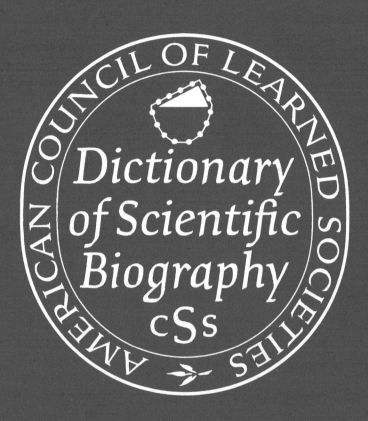

AMERICAN COUNCIL OF LEARNED SOCIETIES

Dictionary of Scientific Biography

cSs

DICTIONARY OF SCIENTIFIC BIOGRAPHY

PUBLISHED UNDER THE AUSPICES OF
THE AMERICAN COUNCIL OF LEARNED SOCIETIES

The American Council of Learned Societies, organized in 1919 for the purpose of advancing the study of the humanities and of the humanistic aspects of the social sciences, is a nonprofit federation comprising thirty-four national scholarly groups. The Council represents the humanities in the United States in the International Union of Academies, provides fellowships and grants-in-aid, supports research-and-planning conferences and symposia, and sponsors special projects and scholarly publications.

MEMBER ORGANIZATIONS

AMERICAN PHILOSOPHICAL SOCIETY, 1743
AMERICAN ACADEMY OF ARTS AND SCIENCES, 1780
AMERICAN ANTIQUARIAN SOCIETY, 1812
AMERICAN ORIENTAL SOCIETY, 1842
AMERICAN NUMISMATIC SOCIETY, 1858
AMERICAN PHILOLOGICAL ASSOCIATION, 1869
ARCHAEOLOGICAL INSTITUTE OF AMERICA, 1879
SOCIETY OF BIBLICAL LITERATURE, 1880
MODERN LANGUAGE ASSOCIATION OF AMERICA, 1883
AMERICAN HISTORICAL ASSOCIATION, 1884
AMERICAN ECONOMIC ASSOCIATION, 1885
AMERICAN FOLKLORE SOCIETY, 1888
AMERICAN DIALECT SOCIETY, 1889
ASSOCIATION OF AMERICAN LAW SCHOOLS, 1900
AMERICAN PHILOSOPHICAL ASSOCIATION, 1901
AMERICAN ANTHROPOLOGICAL ASSOCIATION, 1902
AMERICAN POLITICAL SCIENCE ASSOCIATION, 1903
BIBLIOGRAPHICAL SOCIETY OF AMERICA, 1904
ASSOCIATION OF AMERICAN GEOGRAPHERS, 1904
AMERICAN SOCIOLOGICAL ASSOCIATION, 1905
ORGANIZATION OF AMERICAN HISTORIANS, 1907
COLLEGE ART ASSOCIATION OF AMERICA, 1912
HISTORY OF SCIENCE SOCIETY, 1924
LINGUISTIC SOCIETY OF AMERICA, 1924
MEDIAEVAL ACADEMY OF AMERICA, 1925
AMERICAN MUSICOLOGICAL SOCIETY, 1934
SOCIETY OF ARCHITECTURAL HISTORIANS, 1940
ECONOMIC HISTORY ASSOCIATION, 1940
ASSOCIATION FOR ASIAN STUDIES, 1941
AMERICAN SOCIETY FOR AESTHETICS, 1942
METAPHYSICAL SOCIETY OF AMERICA, 1950
AMERICAN STUDIES ASSOCIATION, 1950
RENAISSANCE SOCIETY OF AMERICA, 1954
SOCIETY FOR ETHNOMUSICOLOGY, 1955

DICTIONARY
OF
SCIENTIFIC BIOGRAPHY

CHARLES COULSTON GILLISPIE
Princeton University

EDITOR IN CHIEF

Volume V

EMIL FISCHER—GOTTLIEB HABERLANDT

CHARLES SCRIBNER'S SONS · NEW YORK

3 5 7 9 11 13 15 17 19 MD/C 20 18 16 14 12 10 8 6 4 2

Printed in the United States of America

Library of Congress Catalog Card Number 69-18090

SBN684-10116-5

Editorial Staff

Panel of Consultants

Contributors to Volume V

The following are the contributors to Volume V. Each author's name is followed by the institutional affiliation at the time of publication and the names of articles written for this volume. The symbol † indicates that an author is deceased.

HANS AARSLEFF
Princeton University
FRANCK, S.; HAAK

KATHLEEN AHONEN
University of Michigan
GLAUBER

GARLAND E. ALLEN
Washington University
FOL

PETER AMACHER
University of California, Los Angeles
FREUD

G. C. AMSTUTZ
University of Heidelberg
GOLDSCHMIDT, V.; GRODDECK

DAVID L. ANDERSON
Oberlin College
GOLDSTEIN

RICHARD P. AULIE
Encyclopaedia Britannica
GAINES

WILLIAM H. AUSTIN
Rice University
GLANVILL

A. ALBERT BAKER, JR.
Grand Valley State College
FISCHER, H.; FRITZSCHE; GABRIEL; GRIGNARD

GEORGE BASALLA
University of Delaware
FITZROY

EDWIN A. BATTISON
Smithsonian Institution
GRAHAM, G.

LUIGI BELLONI
University of Milan
FONTANA

ALEX BERMAN
University of Cincinnati
FORDOS; GAULTIER DE CLAUBRY; GOBLEY; GUIGNARD

MICHAEL BERNKOPF
Pace College
FREDHOLM

ASIT K. BISWAS
Department of the Environment, Ottawa
FORTIN; GAMBEY

MARGARET BISWAS
McGill University
FORTIN; GAMBEY

L. J. BLACHER
Soviet Academy of Sciences
GURVICH

UNO BOKLUND
Royal Pharmaceutical Institute, Stockholm
GAHN

ALFRED M. BORK
University of California, Irvine
FITZGERALD

FRANCK BOURDIER
École Pratique des Hautes Études
GAUDRY; GEOFFROY SAINT-HILAIRE, É.; GEOFFROY SAINT-HILAIRE, I.

W. H. BROCK
University of Leicester
FRANKLAND, E.

JOAN BROMBERG
Niels Bohr Institute
FÖPPL

J. H. BROOKE
University of Lancaster
GERHARDT

THEODORE M. BROWN
City College, City University of New York
GALVANI

STEPHEN G. BRUSH
University of Maryland
FOWLER, R.

WERNER BURAU
University of Hamburg
GÖPEL

J. J. BURCKHARDT
University of Zurich
FUETER; GEISER; GRÄFFE; GROSSMANN, M.

JOHN G. BURKE
University of California, Los Angeles
FORBES, J.; FOUQUÉ

CONRAD BURRI
Swiss Federal Institute of Technology
GRUBENMANN

HAROLD BURSTYN
Carnegie-Mellon University
FOUCAULT

H. L. L. BUSARD
University of Leiden
FRENICLE; GULDIN

LUIGI CAMPEDELLI
University of Florence
FRISI; GHETALDI

ALBERT CAROZZI
University of Illinois
GUYOT

CARLO CASTELLANI
GAGLIARDI; GHISI

JOHN CHALLINOR
GEIKIE, A.; GEIKIE, J.

SEYMOUR L. CHAPIN
Los Angeles State College
FOUCHY; GODIN

JEAN CHÂTILLON
Catholic Institute of Paris
GILES OF ROME

GEORGES CHAUDRON
Laboratoire de Recherches Métallurgiques
GUILLAUME; GUILLET

MARSHALL CLAGETT
Institute for Advanced Study, Princeton
GERARD OF BRUSSELS

EDWIN CLARKE
University College London
FLECHSIG; FRITSCH

I. BERNARD COHEN
Harvard University
FRANKLIN, B.

ROBERT S. COHEN
Boston University
FRANK

WILLIAM COLEMAN
Northwestern University
GAIMARD; GRATIOLET

GEORGE W. CORNER
American Philosophical Society
FLEXNER

CARL W. CORRENS
FRANKENHEIM

ALBERT B. COSTA
Duquesne University
FOWNES; GELMO

PIERRE COSTABEL
École Pratique des Hautes Études
GALLOIS

RUTH SCHWARTZ COWAN
State University of New York at Stony Brook
GATES

CONTRIBUTORS TO VOLUME V

A. C. CROMBIE
University of Oxford
GROSSETESTE

M. P. CROSLAND
University of Leeds
GAY-LUSSAC; GERHARDT

HALLOWELL DAVIS
Central Institute for the Deaf
FORBES, A.

GAVIN DE BEER
GOODRICH

ALLEN G. DEBUS
University of Chicago
FLUDD

RONALD K. DEFORD
University of Texas at Austin
GILBERT, G.

CLAUDE K. DEISCHER
University of Pennsylvania
GMELIN, L.

SUZANNE DELORME
Centre International de Synthèse
FONTENELLE

D. R. DICKS
University of London
GEMINUS

HERBERT DINGLE
University of London
FOWLER, A.

CLAUDE E. DOLMAN
University of British Columbia
FLEMING, A.

J. D. H. DONNAY
McGill University
FRIEDEL

J. G. DORFMAN
Soviet Academy of Sciences
FRENKEL; GOLITSYN

HAROLD DORN
Stevens Institute of Technology
GREGORY, O.

SIGALIA C. DOSTROVSKY
Barnard College
FOSTER, H.

STILLMAN DRAKE
University of Toronto
GALILEI, G.; GALILEI, V.

K. C. DUNHAM
Institute of Geological Sciences
FLETT; GODWIN-AUSTEN

A. HUNTER DUPREE
Brown University
GRAY, A.

BRUCE S. EASTWOOD
Kansas State University
GRIMALDI

FRANK N. EGERTON III
University of Wisconsin-Parkside
FORBES, E.; GRAUNT

GUNNAR ERIKSSON
University of Umeå
FORSSKÅL; FRIES, E.

JOSEPH EWAN
Tulane University
GAERTNER, J.

JOAN M. EYLES
FITTON; GRIFFITH, R.

V. A. EYLES
GREENOUGH

EDUARD FARBER†
FISCHER, E.; FRÉMY

KATHLEEN FARRAR
University of Manchester
GULLAND

FRANK FENNER
Australian National University
FLOREY

KONRADIN FERRARI D'OCCHIEPPO
University of Vienna
GRAFF

MARTIN FICHMAN
York University
GUIBERT

BERNARD S. FINN
Smithsonian Institution
GLAZEBROOK

WALTHER FISCHER
GROTH

C. S. FISHER
Brandeis University
GORDAN

HEINZ FLAMM
University of Vienna
GRUBER

MARCEL FLORKIN
University of Liège
FREDERICQ; GRAMME

ERIC G. FORBES
University of Edinburgh
FREUNDLICH

ROBERT FOX
University of Lancaster
GAUDIN

PIETRO FRANCESCHINI
GALEAZZI; GRASSI

H. C. FREIESLEBEN
GALLE

H. FREUDENTHAL
University of Utrecht
HAAR

JUNE Z. FULLMER
Ohio State University
GARNETT

GERALD L. GEISON
Princeton University
FLETCHER; FOSTER, M.; FRANKLAND, P.; GASKELL

WALTHER GERLACH
University of Munich
GEITEL

GEORGE E. GIFFORD, JR.
Harvard University
GOULD, A.

OWEN GINGERICH
Smithsonian Astrophysical Observatory
FLEMING, W.

EDWARD D. GOLDBERG
Scripps Institution of Oceanography
FORCHHAMMER; GOLDSCHMIDT, V. M.

MORRIS GORAN
Roosevelt University
HABER

J. B. GOUGH
Washington State University
FIZEAU; GOUY

I. GRATTAN-GUINNESS
Enfield College of Technology
FOURIER

FRANK GREENAWAY
Science Museum, London
GRIESS

JOSEPH T. GREGORY
University of California, Berkeley
GRANGER

NORMAN T. GRIDGEMAN
National Research Council of Canada
FISHER; GALTON

A. T. GRIGORIAN
Soviet Academy of Sciences
FRIEDMANN

M. D. GRMEK
Archives Internationales d'Histoire des Sciences
GERBEZIUS; GRISOGONO; GUIDI

V. GUTINA
Soviet Academy of Sciences
GAMALEYA

IAN HACKING
University of Cambridge
GOSSETT

A. RUPERT HALL
Imperial College of Science and Technology
'sGRAVESANDE

MARIE BOAS HALL
Imperial College of Science and Technology
FREIND

CONTRIBUTORS TO VOLUME V

OWEN HANNAWAY
The Johns Hopkins University
GLASER, C.; GOHORY

BERT HANSEN
Fordham University
FÜCHSEL

R. S. HARTENBERG
Northwestern University
GRASHOF

JOHN L. HEILBRON
University of California, Berkeley
GRAY, S.

FRANZ HEIN
German Academy of Sciences
GUTBIER

DAVID HEPPELL
Royal Scottish Museum
GOODSIR

ARMIN HERMANN
University of Stuttgart
HAAS, A.

MAXIMILIAN HERZBERGER
Louisiana State University
GULLSTRAND

BROOKE HINDLE
New York University
GODFREY; GREENWOOD

ANN M. HIRSCH-KIRCHANSKI
University of California, Berkeley
GRIFFITH, W.

MICHAEL E. HOARE
Australian National University
FORSTER, G.; FORSTER, J.

J. E. HOFMANN
University of Tübingen
GUENTHER

GERALD HOLTON
Harvard University
FRANK

BRIGITTE HOPPE
Deutsches Museum
GAERTNER, K.

KARL HUFBAUER
University of California, Irvine
GREN

AARON J. IHDE
University of Wisconsin
FUNK; GOMBERG

JEAN ITARD
Lycée Henri IV
GIRARD, A.

W. O. JAMES
Imperial College, London
GOEBEL

REESE V. JENKINS
Case Western Reserve University
FRAUNHOFER

DANIEL P. JONES
Oregon State University
GORE; GREGORY, W.

PHILLIP S. JONES
University of Michigan
GLAISHER, J. W.

HANS KANGRO
University of Hamburg
GEISSLER

GEORGE B. KAUFFMAN
Fresno State College
FRIEND; GENTH; GRAHAM, T.;
GULDBERG

MARSHALL KAY
Columbia University
GRABAU

A. G. KELLER
University of Leicester
GHINI

SUZANNE KELLY, O.S.B.
Carroll College
GILBERT, W.

MARTHA B. KENDALL
Vassar College
FUHLROTT

H. C. KING
Royal Ontario Museum
GRUBB, H.; GRUBB, T.

STEFAN J. KIRCHANSKI
University of California, Berkeley
GRIFFITH, W.

GEORGE KISH
University of Michigan
GEMMA; GERMANUS

MARC KLEIN
University of Strasbourg
GRAAF

MARTIN J. KLEIN
Yale University
GIBBS, J.

OSKAR KLEIN
University of Stockholm
GORDON

DAVID M. KNIGHT
University of Durham
GIRTANNER

ZDENĚK KOPAL
University of Manchester
GOODRICKE

ELAINE KOPPELMAN
Goucher College
GREGORY, D. F.

SHELDON J. KOPPERL
Grand Valley State College
GADOLIN

HANS-GÜNTHER KÖRBER
Zentralbibliothek des Meteorologischen Dienstes, Potsdam
GUERTLER

FRITZ KRAFFT
University of Mainz
GUERICKE

EDNA E. KRAMER
Polytechnic Institute of Brooklyn
GERMAIN

CLAUDIA KREN
University of Missouri
GUNDISSALINUS

ABRAHAM D. KRIKORIAN
State University of New York at Stony Brook
GREGORY, F.

VLADISLAV KRUTA
Purkyně University
FLOURENS; GMELIN, J.; GRUBY

FRIDOLF KUDLIEN
University of Kiel
GALEN

H. G. KUHN
University of Oxford
FRANCK, J.

EMIL KUHN-SCHNYDER
University of Zurich
GAGNEBIN

P. G. KULIKOVSKY
Soviet Academy of Sciences
GERASIMOVICH

BENGT-OLOF LANDIN
University of Lund
GEER, C.; GYLLENHAAL

HENRY M. LEICESTER
University of the Pacific
FITTIG; FOLIN

JACQUES R. LÉVY
Paris Observatory
GAILLOT; GAUTIER, P.

DAVID C. LINDBERG
University of Wisconsin
FLEISCHER

G. A. LINDEBOOM
Free University, Amsterdam
GRIJNS

DAVID P. C. LLOYD
Rockefeller University
GASSER

MARIO LORIA
GIORGI

MICHAEL McVAUGH
University of North Carolina
FREDERIC II

MICHAEL S. MAHONEY
Princeton University
GOLDBACH

CONTRIBUTORS TO VOLUME V

JEROME H. MANHEIM
Bradley University
FUCHS, I.

BRIAN G. MARSDEN
Smithsonian Institution Astrophysical Observatory
FROST; GOULD, B.

KIRTLEY F. MATHER
Harvard University
FOERSTE

KENNETH O. MAY
University of Toronto
GAUSS

A. MENIAILOV
Soviet Academy of Sciences
FYODOROV

CHARLES R. METCALFE
Royal Botanic Gardens, Kew
GREW

W. E. K. MIDDLETON
University of British Columbia
GLAISHER, J.

WYNDHAM DAVIES MILES
National Institutes of Health
GREEN

MICHAEL E. MITCHELL
University College, Galway
GLEICHEN-RUSSWORM

EDGAR W. MORSE
Sonoma State College
GASSIOT

ALPINOLO NATUCCI
University of Genoa
GRANDI

H. M. NOBIS
Deutsches Museum
FRIES, J.

LOWELL E. NOLAND
University of Wisconsin
GUYER

J. D. NORTH
Museum of the History of Science, Oxford
GELLIBRAND

LUBOŠ NOVÝ
Czechoslovak Academy of Sciences
GUDERMANN

MARY JO NYE
University of Oklahoma
GAUTIER, A.

ROBERT OLBY
University of Leeds
FLEMMING, W.; FRANKLIN, R.

C. D. O'MALLEY†
GEMINUS, T.; GUINTER

LEROY E. PAGE
Kansas State University
FLEMING, J.

JACQUES PAYEN
Conservatoire Nationale des Arts et Métiers
GRAMONT

JON V. PEPPER
Polytechnic of the South Bank
GUNTER

P. E. PILET
University of Lausanne
FOREL; GESNER, J.; GESSNER, K.; GLASER, J.

DAVID PINGREE
University of Chicago
GAṆEŚA

LUCIEN PLANTEFOL
University of Paris
GUILLIERMOND

J. A. PRINS
Technological University of Delft
HAAS, W.

HANS QUERNER
University of Heidelberg
GOETTE

SAMUEL X. RADBILL
College of Physicians of Philadelphia
GESELL

RHODA RAPPAPORT
Vassar College
GUETTARD

J. R. RAVETZ
University of Leeds
FOURIER

NATHAN REINGOLD
Smithsonian Institution
GIBBS, O.

SAMUEL REZNECK
Rensselaer Polytechnic Institute
FITCH

RUTH GIENAPP RINARD
Kirkland College
GRAEBE

GLORIA ROBINSON
Yale University
GAFFKY

BERNARD ROCHOT
École Pratique des Hautes Études
GASSENDI

JOEL M. RODNEY
Elmira College
FOLKES

GRETE RONGE
GEUTHER

B. VAN ROOTSELAAR
State Agricultural University, Wageningen
FRAENKEL; FREGE

HUNTER ROUSE
University of Iowa
FOURNEYRON; FROUDE; GIRARD, P.

CHARLES ROSENBERG
University of Pennsylvania
GOLDBERGER

K. E. ROTHSCHUH
University of Münster/Westphalia
FREY; GOLTZ

MORRIS H. SAFFRON
Rutgers University
GAY

A. P. M. SANDERS
State University of Utrecht
GARNOT; GARREAU

R. SATTLER
McGill University
HABERLANDT

EBERHARD SCHMAUDERER
FUCHS, J.

F. SCHMEIDLER
University of Munich
GROSSMANN, E.

CECIL J. SCHNEER
University of New Hampshire
GRESSLY

HANS HENNING SCHROTH
University of Bonn
GUDDEN

E. L. SCOTT
Stamford High School, Lincolnshire
GLADSTONE; GROVE

ROGER SERVAJEAN
Paris Observatory
FLAMMARION

ELIZABETH NOBLE SHOR
GABB; GILL, T.; GRINNELL; GUTENBERG

GEORGE G. SHOR, JR.
GUTENBERG

ROBERT H. SILLIMAN
Emory University
FRESNEL

DIANA M. SIMPKINS
Polytechnic of North London
FRAZER; FRERE; GOULD, J.; GWYNNE-VAUGHAN

W. A. SMEATON
University College London
FOURCROY; GEOFFROY, C.; GEOFFROY, É. F.; GUYTON DE MORVEAU

E. SNORRASON
Rigshospitalet, Copenhagen
GRAM

T. A. SOFIANO
Soviet Academy of Sciences
FRENZEL

CONTRIBUTORS TO VOLUME V

PIERRE SPEZIALI
University of Geneva
FUBINI; GUCCIA

NILS SPJELDNAES
University of Aarhus
DE GEER

WILLIAM T. STEARN
British Museum (Natural History)
GERARD

FRANÇOIS STOCKMANS
Institut Royal des Sciences Naturelles de Belgique
GOSSELET; GRAND'EURY

R. H. STOY
Royal Observatory, Edinburgh
GILL, D.

J. P. STRADINS
Soviet Academy of Sciences
GROTTHUSS

D. J. STRUIK
Massachusetts Institute of Technology
FRENET; GERBERT; GERGONNE

ROGER H. STUEWER
University of Minnesota
GAMOW

CHARLES SÜSSKIND
University of California, Berkeley
FLEMING, J. A.

LOYD S. SWENSON, JR.
University of Houston
GODDARD; GUYE

F. SZABADVÁRY
Technical University, Budapest
FISCHER, N. W.; FRESENIUS; GÖRGEY

MANFRED E. SZABO
Sir George Williams University
GENTZEN

RENÉ TATON
École Pratique des Hautes Études
FONTAINE; FRANÇAIS, F.; FRANÇAIS, J. F.; GALOIS; GUA DE MALVES

SEVIM TEKELI
Ankara University
ḤABASH AL-ḤĀSIB

OWSEI TEMKIN
The Johns Hopkins University
GLISSON

ANDRÉE TÉTRY
École Pratique des Hautes Études
GIARD; GOLDSCHMIDT, R.

JEAN THÉODORIDÈS
Centre National de la Recherche Scientifique
GEOFFROY, É.-L.

VICTOR E. THOREN
Indiana University
FLAMSTEED; GASCOIGNE

V. V. TIKHOMIROV
Soviet Academy of Sciences
FRENZEL; GOEPPERT

HEINZ TOBIEN
University of Mainz
FREIESLEBEN

THADDEUS J. TRENN
University of Cambridge
GEIGER; GIESEL

HENRY S. TROPP
Smithsonian Institution
GOMPERTZ; GOURSAT

GEORGES UBAGHS
University of Liège
FRAIPONT

PETER W. VAN DER PAS
GOEDAERT

GRAZIELLA F. VESCOVINI
University of Turin
FRANCIS OF MARCHIA; FRANCIS OF MEYRONNES

A. I. VOLODARSKY
Soviet Academy of Sciences
FUSS; GRAVE

GERHARD WAGENITZ
Systematisch-Geobotanisches Institut, Berne
GRISEBACH

EARL WALKER
Johns Hopkins Hospital
FULTON

WILLIAM A. WALLACE, O.P.
Catholic University of America
GERARD OF SILTEO; GILES OF LESSINES

J. B. WATERHOUSE
University of Toronto
HAAST

GEORGE A. WELLS
University of London
GOETHE

D. T. WHITESIDE
Whipple Science Museum
GREGORY, D.; GREGORY, J.

GERALD J. WHITROW
Imperial College of Science and Technology
FORSYTH, A.

W. P. D. WIGHTMAN
King's College, Aberdeen
FRANCESCA

RONALD S. WILKINSON
GROTE

WESLEY C. WILLIAMS
Case Western Reserve University
FLOWER; GAYANT; GRAY, H.

MARY PICKARD WINSOR
University of Toronto
FORBES, S.

DENISE WROTNOWSKA
Institut Pasteur
FOURNEAU

H. WUSSING
University of Leipzig
FROBENIUS

A. P. YOUSCHKEVITCH
Soviet Academy of Sciences
GELFOND

ROBERT M. YOUNG
University of Cambridge
GALL

BRUNO ZANOBIO
University of Pavia
FRACASTORO; GOLGI

DICTIONARY
OF
SCIENTIFIC BIOGRAPHY

DICTIONARY OF SCIENTIFIC BIOGRAPHY

FISCHER—HABERLANDT

FISCHER, EMIL HERMANN (*b.* Euskirchen, near Bonn, Germany, 9 October 1852; *d.* Berlin, Germany, 15 July 1919), *chemistry.*

Fischer was the son of Laurenz Fischer, a successful merchant, and Julie Poensgen Fischer. His father hoped that he would become a businessman; but after a trial period in business ended in failure, the elder Fischer consented to his son's desire for a university education. Fischer entered the University of Bonn in 1871 and attended the lectures of Kekulé. He transferred to Strasbourg the following year, where he studied chemistry under Adolf von Baeyer and obtained the doctorate in 1874. He accompanied Baeyer to Munich in 1875, and qualified as *Privatdozent* in 1878 and as assistant professor in 1879. He became professor of chemistry at Erlangen in 1882, at Würzburg in 1885, and at Berlin in 1892.

Fischer married Agnes Gerlach in 1888; she died seven years later. Two of their three sons were killed in World War I, but the eldest, Hermann Fischer, became an outstanding organic chemist.

Emil Fischer received the Nobel Prize for chemistry in 1902 in recognition of his syntheses in the sugar and purine groups. During World War I he was active in organizing the German chemical resources and headed the commissions for chemical production and food supplies. After the war, he helped to reorganize the teaching of chemistry and to establish research facilities. His work in organic chemistry was primarily on the constitution and synthesis of substances present in organisms. He laid the chemical foundations for biochemistry by his study of sugars, enzymes, purines, and proteins.

Hydrazine Chemistry. Fischer's first publications (1875) dealt with the organic derivatives of hydrazine. He discovered this new group of compounds, considering them to be derivatives of the as yet unknown compound N_2H_4, which he named hydrazine to indicate its relation to nitrogen (azote). In 1866 Kekulé had formulated diazonium compounds as R—N═N—X, similar to the azo formula (R—N═N—R). Since azo compounds were very stable and diazonium compounds were not, chemists disputed Kekulé's formula. In 1871 Adolf Strecker obtained a salt from benzenediazonium nitrate and potassium hydrogen sulfite. Fischer repeated this work and proved that Strecker's salt was a reduction product—potassium phenylhydrazine sulfonate ($C_6H_5NHNH_2$—SO_3K)—of the diazonium compound. This work confirmed the Kekulé formula, and Strecker's compound was a salt of phenylhydrazine. Fischer then prepared phenylhydrazine itself and established its formula by 1878. He prepared many organic derivatives of hydrazine and explored their reactions. The reaction of hydrazines with carbon disulfide led to dyestuffs. Oxidation produced tetrazenes, compounds with chains containing four nitrogen atoms. Aryl hydrazines with ketones and keto acids condensed to form derivatives of indole (the Fischer indole synthesis, 1886).

In 1884 Fischer discovered that phenylhydrazine was a valuable reagent for aldehydes and ketones. It formed solid, crystalline compounds (phenylhydrazones) which had a definite melting point. He then found that it formed not only the hydrazone with carbohydrates but also attacked the hydroxyl group

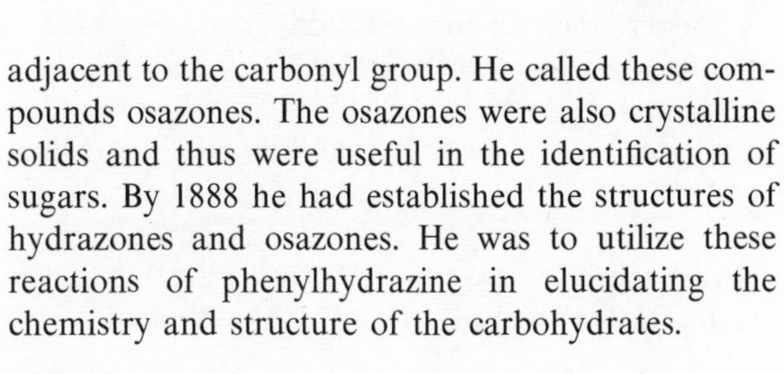

Osazone

adjacent to the carbonyl group. He called these compounds osazones. The osazones were also crystalline solids and thus were useful in the identification of sugars. By 1888 he had established the structures of hydrazones and osazones. He was to utilize these reactions of phenylhydrazine in elucidating the chemistry and structure of the carbohydrates.

Aniline Dyestuffs. Fischer's doctoral thesis had been on the chemistry of colors and dyes. He extended this interest to the new synthetic dyestuffs. He and his cousin Otto Fischer examined the constitution of rosaniline, the basic dyestuff prepared by August von Hofmann in 1862 by the oxidation of toluidine and aniline. There were several conjectures on the constitution of this base but no satisfactory solution until the Fischers succeeded in showing that it was a triphenylmethane derivative. They reduced rosaniline to a colorless derivative, which they called leucaniline and converted, by removal of its nitrogen atoms, into a hydrocarbon of composition $C_{20}H_{18}$. They carried out similar reactions with pararosaniline (from *p*-toluidine and aniline), obtaining a hydrocarbon with the formula $C_{19}H_{16}$, which proved to be identical to triphenylmethane. In 1878 they proved that the rosaniline dyes were homologues and were triamine derivatives of triphenylmethane and its homologues, rosaniline being a derivative of metatolyldiphenylmethane and *p*-rosaniline of triphenylmethane.

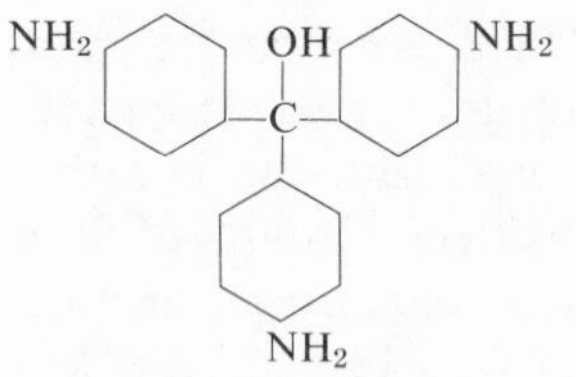

Pararosaniline

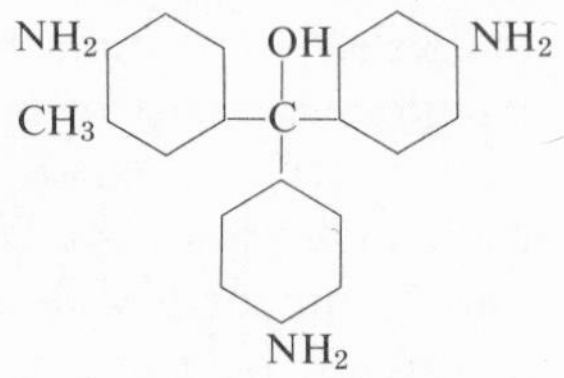

Rosaniline

Purines. Fischer began a study of uric acid and related substances in 1881 and continued his investigations until 1914, when he achieved the first synthesis of a nucleotide. These were biologically important substances. Xanthine, hypoxanthine, adenine, and guanine were present in the cell nucleus of animals. Theobromine, caffeine, and theophylline were stimulants in plants. Baeyer had studied these compounds in the 1860's and partially clarified their relations. The Würzburg chemist Ludwig Medicus proposed structural formulas for several of them in 1875. Fischer became the prime investigator in the field, and it is to him that almost all knowledge of the purines is due. He explored the whole series, established their structures, and synthesized about 130 derivatives by 1900.

Fischer studied the reactions and degradation products of the purines. In 1882 he ventured structural formulas for uric acid, caffeine, theobromine, xanthine, and guanine. He synthesized theophylline and caffeine (1895) and uric acid (1897); but further research convinced him that his structures were incorrect, since his reaction products were not reconcilable to his formulas. In 1897 he provided a new set of formulas. He had come to realize that uric acid and related compounds were oxides of a hypothetical base $C_5N_4H_4$, which he named purine:

$C_5N_4H_4O_3$	$C_5N_4H_4O_2$	$C_5N_4H_4O$
Uric Acid	Xanthine	Hypoxanthine

He proposed that purine was a heterocyclic compound and also proposed the notation system now used in purine chemistry:

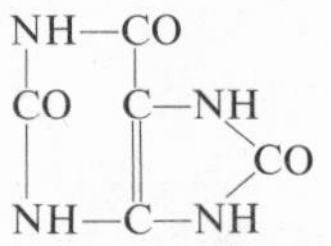

Uric Acid

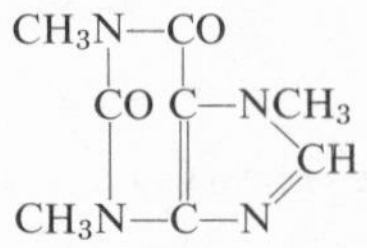

Caffeine

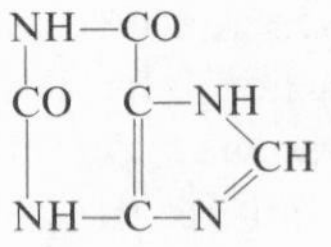

Xanthine

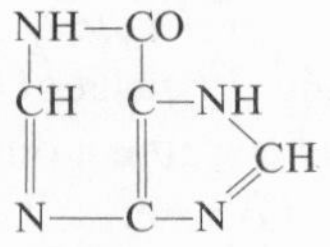

Hypoxanthine

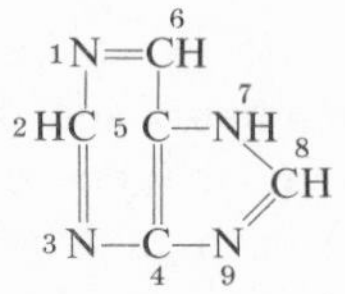

Purine

Subsequently, he synthesized hypoxanthine, xanthine, theobromine, adenine, and guanine. Finally, in 1898 he succeeded in reducing trichloropurine to purine, the parent substance of the class. These researches involved an immense series of preparations and very difficult reactions. He continued this work, combining it with his research on carbohydrates, and in 1914 prepared glucosides of theophylline, theobromine, adenine, hypoxanthine, and guanine. From theophylline-D-glucoside he prepared the first synthetic nucleotide, theophylline-D-glucoside phosphoric acid.

Fischer's purine research was of interest to the German drug industry. His laboratory methods became the basis for the industrial production of caffeine, theophylline, and theobromine. In 1903 he synthesized 5,5-diethyl-barbituric acid. Under various trade names—Barbital, Veronal, and Dorminal—this compound proved to be a valuable hypnotic. Another commercially valuable purine was phenyl, ethylbarbituric acid, prepared by Fischer in 1912 and known as Luminal or phenobarbital.

Carbohydrates. Fischer carried on his purine research simultaneously with his carbohydrate studies and became the prime investigator in both fields. When he began his carbohydrate studies in 1884, there were four known monosaccharides: two aldohexoses (glucose, galactose) and two ketohexoses (fructose, sorbose), all with the formula $C_6H_{12}O_6$. There were three known disaccharides (sucrose, maltose, lactose). The general structure of the simple sugars had been established. Glucose and galactose were straight-chain pentahydroxy aldehydes, and the

FISCHER

ketohexoses were straight-chain pentahydroxy ketones. Fischer in an enormous effort elaborated the complex structures and chemistry of the carbohydrates, synthesized many of them, and established the configurations of the sixteen possible stereoisomers of glucose.

In 1885 Heinrich Kiliani developed the method of lengthening the carbon chain in sugars by means of the addition of hydrocyanic acid to the carbonyl group, followed by hydrolysis and reduction. Fischer utilized this method to convert pentoses into hexoses, the latter into heptoses, etc., synthesizing sugars with as many as nine carbon atoms:

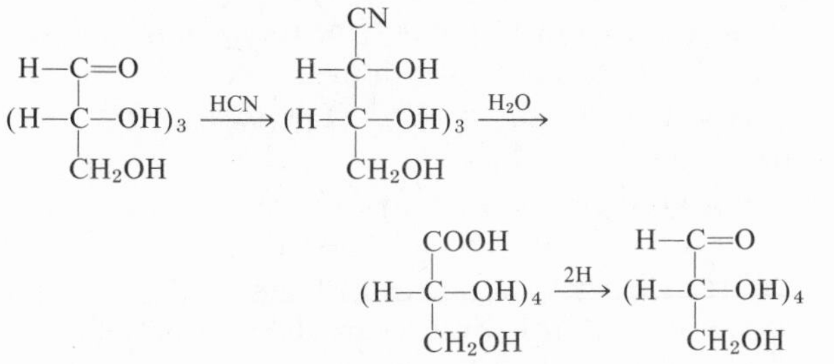

Starting with glycerylaldehyde

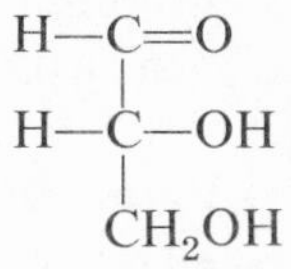

he built up the molecule step-by-step and synthesized several pentoses and hexoses, including glucose, fructose, and mannose, by the Kiliani method.

Fischer achieved his first synthesis of a sugar in 1887. He wanted to synthesize glyceraldehyde and use it as a starting point for building up the carbon chain in sugars. To prepare glyceraldehyde he combined acrolein dibromide and barium hydroxide:

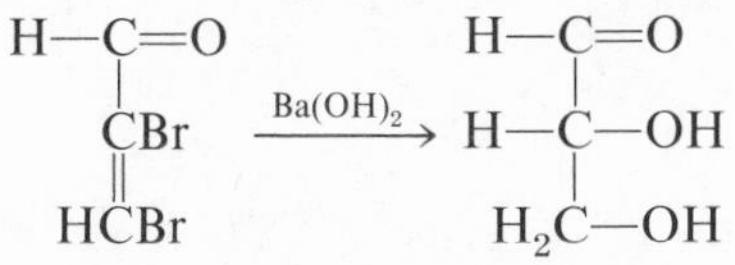

Instead of glyceraldehyde he obtained a syrup which he named acrose:

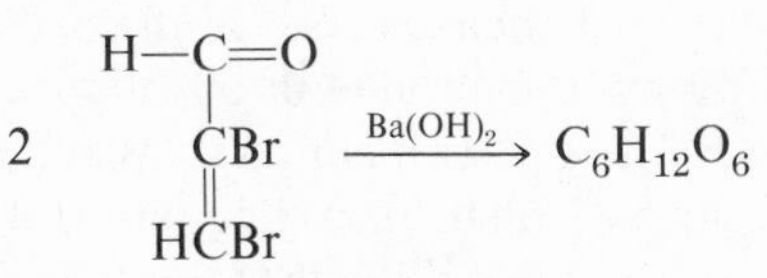

With phenylhydrazine he obtained two different osazones and isolated from them two sugars. He proved that these were fructose and sorbose, the first naturally occurring sugars to be synthesized.

The reaction of sugars with phenylhydrazine yielded first the hydrazone and then the osazone. Fischer found that glucose, fructose, and mannose formed the same osazone. Therefore, the three sugars had the same configuration below the second carbon atom. Osazones on hydrolysis with hydrochloric acid eliminate phenylhydrazine and form osones, a new type of glucose derivative, possessing adjacent carbonyl groups. By reducing these, he obtained sugars, although an aldose is converted into a ketose:

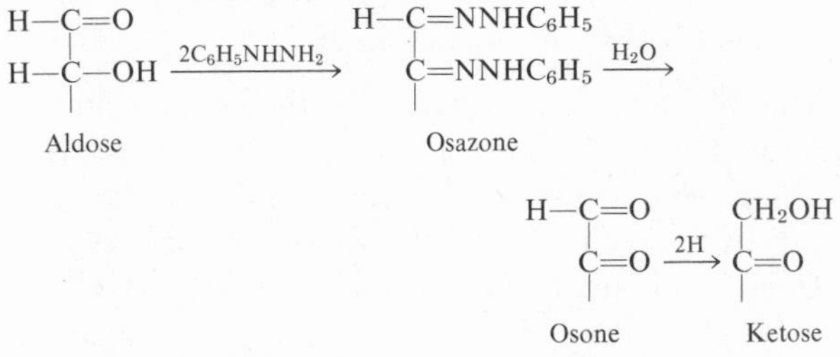

At the other end of the carbon chain the primary alcohol could be reduced or oxidized. Oxidation of this group in glucose gave glucuronic acid; oxidation of the carbonyl group at the other end of the chain, a gluconic acid; and oxidation at both sites, a dicarboxylic acid. By differential reductions and oxidations Fischer could transfer the carbonyl group from one end of the chain to the other, and by testing the products for their properties and their optical rotation of the plane of polarized light, he could elucidate the structures of his compounds.

Using the van't Hoff theory of stereoisomers, Fischer realized that there were sixteen possible configurations for the aldohexoses. By his methods of oxidation, reduction, degradation, addition, etc., he identified the structures of these by 1891. He established the configurations for all members of the D-series of aldohexoses, i.e., those derived from D-glyceraldehyde, where D, according to Fischer's practice, refers to the hydroxyl group's being positioned to the right of the carbon atom next to the primary alcohol group:

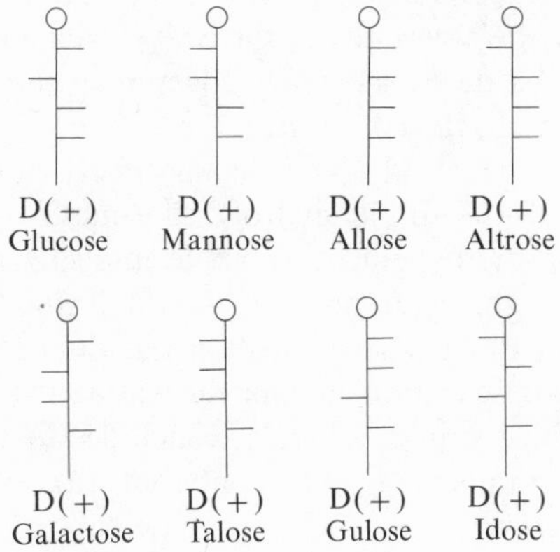

Fischer prepared several artificial sugars. He had established the structures of the natural pentoses arabinose and xylose. He found that by extending the carbon chain of each of these pentoses he obtained two products. The Kiliani method introduced a new asymmetric atom and therefore two reaction products:

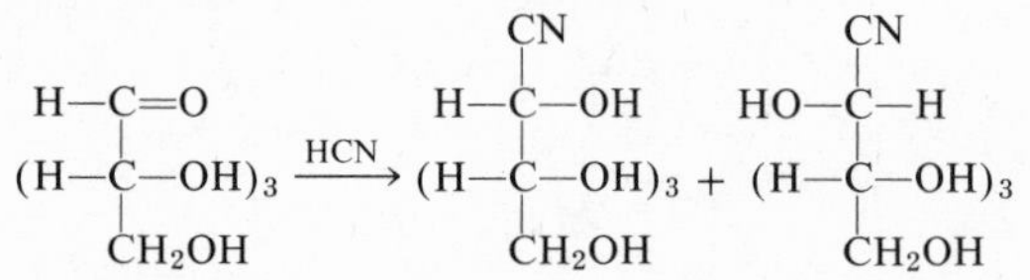

This phenomenon enabled him to prepare the artificial sugars *l*-gulose, *d*-talose, and *d*-idose from *l*-mannonic, *d*-galactonic, and *d*-gulonic acids, respectively; and the pentoses *l*-ribose and *d*-lyxose from *l*-arabonic and *l*-xylonic acids, respectively.

By reaction of the carbonyl group with alcohols, Fischer prepared α- and β-methyl glucoside, the first synthetic glycosides (1893). Since there were two methyl glucosides, he suggested that they must have a cyclic structure:

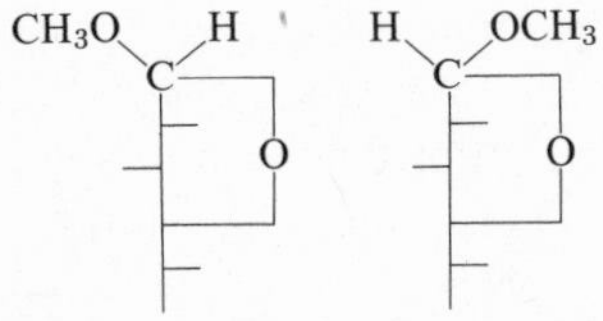

He never extended the ring structure to the sugars themselves, although in 1883 Tollens had suggested ring structures for glucose and fructose. Fischer thought that the disaccharides might have such rings and represented them as two hexoses united through an oxygen linkage: lactose was a glucose-β-galactoside, maltose a glucose-α-glucoside. He regarded the synthesis of glucosides as important because the polysaccharides were glucosides of the sugars themselves, and there was now the possibility of synthesizing polysaccharides.

Fischer examined the properties of enzymes, the substances responsible for the fermentation of sugars. He laid the foundations for enzyme chemistry and provided a new perspective concerning the action of enzymes. In 1894 he tested the action of yeasts on various sugars and noted the specificity of enzymes: maltase, for example, hydrolyzed α-methyl glucoside but not β-methyl glucoside, while emulsin hydrolyzed β-methyl glucoside but not α-methyl glucoside. For sugars of identical composition but different stereometric configuration, an enzyme was active only with a particular configuration. He concluded that enzymes were asymmetric agents capable of attacking molecules of only specific geometric configurations. The action of enzymes in hydrolyzing glucosides led him to use the analogy of a lock-and-key structural relationship between the enzyme and the sugar (1894). Molecular asymmetry gained new significance: the chemical transformations in the organism depended on asymmetry.

As an extension of his work in carbohydrates, Fischer from 1908 studied tannins, the gallic acid derivatives of sugars. In 1912 he showed that tannins were not glucosides but esters and synthesized a pentadigalloylglucose that had the properties of a tannin. In 1918 he established the composition of Chinese tannin as a penta(*meta*-digalloyl)glucose. He also synthesized hepta(tribenzoylgalloyl)-*p*-iodophenylmaltosazone. This derivative of maltose had a molecular weight of 4021, far exceeding that of any synthetic product.

Amino Acids and Proteins. In 1899 Fischer turned to the proteins in the hope of revealing their chemical nature. He knew of thirteen amino acids that had been obtained as hydrolysis products of proteins. He discovered additional amino acids, synthesized several of them, and resolved the *d-l* forms by fractional crystallization of the salts prepared from the benzoyl or formyl derivatives, which he combined with the optically active bases strychnine or brucine.

In 1901 he modified a method for the separation of amino acids developed by Theodor Curtius in 1883. A mixture of amino acids could be separated by esterifying the acids and distilling them at reduced pressure. Furthermore, Curtius showed that the ethyl ester of glycine eliminates alcohol to form a cyclic diketopiperazine, which on ring opening formed glycylglycine:

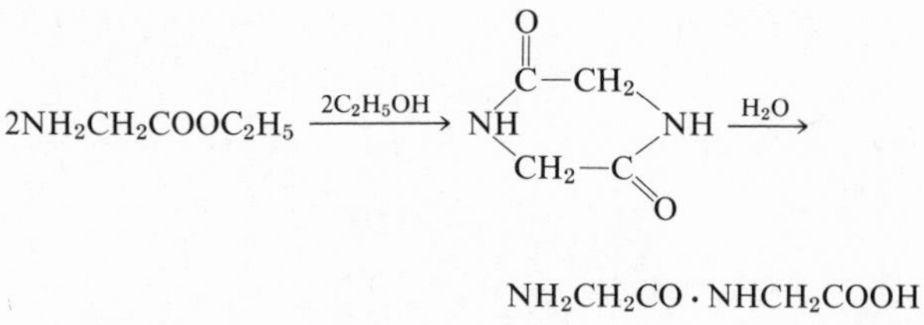

Fischer used Curtius' method to separate mixtures of amino acids from protein hydrolysates by fractionally distilling their esters. He discovered valine, proline, and hydroxyproline in this manner. He prepared the esters of several amino acids and condensed two molecules of them into dipeptides. By 1907 he was preparing polypeptides, the largest one consisting of fifteen glycyl and three leucyl residues and having a molecular weight of 1213: leucyl-triglycyl-leucyl-triglycyl-leucyl-octaglycylglycine. He suggested that the peptide linkage —CONH— was repeated in long chains in the polypeptide molecule. His synthetic methods involved either attacking the amino or the carbonyl group in the amino acid (e.g., using a halogen-containing acid to combine with the amino group and exchanging the halogen by another amino group):

$$CH_2Cl \cdot CO \cdot Cl + NH_2CH(CH_3) \cdot COOH \rightarrow CH_3Cl \cdot CO \cdot NHCH(CH_3) \cdot COOH$$

In this way he could introduce glycyl, leucyl, and other groups into a peptide.

Fischer recognized the complexity of proteins. Even his simple peptides would have numerous isomers, and it would be extremely difficult to establish the constitution and structure of any protein. By 1905 he had differentiated twenty-nine polypeptides and tested their behavior with various enzymes. He characterized proteins by the number, kind, and arrangement of amino acids. In 1916 he summarized his work on the synthesis of about 100 polypeptides and cautioned that these represented only a tiny fraction of the possible combinations that might be found in natural proteins.

Fischer used the Walden inversion in synthesizing amino acids. In 1895 Paul Walden had found that in some substitution reactions the optical antipode of the expected compound was obtained. Fischer examined such reversals of optical rotatory power with regard to amino acids. In 1906 he described the following reaction:

$$l\text{-alanine} \xrightarrow{NOBr} d\text{-}\alpha\text{-bromopropionic acid} \xrightarrow{NH_3} d\text{-alanine.}$$

Comparison with other inversion reactions failed to show at which step the inversion of optical rotation corresponded to a change in the atomic sequence on the asymmetric carbon atom. In 1911 Fischer developed a model to explain such rearrangements, his only excursion into theories of reaction mechanisms. He proposed that substitution is preceded by an addition step in which the entrant group need not take the place of the dislodged one, but that a relative distribution of substituents may take place. Thus, the configuration of the substituted compound may differ from the original.

Fischer's last work was on the esterification of glycerol by fatty acids. The aim of all his investigations was to apply the methods of organic chemistry to the synthesis and processes of substances in living matter.

BIBLIOGRAPHY

I. ORIGINAL WORKS. Fischer's publications were collected in eight large volumes: *Untersuchungen über Aminosäuren, Polypeptide und Proteine, 1899–1906* (Berlin, 1906); *Untersuchungen in der Puringruppe, 1882–1906* (Berlin, 1907); *Untersuchungen über Kohlenhydrate und Fermente, 1884–1908* (Berlin, 1909); *Untersuchungen über Depside und Gerbstoffe, 1908–1919* (Berlin, 1920); *Untersuchungen über Kohlenhydrate und Fermente. II, 1908–1918* (Berlin, 1922); *Untersuchungen über Aminosäuren, Polypeptide und Proteine. II, 1907–1919* (Berlin, 1923); *Untersuchungen über Triphenylmethanfarbstoffe, Hydrazine und Indole* (Berlin, 1924); and *Untersuchungen aus verschiedenen Gebieten, Vorträge und Abhandlungen allgemeinen Inhalts* (Berlin, 1924).

His autobiography is *Aus meinem Leben* (Berlin, 1922), and his Nobel lecture is in *Nobel Lectures. Chemistry 1901–1921* (Amsterdam–New York, 1966), pp. 21–35.

II. SECONDARY LITERATURE. Informative studies of Emil Fischer include Max Bergmann, in G. Bugge, ed., *Das Buch der grossen Chemiker,* II (Berlin, 1930), 408–420; Martin Onslow Forster, "Emil Fischer Memorial Lecture," in *Journal of the Chemical Society,* **117** (1920), 1157–1201; Burckhardt Helferich, in Eduard Farber, ed., *Great Chemists* (New York, 1961), pp. 981–995; and Kurt Hoesch, *Emil Fischer, sein Leben und sein Werk* (Berlin, 1921). "Gedächtnis—Feier für Emil Fischer," in *Berichte der Deutschen chemischen Gesellschaft,* **52A** (1919), 125–164, contains addresses by H. Wichelhaus, Ludwig Knorr, and Carl Duisberg.

EDUARD FARBER

FISCHER, HERMANN OTTO LAURENZ (*b.* Würzburg, Germany, 16 December 1888; *d.* Berkeley, California, 9 March 1960), *biochemistry.*

The son of Emil Fischer, professor of chemistry at the University of Würzburg and famous for his elucidation of the structures of pentoses and hexoses, Hermann was the oldest of three boys. The family moved to Berlin in 1892, when Emil Fischer became director of the Chemical Institute of Berlin University. Fischer attended a Gymnasium in Berlin and decided to become a chemist, while his two brothers chose medical careers. He studied at Cambridge in 1907, then fulfilled his year of military service at Lüneburg. He began his study of chemistry at Berlin and later transferred to Jena. Under Ludwig Knorr's direction he worked on tautomerism of diketones, preparing the enol form of acetyl acetone. After obtaining the doctorate at Jena, Fischer went to Berlin in 1912 to begin research under his father's guidance.

By 1912 Emil Fischer had ceased working on carbohydrates, purines, and proteins and turned his attention to depsides and tannins. He put his son to work on the synthesis of lecanoric acid, which occurs naturally in lichens. Hermann succeeded, showing that lecanoric acid is a didepside, *p*-diorsellinic acid. With the outbreak of World War I, Fischer went to the front in France; both of his brothers joined the military medical service and died in the line of duty. At the end of the war Fischer returned to his father's laboratory. He married in 1922 and was appointed assistant professor at the Chemical Institute of Berlin University.

With Gerda Dangschat, Fischer elucidated the structure of caffeic acid and chlorogenic acid, the depside of quinic acid. They showed that this depside carries the caffeine in coffee and determines the coffee's taste after roasting. Beginning an association with Erich Baer that was to continue for twenty-seven years, Fischer started work on the trioses, dihydroxyacetone, and glyceraldehyde. By 1932 Fischer and his co-workers had succeeded in synthesizing the calcium salt of D, L-glyceraldehyde-3-phosphoric acid which Warburg, Embden, and Meyerhof utilized in developing their schemes of alcoholic fermentation and glycolysis.

Fischer accepted a position at the University of Basel in 1932. He continued work on the trioses, with Baer preparing pure D- and L-glyceraldehydes and synthesizing D-fructose and L-sorbose. In Berlin, Gerda Dangschat continued the elucidation of the configuration of quinic acid and shikimic acid, which later proved to be an important intermediate in the formation of aromatic amino acids in bacterial metabolism.

Fischer accepted the invitation of Sir Frederick Banting, who with Charles Best had discovered insulin, to join the staff at the Banting Institute of the University of Toronto. He arrived there in the fall of 1937 with his wife, two sons and daughter, Erich Baer and other assistants, his private laboratory (including the 9,000 reference compounds representative of all of his father's work), and his father's library. Fischer continued work on trioses, glycerol derivatives, and glycerides. In his laboratory were Baer, J. M. Grosheintz, Leon Rubin, J. C. Sowden, and Henry Lardy, working on the synthesis of selachyl alcohol, the oxidation of glycols, the condensation of aldoses, the cyclization of glucose into myoinositol, and the synthesis of biologically interesting organic phosphates.

Fischer became a member of the new department of biochemistry at the University of California in 1948. On 9 October 1952 he dedicated the Emil Fischer Library, containing his father's books and reference compounds, to the university. Fischer became chairman of the biochemistry department in 1953, holding that position and lecturing on carbohydrates and lipids until his retirement in 1956. Among those who worked with him at Berkeley were D. L. MacDonald, C. E. Ballou, E. A. Kabat, and S. J. Angyal, who investigated sugar disulfones, sugar dialdehydes, inositol derivatives, tetrose phosphates, hexose dialdehydes, D-erythrose-4-phosphate, galactinol, and the confirmational analysis of sugars and inositols. On his retirement Fischer was given space in the Biochemistry and Virus Laboratory, where he conducted research on carbohydrates, assisted by Hans Helmut Baer, from the Max Planck Institute for Medical Research in Heidelberg. Starting from Fischer's observation that a sugar dialdehyde of the pentose series forms, with nitromethane, nitroinositols, Baer worked out the syntheses of 3-amino-3-deoxy-D-ribose and 3-amino-3-deoxy-D-mannose.

Fischer was a member of many professional societies, recipient of the Sugar Research Award of the American Chemical Society in 1949 and of the Adolf von Baeyer Memorial Gold Medal from the Society of German Chemists in 1955, and was named professor emeritus by the University of California in 1956.

BIBLIOGRAPHY

For a short autobiography with portrait, see Hermann O. L. Fischer, "Fifty Years 'Synthetiker' in the Service of Biochemistry," in *Annual Review of Biochemistry,* **29** (1960), 1-14. Early papers on carbomethoxy derivatives of acids written with Emil Fischer can be found in *Berichte der Deutschen chemischen Gesellschaft,* **46** (1913), 1138–1148, 2659–2664; and **47** (1914), 505–512, 768–780. Fischer and Dangschat's work on quinic acid, shikimic acid, and their derivatives is reported in papers found in *Naturwissenschaften,* **19** (1931), 310–311; *Berichte der Deutschen chemischen Gesellschaft,* **65B** (1932), 1009–1031, 1037–1040; and *Helvetica chimica acta,* **17** (1934), 1196–1200, 1200–1207; and **18** (1935), 1204–1206, 1206–1213. Some of the papers written in collaboration with Erich Baer and others on the trioses, dihydroxyacetone and glyceraldehyde, and their derivatives can be found in *Berichte der Deutschen chemischen Gesellschaft,* **60B** (1927), 479–485; **63B** (1930), 1732–1744, 1744–1748, 1749–1753; **65B** (1932), 337–345, 345–352; *Helvetica chimica acta,* **16** (1933), 534–547; **17** (1934), 622–632; **18** (1935), 514–521, 1079–1087; **19** (1936), 519–532; **20** (1937), 1213–1226, 1226–1236; *Naturwissenschaften,* **25** (1937), 588–589, 589; and *Chemical Reviews,* **29** (1941), 287–316.

Fischer published a review of his investigations of chemical and biological relationships between hexoses and inositols in *Harvey Lectures,* **40** (1944–1945), 156–178; and a review of his chemical synthesis of intermediate products of sugar metabolism in *Angewandte Chemie,* **69** (1957), 413–419.

A. ALBERT BAKER, JR.

FISCHER, NICOLAUS WOLFGANG (*b.* Gross-Meseritz, Bohemia [now Mezirici Velké, Czechoslovakia], 15 January 1782; *d.* Breslau, Germany [now Wrocław, Poland], 19 August 1850), *chemistry.*

Very little is known about Fischer's life. He studied medicine in Erfurt and practiced in Breslau, where he also gave lectures at the school of surgery. After the founding of the University of Breslau in 1811, he qualified there as *Privatdozent.* In 1815 the first chair in chemistry was established at the university, and Fischer was appointed to it. He held this position until his death.

In approximately sixty articles published in contemporary German journals, Fischer presented the results of his diversified chemical and medical research. Many of his investigations are of lasting importance.

At first he reported on the triple salt $K_3Co(NO_2)_6$, which entered inorganic chemistry as "Fischer's salt." He employed this salt in the analytical separation of nickel from cobalt.

He appears to have been one of the first to observe the semipermeability of animal bladders in solutions and pure water; moreover, he undertook osmotic investigations and hence observed endosmosis. He gave an account of this research in a heterogeneous article in the part entitled "Über die Eigenschaft der thierischen Blase, Flüssigkeiten durch sich hindurch zu lassen."

Fischer took a great interest in electrochemical phenomena. He investigated the electrochemical reducibility of metals in galvanic cells with the goal of finding the relationship between chemical affinity and galvanism. For this purpose he constructed various cells and observed the so-called galvanoplastic phenomenon (i.e., electroplating), which later, through other researchers, led to the elaboration of technical electroplating.

Fischer made a galvanic cell consisting of silver and zinc electrodes. The former was immersed in dilute sulfuric acid and the latter in moist silver chloride, which he contained in bladders. He thus obtained a voltaic pile which delivered a more or less constant electric current (1812). He therefore belongs among the pioneers in the construction of voltaic cells.

Fischer also concerned himself with, among other things, the investigation of the sensitivity to light of silver chloride, methods for the legal and medical detection of arsenic, and the chemical reactions of the then comparatively new elements tellurium and selenium.

BIBLIOGRAPHY

The article "Über die Wiederherstellung eines Metals durch ein anderes und über die Eigenschaft der thierischen Blase, Flüssigkeiten durch sich hindurch zu lassen und sie in einigen Fällen anzuheben" appeared in *Annalen der Physik,* **12** (1822), 289–307. Poggendorff gives a fairly complete listing of Fischer's articles; he wrote no books.

A biographical notice is J. Schiff, "N. W. Fischer, erster Chemie Professor der Universität Breslau," in *Archiv für die Geschichte der Naturwissenschaften und der Technik,* **8** (1917), 225, and **9** (1918), 29.

F. SZABADVÁRY

FISHER, RONALD AYLMER (*b.* London, England, 17 February 1890; *d.* Adelaide, Australia, 29 July 1962), *statistics, biometry, genetics.*

Fisher's father was a prominent auctioneer and the head of a large family; Fisher was a surviving twin. Chronic myopia probably helped channel his youthful mathematical gifts into the high order of conceptualization and intuitiveness that distinguished his mature work. At Cambridge, which he entered in 1909 and from which he graduated in 1912, Fisher studied mathematics and theoretical physics. His early postgraduate life was varied, including working for an investment house, doing farm chores in Canada, and teaching high school. Fisher soon became interested in the biometric problems of the day and in 1919 joined the staff of Rothamsted Experimental Station as a one-man statistics department charged, primarily, with sorting and reassessing a sixty-six-year accumulation of data on manurial field trials and weather records. In the following decade and a half his work there established him as the leading statistician of his era, and early in his tenure he published the epochal *Statistical Methods for Research Workers.*

Meantime, avocationally, Fisher was building a reputation as a top-ranking geneticist. He left Rothamsted in 1933 to become Galton professor of eugenics at University College, London. Ten years later he moved to Cambridge as Balfour professor of genetics. In 1959, ostensibly retired, Fisher emigrated to Australia and spent the last three years of his life working steadily and productively in the Division of Mathematical Statistics of the Commonwealth Scientific and Industrial Research Organization. Innumerable honors came to him, including election to fellowship of the Royal Society in 1929 and knighthood in 1952.

In 1917 Fisher married Ruth Eileen Guinness and, like his own parents, they had eight children—a circumstance that, according to a friend, was "a personal expression of his genetic and evolutionary convictions." Later in life he and Lady Fisher separated. Slight, bearded, eloquent, reactionary, and quirkish, Fisher made a strong impact on all who met him. The geniality and generosity with which he treated his disciples was complemented by the hostility he aimed at his dissenters. His mastery of the elegantly barbed phrase did not help dissolve feuds, and he left a legacy of unnecessary confusion in some areas of statistical theory. Nevertheless, Fisher was an authentic genius, with a splendid talent for intertwining theory and practice. He had a real feel for quantitative experimental data whose interpretation is unobvious, and throughout his career he was a happy and skillful performer on the desk calculator.

Fisher's debut in the world of mathematical statistics was occasioned by his discovery, as a young man, that all efforts to establish the exact sampling distribution of the well-known correlation coefficient had foundered. He tackled the problem in the context of points in an n-dimensional Euclidean space (n being the size of the sample), an original and, as it turned out, highly successful approach. In the following years he applied similar methods to obtain the distributions of many other functions, such as the regression coefficient, the partial and multiple correlation coefficients, the discriminant function, and a logarithmic function of the ratio of two comparable variances. Fisher also tidied up the mathematics and application of two important functions already in the literature: the Helmert-Pearson χ^2 (the sum of squares of a given number of independent standard normal variates, whose distribution is used to test the "goodness of fit" of numerical observations to expectations) and Gosset's z (the ratio of a normal sample mean, measured from a given point, in terms of its sample standard deviation). The latter was modulated by Fisher to the now familiar t, whose frequency distribution provides the simplest of all significance tests. He seized on Gosset's work to centralize the problem of making inferences from small samples, and he went on to erect a comprehensive theory of hypothesis testing.

The idea here was that many biological experiments are tests of a defined hypothesis, with the experimentalist wanting to know whether his results bolster or undermine his theorizing. If we assume, said Fisher in effect, that the scatter of results is a sample from a normal (Gaussian) distribution whose mean (suitably expressed or transformed) is the "null" hypothesis, we can, using the t distribution, compute the "tail" probability that the observed mean is a random normal sample—in much the same way that we can compute the probability of getting, say, seven or more heads in ten tosses of a fair coin. It might be thought that this probability was all an experimentalist would need, since he would subsequently make his own scientific judgment of its significance in the context of test and hypothesis. However, Fisher advocated the use of arbitrary "cutoff" points; specifically, he suggested that if the probability were $<1/20$ but $>1/100$, a weak judgment against the null hypothesis be made, and if the probability were $<1/100$ a strongly unfavorable judgment be made. This convention, helped by the publication of special tables, became popular, and it has often been used blindly. The real value of the discipline lay in its sound probabilistic structure rather than in its decision-making rules. It is noteworthy that other statistical theorists extended Fisher's ideas by introducing the power of a test, that is, its intrinsic ability, in terms of the parameters and distribution functions, to detect a given difference (between the null hypothesis and the observational estimate) at a prearranged probability level; but, for reasons never made plain, Fisher would not sanction this development.

Fisher devised his own extension of significance testing, the remarkable analysis of variance. This was bound in with his novel ideas on the wide subject of the theory of experimental design. He emphasized not merely the desirability but the logical necessity, in the design of an experiment whose results could not be freed from error, of maximizing efficiency (by devices such as blocks and confounding), and of introducing randomization in such a way as to furnish a valid estimate of the residual error. Whereas the time-honored practice in handling several factors had been to vary only one at a time during the experiment, Fisher pointed out that simultaneous variation was essential to the detection of possible interaction between factors, and that this change could be made without extra cost (in terms of experimental size and operational effort). Entrained with these innovations was the use of randomized blocks and Latin squares for the actual disposition of the test units.

Many would subscribe to the thesis that Fisher's contributions to experimental design were the most praiseworthy of all his accomplishments in statistics. It was to facilitate the interpretation of multifactor experiments carried out in the light of his ideas on design that Fisher introduced the analysis of variance (which he had originally devised to deal with hierarchical classification). In this scheme the variances due to different factors in the experiment are screened out and tested separately for statistical significance

FISHER

(that is, for incompatibility with the null hypothesis of "no effect"). The appeal of the analysis has been great, and here again misuses have not been uncommon among uncritical researchers—for example, some have contented themselves with, and even published, analyses of variance unaccompanied by tabulations of the group means to which the significance tests refer. This itself is a tribute, of a sort, to Fisher.

Arising out of his work on the analysis of variance was the analysis of covariance, a scheme in which the regression effect of concomitant nuisance factors could be screened out so as to purify further the significance tests. (For example, in a multifactor physiological experiment the weight of the animals might be a nuisance factor affecting response and calling for elimination or allowance by analysis of covariance.)

An early landmark in the Fisherian revolution was his long paper "On the Mathematical Foundations of Theoretical Statistics" (1922). Convinced that the subject had progressed too haphazardly and lacked a solid mathematical base, he set out to repair the situation. He drew attention to the shortcomings of the method of moments in curve fitting, stressed the importance of exact sampling distributions, and moved toward a realistic view of estimation. Discussing estimation of a parameter, he urged that a "satisfactory statistic" should be consistent (which means, roughly, unbiased), efficient (having the greatest precision), and sufficient (embracing all relevant information in the observations). His making "information" into a technical term, equatable to reciprocal variance, was a useful step (the reuse of the same word, much later, in C. E. Shannon's information theory is allied but not directly comparable).

To appreciate Fisher's handling of estimation theory, we must look upon it as a subdivision of the general problem of induction that has worried theoreticians since Hume's day. In its simplest and oldest form it is the question of how to arrive at a "best" value of a set of observations. Today we unthinkingly take the arithmetic mean, but in fact the conditions under which this procedure can be justified need careful definition. Broadly speaking, the arithmetic mean is usually the maximum likelihood estimate. This term expressed not a wholly new principle but one that Fisher transformed and named. He urged the need to recognize two kinds of uncertainty and proposed that the probability of an event, given a parameter, should be supplemented by the likelihood of a parameter, given an event. Likelihood has similarities to probability, but important differences exist (for instance, its curve cannot be integrated).

At this point, by way of illustration, we may bring in a modified form of one of Fisher's own examples. It concerns a discrete (discontinuous) distribution. We are given four counts, n_1 through n_4, of corn seedlings (each in a different descriptive category) that are hypothesized to arise from a parameter p, as shown below.

Descriptive category	(i)	1	2	3	4	$\sum$
Fractions expected	(f_i)	$(2+p)/4$	$(1-p)/4$	$(1-p)/4$	$p/4$	1
Numbers observed	(n_i)	1,997	906	904	32	3,839

The problem is to estimate p. Now, by definition, the likelihood, L, will be

$$L = \prod_{i=1}^{4} f_i^{n_i}. \tag{1}$$

Instead of seeking the maximum of this, we shall find it more convenient to handle the logarithm, which is

$$L' = n_1 \log(2+p) + (n_2+n_3)\log(1-p) + n_4 \log p. \tag{2}$$

Differentiating this expression with respect to p, equating the result to zero, and replacing the n_i with the actual observations yields the quadratic

$$3839p^2 + 1655p - 64 = 0, \tag{3}$$

from which we find $\hat{p} = 0.03571$ (the caret is widely employed nowadays to denote "an estimate of"). Therefore, among all possible values of p this is the one most likely to have given rise to the particular tetrad of observed numbers. Fisher now went further and showed that the second derivative of (2) could be equated to the variance of $\hat{p}$. This gives us

$$\text{var}(\hat{p}) = \frac{2p(1-p)(2+p)}{(1+2p)(n_1+n_2+n_3+n_4)}, \tag{4}$$

which, incidentally, is the minimum variance, indicating that the estimate of p is efficient in Fisher's special sense of that term. Substitution of $\hat{p}$ for p in (4) and insertion of the actual n_i, followed by extraction of the square root, gives us the best estimate of the standard error of $\hat{p}$. Thus we can submit $\hat{p} = 0.03571 \pm 0.00584$ as our final result.

Attachment of a standard error to an estimate, as above, is quite old in statistics, and this is yet another matter to which Fisher brought change. He was a pioneer in interval estimation, that is, the specification of numerical probability limits bracketing the point estimate. Fisher's approach is best described in the context of sampling the normal distribution. Imagine such a distribution, with mean μ and variance (second moment) σ^2, both unknown and from which we intend to draw a sample of ten items. Now, in advance of the sampling, various statements can be made about this (as yet) unknown mean, m. One such is

$$(5)\quad P\left(m < \mu - \frac{1.96}{\sqrt{10}}\,\sigma\right) = P\left(m > \mu + \frac{1.96}{\sqrt{10}}\,\sigma\right) = 0.025,$$

the factor 1.96 being taken from a table of the partial integrals of the normal function. The statement is formal, although without practical value. We draw the sample, finding, say, $m = 8.41$ with a standard deviation of $s = 6.325$; then, according to Fisher, a probability statement analogous to (5) can be cast into this form:

$$(6)\quad P\left(\mu < m - \frac{2.23}{\sqrt{10}}\,s\right) = P\left(\mu > m + \frac{2.23}{\sqrt{10}}\,s\right) = 0.025 \equiv P(\mu < 3.95) = P(\mu > 12.87) = 0.025,$$

the factor 2.23 being taken from the t table in the Gosset-Fisher theory of small samples.

Strictly speaking, this is dubious in that it involves a probable location of a parameter, which, by definition, is fixed—and unknown. But, said Fisher, the observed values of m and s have changed the "logical status" of μ, transforming it into a random variable with a "well-defined distribution." Another way of stating (6) is that the values 3.95–12.87 are the "fiducial limits" within which μ can be assigned with probability 0.95. There is no doubt that this is a credibility statement with which an experimentalist untroubled by niceties of mathematical logic should be satisfied. And indeed it might be thought that the notion of fiducialism could be rationalized in terms of a different definition of probability (leaning on credibility rather than orthodox limiting frequency). But Fisher always insisted that probability "obtained by way of the fiducial argument" was orthodox. The doctrine landed Fisher and the adherents of fiducialism in a logical morass, and the situation was worsened by the historical accident that an allied concept, the theory of confidence limits, was introduced by Jerzy Neyman about the same time (*ca.* 1930). Although it, too, had weaknesses, Neyman's theory, as the more mathematically rigorous and widely applicable, was espoused by many statisticians in preference to its rival. Battle lines were drawn, and the next few decades witnessed an extraordinarily acrimonious and indecisive fight between the schools. Fiducialism is still being explored by mathematical statisticians.

This by no means exhausts Fisher's contributions to statistics—topics such as multivariate analysis, bioassay, time series, contingency tables, and the logarithmic distribution are others that come to mind—and in fact it would be hard to do so, if only because he sometimes gave seminal ideas to colleagues to work out under their own names. We must end with some reference to another subject on which Fisher left a deep mark: genetics. In his young manhood natural selection and heredity were in a state of renewed ferment. The rediscovery in 1900 of Mendel's splendid work on particulate inheritance threw discredit not only on Karl Pearson's elaborate researches into blending inheritance but also on Darwinism itself, believed by some to be incompatible with Mendelism. Fisher thought otherwise, and in 1918 he published a paper, "The Correlation Between Relatives on the Supposition of Mendelian Inheritance," that brought powerful new mathematical tools to bear on the issue and that eventually swung informed opinion over to his views—which were, in brief, that blending inheritance is the cumulative effect of a large number of Mendelian factors that are individually insignificant. (This was to blossom into the modern discipline of biometric genetics, although Fisher himself never made any important contributions thereto.)

Fisher came to regard natural selection as a study in its own right, with evolution as but one of several sequelae. His work on the phenomenon of dominance was outstanding. He early pointed out that correlations between relatives could be made to furnish information on the dominance of the relevant genes. He demonstrated that the Mendelian selection process invariably favors the dominance of beneficial genes, and that the greater the benefit, the faster the process. Dominance, then, must play a major role in evolution by natural selection. It may here be added that Fisher's work in this area, as elsewhere, was a careful blending of theory and practice. He carried out breeding experiments with various animals (mice, poultry, and snails were some), often under trying circumstances (for example, much mouse breeding was done in his own home in Harpenden). One of his best experiments concerned the inheritance of whiteness of plumage in white leghorns: by "breeding back" into wild jungle fowl he showed that the responsible dominant gene is a result of artificial selection, and its dominance is quickly lessened when it is introduced into the ancestral wild species.

Fisher also enunciated a "fundamental theorem of natural selection" (for an idealized population) in this form: "The rate of increase in fitness of any organism at any time is equal to its genetic variance in fitness at that time." He was keenly interested in human genetics and, like most eugenicists, held alarmist views about the future of *Homo sapiens.* An important consequence of this special interest was his realization that a study of human blood groups could be instrumental in advancing both theory and practice, and in 1935 he set up a blood-grouping department in the Galton Laboratory. Many good things came out of this enterprise, including a clarification of the inheritance of Rhesus groups.

BIBLIOGRAPHY

I. ORIGINAL WORKS. Over a period of half a century Fisher turned out an average of one paper every two months. The best listing of these is M. J. R. Healy's, in *Journal of the Royal Statistical Society,* **126A** (1963), 170–178. The earliest item, in *Messenger of Mathematics,* **41** (1912), 155–160, is a brief advocacy of the method of maximum likelihood for curve fitting; and the last, in *Journal of Theoretical Biology,* **3** (1962), 509–513, concerns the use of double heterozygotes for seeking a statistically significant difference in recombination values. Key theoretical papers are "On the Mathematical Foundations of Theoretical Statistics," in *Philosophical Transactions of the Royal Society,* **222A** (1922), 309–368; "The Theory of Statistical Estimation," in *Proceedings of the Cambridge Philosophical Society,* **22** (1925), 700–725; and "The Statistical Theory of Estimation," in *Calcutta University Readership Lectures* (Calcutta, 1938). A publication of unusual interest is "Has Mendel's Work Been Rediscovered?" in *Annals of Science,* **1** (1936), 115–137, in which Fisher finds that, probabilistically, some of Mendel's celebrated pea results were a little too good to be true, but in which he also shows that Mendel's insight and experimental skill must have been outstandingly fine. Forty-three of Fisher's most important earlier papers are reproduced in facsimile, with the author's notes and corrections, in *Contributions to Mathematical Statistics* (New York, 1950).

Fisher published five holograph books: *Statistical Methods for Research Workers* (London, 1925; 13th ed., 1958), translated into five other languages; *The Genetical Theory of Natural Selection* (London, 1930; 2nd ed., New York, 1958); *The Design of Experiments* (London, 1935; 8th ed., 1966); *The Theory of Inbreeding* (London, 1949; 2nd ed., 1965); and *Statistical Methods and Scientific Inference* (London, 1956; 2nd ed., 1959). The statistical tables in his first book were subsequently expanded and published separately, with F. Yates, as *Statistical Tables for Biological, Agricultural, and Medical Research* (London, 1938; 6th ed., 1963).

II. SECONDARY LITERATURE. *Journal of the American Statistical Association,* **46** (1951), contains four informative papers by F. Yates, H. Hotelling, W. J. Youden, and K. Mather written on the occasion of the twenty-fifth anniversary of the publication of *Statistical Methods.* The principal commemorative articles published after Fisher's death will be found in *Biometrics,* **18** (Dec. 1962) and **20** (June 1964); *Biographical Memoirs of Fellows of the Royal Society of London,* **9** (1963), 92–129; *Journal of the Royal Statistical Society,* **126A** (1963), 159–170; and *Science,* **156** (1967), 1456–1462. The last contains "An Appreciation" by Jerzy Neyman, who differed with Fisher on several issues, and is therefore of special interest. The writings of Neyman and E. S. Pearson should be consulted for further information on controversial matters. Fisher's contributions to discussions at various meetings of the Royal Statistical Society are also illuminating in this regard (they are indexed in the Healy bibliography). A good philosophical study of statistical reasoning, with particular reference to Fisher's ideas, is Ian Hacking's *Logic of Statistical Inference* (London, 1965).

NORMAN T. GRIDGEMAN

FITCH, ASA (*b.* Salem, New York, 24 February 1809; *d.* Salem, 8 April 1879), *economic entomology, medicine.*

Born into a prominent old Connecticut family that had resettled in eastern New York, Fitch was named for his father, a distinguished physician and farmer. Despite a professional family background, young Asa had an erratic and disconnected education—due in part to the limited facilities that Salem afforded—and spent some time in search of a suitable career. In 1826, almost by chance, he came upon an announcement for the Rensselaer School in nearby Troy, headed by Amos Eaton. The school had an all-science curriculum and was the only one of its kind in the country.

Fitch was drawn to this new venture in scientific education and enrolled in its second class. Indeed, he came just in time to be admitted as a participant in another of Eaton's experiments in scientific education—a traveling school of science, set up on a barge on the newly opened Erie Canal, for the observation of geological formations and the collection of specimens. Fitch became the youngest member of a group of twenty men of all ages and conditions, including Joseph Henry and a son of Governor DeWitt Clinton. On this tour, which is recorded vividly in Fitch's diary, the young man already displayed an interest in and inclination toward the study of insects, which was to be his major occupation. There followed a year at the Rensselaer School, spent in the pursuit of a somewhat haphazard course that was at once all-embracing yet limited in scope and content.

Still in search of a career, Fitch next devoted himself to the study of medicine, attending lectures at medical schools in New York City, Albany, and Castleton, Vermont, and capping it with an apprenticeship to a practicing physician. He served briefly as an assistant professor of natural history at the Rensselaer School, then traveled to the Illinois frontier. Here, at Greenville, he spent an unhappy winter in 1830–1831, seeking to establish himself in the joint pursuit of medicine and science. Unsuccessful, he returned to his home state, where he remained for the rest of his life. Fitch's interest in medicine apparently was secondary to his zeal for natural history, acquired under Eaton's inspiration. He retired to the family farm, giving up medicine for agriculture. With it, however, he combined the assiduous collection and study of insects, especially in respect to their injurious or beneficial effects upon crops.

Fitch, who became known as the "Bug Catcher of Salem," began publishing reports about insects in 1845. Between 1854 and 1870 he received modest financial grants from New York State for his work, and thus he was, perhaps informally, the first entomologist in the service of a state. His numerous reports, published regularly in the *Transactions of the New York State Agricultural Society,* were widely circulated and acknowledged for their combination of sound scientific knowledge of insect life cycles with the conditions and problems of agriculture. From his obscure rural home in upstate New York, Fitch carried on a wide correspondence. His achievement, stemming from Eaton's zeal for applied science, laid the foundation of economic entomology as an American science. Entomology subsequently acquired a more professional character; but Fitch's role in it was perhaps the epitome of early American science, primitive but practical and dedicated.

BIBLIOGRAPHY

I. ORIGINAL WORKS. Asa Fitch's lifelong diary, begun at the age of twelve, is preserved in MS form in the Yale University Library. Many of his notebooks are in the United States National Museum. His writings on entomology began to appear in 1845 in the *American Quarterly Journal of Agriculture* and subsequently in the *Transactions of the New York State Agricultural Society.* Particularly to be mentioned is a series of fourteen "Reports on the Noxious, Beneficial and Other Insects of the State of New York," in *Transactions,* **14–30** (1855–1872). Fitch also prepared "An Historical, Topographical, and Agricultural Survey of Washington County," in *Transactions,* **8–9** (1849–1850). A full bibliography of his entomological work is in J. A. Lintner, *First Annual Report on the Injurious and Other Insects of the State of New York* (Albany, 1882), pp. 289–325.

II. SECONDARY LITERATURE. Aside from brief biographical sketches, especially in *Dictionary of American Biography,* III, 424, there is no full-length study of Fitch, and very little published about him. Fitch's diary is the basis of Samuel Rezneck, "A Traveling School of Science on the Erie Canal in 1826," in *New York History,* **40** (July 1959), 255 ff.; "Diary of a New York Doctor in Illinois, 1830–31," in *Journal of the Illinois Historical Society,* **54** (1961), 25 ff.; see also D. L. Collins, "The Bug Catcher of Salem," in *New York State Bulletin* (March 1954).

SAMUEL REZNECK

FITTIG, RUDOLPH (*b.* Hamburg, Germany, 6 December 1835; *d.* Strasbourg, Alsace [France], 19 November 1910), *chemistry.*

Fittig was the son of Johann Andreas Fittig, the director of a private school in Hamburg. He wished to become a teacher, and at the age of sixteen he taught in a private school. In April 1856 he entered the University of Göttingen, intending to become a teacher of natural science, with special attention to botany. The father of one of his school friends planned to open a dye factory and suggested to young Fittig that he might be employed there. Fittig was interested and therefore took up the study of chemistry, which was then taught at Göttingen by Heinrich Limpricht. He soon decided to make this his career and became assistant to Limpricht in the laboratory and to Friedrich Wöhler, who was still lecturing. In 1858 Fittig received his doctorate and in 1860 became a *Privatdozent* at the university. He married in 1864 and had three sons and three daughters. His wife died while the children were still young, and he raised them by himself.

In 1866 Fittig became extraordinary professor of chemistry and worked closely with Wöhler. At this time he established a friendship with Friedrich Beilstein. In 1865, with Beilstein and Hans Hübner, he took over the editorship of the *Zeitschrift für Chemie und Pharmacie,* which had been edited since 1859 by Emile Erlenmeyer but had lost nearly all its subscribers. The three new editors produced a more successful journal under the title *Zeitschrift für Chemie,* and the venture lasted until 1871. In 1870 Fittig became professor of chemistry at the University of Tübingen, where he remained until he replaced Adolf von Baeyer as professor of chemistry at the University of Strasbourg in 1876. Here he constructed a new chemical laboratory, begun in 1877 and completed in 1882. Fittig served as rector of the university in 1895–1896; he retired in 1902, but continued to publish the results of his researches until nearly the end of his life. During his last years he was made an honorary member of many chemical societies.

Fittig was a prolific author and editor. Besides his activities on the *Zeitschrift für Chemie* he served as an associate editor of the *Annalen der Chemie* from

1895 to 1910, wrote a massive textbook of chemistry which appeared in 1871 and went through a number of editions, and edited the tenth edition of Wöhler's textbook of organic chemistry in 1877. His bibliography lists 399 research papers. Fittig trained many chemists who subsequently became well-known, including a number of Englishmen and Americans. Among the best-known of these were William Ramsay, noted for his work on the inert gases, who received his degree in 1872; and Ira Remsen, whose doctorate was conferred in 1870, and who worked on saccharin and was later president of Johns Hopkins University.

Fittig was essentially an experimentalist, with little interest in theoretical chemistry. He was active at a time when the structural theory of organic chemistry was producing its most striking results, and his extensive studies on preparative organic chemistry contributed much to this development. For his doctoral dissertation he studied the action of sodium on anhydrous acetone, in the course of which work he discovered pinacol. This utilization of sodium in an organic reaction probably led him to extend the studies begun by Wurtz on the reaction of sodium with organic halogen compounds. The action of sodium on benzene halides led Fittig to the discovery of a number of homologous aromatic compounds, including biphenyl. This reaction is known to organic chemists as the Wurtz-Fittig reaction. Fittig was led by these studies to the investigation of other aromatic compounds, and he carried out work on mesitylene and its derivatives, naphthalene, and fluorene. He was an independent discoverer of phenanthrene in coal tar. In 1873 he proposed the quinoid structure for benzoquinone, a structure later used to explain the behavior of numerous organic dyestuffs. After 1873 Fittig worked chiefly on unsaturated acids and lactones. The extent and variety of his work helped greatly to advance the progress of organic chemistry during its period of very rapid development, and he is rightly considered one of the outstanding chemists of his day.

BIBLIOGRAPHY

I. Original Works. A bibliography of the scientific papers of Fittig and his students is given in *Berichte der Deutschen chemischen Gesellschaft,* **44** (1911), 1383–1401. Among the more important papers are "Ueber das Monobrombenzol," in *Liebigs Annalen der Chemie,* **121** (1862), 361–365, in which the work on the Fittig synthesis is first described; "Ueber das Phenanthren, einen neuen Kohlenwasserstoff im Steinkohlenteer," in *Liebigs Annalen der Chemie,* **166** (1873), 361–382; and "Ueber Phenanthren und Anthracen," in *Berichte der Deutschen chemischen Gesellschaft,* **6** (1873) 167–169, in which the quinone formula is suggested.

II. Secondary Literature. An extensive biography with many personal details is F. Fichter, *Berichte der Deutschen chemischen Gesellschaft,* **44** (1911), 1339–1383; and a shorter biography is "R. M.," in *Journal of the Chemical Society,* **99** (1911), 1651–1653.

Henry M. Leicester

FITTON, WILLIAM HENRY (*b.* Dublin, Ireland, January 1780; *d.* London, England, 13 May 1861), *geology.*

Fitton was a son of Nicholas Fitton, a Dublin attorney. The family, long resident in Ireland, was descended from the Fittons of Gawsworth, Cheshire. Fitton entered Trinity College, Dublin, in 1794 and distinguished himself as a classical scholar, being awarded the senior scholarship in 1798 and graduating B.A. in 1799. In 1808 he went to Edinburgh University to study medicine and graduated M.D. in 1810. After a year or two in London he set up as a physician in the county town of Northampton in 1812 and remained there until 1820. During this period Fitton obtained other medical degrees, the M.B. and M.D. from Dublin in 1815 and the M.D. from Cambridge in 1816. In 1816 also he was admitted fellow of the Royal College of Physicians. In June 1820 he married Maria James (by which marriage he had five sons and three daughters) and, since she was a lady of some wealth, he gave up his practice and moved to London, thenceforth devoting himself to scientific, particularly geological, studies. He had been elected a fellow of the Royal Society in 1815 and had become a member of the Geological Society of London in 1816.

Fitton's interest in geology went back to his early years in Dublin, and the first volume of the *Transactions* of the Geological Society of London (1811) contained a paper about minerals found in the vicinity of Dublin, by Fitton and his friend Rev. Walter Stephens. In 1813, under the pseudonym "F," he published in Nicholson's *Journal of Natural Philosophy* two articles entitled "On the Geological System of Werner," a remarkably impartial review of Werner's theoretical views, their value, and their weaknesses. No doubt the fact that he had, while in Edinburgh, attended the lectures of Robert Jameson and T. C. Hope accounts for his being so well informed about the systems of both Werner and Hutton.

While in Northampton, Fitton began to write reviews of geological and medical books for the *Edinburgh Review.* Two published in 1817 and 1818 show that his interest in the early history of geology had been aroused. One of these in particular, his review of the publications of William Smith, directed the attention of geologists and others to the career and remarkable achievements of this still far from well-known man, who in 1815 had published a large-scale geological map of England and Wales but was not even a member of the Geological Society. Fitton made verbatim use of his reviews in some valuable articles, "Notes on the History of English Geology," which he contributed to the *Philosophical Magazine* (1832–1833). An article in the *Edinburgh Review* (1839) on Lyell's *Elements of Geology,* in which the Huttonian theory is discussed, and another on Murchison's *Silurian System* (1841), show that Fitton continued to be interested in the history of his favorite subject.

Fitton is perhaps better known for his contributions to stratigraphy and his elucidation of the succession of the Upper Jurassic and Lower Cretaceous strata of southern England. In his review of Smith's map he had endeavored to point out some of the errors, one of these being a confusion over the position in the stratigraphical succession of the beds of the Weald in southeast England. It was perhaps this which led Fitton, after his return to London from Northampton, to take a closer interest in this area, especially in Kent and Sussex. Then, in 1824, he examined sections in similar beds along the south coast of the Isle of Wight, already described by Thomas Webster in 1816.

In November 1824, Fitton published in Thomas Thomson's *Annals of Philosophy* a masterly account of the beds found below the Chalk in southeast England. Entitled "Inquiries Respecting the Geological Relations of the Beds Between the Chalk and the Purbeck Limestone in the South-east of England," it was accompanied by a colored geological map of the southern half of the Isle of Wight and geological sections showing the succession both there and on the neighboring coast of Dorset. In this article Fitton elucidated and corrected the errors which had arisen through the existence of different beds of ferruginous sands, with clays between.

Although it was some time before a final nomenclature was accepted, it was this paper which made it clear that there was an "Upper Greensand" just below the Chalk, with "Gault Clay" below it, as both William Smith and Thomas Webster had already recognized. Below this was the "Lower Greensand," and all three formations, Fitton pointed out, contained marine fossils. He also showed that the Weald Clay, containing many freshwater fossils, was present beneath the Lower Greensand not only in the Weald but also in the Isle of Wight and on the Dorset coast, and beneath these beds there were ferruginous sands, also with freshwater fossils (which clearly distinguished them from the Lower Greensand). These he named the Hastings Sands, after the town on the Sussex coast where they were well exposed. By providing a tabular "List of Strata From the Chalk to the Hastings Sands, With Synonimes [*sic*] of Different Geologists," he made it clear just what errors had arisen.

Fitton continued to study the Lower Cretaceous and Upper Jurassic strata, both in England and in northern France, and in 1836 published a monograph entitled "On Some of the Strata Between the Chalk and the Oxford Oolite (e.g., Corallian) in the South-east of England" (*Transactions of the Geological Society,* 2nd ser., **4**). This covered much the same field as his earlier paper, but was far longer and embodied many detailed observations, including a number on rocks exposed between Dorset and the Norfolk coast. Accompanied by maps and sections, it is regarded by geologists as a classic contribution to stratigraphy.

Later, between 1843 and 1847, he demonstrated the existence of a clay, the Atherfield Clay, at the base of the Lower Greensand but clearly different from the Weald Clay because it contained marine fossils and marked the readvance of the sea after a long nonmarine episode; he also provided detailed descriptions of an important section along the southwest coast of the Isle of Wight and discussed the equivalents of the Wealden beds in Europe.

Fitton's only separately published work was a small volume entitled *A Geological Sketch of the Vicinity of Hastings* (London, 1833), which gives a good account of the Wealden strata, with sections and a bibliography. He was always ready to instruct naturalist travelers in the principles of geology, and he took a particular interest in the geology of Australia. His last published paper, in the *Proceedings of the Geographical Society* in 1857, was entitled "On the Structure of North-west Australia."

Fitton was secretary of the Geological Society of London from 1822 to 1824 and president from 1827 to 1829. He was largely instrumental in establishing its printed *Proceedings,* which first appeared in 1827. In this publication the presidential addresses were printed, Fitton's being the first to appear, commencing that valuable series in which the progress of geology was annually reviewed. He served as vice-president of the society from 1831 to 1846 and in 1852 was awarded the Wollaston Medal, the society's premier award, in recognition of his important contribution to stratigraphy.

BIBLIOGRAPHY

I. Original Works. Except for his *Geological Sketch of the Vicinity of Hastings* (London, 1833), all of Fitton's contributions to geology appeared in scientific periodicals and are listed in Agassiz's *Bibliographia zoologiae et geologiae* (London, 1850) and the *Catalogue of Scientific Papers (1800–1863)* published by the Royal Society (London, 1868). Both should be consulted.

II. SECONDARY LITERATURE. An obituary notice in the *Quarterly Journal of the Geological Society of London,* **18** (1862), xxx–xxxiv, provides the fullest information about Fitton's life and work; other accounts, all brief, appear to be derived from it. W. Munk's *The Roll of the Royal College of Physicians,* III (London, 1878), 154, gives some additional facts. Biographies of his geological contemporaries do not throw much light on his activities, except for *The Journal of Gideon Mantell,* E. C. Curwen, ed. (London, 1940). J. Challinor, "Some Correspondence of Thomas Webster, Geologist (1773–1844)," in *Annals of Science,* **17–20** (1961–1964), includes twenty-seven letters from Fitton, and there are also interesting references to him in the other letters. A catalog of the sale of his library in 1856 is in the British Museum library.

JOAN M. EYLES

FITZGERALD, GEORGE FRANCIS (*b.* Dublin, Ireland, 3 August 1851; *d.* Dublin, 21 February 1901), *physics.*

FitzGerald was one of the initial group, which included Heaviside, Hertz, and Lorentz, that took Maxwell's electromagnetic theory seriously and began to explore its consequences. Very few others used Maxwell's theory to obtain results beyond those investigated by Maxwell himself. Among the first attempts to use the theory for such results was FitzGerald's paper, "Electromagnetic Theory of the Reflection and Refraction of Light," which Maxwell reviewed for the *Philosophical Transactions,* noting that it related to work carried out by H. A. Lorentz.

It is ironic that FitzGerald is best known for work that was probably of minor importance to him and was outside his work in electromagnetic theory. Together with Lorentz he is credited with being the first to explain the null results of the Michelson-Morley experiment as due to the contraction of an arm of the interferometer, which resulted from its motion through the ether. FitzGerald's ideas on the subject were published in *Science* (1889), and he also discussed the contraction hypothesis with Oliver Lodge. In a paper presented to the Physical Society in May 1892, Lodge commented, "Professor FitzGerald has suggested a way out of the difficulty by supposing the size of bodies to be a function of their velocity through ether."

In 1894 Lorentz wrote to FitzGerald about the hypothesis, and inquired whether he had indeed published on it. In his reply, FitzGerald mentioned his letter to *Science,* but at the same time admitted that he did not know if the letter had ever been printed and that he was "pretty sure" Lorentz had priority. Soon Lorentz began to refer to FitzGerald in his discussions.

Only after FitzGerald's death did English physicists begin to take any further notice. Thus in his Adam's Prize essay, published as *Aether and Matter,* Larmor discussed the Michelson-Morley experiment and the contraction effect in detail, but only Lorentz was mentioned in this connection. Two years later, Larmor, in his introduction to FitzGerald's papers, claimed priority for FitzGerald on the contraction effect. E. T. Whittaker, in the *History of the Theories of Aether and Electricity,* states that Lorentz obtained the hypothesis from FitzGerald; but it appears that Lorentz' concept was independent of FitzGerald's and that he was just giving due credit to FitzGerald.

A further piece of evidence gives additional weight to the argument that the contraction effect was not an important issue with FitzGerald. He carried on an extensive correspondence with Heaviside from 1888 to 1900, in which they discussed many major problems of the physics of the period. In all the surviving correspondence, the Michelson-Morley experiment is mentioned only once. The interest in the Michelson-Morley experiment from the time of the experiment until the development of the theory of relativity has perhaps been exaggerated.

We gather some insight into FitzGerald's view of his work from a letter to Heaviside dated 4 February 1889:

> I admire from a distance those who contain themselves till they worked to the bottom of their results but as I am not in the very least sensitive to having made mistakes I rush out with all sorts of crude notions in hope that they may set others thinking and lead to some advance.

The view is of a speculator, a scientist who generates ideas but does not necessarily develop them. Although FitzGerald's papers contain many examples of sound development, this description seems fair. In the same letter he was excited by Heaviside's work on the electromagnetic field caused by a moving charged sphere:

> I am very glad to hear that you have solved completely the problem. . . . I was anxious to find out how much energy is lost by the earth owing to its magnetisation rotating and going round the sun. . . . to what extent the energy of motion of molecules could be attributed to electrical charges on them and how this part of their energy would be radiated; this might lead to a theory of forces between molecules. . . . You ask what if the velocity be greater than that of light? I have often asked myself that but got no satisfactory answer. The most obvious thing to ask in reply is "Is it possible?"

In an 1893 letter to Heaviside, this speculation is extended supporting this view of his work:

> ... have you considered what would be the extra mass of an atom owing to its atomic charge? A charge of electricity or magnetism acts like an added mass ... this should interfere with Kepler's Laws....

It is worth noting that FitzGerald took seriously his responsibilities as a teacher, both in Trinity College, Dublin, where he spent his academic life as student and teacher, and throughout Ireland through the boards he served on.

BIBLIOGRAPHY

See J. Larmor, ed., *The Scientific Writings of the Late George Francis FitzGerald* (Dublin, 1902).

FitzGerald's communication to *Science* concerning the Michelson-Morley experiment was published as "The Ether and the Earth's Atmosphere," **13** (1889), 390. Steven Brush, "Note on the History of the FitzGerald-Lorentz Contraction," in *Isis,* **58,** no. 2 (1967), 230–232, gives a full account and reproduces the original article and the correspondence between FitzGerald and Lorentz.

ALFRED M. BORK

FITZROY, ROBERT (*b.* Ampton Hall, Suffolk, England, 5 July 1805; *d.* Upper Norwood, London, England, 30 April 1865), *hydrography, meteorology.*

Fitzroy was the second son, by a second marriage, of Lord Charles Fitzroy; his paternal grandfather was Augustus Henry, third duke of Grafton, and his maternal grandfather was the first marquis of Londonderry. As a member of an aristocratic family noted for its association with seafaring, he entered the Royal Naval College at Portsmouth in 1819. He achieved the rank of lieutenant in 1824 and sailed on British naval vessels plying Mediterranean and South American waters.

Fitzroy received his first full command of a ship in 1828, when he was placed in charge of the *Beagle.* Under the command of Captain Philip Parker King, the *Beagle* and the *Adventure* had left England in 1826 with orders to survey the southern coasts of South America. Upon the death of the *Beagle*'s original commander, Pringle Stokes, Fitzroy was asked to complete the hydrographical tasks assigned to the ship. This first *Beagle* voyage to South America ended in the fall of 1830 with the expedition's return to England. During the summer of 1831, the *Beagle* was readied for her second surveying voyage to South America. Fitzroy, as the expedition's commander, chose the young Charles Darwin to accompany him on what was to be one of the most famous scientific expeditions in history. Fitzroy was promoted to captain in July 1835. Upon completion of the work in South America, the expedition returned to England in 1836 and Fitzroy married Mary Henrietta O'Brien.

After publishing the narrative of the two South American expeditions with which he was associated, Fitzroy sought a seat in Parliament and was elected a member for Durham in 1841. His short political career, marked by a violent public quarrel with his chief rival, was interrupted by Fitzroy's appointment to the governorship of New Zealand (1843). The New Zealand interlude proved disastrous for Fitzroy, even though he cannot be held personally accountable for all the troubles that arose during his term of office. By 1845 he had returned home, and in 1848 he was named superintendent of the dockyard at Woolwich. Before his retirement from active naval service in 1850, Fitzroy commanded the navy's first screw-driven steamship, the *Arrogant,* during her initial trial runs. Thus ended Fitzroy's active naval career, but he continued to rise in rank by reason of his seniority—becoming rear admiral in 1857 and vice admiral in 1863.

In the years of his retirement, Fitzroy turned his attention to the emerging science of meteorology and devoted all of his energies to the advancement of its practical aspects. His total absorption in his meteorological work—and his extreme sensitivity to criticisms of it—may have contributed to the mental illness that ended in his suicide.

Fitzroy deserves to be noted in the history of nineteenth-century science because of his association with Charles Darwin and because of his contributions to the fields of hydrography and meteorology.

Darwin, in his *Autobiography,* wrote: "The voyage of the *Beagle* has been by far the most important event in my life and has determined my whole career" (*The Autobiography of Charles Darwin,* Nora Barlow, ed. [New York, 1959], p. 76). Fitzroy, who was more concerned with science than were many naval officers of his day, made it possible for Darwin to visit tropical lands and study their flora, fauna, and geology. The two men shared the same cabin and Fitzroy was attentive to the scientific needs and interests of the young Darwin. Fitzroy's violent temper and his conservative opinions on religion and slavery were responsible for some disagreements between them, but Fitzroy and Darwin remained on friendly terms. So close was their relationship that on the journey home they sent a joint letter to a South African newspaper defending English missionary activity in the South Pacific.

Later in life Fitzroy became worried about the deleterious effect of scientific advances upon religious beliefs. As a result, he joined the opposition to Darwin's *Origin of Species.* At the famous Oxford meeting of the British Association for the Advancement of Science (1860), when Darwinism was the issue in a hot vocal debate, Fitzroy took a public stand against organic evolution. He told the audience he regretted Darwin's publication of the *Origin* and announced his refusal to accept the book as a logical arrangement of the facts of natural history. Darwin, who was not personally involved in the debate, preferred to remember his earlier, happier association with Fitzroy and always spoke kindly of his *Beagle* companion.

While Darwin made his observations in South America and collected his specimens, Fitzroy surveyed the southern coast of that continent. The years of the second *Beagle* voyage marked the beginning of a half-century of supremacy of British hydrography. In the period 1829–1855 Britain's Hydrographic Department was directed by her greatest hydrographer, Sir Francis Beaufort, who sent out some 170 major surveying expeditions. Through these expeditions the Admiralty was able to assemble a collection of accurate charts covering most of the earth's coastlines (with the exclusion of northeast Asia and Japan).

Beaufort ordered Fitzroy to continue the South American charting program begun by King in 1826. Fitzroy and his staff of surveyors furnished the Admiralty with eighty-two coastal sheets, eighty plans of harbors, and forty views covering portions of Patagonia, Tierra del Fuego, Chile, and Peru.

In addition to its surveying equipment, the *Beagle* was supplied with twenty-two chronometers. Utilizing these instruments, Fitzroy established a chain of meridian distances through the Pacific, Indian, and Atlantic oceans. That is, relying upon the accuracy of his chronometers and the celestial observations he made on the voyage, Fitzroy was able to make precise determinations of longitude at a series of positions around the globe.

The surveys he carried out in South American waters established Fitzroy as a first-rate hydrographer and won for him the gold medal of the Royal Geographical Society (1837). Because his marine surveys were accurate to such a high degree they are still used as the foundation for a number of charts of that area.

In 1851 Fitzroy was elected a fellow of the Royal Society of London on the strength of his contributions to hydrography and scientific navigation. These events marked his entrance into another field of scientific endeavor: meteorology.

Ever since his *Beagle* days Fitzroy had shown an interest in the study of the weather. Therefore, when the British government created (1855) the Meteorologic Office, instructed to gather weather information for shipping, it was not surprising that the Royal Society should ask that Fitzroy be placed in charge of it.

While a committee of the Royal Society deliberated about the exact nature of the work to be done by the Meteorologic Office, Fitzroy contacted the ship captains who would make meteorological observations for him. He was not satisfied merely to amass weather information; he wanted to warn sailors and others of approaching weather changes. He began by making available cheap barometers, with accompanying instructions, to coastal fishermen. His next move was to set up a series of stations which would telegraph weather data to the Meteorologic Office in London. Using this data, Fitzroy produced some of the first weather charts and began issuing weather forecasts, a term he helped to popularize. By the end of 1860 the *Times* was printing daily weather forecasts and Fitzroy was gaining recognition as the man who could predict coming weather conditions. At the height of his career as a pioneer forecaster, Fitzroy published a large, introductory *Weather Book* (1863) that summarized his meteorological work.

Fitzroy's position at the Meteorologic Office was clearly defined as "statist," that is, collector of weather information. Forecasting had carried him somewhat beyond his original instructions, and he soon encountered light criticism from the public when his forecasts failed—as they often did—and heavier criticism from scientists who argued that his whole approach to meteorology was marked by an excessive reliance upon the empirical at the expense of theoretical developments. These critics wanted the general theories of the science of meteorology established before weather predictions were made public. In the midst of this controversy Fitzroy took his own life. At his death the theorists won out, but public demand assured that at least his storm warnings would be continued. In retrospect it is clear that Fitzroy's difficulties arose more from the state of the new science of meteorology than from some fundamental failing of his own.

BIBLIOGRAPHY

I. Original Works. Fitzroy's account of the two *Beagle* voyages is to be found in the first two volumes of his *Narrative of the Surveying Voyages of His Majesty's Ships Adventure and Beagle, Between the Years 1826 and 1836,* 3 vols. (London, 1839). Vol. III of the *Narrative* was written by Charles Darwin and has frequently been reprinted as a separate volume. The results of Fitzroy's hydrographical work in South America were incorporated into a series of Admiralty charts issued by the Hydrographic Department. From the *Beagle* period there are also the Fitzroy-Darwin letter on missionary activity, "A Letter Containing Remarks on the Moral State of Tahiti, New Zealand, etc.," in *South African Christian Recorder,* **2,** no. 4 (Sept. 1836), 221–238; and Fitzroy's *Sailing Directions for South America* (London, 1848).

The meteorological contributions of Fitzroy can be studied in publications he wrote for the Board of Trade: *Annual Report of the Meteorologic Office* (London, 1856–1864) and *Barometer and Weather Guide* (London, 1858; final ed., 1877). Fitzroy's *The Weather Book: A Manual of Practical Meteorology* (London, 1863) was intended for a wider audience.

MSS relating to Fitzroy's career as meteorologist are located in the Meteorological Office Archives (London Road, Bracknell, Berkshire). They include correspondence, memoranda, and correspondence books. Other Fitzroy MSS can be found in the J. F. W. Herschel Collection of the Royal Society and at the National Maritime Museum, Greenwich.

II. SECONDARY LITERATURE. H. E. L. Mellersh, *Fitzroy of the Beagle* (London, 1968), is a recent popular but reliable guide to Fitzroy's life. Darwin's remarks on Fitzroy and the *Beagle* voyage are found in Nora Barlow, ed., *The Autobiography of Charles Darwin* (New York, 1959), pp. 71–76. Other aspects of the Darwin-Fitzroy relationship can be pursued in the extensive published material dealing with Darwin's early years.

For Fitzroy as hydrographer see Sir Archibald Day, *The Admiralty Hydrographic Service, 1795–1919* (London, 1967), *passim;* G. S. Ritchie, *The Admiralty Chart* (London, 1967), pp. 183–190, 203–210, 215–220; and H. P. Douglas, "Fitzroy's Hydrographic Surveys," in *Nature,* **129,** no. 3249 (6 Feb. 1932), 200.

Fitzroy's meteorological contributions are discussed in Sir David Brunt, "The Centenary of the Meteorological Office: Retrospect and Prospect," in *Science Progress,* **44,** no. 174 (Apr. 1956), 193–195; Sir Napier Shaw, *Manual of Meteorology: Volume I. Meteorology in History* (Cambridge, 1932), pp. 149–153, 302–303, 311; and *Selected Meteorological Papers* (London, 1955), pp. 236–237; and Roger Prouty, *The Transformation of the Board of Trade* (London, 1957), pp. 52–54.

GEORGE BASALLA

FIZEAU, ARMAND-HIPPOLYTE-LOUIS (*b.* Paris, France, 23 September 1819; *d.* Venteuil, near Jouarre, France, 18 September 1896), *experimental physics.*

Fizeau was the eldest son of a large and relatively wealthy family that had come to Paris from the Vendée. His father held the chair of internal pathology at the Paris Faculty of Medicine from 1823. Fizeau, aspiring to follow in his father's footsteps, began medical studies at the Collège Stanislas, but because of poor health he was obliged to interrupt his education in order to travel to a more agreeable climate. On returning to Paris, he gave up medicine and began an entirely new career in the physical sciences. At the Collège de France, he studied optics with H.-V. Regnault, and he followed the lectures given at the École Polytechnique through the notebooks compiled by one of his brothers. Fizeau's most fruitful educational experience, however, was the course of study he took at the Paris observatory under the tutelage of the famous astronomer François Arago. Arago recognized Fizeau's promise, encouraged his scientific endeavors, and brought his work to the attention of the Academy of Sciences.

Fizeau was made a member of the section of physics of the Academy of Sciences on 2 January 1860. He was vice-president of his section for 1877 and president for 1878. In 1878 he was elected to the Bureau of Longitudes. On 9 July 1856 the five academies constituting the Institut de France awarded him the Triennial Prize, a special award that had just been created by the emperor. From the Royal Society he received the Rumford Medal in 1866 and the title of foreign member in 1875.

On 19 August 1839 Arago made public a description of a new process of "light painting" or heliography that had been invented by L.-J.-M. Daguerre. The daguerrotype, as the result of this process soon came to be called, was a crude forerunner of the modern photograph. Fizeau's earliest work in science was an attempt to improve Daguerre's process and to make the heliograph an instrument of science. He showed that by covering the surface of the developed plate with a salt of gold, oxidation of the surface chemicals could be prevented and the contrasts between light and dark could be considerably heightened. He is often credited with the first use of bromine vapors to hasten the development of the photographic image, but this seems uncertain.[1] Fizeau also introduced a widely used but unpatented method for turning a photograph into a photoetching.

During this early period of his career, Fizeau often worked in collaboration with Léon Foucault, a young man who had also begun his education in medicine. Foucault was one of the most adept mechanicians of his age, and had he been able to tolerate the sight of blood, he might have become a great surgeon. Together the two young scientists worked on the improvement of photographic images, and in 1845 they opened a new and fruitful area of astronomy by taking what were probably the first clear photographs of the sun's surface.[2]

From 1844 Fizeau and Foucault undertook a series of precise and mechanically ingenious optical experiments that would ultimately have a profound effect on the course of physics. By the middle of the nineteenth century, most scientists had come to accept the wave theory of light, formulated near the beginning of the century by Thomas Young and Augustin Fresnel. There remained, however, several gaps in the investigation of the experimental consequences of the theory. For example, in the study of interference fringes produced by two rays of light issuing from the same source, only several dozen fringes on each side of the central band had been observed.

By analyzing the white light source into simpler constituents by means of a spectroscope, Fizeau and Foucault were able to observe fringes produced by interfering light rays with a difference of travel equal to more than 7,000 wavelengths, thus showing that light waves, like sound waves, remain geometrically constant over a large number of periods. But light waves, because of their transverse vibrations, are more complex than sound waves. Light can assume different forms or planes of vibration as well as different intensities. Using the same spectroscopic apparatus as in the preceding experiment, Fizeau and Foucault observed the interaction of two rays produced by passing a single polarized ray through a birefringent crystal. In this case, instead of obtaining alternating bands of light and dark, they obtained bands of light periodically polarized in different planes of vibration.

In 1800 William Herschel, the British astronomer, discovered a form of invisible radiation above the red end of the spectrum which produced a heating effect. The infrared rays (or calorific rays as they were usually called) were shown to follow most laws that had been established for visible light. By using extremely small and delicate thermometers, Fizeau and Foucault demonstrated that calorific rays could produce interference fringes like those produced by visible light, except that instead of appearing as alternating bands of light and dark, the fringes produced by infrared rays appeared as alternating bands of hot and cold.

One of the most important consequences of the wave theory of light that had not yet been demonstrated was that light traveled more slowly in dense than in rare mediums. In 1838 Arago had suggested using a rapidly rotating mirror for the purpose of this demonstration, a technique employed by William Wheatstone in 1834 in an unsuccessful attempt to measure the speed of electricity. In principle, Arago's idea was very simple. A narrow ray of light would be directed into a mirror rotating as rapidly as possible. The light from this mirror would be reflected back over the same path by a fixed mirror placed at a considerable distance. By the time the light had returned, the rotating mirror, having suffered a small angular displacement, would deflect the light off at an angle to the original path. If, in addition, the light returning from the fixed mirror were divided into two rays and one of them were sent through a tube of water, it would then be possible to establish directly, and without having to measure the absolute speeds of the two rays, whether the light had been slowed by its passage through the denser medium. Theoretically, the ray that had come through the tube filled with water would arrive at the rotating mirror a fraction of a second after the ray that had come through the air and would thus be deflected at a greater angle.

In practice, the essential problem was to arrange an optical system such that the narrow, intermittent rays of light were not dispersed in their passage between the two mirrors. After considerable trial, Fizeau and Foucault found a workable system, the essential element of which was a convergent reflector of convenient focal length. Unfortunately, once having solved this problem, the two experimenters broke up their partnership over a personal dispute. Each continued to work on the experiment. On 6 May 1850 two papers on the relative speeds of light in water and in air were submitted to the Academy of Sciences, one signed by Foucault, the other by Fizeau and Louis Bréguet. With almost identical apparatus, the two experiments had yielded substantially the same result. Light did, indeed, travel faster in air than in water.

Fizeau was not satisfied merely with determining the relative velocities of light. He wanted to measure with some precision the absolute velocity. In 1849 he had conceived an ingenious mechanism that would enable him to achieve his goal: a large toothed wheel was spun rapidly about its axis, and a beam of light sent through the spaces between the teeth was reflected back to its source by a fixed mirror. When the wheel was rotated rapidly enough, the intermittent light rays returning from the mirror intersected the path of the teeth and thus became invisible to the observer stationed behind the wheel. As the mechanism was turned faster and faster, the light reappeared and disappeared alternately. The time required for the light to travel through the carefully measured distance was a simple function of the angular displacement of the wheel.

In 1849 Fizeau made a trial of his new method between his father's house at Suresnes and Montmartre. The figure he obtained for the speed of light (about 315,000 kilometers per second) was not quite as accurate as the results of astronomical calculations, but the practicability of the method was established and became the basis of the more precise determinations made by Alfred Cornu in the 1870's.

By substituting for teeth alternating bands of conducting and nonconducting materials, Fizeau attempted with little success to adopt his mechanism to the measurement of the speed of electricity. (A galvanometer, of course, replaced the eye of the observer.) In 1849 Fizeau tried the experiment with the engineer E. Gounelle, but the results were indecisive because of the complex way in which electricity is propagated through a conductor.

In 1848 Fizeau published a paper that was to have a profound effect on the future of astrophysics. He showed that when a body emitting a continuous sound of unvarying frequency is moved, the sound waves do not dispose themselves symmetrically about the source. In front they come at shorter intervals, producing the effect of higher pitch; from behind the frequency appears lowered because of the larger interval between wave crests. (The sound of a passing railroad train is the classic example of this phenomenon.) Fizeau saw the implications of this principle for optics. A moving light source would undergo an analogous change in frequency. From behind, the light waves would be shifted toward the red end of the spectrum; from the front they would be shifted toward the violet.

Unknown to Fizeau, a physicist from Prague, Christian Doppler, had published a paper on exactly the same subject in 1842, six years before the appearance of Fizeau's work. Doppler, however, failed to understand correctly some of the consequences of his own idea. He supposed that light coming from a star moving relative to the earth would experience a change in color.[3] He was apparently unaware of the invisible radiations at the red and violet ends of the spectrum that would, by their shift into the visible range of the spectrum, compensate for the disappearance of any colored rays. The Doppler-Fizeau effect became useful in astronomy only after the work of Gustav Kirchhoff and Robert Bunsen showing that incandescent elements emit discrete frequencies of light. It then became possible, by measuring the shift in the spectra produced by the various elements in a given star, to ascertain the velocity of that star relative to the earth. The first such measurement was made in 1868 by the British astronomer William Huggins, and since then the technique has provided the science of astrophysics with one of its most important tools for measuring the size and structure of the universe.

Nearly all scientists in the nineteenth century believed that some sort of luminiferous ether filled the universe and provided the medium for the propagation of light. One of the many problems that arose with respect to the nature of the ether was whether it could participate in the motion of ponderous matter. In 1818 Fresnel discussed this question in a famous letter addressed to Arago. He assumed that bodies carried with them only as much ether as they contained in excess of that which was present in an equal volume of space void of all ponderous matter. By assuming in addition that the excess of ether contained in a given body of matter was proportional to its refractive index, Fresnel deduced that the percentage of a body's motion that could be communicated to light was equal to $1 - \frac{1}{n^2}$, where n represents the refractive index.

In 1851 Fizeau found a way of overcoming the seemingly impossible difficulty of measuring the small increment in the velocity of light that in theory would be produced by a body in motion. His method was simply to produce interference fringes from rays of light that had passed through two parallel tubes containing a fluid moving in opposite directions. Even a relatively small difference in the velocity of the two light rays would cause a perceptible displacement of the interference fringes. Using air as the test medium, Fizeau discerned no change in the speed of light, a result that he expected because the refractive index of air is equal almost to one. With water, however, the velocity of light was altered by an amount that accorded reasonably well with Fresnel's formula. In 1886 A. A. Michelson and E. W. Morley repeated the experiment on a larger scale and confirmed Fizeau's results.

In a world that was becoming increasingly professional, Fizeau was one of the last great amateurs of science. He was able to employ his personal wealth and virtually unlimited leisure in pursuit of his scientific researches. Except for the Doppler-Fizeau effect, he made no direct contributions to optical theory, but the ingenious experimental techniques that he invented were to supply an invaluable aid to the creation in this century of a new optics. That his reputation has not equaled his deeds is largely because once he had invented a new experimental method, he left it to his followers and collaborators to develop and perfect. Foucault went on to employ the rotating-mirror device in precise measurements of the speed of light; Cornu perfected the toothed-wheel mechanism for the same purpose; and much of the career of A. A. Michelson was built on Fizeau's unfinished business.

Fizeau married a daughter of the famous botanist Adrien de Jussieu. She died early in the marriage, after having given birth to two daughters and a son. After his wife's death, Fizeau retired to his home near Jouarre and came to Paris only rarely, to attend meetings of the Academy of Sciences and the Bureau of Longitudes. He died of cancer of the jaw just five days before his seventy-seventh birthday. His son and younger daughter survived him.

NOTES

1. Historians of photography sometimes give credit for this development to the Englishman J. F. Goddard, but since the photosensitive properties of silver bromide were widely known, the idea of trying bromine vapors in place of iodine was, perhaps, too obvious to be considered an important discovery.
2. A photograph of the moon had been taken as early as 1840 by J. W. Draper of New York.
3. Stars do change color, but not in the way that Doppler thought they did. The intensities of stars' electromagnetic emissions are not equitably distributed throughout the spectrum, and any shift in the maximum energy distribution of a star's visible light will appear as a color change; what Doppler failed to understand was the idea of frequency shift.

BIBLIOGRAPHY

Fizeau wrote no major publications. A list of his scientific articles is in Émile Picard, *Les théories de l'optique et l'oeuvre d'Hippolyte Fizeau* (Paris, 1924), pp. 57–64. There is also a list, presumably complete, in the Royal Society's *Catalogue of Scientific Papers.* Unfortunately there is no major biography of Fizeau. Virtually all the information we have about his life and work comes from Alfred Cornu, "Notice sur l'oeuvre scientifique d'Hippolyte Fizeau," in *Annuaire pour l'an 1898, publié par le Bureau des longitudes* (Paris, 1898[?]), notice C, pp. 1–40. The work by Picard, mentioned above, contains substantially the same information, but Picard has attempted to place his discussion in a broader historical context by relating Fizeau's work to the optical theories that came before and after him. A number of brief biographical notices appeared in various scientific journals just after Fizeau's death. A list of them is found in Picard, p. 64. The Academy of Sciences in Paris is reported to have some of Fizeau's MSS and a portrait.

J. B. GOUGH

FLAMMARION, CAMILLE (*b.* Montigny-le-Roi, France, 26 February 1842; *d.* Juvisy, France, 3 June 1925), *astronomy.*

At the time of Flammarion's birth his parents owned a small store, but his father had been a farmer and Flammarion often mentioned this with pride. He was the oldest of four children. His interest in astronomy dated from his early childhood, when on 9 October 1847 and 28 July 1851 he was able to observe solar eclipses. By the time he was eleven he was busily making astronomical and meteorological observations.

In 1856 his parents' disastrous financial condition led them to move to Paris. For the young Flammarion, this was a decisive event, since Paris offered him immensely greater opportunities for self-improvement. He found employment as apprentice engraver, attended evening courses at the Polytechnic Association, learned English, and pursued his studies of algebra and geometry.

A chance encounter in 1858 marked the start of his career; a physician who was treating Flammarion noticed a bulky, 500-page manuscript written by the young man and entitled *Cosmogonie universelle.* The doctor read it and was so impressed that he brought it to the attention of Le Verrier, who was director of the Paris Observatory. A few days later, Flammarion was hired by the observatory to work in the Bureau de Calcul as an apprentice astronomer.

In 1861 Flammarion wrote *La pluralité des mondes habités,* his first book to be published. In this he revealed the pleasant literary style that was to make him the most important popularizer of science at the turn of the twentieth century. In 1862 he was calculator to the Bureau des Longitudes. He wrote for the *Annuaire du cosmos* and published the *Annuaire astronomique et météorologique,* first in the *Magasin pittoresque,* then later in *L'astronomie.* During the same period he also wrote many popularizing articles for the newspapers and delivered very successful series of lectures in Paris, the provinces, and several other European capitals.

Flammarion became greatly interested in the problems of the atmosphere. Between 1867 and 1880 he made many balloon flights in order to study atmospheric phenomena. In 1871 he published *L'atmosphère. Les terres du ciel* appeared in 1877 and then, in 1880, the famous *Astronomie populaire,* his best-known work, a true best seller that was translated into many languages and which, more than any other book ever written, spread interest in astronomy. It was followed in 1882 by *Les étoiles et les curiosités du ciel.*

At this point in Flammarion's career, his scientific output was considerable and concerned with many subjects, including volcanology, atmospheric electricity, and climatology. Special mention must be made of his research concerning Mars. Scientific opinion of that time held that Mars was the only planet on which traces of life might be found. At the Juvisy Observatory, founded by him in 1883, Flammarion made numerous observations of the planet. As early as 1876 he had noticed the seasonal variations of the dark spots. In 1909 he completed *La planète Mars et ses conditions d'habitabilité,* a compilation of all known observations since 1636.

In 1887 Flammarion founded the French Astronomical Society, a model for all groups aiming to spread interest in science among the general public. For the first time relatively powerful astronomical instruments were put at public disposal, thus allowing numerous amateurs to indulge their taste for science. The activities of the French Astronomical Society created a reservoir of scientists from which emerged most of the outstanding French astronomers of this century.

It was inevitable that Flammarion, who possessed an extraordinary intellectual curiosity and imagination, take an interest in what today is called parapsychology. His taste for scientific precision and his intellectual honesty led him to unmask the inaccuracies, lies, and hoaxes that have always encumbered this field. He directed investigations of and performed experiments in psychic phenomena and gathered most of the results into several books, including *La mort et son mystère, L'inconnu et les problèmes psychiques,* and *Les maisons hantées.*

His love of life and his profound sensitivity led Flammarion to a literary as well as a scientific career. He published several novels, in which science serves as a backdrop.

BIBLIOGRAPHY

Flammarion's most important works in astronomy and geophysics, all published in Paris, are *Astronomie populaire* (1880); *Les étoiles et les curiosités du ciel* (1882); *Les terres du ciel* (1877); *Les merveilles célestes; La planète Mars et ses conditions d'habitabilité* (1892); *La planète Vénus; Les étoiles doubles; L'atmosphère* (1871); *Mes voyages aériens; Tremblements de terre et éruptions volcaniques; L'éruption du Krakatoa; Les caprices de la foudre; Les phénomènes de la foudre* (1905); and *Le monde avant la création de l'homme* (1885).

In philosophy, see *La pluralité des mondes habités; L'inconnu et les problèmes psychiques* (1900); *Les forces naturelles inconnues; La mort et son mystère,* 3 vols. (1920–1921); and *Les maisons hantées,* all published in Paris.

His autobiography is *Mémoires biographiques et philosophiques d'un astronome.* His novels include *Uranie* (1889) and *Stella.*

ROGER SERVAJEAN

FLAMSTEED, JOHN (*b.* Denby, England, 19 August 1646; *d.* Greenwich, England, 31 December 1719), *astronomy.*

The only son of Stephen Flamsteed, a prosperous businessman, and Mary Spateman, he was raised in comfortable circumstances in Derby, England. During a childhood marred by the deaths of his mother and stepmother, he attended the Derby free school and received the normal preparation for university study. Unfortunately, his educational plans were forestalled by a serious breakdown of his health when, at the age of fourteen, he was afflicted with a severe rheumatic condition and complications therefrom, which left him so debilitated as to render his health a subject of grave concern for the rest of his days. His later correspondence is filled with allusions to periodic incapacity and reports of (generally unsuccessful) medication for it. The most immediate consequence of his frailty was his father's refusal to send him on to university in 1662. Flamsteed was deeply disappointed, but his misfortune may well have been a disguised blessing, since, left to his own devices, he was able to follow his own interests to a degree that would otherwise have been impossible. With his introduction to Sacrobosco shortly after leaving school, the direction of those interests was established for life.

The period between 1662 and 1669 was for Flamsteed one of education in the details of astronomical science. The major impediment to his progress seems not to have been the lack of instruction, in which respect he would scarcely have been better off at Oxford or Cambridge, but the fact that his "studies were discountenanced by my father as much in the beginning as they have been since."[1] As late as 1673, Flamsteed was receiving mail through a friend, "that my father might not see all the letters that come to me."[2] The ostensible basis of the father's attitude was, of course, the son's weak constitution; but various of Flamsteed's remarks betray a suspicion that he had been kept away from university more because of the help that a capable only son could render in tending a motherless home and a flourishing business than for any other reason. In spite of the time lost to business and illness, however, Flamsteed persevered. By the end of 1669, he was ready to put himself up for professional consideration.

Flamsteed's debut was a cautious one. Rejecting certain of his efforts that might be "beyond the capacity of the vulgar,"[3] he chose to submit—anonymously—to the Royal Society a small ephemeris of lunar occultations for 1670. He was soon engaged in extensive correspondence with Henry Oldenburg and John Collins, the scientific "clearinghouses" of the day. Through them he was introduced to Sir Jonas Moore, whose interest and influence were to be decisive in the launching of his career. Already from their first meeting in 1670, he emerged with a micrometer and the promise of good telescope lenses, which equipment enabled him to inaugurate his serious observational work. By the winter of 1674–1675 the enthusiastic master of the royal ordinance was attempting to organize patronage for an observatory. In the midst of his labors there appeared at court a French dilettante (sponsored by the king's mistress) who claimed to have solved the problem of determining terrestrial longitudes, long recognized as the principal desideratum for safer navigation. When Moore called upon his protégé for judgment of the claim, Flamsteed replied convincingly that neither the positions of the stars nor the motions of the moon were well enough known to render the proposed method practicable. The result was the immediate realization of Moore's plans and more. The king founded an observatory and installed Flamsteed on 4 March 1675 as his "astronomical observator" at an annual stipend of £100.

With his appointment as astronomer royal and his removal to Greenwich, the pattern of Flamsteed's professional life was essentially established. At Easter of the same year he took orders, having the previous year taken the M.A. at Cambridge by letters-patent, after four years of nonresident enrollment. In 1684 he was granted the living of Burstow, in Surrey, not far from Greenwich; and in 1692, he was married to Margaret Cooke, the granddaughter of his predecessor at Burstow. At his death in 1719, he was succeeded at Greenwich by Edmond Halley and at Burstow by another astronomer, James Pound, an uncle of James Bradley.

The mandate of the newly created *mathematicus regius* was unequivocal: "Forthwith to apply himself with the most exact care and diligence to the rectifying the tables of the motions of the heavens, and the places of the fixed stars."[4] By no means a new idea, it was purely and simply the project conceived by Tycho Brahe a century earlier. The only thing at all remarkable about it was the extent to which it had been neglected during the intervening years. Incredible as it appears to later ages, the invention of the telescope had as yet had virtually no impact on fundamental astronomy. Two generations after Galileo's momentous discoveries, Tycho's star catalog remained the standard of excellence; and the one designed by Hevelius to replace it was likewise being constructed on the basis of naked-eye observations. With respect to the planets, the laws of Kepler were just winning general acceptance, while the observations from which they had been derived were being published (1666) because they still represented the most accurate information available. Flamsteed's assignment, then, was essentially that of dragging positional astronomy into the seventeenth century, of bringing it abreast of the new descriptive astronomy to which the telescope had thus far been almost exclusively applied. It was a project which coincided nicely with his own predilections and one to which he had already dedicated his efforts for some years before 1675. An indefatigable calculator and conscientious observer from the days of his youth, he had early learned that the existing tables and catalogs were unequal to the accuracy of even the most modest instruments. Unfortunately, however, it was one thing to recognize the scandalous state of astronomical science and quite another to do anything about it without professional apparatus. Prior to the fall of 1671, when he finally got his new micrometer-telescope fitted out, Flamsteed was able to do very little in the way of meaningful observation. What he did manage to do was to lay the foundation for his contributions to the solar and lunar theories.

Already several years before his post was created for the express purpose of "find[ing] out the so much-desired longitude of places for the perfecting the art of navigation,"[5] Flamsteed was "esteeming [him]self obliged" to publish predictions of the moon's occultations of stars. In the process of computing these "annual preadmonitions of the lunar appearances,"[6] he necessarily became very familiar with the various accounts of its motion. Since all were conspicuously inadequate, he took considerable interest in the news that the legendary Jeremiah Horrox had left writings pertaining to the lunar theory. Despite the fact that the material involved had been deemed so fragmentary as to be unworthy of publication in the *Opera posthuma* of Horrox—in press at the time—Flamsteed journeyed to Lancashire to look at it. What he found was two letters that together contained a sketch of the proposed model, some computing rules from which he was able to infer the mechanism, and some opinions as to the constants that would be appropriate. Intrigued by the scheme (which stemmed basically from Kepler's ruminations on the subject and featured an elliptical orbit with a librating line of apsides and a variable eccentricity), Flamsteed brought the constants up-to-date and constructed enough tables to put the theory on trial. When observational comparison convinced him that "Bullialdus's, Wing's, and Streete's theories were erroneous, and Horrox's near the truth,"[7] he naturally relayed the information to Collins, and ultimately Wallis, who was editing Horrox' works. The result was a last-minute inclusion of the lunar theory as reworked, tabulated, and elucidated by Flamsteed. Together with it was his defense of the equation of time, which restored it to its rightful status after three generations of confusion involving the annual equation of the lunar theory.

The lunar theory continued to occupy a special place in Flamsteed's work throughout his life. As a result of intermittent reconsiderations of the subject, he revised Horrox' original account at least three times: in 1680 for his *Doctrine of the Sphere,* in the late 1690's, and again about 1703 after the publication of Newton's second efforts on the theory. It was his model in terms of which Newton conceived the moon's motion, his observations by means of which Newton improved the theory, and his incorporation of Newton's revisions that rendered them subject to test, modification, and use. As late as 1746, Flamsteed's last version was published in Lemonnier's *Institutions astronomiques.* To his profound disappointment, however, neither it nor his similarly inspired work with the satellites of Jupiter ever achieved the accuracy requisite for longitude determinations.

Among the various features of Flamsteed's work on the motion of the sun, by no means the least interesting is the fact that he bothered to do it at all. Inherently simple and tractable by virtue of its small eccentricity and unique relation to the earth, the sun remained down to Flamsteed's day the least troublesome of the planets. Yet, for Flamsteed, relative virtue was not sufficient. Every aspect of astronomy had to be as perfect as his researches could make it; and since the solar theory figured in, and hence determined the upper limit of accuracy of, all the other planetary theories, it had a prior claim to the utmost precision attainable. For that reason, Flamsteed issued no fewer than three different sets of tables during his lifetime. The first, published with Horrox' lunar theory, amounted to little more than a computing exercise, since it was constructed before Flamsteed had any original observations on which to base his parameters. The second, computed to a new determination of the eccentricity which pegged it at almost exactly its true value of .01675, appeared in his *Doctrine of the Sphere* (1680). The third was printed in Whiston's *Praelectiones astronomicae* (1707). Common to all three versions was Flamsteed's unique denial of the reality of the generally accepted secular changes in the longitude of apogee and the obliquity of the ecliptic. Strictly a modern in such matters, Flamsteed held that neither the accuracy nor the coherence of the ancient determinations justified their being taken seriously.[8]

That the existing planetary theories were far from any respectable standard of accuracy was one of the early lessons in Flamsteed's astronomical education. Already with the acquisition of his micrometer-fitted telescope he began to look into the possibility of improving them; but neither those investigations nor any of his numerous subsequent attempts yielded the degree of satisfaction he demanded in his work. Aside from a tract on the angular diameters of the planets, composed in 1673 and given to Newton for his preparation of the *Principia,* all that resulted from his efforts was an occasional determination of an isolated orbital element. The hundreds of observations he published in his *Historia coelestis Britannica* were no doubt useful to succeeding generations, but even they have been overshadowed by the six inadvertent observations of Uranus later found in his star catalog. An interesting concomitant of his planetary work was his determination of solar parallax from observations of Mars's perihelion opposition of 1672. Using the rotation of the earth for a base line, he arrived at values of "certainly not 30″" for Mars, and accordingly, "not more than 10″" for the sun's parallax[9]—results essentially identical with those later released by the French and quite reasonably approximate to the true figures.

In 1676, two months after his installation at the Royal Observatory, Flamsteed inaugurated the observations that were to culminate in his celebrated 3,000-star "British Catalogue" (in volume III of his *Historia*). From the beginning, the task proved troublesome. King Charles's initial enthusiasm had sufficed only to the appropriation of funds for an observatory. Flamsteed was left to worry not only about such details as hiring computing assistants and obtaining instruments for the facility, but even whether he would receive his stipulated salary; by the close of 1676 some of it was already overdue, and as late as 1679 it was seventeen months in arrears and "in danger of a total retrenchment."[10] The prestige of the post ameliorated Flamsteed's pecuniary problems by drawing some 140 pupils to him for private mathematical instruction over the years. Sir Jonas Moore eased the want of instruments by giving him two clocks and a seven-foot sextant.

Between 1676 and 1689, Flamsteed made about 20,000 observations with the sextant. Accurate to about 10″, they constituted an improvement on Tycho's work by a factor of perhaps fifteen. Unfortunately, they consisted exclusively of relative distances, having no "anchor" in the celestial sphere. Refusing to refer his star places to Tycho's much less accurate bases, as he had criticized Halley for doing, Flamsteed resolved to underwrite a fixed-meridian instrument himself. A mural quadrant completed in 1683 proved too fragile; but a 140° mural arc made possible by the inheritance from his father's estate solved his problem. In the years following 1689, he did fundamental astronomy with an accuracy unsurpassed before Bradley. He achieved precise determinations of the latitude of Greenwich, the obliquity of the ecliptic, and the position of the equinox and then bypassed them all by devising an ingenious scheme for observing absolute right ascensions. Using matched occasions at which the sun had identical meridian alti-

FLAMSTEED

tudes near each equinox, he measured the time intervals between the passage of the sun and a bright star across the meridian. Halving the difference between the two time intervals then located the solstice and gave the star's right ascension. It is difficult to overstate the advance represented by this method. Not only did it do away with the errors formerly introduced by using an intermediary planet to measure the angle between sun and star, but it eliminated all uncertainties caused by parallax, refraction, and latitude. After using this method to obtain the positions of forty reference stars, Flamsteed computed the rest of his 3,000-star catalog from the intermutual readings already taken with the sextant.

Long before he had readied his observations for publication, Flamsteed had become resigned to the likelihood that he would have to underwrite the end of the project as he had every other aspect of it. Unfortunately, before he could carry the plan through to his own ideal of completion, his long-simmering relations with Newton and Halley boiled over. The wrangle began in 1704 and ended only with the unauthorized printing of Flamsteed's work in 1712. Because the perpetrators of this unorthodox operation were who they were, the incident has received more attention than it deserves. The essence of the situation seems to be that Newton and Halley, who lacked Flamsteed's passion for astronomical precision, felt that Flamsteed was being unnecessarily dilatory in the publication of his observations. Regarding the observations of the publicly supported astronomer royal as public property, they took steps, as officers of the Royal Society, to expedite the entrance of these observations into the public domain. Whatever their motives (and it is difficult to believe that they were purely objective), their action was quite questionable; and in any case, since Flamsteed had disbursed well over half of his life's salary for computing service, construction and repair of instruments, and other operating expenses, their basic premise was open to dispute. In 1714 a turn of the political wheel of fortune gave Flamsteed the satisfaction of burning all but ninety-seven pages of three-quarters of the spurious edition. By the time he died, he had pushed the work far enough that the three-volume *Historia coelestis Britannica* could be published in 1725. The companion *Atlas coelestis* appeared in 1729.

There can be little doubt that Flamsteed's reputation rests on his observational work. As Grant expressed it, "In carrying out views of practical utility, with a scrupulous attention to accuracy in the most minute details, in fortitude of resolution under adverse circumstances, and persevering adherence to continuity and regularity of observation throughout a long career, he had few rivals in any age or country." As is usually the fate of practical scientists, his other qualities and achievements have been either overlooked or denigrated. The fact is that no other astronomer royal until Airy manifested anything like the same concern for the reduction and manipulation of data. Far from bequeathing a mass of raw observations in the manner of Bradley, Flamsteed converted and applied his.

In addition to the numerous efforts already mentioned, one can cite tables of atmospheric refraction and tides. The first tabulation in England of the moon's elliptic inequality according to Kepler's second law was carried out under him.[11] Nor did Flamsteed lack his share of inventiveness in an age in which speculation was rife. He argued vigorously with Newton in behalf of the proposition that two comets of 1680–1681 were in fact appearances of the same comet. Prior to that, he had already noted that the comet of 1677 had appeared in the same place as those of 1653 and 1665. In publishing his observations of it, he posed the question of "what conformity there is betwixt the motions of this and them and whether it may probably be the same returned hither after two revolutions."[12] From reports of the coronal phenomena during a solar eclipse, he inferred the existence of a lunar atmosphere. He has been criticized for his "discovery" of stellar parallax in 1694: what he actually found was aberration of starlight, "the maximum value of which is deducible with an astonishing degree of accuracy" from his observations. The truth remains that whatever interpretive shortcomings might be attributed to him must also be laid at the door of Newton, Halley, Gregory, Wallis, and everyone else who could read the published account of his findings.[13]

One respect in which Flamsteed was conspicuously deficient was an aptitude for dealing with his fellowman. Possessed of an attitude that can only be described as uncompromising, he was an intemperate man even by the standards of an intemperate age. The particular and enduring subject of his passion was Edmond Halley. The last thirty years of Flamsteed's extensive correspondence is infused with vituperous remarks about the man who should have been his most natural and valuable ally. No single cause of such animosity has been convincingly advanced. Professional jealousy was, no doubt, an element: rare indeed was the occasion on which Flamsteed praised any third party, and even rarer was it that he passed up an opportunity to criticize. Basically, however, it was simply a personality clash. Halley's flamboyant nature, frivolous attitude toward religious matters, and hit-and-run approach to astronomy offended the dour Flamsteed, who took everything he did very seriously. Lurking behind it all was Flamsteed's perpetual ill health, which would surely have tried the patience of any man. That he managed to accomplish so much in spite of it and its effect on his relations with his contemporaries is a real tribute to his industry and ability.

NOTES

1. Baily, p. 10.
2. Rigaud, p. 130.
3. Bayle.
4. Baily, p. 111.
5. *Ibid.*
6. Rigaud, p. 120
7. Baily, p. 31.
8. Flamsteed MS, XXXVIII, 149.
9. *Philosophical Transactions,* **7,** 5118.
10. Baily, p. 118.
11. Baily, p. 704.
12. *Philosophical Transactions,* **12,** 873.
13. Wallis, III, 704.

BIBLIOGRAPHY

I. ORIGINAL WORKS. Flamsteed's three major printed works were *The Doctrine of the Sphere* (London, 1680); *Historia coelestis Britannica* (London, 1725); and *Atlas coelestis* (London, 1729). Other lesser works appeared in Horrox' *Opera posthuma* (London, 1673); John Wallis' *Opera mathematica* (London, 1699); and the *Philosophical Transactions of the Royal Society.*

The bulk of the extant Flamsteed MSS is contained in his seventy-odd notebooks preserved at the Royal Observatory and recently published in microfilm, *Observations of the Royal Astronomers* (London, 1969). The most significant material in it is a serialized autobiographical statement, which was published in Francis Baily's *Account of the Revd. John Flamsteed* (London, 1835). Along with it was Baily's revision of the "British Catalogue" according to researches conducted by William and Caroline Herschel.

Flamsteed's extensive correspondence with various of his contemporaries provides a very interesting view of the scientific activity of his day. Many letters were published as early as 1738 in the English version of Bayle's *General Dictionary.* A large number were found in the nineteenth century. Baily printed about 200, while vol. II of Rigaud's *Correspondence of Scientific Men of the Seventeenth Century* (London, 1841) contains numerous others. See also Cudworth's *Life and Correspondence of Abraham Sharp* (London, 1889), and *The Correspondence of Isaac Newton* (London, 1959–). J. L. E. Dreyer found (*Observatory,* **45** [1922], 280–292) some seventy unpublished letters written to Richard Townley preserved in the rooms of the Royal Society at Burlington House. The Southampton Record Office contains Flamsteed's letters to Molyneux, while numerous other unpublished letters are preserved in the notebooks at the Royal Observatory.

II. SECONDARY LITERATURE. The best secondary account of Flamsteed's work is Robert Grant, *History of Physical Astronomy* (London, 1852). Important additional material is presented in Agnes Clerke's article in the *Dictionary of National Biography;* and in E. F. MacPike, *Hevelius, Flamsteed, and Halley* (London, 1937).

VICTOR E. THOREN

FLECHSIG, PAUL EMIL (*b.* Zwickau, Germany, 29 June 1847; *d.* Leipzig, Germany, 22 July 1929), *neuroanatomy, psychiatry, neurology.*

His father, Emil Flechsig, a cultured man and a good friend of Robert Schumann, was a deacon of the Protestant church of St. Mary in Zwickau and much concerned with local social welfare. His mother, Ferdinande Richter, came from a wealthy family. Flechsig was educated in Zwickau, mainly at the Gymnasium, and at the medical school of the University of Leipzig from the spring of 1865 until June 1870, where he was taught in anatomy by E. H. Weber and E. F. W. Weber and in physiology by Karl Ludwig. Ludwig was especially impressed by Flechsig's histological work, and he encouraged and advised him in it.

Flechsig spent two years (1870–1871) in the army during the Franco-Prussian War and on 1 January 1872 became assistant to Ernst Wagner of the Institute of Pathology in the University of Leipzig. He also worked in the medical polyclinic. He was further able to develop his skills in histology and on 1 October 1873 was appointed head of the department of histology in the Institute of Physiology. Here he devoted all his time to research and benefited greatly from the facilities available and the contact with many outstanding German and foreign physiologists. By 1875 he was university lecturer and in 1877 became professor *extraordinarius* in the new chair of psychiatry; he soon was made *ordinarius.* After studying psychiatry at various European centers, on 2 May 1882 he returned to open the clinic of which he was director. Here he spent the rest of his working life and attracted many pupils and visitors, including Beevor, Bekhterev, Blumenau, Darkshevich, Donaldson, Held, Klimor, Martinotti, R. A. Pfeifer, Popov, Schütz, Tschirch, Oskar Vogt, and Yakovenko.

From 1894 to 1895 Flechsig was rector of the University of Leipzig and in 1901, along with the elder Wilhelm His, he helped to found the International Brain Commission, which planned to unify nomenclature, standardize methods, collect material, and encourage research in neuroanatomy. He was made an honorary member of the University of Dorpat in 1903, received the honorary D.Sc. of Oxford in 1904, and became honorary doctor of his alma mater in

1909. At the age of seventy-four he retired but continued working.

Flechsig was a true *Vogtländer,* with a thick neck, a large barrel-shaped trunk, and short legs. He wore a broad-brimmed hat and a velvet cloak with large glass buttons, resembling therefore, it was said by some, his psychiatric patients.

Flechsig had a cyclothymic personality, almost bordering on a true manic-depressive state. Years of intense activity—when he worked ceaselessly and poured out ideas, encouragement, and inspiration—alternated with years when he was irritable, arrogant, intolerant, tyrannical, and suffered from severe depression. Nevertheless his students and followers venerated him, and Pfeifer records that "his guidance was full of spirit and during discussions of various problems his whole youth was awakened." He was devoted to his work and had little time for anything else until late in life. He liked to mix with aristocrats, monarchs, and politicians, in part because of their interest in his work and in part because of his need for extramural research funds.

Flechsig married Auguste Hauff in 1870. After her death, in 1922 he married Irene Colditz, who was thirty years younger than he; she was able to interest him in social events during the closing years of his life.

Although Flechsig contributed to the clinical and pathological study of hysteria, epilepsy, neurosyphilis, and chorea, his fame is due mainly to his technique of myelogenesis for the examination of the brain and spinal cord. As Wagner's assistant, he was impressed by the work of Meynert on the brain and in 1872 began to investigate the myelination in the spinal cord and brain of premature, full-term, and early postnatal infants. He discovered that axones in different parts receive their myelin sheath at different stages of growth, and he could observe the chronological sequence of this process. He was therefore able to differentiate some of the innumerable pathways and concluded correctly that a tract functions adequately only when its axones become fully myelinated. His technique was thus the reverse of Ludwig Türck's and of those of other workers who used the process of secondary or Wallerian degeneration to trace tracts.

Flechsig first examined the spinal cord and, like Türck and others, identified several pathways. He reported this work in 1876 (*Leitungsbahnen im Gehirn und Rückenmark . . .*) and related it to that of Türck; a description of what is now called Flechsig's tract, the dorsal spinocerebellar, is included.

His monumental work on the pyramidal tract—in which for the first time he traced its origin to the cerebral cortex—appeared in parts in 1877 and 1878. It is the first clear account of the upper motor neurone, and the now familiar division of the internal capsule into knee and limbs is his.

In 1893 Flechsig began more intensive study of the cerebral hemispheres and supplemented his myelogenetic findings with clinical observations and data from degeneration experiments. He outlined the auditory radiation and could list twelve cortical areas that are myelinated (and therefore functional) before birth, as well as twenty-four in which myelinization occurs after birth; these he arranged chronologically according to the time of myelinization. He thus isolated primarily projection, or motor and sensory, areas, the fiber connections of which, both corticopetal and corticofugal, mostly mature prenatally; and association areas responsible, he claimed, for higher intellectual functions that develop after birth. From this he evolved a map of cortical function that appeared in a report of 1904 to the Central Committee for Brain Research. Flechsig's conclusions evoked considerable argument, especially from Leonardo Bianchi concerning frontal lobe function and Oskar Vogt on the techniques of myelogenesis. It is now clear that although Flechsig made many errors and ignored the work of others with which his results did not agree, he nevertheless stimulated much beneficial discussion and research.

Flechsig considered the parieto-temporo-occipital association zone to be essential for mental activity (which is at least partially correct), and this is discussed in his rector's oration of 1896, *Gehirn und Seele.* The book he published in 1920, *Anatomie des menschlichen Gehirn und Rückenmarks . . .*, contains most of his data on cortical localization.

BIBLIOGRAPHY

I. ORIGINAL WORKS. There is no bibliography or *opera omnia* of Flechsig, but Pfeifer (1930) has published a list of forty-nine of his most important writings from 1872 to 1920, all but one being on brain anatomy. Among these are *Die Leitungsbahnen im Gehirn und Rückenmark des Menschen auf Grund entwicklungsgeschichtlicher Untersuchungen* (Leipzig, 1876); "Über 'Systemerkrankungen' im Rückenmark," in *Archiv für der Heilkunde,* **18** (1877), 101–141, 289–343, 461–483, and *ibid.,* **19** (1878), 52–90, 441–447; "Zur Anatomie und Entwicklungsgeschichte der Leitungsbahnen im Grosshirn des Menschen," in *Archiv für Anatomie und Physiologie* (Anatomische Abteilung) (1881), pp. 12–75; *Plan des menschlichen Gehirns auf Grund einziger Untersuchungen* (Leipzig, 1883); *Gehirn und Seele* (Leipzig, 1896), his rectorial oration, with extensive notes; "Einige Bemerkungen über die Untersuchungs-methoden der Grosshirnrinde, insbesondere des Menschen. Dem Zentralkomitee für Hirnforschung vorgelegt von . . .," in

Berichte über die Verhandlungen der Sächsischen Akademie der Wissenschaften zu Leipzig, Math.-Phys. Klasse, **56** (1904), 50–104 (with 4 plates), 177–248; and *Anatomie des menschlichen Gehirns und Rückenmarks auf myelogenetischer Grundlage,* vol. I (Leipzig, 1920).

Useful English and French accounts of Flechsig's technique as applied to the cerebral cortex are "Developmental (Myelogenetic) Localisation of the Cerebral Cortex in the Human Subject," in *Lancet* (1901), **2,** 1027–1029; and "Les centres de projection et d'association du cerveau humain," in *Proceedings. XIIIe Congrès International de Médecine* (Section de Neurologie) (Paris, 1900), pp. 115–121. E. Clarke and C. D. O'Malley, *The Human Brain and Spinal Cord* (Berkeley–Los Angeles, 1968), contains English translations of some of Flechsig's writings: on spinal cord tracts, pp. 277–280, 287–290; on cerebral cortical localization, pp. 548–554; on cerebral white matter, pp. 611–619; and on the technique of myelogenesis, pp. 857–858; each contribution is discussed in relation to other work on the same subject.

II. Secondary Literature. There is no biography of Flechsig, and the various brief accounts of his life are based on his autobiography, *Meine myelogenetische Hirnlehre mit biographischer Einleitung* (Berlin, 1927): some of these are W. Haymaker, "Paul Emil Flechsig (1847–1929)," in his ed. of *The Founders of Neurology* (Springfield, Ill., 1953), pp. 31–35 (with a portrait); Henneberg, "Paul Flechsig †," in *Medizinische Klinik,* **25** (1929), 1490–1492; R. A. Pfeifer, "Paul Flechsig †. Sein Leben und sein Wirken," in *Schweizer Archiv für Neurologie und Psychiatrie,* **26** (1930), 258–264; F. Quensel, "Paul Flechsig zum 70. Geburtstag," in *Deutsche medizinische Wochenscrift,* **43** (1917), 818–819; and P. Schröder, "Paul Flechsig," in *Archiv für Psychiatrie and Nervenkrankheiten,* **91** (1930), 1–8.

Concerning Flechsig's work, see L. F. Barker, "The Phrenology of Gall and Flechsig's Doctrine of Association Centers in the Cerebrum," in *Bulletin of the Johns Hopkins Hospital,* **8** (1897), 7–14; and "The Sense-areas and Association-centers in the Brain as Described by Flechsig," in *Journal of Nervous and Mental Diseases,* **24** (1897), 325–356, 363–368 (discussion); W. W. Ireland, "Flechsig on the Localization of Mental Processes in the Brain," in *Journal of Mental Science,* **44** (1898), 1–17; M. P. Jacobi, "Considerations on Flechsig's 'Gehirn und Seele,'" in *Journal of Nervous and Mental Diseases,* **24** (1897), 747–768; J. M. Nielsen, "The Myelogenetic Studies of Paul Flechsig," in *Bulletin of the Los Angeles Neurological Society,* **28** (1963), 127–134; and F. R. Sabin, "On Flechsig's Investigations on the Brain," in *Bulletin of the Johns Hopkins Hospital,* **16** (1905), 45–49.

Flechsig's *Festschrift,* in *Monatsschrift für Psychiatrie und Neurologie,* **26** (1909), 1–416, with 19 plates, has an excellent photograph of him in his laboratory, but no biography or bibliography.

Edwin Clarke

FLEISCHER, JOHANNES (*b.* Breslau, Germany [now Wrocław, Poland], 29 March 1539; *d.* Breslau, 4 March 1593), *optics.*

Fleischer was born into a well-to-do family and received his education at the Goldberg Gymnasium near Breslau and later at the University of Wittenberg, where he matriculated in 1557. During his first years at Wittenberg, Fleischer studied under Philip Melancthon; he returned to Wittenberg after Melancthon's death to concentrate on Hebrew, astronomy, and theology, and in 1589 he was awarded the theological doctorate. Fleischer spent 1568–1569 teaching arts and languages at the Goldberg Gymnasium, and beginning in 1572 he was professor in the Gymnasium attached to St. Elizabeth's Church in Breslau. He also held a series of ecclesiastical posts in Breslau, in St. Maria Magdalena's Church as well as St. Elizabeth's.

Fleischer's only published scientific work is a treatise on the rainbow, which appeared in 1571. This book is remarkable, not for its correct solution to the problem of the rainbow, but for the precision and clarity of its argument, for its emphasis on what occurs in the individual drop of vapor, and for its insistence that both reflection and refraction of solar rays participate in the generation of the rainbow. The essential feature of Fleischer's explanation is that solar rays are refracted by individual drops as they enter the vapor cloud before being reflected back to the observer's eye by denser drops more interior to the cloud. The idea is drawn largely from Witelo, whom Fleischer cites repeatedly, although Fleischer has considerably clarified the mechanism of reflection and refraction described by Witelo.

BIBLIOGRAPHY

I. Original Works. See his *De iridibus doctrina Aristotelis et Vitellionis* (Wittenberg, 1571).

II. Secondary Literature. Fleischer's life is dealt with briefly in C. G. Jöcher, *et al., Allgemeines Gelehrten-Lexicon,* I (Leipzig, 1750), col. 636; and Gustav Bauch, *Valentin Trozendorf und die Goldberger Schule* (Berlin, 1921), pp. 235–237. On Fleischer's theory of the rainbow, see Carl B. Boyer, *The Rainbow: From Myth to Mathematics* (New York, 1959), pp. 163–166; and A. G. Kästner, *Geschichte der Mathematik,* II (Göttingen, 1797), 248–250.

David C. Lindberg

FLEMING, ALEXANDER (*b.* Lochfield, Ayrshire, Scotland, 6 August 1881; *d.* London, England, 11 March 1955), *bacteriology.*

Sir Alexander Fleming's professional career was devoted mainly to investigating the human body's defenses against bacterial infections. Late in life he achieved retrospective fame for discovering penicillin in 1928.

Descended from Lowland farmers, Alexander was the third of four children born to Grace Morton, second wife of Hugh Fleming. Four children of the first marriage survived. His father died when Alec was seven years old, leaving the widow to manage the farm with her eldest stepson. From age five to ten, the boy attended a tiny moorland school. Then he walked daily to school at Dorval, a small town four miles away. Two years later, he attended Kilmarnock Academy, twelve miles distant, which had exacting standards but meager resources. His basic education was thus hard-earned and rather primitive. He learned early to observe nature intimately, to enjoy simple pleasures, and to appreciate unaffectedness.

When just over thirteen, he followed a stepbrother, already a practicing physician, and his brother John to London. The youngest brother, Robert, soon joined them, and a sister kept house. After attending classes at the Regent Street Polytechnic for two years, Alec became a clerk in a shipping company. In 1900 he enlisted in the London Scottish Regiment, but the Boer War ended before he got overseas. He enjoyed life in the ranks and stayed attached to this regiment until 1914. Fleming was short but sturdy, blue-eyed, fair-haired, good at rifle shooting and water polo. At twenty, he inherited a small legacy and decided to study medicine.

Fleming excelled at competitive examinations. He won a scholarship to St. Mary's Hospital Medical School, Paddington, and in 1901 began his lifelong connection with that institution. Capturing numerous class prizes and trophies, he obtained the Conjoint Board Diploma in 1906, and two years later graduated M.B., B.S., with honors and a gold medal from the University of London. In 1909 he completed the fellowship examinations of the Royal College of Surgeons of England.

Upon qualifying in 1906, Fleming joined Sir Almroth Wright's disciples at St. Mary's Hospital. Although he was Wright's antithesis—cautious, unpretentious, and laconic—they were closely associated for forty years. Fleming became assistant director of the Inoculation Department in 1921. The department merged with the Institute of Pathology and Research in 1933; it was renamed the Wright-Fleming Institute in 1948. In that year, Fleming retired as professor of bacteriology, University of London, having held the chair since 1928. He retained the principalship of the institute (to which he succeeded when Wright retired in 1946) until January 1955. Two months later he died suddenly from coronary thrombosis in his Chelsea home. He is buried in St. Paul's Cathedral.

In 1915 Fleming married Sarah Marion McElroy, an Irish farmer's daughter, who had operated a private nursing home. Despite their dissimilar characters, the marriage was happy. They enjoyed gardening at their Suffolk country house, were very hospitable, and collected antiques. Their only child, Robert, born in 1924, became a physician. Fleming's wife died in 1949, and in 1953 he married Dr. Amalia Coutsouris-Voureka, a Greek bacteriologist working at the institute.

Fleming upheld and practiced Wright's doctrine of specific immunization against bacterial infection through vaccine therapy, without necessarily accepting every dictum. His earliest publications (1908) concerned "opsonic index" determinations—Wright's method of assaying the phagocytic power of a patient's blood for a particular microorganism. The procedure was of dubious utility and eventually fell out of favor. Fleming was among the first (1909) to treat syphilis with Salvarsan (606), samples of which Ehrlich had entrusted to Wright.

In World War I, Fleming joined the Royal Army Medical Corps as lieutenant, serving under Wright's colonelcy in a wound-research laboratory at Boulogne. By simple, ingenious techniques, he demonstrated the bactericidal power of pus and the inability of chemical antiseptics to sterilize tortuous wounds. He supported Wright in advocating hypertonic saline solution as a physiological irrigant for septic lacerations. Demobilized with captain's rank, Fleming resumed studying antibacterial mechanisms at St. Mary's in 1919.

His best work followed in the next decade. Using "slide cells," he showed that ordinary germicides damaged the leucocytes in artificially infected blood at dilutions harmless to the bacteria. He therefore condemned the intravenous administration of chemical antiseptics, asserting that ideal therapeutic antibacterial agents should arrest the growth of bacterial invaders without affecting host tissues. Fleming did not systematically search for such entities, but through sharp observation, pertinacious curiosity, and a prepared mind he discovered two outstandingly important antibacterial substances.

In 1921, while inspecting a contaminated culture plate, he observed nasal mucus dissolving a yellowish colony. The bacteriolytic agent was named "lysozyme," and the susceptible organism (at Wright's suggestion) *Micrococcus lysodeikticus.* With V. D. Allison's collaboration, Fleming detected lysozyme in human blood serum, tears, saliva, and milk; and in such diverse animal and plant substances as leucocytes, egg white, and turnip juice. Since inoffensive airborne bacteria were lyzed more readily than pathogenic species, chemical concentration of the active principle was attempted, without success. (Lysozymes were later crystallized in other laboratories; because of their specific disruptive action on the cell wall of certain gram-positive organisms, these enzymes have proved valuable in studies of bacterial cytology.) Fleming then became engrossed with another lytic agent.

In 1928 he noted a culture plate displaying *Penicillium* mold surrounded by lyzed colonies of staphylococci. Culture filtrates of the mold (later identified by C. Thom as *Penicillium notatum*) were antibacterial for many pathogenic species. He reported (1929) that "penicillin" did not interfere with leucocytic function, was nontoxic to laboratory animals, and "may be an efficient antiseptic for application to, or injection into, areas infected with penicillin-sensitive microbes." The intended clinical trials were abandoned because these crude preparations had unpredictable and fleeting potency, which Fleming's knowledge of chemistry was inadequate to overcome. Although he enlisted aid from junior colleagues and from the biochemist H. Raistrick, the problem remained unsolved. Thereafter, he used the "mold juice" mainly for isolating penicillin-insensitive bacteria from mixed cultures.

Following Domagk's work on prontosil (1935), Fleming studied the antibacterial properties of sulfonamides. But he never lost confidence that penicillin would be stabilized and purified, and rejoiced when Ernst Chain, Howard Florey, and their co-workers accomplished this at Oxford in 1940. Within two years, the antibiotic's remarkable powers were established. Mounting war casualties entailed securing the highest priority for its large-scale manufacture, and steps were taken to achieve this in the United States, Britain, and Canada.

As supplies of penicillin expanded and its efficacy became more widely known, tributes and honors showered upon Alexander Fleming. He was elected to fellowship of the Royal Society in 1943; knighted (K.B.) in 1944; received the Nobel Prize in medicine, jointly with Florey and Chain, in 1945; and was awarded numerous foreign decorations and medals, honorary memberships in medical and scientific societies, and doctorates from famous universities. He was elected president of the newly founded Society for General Microbiology (1945) and rector of Edinburgh University (1951) and was given the freedom of Dorval, Chelsea, and Paddington—where he had gone to school, lived, and worked. Between 1945 and 1953, despite his limited eloquence, he undertook a succession of speech-making triumphal tours of the United States and other countries.

Fleming at first accepted the honors and acclaim diffidently, but later came to enjoy them. His main characteristics persisted: the evening game of snooker at the Chelsea Arts Club (where he held a long-treasured honorary membership), the pawky humor, the taciturnity, the basic dedication to the health of mankind.

BIBLIOGRAPHY

I. Original Works. Fleming was sole or senior author of about 100 scientific papers, which appeared mainly in well-known British medical or scientific journals between 1908 and 1954. The majority were reports or reviews of original work on vaccine therapy, wound infection, antiseptics, lysozyme, penicillin, and other antibiotics. Occasionally he described novel techniques or wrote brief biographical memoirs. Philosophical or nonscientific topics were generally beyond his range. He contributed a few individual chapters or sections to composite works and committee reports and was author or coauthor of two books in his own special fields. Among his best papers were those prepared as addresses for endowed lectureships. Certain of these are included in the appended representative list.

No complete bibliography has been printed, but fairly comprehensive lists of his principal publications (containing several minor errors) were appended to Leonard Colebrook's memoir of Fleming and to the biography by André Maurois. A collection of his published works and unpublished manuscripts—including letters, diaries, laboratory notebooks, and many other documents relating to Fleming—is deposited with the Sir Alexander Fleming Museum in the Wright-Fleming Institute.

Fleming's works include "Some Observations on the Opsonic Index, With Special Reference to the Accuracy of the Method and to Some of the Sources of Error," in *Practitioner,* **80** (1908), 607–634; "On the Etiology of Acne Vulgaris and Its Treatment by Vaccines," in *Lancet* (1909), **1,** 1035–1038; "On the Use of Salvarsan in the Treatment of Syphilis," *ibid.* (1911), **1,** 1631–1634, written with L. Colebrook; "On the Bacteriology of Septic Wounds," *ibid.* (1915), **2,** 638–643; "The Action of Chemical and Physiological Antiseptics in a Septic Wound," in *British Journal of Surgery,* **7** (1919), 99–129, the Hunterian lecture; "On a Remarkable Bacteriolytic Element Found in Tissues and Secretions," in *Proceedings of the Royal Society,* **93B** (1922), 306–317; "Lysozyme—A Bacteriolytic Ferment Found Normally in Tissues and Secretions," in *Lancet* (1929), **1,** 217–220, the Arris and Gale lecture; "The Staphylococci," in *A System of Bacteriology in Relation to Medicine,* II (London, 1929), 11–28; "On the Antibacterial Action of Cultures of a Penicillium, With Special Reference to Their Use in the Isolation of *B. influenzae*," in *British Journal of Experimental Pathology,* **10** (1929), 226–236; "The Intravenous Use of Germicides," in *Proceedings of the Royal Society of Medicine,* **24** (1931), 46–58; *Recent Advances in Vaccine and Serum Therapy* (London, 1934), written with G. F. Petrie; "Serum and Vaccine Therapy in Combination With Sulphanilamide or M and B 693," in *Proceedings of the Royal Society of Medicine,* **32** (1939), 911–920; "The Effect of Antiseptics on Wounds," *ibid.,* **33** (1940), 487–502;

"Streptococcal Meningitis Treated With Penicillin," in *Lancet* (1943), **2,** 434–438; "Penicillin: Its Discovery, Development and Uses in the Field of Medicine and Surgery," in *Journal of the Royal Institute of Public Health and Hygiene,* **8** (1945), 36–49, 63–71, 93–105, the Harben lectures; "The Morphology and Motility of *Proteus vulgaris* and Other Organisms Cultured in the Presence of Penicillin," in *Journal of General Microbiology,* **4** (1950), 257–269, written with A. Voureka, I. R. H. Kramer, and W. H. Hughes; *Penicillin* (London, 1946); and "Twentieth Century Changes in the Treatment of Septic Infections," in *New England Journal of Medicine,* **248** (1953), 1037–1045, the Shattuck lecture.

II. SECONDARY LITERATURE. Obituaries include "Sir Alexander Fleming, M.D., D.Sc., F.R.C.P., F.R.C.S., F.R.S.," in *British Medical Journal* (1955), **1,** 732–735, unsigned; "Alexander Fleming, Kt., M.B., Lond., F.R.C.P., F.R.C.S., F.R.S.," in *Lancet* (1955), **1,** 624–626, unsigned; V. D. Allison, "Sir Alexander Fleming, 1881–1955," in *Journal of General Microbiology,* **14** (1956), 1–13; L. Colebrook, "Alexander Fleming, 1881–1955," in *Biographical Memoirs of Fellows of the Royal Society of London,* **2** (1956), 117–127; and R. Cruikshank, "Alexander Fleming, 6th August 1881–11th March 1955," in *Journal of Pathology and Bacteriology,* **72** (1956), 697–708.

A biography is André Maurois, *The Life of Sir Alexander Fleming,* Gerard Hopkins, trans. (London, 1959; Penguin ed., 1963). Lady Fleming persuaded Maurois to undertake this very readable biography, which shows occasional bias and contains some inaccuracies.

Various short appreciations and unusual photographs of Fleming were published in *St. Mary's Hospital Gazette,* **61,** no. 3 (1955), 58–74.

Special references are E. P. Abraham, E. Chain, C. M. Fletcher, H. W. Florey, A. D. Gardner, N. G. Heatley, and M. A. Jennings, "Further Observations on Penicillin," in *Lancet* (1941), **2,** 177–189; E. Chain, H. W. Florey, A. D. Gardner, N. G. Heatley, M. A. Jennings, J. Orr-Ewing, and A. G. Sanders, *ibid.* (1940), **2,** 226–228; R. D. Coghill, "Penicillin: Science's Cinderella," in *Chemical and Engineering News,* **22** (1944), 588–593; R. D. Coghill and R. S. Koch, "Penicillin: A Wartime Accomplishment," *ibid.,* **23** (1945), 2310–2316; L. Colebrook, *Almroth Wright: Provocative Doctor and Thinker* (London, 1954); R. Hare, *The Birth of Penicillin and the Disarming of Microbes* (London, 1970); and M. R. J. Salton, "The Properties of Lysozyme and Its Action on Microorganisms," in *Bacteriological Reviews,* **21** (1957), 82–99.

CLAUDE E. DOLMAN

FLEMING, JOHN (*b.* Kirkroads, near Bathgate, Linlithgowshire, Scotland, 10 January 1785; *d.* Edinburgh, Scotland, 18 November 1857), *zoology, geology.*

The son of Alexander Fleming, a tenant farmer of moderate means, and Catherine Nimmo Fleming, John Fleming completed his studies at the University of Edinburgh in 1805 and was licensed as a minister in the Church of Scotland in 1806. He served in the small parishes of Bressay, Shetland (1808–1810), and Flisk, Fifeshire (1810–1832), and in the larger parish of Clackmannan, near Edinburgh (1832–1834), before becoming professor of natural philosophy at King's College, Aberdeen, in 1834. When the Free Church broke away in 1843, Fleming joined it; and in 1845 he became professor of natural science at New College (Free Church), Edinburgh. He married Melville Christie in 1813, and they had two sons, of whom only one, Andrew, lived to adulthood.

A member of the Wernerian Natural History Society from its founding in 1808, Fleming was elected a fellow of the Royal Society of Edinburgh in 1814. He was later a member of the Royal Physical Society of Edinburgh and other scientific societies. After 1834 he began to suffer spells of ill health, which became more frequent until his death. Fleming's disposition tended to be grave and critical—what humor he had was often sarcastic—but his kindness and honesty were appreciated by those who knew him.

Fleming's scientific career may be divided into four periods: a Wernerian period (1808–1820), when he was a disciple of Robert Jameson; a period of productivity and controversy (1820–1832); a period of reduced productivity (1832–1845), due to the pressure of his duties at Clackmannan and Aberdeen; and a period of renewed activity at New College (1845–1857).

Regarded as Scotland's foremost zoologist as early as 1815, Fleming was concerned largely with the description and classification of freshwater and marine invertebrates. In his *Philosophy of Zoology* (1822), he advocated the binary or dichotomous system of classification, in which a twofold division is made at every level into those animals that possess a certain character and those that do not, a different character being used at each level. Despite his claim that this system was a practical approach to a true natural system, little notice was taken of it by other zoologists because of its artificiality. His *History of British Animals* (1828) was a detailed description and classification of the British fauna, although it omitted the insects, which were supposed to be covered in a succeeding volume that never appeared. The book was noteworthy for its inclusion of fossil species and for its application of the binary system throughout.

Although Fleming always had a low opinion of James Hutton's theory of the earth because of its plutonism and because he considered Hutton an incompetent mineralogist, he did agree with the Huttonians that knowledge of the present was the key to the past. Thus, in the *Philosophy of Zoology* one can find the following views that Fleming's friend,

Charles Lyell, would later develop as a part of his uniformitarian attack on catastrophism: (1) an emphasis on noncatastrophic causes of the extinction of species, particularly (in Fleming's case) man's activities; (2) a tendency to reject the evidence for a progressive increase in the complexity and perfection of life during geologic time; (3) the idea that world climate might have been affected by an increase in the amount of land during the course of geologic history; and (4) the rejection of the theory of an originally molten earth that has slowly cooled down.

From 1824 to 1826, with Jameson's secret encouragement, Fleming engaged in a controversy with William Buckland in which he showed that Buckland's theory of a violent deluge contradicted both the Bible and the scientific evidence. Fleming argued that the Bible represented the deluge as nonviolent, and he attributed the so-called "diluvial" phenomena to local river floods, the bursting of lakes, and uprisings of the sea. In a controversy with William Conybeare in 1829, Fleming disputed the fossil evidence for a warmer climate in the past, insisting that our knowledge of the habits of an existing species can tell us nothing about the behavior of a similar, but not identical, fossil species, since every species is fixed and unique in its behavior.

Fleming had argued in his controversy with Buckland that there must be free inquiry in science without regard for the Bible, yet in his *History of British Animals* he adopted a scheme of reconciliation between geology and Genesis that was originally proposed by a friend, the Reverend Thomas Chalmers, on the basis of Cuvier's idea of successive creations. This theory, which was elaborated by Fleming in his *Lithology of Edinburgh* (1859), assumed that the "pre-Adamic" life had been totally destroyed by some extraordinary cause (probably the darkening of the sun) accompanied by debacles of water rushing over the earth. The species of animals and plants of the present epoch had then been created during the six days (or periods) described in Genesis. Similar revolutions, he believed, had initiated at least five previous epochs in earth history. Thus it can be seen that Fleming rejected Lyell's uniformitarian views for earth history as a whole. The idea of evolution was, of course, anathema to him, and we find him in 1854 citing Scripture in opposition to it.

Fleming was by nature conservative, reluctant to alter his views once they had been firmly established. The discrediting of neptunism around 1820 only served to reinforce his already skeptical attitude toward geological theory. His contributions to geology were therefore essentially negative—the effective criticism of inadequate theories. His views, which were relatively enlightened in the 1820's, when they were opposed to the catastrophist excesses of Cuvier and Buckland, were definitely outmoded by the 1850's. Despite his extensive zoological and paleontological knowledge (he was, for example, the first to discover the remains of fish in the Old Red Sandstone), Fleming had been trained in the old mineralogical school of geology and apparently never fully accepted the new geology, which relied boldly upon paleontological criteria in correlating strata.

BIBLIOGRAPHY

I. ORIGINAL WORKS. Fleming's most important works were *The Philosophy of Zoology,* 2 vols. (Edinburgh, 1822); *A History of British Animals* (Edinburgh, 1828); and *The Lithology of Edinburgh,* ed., with a memoir, by Rev. John Duns (Edinburgh, 1859).

A list of Fleming's works by Alexander Bryson, *Transactions of the Royal Society of Edinburgh,* **22** (1861), 675–680, is fairly complete (129 items, including two, nos. 80 and 109, which are not by Fleming according to W. E. Houghton, ed., *The Wellesley Index to Victorian Periodicals, 1824–1900*).

The list in the Royal Society of London *Catalogue of Scientific Papers* (*1800–1863*), II, contains fifty-three items, of which six are not in Bryson's list. The Royal Society *Catalogue,* however, has fuller and sometimes more correct entries, and it usually gives all the journals in which each article appeared. These lists do not cite all the articles by Fleming in the *Edinburgh Encyclopaedia, Encyclopaedia Britannica,* supp., vol. III (1824), *Edinburgh Monthly Review,* and *New Edinburgh Review.*

There are a few of Fleming's letters still extant, notably several to Lyell at the American Philosophical Society, Philadelphia.

II. SECONDARY LITERATURE. The memoir by Duns (see above) contains extracts from Fleming's correspondence. A memoir by Bryson in *Transactions of the Royal Society of Edinburgh,* **22** (1861), 655–675, emphasizes his scientific work. See also "Scottish Natural Science," in *North British Review,* **28** (1858), 39–55, by Duns, which is largely devoted to Fleming.

L. E. PAGE

FLEMING, JOHN AMBROSE (*b.* Lancaster, England, 29 November 1849; *d.* Sidmouth, Devon, England, 18 April 1945), *electrical engineering.*

The son of a Congregational minister, Fleming moved to London in 1863 and attended University College School and later University College, graduating in 1870. After a period of alternate science teaching and additional study, he entered Cambridge University in 1877 to work under James Clerk Maxwell in the new Cavendish Laboratory. There he helped to repeat the century-old electrical experiments of Henry Cavendish, whose notes on them had recently come to light. Fleming was made demonstrator in 1880, and in the following year he became professor of physics and mathematics in the newly constituted University College at Nottingham.

He resigned after a year to become a consultant to the Edison Electric Light Co. in London. In 1885 he was appointed professor of electrical technology at University College, a post he held for forty-one years. He made many contributions to the design of transformers, to the understanding of the properties of materials at liquid-air temperatures, to photometry, and to electrical measurements in general. He was an outstanding teacher; the right-hand rule (a mnemonic aid relating direction of magnetic field, conductor motion, and the induced electromotive force) is attributed to him. He was also a highly successful popular scientific lecturer.

At University College he experimented widely with wireless telegraphy and gave special courses on the subject. He was aware of Edison's observation of the "Edison effect" (he had visited the United States and met Edison in 1884) of unilateral flow of particles from negative to positive electrode, and he repeated some of the experiments, with both direct and alternating currents, beginning in 1889. During the following years, he cooperated with Marconi in many of his experiments and helped to design the transmitter employed by Marconi in spanning the Atlantic in 1901. Thus it was not until 1904 that he returned to his experiments on the Edison effect, with a view to producing a rectifier that would replace the inadequate detectors then used in radiotelegraphy. He named the resulting device a "thermionic valve," for which he obtained a patent in 1904. This was the first electron tube, the diode, ancestor of the triode and the other multielectrode tubes which have played such an important role in both telecommunications and scientific instrumentation.

Fleming led an incredibly active scientific life. He read the first paper ever presented to the Physical Society on its foundation in 1874 and read his last paper to the same body sixty-five years later, in 1939. His career covered the time from Maxwell to the advent of electronic television. He published more than a hundred important papers. He was an active president of the Television Society from 1930 until his death and received many other honors, including the Hughes Medal in 1910 from the Royal Society (he was made F.R.S. in 1892); the Faraday Medal of the Institution of Electrical Engineers (1928); and the Gold Medal of the Institute of Radio Engineers (1933). He was knighted in 1929. He became professor emeritus after his retirement in 1926 but continued to be scientifically active nearly until his death at the age of ninety-five. In 1933, when he was eighty-four, Fleming, whose first wife (Clara Ripley Pratt) had died in 1917, was married to Olive May Franks, who survived him. He had no children.

BIBLIOGRAPHY

I. Original Works. Fleming wrote several important texts and handbooks on electrical engineering, beginning with the 2-vol. treatise *The Alternate Current Transformer* (London, 1889–1892) and leading up to the monumental *Principles of Electric Wave Telegraphy* (London, 1906), which went into several editions and remained the standard work for many years; it is a rich source of historical information as well. Another of his books to have long-term influence was *The Propagation of Electric Currents in Telephone and Telegraph Conductors* (London, 1911). A collection of his papers is in the library of University College, London, which also houses his own library and a number of the earliest diodes.

II. Secondary Literature. A short illustrated biography published on the fiftieth anniversary of the invention of the diode, J. T. MacGregor-Morris, *The Inventor of the Valve* (London, 1954), contains a list of Fleming's books. The same author prepared the entry in *Dictionary of National Biography, 1941–1950.* There is an obituary by W. H. Eccles in *Obituary Notices of Fellows of the Royal Society,* no. 14 (Nov. 1945), and a tribute in *Notes and Records of the Royal Society* (Mar. 1955).

Charles Süsskind

FLEMING, WILLIAMINA PATON (*b.* Dundee, Scotland, 15 May 1857; *d.* Boston, Massachusetts, 21 May 1911), *astronomy.*

Mrs. Fleming's father, Robert Stevens, a craftsman whose shop sold picture frames, died when she was seven; her mother was Mary Walker Stevens. After a public school education in Dundee, she married James Orr Fleming on 26 May 1877, and they immigrated to Boston at the end of 1878. Shortly thereafter the marriage fell apart, and Mrs. Fleming found it necessary to support herself and her infant son, Edward Pickering Fleming, who was born 6 October 1879. In 1881, after a period of domestic work for Edward C. Pickering, the new director of the Harvard College Observatory, she became a full-time copyist and computer at the observatory itself.

At that time Pickering had just embarked on an extensive program of celestial photography. Through her studies of the objective prism spectrum plates, usually in collaboration with Pickering, Mrs. Fleming became the leading woman astronomer of her day. Her suspicions aroused by the spectral peculiarities she observed, she discovered more than 200 variable stars and ten novae—the latter being a significant fraction of the twenty-eight novae recorded up to the time of her death.

Her most important contribution was the classification of 10,351 stars in the *Draper Catalogue of Stellar Spectra* (published as volume XXVII of the *Annals of Harvard College Observatory* [1890]). The spectra were organized into seventeen categories, lettered from *A* to *Q,* but 99.3 percent of the stars fell in the six classes *A, B, F, G, K,* and *M.* Although it was a great advance over the four types into which Angelo Secchi had visually classified about 4,000 stellar spectra, Mrs. Fleming's system was soon to be enormously refined at Harvard by Annie Jump Cannon.

Mrs. Fleming's keen eyesight, remarkable memory, and industrious nature enabled her to advance to a position of considerable authority at the observatory, so that ultimately she gave assignments to a corps of a dozen women computers. In 1899 she was appointed curator of astronomical photographs, and by 1910 she had examined nearly 200,000 plates. In 1906 she became the fifth woman member (honorary) of the Royal Astronomical Society. Dorrit Hoffleit has written, "Sparkling and friendly though she was, her reputation as a strict disciplinarian lived after her, and as late as the 1930's elderly ladies who had worked with her in their youth still regarded her with awe."

BIBLIOGRAPHY

Mrs. Fleming's principal work appeared in the *Annals of Harvard College Observatory,* including an important paper, "Stars Having Peculiar Spectra," published posthumously in vol. **56** (1912).

Most published biographical material derives from the obituaries by Annie Jump Cannon, in *Astrophysical Journal,* **34** (1911), 314–317; Edward C. Pickering, privately printed (1911), repr. in *Harvard Graduates Magazine,* **20** (1911), 49–51; or from the sketch by Grace A. Thompson, in *New England Magazine,* **48** (1912), 458–467.

The best biography, incorporating some new material, is Dorrit Hoffleit, in *Notable American Women* (Cambridge, Mass., 1971).

OWEN GINGERICH

FLEMMING, WALTHER (*b.* Sachsenberg, Mecklenburg, Germany, 21 April 1843; *d.* Kiel, Germany, 4 August 1905), *anatomy, cytology.*

Flemming's family was Flemish; his father, C. F. Flemming, had moved from Jüterbog to Mecklenburg to become director of a lunatic asylum there. In this region of Germany, Walther was born and brought up. He was educated at the Gymnasium Fridericianum, where he showed great aptitude for literature and philology, but for his university studies he chose medicine. After one semester at Göttingen he went to Tübingen. There followed a semester of intensive study at Berlin, then at Rostock, where, after a long illness from typhoid fever, he completed his medical studies with his thesis on the ciliary muscles of certain mammals (1868).

His subsequent work as assistant in the department of internal medicine under Thierfelder was short-lived, for in 1869 he was able to return to zoological research, first under his former teacher, Franz E. Schulze, and then as private assistant to Semper in Würzburg, studying the sensory epithelia of the mollusks. That autumn saw him in Amsterdam, where, under Willie Kühne, he completed a detailed study of the structure and physiology of fat cells. The Franco-Prussian War obliged him to interrupt his studies and join the medical corps reserve at Saarbrücken, in which he remained active until the autumn of 1871. Then he returned to Rostock and presented his *Habilitationsschrift,* "Über Bindessubstanzen und Gefässwandung bei Mollusken." Here as a *Privatdozent* he worked on connective tissue and gave a public lecture on the microscope, *Über die heutigen Aufgaben des Mikroskops* . . . (Rostock, 1872). That year he moved to Prague, where his work flourished and he formed a happy circle of friends among his colleagues. Only bad feeling among the students, two thirds of whom were Czech nationalists, caused him to leave in 1875 for Königsberg. Finally, in 1876, he settled at the small University of Kiel as professor of anatomy and director of the Anatomical Institute, a position he held until his retirement in 1901. Here he carried out the major part of his great work on cell division published in his classic book, *Zellsubstanz, Kern und Zelltheilung* (Leipzig, 1882). Flemming was a bachelor and for most of his time in Kiel lived with his sister Clara.

In the 1850's attempts to study the process of cell multiplication were vitiated by inadequate techniques of staining and the poor resolving power of lenses. By the 1860's it had become certain that before a cell divides the nucleus must first give rise to two daughter nuclei. This appeared to result either from direct fission or from a more indirect process in which dissolution of the mother nucleus was followed by coagulation of two daughter nuclei about two new centers; but the phases of this metamorphosis remained a mystery. It was seen that nucleoli came and went during indirect division, that their number was constant, and that the midpoint of the division process was marked by the appearance of nuclear granules. In the 1870's these granules were observed to elongate into threadlike structures which split up in some way, yielding the material for two daughter nuclei. It was Flemming's achievement to observe and interpret the stages correctly, to identify them in a wide variety of tissues, and to give indirect division the name by which it is still widely known—mitosis.

With his background in the study of connective tissues, epithelia, and fat cells, Flemming was well-prepared to attack the problem of cell division. His serious study of this subject would appear to date from 1874 while he was in Prague. His third paper in this field ("Beobachtungen über die Beschaffenheit des Zellkerns," in *Archiv für mikroskopische Anatomie,* **13** [1877], 693–717), on the constitution of the cell nucleus, described the use of Hermann's technique of overstaining followed by differentiation in alcohol. This led him to perceive the thread net (*Fadennetz*) with associated vacuoles and nucleoli as a constant feature of the living cell. That winter he still held to the direct-division theory of nuclear multiplication and lectured to that effect in Kiel in February 1878, but by the summer he had studied the same cells in living material as well as in fixed. Then he found what he called the *Äquatorial-platte* ("equatorial plate") stage (early anaphase), which is so easily missed when working only from fixed material, and realized that what he had called direct division was in fact the indirect process. His lecture and correction appeared in *Schriften des naturwissenschaftlichen Vereins für Schleswig-Holstein* (Kiel, February and August 1878).

By December 1879 he had investigated all the stages of mitotic division, the results of which appeared in his three famous papers: "Beiträge zur Kenntnis der Zelle und ihrer Lebenserscheinungen" (pts. 1, 2, and 3, 1879–1881). What had been taken for granules Flemming recognized as sections through threads; what hitherto had appeared as a vague and discontinuous process he saw as a continuous metamorphosis from the skein of the mother nucleus to thread loops (chromosomes) and back again to the skeins of the two daughter nuclei. In 1880 he coined the term "chromatin" for the stainable substance of the nucleus; the nonstaining portions he termed "achromatin." As the cell approaches division, the chromatin separates from the achromatin and becomes organized into a tangled skein (*Knäuel*) which proceeds to break up into figure-eight wreaths (*Kränze*), the loops of which open out to give stars (*Sterne*). At this stage the chromatin is organized with respect to a single center or pole (Flemming's "monocentric" phase), but this soon goes over to organization around two poles ("dicentric" phase). As the poles move apart, the star figures of chromatin pull apart; and because the arms of the stars have doubled along their length, four V-shaped loops (the chromatids) can be discerned, two traveling toward one pole and two toward the other. This is the equatorial plate stage, from which the barrel stage takes the chromatic loops back to the star, wreath, and skein stages of the nascent daughter nuclei.

Flemming was in error in believing that the chromatin loops arise by fragmentation of a continuous skein and that the loops fuse end-to-end at the close of mitosis to generate a skein once more. Hence it is natural that his terminology has been replaced: wreath by prophase, star by metaphase, equatorial plate by early anaphase, and nuclear barrel by telophase. Although he noted the same number of loops in successive divisions he did not perceive their continuity and individuality. This called for material with much lower chromosome numbers than he used. Flemming's contribution was to force the data from a wide range of apparently differing division processes into a single framework, to rule out so-called direct division of nuclei by simple fission, and to perceive longitudinal division of chromatin loops as the basis of nuclear multiplication, rather than transverse division as Strasburger believed.

In the summer of 1879 Flemming turned his attention to nuclear division in the testes and concluded that the spermatozoa are formed from cells whose nuclei have arisen by indirect division, the head of the spermatozoon being composed solely of chromatin. He also failed at this time to observe doubled threads in the closing nuclear figures. In 1882, in his book on cell division, he declared this to have been an error, for now he could detect doubled threads.

It was not until 1887 that he succeeded in clarifying the details of indirect division in the spermatozoa. Then he recognized two divisions, the first of which he termed heterotypic, the second homotypic. In the first, the threads formed curious rings and did not appear to double; in the second, doubling occurred and no ring structures were formed, the resulting nuclei having half the normal complement of chromosomes. In fact, doubling takes place in the first, not the second, division.

What Flemming called ring structures were the paired homologous chromosomes (bivalents) that Jansenns described accurately in 1909. The distinction between meiosis and mitosis is of course a deep and subtle one that Flemming, in his desire to unify the data, failed to appreciate. In 1880 he traveled to the zoological station at Naples to study cell division in the formation of the echinoderm egg and established there also indirect division as the mechanism of cell division.

Flemming's great merit as a theoretician lay in his attempt to find a single process to fit all forms of cell division. History has justified his vision.

In the 1880's attempts were frequently made to tie down the living substance to a particular class of compounds. Flemming would have none of this, for to him life resided in the whole body of the cell. Yet he took sides in the dispute between those who favored a network structure of protoplasm and those who preferred a filar structure. He belonged to the latter group. Such ideas were of course premature, and none has served as a foundation for later developments.

Among Flemming's other contributions may be mentioned his work on amitotic division, which he believed to characterize pathological and senescent tissues only; he improved Flesch's fixative in 1882 by addition of acetic acid to give Flemming's fluid; he introduced Flemming's stain (safranine-gentian violet-Orange G) in 1891. In his later years he returned to his earlier studies of connective tissue development and in 1902 wrote a valuable treatise, "Histogenese der Stützsubstanzen der Bindegewebesgruppe," for O. Hertwig's *Handbuch der vergleichenden und experimentellen Entwickelungsgeschichte der Wirbeltiere.*

BIBLIOGRAPHY

I. Original Works. Flemming published 80 papers and two books, all listed in Spee's obituary notice (below). The majority of his papers appeared in the *Archiv für mikroskopische Anatomie und Entwicklungsmechanik,* beginning with his doctoral dissertation of 1868 and ending with his paper on rod cells 30 years later. Most important are his "Beiträge zur Kenntnis der Zelle," pt. 1, **16** (1879), 302–436; pt. 2, **18** (1880), 152–159; and pt. 3, **20** (1881), 1–86. Pt. 2, setting out the details of mitosis, has been translated into English by Leonie Piternick and is in *Journal of Cell Biology,* **25** (1965), 3–69. Important also are his "Neue Beiträge zur Kenntnis der Zelle," pt. 1, **29** (1887), 389–463; pt. 2, **37** (1891), 685–751, the first analyzing meiosis and the second introducing the Flemming stain.

Flemming's first paper on cell division was "Über die ersten Entwickelungserscheinungen am Ei der Teichmuschel," **10** (1874), 257–292. The first chromatin figures of mitosis are "Studien zur Entwickelungsgeschichte der Najaden," in *Sitzungsberichte der mathematisch-naturwissenschaftlichen Classe der Kaiserlichen Akademie der Wissenschaften,* **71** (1875), pt. 3, 81–212. Major works are *Zellsubstanz, Kern und Zellteilung* (Leipzig, 1882), and "Histogenese der Stützsubstanzen der Bindesubstanzgruppe," in *Handbuch der vergleichenden und experimentellen Entwickelungsgeschichte der Wirbeltiere,* 3 vols. (Jena, 1902–1906).

II. Secondary Literature. No biographies and very few obituaries have been published. The present account is based largely on F. von Spee, "Walther Flemming," in *Anatomischer Anzeiger,* **28** (1906), 41–59, with portrait and complete bibliography, and on a short note by H. J. Conn, "Walther Flemming," in *Stain Technology,* **8** (1933), 48–49, with portrait.

Discussions of Flemming's work may be found in E. B. Wilson, *The Cell in Development and Inheritance* (New York, 1896); and A. Hughes, *A History of Cytology* (London–New York, 1959). Valuable also are W. Coleman, "The Nucleus as the Vehicle of Inheritance," in *Proceedings of the American Philosophical Society,* pt. 3, **109** (1965), 124–158; and A. Bolles Lee, *The Microtomist's Vade-Mecum,* 3rd ed. (London, 1893).

Robert Olby

FLETCHER, WALTER MORLEY (*b.* Liverpool, England, 21 July 1873; *d.* London, England, 7 June 1933), *physiology.*

Fletcher was the youngest of six sons in a family of ten children born to Alfred Evans Fletcher and his wife, Sarah Elizabeth Morley, cousin of the philanthropist Samuel Morley and of the future prime minister H. H. Asquith. Both parents were Congregationalists from Yorkshire. Fletcher's father, who in 1851 had won the gold medal in chemistry at University College, London, was inspector of alkali works for the local government board in Liverpool and later served as chief inspector in London.

Fletcher was educated at University College School in London, where he did not win great distinction, and in 1891 matriculated with a subsizarship at Trinity College, Cambridge. An elder brother, Herbert, had preceded him at Cambridge and, before going on to a medical career, had briefly pursued physiological research in the laboratory founded and directed by Michael Foster. Although Walter also intended to qualify for medical practice, physiology was from the first his chief aim.

Fletcher's intellectual powers matured rapidly in the Cambridge setting, and he took a first class in both parts of the natural sciences tripos in 1894 and 1895. After graduating B.A. in 1894, he was elected to the Coutts Trotter studentship in 1896 and to fellowship of Trinity College in 1897. In the same year he won the Wallingham Medal and an open scholarship at St. Bartholomew's Hospital, where by 1900 he had completed the clinical studies required for medical qualification. During this period Fletcher also taught at Cambridge. He received the M.A. from Cambridge in 1898, M.B. in 1900, M.D. in 1908, and Sc. D. in 1914. He was named senior demonstrator in physiology in 1903 and served as tutor at Trinity College from 1905 to 1914. He was elected a fellow of the Royal Society in 1915 and gave the

Croonian lecture in the same year. Of the students strongly influenced by Fletcher, the most notable is A. V. Hill, who won the Nobel Prize in medicine or physiology in 1922.

Fletcher left Cambridge and original research in 1914, when he was appointed first secretary of the Medical Research Committee, created in 1913 under terms of the National Insurance Act of 1911. He had already demonstrated his organizing powers in administrative work for Trinity College and the University of Cambridge. This previous experience was fortunate, for Fletcher was almost immediately required to mobilize the Medical Research Committee for the war effort. His success was recognized by the award of the K.B.E. in 1918. Of the work done for the committee during the war, Fletcher was particularly intrigued by that which established the cause of rickets, and he thereafter took a special interest in research that offered solutions to nutritional problems.

After the war Fletcher played an important role in securing a new charter for the committee, by which it was freed from the control of the Ministry of Health and established as the independent Medical Research Council under the aegis of the Privy Council (1920). He was criticized for a certain impatience with research that had no immediate practical benefit and for his sometimes naïve optimism about the clinical value of some basic research, but his contributions were on the whole very highly regarded. Until his death in 1933, he wrote an admirable introduction to each of the annual reports of the committee (and later the council).

Fletcher also served on a number of other important government bodies, including the Royal Commission on the Universities of Oxford and Cambridge (1919–1922) and the Indian Government Committee on the Organization of Medical Research (1928–1929), of which he was chairman. In the latter role he helped secure a private gift of £250,000 for research on leukemia. The trustees of the Sir William Dunn Foundation and the Rockefeller Foundation depended heavily on his advice in giving funds for biochemical laboratories at Oxford and Cambridge and for the London School of Hygiene and Tropical Medicine. Fletcher was appointed C.B. in 1929 and received honorary doctorates from the universities of Oxford, Edinburgh, Glasgow, Leeds, Birmingham, and Pennsylvania. In 1904 he married Mary Frances Cropper, who later attracted attention for her popular writing on religion, and by whom he had one son and one daughter.

Like his brother Herbert, Fletcher was a distinguished athlete in track and field, and this may have encouraged his interest in the problem of muscular metabolism and fatigue. All of his published research papers, with the exception of two early notes dealing with minor aspects of the involuntary nervous system, are devoted to this problem. His first major investigation, published in 1898, was the basis for his election to the Trinity fellowship. It presented a serious challenge to the prevailing conception of muscular metabolism, for which the German physiologists Ludimar Hermann and E. F. Pflüger were chiefly responsible. They supposed that there was in muscle a large and complex "inogen" molecule which stored up intramolecular oxygen and then exploded upon contraction to yield the recognized end products of muscular metabolism, chiefly carbon dioxide, water, and lactic acid. This basic conception had been extended by Max Verworn to other tissues, and the general phenomena of cellular metabolism were considered so complex as almost to defy experimental analysis.

The work that led to these ideas was open to the same general criticism that Claude Bernard had applied to the way some German physiologists approached the study of digestion. Their exclusive concern with the initial and end points of the process, said Bernard, was like trying to find out what went on in a house by observing what went in the door and what came out the chimney. Similarly, but without overtly discussing the theoretical implications of his work, Fletcher showed in 1898 that the prevailing theory of muscular metabolism was based on an inadequate understanding of the events taking place between the beginning and the end of the process. He was able to prove this point by adapting for his own uses a sensitive apparatus recently devised by the Cambridge plant physiologist F. F. Blackman for studying the gaseous exchange of leaves. With this apparatus, which made it possible to measure the discharge of even small quantities of carbon dioxide at frequent intervals, Fletcher showed that there was no sudden discharge of carbon dioxide upon contraction but, rather, that most of it was discharged gradually during the process of recovery from fatigue.

All of Fletcher's later research can be considered an extension of this paper. In 1902 he showed that an excised frog muscle would contract and relax in the absence of oxygen but that oxygen greatly facilitated its recovery from fatigue. The next important step was to measure simultaneously the discharges of carbon dioxide and of lactic acid during and after contraction and to study the relationship between them. For this work, which required the development of new methods, Fletcher secured the cooperation of the eminent Cambridge biochemist Frederick Gowland Hopkins.

In 1907 they showed that the confusing and often contradictory results obtained by earlier workers on lactic-acid fatigue could be traced largely to their treatment of the muscle before or during extraction. All of the previous methods—maceration, boiling, and alcohol solutions—tended to stimulate the artificial production of lactic acid and thus to obscure the entire process. They found that the muscle could be preserved in a truly resting and uninjured state by plunging it into ice-cold alcohol. In such a muscle they found very little lactic acid. As the muscle was stimulated to a series of contractions, they found a steady increase in the amount of lactic acid up to a certain maximum, at which irritability was lost. If the fatigued muscle was then placed in oxygen, the lactic acid was greatly reduced, irritability was restored, and carbon dioxide was evolved. The process could be repeated endlessly with the same results. Fletcher and Hopkins concluded that "excised but undamaged muscle when exposed to sufficient tension of oxygen has in itself the power of dealing in some way with the lactic acid which has accumulated during fatigue" ("Lactic Acid in Amphibian Muscle," p. 297).

In 1914, with G. M. Brown, Fletcher showed that none of the processes leading to the discharge of carbon dioxide was directly related to muscular contraction itself. In an extension of his earlier paper with Hopkins, he argued that the absorption of oxygen and the evolution of carbon dioxide were related instead to the removal of lactic acid and other fatigue products. With this established, Fletcher finally criticized the "inogen" theory directly. In a joint Croonian lecture to the Royal Society in 1915, Fletcher and Hopkins incorporated all of this and other work into a new synthesis. They emphasized above all that the main biochemical processes involved in muscular contraction were really quite simple and amenable to experimental analysis. No resort need be made to some complex and hypothetical "inogen" molecule. This point of view greatly stimulated further work on muscular metabolism and on cellular metabolism in general, and Fletcher's basic conception and approach have survived the alterations in detail which that further work inevitably produced.

BIBLIOGRAPHY

I. Original Works. Fletcher's scientific papers are few enough that all may be cited here: "Preliminary Note on the Motor and Inhibitor Nerve Endings in Smooth Muscle," in *Journal of Physiology,* **22** (1898), xxxvii–xl; "The Vaso-Constrictor Fibres of the Great Auricular Nerve in the Rabbit," *ibid.,* 259–263; "The Survival Respiration of Muscle," *ibid.,* **23** (1898), 10–99; "The Influence of Oxygen Upon the Survival Respiration of Muscle," *ibid.,* **28** (1902), 354–359; "Preliminary Note on the Changes in the Osmotic Properties of Muscle Due to Fatigue," *ibid.,* xli–xlii; "The Relation of Oxygen to the Survival Metabolism of Muscle," *ibid.,* 474–498; "The Osmotic Properties of Muscle, and Their Modifications in Fatigue and Rigor," *ibid.,* **30** (1904), 414–438; "Lactic Acid in Amphibian Muscle," *ibid.,* **35** (1907), 247–309, written with F. G. Hopkins; "On the Alleged Formation of Lactic Acid in Muscle During Autolysis and in Post-survival Periods," *ibid.,* **43** (1911), 286–312; "Lactic Acid Formation, Survival Respiration and Rigor Mortis in Mammalian Muscle," *ibid.,* **47** (1913), 361–380; "The Carbon Dioxide Production of Heat Rigor in Muscle, and the Theory of Intra-molecular Oxygen," *ibid.,* **48** (1914), 177–204, written with G. M. Brown; and "Croonian Lecture (1915): The Respiratory Process in Muscle and the Nature of Muscular Motion," in *Proceedings of the Royal Society,* **89B** (1917), 444–467, written with F. G. Hopkins.

II. Secondary Literature. Maisie [Mary Frances Cropper] Fletcher, *The Bright Countenance: A Personal Biography of Walter Fletcher* (London, 1957), a sometimes silly book by Fletcher's widow, at least bears an apt title. It also contains a complete bibliography of his writings, a list of his honors and of his obituary notices, and a valuable forty-page supplement by Sir Arthur MacNalty, which is particularly notable for the excellent survey it gives of the work done by the Medical Research Committee (Council) during Fletcher's period as secretary.

T. R. Elliot, who also worked in the Cambridge physiological laboratory at the turn of the century, has contributed three valuable sketches of Fletcher's life and work: *Dictionary of National Biography (1931–1940),* pp. 284–285; *Nature,* **132** (1933), 17–20; and *Obituary Notices of Fellows of the Royal Society of London,* **1,** no. 2 (1933), 153–163.

See also *The* [London] *Times* (8 June 1933), p. 14; *Cambridge Review* (13 Oct. 1933); *Lancet* (1933), **1,** 1319; and *British Medical Journal* (1933), **1,** 1085.

Gerald L. Geison

FLETT, JOHN SMITH (*b.* Kirkwall, Orkney, Scotland, 26 June 1869; *d.* Ashdon, Essex, England, 26 January 1947), *geology, petrology.*

Educated at the Burgh School, Kirkwall, and George Watson's College, Edinburgh, Flett entered the University of Edinburgh at the age of seventeen. His academic career, of which he left an account (published posthumously), was one of remarkable promise. He read first for the arts degree, and the classics left him with a lifelong love of Horace, Catullus, and Lucretius; the other subjects in the course were mathematics, physics, metaphysics, moral philosophy, English, and political economy. Having graduated M.A. at nineteen, Flett proceeded to the B.Sc. in natural sciences and followed this with the medical degrees M.B. and C.M. in 1894.

After practicing medicine for a short time, Flett returned to the University of Edinburgh to become assistant to the professor of geology, James Geikie, and subsequently was promoted to a lectureship in petrology. His earliest researches were on the stratigraphy and petrology of the rocks of his homeland; this work was accepted for the D.Sc. in 1899. His five years as petrologist at Edinburgh gave Flett a sure grasp of the subject and a growing reputation, especially as a result of his studies of the monchiquite-camptonite suite of minor intrusions.

In 1901 Flett joined the Geological Survey of Great Britain, succeeding Sir Jethro Teall as petrographer and quickly attaining district geologist status. In 1911 he returned to Edinburgh as assistant director in charge of the Geological Survey in Scotland. He became director of the Geological Survey of Great Britain in 1921, occupying this position with great distinction until his retirement in 1935. He was elected a fellow of the Royal Society in 1913 and was created a Knight of the Order of the British Empire in 1925.

Flett's scientific achievements, in addition to his work on Orkney, include important contributions to the geology of Cornwall, especially his work on the sediments, metamorphic rocks, and igneous masses of the Lizard and adjacent areas. That some revision of the dating of the ancient sediments was needed as a result of the work of E. M. Hendricks does not detract from his basic work. Flett's joint study with C. E. Tilley of the unusual cordierite-anthophyllite rocks of the aureole of the Land's End granite is significant in metamorphic petrology, but he is remembered more generally for the formulation, with Henry Dewey, of the spilite suite, a worldwide type characteristic of early geosynclinal history. As Survey petrographer, Flett's work ranged widely over the richly varied rocks of the British Isles and is recorded in contributions to thirty-six issues of the Survey's *Memoirs,* covering areas as separated as Caithness and Meneage (1902–1947). Abroad, his best-known work arose from a Royal Society expedition to St. Vincent after the eruption of Soufrière in 1902; Tempest Anderson was his collaborator.

After 1911 Flett's energies turned to administration, and it was his powerful leadership that left its mark on science. Some of the Geological Survey's best work was done under him, such as the completion of the highly detailed mapping of the Tertiary volcanoes and the revision of the major coalfields. More than this, it was Flett's determination that brought to fruition the move of the Museum of Practical Geology (now called the Geological Museum) from its Victorian site behind Piccadilly to the present splendid building in South Kensington.

Flett became increasingly deaf, but there were those who believed that his success as an administrator was due to his hearing only those proposals according with his own wishes.

BIBLIOGRAPHY

I. Original Works. A full list of Flett's writings is given in the Royal Society obituary notice cited below. Among them are "The Old Red Sandstone of the Orkneys," in *Transactions of the Royal Society of Edinburgh,* **39** (1898), 383–424; "The Trap Dykes of the Orkneys," *ibid.,* **39** (1900), 865–918; "Report on the Eruption of Soufrière in St. Vincent in 1902, and on a Visit to Montagne Pélée, in Martinique," in *Philosophical Transactions of the Royal Society,* **200A** (1903), 353–553, written with T. Anderson; "On Some British Pillow-Lavas and the Rocks Associated With Them," in *Geological Magazine,* 5th ser., **8** (1911), 202–209, 241–248, written with H. Dewey; "Hornfelses from Kenidjack, Cornwall," in *Memoirs of the Geological Survey. Summary of Progress for 1929* (1930), 24–41, written with C. E. Tilley; "Geology of Lizard and Meneage (Explanation of Sheet 359)," in *Memoirs of the Geological Survey of Great Britain* (London, 1912, 2nd ed. [by Flett], 1946), written with J. B. Hill; *The First Hundred Years of the Geological Survey of Great Britain* (London, 1937); and "Memories of an Edinburgh Student, 1886–1894," in *University of Edinburgh Journal,* **15** (1950), 160–182.

II. Secondary Literature. See E. B. Bailey, *Geological Survey of Great Britain* (London, 1952), *passim;* and H. H. Read, "John Smith Flett, 1869–1947," in *Obituary Notices of Fellows of the Royal Society of London,* **5** (1948), 689–696.

K. C. Dunham

FLEXNER, SIMON (*b.* Louisville, Kentucky, 25 March 1863; *d.* New York, N.Y., 2 May 1946), *pathology, bacteriology.*

Flexner was the fourth child of Morris Flexner, member of an educated Jewish family in Czechoslovakia, who immigrated to Kentucky. Starting as a peddler, he became a successful wholesale merchant. Flexner's mother, Esther Abraham, was born in Alsace. Flexner attended public schools in Louisville and was apprenticed to a druggist who sent him to the Louisville College of Pharmacy, from which he was graduated in 1882. He then worked in his eldest brother's drugstore and studied medicine at the University of Louisville, receiving the M.D. degree in 1889. Although the medical school then provided little opportunity for laboratory study, Flexner acquired a microscope, with which he studied pathological tissues and made microscopic examinations for doctors who patronized the Flexner pharmacy.

In 1890, at the suggestion of another of his remarkable brothers, Abraham, Flexner went to Baltimore to study pathology and bacteriology at the Johns Hopkins Hospital with William H. Welch, who gave him a fellowship and in 1892, when the Johns Hopkins Medical School opened, made him his first assistant in the department of pathology. In 1893 Flexner visited Europe, working at Strasbourg with Friedrich von Recklinghausen and at Prague. On his return he became resident pathologist at the Johns Hopkins Hospital. By 1899 he reached full professorial rank. In that year, following the acquisition of the Philippine Islands by the United States, Flexner and two medical students spent several months in Manila studying health conditions. During this stay he isolated an organism that causes a prevalent form of dysentery. This *Bacillus* (now *Shigella*) *dysenteriae* is still commonly known as the "Flexner bacillus."

Soon after his return to Baltimore, Flexner was appointed professor of pathology at the University of Pennsylvania, where he organized an excellent staff, planned a new laboratory building, and carried out important researches on experimental dysentery, on experimental pancreatitis, and on immunological problems, especially with regard to hemolysis and hemagglutination. One of his associates was the brilliant young Japanese physician Hideyo Noguchi, who came from Japan inexperienced and penniless and found in Flexner a lifelong friend and guide.

When bubonic plague broke out in California in 1901, the federal government sent Flexner to San Francisco to study the epidemic. Within a month he and a few associates confirmed the presence of the plague bacillus and made a report to health authorities that aided them in eradicating the disease.

In 1901 John D. Rockefeller and his son John D. Rockefeller, Jr., were planning the creation of the Rockefeller Institute for Medical Research in New York City. Flexner, who by this time, at the age of thirty-eight, was beginning to be nationally known, was appointed to the institute's board of scientific directors, which was composed of seven eminent medical men and headed by his friend and mentor William H. Welch. In 1902 Flexner was chosen to lead a department of pathology and bacteriology in the institute, and soon he established himself as head of the whole enterprise. He brought together a strong group of investigators, including Hideyo Noguchi, S. J. Meltzer, P. A. T. Levene, Alexis Carrel, Jacques Loeb, Eugene Opie, Rufus I. Cole, and Peyton Rous. Flexner's colleagues found him a man of exceedingly keen intelligence, with a reserved manner that concealed a sympathetic heart. He directed his staff with great skill, giving free rein to those who showed independent competence while guiding with a wise hand those who needed advice. His financial acumen impressed the astute patron of the institute, who showed his confidence by successive additions to its funds.

To combat an epidemic of cerebrospinal meningitis in 1906, Flexner produced a serum that remained the best treatment until the sulfa drugs were introduced. When in 1910 poliomyelitis was epidemic in New York, he and his assistants were the first to transfer the virus from monkey to monkey. This success enabled the investigators to keep the virus alive in the laboratory and thus ultimately, after development by others of a less expensive method of perpetuating it (by cultivation in hens' eggs), led to the preparation, in the 1950's, of protective vaccines.

The Rockefeller Institute, quite early in its history, came under strong attack from organizations opposed to the use of animals in experiments on the causes of disease. Flexner's accomplishments in such work and his calm generalship made him a natural leader in the successful deterrence of these opponents.

In 1903 Flexner married Helen Whitall Thomas, member of a prominent Quaker family of Baltimore. She helped to expand his intellectual interests beyond the medical sciences, giving him an appreciation of literature and the arts. Of their two sons, William became a physicist and James Thomas a writer and historian of American culture.

Flexner's medical and biological accomplishments led to public service in various health fields, as chairman of the Public Health Commission of New York State, as medical consultant of the U.S. Army during World War I, and as member of the China Medical Board of the Rockefeller Foundation. When in 1902 William H. Welch wearied of the editorship of the *Journal of Experimental Medicine,* Flexner took it over and for about fifteen years was its chief editor, giving the task much time and attention.

His executive competence was recognized by trusteeships of the Rockefeller Foundation, the Carnegie Foundation for the Advancement of Teaching, and the Johns Hopkins University. A little-known but very important public service was his leadership in establishing fellowships of the National Research Council, provided by the Rockefeller Foundation, for promising young medical scientists. Oxford University called him in 1937–1938 to its Eastman professorship, at a time when his counsel was needed in the organization of Lord Nuffield's endowment of medical professorships. A book, *The Evolution and Organization of the University Clinic* (Oxford, 1939), resulted from this experience. Flexner was elected member of the American Philosophical Society in 1901, the National Academy of Sciences in 1908, and foreign member of the Royal Society in 1919.

During his long career Flexner published several hundred scientific papers, lectures, and essays. At the age of seventy-eight he published jointly with his son James a notable biography, *William H. Welch and the Heroic Age of American Medicine* (New York, 1941). He quietly resigned the directorship of the Rockefeller Institute in 1935.

BIBLIOGRAPHY

Flexner's papers are in the library of the American Philosophical Society, Philadelphia.

Secondary literature includes Stanhope Bayne-Jones, "Simon Flexner, 1863–1946," in *Year Book* [for] *1946. American Philosophical Society* (Philadelphia, 1947), pp. 284–297; George W. Corner, *History of the Rockefeller Institute* (New York, 1965), *passim; Memorial Meeting for Simon Flexner* (New York, 1946), a pamphlet issued by the Rockefeller Institute that contains personal characterizations by John D. Rockefeller, Jr., and others; and Peyton Rous, "Simon Flexner, 1863–1946," in *Obituary Notices of Fellows of the Royal Society of London,* **6** (1948–1949), 409–445, with portrait and complete list of publications.

GEORGE W. CORNER

FLOREY, HOWARD WALTER (*b.* Adelaide, Australia, 24 September 1898; *d.* Oxford, England, 21 February 1968), *pathology.*

Florey's scientific career was devoted to the experimental study of disease processes. His most notable contribution to science was the development of penicillin as a systemic antibacterial antibiotic suitable for use in man.

Florey was the third and last child, and the only son, of Joseph Florey and his second wife, Bertha Mary Wadham, a native of Australia. Joseph Florey owned a boot factory, and the family was in comfortable circumstances. The son attended St. Peter's Collegiate School, Adelaide, as a day boy. He had a brilliant scholastic career, obtaining scholarships at St. Peter's and subsequently for study at the University of Adelaide.

From an early age Florey had decided to study medicine and carry out medical research, rather than learn the management of the family business. He enrolled in the Faculty of Medicine at the University of Adelaide in 1917 and graduated M.B., B.S. five years later. Receipt of the Rhodes Scholarship for South Australia in 1922 enabled him to go to Oxford, where he studied in the Honours Physiology School. His exposure there to the great neurophysiologist Sir Charles Sherrington profoundly affected his outlook on pathology. He was so impressed by the value for aspiring young pathologists of the physiological and biochemical outlook conferred by the Honours Physiology School that when he later became professor of pathology at Oxford, he insisted that all candidates for the Ph.D. should study at the Honours School before beginning experimental work in the Sir William Dunn School. From Oxford, Florey went to Cambridge for a year and then spent a year in the United States as a Rockefeller Foundation traveling fellow. After a short period at the London Hospital he returned to Cambridge, where he took the Ph.D. degree. The most important formative influence at Cambridge came not from the department of pathology but from the biochemist Sir Frederic Gowland Hopkins, then at the height of his career.

In 1926 Florey married Mary Ethel Reed, who had been a fellow medical student at the University of Adelaide; they had a son, Charles, and a daughter, Paquita. Mrs. Florey died in 1966, and in 1967 he married the Hon. Margaret Jennings, a former colleague in his Oxford laboratories.

In 1931 Florey was appointed Joseph Hunter professor of pathology at the University of Sheffield. Four years later he moved to Oxford as professor in charge of the Sir William Dunn School of Pathology; Sir Edward Mellanby played an important part in this appointment. It was a milestone in the history of pathology in Britain, because for the first time a man trained in experimental physiology and viewing pathology with a physiologist's eye came into a position of influence in the teaching of the subject. Florey remained professor of pathology at Oxford from 1935 until 1962, when he resigned to become provost of Queen's College, Oxford.

Florey created a very lively and stimulating atmosphere at Oxford, which led to close contacts between department members, who had been selected to cover a wide range of scientific disciplines. Not only was this spirit of collaboration all-important in the early work on penicillin, but it also resulted in the Sir William Dunn School's becoming the leading center of experimental pathology in Europe, through which a succession of able and brilliant young men passed.

Although he remained in Britain after 1922, with a life centered at Oxford after 1935, Florey remained Australian in accent and outlook. In 1944 he was invited to Australia by the prime minister, John Curtin, to report on the Australian situation in medical research. His report led to the establishment of the Australian National University as a graduate university in 1946. Florey was very closely connected with this university for the next decade, as a senior adviser with a particular interest in the John Curtin School of Medical Research. He played the major role in establishing this school, and he visited the Australian National University for consultation almost every year until 1957. In 1965 he was appointed chancellor of the university and resumed his annual visits to Canberra.

The influence of both Sherrington and Hopkins can be traced throughout Florey's career. He was exceptional among contemporary pathologists in the United Kingdom in that he was interested in the study, by physiological and biochemical methods, of the functional changes of cells which lead to pathological changes, rather than merely in the morphological description of diseased tissues. He also had the pathologist's interest in structure, and in the latter part of his life he made extensive use of electron microscopy to study structure with the greater detail and precision made possible by that instrument. His basic tools were physiological operative techniques, in the use of which he displayed superb skill and ingenuity.

The idea of antibiosis, or microbial antagonism, was not new in Florey's time; Pasteur had made observations on the topic. Neither was penicillin new; Sir Alexander Fleming had discovered it in 1929, although he had looked on it only as a useful antiseptic for local application and had not realized that it was in fact a potent systemic antibacterial substance. Florey and his colleague E. B. Chain transformed what was a bacteriological curiosity into a clinical tool of immense value, and in so doing they opened up the new industry of antibiotic production. In the context of man's cultural evolution, it is interesting to reflect that the utilization of molds for the production of antibiotics represented the first important domestication of a species since prehistoric times.

Shortly after he arrived at Oxford, Florey sought Hopkins' advice on a suitable person to lead a biochemical unit in the Dunn School of Pathology. Hopkins recommended E. B. Chain, a young refugee from Nazi Germany then in Hopkins' laboratory, and Chain moved to Oxford in 1935. This was a critically important development as far as penicillin was concerned, for Chain had the biochemical insight that enabled him to purify penicillin without loss of its potency—a feat that had eluded Harold Raistrick, who had attempted this a decade earlier on behalf of Fleming.

Florey had long had an interest in natural antibacterial substances, and in 1930 he began a study of the antibacterial properties of lysozyme, an enzyme discovered by Fleming in 1921. This work was pursued until the enzyme was purified and the nature of its substrate determined.[1] It was against this background that Florey and Chain, in 1938–1939, initiated a systematic investigation of the biological and chemical properties of the antibacterial substances produced by bacteria and molds. As they recorded in the first publication on penicillin (1940) and in their major book on the subject, *Antibiotics* (1949), they were greatly encouraged by the success of René Dubos and his colleagues in isolating tyrothricin from the soil bacterium *Bacillus brevis* and in purifying its component antibiotic polypeptides, tyrocidin and gramicidin (only to find that although they were effective antibacterial agents, they were too toxic for systemic use).[2]

Florey emphasized that his research on antibacterial agents had been conceived as an academic study with possibilities of wide theoretical interest, not as "war work." By good fortune, and with excellent scientific judgment, Florey and Chain selected Fleming's penicillin as the first substance to be studied in detail. It proved so promising experimentally in mice with streptococci, staphylococci, and gas gangrene organisms (showing true systemic antibacterial potency combined with minimum toxicity) that all the resources of the Oxford laboratory were turned to its production on a scale that would allow clinical trials to be carried out. Many investigations, involving workers in several scientific disciplines, were necessary before penicillin could be used in human medicine. Because of the variety of skills possessed by the scientists Florey had gathered around him, developmental work proceeded rapidly. A simple and effective assay system was devised, the antibacterial spectrum of penicillin was determined, and pharmacological and toxicological studies were made in mice and later in man. In spite of efforts to increase the yield from the cultures of *Penicillium notatum,* it was necessary to process 2,000 liters of culture fluid to obtain enough penicillin to treat a single case of sepsis in man. In order to scale up production very unusual equipment was used, such as enameled bedpans for culture vessels; the "factory" on South Parks Road, Oxford, was far removed from the vast fermentation tanks and sophisticated chemical engineering of the modern antibiotics industry.

In 1941 penicillin was used in treating nine cases of human bacterial infection. All responded dramatically. The next stage called for other skills, at which Florey proved to be as adept as he had been in the laboratory. Industry in wartime Britain could not be expected to produce supplies of penicillin in the amounts so urgently needed, so Florey and his colleague Norman Heatley went to the United States (which had not yet entered World War II) to stimulate interest in its production there. The chairman of the Committee on Medical Research, Office of Scientific

Research and Development, was the pharmacologist A. N. Richards, with whom Florey had worked as a Rockefeller Foundation traveling fellow in 1929–1930. Florey's enterprise and Richards' perspicacity were responsible for the production of penicillin in sufficient quantities for the treatment of war casualties in 1944.[3] Florey journeyed widely to investigate the use of penicillin in the field, traveling to North Africa in 1943 and subsequently to the Soviet Union.

Having acquired such skill in antibiotic research, it was natural that Florey should continue it in the Oxford laboratories well after the end of World War II. The most successful outcome was the development of cephalosporin C. Florey played a part in the early work on the cephalosporins, but later developments were the work of his colleague E. P. Abraham.[4]

After about 1955 Florey returned to research in experimental pathology. His interests ranged widely but showed a continuing preoccupation with the structure and function of the smaller blood vessels and their relation to the movement of lymph and cells in the process of inflammation. In his studies on capillary function and cell migration he could fully indulge his interest in the fine structure of cells and tissues, his pleasure in skilled manipulation, and his enthusiasm for photography. These interests were manifested in his use of the rabbit-ear chamber and other techniques for *in vivo* microscopy, and later of the electron microscope.

The physiology of mucus secretion was another area in which Florey did valuable work, particularly in clarifying its protective function in the respiratory and intestinal tracts. His early recognition of the hormonal control of the secretion of Brunner's glands has recently been confirmed; while a third thread that runs through Florey's work was an interest in human reproduction, initially at the experimental level, where he was interested in the movement of spermatozoa in the female genital tract.

Florey remained an active laboratory investigator all his life. After penicillin, the main topics with which he was concerned were the relatively insoluble antibiotic micrococcin, the electron microscopy of blood vessels, and the nature of atherosclerosis; he published two major works on the structure and function of endothelial cells of blood vessels in 1967, the year before his death.

Florey's other great contribution to science was as president of the Royal Society (1960–1965), the highest office in British science. He was the first Australian and the first pathologist to hold that post. During his tenure, he established the Royal Society Population Study Group and acted as its chairman until the time of his death.

His work was recognized by numerous honors, both public and academic: many honorary degrees from British and Australian universities; the Nobel Prize for physiology or medicine (1945), which Florey shared with Fleming and Chain; the Lister Medal of the Royal College of Surgeons (1945); the Copley Medal of the Royal Society (1957); and the Lomonosov Medal of the Soviet Academy of Sciences (1965).

Florey was elected a fellow of the Royal College of Physicians in 1951, corresponding member of the Australian Academy of Science in 1958, fellow of the Postgraduate Medical Foundation of Australia in 1965, foreign member of the American Philosophical Society in 1963, foreign associate of the National Academy of Sciences of the United States (1963), and foreign honorary member of the American Academy of Arts and Sciences (1964). He was created knight in 1944 and commander of the Legion of Honor in 1946; in 1965 he received the O.M. and was created a life peer, Baron Florey of Adelaide and Marston.

In temperament Florey was reserved but sure of himself. His chief characteristics were his common sense and his intense sense of obligation toward, and responsibility for, his scientific colleagues. He had no liking for speculation: for Florey an idea was not worth having unless it could be used to help design an experiment which would, or could in principle, give a definitive result. Perhaps this is what made him one of the most effective medical scientists of his generation.

NOTES

1. L. A. Epstein and E. Chain, "Some Observations on the Preparation and Properties of the Substrate of Lysozyme," in *British Journal of Experimental Pathology,* **21** (1940), 339–355.
2. R. J. Dubos, "Studies on a Bactericidal Agent Extracted From a Soil Bacillus. I. Preparation of the Agent. Its Activity *in vitro,*" in *Journal of Experimental Medicine,* **70** (1939), 1–17; R. D. Hotchkiss and R. J. Dubos, "Fractionation of the Bactericidal Agent From Cultures of a Soil Bacillus," in *Journal of Biological Chemistry,* **132** (1940), 791–792; and "Chemical Properties of Bactericidal Substances Isolated From Cultures of a Soil Bacillus," *ibid.,* 793–794.
3. See "Alfred Newton Richards, Scientist and Man," in *Annals of Internal Medicine,* **71** (1969), supp. 8, 56; supp. 9, 63–64.
4. E. P. Abraham and G. G. F. Newton, "New Penicillins, Cephalosporin C, and Penicillinase," in *Endeavour,* **20** (1961), 92–100.

BIBLIOGRAPHY

Florey's works include "The Secretion of Mucus by the Colon," in *British Journal of Experimental Pathology,* **11** (1930), 348-361; "Some Properties of Mucus, With Special Reference to Its Antibacterial Functions," *ibid.,* 192–208, written with N. E. Goldsworthy; "Penicillin as a Chemotherapeutic Agent," in *Lancet* (1940), **2,** 226–228, written with E. Chain *et al.;* "Further Observations on Penicillin," *ibid.* (1941), **2,** 177–188, written with E. P. Abraham, E. Chain, *et al.; Antibiotics: A Survey of Penicillin, Streptomycin and Other Antimicrobial Substances From Fungi, Actinomycetes, Bacteria and Plants,* 2 vols. (London, 1949), written with E. Chain *et al.;* and his eds. of *General Pathology* (London, 1954, 1958, 1962, 1970).

A complete bibliography will be found in the memoir on Florey in *Biographical Memoirs of Fellows of the Royal Society* (1971).

FRANK FENNER

FLOURENS, MARIE-JEAN-PIERRE (*b.* Maureilhan, near Béziers, France, 13 April 1794; *d.* Montgeron, near Paris, France, 8 December 1867), *physiology, history of science.*

Pierre Flourens, as he signed his papers, was born into a humble family in a small town in southern France. He studied medicine at the University of Montpellier, graduating at the age of nineteen. The next year, with a letter of recommendation from the famous botanist Augustin de Candolle to Georges Cuvier, Flourens went to Paris, where he decided to abandon medicine and devote all his efforts and ingenuity to physiological research. The protégé of Cuvier, talented, unusually skillful in experimental work, industrious, persevering, and devoted to research and science, Flourens met with early success. In 1821 he was entrusted with lecturing on the physiological theory of sensations before the distinguished scientific Cercle Athénée, and this led him to deeper experimental study of nervous functions. The first results, presented to the Academy by Cuvier in 1822, earned Flourens notoriety and recognition among scientists.

In 1824 and 1825 Flourens received the Montyon Prize twice in succession, and in 1828 he became a member of the Academy of Sciences. That same year Cuvier made Flourens his deputy lecturer at the Collège de France, and he became professor in 1832. The next year, following a wish of Cuvier's expressed before his death, Flourens succeeded him as permanent secretary of the Academy of Sciences. One of his great achievements in this capacity was the founding, with Arago, of the *Comptes rendus,* reports of Academy meetings, which still constitute one of the most important scientific periodicals. In 1838 Flourens was elected deputy for Béziers, and two years later he won election to the French Academy against the celebrated poet Victor Hugo; the election was followed by bitter comments and criticism. In his remaining years Flourens devoted his activity mainly to scientific biographies and philosophical and popular writings. He died at his country house after a long illness.

Flourens' distinguished scientific career began in 1822 with Cuvier's presentation to the Academy of Sciences of the first in a series of his reports on the nervous system; they were collected into a volume in 1824, which was followed by a complementary volume in 1825, and were republished with supplementary material in 1842. These reports are a landmark in the history of the physiology of the nervous system. Flourens' idea was to break down the complicated facts—everything in the mechanisms of life is complex, phenomena as well as organs—into their simple components, to separate all diverse occurrences, to find all distinguishable parts. The art of separating simple facts was for Flourens the whole art of experimenting. In his studies of brain functions he used mainly the technique of ablation—surgical removal of different parts to study their functions—examining systematically one part after the other to differentiate their functions. His hand was sure and precise; his descriptions clear, trenchant, simple, and elegant.

Flourens distinguished three essentially distinct main faculties in the central nervous system: perception and volition (i.e., intelligence), reception and transmission of impressions (i.e., sensibility), and the excitation of muscular contractions. He distinguished excitability from contractility, which is the faculty of muscle to shorten when excited by an adequate stimulus. According to Flourens, the intellect and the faculty of perception reside in the brain proper (cerebral hemispheres), the faculty of immediate excitation of muscular contraction in the spinal cord; and the faculty of coordination of movements willed by the cerebral hemispheres resides in the cerebellum, lesions of which cause disturbances of coordination (i.e., disharmony of movement) and of equilibrium. The idea of coordination introduced by Flourens has played an important role in nervous physiology. For Flourens every part of the brain—"every organ"—had its specific function yet acted as a whole in respect to this function, just as the entire brain functioned as a whole. Thus he thought that there was no localization within each part: all perceptions could concurrently occupy the same seats in the forebrain. Flourens was strongly opposed to Gall's phrenology.

Another important advance was Flourens' discovery of compulsive movements of the head and disturbances of equilibrium after lesions of the semicircular canals of the inner ear (1824–1828). This was a puzzling phenomenon whose physiological background he could not elucidate. It was at that time extremely difficult to realize that the inner ear has not only the receptors of audition (in the cochlea), but also, in its vestibular part, another type of receptor reacting to gravity and accelerative forces. It was explained only fifty years later, in 1873–1874, by Ernst Mach, Josef Breuer, and Alexander Crum Brown simultaneously. Among Flourens' other important contributions to science were his classic localization of the respiratory center (*noeud vital*) in the medulla oblongata, the reunion of nerves (1827), the role of the periosteum in the formation and growth of bone (1842–1847), and the discovery of the anesthetic properties of chloroform on animals (1847).

Flourens had a great influence on the development of physiology, but sometimes it was not beneficial. He was often authoritarian, imposing his opinion without caution or comparison of his experimental results and interpretations with those of other scientists. He was usually right, as in his opposition to Gall's pseudoscience of phrenology, but sometimes wrong, as in his repudiation of every idea of localization in the brain. His most reproachable error was his criticism of Darwin's work (1864).

In his biographies of distinguished scientists Flourens tried to sum up their achievements, relating their work to what was done before and after along the same lines, in a clear, simple, elegant, and engaging style. Some biographies are accompanied by more general studies on the related problems of the history of science. They were very popular, and some are masterpieces which served as models for other biographies.

BIBLIOGRAPHY

I. Original Works. Flourens' writings are *Recherches expérimentales sur les propriétés et fonctions du système nerveux dans les animaux vertébrés* (Paris, 1824, 1842); *Expériences sur le système nerveux . . . faisant suite aux Recherches expérimentales* . . . (Paris, 1825); *Cours sur la génération, l'ovologie et l'embryologie* (Paris, 1836); *Examen de la phrénologie* (Paris, 1842); *Recherches sur le développement des os et des dents* (Paris, 1842); *Mémoires d'anatomie et de physiologie comparées* (Paris, 1843); *Histoire des travaux et des idées de Buffon* (Paris, 1844); *Histoire de la découverte de la circulation du sang* (Paris, 1854, 1857), also trans. into English (Cincinnati, 1859); *De la longévité humaine et de la quantité de vie sur le globe* (Paris, 1854), also trans. into English (London, 1855); *Cours de physiologie comparée* (Paris, 1856); *Recueil des éloges historiques*, 3 vols. (Paris, 1856–1862); *Éloge historique de François Magendie* (Paris, 1858); *De l'instinct et de l'intelligence des animaux. De la vie et de l'intelligence* (Paris, 1858); *Ontologie naturelle ou étude philosophique des êtres* (Paris, 1861); *Éloge historique de A. M. C. Duméril* (Paris, 1863); and *Examen du livre de M. Darwin sur l'origine des espèces* (Paris, 1864).

II. Secondary Literature. On Flourens or his work, see Claude Bernard, "Discours de réception," in *Recueil des discours, rapports et pièces diverses . . . de l'Académie française 1860–1869* (Paris, 1872), II, 319; E. G. Boring, *A History of Experimental Psychology*, 2nd ed. (New York, 1950), pp. 61–67, 69, 77–78; H. Buess, "Flourens, 1794–1867, l'un des créateurs de la neurophysiologie," in *Médecine et hygiène*, **25** (1967), 1377–1379; E. Clarke and C. D. O'Malley, *Human Brain and Spinal Cord. A Historical Study Illustrated by Writings from Antiquity to the Twentieth Century* (Berkeley–Los Angeles, 1968), pp. 483–488, 656–661; V. Kruta, "M. J. P. Flourens, J. E. Purkyně et les débuts de la physiologie de la posture et de l'équilibre," in *Conférences du Palais de la découverte*, no. D98 (1964); M. Neuburger, *Die historische Entwicklung der experimentellen Gehirn und Rückenmark's Physiologie vor Flourens* (Stuttgart, 1897); J. M. D. Olmsted, "Pierre Flourens," in *Science, Medicine and History. Essays in Honour of Charles Singer* (London–New York–Toronto, 1953), II, 290–302; M. Reynaud, *Des derniers ouvrages de M. Flourens et de l'origine des idées modernes sur la vie* (Paris, 1858); and A. Vulpian, *Éloge historique de M. Flourens* . . . (Paris, 1886).

Vladislav Kruta

FLOWER, WILLIAM HENRY (*b.* Stratford-on-Avon, England, 30 November 1831; *d.* London, England, 1 July 1899), *zoology.*

Flower first enrolled at University College, London, and then studied medicine and surgery at Middlesex Hospital, graduating in 1851 from London University. As a student he received medals in zoology and physiology. Soon after becoming a member of the Royal College of Surgeons in March 1854 (he became a fellow in 1857), he volunteered for the Royal Army Medical Service in the Crimea. Upon his return to London, Flower was appointed surgeon, lecturer in anatomy, and curator at the museum of Middlesex Hospital. He remained at Middlesex until late 1861 and during this period published most of his dozen and a half medical papers, including a chapter on injuries to the shoulder region in T. Holmes's *System of Surgery* (1860).

After the death of John Thomas Quekett in 1861 Flower became conservator of the Hunterian Museum at the Royal College of Surgeons. He held the conservatorship until 1884, when he succeeded Richard Owen as superintendent (later director) of the Natural History Departments of the British Museum, remaining in that position until 1898. He was an active member of numerous scientific organizations: he served several terms on the council and was vice-president of the Royal Society, president of the Zoological Society (1879–1899), president of the

Anthropological Institute (1883–1885), trustee of the Hunterian Collection (1885–1899), and president of the British Association for the Advancement of Science (1889). He was made K.C.B. in 1892.

Much of Flower's time and effort was spent on curatorial duties for anatomy and natural history museums, and he often spoke on the aims and organization of such museums. He strongly believed in their twofold function: the education of the public by a small number of expertly presented specimens which tell a story, and the provision of comprehensive collections and related library material for further education and research by knowledgeable experts. Under Flower's directorship the British Museum (Natural History) was developed so that it closely approached this goal.

Few of Flower's papers published before his appointment to the Hunterian conservatorship in 1861 were of a zoological nature. Of by far the greatest interest to Flower were the Mammalia, especially the Cetacea. A concern with problems of classification loomed large in many of his researches, and he made significant contributions to the clarification of the classification of the carnivores (1869), rhinoceroses (1875), and edentates (1882). He helped considerably to consolidate the class Mammalia through two papers on the Marsupialia and Monotremata, in which he demonstrated the essentially mammalian characteristics of the marsupial dentition and the cerebral commissures of both of these aberrant groups.

Beginning in the early 1860's the Cetacea became Flower's prime research interest, nearly a quarter of his published works being directed toward this order. Although hampered by a shortage of information and specimens, he became recognized as the British authority on the Cetacea through his assiduous collecting of all available material. He procured many specimens, first for the Royal College of Surgeons and later for the British Museum (Natural History), and was responsible for adding the whale room at the latter, with its skeletons and life-size models. Flower described and classified many species of whales and dolphins, which he obtained either from specimens washed up on the British coast or from correspondents throughout the world. Of particular interest in this field are his "On the Osteology of the Cachalot or Sperm-whale" (1867) and his long paper "On the Characters and Divisions of the Family Delphinidae" (1883). The latter is the most extensive of his papers on cetacean classification and was long the basis for the study of this family.

Although he was keenly interested in physical anthropology, Flower wrote only a few papers on nonhuman primates, and these were concerned chiefly with the controversy—sparked by Richard Owen in 1860 in opposition to Charles Darwin's *On the Origin of Species* and settled by T. H. Huxley—over certain characteristics of primate brains. Several papers by Flower provided strong evidence that Owen's distinctions between human and nonhuman primate brains were invalid. While at the Hunterian Museum, he added many anthropological specimens, particularly skulls, to the collection and produced a series of papers on the osteology of various primitive tribes. As a result of his researches he adopted the division of the human species into three races—Caucasian, Mongolian, and Ethiopian—which had been proposed by Cuvier sixty years earlier.

Flower was never a teacher in the sense of having students, but he did lecture extensively, particularly as the Hunterian professor of comparative anatomy and physiology (1870–1884). In the introductory lecture to his first Hunterian series he stressed the idea that they should be museum lectures and that he should be a mouthpiece for the specimens. This first series was published as *An Introduction to the Osteology of the Mammalia.* His 1883 series was on the horse, a topic of special interest to him; he published a volume treating the evolutionary development of the horse and related species. With Richard Lydekker, Flower published a comprehensive volume on living and extinct Mammalia (1891), which considers the evolution and classification of the mammals and their geological and geographical distribution.

BIBLIOGRAPHY

I. Original Works. Flower's principal separate publications are *An Introduction to the Osteology of the Mammalia* (London, 1870, 1876; 3rd ed., with Hans Gadow, 1885); *The Horse, a Study in Natural History* (London, 1891); *An Introduction to the Study of Mammals, Living and Recent* (London, 1891), written with Richard Lydekker; and *Essays on Museums and Other Subjects Connected With Natural History* (London, 1898), which contains a collection of essays on the organization and role of museums, on general biology (including whales), and on anthropology.

The following are perhaps the most significant of Flower's papers: "On the Commissures of the Cerebral Hemispheres of the Marsupialia and Monotremata, as Compared With Those of the Placental Mammals," in *Philosophical Transactions of the Royal Society,* **155** (1865), 633–651; "On the Development and Succession of the Teeth in the Marsupialia," *ibid.,* **157** (1867), 631–642; "On the Osteology of the Cachalot or Sperm-whale (*Physeter macrocephalus*)," in *Transactions of the Zoological Society of London,* **6** (1867), 309–372; "On Some Cranial and

Dental Characteristics of the Existing Species of Rhinoceroses," in *Proceedings of the Zoological Society of London* (1876), 443–457; "On the Mutual Affinities of the Animals Composing the Order Edentata," *ibid.* (1882), 358–367; and "On the Characters and Divisions of the Family Delphinidae," *ibid.* (1883), 466–513.

II. SECONDARY LITERATURE. See Charles J. Cornish, *Sir William Henry Flower. A Personal Memoir* (London, 1904), which includes a list of the topics of Flower's Hunterian lectures and a bibliography of Flower's writings compiled by Victor A. Flower; and Richard Lydekker, *Sir William Flower* (London, 1906).

WESLEY C. WILLIAMS

FLUDD, ROBERT (*b.* Milgate House, Bearsted, Kent, England, 1574; *d.* London, England, 8 September 1637), *alchemy, medicine.*

A son of Sir Thomas Fludd and Elizabeth Andros, Fludd came from a well-to-do family connected with the court. His father had been treasurer of war to Queen Elizabeth in France and the Low Countries, and Fludd himself was later to speak of James I as his patron. He attended St. John's College, Oxford, from which he graduated B.A. in 1596 and M.A. in 1598. The following six years he spent as a student of medicine, chemistry, and the occult sciences in France, Germany, Spain, and Italy. On his return to England, Fludd became a member of Christ Church, Oxford, where he received M.B. and M.D. degrees in 1605. After moving to London he sought admission as a fellow to the Royal College of Physicians. Largely because of his contempt for the Galenic system and his insolent manner he repeatedly failed the examination, but he was finally elected a fellow on 20 September 1609 and served as censor in 1618, 1627, 1633, and 1634. His London practice was highly successful, and he was wealthy enough to maintain his own apothecary and a secretary.

Although Fludd had already written a great deal, he had as yet published nothing when the appearance of the *Fama fraternitatis* (1614) initiated a Continental debate over the authenticity of the Rosicrucian texts. When the eminent iatrochemist Andreas Libavius attacked the Rosicrucians, Fludd rose to their defense in a short *Apologia* (1616), which reappeared in considerably expanded form as the *Tractatus apologeticus* (1617). Also in 1617 he began to publish his massive description of the macrocosm and the microcosm, the *Utriusque cosmi maioris scilicet et minoris, metaphysica, physica atque technica historia.* Here and in his other publications Fludd constantly attacked Aristotle, Galen, and the universities, which to him seemed dedicated to preserving the authority of the ancients. He sought instead a new understanding of nature based on Christian principles. His guides were primarily the Mosaic books of the Bible (especially the Creation account in Genesis, which he interpreted as a divine alchemical process) and the Hermetic and Neoplatonic works of late antiquity and the Renaissance, which seemed to mirror the Christian truths. Although Fludd was quite willing to use observational and experimental evidence, he thought that the eternal truths of Scripture and the mysteries of the ancient occultists carried far more weight than the evidence of the senses.

Fludd pictured the universe in terms of a double centrality, a central earth surrounded by the sun, moon, and planets (whose motions were explained by mechanical analogies) and a central sun situated midway between the center of the earth and God. Beyond the fixed stars were the heavens and the region of divinity. He suggested further that relative distances in the heavens might best be found through a study of the celestial monochord and the mathematical musical harmonies.

Fludd sought divine truths in the macrocosm-microcosm analogy and the doctrine of sympathy and antipathy. There was no question that man and divinity were linked through nature. Fludd placed the seat of the Holy Spirit in the sun, from which emanated light and the spirit of life. Life on earth was possible for man only through inspiration of this spirit from the atmosphere—a spirit which he identified as an aerial saltpeter. The source of this spirit affects the human body. Because of the circular motion of the sun, the spirit must have a circular motion impressed on it. Therefore the blood, which carries the spirit, must also circulate. This mystical description of the circulation of the blood was presented by Fludd in his *Anatomiae amphitheatrum* (1623). Yet Fludd was a trained anatomist and had watched Harvey carry out dissections at the Royal College of Physicians. In his later writings he referred to those dissections, and he was the first to support Harvey's *De motu cordis* in print, thinking that the views of his friend confirmed his own cosmological concept of the circulation of the blood (1629).

As a Hermeticist, Fludd had a special interest in the elements. In the first chapter of Genesis he found evidence only for darkness, light, and water as true elements. Therefore the four elements of Aristotle and the three principles of Paracelsus could at best be considered as secondary elements. Heat and cold corresponded to his elements of light and darkness, and he repeatedly employed a graduated thermoscope to show their effects. Here he seemed to have visual evidence of the doctrine of expansion and contraction. Similarly, Fludd entered into the contemporary dispute over the "weapon salve," which was an important test for the validity of sympathetic medicine. In the course of this debate he described William Gilbert's magnetic experiments in detail because they seemed to give valid examples of action at a distance. Here was support by analogy for the truth of the action of the weapon salve. And yet, although Fludd condemned the medicine of the Galenists in general, he accepted the humoral system of disease, which he described in relation to astral influences affecting the body.

The most detailed works on the macrocosm-microcosm universe in the early seventeenth century, Fludd's writings attracted a great deal of attention and controversy. Kepler attacked him after reading his views on the macrocosm and the mathematical harmony of the divine monochord. Mersenne wrote against him several times and was instrumental in having Gassendi write a detailed refutation of Fludd's philosophy. Fludd, in turn, found time to answer these opponents and others in detail. His own work was supported by a number of Continental authors, and in England his writings were proposed as a basis for a Christian understanding of the universe by John Webster in his plea for a reformation of the English universities in 1654.

BIBLIOGRAPHY

I. Original Works. The most complete list of Fludd's works is in J. J. Manget, *Bibliotheca scriptorum medicorum* (Geneva, 1731), I, pt. 2, 298. J. B. Craven's *Doctor Robert Fludd (Robertus de Fluctibus). The English Rosicrucian. Life and Writings* (Kirkwall, 1902; repr. New York, n.d.) also describes Fludd's complex bibliography.

Fludd's first publication, the *Apologia compendiaria Fraternitatem de Rosea Cruce suspicionis maculis aspersam veritatis quasi Fluctibus abluens et abstergens* (Leiden, 1616), was expanded from 23 to 196 pages in the 2nd ed., *Tractatus apologeticus integritatem Societatis de Rosea Cruce defendens* (Leiden, 1617). The work appeared in German translation by Ada Mah Booz (A[dam] M[elchior] B[irkholz]) as *Schutzschrift für die Aechtheit der Rosenkreutzergesellschaft*... (Leipzig, 1782). Also from this period are the *Tractatus theologo-philosophicus* (Oppenheim, 1617) and the first part of the *Utriusque cosmi maioris scilicet et minoris, metaphysica, physica atque technica historia,* subtitled *De macrocosmi historia* (Oppenheim, 1617). The second part appeared as the *De naturae simia seu technica macrocosmi historia*... (Oppenheim, 1618).

The reaction to these works was immediate, and Fludd defended both the Rosicrucians and his own writings to James I in his "Declaratio brevis" (*ca.* 1617). He returned to the same theme in "A Philosophicall Key... Wrighten as a Declaration Unto the Distrustfull and Suspicious, First to Manÿfest, That the Authour Flÿeth on his Owne Wings, and Then to Purifÿ the Adulterat Breath of Spurious Reports as Well of the Ignorant, as Envious Person." This work, probably composed between 1618 and 1620, was also dedicated to the king. Both MSS are currently being prepared for publication by Allen G. Debus.

Kepler attacked Fludd in an appendix to the *Harmonices mundi* (Linz, 1619), which was answered by Fludd in his *Veritatis proscenium... seu demonstratio quaedam analytica, in qua cuilibet comparationis particulae, in appendice quadam a J. Kepplero, nuper in fine harmoniae suae mundanae edita, facta inter harmoniam suam mundanam, et illam R. F., ipsissimis veritatis argumentis respondetur* (Frankfurt, 1621). Kepler replied in his *Prodromus dissertationum cosmographicum... Item ejusdem J. Kepleri pro suo opere Harmonices mundi, apologia adversus demonstrationem analyticam Roberti de Fluctibus* (Frankfurt, 1621–1622), which included a reprint of the *Mysterium cosmographicum* (1596); this, in turn, was answered by Fludd in the *Monochordum mundi replicatio R. F. . . . ad apologiam . . . J. Kepleri adversus demonstrationem suam analyticam nuperrime editam, in qua Robertus validoribus Joannis objectionibus harmoniae suae legi repugnantibus, comiter respondere aggreditur* (Frankfurt, 1622).

Fludd and the Hermeticists were attacked by Mersenne in the *Quaestiones celeberrimae in Genesim*... (Paris, 1623), to which he replied in the *Sophiae cum moria certamen* (Frankfurt, 1629). Gassendi's *Epistolica exercitatio, in qua principia philosophiae Roberti Fluddi, medici, reteguntur, et ad recentes illius libras adversus R. P. F. Marinum Mersennum... respondetur* (Paris, 1630) was answered at length by Fludd in the *Clavis philosophiae et alchymiae Fluddanae sive Roberti Fluddi armageri, et medicinae doctoris, ad epistolicam Petri Gassendi theologi exercitationem responsum* (Frankfurt, 1633).

Of lesser importance was Patrick Scot's *The Tillage of Light* (London, 1623), which was answered by Fludd in "Truth's Golden Harrow," first printed with commentary by C. H. Josten in *Ambix,* **3** (1948), 91–150. Fludd's defense of the weapon salve was criticized by a little-known pastor, William Foster, in the *Hoplocrisma-Spongus: Or a Sponge to Wipe Away the Weapon-Salve* (London, 1631); in reply to this there appeared *Doctor Fludds Answer Unto M. Foster. Or, the Squeesing of Parson Fosters Sponge, Ordained by Him for the Wiping Away of the Weapon-Salve* (London, 1631).

From Fludd's other major works three additional titles may be singled out: the *Anatomiae amphitheatrum effigie triplici, more et conditione varia disignatum* (Frankfurt, 1623), in which Fludd described both the scientific and the mystical anatomy of the body; the *Pulsus* (Frankfurt, n.d. [completed 1629]), which forms part of the *Medicina Catholica, seu mysticum artis medicandi sacrarium* and includes Fludd's first defense of Harvey; and the *Philosophia Moysaica* (Gouda, 1638), later trans. into English (London, 1659), which summarizes Fludd's cosmological views and then goes into the weapon-salve problem and magnetism at great length. A French translation of part of the work on the macrocosm exists: *Étude du macrocosme, annotée et traduite pour la première fois par Pierre Piobb. Traité d'astrologie générale* (*De astrologia*) (Paris, 1907).

II. SECONDARY LITERATURE. The standard biography is that of J. B. Craven cited above. Additional material is given by Josten in the introduction to his "Truth's Golden Harrow" and in his "Robert Fludd's Theory of Geomancy and his Experiences at Avignon in the Winter of 1601 to 1602," in *Journal of the Warburg and Courtauld Institutes,* **27** (1964), 327-335. A general account of Fludd's work is in Allen G. Debus, *The English Paracelsians* (London, 1965; New York, 1966), pp. 105-127; and in "Renaissance Chemistry and the Work of Robert Fludd," in Allen G. Debus and Robert P. Multhauf, *Alchemy and Chemistry in the Seventeenth Century* (Los Angeles, 1966), pp. 1-29.

The Fludd-Kepler exchange is discussed by W. Pauli in "The Influence of Archetypal Ideas on the Scientific Theories of Kepler," in C. G. Jung and W. Pauli, *The Interpretation of Nature and the Psyche,* trans. by Priscilla Silz (New York, 1955), pp. 145-240. An older but still basic study is R. Lenoble, *Mersenne ou la naissance du mécanisme* (Paris, 1948), pp. 103-105, 367-370, and *passim.* Frances A. Yates discusses Fludd's controversies in her *Giordano Bruno and the Hermetic Tradition* (Chicago, 1964), pp. 432-455, and has also shown Fludd's connection with the Vitruvian revival in England and the work of John Dee in her *Theatre of the World* (London, 1969), pp. 42-79. The Gassendi controversy is discussed by L. Cafiero in "Robert Fludd e la polemica con Gassendi," in *Rivista di storia della filosofia,* **19** (1964), 367-410, and **20** (1965), 3-15.

Fludd's physiological concepts and his defense of Harvey are described in Walter Pagel's "Religious Motives in the Medical Biology of the 17th Century," in *Bulletin of the Institute of History of Medicine,* **3** (1935), 97-128, 213-231, 265-312 (see 265-297); and his *William Harvey's Biological Ideas* (Basel-New York, 1967), pp. 113-118; in Allen G. Debus, "Robert Fludd and the Circulation of the Blood," in *Journal of the History of Medicine and Allied Sciences,* **16** (1961), 374-393; and "Harvey and Fludd: The Irrational Factor in the Rational Science of the Seventeenth Century," in *Journal of the History of Biology,* **3** (1970), 81-105. Some aspects of Fludd's defense of the Rosicrucians are discussed by Debus in "Mathematics and Nature in the Chemical Texts of the Renaissance," in *Ambix,* **15** (1968), 1-28. Fludd's relation to the traditional art of memory is the subject of research by Frances A. Yates in *The Art of Memory* (Chicago, 1966), pp. 320-367; C. H. Josten discusses Fludd's alchemical experiment on wheat, taken from the "Philosophicall Key," in *Ambix,* **11** (1963), 1-23; his system of music is described by Peter J. Ammann in "The Musical Theory and Philosophy of Robert Fludd," in *Journal of the Warburg and Courtauld Institutes,* **30** (1967), 198-227. His relationship to Milton is the subject of research by Denis Saurat in *Milton et le matérialisme chrétien en Angleterre* (Paris, 1928); and the relationship of Fludd's thermoscope to the thermometer is described by F. Sherwood Taylor in "The Origin of the Thermometer," in *Annals of Science,* **5** (1942), 129-156 (see 142-150).

Robert Fludd's views on educational reform and the meaning of a new science are taken up in Allen G. Debus, *The Chemical Dream of the Renaissance* (Cambridge, 1968), pp. 20-23; and *Science and Education in the Seventeenth Century. The Webster-Ward Debate* (London-New York, 1970), pp. 23-26. Other aspects of Fludd's work are described by Debus in "The Paracelsian Aerial Niter," in *Isis,* **55** (1964), 43-61; "Robert Fludd and the Use of Gilbert's *De magnete* in the Weapon-salve Controversy," in *Journal of the History of Medicine and Allied Sciences,* **19** (1964), 389-417; and "The Sun in the Universe of Robert Fludd," in *Le soleil à la Renaissance—sciences et mythes, colloque international tenu en avril 1963 . . .* (Brussels, 1965), pp. 259-278.

ALLEN G. DEBUS

FOERSTE, AUGUST FREDERICK (*b.* Dayton, Ohio, 7 May 1862; *d.* Dayton, 23 April 1936), *invertebrate paleontology, stratigraphy.*

The son of John August and Louise Wilke Foerste, A. F. Foerste attended public schools in Dayton, graduating from the old Central High School in 1880. He then taught for three years in a small country school near Centerville, Ohio, before entering Denison University, where he received a B.A. degree in 1887. For graduate work he went to Harvard University, where he studied physical geography under W. M. Davis and petrography under J. E. Wolff, receiving the M.A. in 1888 and the Ph.D. in 1890. During this time he also served in the U.S. Geological Survey as part-time assistant to Nathaniel Shaler and Raphael Pumpelly.

Foerste's doctoral thesis in petrography led to advanced studies in that subject for the next two years at the University of Heidelberg and the Collège de France. He devoted vacations, as before, to work with the Geological Survey, apparently planning a career in that organization. In 1892, when its appropriation was drastically reduced, he had to seek employment elsewhere; for a year he worked as tutor to Pumpelly's children.

In 1893 Foerste returned to Dayton to teach science in the Steele High School, where he remained until his retirement in 1932, at the age of seventy. There were many invitations to teach in colleges and universities, but he felt that his position in Dayton, while providing him with a living as well as opportunities for service to burgeoning technological industries, interfered less with his research than would a more prestigious position elsewhere. During vacations he was employed at various times in the state geological surveys of Indiana, Ohio, and Kentucky, and by the Geological Survey of Canada. Beginning about 1920, his summers were spent at the U.S. National Museum, and after retiring he moved to Washington to continue research there as associate in paleontology. Foerste never married. His home in Dayton had been with his widowed sister and her three children, and it was while visiting them that he died of a heart attack.

Foerste was a fellow of the Geological Society of America and one of the founders of the Paleontological Society, which he served as president in 1928 and later as representative on the National Research Council. He was also a member of the American Association for the Advancement of Science, the Ohio Academy of Science, of which he was president in 1931, and the Washington Academy of Science. The Engineers Club of Dayton presented him with an honorary membership in 1926, and Denison University conferred an honorary Sc.D. on him in 1927.

Foerste's scientific interests were first directed toward flowering plants. Before graduating from high school he had accumulated a herbarium of over a thousand species, all collected within ten miles of Dayton. Attending a lecture by Edward Orton of Ohio State University while still in high school, he first learned the meaning of the word "fossil" and that fossils could be found in the nearby quarries. His interest in paleontology thus awakened, he collected fossils almost daily in the Soldier's Home quarry. Then, during the three years he taught near Centerville, he found many additional specimens in rocks of the same age in a large quarry in that locality. When he entered college he thus had a remarkably complete collection of fossils from the Silurian formation in the "Clinton group," which he later named the "Brassfield." The description of this fauna became the subject of his first papers and started him on his long-continuing specialization in early Paleozoic paleontology and stratigraphy.

At the beginning of Foerste's sophomore year at Denison, C. L. Herrick joined the faculty there as professor of natural history. Herrick was only four years older than Foerste, and the two spent much time together in geological fieldwork. Herrick shared with Foerste his plans for a new scientific publication, and the first issue of the *Bulletin* (now *Journal*) *of the Scientific Laboratories of Denison University* (1885) consists of one paper by Herrick and two by Foerste. In subsequent years about half of Foerste's scientific papers appeared in that publication, the latest during the month of his death. While he was responding to Herrick's influence, Foerste also became acquainted with E. O. Ulrich, with whom he had a lifelong friendship and close association. This had much to do with the devotion of his life to paleontology and stratigraphy rather than to petrography, which had attracted him while at Harvard (although even then he had close contact with Alphaeus Hyatt, curator of paleontological collections in the Boston Museum of Natural History).

Notable among Foerste's many contributions to paleontology was the restudy, redescription, and illustration of hundreds of species of invertebrate fossils inadequately described and figured by earlier writers. Of at least equal value was his systematic study of Ordovician and Silurian cephalopods, in which he emphasized the significance of internal structures rather than relying only on external forms.

BIBLIOGRAPHY

The biography by R. S. Bassler in *Proceedings of the Geological Society of America, 1936* (1937), pp. 143–156, includes a bibliography of 135 titles.

The following is a selected bibliography of Foerste's writings: "The Clinton Group of Ohio," in *Bulletin [Journal] of the Scientific Laboratories of Denison University,* **1** (1885), 63–120; **2** (1887), 89–110, 140–176; **3** (1888), 3–12; "Preliminary Description of North Attleboro Fossils," in *Bulletin of the Museum of Comparative Zoology at Harvard College,* no. 16 (1888), pp. 27–41, written with N. S. Shaler; "Notes on Clinton Group Fossils, With Special Reference to Collections From Indiana, Tennessee, and Georgia," in *Proceedings of the Boston Society of Natural History,* **24** (1889), 263–355; "Fossils of the Clinton Group in Ohio and Indiana," in *Report. Ohio Geological Survey,* **7** (1893), 516–601; and "A Report on the Geology of the Middle and Upper Silurian Rocks of Clark, Jefferson, Ripley, Jennings, and Southern Decatur Counties," in *Indiana Department of Geology and Natural Resources, 21st Annual Report* (1897), pp. 213–288.

See also "Geology of the Narragansett Basin," *Monographs of the U.S. Geological Survey,* no. 33 (1899), written with N. S. Shaler; "Silurian and Devonian Limestones of Western Tennessee," in *Journal of Geology,* **11** (1903), 554–583, 679–715; "The Silurian, Devonian, and Irvine Formations of East-Central Kentucky," *Bulletin of the Kentucky Geological Survey,* no. 7 (1906); "Strophomena and Other Fossils From Cincinnatian and Mohawkian Horizons," in *Bulletin of the Scientific Laboratories of Denison University,* **17** (1912), 17–172; and "The Phosphate Deposits in the Upper Trenton Limestones of Central Kentucky," in *Bulletin of the Kentucky Geological Survey,* 4th ser., **1** (1913), 387–439.

Of further interest are "Notes on the Lorraine Faunas of New York and the Province of Quebec," in *Bulletin of the Scientific Laboratories of Denison University,* **17** (1914), 247–339; "Upper Ordovician Formations in Ontario and Quebec," *Memoirs of the Geological Survey Branch, Department of Mines, Canada,* no. 83 (1916); "The Generic Relations of the American Ordovician Lichadidae," in *American Journal of Science,* 4th ser., **49** (1920), 26–50; "Notes on Arctic Ordovician and Silurian Cephalopods," in *Journal of the Scientific Laboratories of Denison University,* **19** (1921), 247–306; "Upper Ordovician Faunas of Ontario and Quebec," *Memoirs of the Geological Survey Branch, Department of Mines, Canada,* no. 138 (1924);

"Actinosiphonate, Trochoceroid, and Other Cephalopods," in *Journal of the Scientific Laboratories of Denison University,* **21** (1926), 285–383; "American Arctic and Related Cephalopods," *ibid.,* **23** (1928), 1–110; "Three Studies of Cephalopods," *ibid.,* **24** (1930), 265–381; "New Genera of Ozarkian and Canadian Cephalopods," *ibid.,* **30** (1935), 259–290, written with E. O. Ulrich; and "Silurian Cephalopods of the Port Daniel Area on Gaspé Peninsula in Eastern Canada," *ibid.,* **31** (1936), 21–92.

KIRTLEY F. MATHER

FOL, HERMANN (*b.* St. Mandé, France, 23 July 1845; *d.* at sea, March 1892), *biology.*

Although little is known of Fol's immediate family, he was descended from Gaspard Fol, a religious refugee who left Touraine to settle in Geneva in 1590. His father was rich, and one of his brothers became a prominent art scholar and curator of the Musée Fol, which he founded in Geneva; a cousin, Auguste Fol, was a watchmaker and director of Geneva's Caisse Hypothécaire from 1882 to 1891.

Fol himself always retained a strong attachment for Geneva. He received his early education at the Gymnasium there, where his interest was turned toward natural science by Edouard Claparède and F. J. Pictet. On Claparède's recommendation, he went on to study medicine and zoology at the University of Jena. Two of his teachers there were Gegenbauer and Haeckel, both of whom influenced him strongly. In the winter of 1866–1867 Fol joined Haeckel on an extended trip to the western and northern coasts of Africa and the Canary Islands; several collecting trips inland confirmed his enthusiasm for natural history.

In 1867 Fol began to study medicine at Heidelberg (and later at Zurich and Berlin as well); he took the M.D. in 1869, with a thesis on the anatomy and development of Ctenophora. On his return to Geneva in 1870 he continued his zoological researches in preference to practicing medicine and spent several winters collecting and studying marine invertebrates. He married a Mlle. Bourrit in the early 1870's.

In addition to his study on the Ctenophora, Fol worked on the embryology of Mollusca and made microscopic studies of fertilization, cell division, and early embryonic growth. In the 1870's little was actually known about the nature of fertilization and especially about the role in this process of such organelles as the nucleus and centrosome. It had been observed that the nucleus disappeared shortly before the onset of mitosis and that the centrosome and the mitotic spindle appeared by late prophase, but was the spindle system composed of the remains of the nucleus or was it produced by the centrosome? What was the function of the spindle, and what was the function of the chromatin bodies (chromosomes) within the nucleus? Was the sperm nucleus or the centrosome necessary to fertilize the egg, or were they both necessary to fertilization? And did the sperm contribute anything material to the fertilized egg, or was it simply an agent to development?

Among the many theories formulated to answer some of these questions were those of Oscar Hertwig, who noted that immediately after fertilization two distinct nuclei could be seen in the egg cell. From this he concluded that one nucleus had come from the sperm and one from the egg, and went on to theorize that the two nuclei fused and that all the nuclei in all the cells of the developing organism were therefore the descendants of this first fused pair. His inferences were open to dispute, however, and it was pointed out in criticism that he had not actually seen the sperm penetrate the egg. Moreover, some thought the germinal vesicle (the egg nucleus) to be a separate and autonomous cell within the larger cell.

Fol pursued the same line of investigation as Hertwig, apparently quite independently. In two papers, one presented in 1877 and the other in 1879, Fol showed that in sea urchins the egg nucleus is not a separate cell but rather an important structural and functional part of the ovum; that during maturation of the egg three daughter nuclei are cast off as polar bodies so that the mature ovum contains only one nucleus; and that sperm actually penetrates the egg. He made the last observation in 1877 and was thus able to provide more conclusive evidence than Hertwig's about the relationship between the two gametes at the moment of fertilization. Like Hertwig, Fol suggested that the daughter nuclei in all the cells of a growing embryo are descended from the original sperm-and-egg fusion pair.

At the time when Fol and Hertwig were carrying out their studies, the hereditary function of the nucleus was not suspected. Their emphasis on nuclear continuity during maturation of the gametes and during subsequent cleavage was, however, an important step in the understanding of this function. Fol himself did not go on to speculate that the nucleus was the vehicle of heredity; while he reaffirmed the idea of nuclear continuity, he also denied the purity of the fundamental nuclear components; that is, he did not believe that the nucleus had a special structure of its own whereby it could preserve hereditary information from one generation to the next. Fol did not characterize fertilization primarily as the fusion of the sperm-and-egg nuclei; rather, he considered the male nucleus to be a degeneration product of sperm components in contact with egg cytoplasm.

Fol's embryological work emphasized the structural and morphological aspects of fertilization by focusing attention on the material organelles (such as the nucleus); work done prior to his and Hertwig's was physiological in design. His investigations enabled later workers (including T. H. Boveri, August Weismann, and E. A. Strasburger) to clarify the actual hereditary function of the nucleus.

Fol conducted these researches while simultaneously engaged in an academic career. In 1876 he had declined the offer of a chair of comparative anatomy at the University of Naples; two years later he accepted a titular professorship (without pay) in comparative embryology and teratology at the University of Geneva. In addition to his work on sea urchins he applied himself to a wide variety of zoological problems and collected a great deal of material on the comparative embryology of invertebrates. He spent winters in Villefranche, near Nice, where in 1880 he established, at his own expense, a marine laboratory in an abandoned quarantine station; summers he gave courses in parasitology and general zoology at the university.

In 1882, when the International Congress on Hygiene was held in Geneva, Fol became greatly excited by the work of Louis Pasteur and Robert Koch. During the next year he made microscopic studies of various bacteria and, at the request of the city officials, made a detailed analysis of the Geneva water supply. At the same time he became an avid photographer and began to experiment with applying photographic techniques to his microscopic researches. He was founder of the Geneva Photographical Society and published articles in the *Revue suisse de photographie.* He also founded the *Recueil zoologique suisse.*

A somewhat unpredictable and eccentric person, Fol became involved in quarrels with some other members of the university and resigned in 1886 to retire to Villefranche. At the time of his teaching appointment he had given his laboratory there to the French government, which had appointed Jules Barrois to be its director. On his return, the government made Fol a codirector; and there he continued his studies on embryology, cytology, histology, and invertebrate zoology. He further collaborated with Eduard Serasin on a study of the penetration of light into seawater.

His last important microscopic research was a study of the centrosome. In 1889 Rádl had predicted, on strictly a priori grounds, that the centrosomes, like nuclei, would be found to unite at fertilization; by this theory, each gamete would contribute two centrosomes, the product of the fusion dividing to form the two poles of the mitotic spindle. In a paper of 1891, "Le quadrille des centres," Fol again used sea urchins in an experiment that confirmed Rádl's prediction. He showed that each gamete contributed either two centrosomes, or one centrosome that divided immediately after fertilization; the daughter centrosomes then united in such a way that one from the male parent always joined one from the female parent (the movements involved in this pairing reminded Fol of the distribution of cards in the eighteenth-century game of quadrille and thus gave him his paper's title). The paper became somewhat notorious and brought Fol under attack from both Boveri and Hertwig, who agreed with each other that centrosomes were not permanent cell organelles. At a slightly later date, Boveri and E. B. Wilson made specific studies of sea urchins and could observe nothing to substantiate the idea that the centrosomes actually congregate and fuse after fertilization; subsequent investigators also proved Fol wrong.

While working full-time at Villefranche, Fol also made several short collecting trips to the western Mediterranean. Ever since his trip with Haeckel in the 1860's, however, he had wished to make a longer expedition. In 1891 he was given a commission by the French government to lead an expedition to the coast of Tunisia to study the distribution of sponges; he set off with a two-man crew in a new yacht, the *Aster,* on 13 March 1892. Although the boat was rumored to have reached the port of Benodet a few days later, the expedition was never heard from again.

Fol received many honors in his lifetime, including the Legion of Honor for establishing the Villefranche laboratory. He belonged to a number of scientific societies, including those of Moscow and Belgium and the Leopoldina-Carolina.

BIBLIOGRAPHY

I. Original Works. An excellent bibliography is that by Maurice Bedot, cited below. A few of Fol's most crucial papers are "Le premier développement de l'oeuf chez les Géryonides," in *Archives des sciences physiques et naturelles,* 2nd ser., **48** (1873), 335–340; "Sur le commencement de l'hénogénie chez divers animaux," *ibid.,* **58** (1877), 439–472; "Recherches sur la fécondation et le commencement de l'hénogénie chez divers animaux," in *Mémoires de la Société de physique et d'histoire naturelle de Genève,* **26** (1878), 89–250; and "Le quadrille des centres, un épisode nouveau dans l'histoire de la fécondation," in *Archives des sciences physiques et naturelles,* 3rd ser., **25** (1891), 393–420.

II. Secondary Literature. The only available biographical sketch of Fol is Maurice Bedot, "Hermann Fol: sa vie et ses travaux," in *Archives des sciences physiques et naturelles,* **31** (1894), 1–22, which also includes a complete bibliography of Fol's writings from 1869 to 1891. A discussion of Fol's contributions may be found in Arthur Hughes, *A History of Cytology* (London, 1959), pp. 61–63, 70, 82–83; and William Coleman, "Cell, Nucleus, and Inheritance: An Historical Study," in *Proceedings of the American Philosophical Society,* **109** (1965), 124–158, esp. 138–139.

GARLAND E. ALLEN

FOLIN, OTTO (*b.* Asheda, Sweden, 4 April 1867; *d.* Boston, Massachusetts, 25 October 1934), *biochemistry.*

Folin was the son of Nils Magnus Folin, a tanner, and Eva Olson Folin, the village midwife. At the age of fifteen he immigrated to the United States to join his brother Axel, who was living in the lumbering town of Stillwater, Minnesota. He worked for a time on various farms in the region and in 1888 moved to Minneapolis to enter the University of Minnesota, from which he received his B.S. degree in 1892. He then studied with Stieglitz at the University of Chicago, completing a thesis on urethanes in 1896. Since he wished to study biochemistry, he spent two years in Europe, working with Albrecht Kossel at Marburg, Olof Hammarsten at Uppsala, and E. L. Salkowski in Berlin before returning to take his Ph.D. from Chicago in 1898. He was appointed assistant professor of analytical chemistry at the University of West Virginia in 1899, and in the same year he married Laura Grant. He was survived by a son and a daughter. In 1900 Folin took charge of the first laboratory for biochemical research to be established in a hospital, the McLean Hospital for the Insane at Waverley, Massachusetts. In 1907 he was appointed to the first chair of biochemistry in the Harvard Medical School, and there he remained for the rest of his life.

When he began work at the McLean Hospital, Folin decided to seek a method for detecting differences in metabolism between psychotic and normal individuals. He realized that urinary constituents reflect the metabolic state of the body and therefore began to study quantitative methods of urinalysis. He devoted particular attention to nitrogenous compounds and worked out colorimetric methods for their determination. Although his original hopes of obtaining results of psychiatric value were not realized, he grew more and more interested in developing analytical methods for biochemical research, and this field became his specialty. He soon recognized that analysis of blood constituents offered a better guide to metabolic reactions than did urinalysis, and most of his later work concerned blood analysis. He summed up much of this work in his classic paper on microchemical methods of blood analysis, which he published with Hsien Wu in 1919. His work with nitrogenous compounds led him to the concept of endogenous and exogenous metabolism which, although later greatly modified, was very fruitful at the time of its proposal. He established the fact that amino acids are absorbed from the intestine in free form rather than as proteins. His colorimetric methods made possible much of later biochemical analysis.

Folin was active in the organization and administration of various biochemical societies and in aiding the publication of papers on biochemical research. Most of his work appeared in the *Journal of Biological Chemistry,* of which he was a leading supporter. In the latter part of his life he received many honorary degrees, from both European and American universities. At the time of his death he was recognized as the leading authority on biochemical analysis.

BIBLIOGRAPHY

I. ORIGINAL WORKS. Most of Folin's early papers appeared in *Hoppe-Seyler's Zeitschrift für physiologische Chemie* and his later work in the *Journal of Biological Chemistry.* The paper "A System of Blood Analysis," written with Hsien Wu, appeared in *Journal of Biological Chemistry,* **38** (1919), 81–110.

II. SECONDARY LITERATURE. Biographical appreciations of Folin appear in *Science* (New York), **81** (1935), 35–38; and in *Medical Journal of Australia,* **1** (1935), 69.

HENRY M. LEICESTER

FOLKES, MARTIN (*b.* London, England, 29 October 1690; *d.* London, 29 June 1754), *antiquarianism.*

The eldest son of Martin Folkes, a solicitor, and his wife, Dorothy, he first attended the University of Saumur, in France. He entered Clare Hall (Clare College), Cambridge, in 1706, to study mathematics and matriculated in 1709. He was elected a fellow of the Royal Society in 1714, the year of his marriage to Lucretia Bradshaw. The university granted him an M.A. in 1717.

His interest in coins and artifacts led him to be chosen a fellow of the Society of Antiquaries in 1719, and he became vice-president of the Royal Society in 1722. After Newton's death in 1727, he was defeated by Sir Hans Sloan for the presidency but remained vice-president. He continued his numismatic and antiquarian pursuits, but his contributions to the *Philosophical Transactions* were minor.[1]

Upon Sloan's retirement from the presidency of the Royal Society in 1741, Folkes succeeded to the office. His "literary rather than scientific bent" was reflected in the society's meetings which, according to his friend William Stukeley, became "a most elegant and agreeable entertainment for a contemplative person."[2] Other comments on Folkes's leadership were less charitable: the *Philosophical Transactions* for the period of his presidency allegedly contained "a greater proportion of trifling and puerile papers than are anywhere else to be found," and the meetings merely allowed "personages acting the importants . . . to trifle away time in empty forms and grave grimaces."[3] John Hill, the society's severest critic, blamed Folkes for this state of affairs.[4]

Despite these criticisms, Folkes was elected to the Académie des Sciences in 1742, had his *Table of Silver Coins From the Conquest* published by the Society of Antiquaries in 1744, stood (unsuccessfully) for Parliament, received the D.C.L. from Oxford in 1746, and became president of the Society of Antiquaries in 1750. His health began to fail, and he resigned his office in the Royal Society in 1752.

Under Folkes the Royal Society lost much of its professional character. James Jaurin's epitaph best sums up his career: "He was Sir Isaac Newton's friend, and was often singled out . . . to fill his chair."[5]

NOTES

1. E.g., "Remarks on Standard Measures Preserved in the Capitol of Rome," cited in C. Weld, p. 478.
2. Stukeley, III, 472.
3. Weld, pp. 483, 487.
4. Hill, preface.
5. Cited in Weld, p. 479.

BIBLIOGRAPHY

Folkes's publications include *A Dissertation of the Weights and Values of Ancient Coins* (London, 1734); *A Table of Silver Coins From the Conquest* (London, 1744); and *A Table of English Gold Coins From the Eighteenth Year of King Edward II* (London, 1745).

No full-scale biography of Folkes exists. Sketches may be found in Charles R. Weld, *A History of the Royal Society: With Memoirs of the Presidents* (London, 1848); and Warwick Wroth, "Martin Folkes," in *Dictionary of National Biography,* V (London, 1884).

A less formal view of Folkes is presented in William Stukeley, *Family Memoirs,* 3 vols. (London, 1882–1884). The faults of his presidency are most clearly outlined in John Hill, *A Review of the Works of the Royal Society* (London, 1751).

JOEL M. RODNEY

FONTAINE (FONTAINE DES BERTINS), ALEXIS (*b.* Claveyson, Drôme, France, 13 August 1704; *d.* Cuiseaux, Saône-et-Loire, France, 21 August 1771), *mathematics.*

The son of Jacques, a royal notary, and of Madeleine Seytres, Fontaine studied at the Collège de Tournon before his introduction to mathematics at Paris under the guidance of Père Castel. About 1732 he acquired property in the vicinity of Paris and, having formed friendships with Clairaut and Maupertuis, presented several memoirs to the Académie des Sciences, which admitted him as *adjoint mécanicien* on 11 June 1733. Although he was promoted to geometer in 1739 and to pensionary geometer in 1742, Fontaine rarely participated in the work of the Academy and led a rather solitary existence. A difficult personality, he showed almost no interest in the work of others and incurred considerable enmity by claiming priority in certain discoveries. In 1765 he retired permanently to an estate in Burgundy, the purchase of which had almost ruined him. He broke his silence only in order to engage in an imprudent polemic with Lagrange, whom he had initially encouraged. He died before he was able to read Lagrange's reply, however.

Fontaine's work is of limited scope, often obscure, and willfully ignorant of the contributions of other mathematicians. Nevertheless, its inspiration is often original and it presents, amid confused developments, a number of ideas that proved fertile, especially in the fields of the calculus of variations, of differential equations, and of the theory of equations.

One of the first memoirs that Fontaine presented to the Academy in 1734 solved the problem of tautochrones in the case where the resistance of the medium is a second-degree function of the speed of the moving body; the method employed, more general than that of his predecessors (Huygens, Newton, Euler, Johann I Bernoulli, and others), heralds the procedures of the calculus of variations. It won deserved esteem for its author, but Fontaine erred in reconsidering the subject in 1767 and 1768 in order to criticize—unjustly—the method of variations presented by Lagrange in 1762.

On the subject of integral calculus, Fontaine was interested in the conditions of integrability of differential forms with several variables and in homogeneous functions; independently of Euler and Clairaut, he discovered the relation termed homogeneity. He gave particular attention to the problem of notation, utilizing both the Newtonian symbols of fluxions and fluents and the differential notation of Leibniz, which he usefully completed by introducing a coherent symbolism for partial differentials that was successful for a long time before being replaced by δ. One of the first to tackle the study of differential equations of the nth order, he failed in his ambitious plan to regroup all the types of equations that can be solved. He did, however, introduce several interesting ideas that foreshadowed in particular the theory of singular integrals.

In the theory of equations, Fontaine attempted to extend to higher degrees a method of studying equations based on their decomposition into linear factors that had shown its usefulness in the case of equations of the third and fourth degree. His memoir, complex and often unclear, was rapidly outclassed by the works of Lagrange and Vandermonde.

In his work of 1764 Fontaine included a study of dynamics dated 1739 and based on a principle closely analogous to the one that d'Alembert had made the foundation of his treatise of 1743. Although Fontaine did not raise any claim of priority, he attracted the hostility of a powerful rival who subsequently took pains to destroy the reputation of his work, which—without being of the first rank—still merits mention for its original inspiration and for certain fecund ideas that it contains.

BIBLIOGRAPHY

I. Original Works. Fontaine's works are limited to several memoirs published in the *Histoire de l'Académie royale des sciences* for 1734, 1747, 1767, and 1768 and to a volume published as M. Fontaine, *Mémoires donnés à l'Académie royale des sciences non imprimés dans leur temps* (Paris, 1764), repr., without change, as *Traité de calcul différentiel et intégral* (Paris, 1770). Actually, the two successive titles are inexact, because this collection joins to the memoirs already published in 1734 and 1747 ten others, dealing essentially with infinitesimal geometry, integral calculus, mechanics, and astronomy. Only the three memoirs inserted in the volumes of the *Histoire de l'Académie royale des sciences* for 1767 and 1768 are not included in this work.

II. Secondary Literature. On Fontaine and his work, see J. L. Boucharlat, in Michaud, ed., *Biographie universelle,* XV (Paris, 1816), 179–183, and new ed., XIV (Paris, 1856), 323–326; F. Cajori, *A History of Mathematical Notations,* II (Chicago, 1929), esp. 198–199, 206–207, 223–224; J. M. Caritat de Condorcet, "Éloge de M. Fontaine, prononcé le 13 novembre 1773," in *Histoire de l'Académie royale des sciences, 1771* (Paris, 1774), pp. 105–116; J. de Lalande, in *Bibliographie astronomique* (Paris, 1803), pp. 481, 486; M. Marie, *Histoire des sciences mathématiques et physiques,* VIII (Paris, 1886), 39–42; J. F. Montucla, in *Histoire des mathématiques,* new ed., III (Paris, 1802), 44, 177, 343, 627, 657; N. Nielsen, *Géomètres français du XVIIIe siècle* (Copenhagen–Paris, 1935), pp. 174–182; and Poggendorff, *Biographisch-literarisches Handwörterbuch,* I (Leipzig, 1863), col. 766.

René Taton

FONTANA, FELICE (*b.* Pomarolo, Italy, 15 [?] April 1730; *d.* Florence, Italy, 10 March 1805), *neurology, biology.*

Fontana was educated in Rovereto, where he was a student of G. Tartarotti, and at Verona, Parma, and the University of Padua. Toward the end of 1755 he went to Bologna, where he collaborated with L. M. A. Caldani in research on the irritability and sensitivity of the parts of the animal body, an advanced subject proposed to scholars in 1752 by Albrecht von Haller. In 1757 Fontana defended Haller's position in an epistolary dissertation which, published in the collection *Mémoires sur les parties sensibles et irritables du corps animal* (1760), marked the beginning of his fame. From Bologna, Fontana returned for a brief time to the Trentino and then moved to Rome; from there he went to Tuscany, which became his permanent residence until the time of his death.

In 1765 he was appointed to the chair of logic and, in 1766, to the chair of physics at the University of Pisa. Also in 1766, Leopold I, grand duke of Tuscany, who was very interested in natural sciences, summoned Fontana to Florence to organize and develop the court's physics laboratory, which was then located in the Pitti Palace. Fontana reorganized the surviving instruments of the Medici collection—including the relics of Galileo and of the Accademia del Cimento now in the Museum of the History of Science in Florence—and notably increased the collection through the acquisition of scientific instruments and natural objects, as well as by the production of wax models of the human anatomy, prepared under his supervision in an expressly established workshop. In 1775 the Museum of Physics and Natural History, with its important collection of wax models, was opened to the public; it is preserved in a building that was acquired in 1772 to house the growing material. The collection was greatly expanded under Fontana's supervision and during the course of the nineteenth century. In 1786 a duplicate of the collection was sent to Vienna to equip the Austrian medical-surgical military academy, which had been established the preceding year. After the museum had been inaugurated, Fontana was able to begin a long-planned trip in the autumn of 1775 to France and England, to observe, study, and make outstanding acquisitions. This trip, which lasted until January 1780, enabled him to make direct contact with the most significant scientists of the era.

Like his brother Gregorio, a celebrated mathematician, Felice Fontana was an abbot and, like his brother, he was sympathetic to the ideals of the French Revolution. In 1799 he was imprisoned—but only for a few days—by insurgents against the French. On 11 February 1805 he was stricken with apoplexy; he died the following month and was buried in the Church of Santa Croce.

The quality of Fontana's scientific accomplishment is evident from his first work, on irritability and sensitivity, a subject that he continued to pursue so intensely as to earn the praise of Haller in 1767: "Fontana leges irritabilitatis constituit, ingeniosus homo et accuratus." In 1767 there appeared the *De irritabilitatis legibus, nunc primum sancitis, et de spirituum animalium in movendis musculis inefficacia,* revised and translated into Italian as *Ricerche filosofiche sopra la fisica animale* (1775). According to the analysis made in 1955 by Marchand and Hoff,

> The first law concerned Haller's concept of contractility as a property of muscle fiber itself, and pointed out that a contraction follows only after some stimulus. The discussion displayed insight into the underlying nature of tetanic muscular contraction. The second principle was the refractory period discovered by Fontana in heart muscle and applied to better understanding of the function of other muscles. The original third principle was a disproof of the efficacy of a theoretical entity, the "animal spirits." It was a demonstration that the nervous system could excite, but not actually cause contraction of a muscle, and this proposition was illustrated by the classic spark and gunpowder analogy. Not actually a law, this principle was replaced by another in the later Italian version. The newer third law was a description of fatigue as a phenomenon occurring within the muscle fiber itself. In his fourth law, Fontana pointed out the loss of contractility which results from stretching or compressing a muscle, and certain medical applications of this principle. The fifth law was concerned with problems arising from atrophy of disuse. This chapter included a discussion of the behavior of muscles after a relatively brief rest and a progressive shortening related to the "treppe" effect observed on the kymograph record [*Journal of the History of Medicine and Allied Sciences,* **10** (1955), 202].

Initially unwilling to accept the idea of an identification of the nervous flux with electricity, Fontana gradually changed his mind in the course of his research so that finally "he thought in terms of an electric fluid and said the nerves would be the organs destined to conduct this electric fluid and perhaps even to excite it. This is, perhaps, the first suggestion that the production of electricity might be excited by the nerves rather than merely conducted by them as by wires" (Brazier, p. 110).

The research on the movements of the iris (1765) and on viper venom (1767, 1781) is strictly tied to irritability. Fontana observed that the reflex response to light of the pupil of one eye also occurs in the other eye, although it is not exposed to light; in a frightened or excited animal the pupil is dilated and remains so, even if the eye is struck by light; and the pupil of the animal eye is strongly contracted during sleep.

After a series of impressive and ingenious experiments, Fontana retraced the action of the bite of the viper to an alteration in the irritability of the fibers, which he maintained was mediated by the blood: in other words, the viper's poison directly alters the blood, coagulating it, and this in turn alters all parts of the organism—especially the nerve fibers—that the blood would normally nourish. Fontana extended his toxicological experiments to other substances, especially to curare.

Fontana also took advantage of microscopic investigations to complete the characterizations of the parts of the animal body which Haller had based upon irritability and sensitivity. The use of the microscope was at that time especially difficult, because of the illusory images abundantly produced by contemporary instruments. Although Fontana was unable to do away with these images—one can visualize his "tortuous primitive cylinders"—he nonetheless belongs, together with L. Spallanzani, among the major microscopists of the eighteenth century. In the nerve fibers (his "primitive nerve cylinders") he not only distinguished "the axone with myelin sheath and endoneural sheath" (Zanobio [1959], p. 307) but also recognized the fluidity of the axoplasm through accurate research of micromanipulation in which he took advantage of the use of the coverglass (Hoff [1959], p. 377). Thanks to the microscope, Fontana was able to demonstrate in 1778–1779 that the restoration of an interrupted nerve trunk may be traced to a real and actual regeneration of primitive nerve cylinders, or rather, of nerve fibers. Since 1776 Fontana had studied microscopically the "little red globes of the blood" and, discarding the illusory images observed by G. M. della Torre, he attributed to them a spheroidal configuration, modifiable with extreme ease under certain physiological conditions. In fact, the red corpuscles become noticeably elongated (by one third, by one half, or even to twice their diameter) when they cross a blood vessel: the corpuscles assume a cylindrical configuration and retain it as long as the canal remains narrow; but as soon as the canal increases in width, the corpuscles immediately contract and resume their original shape.

In 1766 Fontana demonstrated that the blight which had devastated the Tuscan countryside was caused by parasitic plants that feed on grain and that reproduce by means of spores. Again with the aid of the microscope, he studied the reproduction of cereal Anguillula and its anabiosis. In certain cellular elements (epithelial cells) he observed a nucleus equipped with nucleoli. His discovery of Fontana's canal in the ciliary body of the eye is also famous.

Fontana's biological works, which scholars of science have so far studied only fragmentarily, merit systematic investigation; and the exploration of Fontana's chemical works begun by Icilio Guareschi, also interesting in its applicative aspects, should be continued. Also noteworthy are Fontana's model of the eudiometer (for measuring the salubrity of air), an apparatus for oxygen therapy, and his studies on the absorbent powers of coal.

BIBLIOGRAPHY

I. ORIGINAL WORKS. Bibliographical essays on F. Fontana are contained in the works of Adami (1905), Guareschi, Marchand, and Hoff, cited below.

The principal works of Fontana are "Dissertation epistolaire de Mr. L'Abbé F. Fontana . . . au R. P. Urbain Tosetti . . .," in *Mémoires sur les parties sensibles et irritables du corps animal . . . ouvrage qui sert de suite aux Mémoires de Monsieur de Haller,* III (Lausanne, 1760), 157–243; *Dei moti dell'iride* (Lucca, 1765); *Nuove osservazioni sopra i globetti rossi del sangue* (Lucca, 1766); *De irritabilitatis legibus, nunc primum sancitis, et de spirituum animalium in movendis musculis inefficacia* (Lucca, 1767); *Ricerche fisiche sopra il veleno della vipera* (Lucca, 1767); *Osservazioni sopra la ruggine del grano* (Lucca, 1767); *Descrizione ed usi di alcuni stromenti per misurare la salubrità dell'aria* (Florence, 1774); *Ricerche fisiche sopra l'aria fissa* (Florence, 1775); *Saggio di osservazioni sopra il falso ergot, e tremella* (Florence, 1775); *Saggio del Real gabinetto di fisica e di storia naturale di Firenze* (Rome, 1775); *Traité sur le vénin de la vipère, sur les poisons américains, sur le laurier-cerise et sur quelques autres poisons végétaux . . .* (Florence, 1781); and *Opuscoli scientifici* (Florence, 1783).

II. SECONDARY LITERATURE. Works on Fontana are Casimiro Adami, *Di Felice e Gregorio Fontana scienziati pomarolesi del secolo XVIII* (Rovereto, 1905), and *Felice Fontana pomarolese narrato ai suoi conterranei* (Rovereto, 1930); Luigi Belloni, "Anatomia plastica: III. The Wax Models in Florence," in *Ciba Symposium,* **8** (1960), 129–132; Alberico Benedicenti, *Malati, medici e farmacisti,* II (Milan, 1951), 1180–1190; Guglielmo Bilancioni, "Felice Fontana trentino e gli studi sull'anatomia e sulla fisiologia dell'orecchio e di altri organi di senso nella seconda metà del secolo XVIII," in *Archeion,* **12** (1930), 296–362; Mary A. B. Brazier, "Felice Fontana," in Luigi Belloni, ed., *Essays on the History of Italian Neurology. Proceedings of the International Symposium on the History of Neurology, Varenna 1961* (Milan, 1963), pp. 107–116; Andrea Corsini, "La medicina alla corte di Pietro Leopoldo," in *Rivista Ciba,* **8** (1954), 1509–1540; Fielding H. Garrison, "Felice Fontana: A Forgotten Physiologist of the Trentino," in *Bulletin of the New York Academy of Medicine,* **11** (1935), 117–122; Icilio Guareschi, "Felice Fontana," in *Supplemento annuale 1908–1909 alla Enciclopedia di chimica scientifica e industriale* (Turin, 1909), pp. 411–448; Hebbel E. Hoff, "The History of the Refractory Period. A Neglected Contribution of Felice Fontana," in *Yale Journal of Biology and Medicine,* **14** (1942), 635–672; and "A Classic of Microscopy: An Early, If Not the First, Observation on the Fluidity of the Axoplasm, Micromanipulation, and the Use of the Cover-slip," in *Bulletin of the History of Medicine,* **33** (1959), 375–379; Giuseppe Mangili, *Elogio di Felice Fontana* (Milan, 1813); John Felix Marchand and Hebbel Edward Hoff, "Felice Fontana: The Laws of Irritability. A Literal Translation of the Memoir *De Irritabilitatis Legibus,* 1767; Added Material From *Ricerche Filosofiche sopra la Fisica Animale,* 1775; and Correlation of These Editions With the E. G. B. Hebenstreit German Translation, 1785," in *Journal of the History of Medicine and Allied Sciences,* **10** (1955), 197–206, 302–326, 399–420; Bruno Zanobio, "Le osservazioni microscopiche di Felice Fontana sulla struttura dei nervi," in *Physis,* **1** (1959), 307–320, "L'immagine filamentoso-reticolare nell'anatomia microscopica dal XVII al XIX secolo," *ibid.,* **2** (1960), 299–317, and "Ricerche di micrografia dell'eritrocita nel settecento," in *Actes du symposium international sur les sciences naturelles, la chimie et la pharmacie de 1630 à 1850, Florence–Vinci, 1960* (Florence, 1962), pp. 159–179.

LUIGI BELLONI

FONTENELLE, BERNARD LE BOUYER (or **BOVIER) DE** (*b.* Rouen, France, 11 February 1657; *d.* Paris, France, 9 January 1757), *dissemination of knowledge, mathematics, astronomy.*

Fontenelle's father, François Le Bouyer, *écuyer,* sieur de Fontenelle, was originally from Alençon; his mother, Marthe Corneille, sister of Pierre and Thomas Corneille, came from Rouen. The family was of modest means and lived in rented quarters in Rouen. His father, *sous-doyen des avocats* in the Parlement of Rouen, was "a man of quality but of mediocre fortune" and practiced his profession "with more honor than fame," according to Trublet. Fontenelle was said to resemble his mother, a woman of great intellect, who was also pious and exhorted her children to virtue. Two of them died at an early age, before Bernard was born; two more, Pierre and Joseph Alexis, were born after him—both were to become ecclesiastics. Bernard's two maternal uncles, especially his godfather Thomas Corneille, had a great influence on him; they often invited him to Paris, before he moved there permanently around 1687, and introduced him to the world of the French Academy, the theater, the salons of the *précieuses,* and the *Mercure galant,* which was directed by a friend of Thomas's, Donneau de Visé.

About 1664 the child was placed in the Jesuit *collège* in Rouen, where his uncles had studied. He was, according to his teachers, "a well-rounded child in all respects and foremost among the students." The logic and physics that he was taught seemed to him devoid of meaning: according to Trublet, "He did not find nature in them, but rather vague and abstract ideas which, so to speak, skirted the edge of things but did not really touch them at all." The Jesuits wished to make him one of their own, but Fontenelle did not have a vocation. In deference to his father he became a lawyer, but he pleaded only one case—which he lost—and quit the bar to devote himself to literature and philosophy, which were more to his taste.

Although his parents had dedicated him to St. Bernard and to the Virgin and had made him wear the habit of the Feuillants until the age of seven, Fontenelle never displayed any strong devotion. He maintained the appearance of a Catholic, however, especially toward the end of his life, and in 1684 won the Academy's prize for eloquence with a *Discours sur la patience* that would not have been out of place in a collection of sermons (but did he not take this as a joke?). Nevertheless, his scientific attitude led him to a certain skepticism toward religion. The spirit of tolerance animated him; he had, after all, Protestant paternal ancestors, and in Normandy, where Reformed churchgoers were numerous, he had friends such as the Basnages, to whom he remained faithful after the revocation of the Edict of Nantes.

Fontenelle was born with a very fragile constitution; in his childhood he spat blood and was forbidden to take any violent exercise. He was sparing and careful of himself all his life; this is undoubtedly why he was accused of egotism and of indifference toward others. Although self-centered and considering himself responsible only for his own actions, he was not at all insensitive to the needs of others; on the contrary, he was obliging toward his friends (Mlle. de Launy and Brunel, for example). He was even-tempered—perhaps that is the secret of his longevity. He loved the company of women but never married. Even as a nonagenarian he still frequented their salons, particularly that of Mme. Geoffrin, whom he made his general legatee. In his youth he had been received by Ninon de Lenclos and, from 1710 to 1733, by Mme. de Lambert, at whose home he met men of letters and scholars, such as Houdar de La Motte, Marivaux, Montesquieu, and Mairan. He also attended the duchesse du Maine at her court at Sceaux and was a frequent guest of Mme. de Tencin. He was affable and witty; his all-embracing curiosity made him an excellent listener. Above all, he prized his freedom of mind and independence in his relations with men of rank, like the regent, Philippe d'Orléans, who honored him with his friendship, lodged him in the Palais Royal (until 1730), and awarded him a pension.

Fontenelle received every possible academic honor, although he was refused four times before being accepted into the French Academy in 1691. On 9 January 1697 he entered the Académie des Sciences as *secrétaire perpétuel* and was confirmed in office on 28 January 1699. He was *sous-directeur* in 1706, 1707, 1719, and 1728; *directeur* in 1709, 1713, and 1723; and was made *pensionnaire vétéran* on 9 December 1740. He became a member of the Académie Royale des Inscriptions et Belles-Lettres in 1701 and requested veteran status in 1705. In 1733 he was elected a member of the Royal Society of London. In 1740 he contributed to the foundation of the Académie des Sciences, Belles-Lettres et Arts of Rouen, which received its charter in 1744 and of which he then became an honorary member. He became a member of the Berlin Academy on 4 December 1749, the Accademia dei Arcadi of Rome, and the Academy of Nancy. In 1702 he joined the society formed by the Abbé Bignon to direct the publication of the *Journal des sçavans.*

Commencing with his studies at the Jesuit *collège,* Fontenelle began to write poetry. In 1670 he competed for the prize of the Académie des Palinods of Rouen, writing in Latin on the Immaculate Conception, and his work was judged worthy of printing and was published that year in the *Revue des palinods.* In 1674 he translated an ode by his teacher P. Commire, addressed to the Grand Condé "on the fact that he is subsisting only on milk" (*Mercure galant,* July 1679). In 1677 the *Mercure galant* published his "L'amour noyé" with a very flattering introduction of the author as "nephew of the two Corneille poets." On several occasions Fontenelle competed for the poetry prize of the French Academy, but without great success. His operas, written under the name of Thomas Corneille and set to music by Lully, *Psyché* (1678) and *Bellérophon* (1679), were no more successful; even less so was his tragedy *Aspar* (1680), which was ridiculed by Racine. Under the name of Donneau de Visé he produced a comedy in 1681, *La comète,* inspired by the appearance of the comet of 1680 (the same referred to in Bayle's *Pensées sur la comète*). In it Fontenelle presents—obviously, in an amusing manner—various contemporary explanations of comets, including the most popular as well as the Cartesian theory; and the antiquated notions surrounding these celestial phenomena are held up to ridicule. In the work one can see the dawn of what was to make Fontenelle famous: his taste for the exposition of scientific ideas and his censorious and mocking attitude toward everything that seemed to him to be preconception or myth.

His "Lettre sur la Princesse de Clèves," which appeared in the *Mercure* of May 1678, revealed his talent as a literary critic sensitive to feelings, although he presented himself from this time on as a *géomètre,* with a "mind completely filled with measurements and proportions." Nevertheless, the first work of his period in Rouen was not a scientific one: it was, rather, the *Nouveaux dialogues des morts,* in two volumes, which he published anonymously in 1683. This was followed in 1684 by the *Jugement de Pluton* on the two parts of the first work. Fontenelle sometimes arranged the dialogues between the ancients, sometimes between the moderns, and sometimes between members of the two groups. From occasionally comical situations he draws subtle moral observations in a lively style. One can also find interesting considerations regarding the sciences, all of which have their chimera "which they run after without being able to seize . . . but on the way they trap other very useful knowledge" (dialogue between Artemis and Ramon Lull). He also comments on the role of instruments in the field of scientific knowledge (dialogue between Marcus Apicius and Galileo) and on the difficulty of discovering the truth (dialogue between the third Pseudo-Demetrius and Descartes).

At the same time as this work, which invites serious consideration despite its light touch, there appeared the *Lettres diverses de M. le Chevalier d'Her* * * * (or *Lettres galantes . . .*, depending on the edition), which were attributed to Fontenelle, who disavowed them. No one was deceived, for they clearly bear the mark of his style and his mind and reveal his ability to scrutinize a woman's soul.

In 1685 Fontenelle displayed his taste for mathematical reflection with the publication in the *Nouvelles de la république des lettres,* under the title of "Mémoire composé par M.D.F.D.R. [M. de Fontenelle de Rouen] contenant une question d'arithmétique," of a two-part article on the properties of the number nine. It was only a simple game that did not demonstrate the author's genius in these matters. Yet, if he did not solve the problem, he did pose the question for scholars; the *Nouvelles* published a reply by de Joullieu in February 1686 and a "Démonstration générale de la question . . . touchant les nombres multiples," by J. Sauveur, in October 1686.

This first, scarcely scientific essay was followed in 1686 by Fontenelle's most famous and most frequently published and translated work, *Entretiens sur la pluralité des mondes.* In five "Evenings" (*Soirs*), then six in the 1687 edition, Fontenelle undertook to set forth to a marquise who questioned him during evening promenades in a garden the different astronomical systems: those of Ptolemy, Copernicus, and Tycho Brahe. He spoke to her of the moon and the other worlds—Venus, Mercury, Mars, Jupiter, Saturn, the fixed stars—and discussed the possibility that they might be inhabited. He explained, in terms that could be understood by an intelligent but untrained mind, recent discoveries in the world of the stars, displaying a strong Cartesian bent in his account. In choosing this subject Fontenelle was undoubtedly inspired by a growing interest in the heavenly bodies, as well as by a work that appeared in Rouen in 1655, *Le monde de la lune* (a translation of the *Discovery of a New World* of John Wilkins), and by the *Discours nouveau prouvant la pluralité des mondes* of Pierre Borel (1657), not to mention two books by Cyrano de Bergerac, *L'autre monde: L'histoire comique des états et empires de la lune* (1657) and *L'histoire comique des états et empires du soleil* (1662).

Fontenelle was not an astronomer, and the earliest editions contained a number of errors which he continued to correct until 1742 in order to bring his text into agreement with the scientific data provided him by the members of the Academy of Sciences. The book offered him an opportunity to discuss problems that fascinated him: the relativity of knowledge and the desacralization of the earth—and hence man—attendant upon the recognition of a nongeocentric universe. Our world is not privileged: others might be inhabited, and our present knowledge is limited but grows unceasingly in the course of time. "The art of flying has only just been born; it will be brought to perfection, and someday we will go to the moon" ("Second Evening").

The work's success resulted from the author's having treated supposedly difficult subjects in a light style, playfully and with a touch of affectation that detracted nothing from the seriousness of the given explanations. All this was done in a slightly fictionalized form that permitted a certain lyricism on the enchantment of a summer evening and the immensity of the universe. It is the first example in French of a learned work placed within the reach of an educated but nonspecialized public. It is certainly to these aspects of his work that Fontenelle owed his later academic positions.

Meanwhile, he was active in other fields. He published "Éloge de Monsieur Corneille" in January 1685 in the *Nouvelles de la république des lettres.* (Revised as "Vie de Monsieur Corneille," it appeared in the 1742 edition of his *Oeuvres.*) This was followed in 1686 by *Doutes sur le système physique des causes occasionnelles,* on the theory that Malebranche had presented in the *Recherche de la vérité.* Also in 1686, the self-styled "author of the *Dialogue des morts,*" again under the veil of anonymity, published the *Histoire des oracles.* Actually, he had already set forth his reflections on history: he had sketched the treatise "Sur l'histoire," passages from which were to appear in *De l'origine des fables* (1724). Published along with them were several pages, "Sur le bonheur," also written much earlier and undoubtedly one of the best expressions of Fontenelle's practical philosophy, a human morality independent of religion.

In his reflections on history and on the origin of fables Fontenelle appears as one of the first to treat the history of religion comparatively. He espoused a critical history not only of human events but also of myths, legends, and religions. He studied their formation, showing the role of imagination and how "marvelous" phenomena can be explained by nonsupernatural causes. He found ideas similar to his in *De oraculis ethnicorum dissertationes duae,* a work published in 1683 by the Dutchman A. Van Dale, and he decided to translate it; in the end he preferred to rewrite it entirely in his own manner. This was again done under the cover of anonymity, of course, for it was dangerous to attack superstitions: it led to casting doubt on miracles—fundamental ideas of Christianity that do not agree with scientific truths discovered through reasoning and experiment. Thus, Fontenelle was later attacked by the Jesuits, in particular by Jean-François Baltus, in 1707 and 1708, following the fifth edition of the *Histoire des oracles;* in accordance with his temperamental dislike of dispute and perhaps counseled by his friends as well, he did not reply.

Fontenelle was not content, in 1686, to publish only this dangerous work. He had sent to his friend Basnage in Rotterdam (in order to forward it to Bayle, who published it in the *Nouvelles de la république des lettres* of January) a "Relation curieuse de l'Isle de Bornéo," a so-called extract from a "letter written from Batavia in the East Indies." Involved was a letter between two sisters, Mreo and Eenegu, who were, one quickly discovered, none other than Rome and Geneva. In other words, just after the revocation of the Edict of Nantes, Fontenelle stigmatized the struggle between Catholics and Protestants, besides making a clear allusion to an event of which he deeply disapproved. If he had not at this time had protectors as powerful as the lieutenant of police Marc René de Voyer de Paulmy, marquis d'Argenson, he would have received the *lettre de cachet* that Le Tellier, confessor to Louis XIV, attempted to obtain against him for his unorthodox writings.

Fontenelle settled in Paris around 1687 and resumed his literary activities, publishing in that year *Poésies pastorales de M.D.F., avec un traité sur la nature de l'églogue et une digression sur les anciens et les modernes.* Fontenelle belonged to the party of the moderns, the men of progress, together with his friend Houdar de La Motte, Charles Perrault, and the circle of the *Mercure galant,* in opposition to the party of the ancients, the men of tradition, among whom were Racine, Boileau, and La Bruyère. His relationship with the Corneille family obviously reinforced his hostility toward the partisans of Racine, but it is certain that the *Digression,* leaving aside the question of personalities, shows Fontenelle's reflections concerning science: it is owing to its progress that humanity is improved. Moreover, is not the notion of ancients and moderns really very relative?

Fontenelle wrote another libretto, for the opera *Enée et Lavinie* (1690), and a tragedy, *Brutus* (1691), under the pseudonym of Mlle. Bernard. Received into the French Academy two years before La Bruyère, who in the eighth edition of the *Caractères* (1694) was to mock him under the name of Cydias, Fontenelle published the *Recueil des plus belles pièces des poètes françois, depuis Villon jusqu'à Benserade, avec une préface et des petites vies des poètes* (1692) and the *Parallèle de Corneille et de Racine* (1693).

Thanks to his compatriot and friend Varignon, Fontenelle made the acquaintance of the Parisian scientific circle and became friendly with Nicolas de Malézieu and Guillaume de L'Hospital. For the latter's *Analyse des infiniment petits pour l'intelligence des lignes courbes* (1696), he composed a preface that might have been taken for the author's but which everyone was quite aware was by Fontenelle. In it are displayed his interest in the notion of infinity and his talent as a historian; in a few pages he retraces the history of the mathematical study of curved lines from Archimedes to Newton and Leibniz.

Fontenelle was a friend of the Abbé Bignon and of Pontchartrain, patrons of the Academy of Sciences; and his *Entretiens* was admired for its clear and elegant style, in contrast to the ponderous Latin of the Academy's secretary, Jean-Baptiste du Hamel. In 1697 Fontenelle was invited to replace the latter. The Academy's new statutes of January 1699, of which Fontenelle was in part the author, defined the role of the *secrétaire perpétuel:* he was required to publish each year the memoirs of the academicians drawn from the records, preceded by a sort of *histoire raisonnée* of the Academy's most remarkable accomplishments. He was also to deliver the *éloges* of those academicians who had died during the year and was to publish them in the *Histoire.*

Thus, under the facile pen of a writer who could simplify and clarify and who—without being a specialist—had sufficient knowledge in all areas of science to present its results without distortion, the works of the academicians could become accessible to a cultivated society that balked at Latin. From 1699 to 1740 Fontenelle devoted himself almost exclusively to his task of editing the *Histoire de l'Académie royale des sciences . . . avec les mémoires de mathématique et de physique pour la même année, tirés des registres de cette Académie.* The volume for the year 1699, which appeared in 1702, opens with an untitled preface usually called "Préface [sometimes "Discours préliminaire"] sur l'utilité des mathématiques et de la physique et sur les travaux de l'Académie," which contains essential material on the philosophy of science and is a sort of bridge between Descartes's *Discours de la méthode* and Claude Bernard's *Introduction à l'étude de la médecine expérimentale.* Here one finds the first literary expression of the idea of the interdependence of the sciences and of the constancy of the laws of nature. In 1733 there appeared the history of the early years of the Academy, under the title *Histoire de l'Académie royale des sciences. Tome Ier. Depuis son établissement en 1666, jusqu'à 1686.* Fontenelle covered only the years until 1679 but composed a preface that is an excellent history not only of the founding of the Academy but of the state of contemporary science as well.

Fontenelle eventually published forty-two volumes of the *Histoire de l'Académie,* containing sixty-nine *éloges.* He had already had some experience with this literary genre in the "Éloge de Monsieur Corneille" and especially in the "Éloge de Mons. Claude Perrault de l'Académie royale des sciences et docteur en médecine de la Faculté de Paris . . ." (*Journal des sçavans,* 28 February 1689). The first *éloges* read to the Academy were short, and one senses that Fontenelle had not yet attained complete mastery of the field in which he later proved to be without equal. His ability, evident as early as the *éloge* of Viviani (1703), was still apparent in the last one, that of Du Fay (1739).

No one before him had been able to evaluate so well the works of others nor to report on a life with such verve, nor to sprinkle his text with such subtle psychological and moral observations. The *éloges* were Fontenelle's greatest glory. They remain an astonishing—occasionally unique—source of biographical information on the scientists of the epoch. If one can sometimes reproach Fontenelle for being biased or too Cartesian at a time when science was already Newtonian, he was a good mirror of his times; and one finds in his writing what is undoubtedly the best approach in French to the works of Malebranche, Leibniz, Newton, Johann I Bernoulli, Jean-Dominique Cassini, Varignon, and Boerhaave, to cite only a few names.

The *éloges* enjoyed such success that Fontenelle saw the necessity, as early as 1708, of collecting them in a separate volume under the title *Histoire du renouvellement de l'Académie royale des sciences en M.DC.XCIX et les éloges historiques de tous les académiciens morts depuis ce renouvellement, avec un discours préliminaire sur l'utilité des mathématiques et de la physique.* In 1717 he brought out an edition with seventeen new *éloges,* in 1722 one with eleven more, and in 1733 the *Suite des éloges des académiciens . . . morts depuis l'an M.DCC.XXII.* Finally, in 1742, volumes V and VI of his *Oeuvres* contained the whole series of *éloges.*

As a member of the Academy of Sciences, Fontenelle also wished to do work of his own. In 1727, as a "Suite des mémoires de l'Académie royale des sciences," he published the *Élémens de la géométrie de l'infini.* Some doubted whether it was really the work of a mathematician, but the author believed it was and attached great value to it. He had worked on it for a long time, probably since the period of his preface to the *Analyse des infiniment petits.* The term *élémens* is to be understood in the sense of "first principles." According to Fontenelle, none of the geometers who had invented or employed the calculus of infinity had given a general theory of it; that is what he proposed to do. The work is divided into a preface relating the history of this branch of calculus and into two main parts: "Système général de l'infini" and "Différentes applications ou remarques." The author discusses "the infinite in series or in progressions of numbers" and then examines "the infinite in straight and curved lines," in the words of the Abbé Terrasson, who reviewed the work in the *Journal des sçavans* (July–October 1728).

There was a great deal of discussion in the scientific community about this work, in which mathematicians found numerous paradoxes. Johann I Bernoulli, for example, in his correspondence with Fontenelle allowed his criticisms to show through his praise: he did not understand what was meant by *finis indéterminables.* Fontenelle attempted to defend his theory and above all his distinction between metaphysical infinity and geometric infinity: one must ignore the metaphysical difficulties in order to further geometry, and the *finis indéterminables* ought to be considered "as a type of hypothesis necessary until now in order to explain several phenomena of the calculus" (letter to Johann I Bernoulli, 29 June 1729). "The orders of infinite and indeterminable quantities, like the magnitudes that they represent, are only purely relative entities, hypothetical and auxiliary. The subject matter of mathematics is only ideal," according to the terms of a "Projet de rapport" of Dortous de Mairan to the Academy on this work.

In 1731 the third edition of Thomas Corneille's *Dictionnaire des arts et des sciences* appeared, revised and augmented by Fontenelle with many scientific terms. When he retired from the Academy of Sciences, Fontenelle was feted at the French Academy on the fiftieth anniversary of his election to that body, and for this occasion he composed a "Discours sur la rime" (1741).

In 1743 a small, anonymous volume entitled *Nouvelles libertés de penser* appeared in Amsterdam; it included two articles believed to have been written by Fontenelle: "Les réflexions sur l'argument de M. Pascal et de M. Locke concernant les possibilités d'une vie à venir" and "Traité de la liberté," both of which are completely in accord with his way of thinking.

In 1752 Fontenelle published anonymously through his friend the physician Camille Falconet (who provided a preface) his *Théorie des tourbillons cartésiens avec des réflexions sur l'attraction.* Many were astonished to see the appearance at this time of a work conceived some years previously, and they tried to explain why Fontenelle had decided to present to the learned public a thoroughly outmoded scientific theory. Fontenelle agreed with Newton and the Newtonians to the degree that they did not attempt to give a meaning to "attraction" and contented themselves with calculations. Newton linked formulas with formulas; his method yielded results that corresponded to the facts, but he explained nothing in the sense that Fontenelle would wish, that is, through principles. Fontenelle wished to understand by going back to causes. It was all very well to take "attraction" as a simple word or a sign; one should not, however, endow it with content, and Newtonians who do this return to Scholastic notions and to "occult forces." If Fontenelle remained faithful to the Cartesianism of the *Entretiens,* it was certainly not owing to the stubbornness of age but to a profound conviction of the value of a mechanical explanation in Descartes's sense. This conviction, moreover, was supported by certain works that he analyzed at the Academy of Sciences, in particular those of Privat de Molières, who defended, with some modifications, the theory of vortices (*tourbillons*).

"One must always admire Descartes and on occasion follow him" (*Éloge d'Hartsoëker*): Fontenelle followed him in the matter of the vortices but not in such matters as his theory of animal machines. In his horror of systems that lull thought to sleep, he understood that the important thing is not the results acquired, which are always provisional, but the method of thinking, which consists in completely rejecting all "marvelous" facts, in questioning everything, and in believing only what reason supported by experiment clearly shows. This is the intellectual attitude inherited by the Encyclopedists that characterized the Enlightenment.

In most respects a man of the seventeenth century, Fontenelle was, in others, a man of the eighteenth—perhaps even of the twentieth—century in his unflagging intellectual curiosity and in his belief in the limitless progress of knowledge in a world in which everything must be open to rational explanation.

BIBLIOGRAPHY

I. Original Works. All of Fontenelle's works have been mentioned in the article. Cited here are only the principal eds. of selected and complete works, the most recent critical eds., and several selected texts.

Editions of selected and complete works include *Oeuvres diverses de M. de Fontenelle,* 3 vols. (Amsterdam, 1701, 1716); 2 vols. (London, 1707, 1713, 1714, 1716); 8 vols. (Paris, 1715); 3 vols. (Paris, 1724); 3 vols. (The Hague, 1728–1729), with an engraving by Bernard Picart, "le Romain"; and 5 vols. (The Hague, 1736). *Oeuvres de M. de Fontenelle* appeared in several eds.: 6 vols. (Paris, 1742); 8 vols. (Paris, 1751–1752); 6 vols. (Amsterdam, 1754); 10 vols. (Paris, 1758); 11 vols. (Paris, 1761, 1766); 12 vols. (Amsterdam, 1764); and 7 vols. (London, 1785). The oft-cited Bastien ed., *Oeuvres de Fontenelle,* 8 vols. (Paris, 1790–1792), is not always faithful to Fontenelle's text and cannot be recommended. Later eds. include G. B. Depping, ed., 3 vols. (Paris, 1818), with index; and J.-B. Champagnac, ed., 5 vols. (Paris, 1825).

Critical eds. include Louis Maigron, ed., *Histoire des oracles* (Paris, 1908; repr., 1934); *De l'origine des fables* (Paris, 1932), edited with intro., notes, and commentary by J.-R. Carré; Robert Shackleton, ed., *Entretiens sur la pluralité des mondes. Digression sur les anciens et les modernes* (Oxford, 1955); and *Entretiens sur la pluralité des mondes* (Paris, 1966), with intro. and notes by Alexandre Calame.

Among selected texts are (in chronological order) A. P. Le Guay de Prémontval, ed., *L'esprit de Fontenelle, ou Recueil des pensées tirées de ses ouvrages* (The Hague, 1753); *Oeuvres choisies de Fontenelle,* 2 vols. (Liège, 1779); J. Chass, ed., *Esprit, maximes et principes de Fontenelle* (Paris, 1788); Cousin d'Avallon, ed., *Fontenelliana, ou Recueil des bons mots . . . de Fontenelle* (Paris, 1801); *Oeuvres choisies de Fontenelle,* 2 vols. (Paris, 1883), with a preface by J.-F. Thénard; Henri Pothez, ed., *Pages choisies des grands écrivains, Fontenelle* (Paris, 1909); Émile Faguet, ed., *Textes choisis et commentés* (Paris, 1912); and *Textes choisis* (Paris, 1966), with intro. and notes by Maurice Roelens, the best current ed.

II. Secondary Literature. On Fontenelle's life, one can still profitably consult his first biographer, the Abbé Trublet, in "Mémoires pour servir à l'histoire de la vie et des ouvrages de M. de Fontenelle," a series of articles that first appeared in the *Mercure de France* (1756–1758). They were then collected in 2 vols. (Amsterdam, 1759) and were later added as vols. XI and XII of Fontenelle's *Oeuvres* (Amsterdam, 1764). They were summarized by Trublet in "Fontenelle," in Moreri's *Dictionnaire . . .* (1759).

The essential bibliography concerning Fontenelle and his work is S. Delorme, "Contribution à la bibliographie de Fontenelle," in *Revue d'histoire des sciences,* **10,** no. 4 (Oct.-Dec. 1957), 300-309.

Particularly noteworthy are Grandjeán de Fouchy, "Éloge de Fontenelle," in *Histoire de l'Académie royale des sciences, année 1757;* Louis Maigron, *Fontenelle, l'homme, l'oeuvre, l'influence* (Paris, 1906); J.-R. Carré, *La philosophie de Fontenelle, ou Le sourire de la raison* (Paris, 1932); M. Bouchard, *"L'histoire des Oracles" de Fontenelle* (Paris, 1947); John W. Cosentini, *Fontenelle's Art of Dialogue* (New York, 1952); S. Delorme, G. Martin, D. McKie, and A. Birembaut, in *Revue d'histoire des sciences,* **10,** no. 4 (1957); S. Delorme, A. Adam, A. Couder, J. Rostand, and A. Robinet, "Fontenelle, sa vie et son oeuvre, 1657-1757 (Journées Fontenelle)," in *Revue de synthèse,* 3rd ser., no. 21 (Jan.-Mar. 1961); François Grégoire, *Fontenelle, une philosophie désabusée* (Nancy, 1947); J. Rostand, *Hommes de vérité, Pasteur, Claude Bernard, Fontenelle* (Paris, 1942, 1955); and J. Vendryès, G. Canguilhem, A. Dupont-Sommer, R. Pintard, A. Adam, and A. Maurois, in *Annales de l'Université de Paris,* 27e année, no. 3 (July-Sept. 1957), p. 378 ff.

One should also consult the *Catalogue de l'Exposition Fontenelle à la Bibliothèque Nationale* (Paris, 1957), which is especially useful. See also the bibliographies in the latest critical eds. (Shackleton, Calame, and Roelens, *op. cit.*), and note, particularly from a philosophical point of view, Leonard M. Marsak, "Bernard de Fontenelle: The Idea of Science in the French Enlightenment," in *Transactions of the American Philosophical Society,* n.s. **49,** pt. 7 (1959), 1-64.

SUZANNE DELORME

FÖPPL, AUGUST (*b.* Grossumstadt, Germany, 25 January 1854; *d.* Ammerland, Germany, 12 August 1924), *engineering, physics.*

Föppl's choice of career was determined by the great program of German railway construction in the mid-nineteenth century. In the late 1860's, a line was begun through the Odenwald, near Grossumstadt. Föppl's father, a country physician, was appointed a director of a railway hospital, and both he and his family were thereby drawn into close association with the construction engineers. This contact was decisive for August, who was then just finishing at the Gymnasium. He started engineering studies in Darmstadt, later changing to Stuttgart, and finally graduating from the Polytechnic in Karlsruhe in 1874.

At the time, job opportunities were few for practicing engineers, and Föppl took a temporary, uncongenial position as a bridge engineer. Simultaneously, at the age of twenty-one, he published the results of his first independent research, a paper on bridge construction. The market for engineers was still poor in 1876, when Föppl completed his year of military service, and the young railway engineer hired himself out for a term as teacher in a building-trades school in Holzminden. The work proved unexpectedly to his liking. In the fall of 1877, Föppl accepted a permanent post at the Trades School in Leipzig.

Teaching at Leipzig was at a low level, and Föppl aspired to become a university professor. He decided to make himself known to the university world through publications. His first two books, *Theorie des Fachwerks* and *Theorie der Gewölbe* appeared in 1880 and 1881. In 1886 these two, together with a small textbook for trade school students, served to meet the requirements for a doctorate in his field at the University of Leipzig. The textbook was published in 1890 as *Leitfaden und Aufgabensammlung für den Unterricht in der angewandten Mechanik.*

Although these first books were well received, they did not bring Föppl the desired appointment as a professor of bridge engineering. He gave up the hope of being appointed in his specialty and resolved to master additional fields. In the self-study to which he now gave himself, the problems involved in writing textbooks suitable for independent reading first presented themselves to him. Meanwhile, throughout the early 1880's, electrical artifacts and machines, exhibited in fairs and commercial firms, brought the new field of electrical engineering to public attention. Föppl turned to this area and, to prepare himself, went in late 1893 to work in Gustav Wiedemann's laboratory at the University of Leipzig. He published his work in a series of papers in *Wiedemann's Annalen.* Among them were researches bearing on subjects as fundamental as the nature of electricity.

From Föppl's activity in electromagnetism, together with his interest in the independent student, grew an immensely successful text, the *Einführung in die Maxwellsche Theorie der Elektrizität* (Leipzig, 1894). It was one of the first German-language expositions of Maxwell's ideas. In addition, Föppl had been an early convert to the use of vector calculus in physics, and his *Einführung* was the first German text to incorporate this new mathematics.

During these fifteen years as a schoolteacher, Föppl also continued to work in engineering statics. He was hired by the city of Leipzig for a number of civil engineering assignments; the most noteworthy of these was the design of the iron framework of the Leipzig Markthalle. Föppl here achieved a new solution for roofing over an irregular polygonal space: it later became known as the *Föpplsche Flechtwerk-Hallendächer,* that is, "Föppl's wickerwork roof." He also published a succession of theoretical studies which were collected in 1892 and published as *Das Fachwerk im Raum* (Leipzig, 1892), one of his best books.

The summons to a university finally came in 1892.

The post was the newly created one of extraordinary professor of agricultural machinery and forestry at Leipzig. This was one field in which Föppl had had no experience. He threw himself into it with his customary wholeheartedness. He participated in the systematic program of tests on farm machinery organized by the German Agricultural Society and wrote an article on the theory of plows for the 1893 *Landwirtschaftliches Jahrbuch.* His labors in this new field were cut short, for in 1894 he was appointed to succeed Johannes Bauschinger at the Technische Hochschule in Munich, as ordinary professor of theoretical mechanics and director of the strength-of-materials laboratory.

In Munich, Föppl felt himself to have reached his life's goal and to have achieved a position at the top of his profession. He now turned almost exclusively to engineering mechanics and left it to Max Abraham to carry out the rewriting of subsequent editions of the *Einführung.* In his role as professor, Föppl published a number of texts, of which the most important was the six-volume *Vorlesungen über technischen Mechanik.* By 1927, the third of these volumes received its tenth edition; none of the others went through fewer than four. He also continued his researches, publishing works on gyroscopic phenomena and problems of relative and absolute motion, among other subjects.

In his role as laboratory director, Föppl succeeded in increasing the proportion of laboratory effort in basic science. Under Bauschinger the laboratory was mainly devoted to carrying out tests requested by industry and government. Under Föppl this part of the work was largely carried out by assistants. His own researches at the laboratory were published in a series of articles (making up vols. **24–33**) in the *Mittheilungen aus dem mechanisch-technischen Laboratorium der K. Technischen Hochschule München.* They appeared between 1896 and 1915 and were of diverse kinds: experimental studies of properties of materials, theoretical investigations of dynamical problems arising in engineering practice, and critical scrutinies of the foundations of engineering formulas and tests. In his evaluation of Föppl's Munich work, C. Prinz singled out the article on Laval waves, that is, disturbances in fast-moving waves, as having been of particular importance for both engineering and physics. Prinz also characterized the reorientation Föppl gave the laboratory as a change from an interest in tests on materials to an interest in the several components of a construction regarded in terms of their interrelations. This approach was unusual in Föppl's time and opened new paths.

Föppl gave up his professorship in 1921 but retained direction of the laboratory. In 1924 he had the satisfaction of seeing the appearance of a *Festschrift* on his seventieth birthday, written by former pupils. Among them were his two sons, Otto and Ludwig, as well as Theodor von Kármán, Prandtl, H. Thoma, and Timoschenko. Föppl died suddenly a few months later in his country house in Bavaria.

It was characteristic of Föppl to involve himself in problems as practical as bridge construction and as fundamental as the question of the existence of absolute motion. In both types of investigations, he concerned himself to an unusual degree with a critical examination of the underlying assumptions. His personal qualities were perhaps typical of his century and nation. He was a strict and conscientious father and husband. He was loyal to the cause of German nationalism and German greatness, and conscious of the significance of his field for the industrial and agricultural strength that lay behind Germany's power. Scrupulous and industrious in his work, he succeeded by his considerable effort in attaining the rather precisely defined goal he had set himself.

BIBLIOGRAPHY

In addition to the works mentioned in the text, see the lists in Poggendorff.

Of particular interest is Föppl's autobiography, *Lebenserinnerungen,* which appeared posthumously (Munich–Berlin, 1925).

The *Festschrift* is *Beiträge zur technischen Mechanik und technischen Physik. August Föppl zum siebsigsten Geburtstag* (Berlin, 1924); see esp. the articles "August Föppl," pp. v–viii (unsigned), and C. Prinz, "A. Föppl als Forscher und Lehrer," pp. 1–3.

JOAN BROMBERG

FORBES, ALEXANDER (*b.* Milton, Massachusetts, 14 May 1882; *d.* Milton, 27 March 1965), *physiology.*

Alexander Forbes was the youngest of seven children of a well-educated, well-to-do Unitarian Boston family. His father was William Hathaway Forbes, and his mother was Edith Emerson, the daughter of Ralph Waldo Emerson. Forbes graduated from Milton Academy in 1899 and then attended Harvard (B.A., 1904; M.A., 1905; M.D., 1910). He studied with Charles S. Sherrington at Liverpool (1911–1912) and with Keith Lucas at Cambridge (briefly in 1912). He returned to Harvard Medical School, where he remained until 1948. After 1948 he was professor emeritus and continued his research in the Harvard biological laboratories.

In 1910 Forbes married Charlotte Irving Grinell of New York. The couple had four children. Forbes lived his entire life in Milton, with summers at the Forbes family estate on Naushon Island (Massachusetts) or cruising the North Atlantic. His health was superb and he excelled at yachting, fancy skating, skiing, rock climbing, and canoeing; and for many years he piloted his private airplane. His only physical affliction was a moderate hearing loss, dating from about 1908.

Forbes's primary scientific interest was neurophysiology, but equally strong was his love of the outdoors, the woods, rivers, and hills of New England, particularly the coast of New England and Labrador. He made contributions to navigation and, at the suggestion of Sir Wilfred Grenfell, he mapped the coast of Labrador by aerial photography, using the technique of oblique photogrammetry. For this he was awarded (1938) the Charles P. Daly Gold Medal of the American Geographic Society. He served with the U.S. Navy in both World Wars; in the first he installed radio compasses, and in the second he mapped an aerial route across northern Greenland.

Forbes was a scientific amateur in the best sense of the word. As a man of independent means, he engaged in his laboratory experiments, outdoor sports, yachting, and explorations because he loved them. He did little formal teaching. Not only did he defray much of the expense of his own activities, but for many years he anonymously supported others in the department of physiology.

Forbes's greatest contributions to neurophysiology came early in his career. He was a technical innovator. About 1912 he installed what was probably the first string galvanometer in the New England area for the accurate measurement of the time relations of spinal-cord reflexes. Later, using his experience with radio compasses, he developed a capacity-coupled electronic amplifier for greater sensitivity, and in 1920 he became the first to report the use of electronic amplification in a physiological experiment.

The paper by Forbes (with Alan Gregg, 1915) on the flexion reflex of the decerebrate cat, timed by means of the string galvanometer, was a landmark in neurophysiology. His most influential paper was a review entitled "The Interpretation of Spinal Reflexes in Terms of Present Knowledge of Nerve Conduction" (1922). The properties of the spinal reflexes were chiefly those described by Sherrington and his pupils (including Forbes himself). The knowledge of nerve conduction was developed chiefly by Lucas and E. D. Adrian. Forbes visited Adrian in 1921.

Forbes's great contribution was to unite these two schools of thought and experimentation and thereby establish the form and direction of a major segment of American neurophysiology. In his paper he provided a coherent, consistent interpretation of the major features of reflex activity. Actually, many of the interpretations were erroneous, as Forbes readily admitted, but his ingenious suggestions inspired experiments and theorizing for at least twenty years. Through his influence on Norbert Wiener, Arturo Rosenblueth, and others, he contributed significantly to the development of the science of cybernetics.

Forbes himself considered his single most important scientific contribution to be the final establishment of the all-or-none law of nerve conduction. The experiments, planned by Forbes and carried out by his collaborators, showed that the strength of a nerve impulse is not diminished after it has passed through a local region of partial narcosis where the impulse was weakened but not extinguished. The impulse is a chain reaction, with local contribution of energy in amounts depending on the local condition of the nerve fiber, not on the previous history of the impulse elsewhere. The idea had been formulated previously by Adrian, but with inadequate experimental support. Forbes's experiment was performed independently and simultaneously, with the same result, by Genichi Kato and his associates in Japan.

Forbes's laboratory became a center for the training of both American and European neurophysiologists. Forbes participated in the early use of microelectrodes (large ones by modern standards) and fostered studies of the auditory system and the early development of electroencephalography in the United States. His studies of electrical responses of the brain under Nembutal narcosis paved the way for far-reaching later developments.

BIBLIOGRAPHY

Among the most important of Forbes's writings are the following: "Electrical Studies in Mammalian Reflexes. I. The Flexion Reflex," in *American Journal of Physiology,* **37** (1915), 118–176, written with A. Gregg; "Amplification of Action Currents With the Electron Tube in Recording With the String Galvanometer," *ibid.,* **52** (1920), 409–471, written with C. Thacher; "The All-or-Nothing Response of Sensory Nerve Fibres," in *Journal of Physiology,* **56** (1922), 301–330, written with E. D. Adrian; "The Interpretation of Spinal Reflexes in Terms of Present Knowledge of Nerve Conduction," in *Physiological Reviews,* **2** (1922), 361–414; "The Nature of the Delay in the Response to the Second of Two Stimuli in Nerve and in the Nerve-Muscle Preparation," in *American Journal of Physiology,* **66** (1923), 553–617, written with L. H. Ray and F. R. Griffith, Jr.; "Studies of the Nerve Impulse. II. The Question of Decrement," *ibid.,* **76** (1926), 448–471, written with H. Davis, D. Brunswick, and A. McH. Hopkins; "Tonus in Skeletal Muscle in Relation to Sympathetic Innervation," in *Archives of Neurology and Psychiatry,* **22** (1929), 247–264; "The Mechanism of Reaction," in C. Murchison, ed., *The Foundations of Experimental Psychology* (Worcester, Mass., 1929), pp. 128–168; "The Conflict Between Excitatory and Inhibitory Effects in a Spinal Center," in *American Journal of Physiology,* **95** (1930), 142–173, written with H. Davis and E. Lambert; "Chronaxie," in *Physiological Reviews,* **16** (1936), 407–441, written with H. Davis; "The Effects of Anesthetics on Action Potentials in the Cerebral Cortex of the Cat," in *American Journal of Physiology,* **116** (1936), 577–596, written with A. J. Derbyshire, B. Rempel, and E. F. Lambert; "Activity of Isocortex and Hippocampus: Electrical Studies With Micro-electrodes," in *Journal of Neurophysiology,* **3** (1940), 74–105, written with B. Renshaw and B. R. Morison; and "Electroretinogram of Fresh-water Turtle: Quantitative Responses to Color Shift," *ibid.,* **21** (1958), 247–262, written with H. W. Deane, M. Neyland, and M. S. Congaware.

HALLOWELL DAVIS

FORBES, EDWARD, JR. (*b.* Douglas, Isle of Man, England, 12 February 1815; *d.* Edinburgh, Scotland, 18 November 1854), *biogeography, invertebrate zoology, invertebrate paleontology.*

Both parents were natives of the Isle of Man. His father was involved in local fishery and lumber businesses, but he later switched to banking. His mother, Jane Teare Forbes, owned Manx property, some of which Edward was to inherit. He was the eldest of eight children surviving infancy. A brother, David, became a geologist.

As a child, Edward became deeply engrossed in the natural world which he found on the island and its shores. He also liked to draw, and in 1831 he went to London to study art. Since he did not show sufficient talent, in November of that year he went to Edinburgh to study medicine instead. There he was strongly influenced by Robert Graham in botany and Robert Jameson in geology, but he never channeled his enthusiasm for zoology and botany into an interest in their medical applications. After his mother's death in 1836 he abandoned his medical education. He went to Paris for the winter of 1836–1837 and attended the biological lectures of Henri M. D. de Blainville and Étienne Geoffroy Saint-Hilaire.

Forbes was remarkably friendly and enjoyed a wide popularity. At Edinburgh he organized a social club which, although rather puritanical compared with typical college fraternities, was a source of lifetime friendships. After 1842 he assumed the responsibility of annually persuading naturalists to attend meetings of the British Association for the Advancement of Science, and he organized younger members of the natural history section into a club called the Red Lions. Forbes enjoyed drawing whimsical animal cartoons and composing poems and songs, the best remembered being "The Song of the Dredge" (1839):

Down in the deep, where the mermen sleep,
Our gallant dredge is sinking;
Each finny shape in a precious scrape
Will find itself in a twinkling!
They may twirl and twist, and writhe as they wist,
And break themselves into sections,
But up they all, at the dredge's call,
Must come to fill collections.

He married Emily Marianne Ashworth on 31 August 1848 and remained devoted to her until his death. They had a son and a daughter. After his death, she married Major William Charles Yelverton in 1858.

The range of Forbes's interests was always broad, although from the start most strongly focused upon marine animals and the distribution of species. These interests early inspired him with a desire to travel, and in May 1833 he sailed with a friend to Norway, where he observed the distribution of vascular plants and mollusks. On that voyage and on later trips he concentrated on those groups because of the ease with which they could be collected. They could serve as indicators of the extent of biogeographical provinces. He published brief biogeographical papers in 1835, but more notable were his observations in 1837, "On the Comparative Elevation of Testacea in the Alps" (*Magazine of Zoology and Botany,* **1,** 257–259), which listed the species that appeared in four vegetation zones. This was a small step toward the concept of biotic communities.

He published five papers on mollusks and their distribution in 1839 and then a monograph on British starfish which appeared serially in 1839–1841. In the introduction he divided the British seas into eleven provinces and indicated in a table the distribution of each species within these provinces. Another table indicated the number of species in six families of starfish which are found in four depth zones. He also began studying the relationship between the distribution of fossil and living species, the importance of which subject Charles Lyell had capably expounded in volume II of his *Principles of Geology* (1832).

After leaving medical school Forbes lived on a yearly allowance of £150 from his father, supplemented by fees from occasional teaching and lectures. Gradually he became unhappy because of his inability to find a permanent position as a naturalist. In February 1841 he heard that Captain Thomas Graves of the Royal Navy, who was charged with surveying the coastal waters of Greece and Turkey, wanted a naturalist to accompany him. Like Charles Darwin before him, Forbes jumped at the opportunity for exploration—after asking his father. On this voyage, which began 1 April, Forbes carried out probably the most extensive and systematic dredging for marine animals ever conducted. Along coasts that naturalists had seldom visited since the time of Aristotle he discovered unknown species, both living and fossil. He also studied the rock formations, flora, and fauna of the islands and coastal regions. He planned extensive publications on his findings but was never able to produce them on the scale he desired.

While Forbes was in the Mediterranean, his father notified him that, because of financial reverses, his allowance must cease. His situation was worsened by a serious attack of malaria. Consequently, when his friend John Goodsir arranged for his appointment to the chair of botany at Kings College, London, Forbes reluctantly returned to London, arriving 28 October 1842.

During the next decade Forbes worked long and hard to earn a living as a naturalist. His professorship paid less than £100 per year, and therefore he also accepted the position of curator for the Geological Society of London. This job, which paid £150, involved managing the society's collections and library and editing its journal. He had scant time to prepare his Near Eastern researches for publication, and sickness, apparently the return of malaria, hampered him further. Nevertheless, in 1843 he managed to prepare a report for the British Association, "On the Molluscs and Radiata of the Aegean Sea, and on Their Distribution, Considered as Bearing on Geology." The generalizations in it were important for biogeography and paleontology and carried him closer to the concept of biotic communities. Extrapolating from his data, he postulated an "azoic zone" below 300 fathoms, but later research has revealed that animal life did exist below that depth. These generalizations were more explicitly stated in another paper the following year, "On the Light Thrown on Geology by Submarine Researches; Being the Substance of a Communication Made to the Royal Institution of Great Britain, Friday Evening, the 23d February 1844" (*Edinburgh New Philosophical Journal,* **36** [1844], 318–327).

In 1844 Forbes became a paleontologist for the Geological Survey, under Henry de la Beche, at £300 per year. He was elected a fellow of the Geological Society in 1844 and of the Royal Society in 1845. Although his new position often carried him afield, he still managed to conduct some classes, give lectures, and write articles and book reviews. He was coauthor, with Lieutenant Thomas A. B. Spratt of the Royal Navy, of the two-volume *Travels in Lycia* (London, 1846), but scientifically more important was Forbes's long paper of that year, "On the Connexion Between the Distribution of the Existing Fauna and Flora of the British Isles and the Geological Changes Which Have Affected Their Area" (*Memoirs of the Geological Survey of England and Wales,* **1,** 336–432). In this paper he emphasized hypothetical former land connections with the Continent and also glaciation to account for the discontinuous distribution of species. In 1848–1852 he published with Sylvanus Hanley a four-volume monograph, *The History of British Mollusca.*

An industrious worker who achieved broad experience and knowledge in both field and museum, Forbes was not always fortunate in the conclusions he drew from his studies. The nature of species was of great interest to him, but his thoughts on the subject were entangled by contemporary metaphysical ideas on typology and by his Anglican religion. He believed that his studies of living and fossil species had enabled him to discover God's plan for creating species, which he named "the principle of polarity." Forbes explained this principle in his presidential address to the Geological Society in February 1853 (*Quarterly Journal of the Geological Society of London,* **10** [1854], xxii–lxxxi, esp. pp. lxxvii–lxxxi). He believed that there existed, or had existed, a continuity of forms of species, but this continuity was supposedly the result of a creation plan rather than of evolution. He postulated two major periods of creation, which he labeled "palaeozoic" and "neozoic." He believed that there was a functional parallel between the species of these two epochs, that there had been a "replacement of one group by another, serving the same purpose in the world's economy." In reaction to this paper Alfred Russel Wallace published his paper of 1855 on the replacement of species as evidenced by the geological record. Forbes had earlier attacked the concept of evolution in two anonymous reviews, one on Robert Chambers' *Vestiges of Creation* (*Lancet* [1844], pp. 265–266), and the other on Adam Sedgwick's *Discourse* (*Literary Gazette* [4 January 1851], reprinted in Forbes's *Literary Papers* [London, 1855], pp. 10–24).

In April 1854 Professor Jameson's death resulted in the long-awaited vacancy in the Regius chair of natural history at Edinburgh, and Forbes was appointed to it. He now had the opportunity—it would prove short-lived—to teach and publish as he wished. He soon became sick with diarrhea and vomiting, and before fully recovering he was further weakened by exposure to a hard rain during a field trip. His death, reportedly from a kidney disease, soon followed.

In 1848 Forbes had begun a significant paleontological and stratigraphic study for the Geological

Survey and he was just starting to write the report at the time of his death. This report, *On the Tertiary Fluvio-Marine Formation of the Isle of Wight,* was completed by several of his former colleagues at the Survey, most notably Henry William Bristow, and was edited by Forbes's literary executor, Robert Godwin-Austen (London, 1856).

One of Forbes's most important works was the posthumous *The Natural History of European Seas* (London, 1859). He wrote the first five chapters (126 pages); it was completed by Robert Godwin-Austen. Published in the same year as Darwin's *Origin of Species,* it contained one of the last confident defenses of the idea of centers of creation. On the other hand, it was also a pioneering work, the first general study of oceanography. Although the chapters were organized mainly according to geographical regions, those by Forbes emphasized biogeography and those by Godwin-Austen emphasized physical aspects of oceanography, thereby providing a broad introduction to the science as a whole.

In spite of Forbes's antievolution commitment, it is a tribute to the value of his work that Darwin found numerous occasions to cite him with approval when writing the *Origin of Species.*

BIBLIOGRAPHY

Considering that he died at the age of thirty-nine, Forbes published a great many works. Some of those having particular theoretical interest are mentioned in the text. Almost all of his publications are listed in the short-title bibliography provided by George Wilson and Archibald Geikie, *Memoir of Edward Forbes, F.R.S., Late Regius Professor of Natural History in the University of Edinburgh* (Cambridge-London-Edinburgh, 1861), pp. 575–583, the only extensive study on Forbes.

Several shorter essays and necrologies provide additional information and assessments. Two that contain bibliographies are G. T. Bettany, "Forbes, Edward (1815–1854)," in *Dictionary of National Biography;* and Daniel Merriman, "Edward Forbes—Manxman," in *Progress in Oceanography,* **3** (1965), 191–206.

See also Nils von Hofsten, "Zur älteren Geschichte des Discontinuitätsproblems in der Biogeographie," in *Zoologischen Annalen,* **7** (1916), 197–353, esp. 301–306.

FRANK N. EGERTON III

FORBES, JAMES DAVID (*b.* Edinburgh, Scotland, 20 April 1809; *d.* Clifton, Scotland, 31 December 1868), *physics, geology.*

Forbes's discovery of the polarization of radiant heat strengthened the belief in the identity of thermal and luminous radiation and contributed to the development of the concept of a continuous radiation spectrum. His detailed studies of glaciers aided in the establishment of modern theories of their formation and movement.

Forbes was the youngest son of William Forbes, seventh baronet of Pitsligo, and Wilhelmina Belches, only child and heiress of John Belches Stuart of Fettercairn. Forbes was educated privately until the age of sixteen and developed an early interest in science. He entered the University of Edinburgh in 1825 to pursue legal studies in accordance with the wishes of his father. He distinguished himself in the natural philosophy courses offered by John Leslie and contributed several anonymous papers to David Brewster's *Philosophical Journal.* Upon revealing his authorship, he was encouraged in his scientific work by Brewster, who proposed his membership to the Royal Society of Edinburgh. Forbes was elected to this body upon reaching the age of twenty-one. He received a modest inheritance at his father's death in 1828 and abandoned law in favor of science. He rapidly became acquainted with prominent British scientists and was elected to the Royal Society of London in 1832. In the same year he participated actively in the formation of the British Association.

Forbes was appointed as Leslie's successor to the chair of natural philosophy at Edinburgh in 1833, despite his youth and relative scientific inexperience. This controversial election, in which Brewster was his principal opponent, caused a rift in their friendship which lasted several years. In 1830 Forbes had begun to investigate radiant heat phenomena without significant results. After learning of Melloni's successful detection of the refraction of thermal radiation, he visited Paris in 1833 to confirm Melloni's results, whereupon he requested Melloni to supervise the manufacture of a thermopile for use in his own investigations.

With this instrument Forbes, in November 1834, discovered the polarization of radiant heat by transmission through tourmaline and thin mica plates and by reflection through the latter. Using mica for dipolarization, he was successful in demonstrating the double refraction of thermal radiation, and in 1836 he found that heat could be circularly polarized by two reflections in a Fresnel rhomb of rock salt. He received the Rumford Medal of the Royal Society of London in 1838 for these discoveries and in 1845 was granted a royal pension for his scientific work.

After 1840 Forbes's central interest was geology, although he continued sporadically to study heat conduction in solids and various types of soils, as well as the effects of the atmosphere on solar radiation. He had become an experienced mountaineer during geological field trips in the Pyrenees, in southeastern France, and in the Pennine chain. He turned his attention to the glaciers of the Alps of Savoy when invited there by Agassiz in 1841 on an exploratory expedition. Forbes's early publications on glaciers, claiming priority in noting their veined structure and in demonstrating that the center of a glacier moves faster than its sides, occasioned controversy with Agassiz and others that did not terminate even at Forbes's death.

Forbes pursued detailed studies of the glaciers of the Alps and of Norway during many subsequent summers. He determined that the surface of a glacier moves faster than the ice vertically beneath it and that the velocity of a glacier increases directly with the steepness of its bed. He postulated that a glacier is a viscous body whose movement is due to the mutual pressure of its parts.

Forbes energetically supported the scientific institutions of his time. He served as secretary of the Royal Society of Edinburgh from 1840 to 1851, and he was obliged to decline its presidency in 1867 and that of the British Association in 1864 owing to ill health. He was a corresponding member of many European scientific societies, and he carried on a voluminous correspondence with the leading scientists of the British Isles and Europe. During his tenure at Edinburgh, Forbes sought successfully to reform the Scottish system of higher education by instituting examinations for degrees. He resigned from his chair at Edinburgh in 1860 after his election as principal of the United College of St. Andrews, a position he held until his death.

BIBLIOGRAPHY

I. ORIGINAL WORKS. Forbes's works include *Address to the British Association, 4th General Meeting at Edinburgh* (Edinburgh, 1834); *Travels Through the Alps of Savoy* (Edinburgh, 1843); *The Dangers of Superficial Knowledge* (London, 1849); *Norway and Its Glaciers* (Edinburgh, 1853); "A Review of the Progress of Mathematical and Physical Science in More Recent Times, and Particularly Between the Years 1775 and 1850," in *Encyclopaedia Britannica,* 8th ed. (London, 1853; repr. separately, Edinburgh, 1858); and *Occasional Papers on the Theory of Glaciers* (Edinburgh, 1859).

Forbes also published over 100 scientific papers. His extensive incoming and outgoing correspondence, several journals and notebooks, and his competent watercolors of Alpine landscapes are in the archives of the University of St. Andrews.

II. SECONDARY WORKS. See J. C. Shairp, P. G. Tait, and A. Adams-Reilly, *The Life and Letters of James David Forbes* (London, 1873); John Tyndall, *Principal Forbes and His Biographers* (London, 1873); and George E. Davie, *The Democratic Intellect: Scotland and Her Universities in the Nineteenth Century* (Edinburgh, 1961).

JOHN G. BURKE

FORBES, STEPHEN ALFRED (*b.* Silver Creek, Stephenson County, Illinois, 29 May 1844; *d.* Urbana, Illinois, 13 March 1930), *biology.*

The fifth of the six children of Isaac Forbes and Agnes Van Hoesen, Stephen A. Forbes was raised on a farm in relative poverty. When Stephen was ten, Isaac Forbes died and the elder son, Henry, supported the family. After a year at Beloit Academy, Stephen accompanied Henry into the cavalry on the Union side in the Civil War. Forbes later regarded these years of military service, from September 1861 to November 1865, including four months as a prisoner of war, as a valuable stimulus to his education.

After three years of studying medicine, Forbes decided to study natural history. He supported himself by teaching school in various Illinois towns between 1868 and 1872. Attending the Illinois State Normal University only briefly, Forbes pursued the study of natural history on his own. He married Clara Shaw Gaston in 1873 and had five children. The family was Unitarian, Forbes having moved from the orthodox religion of his childhood to a scientific agnosticism. Throughout his life Forbes was physically and mentally energetic and healthy, enjoying variety in exercise and in reading.

In 1872 he was made curator of the Museum of the State Natural History Society, Normal, Illinois, which he transformed into the Illinois State Laboratory of Natural History in 1877. The laboratory and museum were moved to Urbana when he became a professor at the University of Illinois. This was in 1884, the same year he received his Ph.D. from the University of Indiana. Forbes was appointed state entomologist in 1882. The Office of the Entomologist and the State Laboratory of Natural History were combined when the State Natural History Survey was created. Forbes was chief of the Survey until his death. Forbes's earliest love had been botany, but his first professional concern was how best to teach natural history in the public schools. He was active in the campaign, led by Louis Agassiz, for laboratory and field work. Forbes's first major research was a series of studies of the stomach contents of birds and fish that he collected in Illinois. Naturalists had, of course, made scattered notes of what a particular animal was observed to eat, but Forbes undertook a systematic program to determine directly, often by microscopic examination, what foods had been eaten and in what proportion. He became an authority not only on birds and fish but on the insects and crustacea that they ate. Throughout his career he maintained an interest in limnology, establishing a floating laboratory in the Illinois River in 1894. After his appointment as state entomologist in 1882, most of Forbes's work concerned insects harmful to agriculture. Highly respected in this field, he was president of the American Association of Economic Entomologists in 1893 and 1908, president of the Entomological Society of America in 1912, and elected to the National Academy of Sciences in 1918.

The scientific work of Stephen Alfred Forbes was dominated by his interest in ecology. From the outset he was concerned to investigate scientifically, and quantitatively where possible, the interrelations that make a group of individuals into a functioning system. His viewpoint was clearly and explicitly based upon that of Charles Darwin and Herbert Spencer. He studied the food of fish and birds because he saw the predator-prey relation as the most direct ecological link between species. He expected such studies to help explain not only the geographical distribution and abundance of a species but also its evolution. Forbes found in these studies considerably less specialization than expected, although there were characteristic differences in the proportion of various foodstuffs consumed by each species. The fact that each prey species had many enemies revealed the complexity of the system. Forbes decided that the oscillations in number inherent in a simple predator-prey relation, well described by Spencer (*Principles of Biology,* II, 399), would be damped when these relations were more complex, and he interpreted lack of specialization as an evolutionary adaptation to avoid harmful oscillations. Forbes also found that structural factors were correlated with feeding habits only in a very general sense. The physical adaptation of predator and prey seemed less exact than Darwinists assumed, while the invisible "psychological" factor of food preference, presumed heritable, responded to natural selection.

Spencer had described the stable balance generally found in nature as the result of a physiological law governing reproductive energies, for he thought natural selection unable to produce the necessary mutual adjustment of reproductive rates. But Forbes suggested that natural selection could act on the predator-prey pair as a unit, requiring them to achieve a profitable adjustment to each other or both lose out in the struggle for existence. These apparent enemies have, he said, a common interest. Forbes believed that in the isolated and constant environment of certain lakes, the assemblage of species was "sensible," that is, the entire system was sensitive to whatever affects one species; the assemblage is like an organism composed of interdependent organs. In the microcosm of a lake, the entire complex of species had a "community of interest," so that natural selection would tend to produce maximum productivity and stability of the whole.

Forbes repeated these ideas from his 1880 articles, in a somewhat popularized form, in a lecture read to the Scientific Association of Peoria, Illinois, on 25 February 1887. This lecture, "The Lake as a Microcosm," was later hailed as a minor classic by ecologists for its early statement of the concept of community. Karl Moebius' 1877 booklet on oysters (published in English in 1883) has been similarly hailed. The idea Moebius embodied in his definition of biocoenosis was that an area would hold a given sum of life, so that should the number of oysters be reduced, the number of mussels or other species would increase to maintain the sum.

In 1907 Forbes reviewed his data of thirty years of collecting fish, with the idea of analyzing statistically the geographic distribution of different species. The probability of cooccurrence of two species was predicted from their independent frequencies in his collection; comparing this with their actual cooccurrence yielded his so-called coefficient of association. He applied a similar analysis to data collected in a special survey of birds, giving mathematical expressions for the preference of different species for different types of fields. He had wondered in 1878 whether closely related species living together ever competed for the same food; in 1884 he had described how species of insects feeding on the strawberry plant avoid direct competition by separation in time; in 1907 he hoped to use his coefficient of association to uncover "evasions of competition, and the escape from its consequences, by those closely related and similarly endowed . . ." ("On the Local Distribution of Certain Illinois Fishes," in *Bulletin of the Illinois State Laboratory of Natural History,* 7 [1907], 275). Modern ecologists likewise find the competitive exclusion principle a fruitful basis for research.

While his understanding of the "sensibility" of an assemblage led him to warn of unwanted results if farmers and fishermen tried to alter the balance of nature with inadequate knowledge, his view of the flexibility of natural systems made him hopeful that man could learn how to alter the balance in his favor without disaster. For example, beginning in 1882 Forbes studied the natural diseases of insect pests in the hope of controlling them biologically rather than chemically. He interpreted the agricultural problems with which he dealt as state entomologist as a lack of adjustment of plant and insect, characteristic of the first, primitive stage of association, when evolution had not yet produced mutual adaptation.

In 1859 Darwin had plainly shown not only the possibility of explicitly analyzing the dependencies of organisms but indeed that such an analysis, along with the laws of variation and inheritance, was the key to the origin of species. Yet the existing momentum of academic biology made comparative anatomy, embryology, and paleontology the fields for evolutionary studies, while ecology, like genetics, became well established only in this century. To the modern ecologist Forbes therefore seems remarkably ahead of his time, for he worked on questions not widely appreciated until twenty or thirty years later. What is perhaps more remarkable is that the science of ecology, whose problems and methods had been so clearly defined in the 1880's, had such a long gestation period.

BIBLIOGRAPHY

I. Original Works. Most of Forbes's work appeared in the various publications of the Office of the Illinois State Entomologist, the Illinois State Laboratory of Natural History, the Agricultural Experiment Station of the University of Illinois, and the Illinois State Natural History Survey. An extensive bibliography of his scientific articles, compiled by H. C. Oesterling, is given in *Biographical Memoirs. National Academy of Sciences,* **15** (1934), 26–54.

I have referred particularly to the following: "The Food of Birds," in *Transactions of the Illinois State Horticultural Society,* **10** (1877), 37–44; "The Food of Illinois Fishes," in *Bulletin of the Illinois State Laboratory of Natural History,* **1,** no. 2 (1878), 71–89; "Studies of the Food of Birds, Insects, and Fishes, Made at the Illinois State Laboratory of Natural History, at Normal, Illinois," the subtitle given to no. 3 (1880) and no. 6 (1883) of the same journal.

Among his articles on insects affecting the strawberry is "On the Life-histories and Immature Stages of Three Eumolpini," in *Psyche,* **4** (1884), 123–140. "The Lake as a Microcosm" was published in the first and only volume of the *Bulletin of the Scientific Association of Peoria, Illinois,* pp. 77–87, and reprinted in *Bulletin of the Illinois State Natural History Survey,* **15** (1925), 537–550. "Preliminary Report Upon the Invertebrate Animals Inhabiting Lakes Geneva and Mendota, Wisconsin, With an Account of the Fish Epidemic in Lake Mendota in 1884," is *Bulletin of the United States Fish Commission,* **8** (1890), 473–487.

See also "Summer Opening of the Biological Experiment Station of the University of Illinois," a pamphlet published by the University of Illinois (1896), 24 pp.; "On the Local Distribution of Certain Illinois Fishes: An Essay in Statistical Ecology," in *Bulletin of the Illinois Laboratory of Natural History,* **7** (1907), 273-303; "An Ornithological Cross-section of Illinois in Autumn," *ibid.,* 305–335; and "History of the Former State Natural History Societies of Illinois," in *Science,* **26** (1907), 892–898.

The third *Report on the Natural History Survey of the State of Illinois* (1909) is a monograph by S. A. Forbes and R. E. Richardson entitled *The Fishes of Illinois;* the 2nd ed. of this book was published in 1920.

Of additional interest are "Aspects of Progress in Economic Entomology," in *Journal of Economic Entomology,* **2** (1909), 25–35; "The General Entomological Ecology of the Indian Corn Plant," in *American Naturalist,* **43** (1909), 286–301; and "The Ecological Foundations of Applied Entomology," in *Annals of the Entomological Society of America,* **8** (1915), 1–19.

A posthumously published autobiographical note, written in 1923, is "Stephen Alfred Forbes," in *Scientific Monthly,* **30** (1930), 475–476.

II. Secondary Literature. The fullest account of Forbes is Leland Ossian Howard, in *Biographical Memoirs. National Academy of Sciences,* **15** (1934), 3–54. This incorporates material from the autobiography cited above, from a memorial pamphlet published by the University of Illinois in 1930, and from an obituary by Henry Baldwin Ward, "Stephen Alfred Forbes—A Tribute," in *Science,* n.s. **71** (1930), 378-381.

Mary P. Winsor

FORCHHAMMER, JOHAN GEORG (*b.* Husum, Denmark, 26 July 1794; *d.* Copenhagen, Denmark, 14 December 1865), *geology, oceanography, chemistry.*

Forchhammer was the son of Johan Ludolph Forchhammer, an educator, and Margrethe Elisabeth Wiggers. The elder Forchhammer was a teacher at the Citizens' School in Husum and later became rector of a similar school at Tønder and manager of the teachers' college.

Forchhammer's early education was at the schools in Husum and Tønder. Following the death of his father in 1810, he became an apprentice in a pharmacy at Husum, where he stayed for five years. In 1815 he enrolled at the University of Kiel, studying physics, chemistry, pharmacy, mathematics, and mineralogy. He went to Copenhagen in 1818 and became involved in an investigation of the coal and iron layers of Bornholm, a rocky island in the Baltic. The investigating commission included Hans Oersted, at that time lecturing in physics and chemistry at the University of Copenhagen, and Councillor of Justice L. Esmarch. In 1819 he enrolled at the University of Copenhagen, and upon completion of his thesis "De mangano," he received the doctorate in 1820.

Also in 1820 Forchhammer made a trip to England to further his understanding of geology, and there he became acquainted with such scientists as Prout, Davy, Dalton, Wollaston, Jameson, and Lyell. Together with Sir Walter C. Trevelyan he investigated the geology and coal formations of the Faeroe Islands; the resulting publication led to his becoming a member of the Royal Danish Academy of Sciences.

In 1821 Forchhammer became a lecturer in geology at the University of Copenhagen and also accepted employment at the Royal Copenhagen porcelain factory. Upon the opening of the Polytechnic Institute he became professor of chemistry and mineralogy and manager of one of its two chemical laboratories. He held this position until his death, and during the last fourteen years he was director of the institute. In 1831 Forchhammer was appointed professor of mineralogy and geology at the University of Copenhagen. From 1851 to his death he was secretary of the Royal Danish Academy of Sciences.

Forchhammer's fundamental researches on the composition of seawater brought him international acclaim. He began this work in 1843, more as a geologist than as a chemist, to explain the phenomena that give rise to the deposits on the sea floor. His immediate goals were the factors governing the marine precipitation of calcium carbonate and the influence of volcanic activity on the oceans. He carried out analyses of over 160 samples collected for him over a twenty-year period by the Danish and British navies. He measured chlorine, sulfur, magnesium, calcium, and potassium gravimetrically with 100-pound samples, obtaining sodium from the differences.

The principal consequence of this work was the proposition that although seawaters exhibit marked regional differences in total salt content, the ratios of the major dissolved constituents to each other are almost invariable. With but slight modifications this concept is valid today. Forchhammer also posed in an elegant form the "geochemical balance problem" arising from the major sedimentary cycle: "Thus the quantity of the different elements in sea water is not proportional to the quantity of elements which river water pours into the sea, but inversely proportional to the facility with which the elements are made insoluble by general or organo-chemical action in the sea." He reached this conclusion by noting that although calcium and silicon were often the principal constituents of river waters, they were less plentiful in the oceans. He correctly attributed the decrease in silicon to its incorporation into the skeletal material of the photosynthesizing diatoms but erroneously believed that calcium concentrations were regulated by carbonate-depositing animals.

Forchhammer's pioneering efforts in Danish geology earned him the appellation "the father of Danish geology." His fundamental work, *Danmarks geognostiske Forhold* (1835), was the first work on the structural geology of that country. This work and such other important investigations as those on the weathering of feldspars to clay minerals and the influences of biological materials upon the development of alums were always tinged with chemical insights. Forchhammer strengthened his arguments with chemical analyses. For example, he pointed out that trace quantities of heavy metals were present in almost all rocks as a result of their mobility in groundwaters circulating through fissures. His interest in soil chemistry extended to soil's effect on the growth of plants. As a member of several commissions of the Royal Danish Academy he investigated the origins of the "kitchen middens" along the Danish shores together with zoologists and archaeologists.

BIBLIOGRAPHY

I. Original Works. Forchhammer published about 200 papers on geological and chemical subjects. *Om Sövandets Bestanddele* (Copenhagen, 1859) was translated into English as "On the Components of Sea Water" and published in *Philosophical Transactions of the Royal Society,* **155** (1865), 203–262. His treatise *Danmarks geognostiske Forhold* was published as a University of Copenhagen Report in 1835. He was also the author of several chemical textbooks.

II. Secondary Literature. See S. A. Andersen, in *Dansk biografisk Leksikon,* VII (1935); Axel Garboe, "Fra myte til videnskab," in *Geologiens historie i Danmark,* 2 vols. (1959–1961); Hans Pauly, "G. Forchhammer, en af geokemiens pionerer," in *Naturens verden* (1967), pp. 24–32; I, 204–213, 224–246; and Johannes Steenstrup, "Forchhammer som menneske og personlighed," in *Meddelelser fra Dansk geologisk Forening,* **8** (1935), 438–476.

Edward D. Goldberg

FORDOS, MATHURIN-JOSEPH (*b.* Sérent, France, 3 November 1816; *d.* Paris, France, 1 July 1878), *chemistry.*

Fordos studied pharmacy in Paris, completed an internship in hospital pharmacy, and for the remainder of his professional career directed pharmacy services at three Paris municipal hospitals: Midi (1841–1842), Saint-Antoine (1842–1859), and Charité (1859–1878). A friendship with Amédée Gélis, a fellow pharmacy intern, led to many years of scientific collaboration. Fordos and Gélis were among a group of hospital pharmacy interns who in 1838 founded the Société d'Émulation pour les Sciences Pharmaceutiques, which for several decades provided an important scientific outlet for young pharmacy students serving internships in the Paris hospitals.

The bulk of Fordos's scientific work was carried on jointly with Gélis, who later made a career in industrial chemistry. The two were especially successful in their investigation of inorganic sulfur compounds. In 1842 they published their discovery of sodium tetrathionate, and in 1850 they elucidated the composition of sulfur nitride.

Of the several investigations which Fordos pursued alone, the most important was his chemical isolation of a blue crystalline pigment from purulent bandages, which he called pyocyanine and which Carle Gessard showed in 1882 to be produced by *Pseudomonas pyocyanea* (*Pseudomonas aeruginosa*). Fordos's procedure for obtaining pyocyanine and his description of its physical properties were published in 1860, and by 1863 he was able to perfect his method of extraction and obtain a much greater yield of this substance.

Noteworthy also was Fordos's contribution to public health aspects of lead toxicity. From 1873 to 1875 he conducted experiments showing that drinking water passing through lead pipes, as well as liquids stored in tin-lead alloy utensils, would absorb toxic amounts of lead. His interest in this problem led him to devise and publish (1875) a rapid industrial process for detecting lead in pots and vessels lined with tin.

BIBLIOGRAPHY

I. ORIGINAL WORKS. Among Fordos's most important publications dealing with inorganic compounds of sulfur, written jointly with Gélis, are the following: "Sur un nouvel oxacide du soufre," in *Comptes rendus hebdomadaires des séances de l'Académie des sciences,* **15** (1842), 920–923; and "Sur le sulfure d'azote," *ibid.,* **31** (1850), 702–705. For Fordos's isolation of pyocyanine, see "Recherches sur la matière colorante des suppurations bleues: pyocyanine," *ibid.,* **51** (1860), 215–217; and "Recherches sur les matières colorantes des suppurations bleues: pyocyanine et pyoxanthose," *ibid.,* **56** (1863), 1128–1131.

Representative of Fordos's papers on lead toxicity and the chemical detection of lead are "Action de l'eau aérée sur le plomb," *ibid.,* **77** (1873), 1099–1102; "Action de l'eau de Seine et de l'eau de l'Ourcq sur le plomb," *ibid.,* 1186–1188; "Du rôle des sels dans l'action des eaux potables sur le plomb," *ibid.,* **78** (1874), 1108–1111; "De l'action des liquides alimentaires ou médicamenteux sur les vases en étain contenant du plomb," *ibid.,* **79** (1874), 678–680; "De l'essai des étamages contenant du plomb; procédé d'essai rapide," *ibid.,* **80** (1875), 794–796. A comprehensive listing of Fordos's publications is given in Albert Goris *et al., Centenaire de l'internat en pharmacie des hôpitaux et hospices civils de Paris* (Paris, 1920), pp. 374–376.

II. SECONDARY LITERATURE. See Albert Goris, *op. cit.,* pp. 374, 805; and J. R. Partington, *A History of Chemistry,* IV (London–New York, 1964), 84, 391, 925.

ALEX BERMAN

FOREL, AUGUSTE-HENRI (*b.* near Morges, Switzerland, 1 September 1848; *d.* Yvorne, Switzerland, 27 July 1931), *medicine, neurology, entomology.*

Forel was fascinated very early by the life of insects and particularly by that of ants. Somewhat against his own desires, he studied medicine at the University of Zurich, registering in 1866. Attracted by the courses and clinical studies in psychiatry, he devoted himself to psychology but maintained a never-failing interest in the natural sciences. He became a friend of the famous botanist and paleontologist Oswald Heer, the specialist on Tertiary flora. Later, Forel went to Vienna to work on his thesis on the anatomy of the brain, under the guidance of Theodor Meynert. In 1872 he received his doctorate in medicine. Later that year Forel moved to Munich to work with B. A. von Güdden, who had been one of his teachers in Zurich and whose reputation as a brain specialist was international. In 1877 Forel returned to Zurich, where he was appointed *Privatdozent* at the university. He turned increasingly to psychiatry and in 1879 became professor of psychiatry at the University of Zurich Medical School. At the same time he took on the directorship of the important Burghölzli Clinic. Troubled by the effects of alcoholism, in 1889 he established the Asile d'Ellikon, which became one of the first institutions to treat alcoholics medically and give them the means of reestablishing themselves in society. In 1893 Forel retired prematurely and was thus able to devote himself without distraction to his first interest, the study of ants, as well as to problems concerning social reforms.

Although professionally Forel was one of the important psychiatrists of the last century, he is primarily known as an ant specialist. When very young he went on a study trip to southern Switzerland; the published results of his observations at once brought him high repute as an entomologist and earned him the Schläfli Foundation Prize. As an anatomist Forel studied the internal morphology of ants carefully and thus came to propose a new taxonomy of these members of the order Hymenoptera. In addition, having become engrossed in the psychology of these insects, he contributed greatly to the study of their social instincts. Forel was the first to describe the phenomena of parabiosis and lestobiosis in ants. Having gathered a considerable collection of hymenoptera he described the various species, finding more than 3,500 new ones. Thus he became a remarkable taxonomist.

Forel was also a great brain specialist. While in Munich, under the guidance of Güdden, he was the first to achieve histological preparations of human brain specimens. His specialized studies of particular brain regions made Forel a master of the development of the nervous system's microscopic anatomy. He made remarkable studies of the topography of the trigeminal, pneumogastric, and hypoglossal nerves and gave such a precise description of the hypothalamus that one of its regions was later named the campus Foreli in his honor.

Forel's teaching in Zurich, the direction of his clinic, and his interest in psychology led him to effect innumerable reforms that not only influenced psychiatry in Switzerland but brought about important changes in the penal code. His publications on alcoholism made him one of the pioneers in this field. He himself practiced complete abstinence, as an example, and fought in every way possible the effects of alcoholism on the working classes. Research on hypnotism also fascinated him, and he wrote many papers on that subject. A hygienist as well, Forel published the important book *La question sexuelle,* which was translated into nearly twenty languages.

BIBLIOGRAPHY

I. ORIGINAL WORKS. Forel's writings include *La question sexuelle* (Paris, 1905; 5th ed., Paris, 1922); *L'activité psychique* (Geneva, 1919); *Les fourmis de la Suisse* (La Chaux-de-Fonds, 1920); and *Le testament d'A. Forel* (Lausanne, 1931).

II. SECONDARY LITERATURE. On Forel and his work, see E. Bugnion, "A. Forel. Souvenirs myrmécologiques recueillis," in *Mitteilungen der Schweizerischen entomologischen Gesellschaft,* **15** (1931), 156; H. Kutter, "Verzeichnis des entomologischen Arbeiten von A. Forel," *ibid.,* **15** (1931), 180; A. Von Muralt, "A. Forel," in *Schweizerische medizinische Jahrbuch* (1929), p. 6; and E. Schwiedland, *Bibliographia Foreliana* (Vienna, 1908).

P. E. PILET

FORSSKÅL (also **FORSSKÅHL** or **FORSKÅL**), **PETER** (*b.* Helsinki, Finland [then Sweden], 11 January 1732; *d.* Yarīm, Yemen, 11 July 1763), *botany.*

Forsskål was one of Linnaeus' most gifted pupils and had an unusually broad spectrum of interests. During his university years—1751–1753 in Uppsala, 1753–1756 in Göttingen, and 1756–1760 back in Uppsala—he did not confine himself to natural history; he also mastered economics and philosophy, theology, and the Oriental languages. The combination of knowledge of Arabic and botany made Forsskål unusually suited for the scientific expedition that led to both his fame and his death. In Denmark, under the sponsorship of King Frederick V, a major research voyage to Arabia was planned; its large scientific staff was to include a naturalist, an astronomer, a philologist, a physician, and an artist. Forsskål was accepted as a member of the expedition, received the title of professor, and moved to Copenhagen in 1760. In January 1761 the expedition departed; traveling via Marseilles, Malta, and Constantinople, it reached Egypt that autumn. In October 1762 the voyage continued toward southern Arabia, where Forsskål worked to complete his collections until his death from malaria in July 1763.

Forsskål's contribution to botany consists of a single work: the *Flora aegyptiaco-arabica,* which was saved for posterity by the only surviving member of the expedition, Carsten Niebuhr, and was published at Copenhagen in 1775. This work is of importance both for the greatly increased knowledge it provided about the vegetation in the areas visited (Forsskål proposed fifty new genera, half of which are still valid) and for the valuable and original morphological observations that are often found in the descriptions of the species. But today Forsskål's fame is based mainly upon the introduction to the *Flora,* in which he surveys the phytogeography of Egypt. By comparing the Scandinavian and the Egyptian flora he gave a precise characterization of Egyptian vegetation and clarified its relation to climate and soil. In this respect he can be seen as an often unfairly neglected precursor of Alexander von Humboldt.

BIBLIOGRAPHY

I. ORIGINAL WORKS. Forsskål's most important publication in botany is *Flora aegyptiaco-arabica sive descriptiones plantarum quas per Aegyptum inferiorum et Arabiam felicem detexit, illustravit,* Carsten Niebuhr, ed. (Copenhagen, 1775). A MS of a more general character was published in Swedish as *Resa till lyckige Arabien* (Uppsala, 1950).

II. SECONDARY LITERATURE. On Forsskål or his work, see C. Christensen, *Naturforskeren Per Forskål. Hans rejse til Aegypten og Arabien 1761–63 og hans botaniske arbejder og samlinger* (Copenhagen, 1918); B. Hildebrand and E. Matinolli, "Peter Forsskål," in *Svensk biografiskt lexikon,* XVI (Stockholm, 1965), 359–362; and E. Matinolli, *Petter Forsskål* (Turku, 1960), in Finnish, with a summary in German.

GUNNAR ERIKSSON

FORSTER, (JOHANN) GEORG ADAM (*b.* Nassenhuben [or Nassenhof], near Danzig, Germany [now Gdansk, Poland], 27 November 1754; *d.* Paris, France, 10 January 1794), *natural philosophy, geography.*

Forster was the oldest son of Johann Reinhold Forster and Justina Elisabeth Forster. A precocious child, he was first educated by his father and acquired from him a lively and practical interest in natural history, as well as a thorough grounding in the numerous philological disciplines and languages which Johann Reinhold had mastered. In 1765 he accompanied his father on the survey of the German colonies on the Volga steppes and, for a short period while in Russia, attended the Petrisschule founded by the eminent geographer A. F. Büsching. In 1766 he went to England with his father and in 1767 published his first work, a translation of M. V. Lomonosov's history of Russia. By the age of thirteen he had a command of most of the major languages of Europe.

While his father was in Warrington, Lancashire, Forster was apprenticed to a merchant in London. In the autumn of 1767 he joined his father at the Dissenters' Academy, where he continued his own studies and assisted with the instruction. He also aided his father in the translation of Bougainville's *Voyage autour du monde.* When the elder Forster received the commission to sail on Cook's second voyage (1772–1775), he insisted that his son accompany him as assistant and artist. Afterward the younger Forster published his first major work, *A Voyage Round the World* (London, 1777). As a result of this work, issued without official sanction, Forster became engaged in a spirited polemic with William Wales, the astronomer on the voyage, over the ethics of publishing an independent narrative in defiance of the Admiralty. The *Voyage,* although deliberately lacking the systematic and scholarly presentation of geographic and scientific material found in his father's *Observations,* started a new genre of literary-scientific travel narratives, a genre ably developed later by Alexander von Humboldt, whom Forster influenced greatly by his work and ideas. In 1776 the Forsters issued *Characteres generum plantarum,* and in 1777 the younger Forster was elected a fellow of the Royal Society.

Although his preference was to continue his studies in England, Forster was forced by his family's circumstances to seek positions for himself and his father in Germany, and in 1779 he was appointed professor of natural history at the Collegium Carolinium in Kassel. He was soon in contact with the prominent men of science and letters in Germany, including J. F. Blumenbach, G. C. Lichtenberg, and S. T. Sömmering. Forster was particularly attracted by the intellectual climate of Göttingen. In 1784 he was appointed to the chair of natural history at Vilna, Poland, and the following year he married Therese Heyne, daughter of the eminent Göttingen philologist C. G. Heyne. Forster collaborated with Lichtenberg in editing and writing the *Göttingisches Magazin der Wissenschaften und Litteratur,* and he also published extensively in the *Göttingische Anzeigen von gelehrten Sachen.*

In Vilna, although isolated from the mainstream of European thought, Forster strove to correspond with men of science throughout Europe. In 1786 he published his M.D. dissertation (conferred by Halle), *De plantis esculentis insularum Oceani Australis commentatio botanica* (Berlin–Halle) and *Florulae insularum Australium prodromus* (Göttingen). The latter work was seen by Forster as the basis for a more comprehensive botanical work on the Pacific area, the "Icones plantarum in itinere ad insulas Maris Australis . . . ." He also intended to publish a major study of European exploration in the Pacific. In 1787 Forster published at Göttingen *Fasciculas plantarum Magellanicarum* and *Plantae Atlanticae.* J. D. Hooker, in his later work on the botany of the *Erebus* and *Terror* voyages, drew critically on the work of the Forsters, who in turn were indebted to Daniel Solander, Cook's *Endeavour* botanist. Apart from his botanical work Forster's main contributions to the natural history of Cook's second voyage were his drawings and, later, his philosophical and geographic essays. In 1786 he engaged in a polemic with Kant over his theory of the origins of man.

In 1787, prevented by war from taking up an appointment as naturalist to a Russian expedition, Forster returned to Göttingen; and in October 1788 he was appointed librarian at the University of Mainz. Between March and July 1790, accompanied by Humboldt, he traveled to England via the Rhineland and the Low Countries. His most important prose work, *Ansichten vom Niederrhein* (Berlin, 1791–1794), was a penetrating account of his journey with Humboldt. During the Mainz period his interest and writing turned more to social history and politics. He became absorbed in the French administration which governed Mainz from October 1792. In March 1793, Forster went as a Rhineland deputy to the National Convention in Paris, where he died of illness aggravated by scurvy contracted during the *Resolution* voyage.

Forster wrote of himself in 1789: "Natural science in its broadest sense and particularly anthropology have been my occupation hitherto. What I have written since my voyage is closely related to that." Cook's voyages opened up new areas of investigation to men of science in Europe. Forster, the universal scholar, was a remarkable apologist for the new era of scientific discovery. Fully alive to all the great movements of his day and in contact with the most eminent men in Germany and abroad, Forster, who had been well schooled by his father, did much to convey to the parochial world of German science and letters the significance of the great contemporary empirical advances in the geographic and biological sciences—in some of which disciplines German-speaking scientists were destined to have a profound influence in the ensuing century.

BIBLIOGRAPHY

I. Original Works. The most complete collection of Forster's writings, edited by Gerhard Steiner, is *Georg Forsters Werke, Sämtliche Schriften, Tagebücher, Briefe,* which is being published by the Deutsche Akademie der Wissenschaften zu Berlin (1958–). To date only vols. I-III, VII, and IX have appeared. Two earlier, smaller collections are L. F. Huber, ed., *Kleine Schriften. Ein Beytrag zur Völker- und Länderkunde, Naturgeschichte und Philosophie des Lebens,* 6 vols. (Leipzig, 1789-1797); and G. G. Gervinus, ed., *Georg Forster's Sämmtliche Schriften,* 9 vols. (Leipzig, 1843).

Collected eds. of some of Forster's prolific correspondence are Therese Huber, ed., *Johann Georg Forster's Briefwechsel nebst einigen Nachrichten von seinem Leben* (Leipzig, 1829); and H. Hettner, ed., *Georg Forster's Briefwechsel mit S. Th. Sömmering* (Brunswick, 1877). Summaries of some of his English letters are in Warren R. Dawson, ed., *The Banks Letters. A Calendar of the Manuscript Correspondence of Sir Joseph Banks . . .* (London, 1958). MSS copies of his scientific papers, correspondence, etc. are extant in many collections throughout Europe, North America, and Australasia.

A good bibliography is in Johann Georg Meusel, *Lexikon der vom Jahr 1750 bis 1800 verstorbenen Teutschen Schriftsteller,* III (Leipzig, 1804), 419–430; some individual works are listed in Poggendorff, I, 776.

II. Secondary Literature. Because of the universal nature of his work, Forster is cited by historians in many disciplines. He is also the subject of fictional writing. The fullest bibliography and assessment of his work are in Ludwig Uhlig, *Georg Forster. Einheit und Mannigfaltigkeit in seiner geistigen Welt* (Tübingen, 1965). Very little scholarly work on Forster is available in English: some appreciation of his science and writings can be found in E. D. Merrill, *The Botany of Cook's Voyages* (Waltham, Mass., 1954); and L. Bodi, in *Historical Studies, Australia and New Zealand,* **8** (1959), 345–363.

No satisfactory full-length biography of Forster exists. The standard note is still A. Dove, in *Allgemeine deutsche Biographie,* VII (1878), 173–181. Also useful is K. Karsten, *Der Weltumsegler* (Bern, 1957).

Michael E. Hoare

FORSTER, JOHANN REINHOLD (*b.* Dirschau [now Tczew], Poland, 22 October 1729; *d.* Halle, Germany, 9 December 1798), *natural philosophy, geography.*

Forster was descended from a landed Yorkshire family that had emigrated to Germany about 1642. He was educated at Marienwerder and Berlin in 1743–1748 and then, against his wishes, as a Reformed clergyman at the University of Halle in 1748–1751. He became pastor at Nassenhuben (or Nassenhof), near Danzig, in 1753.

Forster began to maintain a wide scientific correspondence with such men as the elder Linnaeus, Thomas Pennant, and, later, Joseph Banks. In 1765 he was commissioned by the Russian government to undertake a survey of the Saratov-Tsaritsyn region of the lower Volga. In 1766, deprived of advancement in Russia and of his pastorate in Prussia, Forster went to England and soon succeeded Joseph Priestley as a tutor at the Dissenters' Academy in Warrington, Lancashire, teaching natural history and classical and modern languages.

Forster became known in Britain through his scientific writing. He was asked by the Royal Society of London to describe a collection presented by the Hudson's Bay Company. His papers on zoology, ornithology, and ichthyology were published in the *Philosophical Transactions of the Royal Society* (1772, 1773). Reprinted by the Willughby Society in 1882, they were recognized as having been written by "one of the earliest authorities on North American zoology." He published *An Introduction to Mineralogy* in 1768; two years later he issued *A Catalogue of British Insects,* and in 1771 he published works on American flora and on entomology. He also worked on the translation and editing of works on North America by the itinerant naturalists Peter Kalm and Nicholas Bossu and on Asia by Petrus Osbeck. In 1772 he published an edited translation of Bougainville's *Voyage autour du monde.* On 27 February 1772 Forster was elected fellow of the Royal Society.

In June 1772 Forster and his son Georg, "gentlemen skilled in Natural history and Botany but more especially the former," were appointed with ten days' notice to H.M.S. *Resolution,* bound, under Captain James Cook, to search for the hypothetical southern continent. Linnaeus the elder commended Forster as an outstanding man for such a charge. At Cape Town, Forster took on as an assistant Anders Sparrman, one of Linnaeus' pupils. The Forsters returned with Cook in the summer of 1775.

The voyage included a great part of the Pacific basin. In 1776 the Forsters published *Characteres generum plantarum,* a small, hurried, and preliminary account of the botany of the voyage. The remainder of the botanical specimens were dealt with later by Georg in Germany and by Daniel Solander privately. Forster's most significant publication was *Observations Made During a Voyage Round the World* (1778), the sum of his work "on physical geography, natural history and ethnic philosophy." Forster read deeply in the science of his day, including the work of Buffon and Torbern Bergman; he was able to test armchair hypotheses empirically against the facts of the field. The *Observations* is a remarkable systematic study of oceanographic, geographic, and ethnographic problems in the infancy of those sciences, a study characterized by perceptive observation, analogy, and experimentation. Forster predicted the scope and methods of Alexander von Humboldt's work and, in the same region, investigated those phenomena (e.g., coral reefs and volcanoes) which Charles Darwin examined sixty years later on the *Beagle* voyage. Forster also influenced the work of Blumenbach and the growing science of comparative anthropology.

After moving to Halle in 1780 as professor of natural history and mineralogy, Forster published extensively on zoological subjects, many of them connected with the *Resolution* voyage. He was associated with Pennant in the translation and later editions of his *Indian Zoology.* From 1790 he edited the *Magazin von merkwürdigen neuen Reisebeschreibungen,* which did a great deal to introduce the results of important scientific voyages to the German public. Forster published a history of northern maritime discovery in 1784. In the year of his death he published an essay containing his thoughts on a future theory of the history of the earth.

In 1844 H. Lichtenstein published *Descriptiones animalium . . .,* the zoological work of the *Resolution* voyage, which has since been attributed to Forster without reservation.

The whole of Forster's scientific career was affected by a tragic quarrel with the British Admiralty. He was a man of pride and quick temper. The considerable scientific data assembled on the *Resolution* voyage was, for this reason, scattered throughout the world, and the scientific publications of the Forsters, although competent, were fragmentary and obscure. The real merit of Forster's work has often been overlooked by authors more zealous to describe his weaknesses of character than to appraise his contribution to science.

BIBLIOGRAPHY

I. Original Works. See bibliography in Johann Georg Meusel, *Lexikon der vom Jahr 1750 bis 1800 verstorbenen Teutschen Schriftsteller,* III (Leipzig, 1804), 430–439; and Poggendorff, I, 775–776.

No complete collection of Forster's works or papers exists. His unedited correspondence is scattered in Australasia, London, Germany, North America, and many European centers. Published works besides those cited in the text include *Florae Americae septentrionalis* (London, 1771); *Novae species insectorum centuria* (London, 1771); *Enchiridion historiae naturali inserviens . . .* (Halle, 1788); and numerous translations of accounts of voyages, with his own scientific appendixes and commentaries. He also contributed to a number of Continental scientific journals. His MS journal of his voyage (6 vols.) is in the Stiftung Preussischer Kulturbesitz, Berlin.

II. Secondary Literature. There is no biography of Forster. The best biographical note is A. Dove, in *Allgemeine deutsche Biographie,* VII (1878), 167–172. For his scientific work, see J. C. Beaglehole, ed., *The Voyage of the Resolution and the Adventure 1772–1775* (Cambridge, 1961), pp. xlii–xlix; and M. E. Hoare, "Johann Reinhold Forster, the Neglected 'Philosopher' of Cook's Second Voyage (1772–1775)," in *Journal of Pacific History,* **2** (1967), 215–224.

Michael E. Hoare

FORSYTH, ANDREW RUSSELL (*b.* Glasgow, Scotland, 18 June 1858; *d.* London, England, 2 June 1942), *mathematics.*

Forsyth was the son of John Forsyth, a marine engineer, and of Christina Glenn, of Paisley. The family moved to Liverpool, where Forsyth soon revealed his mathematical ability. He entered Trinity College, Cambridge, in 1877 and was senior wrangler in January 1881. He became a fellow of Trinity the same year with a remarkably powerful thesis on double theta functions. In 1882 he was appointed to the chair of mathematics at University College, Liverpool, but in 1884 he returned to Cambridge as a lecturer. He was elected a fellow of the Royal Society in 1886.

As a mathematician Forsyth belonged to the school of his Cambridge master, Cayley, and was outstanding in his ability to marshal complicated formulas. His importance in the history of British mathematics is due, however, to his being a great traveler and a good linguist; he was thus the first to realize the deficiencies of the Cambridge school, which was almost completely ignorant of Continental mathematics. Forsyth was determined to rectify this situation, and in 1893 he published his *Theory of Functions,* which, according to Sir Edmund Whittaker, "had a greater influence on British mathematics than any work since Newton's *Principia*." As a result, for many years function theory dominated Cambridge mathematics.

In 1895 Forsyth succeeded Cayley as Sadlerian professor of pure mathematics but resigned in 1910 in order to marry Marion Amelia Boys, the former wife of the physicist C. V. Boys. After a short time in Calcutta, he was appointed chief professor of mathematics at Imperial College, London, in 1913. Although he retired in 1923, he continued to write mathematical treatises; but his point of view was antiquated, his work being based on manipulative skill rather than on logical processes.

Ironically, Forsyth's main achievement was having brought to Cambridge the modern style of mathematics that superseded his own, and as a result his reputation in his later years was less than it deserved to be.

BIBLIOGRAPHY

I. ORIGINAL WORKS. Forsyth's most important books were *A Treatise on Differential Equations* (London, 1885; 6th ed., 1931), also trans. into German and Italian; *Theory of Differential Equations,* 6 vols. (Cambridge, 1890–1906); and *Theory of Functions of a Complex Variable* (Cambridge, 1893; 3rd ed., 1917). He also published *Lectures on the Differential Geometry of Curves and Surfaces* (Cambridge, 1912); *Lectures Introductory to the Theory of Functions of Two Complex Variables* (Cambridge, 1914); *Calculus of Variations* (Cambridge, 1927); *Geometry of Four Dimensions,* 2 vols. (Cambridge, 1930); and *Intrinsic Geometry of Ideal Space,* 2 vols. (London, 1935). He also contributed to British mathematical journals, *Proceedings of the Royal Society,* and other publications.

II. SECONDARY LITERATURE. Biographical notices are E. H. Neville, in *Journal of the London Mathematical Society,* **17** (1942), 237–256; and E. T. Whittaker, in *Obituary Notices of Fellows of the Royal Society of London,* **4** (1942–1944), 209–227. The latter contains a complete bibliography of Forsyth's writings. See also the article on Forsyth by E. T. Whittaker, in *Dictionary of National Biography,* supp. VI (1941–1950), 267–268.

G. J. WHITROW

FORTIN, JEAN NICOLAS (*b.* Mouchy-la-Ville, Île-de-France, France, 9 August 1750; *d.* Paris, France, 1831), *scientific instruments.*

Fortin was one of the most skilled precision mechanics and scientific instrument makers of his time. Lavoisier realized his potential and asked him, at the beginning of his career, to make several new laboratory instruments for him. Of special note is a precision balance made in 1788, which had an arm one meter long and was sensitive to weights as slight as 1/400 ounce. For the Commission of Weights and Measures he made a similar precision balance with the necessary weights, and another instrument to compare the dimensions of the cylinders that constituted the standards for weights. In 1799 Fortin adjusted the platinum kilogram standard that was deposited in the National Archives of France. He also made instruments for the Paris observatory.

Around 1800 Fortin made a barometer whose distinctive feature was the combination of a leather bag containing mercury, an ivory pointer indicating the zero point of the barometric scale, and a glass cylinder. By this simple combination Fortin made it possible to adjust the level of the mercury surface in the cylinder to coincide with zero on the scale. The device made transportation of barometers easier, and later any barometer in which the mercury could be adjusted to touch a point was known as a Fortin barometer.

Fortin devised many instruments that were used by scientists and engineers in famous experiments: the study of the expansion of gases by Gay-Lussac; the verification of the Boyle-Mariotte law at high pressures by Arago and Dulong; the triangulations between Barcelona and Formentera by Biot and Arago; and so on. He was a member of the Bureau des Longitudes, and in 1776 he reduced Flamsteed's *Atlas céleste* to about a third of its former length.

BIBLIOGRAPHY

Fortin's only publication was his edition of J. Flamsteed's *Atlas céleste* (Paris, 1776).

On his work, see M. Daumas, *Les instruments scientifiques aux XVIIe et XVIIIe siècles* (Paris, 1953), *passim.*

ASIT K. BISWAS
MARGARET R. BISWAS

FOSTER, HENRY (*b.* Wood Plumpton, England, August 1797; *d.* Chagres River, Isthmus of Panama, 5 February 1831), *geophysics.*

Henry Foster was involved with geophysical observations throughout his career in the British navy. Foster joined the Royal Navy in 1812. Early projects included surveys and, on a trip to South America with Captain Basil Hall, determination of the acceleration of gravity. In 1824 Foster was made lieutenant and became a fellow of the Royal Society. He performed most of his investigations while on expeditions to the Arctic in 1824–1825 and to the South Seas in 1828–1831. He spent the winter of 1824–1825 at Port Bowen, north of the Arctic Circle, as astronomer of an expedition led by Sir William Edward Parry; he studied geomagnetism, the velocity of sound, atmospheric refraction, and the acceleration of gravity. The Board of Longitude printed a detailed account of his observations.[1] In 1827 Foster received the rank of commander and the Copley Medal of the Royal Society for these researches. In the spring of 1828 he sailed to the South Seas as commander of a sloop sent on a geophysical expedition, at the suggestion of the Royal Society, to study geomagnetism, gravity, meteorology, and oceanography.

Foster was on many occasions occupied with the indirect measurement of the acceleration of gravity. The project, generally referred to as a determination of the length of a seconds pendulum, was popular at the time and was sponsored officially. Foster used the method recently devised by Henry Kater[2] and observed coincidences between a pendulum of known length and the pendulum of a clock whose rate is determined by astronomical transit measurements. The final object of the observations at various latitudes was a determination of the ellipticity of the earth.

Foster was interested primarily in observations and performed them carefully.[3] He had a minor interest in theory—he speculated, for example, on the source of the diurnal variation in the earth's magnetic field. He was in some contact with other scientists: at Port Bowen, for example, he repeated some of Samuel Christie's experiments at the latter's request.[4]

NOTES

1. Published as *Philosophical Transactions of the Royal Society,* **26,** pt. 4 (1826).
2. Henry Kater, "An Account of Experiments for Determining the Length of the Pendulum Vibrating Seconds in the Latitude of London," *ibid.,* **18** (1818), 33–109; "An Account of Experiments for Determining the Variation in the Length of the Pendulum Vibrating Seconds," *ibid.,* **19** (1819), 336–508.
3. Such was the opinion of Gerard Moll, "On Captain Parry's and Lieutenant Foster's Experiments on the Velocity of Sound," *ibid.,* **28,** pt. 1 (1828), 97–104.
4. Henry Foster, "Account of the Repetition of Mr. Christie's Experiments on the Magnetic Properties Imparted to an Iron Plate by Rotation . . .," *ibid.,* **26,** pt. 4 (1826), 188–199.

BIBLIOGRAPHY

I. Original Works. Foster's writings include "Experiments With an Invariable Pendulum," in *Edinburgh Philosophical Journal,* **10** (1824), 91–95, written with Basil Hall; "Account of Experiments Made With an Invariable Pendulum . . .," in *Philosophical Transactions of the Royal Society,* **26,** pt. 4 (1826), 1–70; "Magnetical Observations at Port Bowen," *ibid.,* 73–117, written with W. E. Parry; and "Observations on the Diurnal Changes in the Position of the Horizontal Needle . . .," *ibid.,* 129–176. For a complete listing of Foster's publications, see the Royal Society of London, *Catalogue of Scientific Papers, 1800–1863,* II (London, 1868), 673–674.

II. Secondary Literature. See Francis Baily, "Report on the Pendulum Experiments Made by the Late Captain Henry Foster, R.N., in His Scientific Voyage in the Years 1828–1831, With a View to Determine the Figure of the Earth," in *Memoirs of the Royal Astronomical Society,* **7** (1834), 1–378. An account of Foster's expedition of 1828–1830, written by the surgeon of the sloop, is William H. B. Webster, *Narrative of a Voyage to the Southern Atlantic Ocean,* 2 vols. (London, 1834); the appendix contains measurements made on the expedition (II, 211–253). See also *Annual Biography and Obituary,* XVI (London, 1832), 436–437; and *Proceedings of the Royal Society,* **3A** (1830–1837), 82.

Sigalia Dostrovsky

FOSTER, MICHAEL (*b.* Huntingdon, England, 8 March 1836; *d.* London, England, 28 January 1907), *physiology.*

Foster was descended from a well-known family of religious Nonconformists who had farmed for many generations in Hertfordshire and Bedfordshire. His father, also named Michael, broke the yeoman tradition and became a medical practitioner. From 1831 to 1833 the elder Michael Foster studied medicine at the University of London (later University College), where he won many prizes. He practiced at Huntingdon from 1833 and was created fellow of the Royal College of Surgeons in 1852. A fervent Baptist, he was a prominent religious and civic leader in Huntingdon.

The younger Michael Foster, the eldest of ten children, was educated at the local grammar school in Huntingdon until 1849, when he was sent to University College School in London. In 1852 he entered University College, from which he graduated B.A. in 1854, placing first on the honors list in classics and receiving the college scholarship in that faculty. Foster might have pursued a career in classics at the University of Cambridge, but religious tests prevented his competing for a fellowship there. Instead, he immediately entered the medical school at University College, where in 1856 he won gold medals in anatomy and physiology and in chemistry. He graduated M.B. in 1858 and M.D. in 1859, and spent part of the next two years studying clinical medicine in the Paris hospital schools.

In the autumn of 1860, after impairment of his health led to fears of consumption, Foster signed on as ship's surgeon of H.M.S. *Union,* which was bound for the Red Sea to take part in the building of a lighthouse near Mt. Sinai. He signed on partly for the sake of his health and partly in the hope of studying the natural history of the area. After his attempts to make such studies were repeatedly discouraged or prevented, he returned to Huntingdon in March 1861. His health remained uncertain for many years and contributed to his later decision to leave London for Cambridge. From 1861 to 1866 he practiced medicine with his father in Huntingdon, but during all this time he longed for a career in science.

In January 1867, at the invitation of William Sharpey, Foster became instructor in practical physiology and histology at University College. In 1869 he was promoted to a professorship in the same subject. Meanwhile he had established a course of laboratory instruction, including elementary experimental physiology, that was the first of its kind in England. Also in 1869 he was appointed Fullerian professor of physiology at the Royal Institution.

In May 1870, Foster was appointed to a newly established prelectorship in physiology at Trinity College, Cambridge. In choosing both physiology as the subject of the prelectorship and Foster as the man to fill it, the Trinity seniority followed the recommendation of Thomas Henry Huxley. Foster remained prelector at Trinity College until 1883, when he was chosen to occupy the first chair of physiology in the university. Upon his resignation in 1903, the chair went to his former student John Newport Langley.

When Foster arrived at Cambridge in 1870, the biological sciences and the medical school were largely moribund. Neither Charles Babington, professor of botany, nor Alfred Newton, professor of zoology, was particularly receptive to the movement toward laboratory training in biology, and both were indifferent teachers. From the first Foster was determined to change this situation and to build a great school of biology and physiology at Cambridge, even though his original position made him responsible only to Trinity College. Before teaching his first class, Foster obtained the consent of the Trinity seniority to open his course to all students in the university. The university responded by giving him the use of one small room, which was furnished with the basic necessities by Trinity College. This accommodation very soon proved inadequate as Foster attracted ever larger numbers of students to his courses in physiology and elementary biology. New buildings were completed in 1879 and 1891, but even these were becoming overcrowded by the time Foster retired. From 1870 to 1883, the number of students attending his courses in physiology grew from about twenty to 130, while the number attending his course in elementary biology grew from about forty-five at his initial class in 1873 to more than eighty in 1883. In that year Foster turned the latter course over to two of his former students, and enrollment continued to grow dramatically. He then concentrated on the courses in physiology, which were drawing about 300 students when he retired in 1903.

Like other great teachers, Foster is probably best remembered for his students, many of whom remained at Cambridge to develop the principles and programs he had inaugurated. On leaving London for Cambridge in 1870, Foster had invited his two favorite students at University College to join him. Edward Sharpey-Schafer declined, on his father's advice, and remained at University College as assistant and later successor to John Burdon-Sanderson in the Jodrell chair of physiology. H. Newell Martin joined Foster at Cambridge and served as his right-hand man until 1876, when he was called to the United States as first occupant of the chair in biology at the newly established Johns Hopkins University. Martin thus carried to America the methods of teaching he had learned from Foster and Huxley.

While at Cambridge, Foster attracted a group of students as remarkable for the breadth of their interests as for their later eminence. Apart from physiologists, they include the embryologist Francis Maitland Balfour; the biologist G. J. Romanes; the anthropologist A. C. Haddon; the psychologist C. S. Myers; the neurologist Henry Head; the pathologist J. G. Adami; the botanists S. H. Vines, F. O. Bower, and H. Marshall Ward; and the morphologists A. Milnes Marshall, Adam Sedgwick, D'Arcy Wentworth Thompson, and A. E. Shipley. Of these, Balfour, Vines, Haddon, Ward, Sedgwick, and Shipley became leading members of the Cambridge faculty; and through them Foster remained a living influence on Cambridge biology long after his own direct role had come to an end.

But Foster was above all else the founder of the Cambridge School of Physiology, and the eminent physiologists trained while he was there are his chief contributions to science. Three of his earliest students were John Langley, Walter Holbrook Gaskell, and Arthur Sheridan Lea. Except for brief periods of study in Germany, all three remained at Cambridge throughout their careers, and all three were elevated to university lectureships in physiology when Foster was appointed to the professorship in 1883. Especially through the work of Langley on glandular secretion, of Gaskell on heart action, and of both on the involuntary nervous system, Cambridge soon became recognized as one of the world's leading centers for physiological research.

The list of physiologists trained at Cambridge later in Foster's career is one of almost staggering eminence. It includes Charles Scott Sherrington (matriculated at Cambridge in 1879, major work on reflexes and the integrative action of the nervous system); W. B. Hardy (1884, colloid chemistry); Walter Morley Fletcher (1891, muscle metabolism); Joseph Barcroft (1893, blood gases, respiration, and homeostasis); Henry H. Dale (1894, chemical transmission of nerve impulses); T. R. Elliott (1896, sympathomimetic drugs); and Keith Lucas (1898, conduction of nerve impulses). Sherrington and Dale went on to win the Nobel Prize in physiology or medicine in 1932 and 1936, respectively. Hardy, Fletcher, Barcroft, and Lucas joined the staff at Cambridge, with Barcroft succeeding Langley as professor of physiology in 1925.

Because Foster epitomizes the concept of a great teacher, it is interesting to consider his approach and the reasons for his success. He owed much to William Sharpey, who taught him at University College and first aroused his interest in physiology, and to Thomas Huxley, who very early perceived the remarkable kinship of mind and spirit between Foster and himself. Both taught Foster that physiology should be viewed broadly, as one of the biological sciences, and both encouraged his appreciation of the experimental approach, although neither made much use of that approach in his own work. Of the two, Huxley's influence was the more lasting and profound.

Foster first met Huxley in 1856, when the latter examined him in anatomy and physiology at University College. From then on, Huxley was his main guide and chief agent. The two rarely, if ever, disagreed on any issue of substance, and their educational philosophies are virtually indistinguishable. Both Huxley and Foster insisted that science must take equal place with mathematics and classics in the English educational system, and both urged students to undertake original laboratory research at an early stage. There are even two striking parallels in the course of their careers: Foster succeeded Huxley as Fullerian professor of physiology in 1869 and as biological secretary of the Royal Society in 1881.

In the summer of 1871, when Huxley introduced a laboratory course in elementary biology to a group of schoolmasters at South Kensington, he selected Foster as the first of his demonstrators. After a second summer as Huxley's demonstrator, Foster established his own one-term course in elementary biology at Cambridge in 1873. Both courses were taught on evolutionary principles, with a very few organisms being dissected and studied as representative "types." Huxley's course, which was the model, is considered the origin of the modern method of teaching introductory biology. Foster's very similar course seems to have been the first such course taught in a true university setting. It illustrates his broadly biological approach to physiology and helps to explain the breadth of his influence on Cambridge biology and physiology, for Foster designed this course in such a way that it became the standard means by which students were introduced to all of the biological sciences at Cambridge. In this way he was able to exert an influence on students who became botanists or morphologists as well as on those who became physiologists.

Another important factor in Foster's success was that the University of Cambridge was in a state of transition when he arrived. After decades of defending the virtual monopoly enjoyed by mathematics and classics at Oxford and Cambridge, many Cambridge dons were ready at last to give a more sympathetic hearing to the advocates of science and other "modern" studies. It was an excellent opportunity for Foster, who had a clear vision of how much could be done and how to go about doing it. With the support of several influential allies, especially G. M. Humphry, professor of anatomy, and Coutts Trotter, a fellow of Trinity College who was a leading force in university administration, he pressed the claims of physiology upon the university with remarkable success for a mere collegiate lecturer. That this success depended in part on a new attitude in the university at large is suggested by the comparable success of the famous Cambridge School of Physics, whose development paralleled almost exactly that of the School of Physiology.

Foster's achievement at Cambridge depended also on his own great clarity of aim and charm of manner. Even more important was his capacity for inspiring others to undertake original research. Many of his students have testified that they chose a career in research only because Foster promoted the enterprise with so much enthusiasm and with such a sense of adventure. Because Foster's own contributions to original research were few and largely ignored, he has acquired a reputation as a discoverer of men rather than of facts, as a great teacher of research who did not himself practice what he so effectively taught. But it is crucial to recognize that Foster did engage in original research. Throughout his brief career in research, the problem of the heartbeat held a special fascination for him.

The issue to be settled about the heartbeat was whether it depended ultimately on nerve discharges or rather on an inherent rhythmicity in active cardiac muscle—in other words, whether the heartbeat was neurogenic or myogenic. When Foster began his work, the issue had apparently been decided in favor of the neurogenic theory, especially because a number of German investigators had found that in the vertebrate heart, nerve ganglia were concentrated precisely in those regions of the cardiac tissue where excision or ligature disturbed the spontaneous rhythm of the heartbeat.

In 1859 Foster found that even very tiny pieces cut from the beating heart of a snail continued to beat rhythmically for some time. But no ganglia had been found anywhere in the snail's heart; and even if they were there, it seemed impossible to Foster that they could be so widely diffused as to appear in each and every part of the heart. He therefore concluded that, in the snail at least, the rhythmic beat must depend not on nerve ganglia but on the inherent properties of the general cardiac tissue.

In 1869 Foster published his first challenge to the neurogenic theory in vertebrate hearts. He showed that the lower two-thirds of a frog's ventricle, where no ganglia were known to exist, could nonetheless be induced to rhythmic pulsations by direct application of an interrupted current of appropriate strength. He therefore argued that the frog's cardiac musculature, like the snail's, must possess an inherent tendency to rhythmic pulsation.

Returning in 1871 to the snail's heart, Foster showed that when weak currents were applied directly to its muscular tissue, the result was an inhibition exactly like that produced in the vertebrate heart by stimulating the vagus nerve. Since in the ganglion-free snail's heart this inhibition could not be the result of any nervous mechanisms, Foster attributed it instead to the direct effects of weak electrical currents on the fundamental properties of active contractile tissue.

Between 1875 and 1877 Foster published four papers on the heartbeat, three of them in collaboration with his student A. G. Dew-Smith. Two of these were elaborate extensions of Foster's own earlier work on the snail's heart and on the frog's. The third, in 1877, was written in reply to a German scientist's claim that he had detected ganglia in the snail's heart. Foster and Dew-Smith argued that what the German had taken for ganglia were in fact pyriform connective-tissue cells.

The fourth paper, by Foster alone, concerned the effects of the poison upas antiar on the frog's heart. He emphasized the remarkable effect that vagus stimulation produced in a heart thus poisoned. The eventual result was not the usual inhibition but an opposite accelerating effect, which increased as the influence of the poison increased. Again Foster rejected the idea that nerve ganglia were somehow responsible. Antiar was known to be a muscular poison, and if it were admitted that vagus inhibition also resulted from direct action on the cardiac musculature, then the marked acceleration eventually observable under their combined influence could be explained simply as an exaggerated reaction by the muscle tissue to a previously exaggerated inhibition.

In all of this, the general trend of Foster's conclusions is clear. The causes both of inhibition and of the rhythmic heartbeat itself were to be sought not in nerve ganglia but in the basic properties of contractile tissue. Less obvious, but very definitely present in two of the papers with Dew-Smith, is the evolutionary basis for Foster's conviction. Impressed by the rhythmic capacity of undifferentiated protoplasm—in amoebas, in ciliates, and in the simple snail's heart—he saw no reason why differentiated nerve ganglia should be necessary for the same function in higher organisms. Apart from some ambiguity about whether the general cardiac tissue was purely muscular or rather neuromuscular in character, the chief difficulty in Foster's scheme was his concession that in the frog (and presumably other vertebrates) the ganglia might serve to coordinate the sequence of beats. In the undifferentiated and ganglion-free snail's heart, Foster attributed coordination to a muscular sense inherent in the general cardiac tissue, so by his own evolutionary criteria, differentiated ganglia should not have been required to perform the same function in higher organisms.

By 1900 the myogenic theory had largely replaced the neurogenic, but Foster's work was for a long time generally ignored and was not itself greatly influential in changing the direction of the debate. It is nonetheless important for at least three reasons. First, it reveals Foster as a competent research physiologist and suggests that this experience may have been a crucial factor in his success as a teacher. Without some such experience, it seems unlikely that he could have promoted research so convincingly or that he could have developed the critical acumen so essential to a director of research. Second, the problem of the heartbeat was the starting point or focus for much of the research carried out by the Cambridge School of Physiology during its crucial early years. Under Foster's direction Lea, Langley, Romanes, Francis Darwin, and Gaskell were all attracted to the problem during the 1870's. Like Foster himself, Romanes and Gaskell saw the problem of the heartbeat as part of the more general problem of rhythmic motion, and they pursued the issues with significant success. Although the others rather quickly found different research interests, their work on the heart was crucial in establishing a research tradition in physiology at Cambridge. Third, Foster's work on the heart provides a concrete illustration of his broadly biological and evolutionary approach to physiology and suggests again that this approach may have contributed greatly to his success and to that of the embryonic Cambridge School of Physiology. This seems even more likely because Gaskell, who did more than anyone else to resolve the problem in favor of the myogenic theory, depended very heavily on the evolutionary approach he had learned from Foster.

Foster's impact on physiology and science extended far beyond his contributions as original investigator and as founder and director of the Cambridge School of Physiology. His name was attached to several important textbooks, including the pioneering *Handbook of the Physiological Laboratory,* edited by John Burdon-Sanderson (1873), for which he wrote the section on nerve and muscle; *The Elements of Embryology,* which he published with his student F. M. Balfour in 1874; and *A Course of Elementary Practical Physiology and Histology,* which he published with Langley's assistance in 1876. The first edition of his famous *Text-Book of Physiology* appeared in 1877. Distinguished for its literary style, balanced judgment, and evolutionary perspective, this work was translated into Russian, Italian, and German. It went through six complete editions and part of a seventh.

Foster was also the leading figure in the professionalization of physiology in Victorian England. A conspicuous opponent of popular antivivisection sentiment, he was largely responsible for the founding in 1876 of the British Physiological Society. In 1878 he founded the *Journal of Physiology,* which he edited until 1894.

As he became increasingly occupied with these and other organizational activities, Foster abandoned original research in physiology and delegated to former students most of the responsibility for teaching the advanced classes at Cambridge and for directing the day-to-day activities of the research laboratory. By about 1880 the shift was complete. Foster concentrated thereafter on elementary teaching and on exercising his talent for organization. At Cambridge he led the fight for the establishment of a school of scientific agriculture in the 1890's. In 1898 he induced Frederick Gowland Hopkins to join his staff at Cambridge as teacher of biological chemistry. Hopkins went on to become founder of the Cambridge School of Biochemistry and to share the Nobel Prize in physiology or medicine in 1929.

Foster became a leader as well in the national and international organization of science. At the Royal Society, of which he was elected fellow in 1872, he served as biological secretary from 1881 to 1903. In this influential and burdensome office he supported a wide range of scientific expeditions and was a vigorously successful advocate of a closer partnership between the Society and the government. He was vice-president of the Society in 1903–1904. He was also active in the affairs of the Royal Horticultural Society and of the British Association for the Advancement of Science, of which he was president in 1899. In the founding of the International Physiological Congresses, the first of which was held in 1889, he played a major role, as he did in the establishment of the International Association of Academies and in the preliminary arrangements for the *International Catalogue of Scientific Literature.*

Foster served on national commissions dealing with vaccination, tropical disease, disposal of sewage, and the reorganization of the University of London. In 1901 he was designated chairman of the Royal Commission on Tuberculosis. From 1900 to 1906 he was Member of Parliament for the University of London. Because he opposed the Liberal bill for Irish home rule, he stood originally as a Conservative; later he joined the Liberal opposition because of his stand on the education bill. On seeking reelection in 1906, he lost by the narrow margin of twenty-four votes.

Despite all these administrative duties, Foster coedited *The Scientific Memoirs of T. H. Huxley* (1898–1902) and several times revised Huxley's *Lessons in Elementary Physiology.* In 1899 he published a biography of Claude Bernard and in 1901 *Lectures on the History of Physiology During the Sixteenth, Seventeenth and Eighteenth Centuries.* Even in gardening, which was his chief source of relaxation, Foster exhibited leadership. He hybridized several new varieties of iris and was for a long time the internationally acknowledged expert on the genus. In fact, he published more original papers in horticulture than in physiology.

A member or fellow of a vast number of scientific societies, both British and foreign, Foster received honorary doctorates from the universities of Glasgow, St. Andrews, McGill, and Dublin. At Cambridge he was made honorary M.A. in 1871, and the full degree was conferred upon him in 1884. He was created K.C.B. in 1899.

Foster was twice married to women from Huntingdon: in 1863 to Georgina Edmonds, who died in 1869, and in 1872 to Margaret Rust, who survived him. By his first wife he had a daughter, Mercy, and a son, Michael George.

BIBLIOGRAPHY

I. Original Works. Foster's papers on the heartbeat are the following: "On the Beat of the Snail's Heart," in

Report of the Twenty-ninth Meeting of the British Association for the Advancement of Science (London, 1860), transactions of the sections, p. 160; "Note on the Action of the Interrupted Current on the Ventricle of the Frog's Heart," in *Journal of Anatomy and Physiology,* **3** (1869), 400–401; "Ueber einen besonderen Fall von Hemmungswirkung," in *Pflüger's Archiv für die gesamte Physiologie des Menschen und der Tiere,* **5** (1872), 191–195; "On the Behaviour of the Hearts of Mollusks Under the Influence of Electric Currents," in *Proceedings of the Royal Society,* **23** (1875), 586–594, written with A. G. Dew-Smith; "The Effects of the Constant Current on the Heart," in *Journal of Anatomy and Physiology,* **10** (1876), 735–771, written with A. G. Dew-Smith; "Some Effects of Upas Antiar on the Frog's Heart," *ibid.,* 586–594; and "Die Muskeln und Nerven des Herzens bei einigen Mollusken," in *Archiv für mikroskopische Anatomie und Entwicklungsmechanik,* **14** (1877), 317–321, written with A. G. Dew-Smith.

The most complete bibliography may be found in the article by Henry Dale (see below). A slightly less complete bibliography can be obtained by combining the citations in the *Royal Society's Catalogue of Scientific Papers,* II, 674; VII, 692; IX, 906; XV, 69; and in the *British Museum General Catalogue of Printed Books,* LXXVI, cols. 241–243. Several publications are omitted from all of these sources. A series of popular articles on science (some unsigned), including one on the snail's heart, appeared in the *Christian Spectator* in 1863 and 1864. Foster expresses his views on education in the unsigned article "Science in the Schools," in *London Quarterly Review,* **123** (1867), 244–258; in "Vivisection," in *Macmillan's Magazine,* **29** (1874), 367–376, he defends physiologists against the charges of the antivivisectionists; and in "Reminiscences of a Physiologist," in *Colorado Medical Journal,* **6** (1900), 419–429, he gives a rambling account of his education and early career.

There is no central repository for Foster's private papers and correspondence. Of the Foster–Huxley correspondence, more than 200 letters are preserved in the Huxley Papers at Imperial College, London, and nearly as many, from Huxley to Foster only, at the Royal College of Physicians. Many letters from both collections are quoted in Leonard Huxley, *Life and Letters of Thomas Henry Huxley,* 2 vols. (London, 1900). Sir Robert Mordant Foster, grandson of Sir Michael, possesses more than twenty letters sent home by Foster during his brief career as ship's surgeon. The rest of Foster's extant letters are scattered among various collections in England, including the J. D. Hooker and W. T. Thistleton-Dyer letters at the Royal Botanical Gardens in Kew, and the E. A. Sharpey-Schafer Papers at the Wellcome Institute for the History of Medicine.

At the library of the Cambridge Physiological Laboratory is a bound MS volume in Foster's hand with the heading "Three Lectures on the 'Involuntary Movements of Animals' Delivered Before the Royal Institution of Great Britain, February 1869." This MS reveals the central thrust—as well as the difficulties and ambiguities—of Foster's later ideas on the rhythmic heartbeat.

II. SECONDARY LITERATURE. This article is based on Gerald L. Geison, "Sir Michael Foster and the Rise of the Cambridge School of Physiology, 1870–1900," unpublished Ph.D. thesis (Yale, 1970). Of the many available sketches of Foster's work and career, the most valuable are J. N. Langley, in *Journal of Physiology* (London), **35** (1907), 233–246; and in *Dictionary of National Biography,* suppl. I (1901–1911), 44–46; W. H. Gaskell, in *Proceedings of the Royal Society,* **80B** (1908), lxxi–lxxxi; and Henry Dale, in *Notes and Records. Royal Society of London,* **19** (1964), 10–32.

For general background, see E. A. Sharpey-Schafer, *History of the Physiological Society During Its First Fifty Years, 1876–1926* (London, 1927); G. L. Geison, "The Stagnancy of English Physiology, 1850–1870," in *Bulletin of the History of Medicine* (in press); and Richard D. French, "Some Problems and Sources in the Modern Foundations of British Physiology," in *History of Science* (in press). French has also drawn attention to the evolutionary context of the cardiological research of Foster and Gaskell. See "Darwin and the Physiologists, or the Medusa and Modern Cardiology," in *Journal of the History of Biology,* **3** (1970), 253–274.

GERALD L. GEISON

FOUCAULT, JEAN BERNARD LÉON (*b.* Paris, France, 19 September 1819; *d.* Paris, 11 February 1868), *experimental physics.*

The son of a bookseller-publisher, Foucault received his education at home because of his delicate health. An indifferent student, he passed the *baccalauréat* only after special coaching and began to study medicine, hoping to put to use as a surgeon the considerable dexterity he had demonstrated (from the age of thirteen) in making a number of scientific toys, including a steam engine. Revolted by the sight of blood and suffering and stimulated in new directions by the invention of daguerreotypy, Foucault abandoned his medical studies, although not before he had come to the attention of Alfred Donné, teacher of clinical microscopy at the École de Médecine. Donné made him assistant in the microscopy course, then coauthor of its textbook (published in 1844–1845). Foucault finally succeeded his master as science reporter for the newspaper *Journal des débats* (1845), thereafter writing, in a brilliant style at once lively and precise, a regular column in which he discussed for a general audience the latest from the world of science.

From 1844 to 1846 Foucault published geometry, arithmetic, and chemistry texts for the *baccalauréat.* Thereafter, except for his newspaper articles, he published only scientific papers. Foucault worked in a laboratory set up in his home until, following the award of the Cross of the Legion of Honor in 1851 (for his pendulum experiment) and the *docteur ès sciences physiques* in 1853 (for his thesis comparing the velocity of light in air and water), he was given a place as physicist at the Paris observatory by Napoleon III. Further honors followed: the Copley Medal of the Royal Society in 1855, officer of the Legion of Honor and member of the Bureau des Longitudes in 1862, and foreign member of the Royal Society (1864) and the academies of Berlin and St. Petersburg. Finally, after having failed to be elected in 1857, Foucault was chosen in 1865, following the death of Clapeyron, a member of the Académie des Sciences.

A nonobserving Catholic until his final illness returned him to the church, Foucault led a quiet life of total devotion to scientific research. Small and frail, he managed to preside gracefully over the group of scientific friends who gathered on Thursdays at his house in the rue d'Assas. He died of brain disease at the age of forty-eight after a seven-month illness.

Foucault is best-known for two of the most significant experiments of the mid-nineteenth century—the laboratory determination of the velocity of light (1850, 1862) and the mechanical demonstration of the earth's rotation (1851, 1852)—and for his advancement of the technology of the telescope. He also performed a number of other important experiments, chiefly in optics, and developed several devices which were widely used in both experimental science and technology.

In 1834 Charles Wheatstone developed a rotating-mirror apparatus to measure the velocity of electricity, and in 1838 Arago suggested that the same principle might be applied to determining the velocity of light terrestrially (earlier determinations were astronomical). A comparison of this velocity in air and in water would be a clear experimental test between the wave and particle theories of light, since the former required light to travel faster in air; the latter, in water. Arago's attempts to carry out the experiment were unsuccessful, and failing eyesight forced him to abandon them. Immediately Foucault and Hippolyte Fizeau, with whom Foucault had collaborated on optical researches between 1845 and 1847, began independently to attempt to overcome the obstacles that had defeated Arago.

Fizeau was the first to succeed; by replacing the rotating-mirror apparatus in the laboratory with a toothed wheel interrupting a ray of light traveling over a long terrestrial path, he obtained the first precision measurement of the velocity of light at the earth's surface in 1849. Fizeau returned to the rotating mirror to compare light's velocity in rare and dense media, but here he was beaten by Foucault, who announced on 30 April 1850 that "light travels faster in air than in water" (*Recueil,* p. 207). His apparatus is diagramed in Figure 1. A source of light at *a* is reflected by a mirror *m,* rotating at 800 revolutions per second, to a spherically concave stationary mirror *M* and back again to *a'*. (The glass plane *g* permits the observer at *O* to see both source and reflection.) By the use of both an air path (upper half of diagram, image *a'*) and a water path (lower half of diagram,

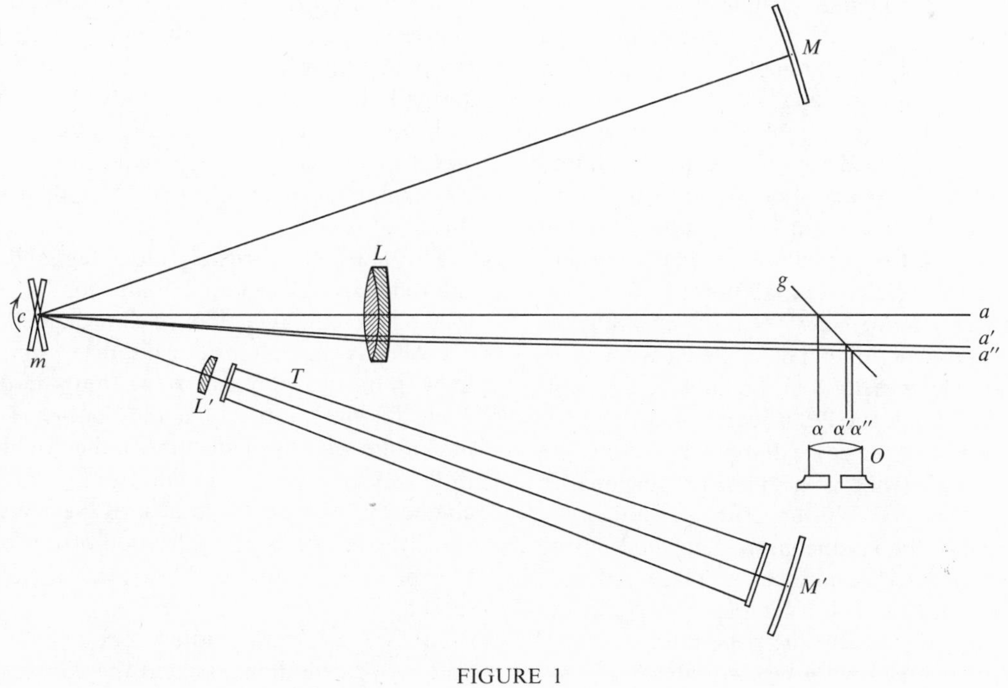

FIGURE 1

water-filled tube *T,* image *a''*), the velocity of light, which is a function of the displacement of the reflected image *a'* or *a''* from the source image *a,* can be compared in the two media. Since the water image *a''* is deflected more than the air image, light must travel faster in air than in water.

Foucault's first experiment, carried out in 1850 and written up in full in his doctoral thesis of 1853, was purely comparative; he announced no numerical values until 1862. Then, with an improved apparatus, he was able to measure precisely the velocity of light in air. This result, significantly smaller than Fizeau's of 1849, changed the accepted value of solar parallax and vindicated the higher value which Le Verrier had calculated from astronomical data. Foucault's turning-mirror apparatus was the basis for the later determinations of the velocity of light by A. A. Michelson and Simon Newcomb.

With Fizeau, Foucault had pioneered in astronomical photography by making the first daguerreotype of the sun in 1845. The long exposures necessary for photographing the stars required that the telescope remain continuously pointed at the heavenly object. To regulate the drive for such a telescope, Foucault in 1847 brought into practice Christian Huygens' abortive seventeenth-century project for a clock with a conical pendulum. Foucault's clock had a steel rod to support the bob of its pendulum, and he noticed that such a rod, set vibrating while clamped in the chuck of a lathe, tended to maintain its plane of vibration when the lathe was rotated by hand.

This unexpected behavior of the rod suggested to Foucault an experimental demonstration of the earth's rotation. In the cellar of his house he mounted a pendulum with a five-kilogram bob suspended from a steel thread two meters long, free to swing in any direction and tied at the extremity of its swing with a thread. When the thread was set afire, the pendulum began swinging, and at 2 A.M. on Wednesday, 8 January 1851, Foucault was rewarded by the sight of the plane of swing of the pendulum gradually turning "in the direction of the diurnal movement of the celestial sphere" (*Recueil,* p. 378, n.). Repeating the experiment in the meridian hall of the Paris observatory with an eleven-meter-long pendulum, Foucault reported to the Académie des Sciences on 3 February 1851 his finding that the circle described by the plane of the pendulum's swing is inversely proportional to the sine of the latitude. This experiment, soon scaled up and moved to the Panthéon, was repeated during the next two years in a number of places all over the world and gave rise to a tenfold increase in the scientific papers devoted to the pendulum.

As Foucault claimed in his report to the Academy, his finding illustrated Poisson's theoretical treatment of the deflecting force of the earth's rotation (*Journal de l'École polytechnique,* **16** [1838], 1–68), but Poisson had explicitly denied that the effect on the pendulum could be observed (p. 24).

Continuing to experiment on the mechanics of the earth's rotation, Foucault in 1852 invented the gyroscope, which, he showed, gave a clearer demonstration than the pendulum of the earth's rotation and had the property, similar to that of the magnetic needle, of maintaining a fixed direction. Foucault's pendulum and gyroscope had more than a popular significance (which continues to this day). First, they stimulated the development of theoretical mechanics, making relative motion and the theories of the pendulum and the gyroscope standard topics for study and investigation. Second, prior to Foucault's demonstrations the study of those motions on the earth's surface in which the deflecting force of rotation plays a prominent part (especially winds and ocean currents) was dominated by unphysical notions of how this force acted. Foucault's demonstrations and the theoretical treatments they inspired showed conclusively that this deflecting force acts in all horizontal directions, thus providing the sound physical insight on which Buys Ballot, Ferrel, Ulrich Vettin, and others could build.

Their daguerreotype of the sun was only one fruit of the collaboration between Foucault and Fizeau. Together, between 1844 and 1847, they carried out half a dozen researches. Two were of special importance: in 1845 and 1846 they extended the experiments of Thomas Young and Fresnel to show that interference took place between rays of light of which the paths differed by several thousand wavelengths, and in 1847 they showed, by studying the interference of heat rays from the sun, that radiant heat has a wavelike structure identical with that of light. These two experiments considerably strengthened the wave theory of light.

With his close friend Jules Regnault, Foucault showed in 1848 how the brain combines into one image two separate colors, each presented to a single eye. Shortly thereafter Foucault threw sunlight on the light from a carbon arc to superimpose the spectra. From his observation that the double bright-yellow line of the arc was identical with the double dark line in the solar spectrum (D line from sodium), he concluded that the arc could absorb the same light that it emitted, but the generalization of this observation to explain the Fraunhofer lines was left for Kirchhoff in 1859.

In 1853 Foucault studied conductivity in liquids, and in 1855 he demonstrated the conversion of mechanical work into heat by turning with a crank a copper disk placed between the poles of an electromagnet and measuring the heat produced in the disk.

No one in his time exceeded Foucault in technical inventiveness. From his first published papers on improvements in daguerreotypy (1841, 1843) to the completion of his siderostat shortly after his death, the devices designed by Foucault and executed, first by himself and later with the help of others, solved outstanding problems of practice in both science and technology. He developed a regulator for the arc lamp, which made it possible for gas to be supplanted by electricity in the supply of artificial light to the microscope (1843), and his improvement to this regulator (1849) brought the arc lamp into the theater. He designed a photometer (1855). His mercury interrupter (1856) improved the performance of Ruhmkorff induction coils, and his birefringent prism (1857), using air rather than balsam between the two pieces, made it possible to obtain plane polarized light into the ultraviolet. About 1860 he returned to the problem of making mechanical motion uniform, which had led him to the pendulum experiment, and he developed a whole series of mechanical regulators which went considerably beyond James Watt's governor in their effectiveness. These regulators were used first in machines which kept a telescope pointed continuously at the sun (heliostat) or a star (siderostat) and then in large steam engines, both in factories and at the Paris Exposition of 1867.

None of these inventions, however, was as significant for science as Foucault's introduction of the modern technique for silvering glass to make mirrors for reflecting telescopes (1857) and his simple but accurate methods for testing and correcting the figure of both mirrors and lenses (1858). Glass proved much superior to the speculum metal previously used in reflecting telescopes because it is much lighter in weight, easier to grind and figure, and easier to resurface if it becomes tarnished or damaged.

Foucault's extraordinary command of a precise language in both word and deed was not always taken at its true worth by his contemporaries among the masters of the French analytic tradition, for whom his sparing use of mathematics condemned him as merely a lucky tinkerer. His pungent newspaper articles, although never vicious, were also a source of hostility. Foucault's interest in astrophysics met the firm opposition of Le Verrier, director of the Paris observatory, a theoretical astronomer of the old school, and Foucault was therefore prevented from installing his siderostat in the observatory. Nevertheless, before he died, Foucault had acquired the respect of all as an outstanding experimentalist; and his reputation grew after his death as modern telescopic astronomy developed on the basis of the optical techniques he had inaugurated.

BIBLIOGRAPHY

I. Original Works. Foucault's papers, published mostly in the *Comptes rendus hebdomadaires des séances de l'Académie des sciences,* were collected and issued together with a number of unpublished papers in *Recueil des travaux scientifiques de Léon Foucault,* 2 vols. in one (Paris, 1878). Figure 1 in the text is taken from Plate 4 of the *Recueil,* which is in turn taken from Foucault's thesis, *Sur les vitesses relatives de la lumière dans l'air et dans l'eau* (Paris, 1853).

II. Secondary Literature. The two chief sources for Foucault's life and work are also in the *Recueil:* J. Bertrand, "Avertissement", I, i–iv, and "Des progrès de la mécanique," I, v–xxviii, the latter originally published in *Revue des deux mondes,* **51** (1 May 1864), 96–115, in order to help Foucault's candidacy for the Académie des Sciences; and J. A. Lissajous, "Notice historique sur la vie et les travaux de Léon Foucault," II, 1–18. Also useful is P. Gilbert, "Léon Foucault, sa vie et son oeuvre scientifique," in *Revue des questions scientifiques,* **5** (1879), 108–154, 516–563. Bertrand alludes in his article to the opposition Foucault faced in the Academy; the opposition of Le Verrier is mentioned in P. Larousse, *Grand dictionnaire universel du XIXe siècle,* VIII (Paris, 1872), 649.

Harold L. Burstyn

FOUCHY, JEAN-PAUL GRANDJEAN DE (*b.* Paris, France, 10 March 1707; *d.* Paris, 15 April 1788), *astronomy.*

He was the son of Marie-Madeleine Hynault and Philippe Grandjean de Fouchy, a Mâconnais noble who perfected the printing of deluxe editions under Louis XIV. Trained to succeed his father, Fouchy (who called himself alternately Grandjean, Grandjean de Fouchy, and de Fouchy) made some contributions in that area but soon found his art less appreciated and the demand for such work diminished. He became auditor of the Chambre des Comptes and secretary to the duc d'Orléans. More important, he undertook the study of science, devoting himself particularly to astronomy as a student of Joseph Nicolas Delisle.

In 1726 he became part of the newly formed Society of Arts in Paris. Among the several papers he presented to this group was one on the meridian of mean time, an innovation destined to be his most lasting contribution to astronomy. Named to the Academy of Sciences as a supernumerary assistant astronomer in 1731, he succeeded to regular membership in astronomy by the end of 1733. The first decade of his membership therein was his most productive scientific period.

Many of the memoirs he offered during that period were simply observational reports of specific phenomena such as eclipses, occultations, and the 1736 transit of Mercury. A few were more general: in 1731, a proposal for giving astronomical tables a more commodious form; in 1732, a memoir dealing with the reason for the disappearance of Jupiter's satellites from view before immersion and their reappearance only after a segment had emerged from Jupiter's shadow, and establishing rules to calculate the size of the segments involved based upon a new observational technique; in 1733, a method of employing bright spots on the moon for longitude determination; in 1737, his observation of Mercury's transit by a new means; in 1738, the proposal of a method to determine the eccentricity of the earth's orbit and that of the inner planets; in 1740, the extension of this method to any planet; and finally, also in 1740, a suggestion for improving Hadley's quadrant by substituting a telescope for open sights. Several other ideas for instrumental improvements, including a new level, a universal micrometer, and a device for moving a large quadrant, appeared in the collection *Machines et inventions approuvées par l'Académie.*

Unfortunately, these works were not as significant as they might seem. Few of them offered the advantages claimed by Fouchy, who, moreover, was much more prone to propose than to pursue. In the case of Jupiter's satellites, for example, it remained for Jean Sylvain Bailly to develop his idea and arrive at important results. Thus, Delambre's judgment that Fouchy was more an amateur than a true astronomer seems valid. This evaluation becomes even more appropriate after 1743, when Fouchy became the Academy's perpetual secretary. He served alone in that capacity for thirty years; but from 1773 until he resigned in 1776, he asked for and received the aid of Condorcet. During that period he wrote over sixty *éloges,* which, although lacking the style and philosophy of those of Fontenelle and Condorcet, were noteworthy for their information on, and analysis of, the scientific work of others.

During his secretariat his scientific contributions consisted mainly of meteorological observations but also included observations of eclipses and of the transits of Venus of 1761 and 1769. Some of these activities he continued thereafter, for he remained active nearly to the end of his life, even dispassionately describing a strange malady that afflicted him in 1784. His long career brought him membership both in the Academy of Sciences of Berlin and the Royal Society of London.

Fouchy was married twice, to Mlle. de Boistissandeau and to Mlle. Desportes-Pardeillan. The first union produced one daughter; the second, one daughter and two sons, both of whom pursued military rather than scientific careers.

BIBLIOGRAPHY

I. Original Works. The most important of Fouchy's contributions to the *Mémoires de l'Académie royale des sciences* were "Sur la forme la plus avantageuse qu'on puisse donner aux tables astronomiques" (1731), 433–442; "Sur la féconde inégalité des satellites de Jupiter" (1732), 419–427; "Observation du passage de Mercure sur le disque du Soleil, arrivé le 11 novembre 1736" (1737), 248–252; "Méthode pour déterminer par observation, l'excentricité de la Terre, et celle des planètes inférieures" (1738), 185–192; "Second mémoire sur l'excentricité des planètes" (1740), 235–242; and "Mémoire concernant la description et l'usage d'un nouvel instrument pour observer en mer les hauteurs et les distances des astres" (1740), 468–482. His longitude determination proposal was recorded, under the heading of "Sur une nouvelle méthode pour les longitudes," in the *Histoire de l'Académie royale des sciences* (1733), 76–79. His various instrument proposals may be read in *Machines et inventions approuvées par l'Académie royale des sciences depuis son établissement jusqu' à présent, avec leurs descriptions,* 7 vols. (Paris, 1735–1777), V, 91–92; VI, 45–47, 79–81, 113–114; and VII, 47–48. His *éloges* appeared in his annual histories of the Academy's work that preface the *Mémoires.* Those which appeared in the first sixteen years of his secretariat were also collected and published separately as *Éloges des académiciens de l'Académie royale des sciences, morts depuis l'an 1744* (Paris, 1761).

II. Secondary Literature. The archives of the Académie des Sciences contain an interesting MS of notes by one of Fouchy's sons for Condorcet's use in preparing the official *éloge.* Condorcet's product is in *Oeuvres complètes de Condorcet,* Marie Louise Sophie de Grouchy, Marquise de Condorcet, ed., 21 vols. (Paris, *an* XIII [1804]), IV, 3–26. A far more valuable estimation of his work is in J. B. J. Delambre, *Histoire de l'astronomie au dix-huitième siècle* (Paris, 1826), pp. 327–331. For a very brief treatment, see Niels Nielsen, *Géomètres français du dix-huitième siècle* (Paris, 1935), pp. 184–185.

SEYMOUR L. CHAPIN

FOUQUÉ, FERDINAND ANDRÉ (*b.* Mortain, Manche, France, 21 June 1828; *d.* Paris, France, 7 March 1904), *geology, mineralogy.*

Fouqué made three important contributions to science. First, he added significantly to the knowledge of volcanic phenomena and volcanic products, in particular generalizing Henri Sainte-Claire Deville's explanation of the chemical composition of the emanations of fumaroles. Second, in collaboration with Auguste Michel-Lévy, he introduced into France the study of rocks by microscopical petrography. Third, again in collaboration with Michel-Lévy, he successfully synthesized a large number of igneous rocks in an attempt to determine the conditions necessary for the production of their mineralogical constituents.

Fouqué had some difficulty in settling upon a career. He attended Saint-Cyr (1847), the École d'Administration (1848), and the École Normale Supérieure (1849). He became a laboratory assistant at the latter and collaborated in 1853 with Sainte-Claire Deville in a memoir concerning the action of heat on topaz. After working briefly in the chemical industry, he commenced medical studies and received his doctorate in medicine in 1858. His lasting interest in volcanic phenomena was aroused when he accompanied Sainte-Claire Deville in 1861 to Vesuvius, then in eruption, to observe the fumaroles.

During the next twenty years, Fouqué traveled extensively to study volcanoes, both active and extinct. He was present at the eruption of Etna in 1865 and of Santorin (now Thíra, Greece) in 1866; and he investigated the volcanic chemistry of the Lipari Islands, Vesuvius, Solfatara, and the Cantal. His research resulted in several important publications: *Recherches sur les phénomènes chimiques qui se produisent dans les volcans* (1866), which was accepted as his thesis for the doctorate in physical sciences; *Les anciens volcans de la Grèce* (1867); and *Santorin et ses éruptions* (1879). His most important finding was that the chemical products of fumaroles are primarily a function of temperature, thus relating the product composition, the site of the fumarole with respect to the center of the eruption, and the elapsed time between the emergence of the vent and the beginning of the eruption.

Fouqué's studies of volcanoes led naturally to his other scientific activity, in which he collaborated closely with Michel-Lévy. Both had heard of Henry Clifton Sorby's work in the microscopical examination of thin sections of rocks, and they perfected this technique. Their two-volume work *Minéralogie micrographique* (1879) introduced this new petrographic method into France. Further, they laid the foundations of modern petrography by introducing a classificatory system based on the mineralogical composition, the structure, and the chemical composition of volcanic rocks.

From 1878 to 1882, Fouqué and Michel-Lévy worked continuously on the artificial synthesis of igneous rocks, primarily to determine the conditions surrounding their origins. They were successful in producing the majority of volcanic rocks with the identical mineralogical composition and structural peculiarities found in nature. Their work verified the importance of the rate of cooling on the extent of crystallization and the sizes of grain, and demonstrated that rocks of distinctly different mineralogical composition would be formed from the same magma, depending on the conditions of crystallization.

Fouqué received the Cuvier Prize in 1876, and in 1877 he became professor of natural history at the Collège de France. He was named to the French geological survey commission in 1880, and in this position he made contributions to the stratigraphic geology of the Haute-Auvergne region. He was elected to the Académie des Sciences in 1881 and presided over it in 1901. In 1884, following earthquakes in Andalusia, he directed a group sent there by the Institut de France to study these phenomena. This mission led to Fouqué's experiments on the speed of propagation of shock waves in a variety of soils. His last important work, completed in 1896, was a petrographic study of the plagioclase feldspars.

BIBLIOGRAPHY

I. ORIGINAL WORKS. Fouqué's chief publications are *Recherches sur les phénomènes chimiques qui se produisent dans les volcans* (Paris, 1866); *Les anciens volcans de la Grèce* (Paris, 1867); *Santorin et ses éruptions* (Paris, 1879); *Minéralogie micrographique: Roches éruptives françaises,* 2 vols. (Paris, 1879), written with A. Michel-Lévy; *Synthèse des minéraux et des roches* (Paris, 1882), written with A. Michel-Lévy; and *Les tremblements de terre* (Paris, 1888). He published approximately 100 memoirs, some in collaboration with Michel-Lévy.

II. SECONDARY LITERATURE. See A. Michel-Lévy, "Notice sur F. Fouqué," in *Bulletin de la Société française de minéralogie,* **28** (1905), 38–56; and Alfred Lacroix, *Notice historique sur Auguste Michel-Lévy* (Paris, 1914).

JOHN G. BURKE

FOURCROY, ANTOINE FRANÇOIS DE (*b.* Paris, France, 15 June 1755; *d.* Paris, 16 December 1809), *chemistry, medicine.*

A member of a noble family that had declined, Fourcroy was the son of Jean Michel de Fourcroy, an apothecary, and Jeanne Laugier. He left the Collège d'Harcourt in Paris at the age of fifteen, and after studying for a year under a writing master, became a clerk in the office of the chancellory. There he would have remained but for his good fortune in meeting F. Vicq d'Azyr, the anatomist, who persuaded his father to let Fourcroy study at the Paris Faculty of Medicine. Aided financially by members of the Société Royale de Médecine, of which Vicq d'Azyr was secretary, Fourcroy graduated as a doctor in 1780, but he did not practice medicine.

As a student he had shown great ability in chemistry and had lectured in the private laboratory of J. B. M. Bucquet, his teacher. Every winter from Bucquet's death in 1780 until 1791 or 1792 Fourcroy gave a course of seventy lectures in his own laboratory which was published as *Leçons élémentaires d'histoire naturelle et de chimie* (Paris, 1782), and from 1782 to 1784 he also gave a summer course in materia medica. In all his lectures Fourcroy emphasized the relations between chemistry and natural history and their application to medicine. Fieldwork in natural history led him to publish *Entomologia parisiensis* (Paris, 1785), a detailed account of the insects of the Paris region, and about this time he also did some research on the anatomy of muscles; but he soon decided to concentrate on chemistry.

In 1783 Fourcroy received his first public appointment as chemistry professor at the Ecole Royale Vétérinaire, at Alfort, near Paris, but this ended in 1787 when plans to expand the school were abandoned. His career did not suffer, for in 1784 he had succeeded P. J. Macquer in the important chair of chemistry at the Jardin du Roi. Here he lectured every summer to very large audiences and achieved fame by his brilliant exposition of a rapidly changing subject. From 1787 he added to his reputation by lecturing at the Lycée, a private educational institution on rue de Valois founded by J. F. Pilatre de Rozier.

The Société Royale de Médecine allowed Fourcroy to take part in its work while he was still a student and elected him to membership as soon as he graduated; he subsequently became one of its leading members, and his talent was further recognized in 1785 by his election to the Académie Royale des Sciences. Here he was in contact with A. L. Lavoisier, whose antiphlogistic theory he adopted in 1786, after several years of hesitation during which he had given his students a comparative account of the phlogistic and antiphlogistic theories. Most of the second edition of his *Leçons élémentaires,* retitled *Élémens d'histoire naturelle et de chimie* (Paris, 1786), was printed before 1786, and he announced his conversion in a specially written introduction. His *Principes de chimie* (Paris, 1787) was the first textbook written entirely according to the antiphlogistic theory.

In 1787 Fourcroy collaborated with Lavoisier, L. B. Guyton de Morveau, and C. L. Berthollet in the revision of chemical nomenclature, and he undertook the great task of completing the chemical section of the *Encyclopédie méthodique,* which Guyton had to abandon after completing volume I (Paris, 1789). Fourcroy was a teacher who always tried to arrange the fundamental principles of chemistry in a systematic order, and in his article "Axiomes" in the second volume of *Encyclopédie méthodique* (1792) he classified the chief facts of chemistry under twelve headings. When published separately as a little book entitled *Philosophie chimique* (Paris, 1792), this proved to be a very popular summary of antiphlogistic chemistry and was translated into eleven languages. Fourcroy also helped to advance the new chemistry as one of the editors of *Annales de chimie,* the journal founded in 1789 by Lavoisier and his colleagues; but he was more active as the editor of his own periodical, *La médecine éclairée par les sciences physiques,* which appeared fortnightly during 1791 and 1792 and was intended for medical practitioners wishing to keep up to date in all relevant branches of science.

While establishing his reputation as a professor and author, Fourcroy was also busy in the laboratory. One of the duties of the Société Royale de Médecine was to analyze mineral waters and assess their medicinal value, and in 1782 Fourcroy published a valuable account of the qualitative analysis of mineral waters by means of reagents, a method that was replacing the older analysis by evaporation to dryness. He considered that many of the reagents recommended in 1778 by T. O. Bergman were unnecessary and reduced the number from about twenty-five to eleven. Further, Bergman had not suggested any particular order for the reagents, but Fourcroy described a systematic analysis, using reagents that had the least effect on mineral waters before those that caused more complicated changes. A separate sample of the water was used for each test.

Fourcroy noticed that ammonia did not always completely precipitate magnesia from a mineral water containing it in solution. This led him in 1790 to investigate the reactions between salts of ammonia and of magnesia, and to the discovery of the crystalline double sulfates and double phosphates of the two bases. Bergman had recognized the existence of such salts in 1783, but few had been characterized.

Fourcroy's interest in the application of chemistry to medicine led him to study various solids and fluids of the human and animal body in health and sickness. In 1785 he found that both human and animal muscle fiber contained a substance chemically similar to the fibrous matter in coagulated blood. This fibrous matter must have been derived from the animal's food, which was inanimate; Fourcroy seems to have thought that it was converted into living muscle fiber by the agency of a vital force. C. W. Scheele and Berthollet had found nitrogen in animal matter, and in 1788 Fourcroy showed that there was a greater proportion of nitrogen in muscle fiber than in any other part of the body, and that the proportion of nitrogen contained in these fibers was the same for carnivorous and herbivorous animals. By 1789 he had found nitrogen in many vegetables, and it was therefore possible to account for its presence in herbivores without necessarily assuming that the animal absorbed it from the atmosphere.

Some parts of the body putrefied to form a white, waxy material resembling spermaceti, but in 1786 Fourcroy showed that it had a lower melting point than spermaceti and was more soluble in alcohol. Gallstones contained another similar substance (now known as cholesterol) which was only slightly soluble in alcohol and melted at a higher temperature than the others. This use of measurable physical properties to distinguish substances was very unusual before the nineteenth century.

Vegetable chemistry also interested Fourcroy, but to a lesser extent. His most important contribution was a detailed analysis of cinchona bark, which he extracted in a systematic manner with water, alcohol, alkalies, and acids. He did not isolate the active principle, but his analysis prepared the way for techniques that led to the extraction of cinchonine and quinine by P. J. Pelletier and J. B. Caventou in 1820.

About 1790 Fourcroy gave his first course in animal chemistry at the Lycée. He was assisted by N. L. Vauquelin, who collaborated in much of his research, but this joint work was done later, for Fourcroy's scientific activities were interrupted by his entry into politics.

Like most French scientists, Fourcroy held liberal opinions and supported the moves that led to the French Revolution. He was one of about 400 representatives of the Third Estate in Paris who met in April and May 1789 to elect twenty deputies to the Estates General, but he took no further part in politics until 1792. In the meantime he served on local committees of health, education, and public welfare and continued his scientific work.

The government called on scientists to assist in solving the country's economic difficulties. In 1790 Fourcroy successfully applied his chemical knowledge to the problem of extracting copper (needed for coinage and later for cannon manufacture and shipbuilding) from its alloy with tin, which, with the closing of many churches, was available in the form of bells. He heated the molten metal in air until the gain in weight showed that enough oxygen had been absorbed to oxidize the tin but not the copper. But at this stage some oxygen was combined with copper and some tin was uncombined, so, knowing that oxygen had a greater affinity for tin than for copper, he continued the heating in the absence of air. This caused all the oxygen to be transferred to the tin, leaving tin oxide and pure copper. The process gave a good yield of copper and was employed on a large scale for at least ten years.

The suspension of the monarchy and dissolution of the National Assembly on 10 August 1792 were followed by the election of a new National Convention and the declaration of the republic. Fourcroy became a member of the electoral assembly of Paris, the body that elected the deputies, but he had no ambition to enter politics actively and wished only to serve his country by continuing his scientific work. He stated this clearly on 10 September 1792, when he wrote to the government declining the position of *régisseur des poudres et salpêtres* (an administrative position concerned with gunpowder manufacture); but he failed in his attempt to remain a private citizen and on 21 September was elected fourth substitute deputy for Paris. He was called to take his seat in the Convention on 22 July 1793, after J. P. Marat's assassination. Fourcroy now showed some enthusiasm for politics. He joined the Jacobin Club and became a member of the Committee of Public Instruction of the Convention.

After 10 August 1792 Fourcroy supported the expulsion from the Société Royale de Médecine and the Académie Royale des Sciences of émigrés and counterrevolutionaries, but none of the active members still resident in France were affected. He also supported the decision of the Convention on 8 August 1793 to suppress these bodies and all other academies that had enjoyed privileges under the monarchy. This did not affect certain independent societies, such as the Lycée des Arts (not to be confused with the Lycée), which was particularly concerned with the applications of science and included among its members Fourcroy, Lavoisier, and other academicians.

The suppression of the academies was not intended to be an attack on their members, and as a member of the Committee of Public Instruction, Fourcroy became partly responsible for organizing commissions of scientists to continue the most important work in progress. But in fact, the political and military problems of the day made it possible to set up only the commission that developed the metric system of weights and measures. Lavoisier was a member of this commission until after his arrest, with the other farmers-general of taxes, in November 1793. His trial and execution on 8 May 1794 came as a great shock to his fellow scientists, and there is evidence that Fourcroy made an unsuccessful last-minute appeal on his behalf to Robespierre and the other members of the Committee of Public Safety.

Fourcroy served on the government committee that

founded the École Polytechnique in Paris (called the École Centrale des Travaux Publics when it opened in 1794) and new medical schools in Paris, Strasbourg, and Montpellier, which opened in 1795. These were urgently needed to train engineers and doctors for the army, but the École Polytechnique and the École de Médecine at Paris also became important research centers. Fourcroy was a professor at each until his death, and he also retained his chairs at the Lycée and the Jardin du Roi, which was reorganized in 1793 as the Muséum National d'Histoire Naturelle.

On 1 September 1794 Fourcroy was elected to the Committee of Public Safety, which had diminished powers after Robespierre's downfall, and for several months he was deeply involved in the organization of munitions manufacture. From July to October 1795 he was again on the Committee of Public Instruction and helped to prepare an ambitious plan for national education which was to include *écoles centrales* for boys aged eleven to eighteen. Much science was to be taught in them, but few were successful, largely because of the shortage of science teachers. Fourcroy was also one of the planners of the Institut National des Sciences et des Arts, which replaced the old learned societies, and he became a member soon after it opened in 1795.

Fourcroy was elected to the Conseil des Anciens, one of the two assemblies that succeeded the Convention in 1795, but he did not serve on any of its committees and was not reelected in 1797. His return to private life lasted only two years, for on 25 December 1799 Napoleon appointed him to the council of state. By this time he had resumed his scientific work, and he was able to continue it while a councillor. He published a new treatise on chemistry, *Systême des connaissances chimiques* (Paris, 1801) and many research papers, but most of these were joint publications, generally with Vauquelin.

A useful contribution to inorganic chemistry was made by Fourcroy and Vauquelin in 1796, when they gave clear descriptions of the preparation and properties of sulfites and phosphites, including some new salts. In 1803, independently of H. V. Collet-Descotils, they examined the residue left when crude platinum dissolved in aqua regia and showed that it contained a new metal (which they named iridium), but they missed the second metal (osmium) that was discovered in 1804 by J. Smithson Tennant. In 1801 L. J. Thenard was Fourcroy's collaborator in a masterly study of the oxides and salts of mercury, which definitely established the existence of two series of compounds containing mercury in different degrees of oxidation.

The action of sulfuric acid on vegetable substances was studied by Fourcroy and Vauquelin in 1797, and they showed that it did not always act as an oxidizing agent, as was generally believed, but sometimes decomposed vegetable matter by removing water from it, even though the water was not originally present as such but only as its elements. The sulfuric acid was unaltered chemically, and the reaction ceased when it became too dilute. In the particular case of alcohol, which yielded ether when treated with sulfuric acid, they considered that hydrogen and oxygen were removed from the alcohol, forming water, but the liberation of carbon that they observed led them to believe that the reaction was more complicated. Later, chemists recognized that the carbon came from impurities in the alcohol, but Fourcroy and Vauquelin had made an important contribution to the development of the theory of etherification.

Animal chemistry was still of great interest to Fourcroy, and with Vauquelin he examined many solids and fluids, including brains, mucus, nasal humor, and bile, and tried to explain their formation and function in chemical terms and to find medicaments that would restore them to their original state when altered by disease. Like most animal chemists of the day, they did not characterize any organic constituents of these animal substances, which, unlike vegetables, rarely yield crystalline and easily purifiable compounds.

Fourcroy and Vauquelin achieved more when they examined the inorganic constituents of animal matter. They found, for example, that the phosphates of lime and magnesia were present in the same proportions in milk as in bones, and that phosphorus in the soft roe of a fish was combined in such a way that it did not give the usual reactions of a phosphate.

Hundreds of concretions from various parts of human and animal bodies were analyzed by Fourcroy and Vauquelin. Most were urinary calculi which, independently of W. H. Wollaston, they classified according to chemical composition from 1798 onward. They confirmed the frequent presence of uric acid and phosphate of lime (discovered in calculi by Scheele and George Pearson respectively) and also found urate of ammonia, the double phosphate of magnesia and ammonia, and occasionally other compounds. Fourcroy hoped that the analysis of urinary calculi would lead to the discovery of solvents suitable for dissolving them by injection into the bladder, but this was not achieved.

In an attempt to find why urinary calculi were formed, Fourcroy and Vauquelin investigated urine, and in 1799 they gave the first satisfactory account of urea, which they named. (H. Boerhaave and H. M. Rouelle had previously observed a crystalline substance in evaporated urine but had not examined its properties.) Fourcroy and Vauquelin isolated it by recrystallization from alcohol and, in 1808, achieved a purer state by adding alkali to the crystalline nitrate that they had discovered. They found that urea yielded carbonic and acetic acids and ammonia when its aqueous solution was boiled; these were also the products of putrefaction, and they thought that calculi containing ammonia might be formed by the partial fermentation of urea in the bladder. Such speculations provided a valuable stimulus to the next generation of animal chemists.

As councillor of state, Fourcroy played a large part in drafting a new educational system, from primary schools to advanced colleges, and in 1802 Napoleon appointed him director-general of public instruction, with the great task of implementing the proposals. He achieved considerable success, and it was a disappointment when, in March 1808, he was not made grand master of the Imperial University, the corporation that was to control the entire system. It is probable that Napoleon wanted a grand master who was completely acceptable to the Roman Catholic Church, and he knew that Fourcroy was a freethinker. The post was given to Louis de Fontanes, a man of letters with orthodox religious views.

The title of count of the empire was conferred on Fourcroy in 1808, and he remained a councillor of state. During 1809 he was occupied in drafting new mining legislation, and Napoleon may have intended to appoint him director-general of mines. But Fourcroy's health had begun to decline in 1808 and he died, aged fifty-four, before the mining law was passed.

Fourcroy was married to Anne Claude Bettinger in 1780; they had a son, an army officer who was killed in action in 1813, and a daughter. This marriage was dissolved in 1799, and in 1800 Fourcroy married Adelaide Flore Belleville, the widow of Charles de Wailly, a well-known architect. There were no children from the second marriage.

BIBLIOGRAPHY

I. Original Works. An extensive bibliography of Fourcroy's scientific writings is given by W. A. Smeaton (see below), pp. 211–252, with supplementary information in "Some Unrecorded Editions of Fourcroy's *Philosophie Chimique,*" in *Annals of Science,* **23** (1967), 295–298.

II. Secondary Literature. There are two comprehensive accounts of Fourcroy's life and work: W. A. Smeaton, *Fourcroy, Chemist and Revolutionary* (London, 1962); and Georges Kersaint, *Antoine François de Fourcroy, sa vie et son oeuvre* (Paris, 1966). Both books contain many references to manuscripts and printed sources.

W. A. Smeaton

FOURIER, JEAN BAPTISTE JOSEPH (*b.* Auxerre, France, 21 March 1768; *d.* Paris, France, 16 May 1830), *mathematics, mathematical physics.*

Fourier lost both his father (Joseph, a tailor in Auxerre) and his mother (Edmée) by his ninth year and was placed by the archbishop in the town's military school, where he discovered his passion for mathematics. He wanted to join either the artillery or the engineers, which were branches of the army then generally available to all classes of society; but for some reason he was turned down, and so he was sent to a Benedictine school at St. Benoît-sur-Loire in the hope that he could later pursue his special interests at its seminary in Paris. The French Revolution interfered with these plans, however, and without regret he returned in 1789 to Auxerre and a teaching position in his old school.

During the Revolution, Fourier was prominent in local affairs, and his courageous defense of the victims of the Terror led to his arrest in 1794. A personal appeal to Robespierre was unsuccessful; but he was released after Robespierre's execution on 28 July 1794 and went as a student to the ill-fated École Normale, which opened and closed within that year. He can have spent only a short time there, but nevertheless he made a strong impression; and when the École Polytechnique started in 1795 he was appointed *administrateur de police,* or assistant lecturer, to support the teaching of Lagrange and Monge. There he fell victim of the reaction to the previous regime and was, ironically, arrested as a supporter of Robespierre (who had declined his earlier appeal). But his colleagues at the École successfully sought his release, and in 1798 Monge selected him to join Napoleon's Egyptian campaign. He became secretary of the newly formed Institut d'Égypte, conducted negotiations between Napoleon and Sitty-Nefiçah (the wife of the chief bey, Murad), and held other diplomatic posts as well as pursuing research. He does not appear to have been appointed governor of southern Egypt, however, as has often been reported.

After his return to France in 1801, Fourier wished to resume his work at the École Polytechnique; but Napoleon had spotted his administrative genius and appointed him prefect of the department of Isère, centered at Grenoble and extending to what was then the Italian border. Here his many administrative achievements included the reconciliation of thirty-seven different communities to the drainage of a huge area of marshland near Bourgoin to make valuable farming land, and the planning and partial construction of a road from Grenoble to Turin (now route N91-strada 23), which was then the quickest route between Turin and Lyons. In 1808 Napoleon conferred a barony on him.

While in Egypt, Fourier suggested that a record be made of the work of the Institut d'Égypte, and on his return to France he was consulted on its organization and deputed to write the "Préface historique" on the ancient civilization and its glorious resurrection. This he completed in 1809, but some of its historical details caused controversy. Napoleon supported it, and it appeared in the *Description de l'Égypte.*

Fourier was still at Grenoble in 1814 when Napoleon fell. By geographical accident the town was directly on the route of the party escorting Napoleon from Paris to the south and thence to Elba; to avoid an embarrassing meeting with his former chief Fourier negotiated feverishly for a detour in the route of the cortege. But no such detour was conceivable on Napoleon's return and march on Paris in 1815, and so Fourier compromised, fulfilling his duties as prefect by ordering the preparation of the defenses—which he knew to be useless—and then leaving the town for Lyons by one gate as Napoleon entered by another. He did return, however, and the two friends met at Bourgoin. Fourier need have had no fears, for Napoleon made him a count and appointed him prefect of the neighboring department of the Rhône, centered at Lyons. But before the end of Napoleon's Hundred Days, Fourier had resigned his new title and prefecture in protest against the severity of the regime and had come to Paris to try to take up research full time (it had previously been only a spare-time activity).

This was the low point of Fourier's life—he had no job, only a small pension, and a low political reputation. But a former student at the École Polytechnique and companion in Egypt, Chabrol de Volvic, was now prefect of the department of the Seine and appointed him director of its Bureau of Statistics, a post without onerous duties but with a salary sufficient for his needs.

In 1816 Fourier was elected to the reconstituted Académie des Sciences, but Louis XVIII could not forgive his having accepted the prefecture of the Rhône from Napoleon, and the nomination was refused. Diplomatic negotiation eventually cleared up the situation, and his renomination in 1817 was not opposed. He also had some trouble with the second edition of the *Description de l'Égypte* (for now his references to Napoleon needed rethinking) but in general his reputation was rising fast. He was left in a position of strength after the decline of the Société d'Arcueil, led by Laplace in the physical sciences, and gained the favor and support of the aging Laplace himself in spite of the continued enmity of Poisson. In 1822 he was elected to the powerful position of *secrétaire perpétuel* of the Académie des Sciences, and in 1827—after further protests—to the Académie Française. He was also elected a foreign member of the Royal Society.

Throughout his career, Fourier won the loyalty of younger friends by his unselfish support and encouragement; and in his later years he helped many mathematicians and scientists, including Oersted, Dirichlet, Abel, and Sturm. An unfortunate incident occurred in 1830 when he lost the second paper on the resolution of equations sent to the Academy by Evariste Galois; but this would appear to be due more to the disorganization of his papers than—as Galois believed—to deliberate suppression.

The Egyptian period of his life had one final consequence in his last years. While there he had caught some illness, possibly myxedema, which necessitated his increasing confinement to his own heated quarters. He lived at 15 rue pavée St. André des Arts (now 15 rue Séguier) until 1829, then at 19 rue d'Enfer (now the site of 73 Boulevard St. Michel) until his death. On 4 May 1830 he was struck down while descending some stairs, and he allowed the symptoms to become worse until he died twelve days later. The funeral service took place at the Église St. Jacques de Haut Pas, and he was buried in the eighteenth division of the cemetery of Père Lachaise.

Various memorials have been made to Fourier. A bust by Pierre-Alphonse Fessard was subscribed in 1831 but was destroyed during World War II. A similar fate overtook the bronze statue by Faillot erected in Auxerre in 1849; the Nazis melted it down for armaments. During the night before its destruction, however, the mayor rescued two of its bas-reliefs, which were mounted on the walls of the town hall after the war. A medallion was founded in the town in 1952, and since 1950 the *Annales de l'Institut Fourier* have been published by the University of Grenoble. In 1968 the bicentenary of his birth was celebrated and the secondary school in Auxerre was renamed the Lycée Fourier.

Heat Diffusion and Partial Differential Equations. Fourier's achievements lie in the study of the diffusion of heat and in the mathematical techniques he introduced to further that study. His interest in the problem may have begun when he was in Egypt, but the substantial work was done at Grenoble. In 1807 he presented a long paper to the Academy on heat diffusion between disjoint masses and in special continuous bodies (rectangle, annulus, sphere, cylinder, prism), based on the diffusion equation

$$\frac{\partial^2 v}{\partial x^2} + \frac{\partial^2 v}{\partial y^2} + \frac{\partial^2 v}{\partial z^2} = k\frac{\partial v}{\partial t} \quad (1)$$

(in three variables). Of the examiners, Laplace, Monge, and Lacroix were in favor of accepting his work, but Lagrange was strongly opposed to it—due, to some extent, to the Fourier series

$$f(x) = \frac{1}{2\pi}\int_{-\pi}^{\pi} f(t)\,dt + \frac{1}{\pi}\sum_{r=1}^{\infty}\left[\cos rx\int_{-\pi}^{\pi} f(t)\cos rt\,dt + \sin rx\int_{-\pi}^{\pi} f(t)\sin rt\,dt\right] \quad (2)$$

required to express the initial temperature distribution in certain of these bodies, which contradicted Lagrange's own denigration of trigonometric series in his treatment of the vibrating string problem in the 1750's. The paper was therefore never published.

A prize problem on heat diffusion was proposed in 1810, however, and Fourier sent in the revised version of his 1807 paper, together with a new analysis on heat diffusion in infinite bodies. In these cases the periodicity of the Fourier series made it incapable of expressing the initial conditions, and Fourier substituted the Fourier integral theorem, which he wrote in forms such as

$$\pi f(x) = \int_{\infty}^{\infty} f(t)\,dt\int_{0}^{\infty}\cos q(x-t)\,dq. \quad (3)$$

The last sections of the paper dealt with more physical aspects of heat, such as the intensity of radiation, and these became more important in Fourier's thought during his later years. Fourier's paper won the competition, but the jury—probably at the insistence of Lagrange—made criticisms on grounds of "rigor and generality," which Fourier considered an unjustified reproach. He expanded the mathematical parts of the paper into his book *Théorie analytique de la chaleur.* An extended treatment of the physical aspects was first planned for further chapters of this book and then for a separate book, *Théorie physique de la chaleur,* but it was never achieved.

The history of Fourier's main work in mathematics and mathematical physics has long been confused by an exclusive concentration on only two results, Fourier series and Fourier integrals, and by the application of anachronistic standards of rigor in judgments on their derivation. Fourier's achievement is better understood if we see it as twofold: treating first the formulation of the physical problem as boundary-value problems in linear partial differential equations, which (together with his work on units and dimensions) achieved the extension of rational mechanics to fields outside those defined in Newton's *Principia;* and second, the powerful mathematical tools he invented for the solution of the equations, which yielded a long series of descendants and raised problems in mathematical analysis that motivated much of the leading work in that field for the rest of the century and beyond.

Fortunately for the historian, Fourier reproduced, nearly intact, almost all his successful results in the several versions of his basic work. A comparison of these, in correlation with unpublished sources, biographical information, and separate papers, enables a firm reconstruction of the sequence of his researches. Moreover, from this sequence and from his style of presentation, we can identify several crucial points at which he failed to solve problems as well as the reasons for his failure.

Fourier's first work in the rational mechanics of heat used a model of heat being transferred by a shuttle mechanism between discrete particles. The physical theory was a simple method of mixtures, and the mathematics was of the 1750's. Of the two problems he attacked, the second, with the n particles arranged in a ring, yielded a complete solution for the finite case. Fourier wished to extend this to the continuous case but could not, for as n increased, the time constants in the exponentials tended to zero, obliterating the time dependence of the solution. Only later did he understand how to modify his transfer model to avoid this anomaly; and by his concentration on the complete solution and its difficulties, he failed to notice that at $t = 0$ his solution gave an interpolation formula which would yield the Fourier series in the continuous case. (Lagrange's earlier failure to discover the Fourier series can be similarly explained; it had nothing to do with the scruples of rigor which are usually held to be the cause.)

Fourier's successful establishment of the equation of heat flow was probably indebted to early work of J. B. Biot on the steady temperatures in a metal bar, wherein Biot distinguished between internal conduction and external radiation. Biot's analysis was crippled by a faulty physical model for conduction which yielded an "inhomogeneous" equation $d^2v - kv\,dx^2 = 0$; and Fourier was able to concoct a physical model which resolved the difficulty. The full time-dependent equations for one and two dimensions of the type (1) then came easily.

Fourier's masterstroke was in the choice of configuration for a problem in which to apply the equation. The semi-infinite strip, uniformly hot at one end and uniformly cold along the sides, combines the utmost simplicity with physical meaning, in the tradition of rational mechanics deriving from the Bernoullis and Euler. The steady-state case is simply Laplace's equation in Cartesian coordinates. Fourier probably tried complex-variable methods (a solution along these lines, probably retrospective, is in the *Théorie*) but then used separation of variables to yield a series solution and thus the boundary-condition equation

$$1 = \sum_{r=0}^{\infty} a_r \cos rx. \quad (4)$$

The solution of the equation and its generalization for an arbitrary function $f(x)$ by infinite-matrix methods have been analyzed and criticized many times. It is well to remember that this work was done several decades before the Cauchy-Weierstrass orthodoxy was established. Fourier was not a naive formalist: he could handle problems of convergence quite competently, as in his discussion of the series for the sawtooth function. The leading technical ideas of several basic proofs, such as that of Dirichlet on the convergence of the Fourier series, can be found in his work. Moreover, he saw, long before anyone else, that term-by-term integration of a given trigonometric series, to evaluate the coefficients, is no guarantee of its correctness; the completeness of a series is not to be assumed. The great shock caused by his trigonometric expansions was due to his demonstration of a paradoxical property of equality over a finite interval between algebraic expressions of totally different form. Corresponding to any function in a very wide class, there could be constructed a trigonometric series whose values, on an assigned interval, are the same as those of the function. As he showed by example, the given function could even be a mixture of different algebraic expressions, each defined on disjoint subintervals of the basic one. Both trigonometric expansions and arbitrary functions had been used by others (including Poisson); but the former were restricted to problems involving periodic phenomena, and the latter, when they appeared in the solutions of partial differential equations, were assumed by their nature to be incapable of an algebraic expression.

The earliest records of this first successful investigation show its exploratory character and Fourier's excitement with his achievement. Also, in this work there are traces of the influence of Monge in the notation, in the representation of the solution as a surface, and in the separate expression of boundary values in determining the solution of a differential equation. Thenceforth, Fourier proceeded into new territory with assuredness. The three-dimension case caused some difficulties, which were resolved by splitting the original equation into two, one for interior conduction and the other relating radiation to the temperature gradient at the surface. Applied to the sphere, in spherical coordinates, this gave a nonharmonic trigonometric expansion, where the eigenvalues are the roots of a transcendental equation. Fourier used his knowledge of the theory of equations (see below) to argue for the reality of all roots, but the question caused him trouble for many years. The problem of heat conduction in a cylinder gave rise to a further generalization. Fourier's solution was in what are now called Bessel functions—derived several years before Friedrich Bessel—by techniques made fully general in the theory created by Fourier's later associates, J. Charles François Sturm and Joseph Liouville.

The study of diffusion along an infinite line, involving the development of the Fourier integral theorem, probably depended on the idea of Laplace of expressing the solution of the heat equation as an integral transform of an arbitrary function representing the initial temperature distribution. Fourier derived the cosine and sine transforms separately for configurations symmetrical and antisymmetrical about the origin, by the extension of the finite-interval expansion. Only gradually did he come to appreciate the generality of the odd-and-even decomposition of a given function.

Fourier's last burst of creative work in this field came in 1817 and 1818, when he achieved an effective insight into the relation between integral-transform solutions and operational calculus. There was at that time a three-cornered race with Poisson and Cauchy, who had started using such techniques by 1815. In a crushing counterblow to a criticism by Poisson, Fourier exhibited integral-transform solutions of several equations which had long defied analysis, and gave the lead to a systematic theory. This was later achieved by Cauchy, en route to the calculus of residues.

As a mathematician, Fourier had as much concern for practical problems of rigor as anyone in his day except Cauchy and N. H. Abel, but he could not conceive of the theory of limiting processes as a meaningful exercise in its own right. The famous referees' criticisms of the 1811 prize essay, concerning its defects of rigor and generality, have long been misinterpreted. Much of the motivation for them was political; Poisson and Biot, outclassed rivals in the theory of heat diffusion, tried for years to denigrate

Fourier's achievements. The criticism of rigor was probably based on Poisson's point that the eigenvalues in the sphere problem were not proven to be all real; and complex roots would yield a physically impossible solution. (Poisson himself solved the problem for Fourier years later.) The supposed lack of generality in Fourier's series solution (2) was probably by way of contrast to an integral solution already achieved by Laplace, in which the arbitrary function was neatly encased in the integrand.

Fourier's sensibility was that of rational mechanics. He had a superb mastery of analytical technique and notation ($\int_a^b$ is his invention, for example); and this power, guided by his physical intuition, brought him success. Before him, the equations used in the leading problems in rational mechanics were usually nonlinear, and they were solved by ad hoc approximation methods. Similarly, the field of differential equations was a jungle without pathways. Fourier created and explained a coherent method whereby the different components of an equation and its series solution were neatly identified, with the different aspects of the physical situation being analyzed. He also had a uniquely sure instinct for interpreting the asymptotic properties of the solutions of his equations for their physical meaning. So powerful was his approach that a full century passed before nonlinear differential equations regained prominence in mathematical physics.

For Fourier, every mathematical statement (although not all intermediate stages in a formal argument) had to have a physical meaning, both in exhibiting real motions and in being capable, in principle, of measurement. He always interpreted his solutions so as to obtain limiting cases which could be tested against experiment, and he performed such experiments at the earliest opportunity. He rejected the prevailing Laplacian orthodoxy of analyzing physical phenomena through the assumption of imperceptible molecules connected by local Newtonian forces; because of his approach to physical theory, together with his enmity to Poisson, he was adopted as philosophical patron by Auguste Comte in the development and popularization of *philosophie positive.*

Although the physical models of his earliest drafts were very sketchy, by the time of the 1807 paper he had fully incorporated physical constants into his theory of heat. The concern for physical meaning enabled him to see the potential in his formal technique for checking the coherence of the clumps of physical constants appearing in the exponentials of the Fourier integral solutions. From this came the full theory of units and dimensions (partly anticipated by Lazare Carnot), the first effective advance since Galileo in the theory of the mathematical representation of physical quantities. A comparison with the confused struggles of contemporaries such as Biot with the same problem illuminates Fourier's achievement.

Although Fourier studied the physical theory of heat for many years, his contributions, based primarily on the phenomena of radiation, did not long survive. His concern for applying his theory produced an analysis of the action of the thermometer, of the heating of rooms, and, most important, the first scientific estimate of a lower bound for the age of the earth. It is puzzling that in spite of his faith in the importance of heat as a primary agent in the universe, Fourier seems to have had no interest in the problem of the motive power of heat; and so, along with nearly all his contemporaries, he remained in ignorance of the essay on that topic by Lazare Carnot's son, Sadi.

On the side of real-variable analysis, the problems suggested especially by Fourier series lead directly through Dirichlet, Riemann, Stokes, and Heine to Cantor, Lebesgue, F. Riesz, and Ernst Fischer. Such deep results are not the chance products of algebraic doodling. None of Fourier's predecessors or contemporaries did—or could—exploit trigonometric expansions of arbitrary functions to their full effectiveness, nor could they recognize and accept their implications for the foundations of pure and applied analysis. Such achievements required a great master craftsman of mathematics, endowed with a lively imagination and holding a conscious philosophy of mathematics appropriate for his work. For Fourier, this was expressed in his aphorism, "Profound study of nature is the most fertile source of mathematical discoveries."

Theory of Equations. In contrast with his famous work on heat diffusion, Fourier's interest in the theory of equations is remarkably little known. Yet it has a much longer personal history, for it began in his sixteenth year when he discovered a new proof of Descartes's rule of signs and was just as much in progress at the time of his death. This rule may be stated as follows:

$$\text{Let } f(x) = x^m + a_1x^{m-1} + \cdots + a_{m-1}x + a_m.$$

Then there will be a sequence of signs to the coefficients of $f(x)$. If we call a pair of adjacent signs of the same type (i.e., $+\ +$ or $-\ -$) a preservation and a pair of the opposite type a variation, then the number of positive (or negative) roots of $f(x)$ is at most the number of variations (or preservations) of sign in the sequence. Fourier's proof was based on multiplying $f(x)$ by $(x + p)$, thus creating a new polynomial which contained one more sign in its sequence and one more positive (or negative) root, according as p was less (or greater) than zero, and showing that the number of preservations (or variations) in the new sequence was not increased relative to the old sequence. Hence the number of variations (or preservations) is increased by at least one, and the theorem follows. The details of the proof may be seen in any textbook dealing with the rule, for Fourier's youthful achievement quickly became the standard proof, even if its authorship appears to be virtually unknown.

Fourier generalized Descartes's rule to estimate the number of real roots $f(x)$ within a given interval $[a,b]$, by taking the signs of the terms in the sequence

$$f^{(m)}(x), f^{(m-1)}(x), \cdots, f''(x), f'(x), f(x).$$

When $x = -\infty$ the series will be made up totally of the variations

$$+ - + - \cdots\cdots$$

while at $x = +\infty$ it is entirely preservations:

$$+ + + + \cdots\cdots.$$

Fourier showed that as x passes from $-\infty$ to $+\infty$ the variations are lost by the crossing of a real (possibly multiple) root, or the skirting of a pair of complex conjugate roots, and that the number of real roots within $[a,b]$ is at most the difference between the number of variations in the sequence when $x = a$ and the number when $x = b$. This theorem received an important extension in Fourier's own lifetime by Sturm, who showed in 1829 that the number of real roots is exactly the difference in the number of variations formulated above for the sequence of functions

$$f_m(x), f_{m-1}(x), \cdots, f_2(x), f'(x), f(x)$$

where $f_2(x), \cdots\cdot$ are defined algorithmically from $f(x)$ and $f'(x)$. This is the famous Sturm's theorem.

Fourier appears to have proved his own theorem while in his teens and he sent a paper to the Academy in 1789. However, it disappeared in the turmoil of the year in Paris, and the pressure of administrative and other scientific work delayed publication of the results until the late 1810's. Then he became involved in a priority row with Ferdinand Budan de Bois-Laurent, a part-time mathematician who had previously published similar but inferior results. At the time of his death, Fourier was trying to prepare these and many other results for a book to be called *Analyse des équations déterminées;* he had almost finished only the first two of its seven *livres.* His friend Navier edited it for publication in 1831, inserting an introduction to establish from attested documents (including the 1789 paper) Fourier's priority on results which had by then become famous. Perhaps Fourier was aware that he would not live to finish the work, for he wrote a synopsis of the complete book which also appeared in the edition. The synopsis indicated his wide interests in the subject, of which the most important not yet mentioned were various means of distinguishing between real and imaginary roots, refinements to the Newton-Raphson method of approximating to the root of an equation, extensions to Daniel Bernoulli's rule for the limiting value of the ratio of successive terms of a recurrent series, and the method of solution and applications of linear inequalities. Fourier's remarkable understanding of the last subject makes him the great anticipator of linear programming.

Fourier's other mathematical interests included a general search for problems in dynamics and mechanics, shown by a published paper on the principle of virtual work. In his later years his directorship of the Bureau of Statistics brought him in touch with the problems of probability and errors, and he wrote important papers on estimating the errors of measurement from a large number of observations, published in the Bureau's reports for 1826 and 1829.

BIBLIOGRAPHY

I. Original Works. Fourier's most famous work is *Théorie analytique de la chaleur* (Paris, 1822; repr. Breslau, 1883). An English trans. was prepared by A. Freeman (Cambridge, 1878; repr. New York, 1955). A 2nd French ed. appeared in 1888 as vol. I of the *Oeuvres* of Fourier, Gaston Darboux, ed. Vol. II, containing the majority of the rest of Fourier's published works, appeared in 1890. The list of works given by Darboux in the intro. to this vol. shows that his principal omission was the *Analyse des équations déterminées* (Paris, 1831). Two German trans. of this book have been made: by C. H. Schnuse (Brunswick, 1836; notes added in 1846), and by A. Loewy, Ostwald's Klassiker, no. 127 (Leipzig, 1902). The other main omissions from Darboux's ed. were the first 79 articles of the 1811 prize paper on heat diffusion, in *Mémoires de l'Académie des sciences,* **4** (1819–1820), 185–555, which were largely in common with secs. of the book, and a joint paper with H. C. Oersted on thermoelectric effects, in *Annales de chimie et de physique,* **12** (1823), 375–389. Darboux's list also omitted the papers read by Fourier at the Institut d'Égypte, which are listed in Cousin's obit. of Fourier cited below and partially in Navier's introduction to the *Analyse.* As *secrétaire perpétuel* of the Académie des Sciences, Fourier wrote the *Analyse des travaux* (1823–1827), and *éloges* on Delambre, Herschel, Breguet, Charles, and Laplace. The references are in Darboux's list.

The main source of unpublished MSS is the twenty-nine vols. in the Bibliothèque Nationale (MSS fonds franç. 22501–22529), totaling about 5,200 sheets. Of these, 22501 is a set of miscellaneous studies and letters; 22502–22516 deal with the theory of equations, including topics only summarized in the *Analyse;* 22517–22522 cover extended work in mechanics, dynamics, and errors of measurement, etc.; and 22523–22529 are concerned with various aspects of heat diffusion and its associated mathematics and experimental work, including, in 22525, fols. 107–149, the "first draft" of his 1807 paper on heat diffusion. This paper itself was discovered by Darboux in the library of the École Nationale des Ponts et Chaussées (MS 267, now numbered 1851), which also contains several *cahiers* of lecture notes, totaling 386 pp., given by Fourier at the École Polytechnique in 1795–1796 (MS 668, and 1852). Another set of lecture notes, partly in common with this set, is in a vol. of 559 pp. in the Bibliothèque de l'Institut de France (MS 2044) where an early four-page article on Descartes's rule (MS 2038) may also be found. There is a scattering of letters in connection with his secretaryship of the Academy and his prefectures in various public MS collections in France and in the archives of various learned institutions.

With regard to his extrascientific writings, his notebook of the Egyptian campaign may be read in *Bibliothèque Égyptologique,* VI (Paris, 1904), 165–214. The various versions of the "Préface historique" are best compared on pp. 88–172 of the book by J. J. Champollion-Figeac cited below. Fourier wrote an article in the *Description* on the government of Egypt, and another on the astronomical monuments of the country (including a discussion of the Zodiacs). Details are given in the bibliographical account and collation of the *Description de l'Égypte* (London, 1838). He also contributed notes to a trans. by A. de Grandsagne of Pliny's *Natural History* and, although they are unsigned, it is clear that he annotated Pliny's discussion of Egypt, in *Histoire naturelle,* 20 vols. (Paris, 1829–1840), IV, 190–209. He also wrote the articles "Rallier des Ourmes," "Viète," and "Jean Wallis" in the *Biographie universelle,* 52 vols. (Paris, 1811–1829).

II. Secondary Literature. The main biographical work is by the archaeologist Jacques Joseph Champollion-Figeac, who was encouraged by Fourier at Grenoble: *Fourier, Napoléon, l'Égypte et les cent jours* (Paris, 1844). The other primary sources of biography are Victor Cousin, *Notes biographiques sur M. Fourier* (Paris, 1831), with an addition; also in his *Fragments et souvenirs,* 3rd ed. (Paris, 1857), 283–392; François Arago, "Éloge historique de Joseph Fourier," in *Mémoires de l'Académie des Sciences,* **14** (1838), lxix–cxxxviii; also in his *Oeuvres* (Paris, 1854), V, 295–369, and in an English trans. in *Biographies of Distinguished Scientific Men* (London, 1857), 242–286; and in *Annual Reports of the Smithsonian Institution* (1871), 137–176. See also Aimé-Louis Champollion-Figeac, *Chroniques dauphinoises. Les savants du département de l'Isère . . .* (Vienne, 1880) and *Seconde période historique 1794–1810* (Vienne, 1881); Victor Parisot, "Fourier," in *Biographie universelle,* XIV (Paris, 1856), 525–534; and Georges Mauger, "Joseph Fourier," in *Annuaire statistique de l'Yonne* (1837), 270–276.

Some discussion of Fourier's work is to be found in Heinrich Burkhardt, "Entwicklungen nach oscillierenden Functionen . . .," in *Jahresbericht der Deutschen Mathematikervereinigung,* **10,** pt. 2 (1901–1908), esp. chs. 7 and 8; Gaston Bachelard, *Étude sur l'évolution d'un problème de physique . . .* (Paris, 1928), esp. chs. 2–4; and Ivor Grattan-Guinness in collaboration with Jerome Ravetz, *Joseph Fourier 1768–1830* (in press), which contains the full text of the 1807 paper on heat diffusion.

Jerome R. Ravetz
I. Grattan-Guinness

FOURNEAU, ERNEST (*b.* Biarritz, France, 4 October 1872; *d.* Ascain, France, 5 August 1949), *chemistry.*

Of Spanish origin, Fourneau retained the appearance and elegant manner of that culture. His grandfather, the owner of a spinning mill, had established himself in France in the Basque country; his parents managed a large hotel in Biarritz. He received an excellent education; was fluent in English, German, and Spanish; and was interested in philosophy, literature, music, and painting, which he engaged in. He was also a brilliant conversationalist, owing to his education and to the cultivated circles that he frequented.

Following his secondary studies in Bayonne, he began studying pharmacy with Félix Moureu. In 1898 he obtained his diploma in Paris as a pharmacist; he then worked with the chemist Charles Moureu, brother of Félix. Having found his calling, he began to publish. In 1899 he commenced a three-year period of training in Germany under Theodor Curtius, Ludwig Gatterman, Emil Fischer (amino acids and barbiturate medications), and Richard Willstätter (chlorophyll). A witness to the birth of the German pharmaceutical industry, Fourneau returned to France and convinced the Poulenc brothers (Camille, Gaston, and Émile) of the necessity of creating a pharmaceutical chemistry laboratory. With the support of Camille Poulenc, he became the director of a laboratory in the factory at Ivry-sur-Seine. A born chemist and dextrous experimenter, there he was able to develop his talents. In 1904 he discovered an anesthetic that he named stovaine, a translation of the word *fourneau* ("stove").

In 1911, Émile Roux was director of the Institut Pasteur. Always alert to scientific progress, he welcomed Fourneau into the Grande Maison and named him chief of the new therapeutic chemistry service, which rapidly became world famous. Fourneau surrounded himself with remarkable researchers: chemists, microbiologists, physiologists, and physicians, notably Jacques and Thérèse Tréfouël (in 1921), and Daniel Bovet and Frédéric Nitti (in 1931). The service became a center for chemotherapeutic research.

From his marriage in 1906 to the daughter of the surgeon Paul Segond, he had three sons; one also became a chemist and director of a pharmaceutical laboratory. Fourneau reached retirement age in 1942 but continued to work at the Institut Pasteur until 1946. The Rhône-Poulenc chemical company then offered him a laboratory in Paris, where he continued his work. He was secretary-general of the Société Chimique de France, to which he gave great stimulus by his constant interest in the École de Pharmacie. He was an officer of the Légion d'Honneur (1903), and many orders of other societies were conferred upon him. He was a member of the Académie de Médecine (1919) and of a number of other French and foreign academies.

During World War I Fourneau was entrusted by the ministries of war and munitions with the study of various topics for the general dispensary (Pharmacie Générale) of military hospitals; in 1939 he was a member of the army's scientific commissions, and his laboratory was joined to the general staff.

Fourneau had lost his wife in 1942 at Ascain, to which he asked in 1949 to be transferred, being ill himself. Several days later, surrounded by his memorabilia, he passed away.

Fourneau published more than two hundred books, articles, and lectures in collaboration with other researchers on amino alcohols and ethylene oxides (stovaine). A master of this material, he was entrusted with the important chapter (XII) on it in the *Traité de chimie organique* of Victor Grignard (1941). As early as 1910 he had summarized his investigations with enumerations and descriptions of amino alcohols, oxaminated acids, *m*-acetylamino *p*-oxyphenylarsenic acid or stovarsol (Fourneau 190), and its isomer tryparsamide (Fourneau 270). As a natural continuation of his work he turned to the alkaloids (the ephedrines). He then studied corysanthine (the lysocythin of cobra venom) and glycerine esters and investigated the separation and the quantitative analysis of bismuth. Later he studied the stereochemistry of arsenic compounds, synthetic antipaludics (antimalarials), antihistamine derivatives and spasmolytics, and sulfur derivatives. He determined the formula of suramin sodium (Fourneau 309, Bayer 205) and its antibacterial action. Next he turned to the sulfamides (with the Tréfouëls, Bovet, and Nitti) and to sulfamidotherapy.

With his broad vision, Fourneau helped to establish the fundamental laws of chemotherapy that have saved so many human lives.

BIBLIOGRAPHY

I. Original Works. Fourneau's writings include "Stovaïne anesthésique local," in *Journal de pharmacie et de chimie,* 6th ser., **20** (1904), 108–109; "Ephédrines synthétiques," *ibid.,* **20** (1904), 481–499, and **25** (1907), 593–640; *Préparation des médicaments organiques* (Paris, 1921); "Anesthésiques locaux. Acides oxyaminés," in *Bulletin de la Société chimique de France,* 4th ser., **29** (1921), 413–416; "Recherches de chimiothérapie dans la série du 205 Bayer," in *Annales de l'Institut Pasteur,* **38** (1924), 81–114, written with J. Tréfouël and J. Vallée; "Sur une nouvelle méthode de sensibilité extrême pour la recherche, la séparation et le dosage du bismuth," in *Comptes rendus hebdomadaires des séances de l'Académie des sciences,* **181** (1925), 610–611, written with A. Girard; "Progrès récents dans le domaine des applications de la chimie à la thérapeutique," in *Bulletin des sciences pharmacologiques,* **35,** nos. 8 and 9 (1928), 499–516; "Préparation de dérivés en vue d'essais thérapeutiques: I, Amino alcools; II, Dérivés de l'atopian; III, Dérivés du carbostynyle; IV, Dérivés quinoléiniques et quiholéine arsinique," in *Annales de l'Institut Pasteur,* **44** (1930), 719–751, written with J. and T. Tréfouël and G. Benoit; "Sur une nouvelle classe d'hypnotique," in *Journal de pharmacie et de chimie,* **8** (1934), 49–54, written with J. R. Dilleter; "Chimiothérapie de l'infection pneumococcique par la di (p-acétylaminophényl) sulfone," in *Comptes rendus hebdomadaires des séances de l'Académie des sciences,* **205** (1937), 299–300, written with J. and T. Tréfouël, F. Nitti, and D. Bovet; "L'évolution de la chimiothérapie anti-bactérienne," in *Annales de l'Institut Pasteur,* **61** (1938), 799–811; "Quelques notions d'ordre chimique et rappel historique. L'antisepsie interne des maladies microbiennes par des dérivés du soufre," in *Gazette des hôpitaux civils et militaires,* **112,** no. 34 (1939), 577–581; "Aminoalcools," in Victor Grignard, *Traité de chimie organique,* XII (Paris, 1941), 393–635; and "La muscarine," in *Annales pharmaceutiques françaises,* **1,** no. 3 (1944), 120.

II. Secondary Literature. On Fourneau and his work, see M. Delépine, "Notice sur la vie et les travaux de Ernest Fourneau," in *Bulletin de la Société chimique de France,* 5th ser., **17** (1950), 953–982; P. Deloncle, "La science au service de l'action coloniale. Le laboratoire de chimiothérapie de l'Institut Pasteur," in *La dépêche coloniale* (27 Feb. 1927); T. A. Henry, "Ernest Fourneau," in *Journal of the Chemical Society,* **1** (1952), 261–266; R. Tiffeneau, "Ernest Fourneau," in *Paris-Médical,* **138** (1949), 470–471; J. Tréfouël, "Ernest Fourneau," in *Bulletin de la Société de pathologie exotique,* **42** (1949), 427–428; "Ernest Fourneau," in *Annales de l'Institut Pasteur,* **77** (1949), 644–647; and "Ernest Fourneau," in *Bulletin de l'Académie nationale de médecine,* **31–32** (1949), 589–595.

Denise Wrotnowska

FOURNEYRON, BENOÎT (*b.* Saint-Étienne, Loire, France, 31 October 1802; *d.* Paris, France, 8 July 1867), *hydraulic machinery.*

The son of a geometrician, Fourneyron prepared in mathematical sciences before entering at the age of fifteen a new school of mines at Saint-Étienne, from which he graduated at the top of the first class. His early activities were devoted to developing the mines at Le Creusot, prospecting for oil, laying out a railroad, and finally initiating the fabrication of tinplate —until then an English monopoly—at Pont-sur-l'Ognon, Haute-Saône. Involved in the latter process was a waterwheel of low efficiency, and Fourneyron became obsessed with the idea of producing a high-efficiency machine. At about the same time, one of his former professors at the school of mines, Claude Burdin, submitted to the Académie des Sciences a paper on hydraulic turbines; formally approved in 1824, it was noteworthy largely for its first use of the term. Both Burdin and Fourneyron then competed for a prize offered by the Société d'Encouragement pour l'Industrie Nationale for the first person to "succeed in applying at large scale, in a satisfactory manner, in mills and factories, the hydraulic turbines or wheels with curved blades of Bélidor." Burdin was a theoretician and was never able to produce a working model. Fourneyron, on the contrary, after four years of experimentation, had constructed by 1827 an operating unit of the outward-flow type, the power (6 h.p.) and efficiency (80 percent) of which he determined through the first practical application of the newly invented Prony brake. The Société Industrielle de Mulhouse that year awarded prizes to both inventors. Fourneyron patented the general design of his first three turbine installations in 1832. Although these were of the free-efflux type, he also foresaw the possibilities of efflux into a diffuser, and in 1855 he patented an outflow diffuser in the form of the present-day inflow scroll case. He was eventually to build more than one hundred hydraulic turbines of various forms for different parts of the world. His writings on water pressure, pipe design, and lock gates may be found in the *Mémoires* and *Comptes rendus* of the Académie des Sciences in the early 1840's.

BIBLIOGRAPHY

Relevant materials include B. Fourneyron, "Mémoire sur l'application en grand dans les mines et manufactures, des turbines hydrauliques ou roues à palettes courbes de Bélidor," in *Bulletin de la Société d'Encouragement pour l'Industrie Nationale,* **33** (1834), 3–17, 49–61, 85–96; M. Crozet-Fourneyron, *Invention de la turbine* (Paris, 1924); and H. Rouse and S. Ince, *History of Hydraulics* (New York, 1963), pp. 146–148.

HUNTER ROUSE

FOWLER, ALFRED (*b.* Wilsden, Yorkshire, England, 22 March 1868; *d.* Ealing, London, England, 24 June 1940), *astrophysics.*

Alfred Fowler was the eighth child and seventh son of Hiram Fowler and his wife, Eliza Hill Fowler. The family was of working-class origin, and Alfred attended elementary schools at Keighley, the largest neighboring town, to which the family moved about 1876. In 1880 he obtained a scholarship to the local trade and grammar school; in 1882, with the aid of a Devonshire exhibition, he proceeded to the Normal School of Science (later the Royal College of Science, now forming a constituent of the Imperial College of Science and Technology) at South Kensington. Here, after a successful career as a student of mechanics, he obtained an appointment as a teacher in training under Norman Lockyer, who had shortly before become director of the Solar Physics Observatory at South Kensington and lecturer in astronomy at the Normal School of Science. This began Fowler's close association with Lockyer and participation with him in the then new field of the application of the spectroscope to astronomy. The association lasted until Lockyer's retirement from the Royal College of Science in 1901, whereupon Fowler succeeded him as assistant professor, and later as professor, of astrophysics. He held this post until 1923, when he was appointed one of the first two Yarrow research professors of the Royal Society. He was thus enabled to continue research at the college but was relieved of teaching duties (other than the direction of research students). He remained there until his retirement in 1934.

In 1892, Fowler married Isabella Orr, who survived him, as did a daughter and a son. His life, apart from his astrophysical work, was uneventful, his interests being concentrated almost entirely on his scientific research and duties arising from his involvement in the organization of science. He successfully directed his students' activities, and many who later achieved distinction in spectroscopy owed much to their early research under his guidance. When the International Astronomical Union was formed in 1919, Fowler became its first general secretary, a position he retained until 1925. The original statutes of the union were drafted by Fowler and adopted almost without change.

During his association with Lockyer, much of Fowler's work was incorporated into that of the senior man, and it was not until he became an independent investigator that his own abilities began to be recognized. Consequently, honors came to him slowly at first, but later in good measure. Temperamentally he was a striking contrast to Lockyer; and their association, although not without occasional misunderstandings, was in many respects fortunate for both. Lockyer's impetuous development of an idea until it became a hypothesis too massive for its frail observational basis was tempered, and often supported, by Fowler's insistence on the primacy of facts and his great skill in acquiring them; while Fowler never forgot, or failed to acknowledge, the inspiration he received, especially in his early days, from Lockyer's enthusiasm. Fowler's life was marked by a quiet integrity and amiability that endeared him to all his associates.

His contributions to astrophysics were based on an exceptionally intimate knowledge of the characteristic spectra of the elements, acquired during his apprenticeship with Lockyer, and an almost uncanny skill in recognizing the identity of celestial spectra and those obtained under vastly different laboratory conditions. These abilities enabled him to assign the band spectra yielded by the cool stars (type M) to titanium oxide, to detect the presence of magnesium hydride in sunspots, to identify bands observed in comet tail spectra with those of low-pressure carbon monoxide, and, with R. J. Strutt (later Lord Rayleigh), to prove that the termination of solar and stellar spectra in the near ultraviolet was caused by ozone in the earth's atmosphere.

His outstanding achievements, however, followed the sudden enlargement of interest in spectroscopy created by Bohr's successful theory of the origin of spectra that appeared in 1913. This made possible a theoretical analysis of spectra that demanded a knowledge of their details, in which Fowler was unrivaled. His work as Lockyer's assistant had involved not only investigations of laboratory spectra from all available sources and of as great a range of celestial spectra as the atmospheric conditions at South Kensington allowed, but also participation in several expeditions to observe total eclipses of the sun. Moreover, under the influence of Lockyer's dissociation hypothesis Fowler had acquired a large amount of information on the variation of spectra with physical conditions, although the general disfavor extended to that hypothesis had discouraged its publication.

The Bohr theory showed the significance and value of such data, and Fowler accordingly took a leading part in the subsequent elucidation of the structure of the various atoms from the characteristics of their spectra. As a first reaction to the Bohr theory he pointed out a discrepancy between the wavelength of the so-called cosmic hydrogen line at λ4686 Å, which he had observed in the spectrum of the sun's chromosphere, and that calculated by Bohr as λ4688 Å and ascribed to ionized helium—an anomaly that resulted in the first refinement of the theory, in which account was taken of the finite ratio of the masses of the proton and the electron. There ensued a continuous interaction between theory and observation in which Fowler played a leading part.

It is fortunate that the period during which spectroscopy stood in the vanguard of physical advance coincided with that in which Fowler, with unique experience and possession of the necessary observational data, could place such data, with no preconceptions, at the service of theoretical investigators. His career offers one of the best examples we have of the variety of possible interactions of theory and observation in the advancement of science.

BIBLIOGRAPHY

Fowler wrote little beyond his original papers, mainly in *Proceedings of the Royal Society* and *Monthly Notices of the Royal Astronomical Society.* "I was too keenly interested in research," he wrote, "to give much thought to the writing of books." Nevertheless, he published a handbook entitled *Popular Telescopic Astronomy* (London, 1895), with the subtitle *How to Make a 2-inch Telescope and What to See With It,* and he contributed about 190 pages on "Geometrical Astronomy and Astronomical Instruments" to a volume entitled *The Concise Knowledge Astronomy* (London, 1896). His only work on his chief specialty was *Report on Series in Line Spectra* (London, 1922), which contains all the data then available on the regularities in spectra (much of which he had brought to light) together with a general account of the subject. He contributed a chapter to *Life and Work of Sir Norman Lockyer,* by T. Mary Lockyer and Winifred L. Lockyer (London, 1928), in which he gives some account of his relations with Sir Norman.

No biography of Fowler exists; the notice in *Obituary Notices of the Royal Society, 1940* is probably the fullest that has appeared.

HERBERT DINGLE

FOWLER, RALPH HOWARD (*b.* Roydon, Essex, England, 17 January 1889; *d.* Cambridge, England, 28 July 1944), *physics.*

Fowler was the oldest son of Howard Fowler, a London businessman, and Ena, daughter of George Dewhurst, a Manchester businessman. He was educated at Winchester and at Trinity College, Cambridge (B.A., 1911); as a student he showed considerable ability in golf and cricket as well as winning prizes in mathematics. After taking his degree he published some work on the theory of solutions of differential equations and as a result was elected to a fellowship at Trinity in October 1914.

By this time Fowler had obtained a commission in the Royal Marine Artillery. He was wounded in the Gallipoli campaign, and while convalescing in 1916 was persuaded to join a group of scientists, led by A. V. Hill, who were doing research on such military problems as tracking the flight of airplanes and computing trajectories of cannon shells. This early introduction to applied mathematics seems to have influenced Fowler's subsequent interest in physical problems, although he did not entirely abandon his earlier commitment to pure mathematics.

In 1921, two years after returning to Cambridge as a fellow, he married Eileen, the only daughter of Sir Ernest Rutherford. They had four children.

In 1922 Fowler and C. G. Darwin published a series of papers on statistical mechanics in which they developed methods for calculating the "partition functions" associated with the distribution of energy in quantum systems. (By using the theory of functions of a complex variable they were able to avoid some of the usual approximations.)

Fowler then extended these methods in statistical mechanics to deal with the equilibrium states of ionized gases at high temperatures. His results could be immediately applied to the interpretation of stellar spectra and provided a new method for estimating the temperatures and pressures of stellar interiors. Fowler also provided one of the earliest applications of the new "quantum statistics" of E. Fermi and P. A. M. Dirac when in 1926 he proposed that white dwarf stars consist of a "degenerate" gas of extremely high density. Thus Fowler was one of the founders of modern theoretical astrophysics. (His work on the solutions of Emden's equation was another contribution to this field.)

By the early 1920's Fowler was among the very few workers at Cambridge who maintained a continuing interest in the progress of the quantum theory; he kept in touch with recent developments through correspondence and visits to Copenhagen. Those students—such as Dirac—who turned their attention to the quantum theory had usually been introduced to it by Fowler, and it was he who gave Dirac the galley proofs of Heisenberg's "matrix article" of 1925, which led to Dirac's discovery of Poisson-Bracket relations (according to private communication from T. S. Kuhn, based on information in the Archive for History of Quantum Physics). Because of his connection with Rutherford, Fowler was particularly well placed to introduce problems from the quantum theory into the discussions of the more experimentally inclined physicists who gathered at the Cavendish Laboratory and in the Kapitza Club. Much of the early work at Cambridge on this aspect of physics was therefore stimulated by him.

Fowler was awarded the Adams Prize at Cambridge University in 1924 for an essay on statistical mechanics. In 1929 he published a revised version of this essay, including the application of quantum statistics and ionization theory to states of matter at high pressures and high temperatures. *Statistical Mechanics* became the standard reference work on the subject in English-speaking countries for the next decade; it was followed by a second edition (1936) and by *Statistical Thermodynamics* (1939), a book emphasizing applications to physical chemistry, written with E. A. Guggenheim.

Fowler was elected to the Plummer chair of theoretical physics at Cambridge in 1932 and continued to pioneer the applications of statistical mechanics and to explore other areas of theoretical physics. Together with such students and colleagues as E. A. Guggenheim and R. F. Peierls he developed the "Ising model" as a theory of phase transitions and cooperative phenomena in magnets, alloys, and solutions.

In 1938 he was appointed director of the National Physical Laboratory, to succeed Sir Lawrence Bragg, but had to decline the appointment almost immediately because of illness. In World War II he served as a consultant to the Ordnance Board and the Admiralty. In 1942 he was knighted for his services to the government, in particular for establishing scientific liaison between research efforts on military problems in England and in Canada, and for his accomplishments during an important mission to Canada and the United States.

BIBLIOGRAPHY

The best source of information about Fowler is the comprehensive memoir by his friend and colleague E. A. Milne, in the *Obituary Notices of Fellows of the Royal Society of London,* **5** (1945–1948), 61–78, which contains a portrait, bibliography, and many personal recollections.

STEPHEN G. BRUSH

FOWNES, GEORGE (*b.* London, England, 14 May 1815; *d.* Brompton, England, 31 January 1849), *chemistry.*

Fownes worked in his father's glove business until 1837, when he began to study science with Thomas Everitt, lecturer in chemistry at the Middlesex Hospital. In 1839 he earned the doctorate degree under

Liebig at Giessen. On his return to London he became Thomas Graham's assistant at University College. He held lectureships in chemistry at Charing Cross and Middlesex hospitals. In 1842 he became professor of chemistry to the Pharmaceutical Society and began a lecture series on organic chemistry at the Royal Institution. He was the first director of the newly established Birkbeck Laboratory at University College (1845). Pulmonary disease obliged him to resign his lectureships by 1846, and after three years of poor health he died of consumption.

Fownes accomplished the bulk of his work in only four years (1842–1846). His most notable achievement was the isolation of two new organic bases. In 1845 he prepared furfural by the action of sulfuric acid on bran. In the same year he isolated benzoline (hydrobenzamide) from the oil of bitter almonds. In 1839 he accurately determined the equivalent weight of carbon by means of the combustion of naphthalene; Fownes reported that the accepted value as determined by Berzelius and others was too high. He prepared potassium cyanide by passing nitrogen over potassium carbonate and charcoal at high temperature, a process that was used industrially for a time. In 1844 he discovered the presence of phosphate in igneous rocks and suggested that this was the original source of phosphate in clay and soil.

He published two widely read books. In 1843 he was awarded the Royal Institution's Acton Prize for his *Chemistry, As Exemplifying the Wisdom and Beneficence of God,* an argument for design in the universe based on the chemical constitution of the earth, sea, and atmosphere. His *Manual of Elementary Chemistry* (1844) was a very popular textbook for half a century.

BIBLIOGRAPHY

I. ORIGINAL WORKS. Fownes's *Manual of Elementary Chemistry, Theoretical and Practical* (London, 1844) appeared in many eds. under the editorship of H. B. Jones, A. W. Hofmann, H. Watts, and W. A. Tilden; the final ed. was published in 1889. His *Chemistry, As Exemplifying the Wisdom and Beneficence of God* had two eds. (London, 1844, 1849). Fownes also published *An Introduction to Qualitative Analysis* (London, 1846) and *Rudimentary Chemistry* (London, 1848). Significant papers include "On the Equivalent of Carbon," in *The Philosophical Magazine,* ser. 3, **15** (1839), 62–65; "On the Formation of Cyanogen From Its Elements," in *Pharmaceutical Journal and Transactions,* **1** (1842), 338–343; "On the Existence of Phosphoric Acid in Rocks of Igneous Origin," in *Philosophical Transactions of the Royal Society,* **134** (1844), 53–56; "An Account of the Artificial Formation of a Vegeto-Alkali," *ibid.,* **135** (1845), 253–262; and "On Benzoline, a New Organic Salt-Base From Bitter Almond Oil," *ibid.,* 263–268.

II. SECONDARY LITERATURE. The most detailed notice on Fownes is J. S. Rowe, "The Life and Work of George Fownes, F.R.S. (1815–49)," in *Annals of Science,* **6** (1948–1950), 422–435. Several brief obituary notices appeared at the time of his death: *Journal of the Chemical Society,* **2** (1849), 184–187; *Pharmaceutical Journal and Transactions,* **8** (1849), 449–450; and *Proceedings of the Royal Society,* **5** (1849), 882–883.

ALBERT B. COSTA

FRACASTORO, GIROLAMO (*b.* Verona, Italy, *ca.* 1478; *d.* Incaffi [now hamlet of Affi, Verona], 6 August 1553), *medicine, philosophy.*

Descendant of a patrician Veronese family and the sixth of seven brothers, Fracastoro received his first literary and philosophical instruction from his father; his mother, Camilla Mascarelli, seems to have died when he was still very young.

As an adolescent, he was sent to the Academy in Padua, where he was entrusted to a family friend, Girolamo Della Torre, a Veronese who taught and practiced medicine there. Fracastoro studied literature, mathematics, astronomy, philosophy (the latter under the guidance of Pietro Pomponazzi and Nicolò Leonico Tomeo), and medicine, in which he was instructed by Girolamo Della Torre and his son Marcantonio, and Alessandro Benedetti. Fracastoro was a fellow student of the brothers Giovan Battista and Raimondo Della Torre, of the future cardinals Ercole Gonzaga and Gaspare Contarini, and of Andrea Navagero; and he established relationships with Giovanni Battista Ramusio and Pietro Bembo that proved of primary importance. Immediately after receiving his degree (1502) he became an instructor in logic at the University of Padua, where he was also *conciliarius anatomicus.* His contacts with Copernicus, who had enrolled in medicine at Padua in 1501, date from this time. While he was still young, Fracastoro married (1500?) Elena de Clavis (or Schiavi), by whom he had five children: four sons—Giovanni Battista; Paolo and Giulio, who died at an early age and were lamented by their father in one of his odes; and Paolo Filippo, born in 1517 and the only son to survive his father—and a daughter, Isabella.

After the death of his father and the closing of the University of Padua and with the threat of war between Venice and the Emperor Maximilian I, Fracastoro left Padua and in 1508 followed Bartolomeo d'Alviano to Porto Naone (now Pordenone) in Friuli, where Alviano presented him at the Accademia Friulana. After a short stay, he followed Alviano to the border of the Veneto, apparently as a doctor. Alviano was taken prisoner at Giara d'Adda, after the Venetian defeat at the battle of Agnadello (1509). Fracastoro returned to Verona and established residence in the area of the church of Santa Eufemia.

He then dedicated himself to his studies, to reorganizing his estate, and, for a while, to medical practice, treating patients from all over Italy. He actively participated in the life of the local *collegio dei fisici,* where he had already matriculated in 1501 and of which he was four times prior and eight times councillor. Although interested in politics, he never held public office.

From 1511 he began to alternate his residence in Verona with long sojourns at his villa in Incaffi, on the slopes of Monte Baldo, where his learned friends gathered for philosophical and scientific meetings. Meanwhile he maintained relations with such leading figures as Gian Matteo Giberti, bishop of Verona, a man of great culture and patron of writers, scientists, and artists, whose guest Fracastoro was at Malcesine. He was also expanding his cultural interests, which touched not only on philosophy and medicine but on the liberal arts and natural sciences in general; and he attained noteworthy erudition and competence in each area, as his surviving writings testify.

Fracastoro's fame, esteem, and acquaintances in ecclesiastical circles contributed to his nomination by Pope Paul III in 1545 as *medicus conductus et stipendiatus* of the Council of Trent, to which he went upon request, a guest of Cardinal Madruzzo. His presentiment of a terrible epidemic seems to have influenced the transfer (1547), which the pope desired, of the Council from Trent to Bologna. Around 1546 Fracastoro was made canon of Verona, with special dispensations.

His mental faculties undimmed by age, Fracastoro suffered a stroke that killed him within the day, on 6 August 1553, almost certainly in his house at Incaffi. His body was transported to Verona and was buried in the church of Santa Eufemia, where it rested probably until 1740; the remains have since been lost. In 1555 a statue was erected to him in Verona, in the Piazza dei Signori, near the existing statues of Pliny and Catullus.

Fracastoro's scientific personality matured in the atmosphere of Padua, where he had ample opportunity to enter into the disputes of the Scholastics and the followers of Alexander of Aphrodisias and Ibn Rushd (Averroës). Philosophical considerations were thus always inherent in his more purely scientific work. His thought, although not always organic, is framed in those philosophies of nature which were developed by various writers of the Italian Renaissance and which are the result of two components, a diminished interest in theological subjects and metaphysics in general and an increased interest in the study of nature, in which man lives and which is held to be the only subject appropriate to his understanding, which requires certainty. (Significant in this regard is the beginning of the posthumously published *Turrius sive de intellectione dialogus.*) This interest in nature differs from that of the preceding era, that is, of the humanists: the contemplative aspect gives way to the operative one. That is, nature is considered as an autonomous reality, upheld by its own laws, in which a mixture of good and bad is inherent and before which any recourse to supernatural intervention is useless; to derive the most profit and happiness, man must rely only on himself and on his capacity for progressive understanding of the world's regulating principles. These ideas emerge in the narrative poem *Syphilis sive morbus Gallicus* (1530), which brought Fracastoro universal fame, as is attested by numerous editions and translations in various languages; in it the nature and cure of lues are illustrated.

Composed in 1521, the poem was initially divided into two books. In the final draft it was published in three books, despite advice to the contrary by Pietro Bembo (in his letter of 5 January 1526 to Fracastoro, in which he also firmly asserted that some passages be eliminated), to whom it is dedicated and by whom it was esteemed and praised, both when it was sent to him by Fracastoro for a preliminary reading in 1525 and subsequently.

The poem, drafted in Latin hexameter (about 1,300 verses) of exquisite beauty, occupies a prominent place in the literature of the times and represents a magnificent paradigm of formal sixteenth-century virtuosity in refined Latin of a didactic quality reminiscent of Vergil's *Georgics.* Through the work the name of the sickness became definitively established; the name was, in fact, considered to derive from that of the hero of Fracastoro's treatise, the unfortunate shepherd Sifilo. Others believe that the word *sifilo* derived from *sifilide,* a term already in use in the local dialect of the Veneto.

According to Fracastoro's mythological tale, the terrible disease originated as the punishment (an unclean ulcer on the body) inflicted by the sun god on the young shepherd Sifilo, who had become unfaithful to him. The misdeed was, however, forgiven, and the guaiacum, a great leafy tree, was born. Humanity learned to extract from it the medicament that cured the disease. Also effective against lues is mercury, which the nymph Lipare advised the shepherd Ilceo to use. The ample and exhaustive description of the various luetic manifestations demonstrates Fracastoro's lucid knowledge of the clinical events and the related course of the illness.

In *De morbo Gallico* the author lays the first foundations of his doctrine of infections, since he was already familiar with the *semina morbi* of Lucretius through Andrea Navagero's edition of *De rerum natura* (1515). The concepts of contagion indicated in *De morbo Gallico* were further developed in Fracastoro's prose treatise on syphilis, written in 1553 but not published until 1939, which served as preparation for the subsequent formulation of the Fracastorian doctrine of contagion. Some authors consider noteworthy in *De morbo Gallico* not so much the illustrations of the pathological phenomena as Fracastoro's manner, his feeling for human suffering, as exemplified in the episode of the death from syphilis of a young man from Brescia, and in the vivid description of the misfortunes that pervaded Europe, and especially Italy, in the first half of the sixteenth century. The work also provided the poet with an opportunity to celebrate the great geographical discoveries of the century.

The theory has also been advanced that the subject dealt with in *De morbo Gallico* is only a pretext for posing a problem of greater significance. The dominant theme of the first book is that of the mutations that take place in nature. Nature creates and destroys and gives misery and happiness, and it is useless to try to appease the gods. Science, whose power alone can give joy, dictates man's actions.

For the construction of a philosophy of nature that starts from the above premise, a fundamental question obviously is posed—that of method. For Fracastoro the only valid one is that of experience, as he does not hesitate to declare in the *Homocentrica sive de stellis* (1538), a work on astronomy in which the movements of the heavens and the celestial spheres with their orbits, the seasons, and various types of days (civil, solar, sidereal) are illustrated, and in which Fracastoro again reinstates in a place of honor the most ancient astronomical theory, the Eudoxian. Apart from the intrinsic value of the work, its attempts to solve certain problems in astronomical and terrestrial physics are interesting, as are the studies on refraction. In the course of the latter Fracastoro points out the apparent enlargement and approach of celestial objects (as well as the moon) observed through two superimposed lenses, analogous to the appearance of a body immersed in water, which varies exactly according to the quantity and density of the water itself.

The discourse on experience, begun in the *Homocentrica,* is developed in *De causis criticorum dierum libellus* (1538). Experience, in order to be fruitful, must be collected and examined by secure concepts; these keep it from degenerating into a dispersion of multiplicities or into fantasy and magic, which would constitute a renewed victory of the transcendentalist attitude toward nature. In *De causis* Fracastoro gives an example of badly interpreted experience: critical days really exist in the course of an illness, but it is an error to look for the explanation of this solely in astral influences or certain numerological relationships. The cause lies in the nature of the disease itself, that is, in the humoral modifications; the crisis is an expression of the organic actions and reactions determined by the qualitative and quantitative alteration of the humor or humors involved.

That which unifies experience is the Aristotelian concept of cause. The type of cause capable of unifying natural phenomena is not of the order of most general causes; Fracastoro considers these useless because they are *remotissimae a rebus.* It is, rather, that of the closest and most particular causes, that is, the middle causes; furthermore, one must strive to arrive at those causes which are *propinquissimae et propriae.* Thus the traditional position of philosophy is turned upside down: philosophy is such to the extent that it investigates not abstract but concrete nature. To proceed along the path of universals and principles of things is to condemn philosophy—so far as it concerns nature—and to leave *innumera intacta* and other things *non plana discussa.*

In *De sympathia ed antipathia rerum* (1546) Fracastoro recognizes that the principle immanent in nature and explaining it is *simpatia,* which Fracastoro conceives of in a sense different from that of the humanists. To Fracastoro sympathy is a principle of spiritual order; it is the *species spiritualis* that unifies the world. In particular, it is to be brought down to the plane of natural things that are to be studied naturalistically.

Bound to the cosmological principle of sympathy are Fracastoro's anthropological and esthetic concepts. It is sympathy, in fact, that gives nature an unbroken gradualism, so that there is no disruption in man's faculties; sense and intellect are both passive and both have a *species,* even though of a different unifying power. That which really belongs to the intellect is judgment, conceived as a synthesis of sensory data and of the universal. The pure sensations, on the other hand, attain a unity of their own in the forces of the *subnotiones,* which distinguish them from one another and place them in interrelation. Fracastoro expresses these ideas in the *Turrius sive de intellectione dialogus,* in which he conceived of knowledge as a progressive unification of multiplicities, rather as did Kant. Similarly, in the *Naugerius sive de poetica dialogus* (1549), the essence of poetry is rendered neither by the content with which the poet deals nor by the form, which can be various, but rather by the intuition of beauty, which is then the universal, present in all things and expressing itself in the sympathy that regulates them. This differentiates the poet from the historian, who deals with particulars.

Fracastoro's scientific thought culminates and concludes with *De contagione et contagiosis morbis et curatione* (1546), which assures him a lasting place in the history of epidemiology. In it he clearly describes numerous contagious diseases, with chapters of principal interest, such as that on phthisis, whose contagion and affinity for the lungs he affirms. In the work's most significant part Fracastoro illustrates the three means by which contagion can be spread: by simple contact (as in scabies and leprosy); by *fomites,* corresponding to carriers (clothing, sheets); and at a distance, without direct contact or carriers (as in plague, smallpox, and the like). Fracastoro imagines that in the last case the *seminaria* propagate either by choosing the humors for which they have the greatest affinity or by attraction, penetrating through the inspiration of the vessels. According to Fracastoro the seeds of contagion are in fact responsible for contagion; they are distinct imperceptible particles, composed of various elements. Spontaneously generated in the course of certain types of putrefaction, they present particular characteristics and faculties, such as that of increasing themselves, having their own motion, propagating quickly, enduring for a long time, even far from their focus of origin, exerting specific contagious activity, and dying.

In *De contagione* the epidemiological problems and the *principia contagionum* are delved into with great acuteness. Fracastoro's sheer prophetic intuition yielded hypotheses on causes and ways of infections that were verified in succeeding centuries.

In certain passages the Fracastorian *seminaria* seem to be like our microorganisms. Undoubtedly, the *seminaria* derive from Democritean atomism via the *semina* of Lucretius and the gnostic and Neoplatonic speculations renewed by St. Augustine and St. Bonaventura (*rationes seminales*); but the Fracastorian *seminaria* differ greatly from traditional *semina.* It is difficult—perhaps impossible—to establish incontrovertibly whether Fracastoro really foresaw, as some would like to believe, the existence of microbes. He seems to attribute certain vital faculties to his *seminaria* and to use suggestive terminology for them (such as generation, birth, and life), but in light of the state of knowledge at the time—the inability to distinguish clearly between the organic and inorganic and belief in spontaneous generation—Fracastoro could not assign to his *seminaria* all the typical characteristics of microorganisms.

Fracastoro left works on other subjects, including botany, geology, and medicine. Among those in which the philosophical and literary content merits mention are the *Fracastorius sive de anima dialogus,* in which he affirms the immortality of the soul; and the short poems *Alcon seu de cura canum venaticorum* and *Ioseph.*

BIBLIOGRAPHY

I. Original Works. Fracastoro's works were published in one vol. as *Opera omnia* (Venice, 1555); there were various reprintings, of which the Cominiana ed. (Padua, 1739) is important. Included in the first ed. are *Homocentricorum sive de stellis, liber unus; De causis criticorum dierum libellus; De sympathia et antipathia rerum liber unus; De contagionibus et contagiosis morbis et eorum curatione libri tres; Naugerius sive de poetica dialogus; Turrius sive de intellectione dialogus; Fracastorius sive de anima dialogus; De vini temperatura sententia; Syphilis sive morbus Gallicus, libri tres; Ioseph libri duo;* and *Carminum liber unus.*

Some letters of Fracastoro to G. B. Ramusio, of interest because they refer to the scientific life of the era, were published in 1564 in Tommaso Poracchi, *Lettere di XIII huomini illustri.* A later ed. (Venice, 1632) also contains a letter from Fracastoro to Paolo Ramusio. See also the prose treatise on syphilis, Codice CCLXXV-I, Biblioteca Capitolare, Verona (Verona, 1939); and a vol. of *Scritti inediti* (Verona, 1955); other works are scattered in various publications. Many MSS, partially unpublished, are preserved in the Biblioteca Capitolare.

II. Secondary Literature. The indicated works serve as bibliographical sources: L. Baumgartner and J. F. Fulton, *A Bibliography of the Poem Syphilis sive Morbus Gallicus by Girolamo Fracastoro of Verona* (New Haven, 1935); E. Cassirer, *Storia della filosofia moderna,* A. Pasquinelli, G. Colli, and E. Arnaud, trans., I (Turin, 1964), 258–264, *passim;* B. Croce, "Il dialogo di Fracastoro sulla poetica," in *Quaderni della critica,* no. 9 (Nov. 1947), 56–61; E. di Leo, *Scienze ed umanesimo in Girolamo Fracastoro,* 2nd ed. (Salerno, 1953); E. Garin, *Storia della filosofia italiana,* II. *Il Rinascimento,* 2nd ed. (Turin, 1966), 627–629, *passim;* F. Pellegrini, *Fracastoro* (Trieste, 1948); F. Pellegrini, G. Alberti, A. Spallicci, *et al., Studi e memorie nel IV centenario* (Verona, 1954); and G. Saitta, *Il pensiero italiano nell'umanesimo e nel Rinascimento,* II. *Il Rinascimento,* 2nd ed. (Florence, 1961), 177–212, *passim.*

Bruno Zanobio

FRAENKEL, ADOLF ABRAHAM (*b.* Munich, Germany, 17 February 1891; *d.* Jerusalem, Israel, 15 October 1965), *mathematics.*

Fraenkel studied at the universities of Munich, Marburg, Berlin, and Breslau. From 1916 to 1921 he was a lecturer at the University of Marburg, where

FRAENKEL

he became a professor in 1922. In 1928 he taught at the University of Kiel, and then from 1929 to 1959 he taught at the Hebrew University of Jerusalem. A fervent Zionist with a deep interest in Jewish culture, he engaged in many social activities. His interest in the history of mathematics appears in his papers "Zahlbegriff und Algebra bei Gauss" (1920), "Georg Cantor" (1930), and "Jewish Mathematics and Astronomy" (1960). As a mathematician he was interested in the axiomatic foundation of mathematical theories. His first works were on algebra, notably on the axiomatics of Hensel's p-adic numbers and on the theory of rings. He soon turned to the theory of sets, and in 1919 his remarkable *Einleitung in die Mengenlehre* appeared, which was reprinted several times. Engaged in a proof of the independence of the axiom system of Ernst Zermelo (1908), Fraenkel noticed that the system did not suffice for a foundation of set theory and required stronger axioms of infinity. At the same time he found a way to avoid Zermelo's imprecise notion of definite property.

Briefly stated, Zermelo's set theory is about a system B of objects closed under certain principles of set production (axioms). One of these axioms, the axiom of subsets, states that if a property E is definite in a set M, then there is a subset consisting precisely of those elements x of M for which $E(x)$ is true. Property E is definite for x if it can be decided systematically whether $E(x)$ is true or false. Another one is the famous axiom of choice, stating that the union of a set T of nonvoid disjoint sets contains a subset that has precisely one element in common with the sets of T.

Instead of Zermelo's notion of definite property Fraenkel used a notion of function, introduced by definition; and he replaced Zermelo's axiom of subsets by the following: If M is a set and ϕ and ψ are functions, then there are subsets M_E and $M_{E'}$ consisting of those elements x of M for which $\phi(x)$ is an element of $\psi(x)$, and $\phi(x)$ is not an element of $\psi(x)$ respectively. Using this axiom Fraenkel proved the independence of the axiom of choice, having recourse to an infinite set of objects that are not sets themselves. A proof avoiding such an extraneous assumption proved to be far more difficult and was given in 1963 by P. J. Cohen for a slightly revised system, ZFS, named after Zermelo, Fraenkel, and Thoralf Skolem. This system derives from a modification proposed by Skolem in 1922, consisting in the interpretation of definite property as property expressible in first-order logic.

In a series of papers Fraenkel developed ZF set theory to include theories of order and well-order. His encyclopedic knowledge of set theory is preserved in his works *Abstract Set Theory* (1953) and *Foundations of Set Theory* (1958). As early as 1923 he emphasized the importance of a thorough investigation of predicativism, based on ideas of H. Poincaré and undertaken much later by G. Kreisel, S. Feferman, and K. Schütte, among others.

BIBLIOGRAPHY

I. ORIGINAL WORKS. Fraenkel's writings include "Axiomatische Begründung von Hensels p-adischen Zahlen," in *Journal für die reine und angewandte Mathematik,* **141** (1912), 43–76; "Über die Teiler der Null und die Zerlegung von Ringen," *ibid.,* **145** (1915), 139–176; *Einleitung in die Mengenlehre* (Berlin, 1919); "Zahlbegriff und Algebra bei Gauss," in *Nachrichten von der Königlichen Gesellschaft der Wissenschaften zu Göttingen,* Math.-phys. Kl. (1920), pp. 1–49; "Über einfache Erweiterungen zerlegbarer Ringe," in *Journal für die reine und angewandte Mathematik,* **151** (1921), 121–167; "Über die Zermelosche Begründung der Mengenlehre," in *Jahresbericht der Deutschen Mathematikervereinigung,* **30** (1921), 97–98; "Zu den Grundlagen der Cantor-Zermeloschen Mengenlehre," in *Mathematische Annalen,* **86** (1922), 230–237; "Axiomatische Begründung der transfiniten Kardinal-zahlen. I," in *Mathematische Zeitschrift,* **13** (1922), 153–188; "Der Begriff 'definit' und die Unabhängigkeit des Auswahl-axioms," in *Sitzungsberichte der Preussischen Akademie der Wissenschaften,* Math.-phys. Kl. (1922), pp. 253–257; "Die neueren Ideen zur Grundlegung der Analysis und Mengenlehre," in *Jahresbericht der Deutschen Mathematikervereinigung,* **33** (1924), 97–103; "Untersuchungen über die Grundlagen der Mengenlehre," in *Mathematische Zeitschrift,* **22** (1925), 250–273; "Axiomatische Theorie der geordneten Mengen," in *Journal für die reine und angewandte Mathematik,* **55** (1926), 129–158; *Zehn Vorlesungen über die Grundlegung der Mengenlehre* (Leipzig-Berlin, 1927); "Georg Cantor," in *Jahresbericht der Deutschen Mathematikervereinigung,* **39** (1930), 189–226; "Das Leben Georg Cantors," in *Georg Cantor Gesammelte Abhandlungen,* E. Zermelo, ed. (Berlin, 1932; Hildesheim, 1966), pp. 452–483; "Axiomatische Theorie der Wohlordnung," in *Journal für die reine und angewandte Mathematik,* **167** (1932), 1–11; *Abstract Set Theory* (Amsterdam, 1953); *Axiomatic Set Theory* (Amsterdam, 1958), written with P. Bernays; *Foundations of Set Theory* (Amsterdam, 1958), written with Y. Bar-Hillel; "Jewish Mathematics and Astronomy," in *Scripta mathematica,* **25** (1960), 33–47; and *Lebenskreise, aus den Erinnerungen eines jüdischen Mathematikers* (Stuttgart, 1967).

II. SECONDARY LITERATURE. On Fraenkel and his work, see (in chronological order) T. Skolem, "Einige Bemerkungen zur axiomatischen Begründung der Mengenlehre," in *Wiss. Vorträge gehalten auf dem 5. Kongress der skandinav. Mathematiker in Helsingfors 1922* (1923), pp. 217–232; J. von Neumann, "Über die Definition durch transfinite Induktion und verwandte Fragen der allgemeinen Mengenlehre," in *Mathematische Annalen,* **99** (1928), 373–391; G.

Kreisel, "La prédicativité," in *Bulletin de la Société mathématique de France,* **88** (1960), 371–391; K. Schütte, *Beweistheorie* (Berlin, 1960); S. Feferman, "Systems of Predicative Analysis," in *Journal of Symbolic Logic,* **29** (1964), 1–30; P. J. Cohen, *Set Theory and the Continuum Hypothesis* (New York, 1966); and J. van Heijenoort, *From Frege to Gödel* (Cambridge, Mass., 1967).

B. VAN ROOTSELAAR

FRAIPONT, JULIEN (*b.* Liège, Belgium, 17 August 1857; *d.* Liège, 22 March 1910), *zoology, paleontology, anthropology.*

At the end of his intermediate studies, Fraipont entered the offices of the bank of which his father was director. However, attracted since childhood by the natural sciences, he attended at the same time the zoology courses given at the University of Liège by Edouard Van Beneden. He became one of Van Beneden's favorite students, and then abandoned the career for which he had seemed destined in order to pursue his scientific vocation. He was soon named student assistant and then became Van Beneden's *préparateur* (1878) and his assistant (1881). He was then hired to teach the following subjects at the University of Liège: animal paleontology (1884), animal geography (1885), and systematic zoology (1885). He was named professor in 1886 and, in 1909, a few months before his death, rector of the University of Liège. He was elected a foreign member of the Leopoldinisch-Karolinische Deutsche Akademie der Naturforscher in 1890, replacing L.-G. De Koninck, and a foreign member of the Imperial Society of Naturalists of Moscow in 1895. He became a member of the Académie Royale des Sciences de Belgique in 1895 and director of its science section in 1908.

Fraipont's zoological works (fifteen publications appeared between 1877 and 1908) deal with systematics, but above all with the morphology of Protozoa (*Acineta*), Hydrozoa (*Campanulariae*), Trematoda, Cestoda, and Archiannelida. They also include a monograph (1907) on the genus *Okapia* in which the author endeavors to demonstrate that this mammal, discovered in 1900 in the Belgian Congo, represents a form perfectly intermediate between the Cenozoic Giraffidae and present-day giraffes.

Fraipont's most important contribution to zoology probably consists of his studies on the Archiannelida (1884–1887), a group which had recently come to prominence through the investigations of B. Hatschek. Fraipont's studies began with the cephalic nephridia (1884) and the central and peripheral nervous systems of certain of these organisms (1884) and were completed by a monograph on the genus *Polygordius* (1887). As in all his preceding works, Fraipont was inspired by the example and the teaching of his mentor Van Beneden. He gave a minute description of the anatomy, histology, development, habits, and habitat of the genus, as well as of its geographic distribution and position in the class of the Annelida. In his conclusions he agreed, although not without some reservations, with Hatschek's opinion and accepted, like him, the group of the Archiannelida.

Fraipont was especially occupied with paleontological research during the period from 1883 to 1890. In particular he studied various fossils of the Upper Devonian and the Lower Carboniferous. In 1885 he published, in collaboration with De Koninck, the fifth part (devoted to the Lamellibranchia) of De Koninck's monumental work on the fauna of the Lower Carboniferous in Belgium.

During this period Fraipont also began to take a lively interest in prehistory, continuing the work done before him in Belgium by P.-C. Schmerling and E.-F. Dupont. Alone or with collaborators he explored several caves in the province of Liège, discovering numerous archaeological levels ranging from the Lower Mousterian to the Neolithic. He was also involved in study of the human fossils discovered at Spy, near Namur (Belgium), during the summer of 1886 by his friends the geologist Max Lohest and the prehistorian Marcel De Puydt.

This discovery played a considerable role in the history of human paleontology. The material found consisted of the remains of two human skeletons, associated with a great quantity of Quaternary mammalian bones and with lithic implements of the Mousterian type. This was the first discovery of relatively complete documents of Neanderthal man, exhumed in perfectly established stratigraphic conditions that fixed their age (known today to date from the Würm I stage) and guaranteed their authenticity. The principal observations and measurements of the two skeletons were carried out by Fraipont. They are remarkable for their precision, especially since Fraipont was not a professional anatomist. The results of these investigations were the subject of a memoir published jointly by Fraipont and Lohest in 1887.

This memorable discovery at Spy permitted the interpretation of fragmentary pieces previously brought to light, such as the jaw found at La Naulette (Belgium) in 1865 by E.-F. Dupont, and it completed and confirmed the knowledge of a type of human fossil whose special characteristics some in this period were still trying to explain by the action of pathological factors. Fraipont devoted several other articles to the Spy fossils between 1888 and 1893. He also published an interesting study on the tibia (1888) in its relation to the erect posture of man and the Pongidae, and in 1900 he presented a thorough study of certain Neolithic skeletons found in various Belgian caves.

Highly esteemed by everyone, Fraipont was a modest man, extremely kind and courteous, devoted to his teaching duties and to his students. His complete moral integrity is reflected in his work. One may reproach that work for too great a diversity in subject matter and for certain factual or interpretive errors; yet it preserves a fundamental unity of method and of thought, that of a zoologist devoted to the facts as he perceived them, rather than to constructing brilliant but hazardous speculative systems.

BIBLIOGRAPHY

I. ORIGINAL WORKS. Fraipont published 46 works (15 in zoology, 11 in paleontology, and 20 in anthropology and prehistory) in addition to a great many reports and conference papers.

The principal works are "Faune du calcaire carbonifère, 5e partie, Lamellibranches," in *Annales du Musée royal d'histoire naturelle de Belgique,* **11** (1885), 1-33, written with L.-G. De Koninck; "Monographie du genre Polygordius," in *Fauna und Flora des Golfes von Neapel,* **14** (1887), 1-125; and "La race humaine de Neanderthal ou de Canstadt en Belgique. Recherches ethnographiques sur des ossements humains, découverts dans des dépôts quaternaires d'une grotte à Spy et détermination de leur âge géologique," in *Archives de biologie,* **7** (1887), 587-757, written with Max Lohest.

II. SECONDARY LITERATURE. Of the obituaries published, the best, which includes a complete list of publications, is M. Lohest, C. Julin, and A. Rutot, "Notice sur Julien Fraipont," in *Annuaire de l'Académie royale de Belgique,* **91** (1925), 131-197. On the discoveries at Spy, see the interesting critical chapter in Aleš Hrdlička, *The Skeletal Remains of Early Man,* Smithsonian misc. coll., **83** (Washington, D.C., 1930), 178-212.

G. UBAGHS

FRANÇAIS, FRANÇOIS (JOSEPH) (*b.* Saverne, Bas-Rhin, France, 7 April 1768; *d.* Mainz, Germany, 30 October 1810); **FRANÇAIS, JACQUES FRÉDÉRIC** (*b.* Saverne, Bas-Rhin, France, 20 June 1775; *d.* Metz, France, 9 March 1833), *mathematics.*

The mathematical works of the Français brothers, François and Jacques Frédéric, are so poorly distinguished by most authors and their biographies so imprecise that it is necessary to devote a common article to the two of them. Sons of Jacques Frédéric Français, a grocer, and of Maria Barbara Steib, they were both born at Saverne, seven years apart. In 1789, François, the elder, became a seminarist. Named professor at the *collège* in Colmar in June 1791, he assumed the chair of mathematics at the *collège* in Strasbourg in September 1792. He participated actively in political life and was a secretary of the *société populaire* of Strasbourg. He took part in the Vendée campaign from May to October 1793 and, after a brief return to civilian life, went back to the army as an officer until October 1797, when he was named professor of mathematics at the École Centrale du Haut-Rhin in Colmar. He left this position in September 1803 to teach mathematics, first at the lycée in Mainz, then at the École d'Artillerie at La Fère (1804), and, finally, at the École d'Artillerie in Mainz. At his death he left four small children, whom his younger brother adopted soon afterward.

Jacques Frédéric Français, after having been an outstanding student at the *collège* of Strasbourg, enrolled as a volunteer in 1793 and was named assistant in the corps of engineers in September 1794. He was admitted to the École Polytechnique on 30 December 1797, and from there he went, in March 1800, to the École du Génie. A first lieutenant in January 1801, he participated in the expedition sent by Napoleon to attempt to save the French army in Egypt. On his return he was quartered at Toulon and was named captain of the sappers in December 1801; in November 1802, he became second in command of the staff headquarters of the corps of engineers. In this capacity he participated, with Admiral Villeneuve's squadron, in the expedition to the Antilles and in the naval battles of Cape Finisterre and Trafalgar (1805). Beginning at the end of that year, he was successively assigned to garrisons at Condé-sur-Escaut; then Kehl (1806); Strasbourg (1807), under the command of Malus; and Metz (from 1808), to the staff headquarters of the École d'Application. Promoted to first in command in July 1810, he was named, at the beginning of 1811, professor of military art at the École d'Application du Génie et de l'Artillerie in Metz. He held this last position until his death.

In July 1795 François Français presented a memoir on the integration of partial differential equations; a new version of this paper, addressed to the Académie des Sciences in 1797, is mentioned by S. F. Lacroix (*Traité du calcul différential et du calcul intégral,* III, 598) as an important contribution to the theory of these equations. According to the testimony of Biot (*Procès-verbaux de l'Académie des sciences,* III, 204-205), Français then assisted "his uncle" Louis-François Arbogast in the elaboration of the "calculus of derivations" and in the preparation of a treatise that he devoted to this subject (1800). Having inherited Arbogast's papers in April 1803, he continued to work on the development of the calculus of derivations and its applications; thus, in a memoir presented to the Academy in November 1804, he applied this calculus to the movement of projectiles in a resistant medium. Highly esteemed by the mathematicians of the Paris Academy—Lagrange, Legendre, Lacroix, and Biot—François Français pursued original mathematical investigations, but without publishing anything. Following his death his brother Jacques Frédéric included several brief extracts in the *Annales de mathématiques* from his unpublished papers (the application of the calculus of derivations; formulas concerning polygons and polyhedra; and a study of a special curve, the tractrix); these papers were, moreover, a precious source of inspiration to him.

After having presented a memoir, now lost, on the complete integral of first-order partial differential equations in 1800, Jacques Frédéric Français did not return to mathematics until 1807–1808. He then published, on the urging of Malus, two memoirs on analytic geometry; they treated the equation of the straight line and of the plane in oblique coordinates and the transformation of the systems of oblique coordinates. Applying his method to the famous problem of finding a sphere tangent to four given spheres, he gave a solution to it in 1808, which he corrected immediately before completing it in 1812.

The study of his brother's papers attracted him once more to infinitesimal calculus and especially to the development of the calculus of derivations, to which he in turn devoted two important memoirs: one in 1811 (published in 1813) on the separation of the scales of differentiation and the integration of those functions which they determine; and the other in 1815, on the principles of this calculus. In April 1811 he presented a memoir to the Academy, published in 1812 and 1813 in the *Annales de mathématiques,* in which he put forth an unusual example in the theory of the extrema of functions of several variables. In 1813 he published a rather fully developed study on the rotation of solid bodies, in which, in the words of Cauchy (*Procès-verbaux de l'Académie des sciences,* VIII, 523–525), "interesting research is mixed with several errors."

In September 1813 Français published in the *Annales de mathématiques* a resounding article in which he presents the principles of the geometric representation of complex numbers and draws from them several applications. However, in the final paragraph, he acknowledges having taken a portion of his ideas from a letter of 1806 in which Legendre gave his brother François information about a manuscript study on this same subject that had been entrusted to him by an anonymous young author, and he requested that this author reveal himself. In fact, in the following issue of the *Annales de mathématiques,* this author, Jean-Robert Argand, whose study, although printed, had remained practically unknown, replied with a summary of the main conceptions of his work (*Essai sur une manière de représenter les quantités imaginaires dans les constructions géométriques* [Paris, 1806]). A polemic then arose in the *Annales,* in 1813 and 1814, between Argand himself, Français, and François-Joseph Servois: the first two attempted to justify the principle itself of this geometric representation, while Servois was concerned above all else to preserve the rigor and purity of algebra. These publications had the great merit of widely diffusing an innovation whose essence, although presented by Caspar Wessel in Copenhagen in 1797 (and published in 1799), by the Abbé Adrien-Quentin Buée in London in 1805, and by Argand in Paris in 1806, had remained unnoticed by the leading mathematicians.

Although Jacques Frédéric Français's mathematical publications were interrupted rather suddenly at the end of 1815, it does not seem that his curiosity was extinguished, and Poncelet's long stay in Metz certainly contributed to maintaining it. While not of the first rank, the mathematical activity of the Français brothers merits mention for its originality and diversity.

J. F. Soleirol, in his *Éloge de Monsieur Français . . . prononcé sur sa tombe le 11 mars 1833* . . . (Metz, 1833), points out that Français also composed a course on military art, a course on geodesy, and two memoirs, one on permanent fortifications and the other on the thrust of the earth.

A final point remains to be made. Upon the death of Arbogast in April 1803, his writings, his important mathematical library, and the rich collection of scientific manuscripts that he had gathered passed to his "nephew," François Français. When François died, he bequeathed this collection of manuscripts and books, augmented by his own writings, to his brother Jacques Frédéric, who announced in December 1823 that they were being placed on sale (see *Bulletin général et universel des annonces* . . . I, fasc. 3 [1823], 493–495). Upon the latter's death the essential portion of the collection, not yet sold, passed into the hands of a bookseller in Metz, at whose shop Count Libri was still able to find various valuable manuscripts in 1839. With the sale of Libri's library, these items were dispersed; some are now in the Biblioteca Medicea-Laurenziana in Florence (in particular, certain papers of François Français) and in the Bibliothèque Nationale de Paris, while others, which are very precious, have not yet been found. It is hoped that a thorough investigation will be undertaken in order to locate them.

BIBLIOGRAPHY

I. ORIGINAL WORKS.

(1) François Français. His work amounts to four posthumous memoirs published by his brother in the *Annales de mathématiques pures et appliquées.* They deal with an aspect of the "Calcul des dérivations" ("Méthode de différentiation indépendante du développement des fonctions en séries," in *Annales,* **2** [May 1812], 325–331); with theorems concerning polyhedra and polygons (*ibid.,* **3** [Dec. 1812], 189–191, and **5** [May 1815], 341–350); and with the tractrix (**4** [Apr. 1814], 305–319). Two important memoirs presented to the Académie des Sciences remain unpublished but were known and utilized by different authors—the memoir on the integration of partial differential equations, presented in 1797 (see S. F. Lacroix, *Traité du calcul différentiel et du calcul intégral,* 2nd ed., III [Paris, 1819], 598); and the memoir on the movement of projectiles in resisting media, presented on 26 Nov. 1804, which, moreover, was the object of a flattering report by Biot on 22 April 1805 (*Procès-verbaux de l'Académie des sciences . . .,* III [Hendaye, 1913], 159, 204–205).

(2) Jacques Frédéric Français. His work includes an individual publication, *Mémoire sur le mouvement de rotation d'un corps solide libre autour de son centre de masse* (Paris, 1813); and a series of memoirs published in the *Correspondance sur l'École polytechnique* (*C.E.P.*), the *Journal de l'École polytechnique* (*J.E.P.*), and the *Annales de mathématiques pures et appliquées* of Gergonne (*Annales*). They are listed below by subject and in chronological order.

Analytic Geometry: letter to Hachette, in *C.E.P.,* **1,** no. 8 (May 1807), 320–321; on the straight line and the plane in oblique coordinates, in *C.E.P.,* **1,** no. 9 (Jan. 1808), 337–346; on a sphere tangent to four spheres in the following issues of *C.E.P.:* **1,** no. 9 (Jan. 1808), 346–349; **1,** no. 10 (Apr. 1808), 418–421; **2,** no. 2 (Jan. 1810), 63–66; **2,** no. 5 (Jan. 1813), 409–410; and in *Annales,* **3** (Nov. 1812), 158–161; on the transformation of oblique coordinates, in *J.E.P.,* **7,** *cahier* 14 (Apr. 1808), 182–190; and on various problems, in *C.E.P.,* **2,** no. 2 (Jan. 1810), 60–70.

Infinitesimal Calculus: on a singular case of the theory of the extrema of functions of several variables, in *Annales,* **3** (Oct. 1812), 132–137; and *ibid.,* **3** (June 1813), 197–206; on scales of differentiation and integration, *ibid.,* **3** (Feb. 1813), 244–272; on the calculus of derivations derived from its true principles, *ibid.,* **6** (Sept. 1815), 61–111.

Solid Mechanics: on rotation of solid bodies, in *Annales,* **3** (Jan. 1813), 197–206.

Geometric Representation of Imaginary Numbers: articles in *Annales,* **4** (Sept. 1813), 61–71; **4** (Jan. 1814), 222–227; **4** (June 1814), 364–366; and articles repr. in J. Hoüel, ed. (see below), pp. 63–74, 96–101, 109–110.

Other Topics: problems concerning the calendar, in *Annales,* **4** (Mar. 1814), 273–276, and *ibid.,* **4** (May 1814), 337–338; remarks on the tractrix, *ibid.,* 332–336; and a problem involving the pendulum and the flying bridge, *ibid.,* **6** (Oct. 1815), 126–129.

II. SECONDARY LITERATURE. On the brothers Français, see M. Chasles, *Rapport sur les progrès de la géométrie* (Paris, 1870), p. 57 (on François), pp. 35, 61 (on Jacques Frédéric); S. F. Lacroix, *Traité du calcul différentiel et du calcul intégral* (Paris, 1819), II, pp. 656–658, 789, III, p. 598, 726, 752 (on François), pp. 631–632, 752 (on Jacques Frédéric); N. Nielsen, *Géomètres français sous la Révolution* (Copenhagen, 1929), pp. 96–97 (on François), pp. 97–103 (on Jacques Frédéric); and the Royal Society *Catalogue of Scientific Papers,* II (London, 1868), 694–695: nos. 4, 7, 14, and 16 are on François, the others on Jacques Frédéric. Baptism records may be found in the municipal archives of Saverne.

On François Français, see (in chronological order), *Almanach national* (later *Almanach impérial*) for *an* VII (1798–1799) to 1810; *Procès-verbaux du Comité d'instruction publique de la convention nationale,* VI (Paris, 1907), 452; *Procès-verbaux de l'Académie des sciences,* III (Hendaye, 1913), 59, 159, 204–205, 262, 504; and J. Joachim, *L'école centrale du Haut-Rhin* (Colmar, 1934), esp. pp. 151–155, where there is partial confusion with Louis François Français, war commissioner. See also the archives of the Département du Haut-Rhin.

On Jacques Frédéric Français, see R. Argand, *Essai sur une nouvelle manière de représenter les quantités imaginaires dans les constructions géométriques,* 2nd ed. (Paris, 1874), pp. v–xvi, 63–74, 96–101, 109–110; S. Bachelard, *La représentation géométrique des quantités imaginaires au début du XIXe siècle* (Paris, 1966), pp. 11–13, 30; C. B. Boyer, *History of Analytic Geometry* (New York, 1956), pp. 222–223; A. Fourcy, *Histoire de l'École polytechnique* (Paris, 1828), p. 403; G. Libri, in *Comptes rendus hebdomadaires des séances de l'Académie des sciences,* **9** (1839), 357–358, and "Fermat," in *Revue des deux mondes* (15 May 1845), pp. 679–707; G. Loria, "Origines, perfectionnement et développement de la notion de coordonnées," in *Osiris,* **8** (1948), esp. 220–223, where there is confusion with Frédéric Louis Lefrançois; and J. V. Poncelet, *Applications d'analyse et de géométrie,* II (Paris, 1864), 592–595; and J. F. Soleirol, *Éloge de Monsieur Français . . . prononcé sur sa tombe le 11 mars 1833 . . .* (Metz, 1833). Further material may be found in *Almanach national* (later *Almanach impérial,* then *Almanach royal*) for *an* VII (1798–1799) to 1833; Férussac, ed., *Bulletin général et universel des annonces et des nouvelles scientifiques,* **1,** fasc. 3 (1823), 493–495; and *Procès-verbaux de l'Académie des sciences,* III–V (Hendaye, 1913–1914), III, 265; IV, 475, 554; V, 152, 168, 524.

Part of the original documentation of this article comes from the archives of the École Polytechnique, the Service Historique de l'Armée, and the archives of the Legion of Honor.

RENÉ TATON

FRANCESCA, PIERO DELLA (or **Piero dei Franceschi**), also known as **Petrus Borgensis** (*b.* Borgo San Sepolcro [now Sansepolcro], Italy, between 1410 and 1420; *d.* Sansepolcro, 12 October 1492), *mathematics.*

Vasari's reason (in *Lives of the Artists*) for the adoption of the feminine form "Francesca" in Piero's name has been invalidated by the authentication of his father as "dei Franceschi" and his mother as Romana di Perino da Monterchi. Of Piero's early life—as the wide uncertainty of his birthdate reveals—nothing is known until 7 September 1439, when he was an associate of Domenico Veneziano at Florence. He is not named by Alberti in the famous dedication to his colleagues in *Della pittura* (1436), but Alberti's influence is revealed in the clearest manner in the architectural studies from Piero's workshop at Urbino.

Piero's value to science lay in his pioneering efforts to explore the nature of space and to construct it by his sophisticated study of linear perspective and masterly juxtaposition of color masses. Although his major work on the mathematics of painting, *De prospettiva pingendi,* was written only after his career as an artist was at an end, it can hardly be doubted that the diminution in the successive members of the black and white pavement in the *Flagellation* at Urbino must have been achieved by such complex calculations as are subsequently displayed in the *Prospettiva.* These represent a synthesis of the two operational diagrams that he probably learned from Alberti.

But a more strikingly original contribution of Piero's was his measuring of the distances between successive surfaces of a human head and transferring the plane sections thus obtained into a contoured plan. Luca Pacioli, whose influence in spreading the study of mathematics in the early *cinquecento* is well known, testified to the assistance of his fellow townsman but later paid him the dubious compliment of including (unacknowledged) in his *De divina proportione* a large part of Piero's last work, *De quinque corporibus regolaribus.*

BIBLIOGRAPHY

I. Original Works. The *De prospettiva pingendi* was written in the vernacular; a transcript exists in the Palatina at Parma and forms the basis of the definitive text edited by G. Fasola (Florence, 1942). There is a transcript of the (contemporary) Latin trans. in the Ambrosian Library at Milan. Piero's *De quinque corporibus regolaribus* exists in a transcript (with figs. by him) in the Vatican Library (Urbinas 632). Excerpts from the original works (in English) are available in E. G. Holt, ed., *A Documentary History of Art,* I (New York, 1957), 256–267.

II. Secondary Literature. A detailed and analytical study of Piero's life and work is Roberto Longhi, *Piero della Francesca* (London, 1930), Leonard Penlock, trans. The Introduction by Sir Kenneth Clark to the Phaidon review of his pictures, *Piero della Francesca* (London, 1951), is both readable and scholarly.

William P. D. Wightman

FRANCIS OF MARCHIA (*b.* Appignano, Italy; *fl.* first half of the fourteenth century), *theology, natural philosophy.*

Francis was a Friar Minor (Franciscan) whom Sbaralea identifies as a native of Pignano (Appignano), in the province of Ascoli Piceno, March of Ancona.[1] Many other names were incorrectly attributed to him: he was variously called di Apiniano (Esculo), D'Ascoli (Asculanus), and Rossi (Rubeus). He completed his studies at the University of Paris, where he received his degree as a teacher of theology. In all probability he commented on the *Sentences* during 1319 and 1320 in accordance with the theological program at Paris.[2] Later, around 1328, he was a lecturer at the Studio Generale of the Franciscans at Avignon.[3] In the fifteenth century he was given the honorary title of *doctor succinctus et praefulgens,* which can be seen in the inscriptions on one of the frescoes in the Franciscan convent at Bolzano.

Francis took an active part in the internal struggles regarding poverty that were then dividing the order. Together with Michael of Cesena, William of Ockham, and Bonagrazia of Bergamo, he supported a rule of absolute poverty for the successors of Christ and for the church. He rebelled against Pope John XXII, supporting his opponent, Emperor Louis IV the Bavarian.[4] He was excommunicated by the pope and joined Louis in Pisa in 1328 and once again rebelled to protest his excommunication (1329–1331).[5]

Francis was expelled from the order in 1329. He was persecuted by ecclesiastical authorities in Italy in 1341. In 1344 he made a formal recantation (which was to serve as an example to all later dissidents) and was reconciled with the church and with the order.[6] The date of his death is not known.

Francis' scientific thought is contained in his comments on Aristotle's *Physics* and in his theological writings. In these works he shows an original approach to certain problems of mechanics. He was the first of the medieval philosophers to employ the theory of impetus (anticipating the principle of inertia) to explain the movement of projectiles.[7] The term "impetus" was not used by him in the technical sense as it later was by Jean Buridan; rather he speaks of a force left or impressed (*vis derelicta*), which is the intrinsic cause—transmitted by the motor to the object moved—of the movement of the projectile. He was also the first to maintain that the movement of a projectile is not caused by something extrinsic (*ab alio*) to the object moved. It is not a movement transmitted by the motor to the projectile via the medium through which it moves. He supposes that the *proiciens* leaves in the projectile a part of its force that then causes subsequent motion. In other words,

FRANCIS OF MARCHIA

the moving force (*vis motrix*) in the launching of a projectile is not transmitted to the medium (air or water) and thence to the projectile, but rather directly to the body itself.[8]

Francis thus corrects Aristotle's doctrine. The cause of the movement of projectiles is not to be sought in the activity of a force derived through the vortical movement of air or in its heaviness or lightness; it does not depend on the form of the heavens and is not transmitted by the medium.[9] The cause is a *vis derelicta* impressed by the motor on the object itself.[10] The medium contributes to the movement of the projectile but is not the cause of it. The impressed or *derelicta* force is neither a permanent form (such as heat generated by fire) nor is it a *simpliciter fluens* form (that is, one which flows simply, as the heating of water) but rather an intermediate form—that is, one that has a form that lasts for only a limited period of time (*esse permanens ad determinatum tempus*).[11] The movement of the projectile diminishes in speed and exhausts itself not because of the destruction of the *subiectum*—the projectile—but because of the cessation of the motivating force, which occurs in two ways: a pure and simple slackening in the force of the motor or a slackening in the force of the motor in the projectile, whose movement lasts only a short time because of the existential imperfection of the movement.[12] In the latter case the movement of the projectile diminishes just as images impressed on the eye by a source of light are exhausted and disappear when the source of light is removed.[13]

Francis also invoked this principle to explain the movement of the celestial spheres. He suggested the idea that the divine intelligence impresses a driving power of this type on the celestial spheres—that is, an impetus implanted in the heavens themselves.[14] He thus gave a purely mechanical explanation for the movement of the celestial bodies.

Francis was also a proponent of the then new theory of actual infinity. He derived this concept from that of divine cause. There exists an infinity that is positively real, being the effect of divine causality or omnipotence. This is an actual infinite which exceeds any finite beyond any determined proportion, accepted or acceptable.[15] This actual infinite is so according to size, multiplicity, and extension. It is more a transfinite than a maximum.[16] Francis also admits as a variation of this actual infinity an actual infinity according to succession. Movement and time would be in this category and are therefore conceived of by Francis as an actual successive infinity. In other words, on admitting actual infinity according to succession, Francis came to conceive of a world of infinite space, a new concept in medieval cosmology.

NOTES

1. G. Sbaralea, *Supplementum et castigatio ad scriptores,* I (Rome, 1908), 257.
2. Cf. MS Naples, Biblioteca Nazionale, VII, C. 27: "Explicit fratris Francisci de Marchia super primum Sententiarum secundum reportationem factam sub eo tempore, quo legit Sententias Parisius anno Domini 1320."
3. Cf. Etienne Baluze and J. D. Mansi, *Miscellanea,* II (Lucca, 1761), 140.
4. Cf. M. D. Lambert, *Franciscan Poverty: The Doctrine of the Absolute Poverty of Christ and the Apostles* (London, 1961).
5. Cf. MS Florence, Biblioteca Laurenziana, Santa Croce, pluteo 31, sinistra 3, fols. 1–63.
6. Cf. Wadding, VII, 371–372.
7. Cf. Clagett, pp. 530–531.
8. *La teoria dell'impeto,* pp. 59 f. Cf. Maier, *Zwei Grundprobleme,* pp. 168 f., and Clagett, pp. 527 f.
9. *La teoria dell'impeto,* p. 10.
10. *Ibid.,* p. 9.
11. *Ibid.,* p. 11.
12. *Ibid.,* pp. 20–21.
13. *Ibid.,* p. 21.
14. *Ibid.,* pp. 18–19; cf. Clagett, p. 531.
15. *In Sententias,* d. 2, MS, Rome, Biblioteca Vaticana (Chigiano), B. VII 113, fols. 28v–33v; and Vat. lat. 4871, fols. 100r–101v.
16. Cf. A. Maier, *Ausgehendes Mittelalter,* I, 68 f.

BIBLIOGRAPHY

I. Original Works. Most of Francis' writings, not having been published, exist only in MS. The works fall into three categories, according to the subjects with which they are concerned: (1) politics, (2) theology, and (3) science and philosophy. A partial listing of MSS follows.

Political Works. MS Florence, Laurenziana, Santa Croce, pluteo 31, sinistra 3, fols. 1–63, contains his protest against the pope. His formal retraction was published in L. Wadding, *Annales minorum* (Florence, 1932), vol. VII.

Theological Works. Many of Francis' theological writings were in the form of commentaries on the *Sententiae* of Peter Lombard. Various MSS are cited in F. Stegmüller, *Repertorium commentariorum in Sententias* (Würzburg, 1947), pp. 237, 302; V. Doucet, "Commentaires sur les Sentences, Supplément au répertoire de F. Stegmüller," in *Archivum franciscanum historicum,* **47** (1954), 116–117; A. Maier, *Ausgehendes Mittelalter,* I (Rome, 1964), 68 ff.; and P. O. Kristeller, *Iter italicum,* II (London–Leiden, 1967), 445.

Scientific and Philosophical Works. Several of the works in this class took the form of *Quodlibeta* (MS Paris, Bibliothèque Nationale, lat. 16110, sec. XIV); and commentaries on Aristotle, among them *Quaestiones super primum et secundum librum Metaphysicorum* (MS Florence, Laurenziana, Fesulano, supp. 161, fols. 67–73) and *Expositio super Physicam* (Rome, Vaticana Ottoboniano, lat. 1816, fols. 30r–49r). Garcia y Garcia and Piana also attribute Bologna, Biblioteca del Real Collegio di Spagna, MS 104, fols. 48*ra*–102*vb*, to Francis, although P. Kuenzle credits it to Francis of Méyronnes. *La teoria dell'impeto,* G. Federici Vescovini, ed. (Turin, 1969), pp. 1–21, presents *In Sententias IV,* 1, MS Biblioteca Vaticana (Chigiano), B. VII, 113, fols. 175*ra*–177*va,* as part of a collection of medieval Latin texts dealing with impetus.

II. SECONDARY LITERATURE. On Francis and his works, see M. Clagett, *The Science of Mechanics in the Middle Ages* (Madison, Wis., 1959), pp. 526–531, which includes an English trans. of the text on impetus; F. Ehrle, "Der Sentenzenkommentar Peters von Candia," in *Franziskanische Studien,* supp. IX (1925), pp. 253–259; A. Garcia y Garcia and C. Piana, "Los manuscritos filosofico, historico y cientificos del Real Colegio de Espagna de Bolonia," in *Salmanticensis,* **14** (1967), 81–169; P. Kuenzle, "Petrus Thomae oder Franciscus de Mayronis?," in *Archivum franciscanum historicum,* **61** (1968), 462–463; A. Maier, *Die Vorlaüfer Galileis im 14. Jahrhundert* (Rome, 1949), pp. 133 ff.; *Zwei Grundprobleme der scholastischen Naturphilosophie* (Rome, 1952), pp. 166–180, which contains a portion of the impetus text; *Ausgehendes Mittelalter,* I (Rome, 1964), 357, 461, and II (1967), 467, 478; M. Schmaus, "Der *Liber propugnatorius* des Thomas Anglicus," in *Beiträge zur Geschichte der Philosophie des Mittelalter,* **29** (1930), 34, n. 59; and A. Teetaert, "Pignano (François de)," in *Dictionnaire de théologie Catholique,* XII (1935), cols. 2104–2109.

GRAZIELLA FEDERICI VESCOVINI

FRANCIS OF MEYRONNES (*b.* Méyronnes, Provence, France, *ca.* 1285; *d.* Piacenza, Italy, *ca.* 1330), *theology, natural philosophy.*

The dates of Francis' birth and death are uncertain; he lived in the first half of the fourteenth century and was called de Mayronis, after his birthplace in the canton of St. Paul in the Basses-Alpes. He entered the Franciscan order of Provence, probably in the convent of Digne. Pope John XXII calls him Franciscus de Maironis de Digna in a letter of 23 May 1323.[1] He was a pupil of Duns Scotus and, according to the Benedictine scholar Johannes Trithemius, he taught in England; but it is not known if this was before or after he came to Paris (between 1302 and 1307).[2]

As bachelor of the faculty of theology at Paris, Francis lectured on Peter Lombard's *Sentences* and became a doctor of theology in 1323.[3] He is reported to have inaugurated, between 1315 and 1320, the *actus sorboniens.* This was the scholastic debate that took place every Friday during the summer season and lasted twelve hours consecutively; during these debates, speakers had to respond to and hold their own against all adversaries who appeared.[4] (The adoption of this scholastic practice, however, dates from before 1312 and is traceable to Robert de Sorbon.)[5] The debate between Francis himself and Pierre Roger (later Pope Clement VI) in 1321 was famous and is probably what is referred to as the *certamen Mayronicum.*[6]

In the spring of 1324 Francis was in Avignon. That year Pope John XXII sent him, together with the Dominican monk Domenico Grima, to Gascony to try to prevent a conflict between the armies of Charles IV of France and Edward III of England. Between 1323 and 1324 he was also minister provincial of Provence.[7] His death took place in the convent of Piacenza sometime between 1327 and 1333; according to Roth, he was still alive in 1328.[8]

Francis was a follower of the doctrines of Duns Scotus. His studies included science, metaphysics, and theology. As a theologian he commented on Aristotle's cosmology, correcting it in the light of the physics presented in the Scriptures, a methodological position that was later to be definitively examined and abandoned by Galileo. The facts of Aristotelian physics that Francis inherited from medieval science thus came to be integrated with those of the Bible.[9]

According to Francis, the universe was constituted of fourteen spheres: the empyrean, the crystalline, the firmament, Saturn, Jupiter, Mars, sun, Venus, Mercury, moon, fire, air, water, and earth; each of these has its own composition. At the center of these spheres, which are all in circular motion, is the immobile earth. Francis does not admit the possibility of the earth's movement or the immobility of the heavens, a possibility that was beginning to be argued in Paris—as he himself relates in connection with a teacher who would consider that the earth moves and that the skies are immobile.[10]

The world has been created by God, and Francis does not believe it to be *ab aeterno* or infinite. The reasoning that he uses to disavow the actual infinity of the world is of a philosophical and metaphysical nature. The world, because it was created, was begun, and what has a beginning must also have an end. But that which has an end or a conclusion is not infinite. Therefore, the physical world is not infinite. For this reason, Francis excludes the possibility that the world is actually infinite (*infinitum in actu*);[11] such infinity belongs only to divine omnipotence. Movement, time, discrete quantity, and number—which are determinations of the physical world and are successions—cannot be constituents of the infinite.

Francis does admit that God, as omnipotent infinity, can cause through his infinite power an infinite world, but with the limitation that it be according to continuous quantity and according to intensity or degree. That is, it can never be caused according to numerical succession, for the elements of a series can always be reenumerated. In other words, Francis admits that the physical world is potentially infinite, in the manner of the continuous quantity (infinitely divisible material) that constitutes it.[12]

In his doctrine on the movement of physical bodies Francis does not substantially modify the Aristotelian

FRANCIS OF MEYRONNES

system of explaining the movement of projectiles. It is a movement that originates from without, and its cause is the medium, with the concurrence of four factors whereby the projectile is moved by whatever pushes it (*motus pellentis*), which divides the medium violently from behind; the medium then closes so that a void does not arise and this closing (*clausio*) pushes the moving body.[13]

More original, on the other hand, is Francis' philosophical explanation of motion, which he understands as a *fluxus formae* (flux of form) rather than as a *forma fluens* (flowing form). In his exposition he embellishes the doctrines of Aristotle with new content.[14]

Francis does not completely accept the fundamental rules of Aristotelian dynamics and kinematics (*Physics* VII 5, 250a, 1–20) as they had been formulated by the medieval scientific tradition. He asserts that the relationship (*comparatio*) established by Aristotle between the force of the mover, space, and time is not true; by means of this relationship it was argued that if a force can move an object in space for a certain time, the same force can move double the object through half the space in the same time. In fact, Francis argues, if, for example, Socrates can carry a quintal for a league, it does not follow that he can carry two quintals for half a league. According to Francis the inverse rule attributed to Aristotle is also not exact; for if a force can move an object in a given space for a certain time, it does not follow that half this force can move the entire object through half the space in the same time. For example, if thirty men can move a ship for thirty paces, it does not follow that fifteen men can move the same ship for fifteen paces in the same time.[15]

NOTES

1. Cf. P. W. Lampen, "Francis de Meyronnes," in *France franciscaine,* **9** (1926), 215–222; E. d'Alençon, "Francis de Meyronnes," in A. Vacant *et al.*, eds., *Dictionnaire de théologie catholique,* X (Paris, 1929), cols. 1634–1646.
2. J. Trithemius, *De scriptoribus ecclesiasticis* (Paris, 1494), fol. 123b.
3. H. Denifle and E. Chatelain, eds., *Chartularium universitatis Parisiensis,* II (Paris, 1891), 272, no. 823; P. Feret, *La faculté de théologie de Paris, Moyen-âge,* III (Paris, 1896), 323, no. 2.
4. Bartholomaeus de Rinonico Pisanus, *De conformitate vitae* IV (Florence, 1906), 339, 523, 540, 544; Gilberti Genebrardi, *Chronographiae libri,* IV (Cologne, 1518), 1014.
5. Cf. Vatican Library, MS Borghese 39; cf. A. Maier, *Ausgehendes Mittelalter,* I (Rome, 1964), 333; II (Rome, 1967), 257 ff.
6. Cf. P. Glorieux, "L'enseignement au moyen-âge, techniques et méthodes en usage à la Faculté de Théologie de Paris," in *Archives d'histoire doctrinale et littéraire du moyen-âge,* **35** (1968), 134.
7. Biblioteca Comunale, Assisi, MS 684. Cf. d'Alençon, col. 1646.
8. B. Roth, *Francis von Meyronnes, sein Leben, seine Werke, seine Lehre vom Formalunterschied in Gott* (Weil in Westfalen, 1936), p. 49.
9. *Commentum in secundum librum Sententiarum* (Venice, 1520), distinctio 14, quaestio V, fol. 150v, cols. a–b.
10. *Ibid.,* fol. 150v, col. b. Cf. P. Duhem, "Francis de Meyronnes et la question de la rotation de la terre," in *Archivum franciscanum historicum,* **6** (1913), 23–25.
11. *Commentum in primum librum Sententiarum,* dist. 43, qu. X, fol. 128v, col. b; dist. 43, qu. IX, fol. 127v, cols. a–b; dist. 44, qu. X, fol. 129v, col. a; *Expositio in Physicam,* bk. III (Ferrara, 1495), fol. Gv, cols. a–b; fol. Kr, cols. a–b.
12. *Ibid.,* fol. Kr, cols. a–b; fol. K^{ii}r, col. a ff., *Commentum in primum librum Sententiarum, loc. cit.*
13. *Ibid.,* dist. 14, qu. VII, fol. 151r, col. b.
14. *Ibid.,* dist. 16, qu. IV, fol. 68r, col. b; dist. 14, qu. IX, fol. 152r, col. b; *Expositio in physicam,* bk. V, fol. Mv, col. a.
15. *Ibid.,* bk. VII, fol. Ov, cols. a–b.

BIBLIOGRAPHY

I. ORIGINAL WORKS. Francis of Meyronnes was the author of numerous writings on various subjects, including theology, metaphysics, logic, physics, politics, and piety; almost all are in MS or in eds. published at the end of the fifteenth and beginning of the sixteenth centuries. There are no modern eds. of his scientific works. For a detailed indication of the MSS and first eds. of all his works, see B. Roth, pp. 50 ff. (see n. 8); on his political thought, see P. de Lapparent, "L'oeuvre politique de Francis de Méyronnes," in *Archives d'histoire doctrinale et littéraire du moyen âge,* **13** (1942), 57–74. On his comments to the *Sentences,* see F. Stegmüller, *Repertorium commentariorum in libros Sententiarum* (Würzburg, 1947), and V. Doucet, "Commentaires sur les Sentences, Supplément au répertoire de F. Stegmüller," in *Archivum franciscanum historicum,* **47** (1954), 114–116; and annals of the *Archivum:* XLVI, 164–166, 342; XLVII, 98, 114–116; 149, 153, 403; L, 203; LIV, 230; LV, 369, 531; LVI, 209; LVII, 363, 408, 573 (indications of MSS of his commentaries on Aristotle); LVIII, 187, 192, 264, 408; LIX, 86; LX, 263, 450, 466; LXI, 462–463. See also P. O. Kristeller, *Iter italicum,* I (London, 1963), 76, 312, 317, 420; II, 71, 216, 326, 390, 413, 465–466.

Francis' scientific thought is contained in his commentaries on Aristotle, especially in *Expositio in physicam* (Ferrara, 1495; Venice, 1517), in his comments to the *Sentences;* and in the *quaestiones quodlibetales.* For indications of MSS and rare eds., see especially Roth.

II. SECONDARY LITERATURE. Bibliographical indications are in Roth, which is the most nearly complete study to date. For more recent indications of Francis' political and theological thought, see the annals of the *Archivum franciscanum historicum, loc. cit.* On his scientific thought, in addition to the study by Duhem cited in note 10, see his *Système du monde,* vols. VI–X (Paris, 1956–1959), *passim,* and particularly VI, 451–474. See also A. Maier, *Zwischen Philosophie und Mechanik* (Rome, 1958), p. 96; *Ausgehendes Mittelalter,* I (Rome, 1964), 71, 247, 468; and *Zwei Grundprobleme der scholastischen Naturphilosophie* (Rome, 1951), pp. 51, 53, 56, 164, 197, 232, 238. See also B. Nardi, "La filosofia della natura nel Medioevo," in *Acts of the*

Third International Conference of Medieval Philosophy, La Mendola, 1964 (Milan, 1966), p. 23.

GRAZIELLA FEDERICI VESCOVINI

FRANCK, JAMES (*b.* Hamburg, Germany, 26 August 1882; *d.* Göttingen, Germany, 21 May 1964), *physics.*

Franck was the son of Jacob Franck, a banker, and Rebecca Franck. His scientific activity extended over about sixty years, from the beginning of the twentieth century, when the foundations of atomic physics and quantum theory were being laid, to a time when these disciplines had reached a high degree of sophistication. Although Franck was primarily a physicist, his work had a profound influence on chemistry and on the branch of biology concerned with the fundamental process by which the energy of sunlight is converted into the forms of energy that maintain life on earth. In all the varied phenomena that he studied one can recognize a unity of approach in his attempt to understand the processes of transfer of energy in atomic systems.

In the two semesters (1901–1902) of his studies at Heidelberg, Franck met Max Born and formed a friendship with him that lasted throughout his life. His serious study and research in physics began in 1902 when he moved to Berlin, at that time the center of physics in Germany. Rubens, Emil Warburg, and Planck (later Drude and Einstein) were professors in Berlin, and their joint colloquium was one of the great formative influences in Franck's life. He entered Warburg's laboratory and started work on corona discharges, a topic he soon abandoned in favor of the more fundamental study of ion mobilities. He found that collisions of electrons with noble gas atoms were mainly elastic, without loss of kinetic energy. His younger colleague, Gustav Hertz, joined him in a thorough study of elastic collisions, and this work led to the discovery of quantized transfer of energy in inelastic collisions between electrons and atoms. In their famous experiments, Franck and Hertz[1] showed that electrons could impart energy to a mercury atom only if they had a kinetic energy exceeding 4.9 ev., and that exactly this quantum of energy was taken up by the mercury atom, causing it to emit light of the resonance line Å 2537. It was the first direct proof of the quantized nature of the energy transfer and of the connection of the quantum ΔE of energy with the frequency $\nu = \Delta E/h$ of the light emitted as the result of the transfer. These experiments are rightly regarded as the first decisive proof of the reality of the quantized energy levels that had just been postulated by Niels Bohr. Misled by the observation of ions in their experiments and in those of other workers in the same conditions, Franck and Hertz initially believed ionization to occur simultaneously with emission of resonance radiation, so that $h\nu$ was to be regarded as the ionization energy; this was in accordance with current speculations by Stark and others but contradicted Bohr's theory.

The outbreak of World War I interrupted most scientific work and exchange of ideas. Franck served briefly in the German army but became seriously ill and was sent home to recover. It was probably due to this interruption of scientific activities and contacts in Europe that Franck and Hertz held to their views on ionization as late as 1916. The spurious origin of the ions was proved mainly by work in the United States and was recognized after the war by Franck and Hertz.[2] The fundamental importance of their experiments was acknowledged in 1926 by the award of the Nobel Prize to Franck and Hertz.

From 1917 to 1921 Franck was assistant professor and head of a section of the Kaiser Wilhelm Institut für Physikalische Chemie (later the Max Planck Institut), whose director was Fritz Haber. With a number of co-workers he extended the study of inelastic collisions of electrons with atoms and molecules and measured excitation and ionization potentials. With Knipping and Reiche he introduced the concept of metastable levels, excited states that can lose energy not by radiation but only by collisions. They play an important part in gas discharges and many other phenomena. The postwar years in Berlin marked the beginning of Franck's friendship with Niels Bohr, for whom he had a profound admiration as a scientist and a warm affection. The obituary of Bohr that Franck wrote not long before his own death[3] is a moving testimony to their friendship.

In 1921 Franck accepted the chair of experimental physics and directorship of the Zweite Physikalische Institut in Göttingen, where R. Pohl occupied the other chair as director of the Erste Physikalische Institut, located in the same building. Max Born had just accepted the chair of theoretical physics on the condition that a chair and department be established for Franck. For the next twelve years Franck and Born, linked by close ties of friendship and common interests, formed the nucleus of an active scientific community in Göttingen.

A central theme in the great variety of publications of that period may be described as the study of atoms in collision, and the formation and dissociation of molecules and their vibration and rotation. In two papers[4, 5] Born and Franck developed the use of the now familiar potential energy curves for treating two-atom systems, and they introduced the concept of quasi-molecules. Applying these ideas to the transfer of energy from electronic to vibrational motion in molecular spectra, Franck was led to the method of determining the energy of dissociation of molecules by extrapolation of vibrational levels and to the principle which, after its wave-mechanical formulation by Condon, became known as the Franck-Condon principle. It has since provided the key to the understanding of a wide range of phenomena in molecular physics, such as continuous molecular spectra, the intensity distribution in band spectra, predissociation, photodissociation, and pressure broadening of spectral lines.

Problems of energy transfer in collisions had occupied Franck since he started research, and in 1926 his only publication in book form[6] appeared; written with P. Jordan, it contains the basic ideas of most of his work to that date.

Political events in Germany in 1933, after Hitler came to power, brought most of the scientific work in Göttingen to an abrupt end. Franck, although Jewish, was initially allowed to continue in office, but new legislation would have forced him to dismiss co-workers and students who were either non-Aryan or politically committed. He refused to accept this, and in April 1933 he resigned his professorship and published a courageous statement of protest against the new laws. Within a few months not only Franck and Born but most of their co-workers had left Germany.

After spending over a year in Copenhagen, Franck immigrated to the United States in 1935 and accepted a professorship at Johns Hopkins University in Baltimore. In 1938 he was appointed professor of physical chemistry at the University of Chicago, where the Samuel Fels Foundation had established a laboratory for photosynthesis; he directed it until his retirement in 1949 and took an active part in it long afterward. At Göttingen and Baltimore, Franck and his colleagues had begun to extend the understanding of excitation and photodissociation from diatomic molecules to liquids and solids and finally to the process of photosynthesis in plants. This work was bound to involve Franck in all the complexities of biochemistry, but it attracted him by its fundamental importance. His contribution to the exciton theory and the photographic process, made jointly with Teller,[7] also belongs to this period, but it was to the problem of photosynthesis that most of his remaining work was devoted.

During World War II, he joined the metallurgical project in Chicago, which formed part of the atomic bomb project. After the surrender of Germany, he and many other scientists working on the project became seriously concerned about the consequences of using the new weapon. In a document later released and known as the Franck Report,[8] they urged the government to consider the use of the bomb a fateful political decision and not merely a matter of military tactics. After the end of the war, Franck resumed his research at Chicago. His wife Ingrid had died in 1942 after a long illness, and in 1946 he married Hertha Sponer, professor of physics at Duke University.

The work on photosynthesis involved Franck in much controversy. On the experimental side, he rejected the measurements of Warburg as being in conflict with basic thermodynamic principles and in disagreement with the work at other laboratories. On the theoretical side, Franck developed a model that assumed a two-step process in one single chlorophyll molecule and accounted for most of the experimental facts, although some details of his views are still contested. The award of the Rumford Medal of the American Academy of Arts and Sciences in 1955 for his work on photosynthesis showed the increasing recognition of his contribution to this field. It was one of the numerous honors he received in addition to the Nobel Prize and memberships in academies and learned societies, including the Royal Society of London. Honors also came to him after World War II from Germany: he received the Max Planck Medal of the German Physical Society and was made an honorary citizen of Göttingen, where he died while on a tour of Germany to visit old friends.

NOTES

1. J. Franck and G. Hertz, in *Verhandlungen der Physiologischen Gesellschaft zu Berlin,* **16** (1914), 512.
2. J. Franck and G. Hertz, in *Physikalische Zeitschrift,* **20** (1919), 132.
3. J. Franck, "Niels Bohr's Persönlichkeit," in *Naturwissenschaften,* **50** (1963), 341.
4. J. Franck and M. Born, in *Annalen der Physik,* **76** (1925), 225.
5. J. Franck and M. Born, in *Zeitschrift für Physik,* **31** (1925), 411.
6. J. Franck and P. Jordan, *Anregungen von Quantensprüngen durch Stösse* (Berlin, 1926).
7. J. Franck and E. Teller, in *Journal of Chemical Physics,* **6** (1938), 861.
8. Franck Report, *Bulletin of the Atomic Scientists* (*of Chicago*), **1**, no. 10 (1946), 1-5.

BIBLIOGRAPHY

A more detailed biography of James Franck is H. G. Kuhn, "James Franck 1882–1964," in *Biographical Memoirs of Fellows of the Royal Society,* **11** (1965), 53–74; it includes a complete bibliography by R. L. Platzman.

H. G. KUHN

FRANCK, SEBASTIAN (*b.* Donauwörth, Bavaria, Germany, 20 January 1499; *d.* Basel, Switzerland, 1542), *theology.*

We have no precise information about Franck's parents and early life. He may have attended the grammar school in Nördlingen before matriculating, in March 1515, in the Arts Faculty of the University of Ingolstadt, where he received a humanistic education that included Latin and Greek but not Hebrew. After graduation in December 1517, he went to Heidelberg in January 1518 to study theology at the Dominican college that was incorporated with the university. The theological faculty was then dominated by Aristotelian Scholasticism, but a few months after his arrival Franck heard the new Augustinian voice when he attended Luther's famous Heidelberg disputation. Among his fellow students were his later opponents Martin Frecht and the Strasbourg reformer Martin Bucer. We do not know when Franck left Heidelberg. He entered the Catholic priesthood, but by the end of 1527 he was a Protestant pastor in Gustenfelden, near Nuremberg. In 1528 he married Ottilie Beham, the sister of Albrecht Dürer's pupils Barthel and Hans Sebald Beham, both known for their Anabaptist leanings and for their association with Hans Denck. At this time, during the turbulent years that followed the Peasants' War, Franck adopted the spiritualist views that put him in strong opposition to Luther.

He left his pastorate before the end of 1528, and for the rest of his life he earned his living as a popular writer, printer, and, for a while, soapmaker, wandering from place to place with his family as he was banned from one town after another for his unorthodox writings. For a while he was in Nuremberg, where he published his first writings, but in 1529 he was in Strasbourg, then known for its liberal religious atmosphere and as a gathering place for radical reformers, who during these years included Michael Servetus, Hans Bünderlin, and Kaspar von Schwenkfeld. Here Franck published his great work *Chronica, Zeitbuch und Geschichtbibel* (1531), which immediately brought complaints from many sides, including one from Erasmus, whom Franck greatly admired. The book was confiscated, Franck was arrested, and at the end of the year he was expelled from Strasbourg.

In 1534 Franck became a citizen of Ulm, where he almost immediately faced new difficulties owing to his publications there, the *Paradoxa ducenta octoginta, das ist CCLXXX Wunderred und gleichsam Räterschaft, aus der Heiligen Schrift* (1534), his most characteristic theological work, and *Das theur und künstlich Büchlein Morie encomion* (1534), which Franck also called "die vier Kronbüchlein." It developed his spiritual doctrine by showing that all worldly piety and wisdom are folly before God. This work contained German versions of Erasmus' *In Praise of Folly* and of Agrippa von Nettesheim's *De incertitudine et vanitate omnium scientiarum et artium* as well as two pieces by Franck, *Ein Lob des thörichten Göttlichen Worts* and *Vom Baum des Wissens Gutes und Böses,* which alone among Franck's writings has been published in English. It was translated by the mystic John Everard, under the title *The Forbidden Fruit: Or a Treatise of the Tree of Knowledge* (1640).

Franck was now accused of rejecting the efficacy of preaching and the authority of the Bible but was allowed to remain in Ulm, provided he submitted to censorship. He published his next books in Tübingen, Augsburg, and Frankfurt. They included a book of geography (including the New World), folklore, and anthropology, *Weltbuch: Spiegel und Bildniss des ganzen Erdbodens* (1534); a history and description of Germany called *Germaniae chronicon* (1538); and *Die Güldin Arch* (1538), which is a sort of concordance to Scriptures designed to awaken the reader to the inward word. It was followed by *Das verbütschierte mit 7 Siegeln verschlossene Buch* (1539), a "discordance" in which Franck deliberately juxtaposed contradictory Scriptural passages. His presence in Ulm again became controversial and, with Schwenkfeld, he was banished from the city in January 1539. With his wife, his ten children, and his printing press he left for Basel, where he was allowed to live until his death in 1542. His first wife died in 1540, and the following year he married Margarete Beck, the daughter of the printer Reinhard Beck and the stepdaughter of Balthasar Beck, who had printed Franck's *Chronica.* Franck's last works, including a collection of German proverbs, were published at Basel.

Franck's thought presents a mixture of theology and philosophy. It was neither highly original nor entirely consistent, but what he borrowed he molded into a powerful and unusual statement of the spiritual freedom and self-sufficiency of the individual. It was guided by the principle that all men, regardless of time and place, are given equal capacity for moral, intellectual, and religious insight. From the beginning of history, God has in His creation revealed Himself unambiguously and uniformly to all mankind, and this revelation in nature is surer and more universal testimony to His power, wisdom, and goodness than the Scriptures are. The Scriptures are recorded in the dead letter of writing, full of contradictions and available only to part of mankind. Since God is impartial, faith and divine favor cannot depend on Scripture alone.

Hence the Incarnation and the historical Christ have no place in Franck's theology. Adam and Christ, the flesh and the spirit, the outward and the inward man, are qualities that lie in human nature. The common creation of the macrocosm and the microcosm ensures their conformity as well as the uniformity of human nature. Thus all men are born with the ability to gain divine insight. Reason, or the light of nature, combined with experience is the means man has been granted to gain this insight. Taken together with his individualism, this aspect of Franck's thought has a rationalist and naturalist quality that is absent in his German contemporaries but somewhat reminiscent of the philosophy of the late seventeenth century.

Franck is generally grouped with the spiritual reformers or mystics of his own century because, like them, he rebelled against the increasing dogmatism and growing institutional rigidity of the Protestant churches. But his rationalism and radical universalism set him apart from them. Unlike the true mystics—Valentin Weigel and Jacob Boehme, for instance—Franck never claimed authority and special insight by virtue of some unique personal revelation; the knowledge that was open to him was open to all. He was no enthusiast. Similarly, he had no fondness for esoteric and cabalistic lore, did not engage in fanciful verbal mysticism, and had no predilection for magic.

Although it may appear curious, Franck's outlook resembles that of John Locke (no influence is postulated). Both believed that the play of reason on experience was a God-given and certain avenue to all knowledge, both natural and moral; that this knowledge was equally open to all mankind; and that it agreed with the moral and religious precepts of the New Testament. Both had profound doubts about the Trinity and the divinity of Christ; both insisted on God's impartiality and therefore gave tolerance a prominent place in their concerns; and both took an interest in comparative anthropology. Their agreement on so many fundamental points is summed up in their mutual abhorrence of enthusiasm as an enemy of reason and tolerance. This position is not incompatible with the chiliasm which Franck shared with so many in his own and the following century, although it did not play a prominent role in his writings. Chiliasm gave a strong impulse to rationalism; being God-given and Godlike, only reason can discover the proper method for the speedy increase of knowledge.

Franck taught the most radical form of spiritualism. True belief depends on the illumination of the individual soul by the inward spirit, which is also called Christ, truth, and the inward word. Having created man in his own image, God has planted this spirit in man and has made it innate. All men are in this respect equal, whether they have heard the outward word or not. Just as many who have never heard of Adam live according to the flesh, so many who have not heard of Christ are filled with the spirit. God is impartial. He is wholly love, and this love is extended to all of creation, which gives testimony to his love and power. God is essentially without will. Self-will entered the world with the Fall, but the loving God will not use force against it. Union with God can occur only when man is rightly moved by the spirit, making himself altogether empty of will and thus becoming independent of outward things. This will-less state of the soul is called *Gelassenheit,* a term common among the spiritual reformers, who found it in the writings of late medieval mystics. It was also used by Luther and later regained importance among the Pietists. To ensure that man is indeed capable of this will-less spiritual state, Franck argued that man can actively exercise free will by prevenient grace alone, that is, grace before conversion and baptism. Predestination and election are contrary to the essential love and impartiality of God.

Within these terms, so very different from Luther's, Franck agreed with Luther that justification occurs by faith alone, but he firmly rejected Luther's scripturalism (the necessity of the outward word, even though insufficient, prior to the awakening of the inward spirit). God's word and truth cannot be written and read, spoken and taught. As reason will not submit to written rules, so the spirit cannot be contained in the dead letter. The only possible church is the invisible church of individual believers, each man gaining faith by his own private efforts. All men being endowed with the spirit and allowed full freedom of will, they are genuinely capable of making a responsible and free choice. The Old and New Testaments are written in the hearts of all men. When Franck revealed, in the *Paradoxa* and in other works, the contradictions contained in the Bible, he sought to weaken man's faith in the dead letter in order to guide him toward his own reliance on the spirit within. In this sense Franck can be said to have advocated an extreme and fundamental form of individualism. Still, the importance he attached to the Bible (when understood with spiritual guidance) is sufficiently strong to relieve him of mere pantheism.

Although Franck held that the hidden God can be understood only in the truth and faith that are the fruits of spiritual insight, he did not believe that this insight can be gained directly. Guided by the light of nature or reason, the experience of outward things, whether they were made by God or man, is the means by which man may learn to find the truth that lies hidden behind the mask of appearance. The world of man and his institutions has always been dominated by man's will, except among the apostles. It is the world of Antichrist, and it is an unending record of chaos, decay, violence, and intolerance. The events of history offer instruction when they are seen as the very opposite of truth, a view that forms the powerful theme of the *Chronica.* The world, Franck says in the preface, is God's carnival play; appearance is the reverse of truth. The most characteristic part of this work is the book devoted to the men who have been judged heretics by the Roman Church. Among them Franck included Luther, Erasmus, Zwingli, and the Anabaptists. As victims of mere human authority, will, and force, all heretics have become witnesses to truth by following their own consciences.

Tolerance and impartiality are duties man owes to man by virtue of being created in the image of God. Experience, truth, and faith will always be private and individual. For this reason Franck made no basic distinction between pagans and Christians. He accorded equal significance to citations from the Bible and from Plato, Seneca, Proclus, Plotinus, and Hermes Trismegistus, whom he knew from Ficino's Latin translation and commentary. They saw the good by means of experience and the inner light or reason that is common to all mankind. Although he cited them often, Franck admitted no special authority for the Church Fathers. He agreed with Erasmus that the wisdom of the learned is folly before God. In line with what may perhaps be called Franck's democratic spiritualism, he found wisdom in the proverbs of the common folk.

Franck's position in his own time was as independent as his theology. Although he had much sympathy for the Anabaptists, he was as little inclined to join them as any other sect. He was strongly influenced by Erasmus and the young Luther, as well as by late medieval German mysticism, especially by Johannes Tauler and the *Theologia Germanica.* He was indebted to a number of his contemporaries among the spiritual reformers, especially Hans Denck, Johann Bünderlin, and Michael Servetus. The distinctive quality of his thought was determined by his heavy debt to Renaissance humanism and the Neoplatonic tradition. It was his special accomplishment to make this tradition available to the public at large. As a writer of German prose, Franck was second only to Luther.

Franck and his teachings were condemned in the strongest terms by Luther, Zwingli, Calvin, and Melanchthon. He naturally formed no sect, but his writings, although often banned and burned, were reprinted with some frequency in Germany. Yet it was in the Netherlands that Franck gained his greatest following. He had a direct influence on David Joris and Dirck Coornhert, and some of his writings are preserved only in translations made for the Dutch spiritualists and published at Gouda. Valentin Weigel cites Franck with approval, but the true extent of his influence on later German spiritualists is not easily determined. The title of Gottfried Arnold's *Unparteiische Kirchen- und Ketzer-Historie* (1699–1700) is a reminder that Franck was not forgotten by the Pietists.

BIBLIOGRAPHY

I. Original Works. Although not complete, the best list of Franck's works is Karl Goedeke, *Grundrisz der Deutschen Dichtung aus den Quellen,* II, *Das Reformationszeitalter,* 2nd ed. (Dresden, 1886), 8–14. There is an unsatisfactory edition of the *Paradoxa* by Heinrich Ziegler (Jena, 1909). The original works are rare, but good selections will be found in the following: G. H. Williams, ed., *Spiritual and Anabaptist Writers* (Philadelphia, 1957), pp. 145–160 ("A Letter to John Campanus"); Heinold Fast, ed., *Der Linke Flügel der Reformation* (Bremen, 1962), pp. 217–248 ("Letter to Campanus" and preface to the book on the Roman heretics in *Chronica*); Kurt von Raumer, ed., *Ewiger Friede, Friedensrufe und Friedenspläne seit der Renaissance* (Freiburg–Munich), pp. 249–288 (extensive excerpts from *Kriegbüchlein des Friedes* [1539]). Good excerpts from various sources are also in Peter Meinhold, ed., *Geschichte der kirchlichen Historiographie,* I (Freiburg–Munich, 1967), 301–310; and in Ernst Staehelin, ed., *Die Verkündigung des Reiches Gottes in der Kirche Jesu Christi,* IV (Basel, 1957), 342–356.

II. Secondary Literature. The secondary literature is listed in Karl Schottenloher, *Bibliographie zur Deutschen Geschichte im Zeitalter der Glaubensspaltung 1517–1585,* I (Leipzig, 1933), 263–266; V (Leipzig, 1939), 92; VII (Stuttgart, 1962), 79–80. See also E. Teufel, "Die *Deutsche Theologie* und Sebastian Franck im Lichte der neueren Forschung," in *Theologische Rundschau,* **12** (1940), 99–129.

The standard work on Franck and still the best is Alfred Hegler, *Geist und Schrift bei Sebastian Franck, eine Studie zur Geschichte des Spiritualismus in der Reformationszeit* (Freiburg, 1892). This work should be supplemented by Hegler's "Sebastian Franck," in Albert Hauck, ed., *Realencyklopädie für protestantische Theologie und Kirche,* 3rd ed., VI (Leipzig, 1899), 142–150. The best biography is E. Teufel, *"Landräumig" Sebastian Franck, ein Wanderer an Donau, Rhein und Neckar* (Neustadt an der Aisch, 1954). Somewhat diffuse, with extensive quotations from the works, is Will-Erich Peuckert, *Sebastian Franck, ein Deutscher Sucher* (Munich, 1943). Wilhelm Dilthey devoted an influential section to Franck in *Weltanschauung und Analyse des Menschen seit Renaissance und Reformation, Gesammelte Schriften,* II (Leipzig–Berlin, 1914), 81–89.

General aspects are dealt with in Rudolf Stadelmann, *Vom Geist des ausgehenden Mittelalters, Studien zur*

Geschichte der Weltanschauung von Nikolaus Cusanus bis Sebastian Franck (Halle, 1929). A special issue of *Blätter für Deutsche Philosophie,* **2** (1928–1929), was devoted to Franck. See also Alexandre Koyré, "Sébastien Franck," in *Mystiques, Spirituels, Alchimistes du XVI*[e] *siècle allemand* (Paris, 1955), pp. 21–43; and Walter Nigg, *Das Buch der Ketzer* (Zurich, 1949), pp. 382–392. G. H. Williams, *The Radical Reformation* (Philadelphia, 1962), deals with Franck on pp. 264–268, 457–466, and 499–504. Good general introductions are offered in Rufus M. Jones, *Spiritual Reformers of the 16th and 17th Centuries* (New York, 1914), pp. 46–63; and Doris Rieber, "Sébastian Franck," in *Bibliothèque d'humanisme et renaissance,* **20** (1958), 218–228.

Special topics are dealt with in Kuno Räber, *Studien zur Geschichtsbibel Sebastian Francks* (Basel, 1952), which is vol. XLI in Basler Beiträge zur Geschichtswissenschaft. Joseph Lecler, *Histoire de la tolérance au siècle de la réforme,* I (Paris, 1955), 177–187, is excellent. Meinulf Barbers, *Toleranz bei Sebastian Franck* (Bonn, 1964), has a good bibliography (this is n.s. 4 in Untersuchungen zur allgemeinen Religionsgeschichte). See also Robert Stupperich, "Sebastian Franck und das münsterische Täufertum," in Rudolf Vierhaus and Manfred Botzenhart, eds., *Dauer und Wandel der Geschichte . . . Festgabe für Kurt von Raumer zum 15. Dezember 1965* (Münster, 1966), pp. 144–162. On Gottfried Arnold and Franck, see Erich Seeberg, *Gottfried Arnold, die Wissenschaft und die Mystik seiner Zeit* (Meerane, 1923; repr. Darmstadt, 1964), pp. 516–534. Franck's role in the study of comparative anthropology and folklore is demonstrated in Erich Schmidt, *Deutsche Volkskunde im Zeitalter des Humanismus und der Reformation,* Historische Studien, E. Eberling, ed., no. 47 (Berlin, 1904), pp. 108–131.

There is an excellent chapter on the general outlook of the Anabaptists in Claus-Peter Clasen, *Die Wiedertäufer im Herzogtum Württemberg und in benachbarten Herrschaften: Ausbreitung, Geisteswelt und Soziologie* (Stuttgart, 1965), pp. 69–117.

HANS AARSLEFF

FRANK, PHILIPP (*b.* Vienna, Austria, 20 March 1884; *d.* Cambridge, Massachusetts, 21 July 1966), *physics, mathematics, philosophy of science, education.*

Frank obtained his doctorate in physics in 1907 from the University of Vienna as a student under Ludwig Boltzmann. Frank later wrote of this period:

> . . . the domain of my most intensive interest was the philosophy of science. I used to associate with a group of students who assembled every Thursday night in one of the old Viennese coffee houses. . . . We returned again and again to our central problem: How can we avoid the traditional ambiguity and obscurity of philosophy? How can we bring about the closest possible *rapprochement* between philosophy and science?

As a physicist Frank was a creative contributor, working on fundamental problems of theoretical physics during an exciting period of its growth. Perhaps his most widely known publication of those years was the two-volume collection, edited with his lifelong friend Richard von Mises, *Die Differential- und Integralgleichungen der Mechanik und Physik.* Frank's own research was concerned with variational calculus, Fourier series, function spaces, Hamiltonian geometrical optics, Schrödinger's wave mechanics, and relativity theory. In an early paper with Hermann Rothe he derived the Lorentz transformation equations without assuming constancy of light velocity from the fact that the equations form a group.

But his first and most lasting love was the philosophy of science. From the beginning Frank was intrigued by Poincaré's neo-Kantian idea that many basic principles of science are purely conventional. In 1907 Frank took the bold step of using that idea to analyze the law of causality. This paper attracted Einstein's attention and started a lasting friendship. In 1912 Einstein recommended Frank as his successor as professor of theoretical physics at the German University of Prague, a position Frank held until 1938. Frank's original paper on causality—which Lenin criticized in his 1908 book on positivist philosophy and the sciences—was later expanded into his widely influential work *Das Kausalgesetz und seine Grenzen* (1932). In 1947 Frank published an authoritative biography, *Einstein: His Life and Times.*

Frank was a logical positivist, although a less doctrinaire one than many of those with whom he formed the Vienna circle in the 1920's. The breadth of interest which he exhibited in his work and fostered in his students made science a liberal discipline and reflected a style of life as well as of mind. As he once remarked, he sought always to achieve a balanced outlook on man and nature; and for him physics not only provided reliable answers to particular technical problems but also raised and illuminated important questions concerning the nature, scope, and validity of human knowledge. Indeed, Frank believed that a stable perspective on life can best be achieved through the critical, intellectual method of modern natural science.

He therefore saw it as a misfortune that science and philosophy are widely regarded as unrelated and incongruous. But it was also his conviction that this breach between a scientific and a humanist orientation toward life—a breach that he thought to be of relatively recent origin—could be diminished, if not overcome, by an adequate philosophy of science.

Holding that the meaning and validity of theoretical assumptions can be determined only if detailed consideration is given to the verifiable consequences which the assumptions entail, Frank called attention to certain misinterpretations of relativity theory and quantum mechanics and their fallacious use in support of questionable doctrines. The titles of some of his works indicate these concerns—"Das Ende der mechanistischen Physik" (1935), *Interpretations and Misinterpretations of Modern Physics* (1938), and *Philosophy of Science: The Link Between Science and Philosophy* (1957).

Frank was organizer or chief participant in the *International Encyclopedia of Unified Science,* the Philosophy of Science Association, *Synthèse,* the Institute for the Unity of Science, and the Boston Colloquium for the Philosophy of Science.

In 1938 Frank and his wife, Hania, came to the United States. After serving as a visiting lecturer, he remained as lecturer on physics and mathematics at Harvard, where his influential course on philosophy of science, his erudite mastery, and his warm and witty manner were remembered long after his retirement in 1954.

BIBLIOGRAPHY

I. ORIGINAL WORKS. Frank's books include *Die Differential- und Integralgleichungen der Mechanik und Physik,* 2 vols. (Brunswick, 1925; last rev. ed., 1935), trans. into Russian (Moscow, 1937), written with Richard von Mises; *Das Kausalgesetz und seine Grenzen* (Vienna, 1932), also trans. into French (Paris, 1937); the collection of papers in philosophy of science, *Between Physics and Philosophy* (Cambridge, Mass., 1941), later repr. and enl. as *Modern Science and Its Philosophy* (New York, 1949); *Einstein: His Life and Times* (New York, 1947; rev. 1953), published in German (Munich, 1949); *Relativity: A Richer Truth* (Boston, 1950); and *Philosophy of Science: The Link Between Science and Philosophy* (Englewood Cliffs, N.J., 1957).

Frank's papers in theoretical physics include "Das Relativitätsprinzip und die Darstellung der physikalischen Erscheinungen im vierdimensionalen Raum," in Ostwald's *Annalen der Naturphilosophie,* **10** (1911), 129–161; "Die statistische Betrachtungsweise in der Physik," in *Naturwissenschaften,* **7** (1919), 701–740; "Über die Eikonalgleichung in allgemein anisotropen Medien," in *Annalen der Physik,* 4th ser., **84** (1927), 891–898; "Relativitätsmechanik," in *Handbuch für physikalische und technische Mechanik,* II (Leipzig, 1928), 52 ff.; "Die Grundbegriffe der analytischen Mechanik als Grundlage der Quanten- und Wellenmechanik," in *Physikalische Zeitschrift,* **30** (1929), 209–228; "Statistische Mechanik Boltzmanns als Näherung der Wellenmechanik," in *Zeitschrift für Physik,* **61** (1930), 640–643, written with W. Glaser.

His epistemological writings include "Kausalgesetz und Erfahrung," in Ostwald's *Annalen der Naturphilosophie,* **6** (1908), 445–450; "Über die Anschaulichkeit physikalischer Theorien," in *Naturwissenschaften,* **16** (1928), 122–128; "Was bedeuten die gegenwärtigen physikalischen Theorien für die allgemeine Erkenntnislehre?," *ibid.,* **17** (1929), 971–977; "Das Ende der mechanistischen Physik," in *Einheitswissenschaft,* **5** (1935), 23–25; "The Mechanical Versus the Mathematical Conception of Nature," in *Philosophy of Science,* **4** (1937), 41–74; *Interpretations and Misinterpretations of Modern Physics* (Paris, 1938); "Physik und logischer Empirismus," in *Erkenntnis,* **7** (1938), 297–301; *Foundations of Physics,* I, no. 7 of the *International Encyclopedia of Unified Science* (Chicago, 1946); and "Metaphysical Interpretations of Science," in *British Journal for the Philosophy of Science,* **1** (1950), 60–91.

Frank's papers on sociological and cultural aspects of science include "Mechanismus oder Vitalismus? Versuch einer präzisen Formulierung der Fragestellung," in Ostwald's *Annalen der Naturphilosophie,* **7** (1908), 393–409; "Die Bedeutung der physikalischen Erkenntnistheorie Machs für das Geistesleben der Gegenwart," in *Naturwissenschaften,* **5** (1917), 65–72; "The Philosophical Meaning of the Copernican Revolution," in *Proceedings of the American Philosophical Society,* **87** (1944), 381–386; "Science Teaching and the Humanities," in *ETC: A Review of General Semantics,* **4** (1946), 3–24; "The Place of Logic and Metaphysics in the Advancement of Modern Science," in *Philosophy of Science,* **15** (1948), 275–286; "Einstein, Mach, and Logical Positivism," in *Albert Einstein: Philosopher-Scientist,* P. A. Schilpp, ed. (Chicago, 1949), pp. 271–286; "Einstein's Philosophy of Science," in *Review of Modern Physics,* **21** (1949), 349–355; "The Logical and Sociological Aspects of Science," in *Proceedings of the American Academy of Arts and Sciences,* **80** (1951), 16–30; "The Origin of the Separation Between Science and Philosophy," *ibid.* (1952), 115–139; "The Variety of Reasons for the Acceptance of Scientific Theories," in *The Validation of Scientific Theories,* Philipp Frank, ed. (Boston, 1956), pp. 3–17, first pub. in *Scientific Monthly,* **79**, no. 3 (1954), 139–145; and "The Pragmatic Component in Carnap's 'Elimination of Metaphysics,'" in *The Philosophy of Rudolf Carnap,* P. A. Schilpp, ed. (Chicago, 1963), pp. 159–164.

Frank edited a number of works, including *The Validation of Scientific Theories* (Boston, 1956) and *The International Encyclopedia of Unified Science* (Chicago, various dates). He also served on the editorial boards of the journals *Synthèse* (1946–1963) and *Philosophy of Science* (1941–1955).

II. SECONDARY LITERATURE. A *Festschrift* for Philipp Frank was published as vol. II of *Boston Studies in the Philosophy of Science,* R. S. Cohen and M. W. Wartofsky, eds. (Dordrecht–New York, 1965), with tributes by Peter G. Bergmann, Rudolf Carnap, R. Fürth, Gerald Holton, Edwin C. Kemble, Henry Margenau, Hilda von Mises, Ernest Nagel, Raymond J. Seeger, and Kurt Sitte, and essays in the philosophy of science.

A memorial booklet based on talks delivered by some of Frank's colleagues and friends at the memorial meeting of 25 October 1966 at Harvard University was distributed the following year, and an article "In Memory of Philipp Frank" appeared in *Philosophy of Science,* **35** (1968), 1–5.

GERALD HOLTON
ROBERT S. COHEN

FRANKENHEIM, MORITZ LUDWIG (*b.* Brunswick, Germany, 29 June 1801; *d.* Dresden, Germany, 14 January 1869), *crystallography.*

Frankenheim attended the Gymnasium in Wolfenbüttel and Brunswick. In 1820 he began his university studies in Berlin with philology but changed to mathematics and physics. In 1823 he received a doctorate for his dissertation, *De theoria gasorum et vaporum.* He qualified as a university lecturer in 1826, also in Berlin. In 1827 he was appointed assistant professor at Breslau, where he became professor of physics in 1850; he held this position until 1866.

Frankenheim's importance lies especially in the field of crystallography. In his work *Die Lehre von der Kohäsion . . .* (1835), he was the first to examine whether or not the geometrically possible types of crystal lattices agree in their symmetry relations with those actually observed in crystals. He showed that there could be only fifteen different "nodal," i.e., space lattice, type configurations. Bravais, in his "Mémoires sur les systèmes formés par des points distribués régulièrement sur un plan ou dans l'espace" (1848), acknowledged Frankenheim's achievement: "Frankenheim, in his beautiful researches in crystallography, arrived at the same classification." In 1856 he corrected himself: there could be only fourteen, because two of the proposed monoclinic subdivisions proved to be identical.

In his 1829 work *De crystallorum cohaesione* Frankenheim established that the hardness of crystals is always the same in the same crystallographic directions but varies with the direction through the crystal. He was also the first to investigate experimentally the influence of a crystal on oriented overgrowth from a crystal seed (epitaxy). In 1830 he investigated more exactly with the microscope the overgrowth of sodium carbonate on calcium carbonate that he had observed in his study of cohesion. In 1836 he grew potassium iodide on mica, a spectacular example of oriented overgrowth still used for demonstration. Frankenheim also introduced the concept of isodimorphism, which he derived from observations on sodium nitrate and potassium nitrate on the one hand and on calcite and aragonite on the other.

Frankenheim devised an experiment that even today is a suitable lecture demonstration. Out of a drop of warm supersaturated potassium nitrate solution, a rhombohedral unstable modification precipitates out onto the microscope slide. With further cooling needlelike orthorhombic crystals form outward from the edge, and the rhombohedrons in the vicinity of the orthorhombic needles dissolve. If one of the needles is touched by a rhombohedron, the latter is very quickly transformed into an aggregate of rhombic crystals.

Frankenheim repeatedly took a position on the question of amorphous minerals in a polemic with the Munich mineralogist J. N. von Fuchs. In 1851 he held that these bodies were aggregates of many crystals of imperceptible dimensions. Much later the introduction of X-ray investigation showed that this conception was correct in the case of a great many substances formerly considered amorphous.

As early as 1860, Frankenheim used a new kind of polarizing microscope; the specimen could be rotated so that the angles between two directions in the specimen, as well as its position relative to the orientation of the Nicol prisms, could be exactly determined.

BIBLIOGRAPHY

I. Original Works. Frankenheim's works include *De theoria gasorum et vaporum* (Berlin, 1823); *De crystallorum cohaesione* (Vratisl, 1829); *Die Lehre von der Kohäsion, umfassend die Elastizität der Gase, die Elastizität und Kohärenz der flüssigen und festen Körper und die Kristallkunde* (Breslau, 1835); "Über die Verbindung verschiedenartiger Krystalle," in *Annalen der Physik,* **37** (1836), 516–522; "System der Kristalle, ein Versuch," in *Nova acta Academiae Caesarae Leopoldina Carolinae germanicae naturae curiosorum,* Abt. II, **19** (1842), 471–660; "Krystallisation und Amorphie," in *Journal für praktische Chemie,* **54** (1851), 430–476; "Die Anordnung der Moleküle im Kristalle," in *Annalen der Physik,* **97** (1856), 337–382; "Entstehen und Wachsen der Kristalle, mikroskopische Beobachtungen," *ibid.,* **111** (1860), 37 ff.; *Zur Kristallkunde I. Charakteristik der Kristalle* (Leipzig, 1869), unfinished.

II. Secondary Literature. On Frankenheim and his work, see A. Bravais, "Mémoires sur les systèmes formés par des points distribués régulièrement sur un plan ou dans l'espace," in *Journal de l'École polytechnique,* **19** (1848), 1–128, presented to the Académie des Sciences on 11 Dec. 1848; it was translated by C. and E. Blasius as *Abhandlung über die Systeme von regelmässig auf einer Ebene oder im Raum verteilten Punkten* (Leipzig, 1897). See also P. Groth, *Entwicklungsgeschichte der mineralogischen Wissenschaften* (Berlin, 1926); and Poggendorff, I, 792, and III, 469.

Carl W. Correns

FRANKLAND, EDWARD (*b.* Catterall, near Churchtown, Lancashire, England, 18 January 1825; *d.* Golaa, Gudbrandsdalen, Norway, 9 August 1899), *chemistry.*

Frankland was the illegitimate son of Peggy Frankland, the daughter of a calico printer. After education in seven schools, including Lancaster Grammar School, Frankland was apprenticed by his stepfather, William Helm, to a Lancaster druggist, Stephen Ross. The drudgery of the years from 1840 to 1845, during which Ross taught him little, haunted Frankland's dreams for the remainder of his life. Through the efforts of two local doctors, Christopher and James Johnson, he was given facilities to perform chemical experiments in his spare time, and in 1845 they found him employment in Lyon Playfair's laboratory at the government's Museum of Economic Geology in London. There he met the brilliant German chemist A. W. H. Kolbe, who taught him Robert Bunsen's methods of gas analysis—a technique Frankland exploited in his later researches.

In 1846 Frankland became Playfair's assistant at the Civil Engineering College at Putney, London, and during the summer of 1847 he accompanied Kolbe to Marburg in order to study with Bunsen. From 1847 to 1848 he taught science with John Tyndall at the progressive Quaker school run by George Edmondson at Queenwood, Hampshire. Frankland completed his training with Bunsen at Marburg from 1848 to 1849, obtained his doctorate, and briefly studied with Justus Liebig at Giessen before returning to London to take Playfair's chair of chemistry at Putney from 1850 to 1851. He became professor of chemistry at Owens College, Manchester, in 1851, but this position proved unsatisfactory. In 1857 he returned to London, where, until 1864, he was lecturer in chemistry at St. Bartholomew's Hospital.

Frankland also indulged in the pluralism of a lectureship in science at Addiscombe Military College from 1859 to 1863, and from 1863 to 1869 he was professor of chemistry at the Royal Institution. Finally, in 1865, he succeeded A. W. Hofmann as professor of chemistry at the Royal College of Chemistry, a position he retained through the college's many transformations until his retirement in 1885. From 1865, Frankland made official monthly analyses of the water supplies of London, and from 1868 to 1874 he served on the important Royal Commission on Rivers Pollution. For these services he was knighted in 1897.

At the age of eighteen Frankland underwent an extreme form of evangelical conversion, but after 1848 he lapsed into skepticism. Together with Tyndall, T. H. Huxley, J. D. Hooker, and others he was an active member of an informal scientific pressure group which called itself the X Club. Yet the club was unable to gain for Frankland the presidency of the Royal Society or of the British Association for the Advancement of Science, owing to his modesty and poor ability in public debate. But he did serve as president of the Chemical Society from 1871 to 1873 and was the founder and first president of the Institute of Chemistry (the society for professional chemists) from 1877 to 1880.

Frankland is an outstanding example of a pure scientist who was deeply conscious of the significance and importance of applied science; but his public service in the improvement of water and gas supplies and his contributions to the development of British scientific education await proper assessment. Frankland possessed a voracious appetite for travel, which he combined with mountaineering, yachting, and fishing. He was also a keen gardener, music lover, and amateur astronomer. In 1874, following the death of his first wife, Sophie Fick, by whom he had three sons and two daughters, he married Ellen Grenside, by whom he had two daughters.

Frankland's extraordinary practical and manipulative ability, as well as his power, like Bunsen's, to combine physics with chemistry, was exemplified in all three of the broad categories of his research: organic, physical, and applied chemistry. In 1844 H. Fehling had obtained a new compound, benzonitrile, C_7H_5N (i.e., phenyl cyanide), by the dry distillation of ammonium benzoate. Following A. Schlieper's preparation of valeronitrile, C_5H_9N (i.e., butyl cyanide), in 1846, Kolbe and Frankland noted that both nitriles were easily hydrolyzed to their corresponding acids (i.e., benzoic and valeric acids). In their joint work of 1847 they pointed out that if these so-called nitriles were really cyanides, then their hydrolysis would agree with Berzelius' iconoclastic suggestion that acetic acid was a methyl radical conjugated with oxalic acid ($C_2H_3 \cdot C_2O_3 \cdot HO, C = 6, O = 8$). If both these assumptions were made, it followed that the homologues of acetic acid (e.g., propionic acid) arose from the conjugation of oxalic acid with ethyl (alkyl) radicals. Their production of propionic acid from ethyl cyanide in 1847[1] led Frankland and Kolbe to attempt separately the isolation of alkyl radicals from acids: Kolbe by the electrolysis of acids (1849) and Frankland by using a reaction between alkyl iodides and zinc based on analogy with Bunsen's celebrated isolation of cacodyl in 1837. But after much controversy and the reform of atomic weights, Frankland was forced to admit that the formulas of the radicals he prepared between 1848 and 1851 had to be doubled and that the radicals were in fact inert hydrocarbons of the paraffin series.

The work on radicals also led Frankland in 1849 to the isolation of a new reactive organometallic compound, zinc methyl; this, together with the alkyltin compounds which he prepared in 1850 by the action of sunlight on alkyl halides in the presence of tin, produced the following problem. If, as the conjugation theories of Berzelius and Liebig held, the different alkyl groups associated with oxalic acid (i.e., a carboxylic group) had little or no influence on the combining properties of the acid, why did alkyl-conjugated metals have combining powers different from those of the metals alone? For example, tin diethyl (stanethylium) formed only one oxide, whereas tin itself formed at least two oxides. Zinc methyl, on the other hand, seemed to possess the same singular combining power as zinc. Here was the seed of the concept of valence, which, with international agreement on atomic weight values, was to unite the rival theoretical schools of chemistry during the 1860's into the common aim of structural chemistry.

On 10 May 1852 Frankland read to the Royal Society a paper on organic metallic compounds in which he made the empirical observation that elements possessed fixed combining powers, or "only room, so to speak, for the attachment of a fixed and definite number of the atoms of other elements."[2] The expression "valence" or "valency" began to be used by other chemists only after 1865, whereas Frankland tended to use the misleading term "atomicity." Although the development of valence as an architectural concept for linking atoms together within a molecule owed more to the work of Kekulé in the 1850's and 1860's, Frankland's teaching position at the Royal College of Chemistry and his influence on the Department of Science and Art science examinations enabled him to spread the idea through the younger generation of British chemists. In 1866 he published an influential textbook, *Lecture Notes,* in which he adopted Crum Brown's graphic (structural) formulas and argued (against Kekulé) that elements could exhibit more than one valence below a fixed upper maximum. He also developed a special shorthand structural notation,[3] but it proved confusing and its use did not persist into the twentieth century.

Frankland was quick to see that the analytical techniques he had developed and the organometallic compounds he had prepared would be powerful aids to synthesis, by which he meant the chemist's ability to build up compounds "stone by stone" with a view to understanding their atomic configurations. From 1863 to 1870 he and Baldwin Duppa exploited zinc ethyl and other organic reagents, including ethyl acetate, in the synthesis of ethers, dicarboxylic acids, unsaturated monocarboxylic acids, and hydroxy acids. This meticulous work revealed clearly the structure and relationship of these compounds, and of course its methodology had great bearing on the growth of the chemical industry.

Intermittent work on combustion during the 1860's was initiated by a memorable ascent of, and night on, Mont Blanc with Tyndall in 1859. Frankland found that Humphry Davy's views on the nature of flame were unsound and that pressure variations produced striking changes in the illuminating power of flames.[4] He showed the relevance of this finding to the supply of domestic illuminating gas and, in 1868, to stellar spectroscopy. During the latter brief investigation in collaboration with the astronomer J. N. Lockyer, lines of helium were first observed in the sun; but Frankland did not agree with Lockyer's interpretation that helium was a new element.[5]

Frankland's wide interests included biology. In 1865, together with Adolf Fick and Johannes Wislicenus, he designed an experiment to test Liebig's theory that the source of muscular energy was the oxidation of nitrogenous muscular tissue. The two Germans performed this experiment by ascending Mt. Faulhorn in Switzerland while on a protein-free diet, then measuring the nitrogen output in their urine.[6] They confirmed their suspicion that muscular energy comes principally from the oxidation of non-nitrogenous materials. It remained for Frankland to confirm in the laboratory that the oxidation of carbohydrates and fats produces sufficient energy to account for the mechanical work of an organism.[7] His calorimetric experiments of 1866 on the energy values of common foodstuffs laid the foundation for quantitative dietetics.

In 1867, together with H. E. Armstrong, Frankland devised a method for analyzing water by combustion analysis of organic carbon and nitrogen *in vacuo.*[8] A rival method developed by J. A. Wanklyn in the same year,[9] which identified nitrogen content as ammonia, led to acrimonious disputes between the two men over the respective merits of their systems. Frankland's method, although extremely accurate, proved too cumbersome and difficult for the unskilled, so Wanklyn's simpler but less reliable technique was usually preferred by public analysts. Frankland's humanitarian and scientific interest in water analysis was continued by his son Percy.

NOTES

1. E. Frankland and H. Kolbe, "On the Chemical Constitution of Metacetonic Acid, and Some Other Bodies Related to It," in *Memoirs of the Chemical Society,* **3** (1845–1848), 386–391.
2. E. Frankland, "On a New Series of Organic Bodies Containing Metals," in *Philosophical Transactions of the Royal Society,* **142** (1852), 417–444, see p. 440. Publication of this paper was delayed by the oversight of the Society's secretary, G. Stokes (see Frankland's autobiography, 1902 ed., p. 187).
3. E. Frankland, "Contributions to the Notation of Organic and Inorganic Bodies," in *Journal of the Chemical Society,* **4** (1866), 372–395.
4. E. Frankland, "On the Influence of Atmospheric Pressure Upon Some of the Phenomena of Combustion," in *Philosophical Transactions of the Royal Society,* **151** (1861), 629–653.
5. Letter to Lockyer, 9 Sept. 1872, in the archives of the Sir J. N. Lockyer Observatory, Sidmouth, Devonshire.

6. A. Fick and J. Wislicenus, "On the Origin of Muscular Power," in *Philosophical Magazine,* 4th ser., **31** (1866), 485–503.
7. E. Frankland, "On the Origin of Muscular Power," *ibid.,* **32** (1866), 182–199.
8. E. Frankland and H. E. Armstrong, "On the Analysis of Potable Waters," in *Journal of the Chemical Society,* **6** (1868), 77–108.
9. J. A. Wanklyn, E. T. Chapman, and M. H. Smith, "Water Analysis: Determination of the Nitrogenous Organic Matter," *ibid.,* **5** (1867), 445–454.

BIBLIOGRAPHY

I. ORIGINAL WORKS. Frankland published over 130 papers, of which the *Royal Society Catalogue of Scientific Papers* (London, 1867–1925) lists 107; see II, 699–700, VII, 700–701, IX, 918, and XV, 101; sixty-four were republished, some in a revised form, by Frankland in his 1877 book. To these should be added "A Course of Ten Lectures at the Royal Institution," in *Chemical News,* **3** (1861), 99–104, 118–122, 132–136, 166–170, 185–187, 201–203, 215–219, 291–299, 377–381, and **4** (1861), 51–54, 65–68, 93–97; "Chemical Research in England," in *Nature,* **3** (1870–1871), 445; an untitled paper on chemical apparatus read to the Kensington Science Conferences of 1876, in *Nature,* **14** (1876), 73–76—see also *South Kensington Museum. Conferences Held in Connection With the Special Loan Collection of Scientific Apparatus,* 3 unnumbered vols. (London, 1876), "Chemistry, Biology," pp. 1–13; the presidential address to the Institute of Chemistry, in *Chemical News,* **37** (1878), 57–59; reply to Lockyer's attack on the Institute of Chemistry, *ibid.,* **52** (1885), 305–306. Note also Frankland's important evidence to the Select Committee on Scientific Instruction for Industrial Classes, 1867–1868, in *Parliamentary Papers 1867–1868,* XV (432), pars. 8033–8177; and to the Devonshire Commission on Scientific Instruction and the Advancement of Science, 1871–1875, *ibid., 1872,* XXV (C.536); *1874,* XXII (C.1087); and *1875,* XXVIII (C.1298), pars. 40–47, 516–518, 758–835, 980–982, 2473–2488, 5667–5896, 11,053–11,108, and index. Finally, note Frankland's influence in George S. Newth, *Chemical Lecture Experiments. Non-metallic Elements* (London, 1892, 1896).

Frankland's books were *Ueber die Isolirung des Radicales Aethyl* (Marburg–Brunswick, 1849), his Ph.D. diss.; *Lecture Notes for Chemical Students (Embracing Mineral and Organic Chemistry)* (London, 1866), the 2nd ed., 2 vols., published as I, *Inorganic Chemistry* (1870), and II, *Organic Chemistry* (1872), and a 3rd ed. of II, rev. by F. R. Japp (1881)—see below for the 3rd ed. of I; *Reports of the Rivers Pollution Commission (1868)*, 6 vols. (London, 1870–1874), also in *Parliamentary Papers, 1871,* XXV, XXVI; *1872,* XXXIV; and *1874,* XXXIII; *Experimental Researches in Pure, Applied, and Physical Chemistry* (London, 1877), Frankland's edited version of his papers, dedicated to Bunsen; *How to Teach Chemistry; Hints to Science Teachers and Students,* George Chaloner, ed. (London–Philadelphia, 1875); *Water Analysis for Sanitary Purposes* (London, 1880, 1890); *Inorganic Chemistry,* rev. by J. R. Japp, 3rd ed. of *Lecture Notes,* I; *Sketches From the Life of Edward Frankland* (London, 1901); and *Sketches From the Life of Sir Edward Frankland,* edited and completed by M. N. W. [West] and S. J. C. [Colenso] (Frankland's daughters).

For Kekulé's claim to priority in valence theory, see his unpublished MS "Zur Geschichte der Valenztheorie," in R. Anschütz, *August Kekulé,* I (Berlin, 1929), 555–569, repr. in facs. in R. Kuhn, ed., *Cassirte Kapitel aus der Abhandlung: Über die Carboxytartronsäure und die Constitution des Benzols* (Weinheim, 1965). Frankland's polemics with Wanklyn may be traced from *Chemical News,* **17** (1868), 45, 79, 97; **33** (1876), 85, 104–106; and **66** (1892), 103, 119. On the X Club, see Frankland's autobiography.

MS material is located in London in the Royal Institution (where the Tyndall papers may also be found), the Royal Society, and Imperial College archives. Other archives containing MS papers are those at Liverpool University (the Reade papers), the Lancaster Public Library (the Lancastrian Frankland Society), and the Sir J. N. Lockyer Observatory, Sidmouth. Unlisted papers held by the Frankland family are not yet available for study. Oddments of Frankland's apparatus are to be found at the Royal Institution and the City of Lancaster Museum.

II. SECONDARY LITERATURE. The best obituaries are J. Wislicenus, in *Berichte der Deutschen chemischen Gesellschaft,* **33** (1900), 3847–3874, with photograph and list of papers; H. McLeod, in *Journal of the Chemical Society,* **87** (1905), 574–590; and [J. R. Japp], in *Minutes of Proceedings of the Institution of Civil Engineers,* **139** (1900), 343–349. A full version of H. E. Armstrong's Frankland memorial lecture to the Chemical Society was never published, but see his interesting "First Frankland Memorial Oration to the Lancastrian Frankland Society," in *Journal of the Society of Chemical Industry,* **53** (1934), 459–466. See also Sir W. Tilden, *Famous Chemists* (London, 1921), pp. 216–227; and J. R. Partington, *A History of Chemistry,* IV (London–New York, 1964), ch. 16. For an extremely thorough analysis of Frankland's contributions to valence theory, see C. A. Russell, *History of Valency* (Leicester, 1971). Frankland's period as a schoolteacher is sketched in D. Thompson, "Queenwood College, Hampshire," in *Annals of Science,* **11** (1955), 246–254; and his contribution to biochemistry in E. McCollum, *A History of Nutrition* (Boston, 1957), pp. 127–129. For Frankland's activities on behalf of professional chemists, see R. B. Pilcher, *The Institute of Chemistry of Great Britain and Ireland, History of the Institute, 1877–1914* (London, 1914), *passim.*

W H. BROCK

FRANKLAND, PERCY FARADAY (*b.* London, England, 3 October 1858; *d.* House of Letterawe, on Loch Awe, Argyllshire, Scotland, 28 October 1946), *chemistry, bacteriology.*

Frankland was the second son of Edward Frankland, professor of chemistry at the Royal School of Mines in London. His middle name was given in honor of the eminent chemist Michael Faraday, who was his godfather. After studying at University College School in London from 1869 to 1874, Frankland entered the Royal School of Mines in 1875. His teachers there included his father and Thomas Henry Huxley. In 1877 he won a Brackenbury scholarship at St. Bartholomew's Hospital, but his father dissuaded him from a medical career and induced him to take up chemistry instead. From 1878 to 1880 he studied organic chemistry under Wislicenus at the University of Würzburg, taking his Ph.D. summa cum laude in the latter year. He was then appointed demonstrator under his father at South Kensington, where the Royal School of Mines had been transferred and its name changed to the Normal School of Science. He took his B.Sc. in 1881 from the University of London, which was then merely an examining and degree-granting body.

Frankland was professor of chemistry at University College, Dundee, from 1888 to 1894 and at Mason Science College (later the University of Birmingham) from 1894 to 1919. At the latter institution he also served as dean of the Faculty of Science from 1913 until his retirement. He was president of the Institute of Chemistry from 1906 to 1909 and of the Chemical Society in 1912 and 1913. During World War I, Frankland worked with the Chemical Warfare Committee on synthetic drugs, explosives, and mustard gas. These efforts led to his being named C.B.E. in 1920. Elected a fellow of the Royal Society in 1891, Frankland was awarded its Davy Medal in 1919. He was also awarded honorary doctorates by the universities of St. Andrews (1902), Dublin (1912), Birmingham (1924), and Sheffield (1926). Following his death a memorial lecture was established in his name at the Royal Institute of Chemistry.

Frankland's wife, Grace Coleridge Toynbee, whom he married in 1882, was the youngest daughter of Joseph Toynbee, the pioneer ear specialist. She was herself a research bacteriologist and frequently contributed to her husband's scientific work. Her death preceded his by a few weeks. They left a son, Edward.

Frankland's early research work seems to have been strongly influenced by his father. In the early 1880's he undertook a systematic study of the coal gas supplied to consumers in the larger British towns, thus following a path his father had trod thirty years before. Comparing his results with his father's, Frankland noted that the nitrogen content had increased because of a change in the methods of combustion. This study led to the publication of a series of five papers on the illuminating power of various hydrocarbons.

Frankland's interest in water analysis probably also derived originally from his father, who had concentrated on the purely chemical aspects of water analysis; Frankland was also attracted to its biological or bacteriological aspects. From 1885 to 1895 much of his research had as its goal the elucidation of the chemical reactions taking place in the presence of fermentative bacteria, and especially the development of effective methods for analyzing and preventing the bacterial contamination of water supplies. Largely as a result of his efforts, a monthly bacteriological examination of London's water supplies was inaugurated in 1885. He tested the efficacy of such materials as coke and greensand as agents for filtering bacteria from water and studied alterations in the viability and virulence of the anthrax and typhoid bacilli in drinking water. From 1892 to 1895 Frankland was coauthor, with Harry Marshall Ward, of four experimentally based reports to the Water Research Committee of the Royal Society. He also acted as private consultant to many of the largest water companies in Great Britain. His experience in original research added to the authority of his book, written with his wife, *Micro-organisms in Water: Their Significance, Identification and Removal* (London, 1894). Frankland also wrote a more popular book on bacteriology, *Our Secret Friends and Foes* (London, 1893), which went through four editions by 1899.

Most of the rest of Frankland's research concerned the stereochemistry of optically active substances. His interest in this topic was first aroused while he was working on his Ph.D. under Wislicenus, and it ultimately became his major preoccupation. By carrying out an exhaustive study of the rotatory effects of a large number of molecular groups, Frankland developed valuable methods for testing the quantitative relationship between molecular structure and degree of optical activity. Although he thought he had uncovered a few regularities, he admitted that his research had not produced any broad generalizations. His work showed mainly that the relationship between structure and optical activity was too complex to be explained by existing theories. No great original contributions resulted from his bacteriological work either.

In his scientific interests and approach Frankland recognized a kinship between himself and Louis Pasteur. With his wife he wrote an admirable biography bearing the simple title *Pasteur* (London, 1898), to which William Bulloch frequently referred in his *History of Bacteriology* (London, 1938). A leading advocate of original research by students, Frankland was considered an inspiring, if rather stern and demanding, teacher.

BIBLIOGRAPHY

I. ORIGINAL WORKS. Besides the books mentioned in the text, Frankland published well over 100 papers, several of which cover much the same ground and many of which were written in collaboration with his students and colleagues. Most of his early papers appeared in the *Journal of the Chemical Society* (London). A complete bibliography of his works published before 1900 may be found in the *Royal Society Catalogue of Scientific Papers,* IX (1891), 919; and XV (1916), 101–103. The most important of these and of his later papers are cited by Garner in the longer of his two biographical sketches of Frankland.

II. SECONDARY LITERATURE. See W. E. Garner, "Frankland, Percy Faraday," in *Dictionary of National Biography* (1941–1950), pp. 270–271; and "Percy Faraday Frankland," in *Obituary Notices of Fellows of the Royal Society of London,* **5,** no. 16 (1947), 697–715. The latter notice contains a bibliography of ninety-one "main publications" by Frankland between 1880 and 1927, as well as a detailed account of Frankland's research work, especially that on stereochemistry.

GERALD L. GEISON

FRANKLIN, BENJAMIN (*b.* Boston, Massachusetts, 17 January 1706; *d.* Philadelphia, Pennsylvania, 17 April 1790), *electricity, general physics, oceanography, meteorology, promotion and support of science and international scientific cooperation.*

Benjamin Franklin was the first American to win an international reputation in pure science and the first man of science to gain fame for work done wholly in electricity. His principal achievement was the formulation of a widely used theory of general electrical "action" (explaining or predicting the outcome of manipulations in electrostatics: charge production, charge transfer, charging by electrostatic induction). He advanced the concept of a single "fluid" of electricity, was responsible for the principle of conservation of charge, and analyzed the distribution of charges in the Leyden jar, a capacitor. He introduced into the language of scientific discourse relating to electricity such technical words as "plus" and "minus," "positive" and "negative," "charge" and "battery." By experiment he showed that the lightning discharge is an electrical phenomenon, and upon this demonstration (together with his experimental findings concerning the action of grounded and of pointed conductors) he based his invention of the lightning rod.

Franklin made contributions to knowledge of the Gulf Stream, of atmospheric convection currents, and of the direction of motion of storms. His observations on population were of service to Malthus. He was the principal founder of the American Philosophical Society, the New World's first permanent scientific organization.

Early Life and Career

Benjamin Franklin's father, Josiah, who was descended from a family of British artisans, immigrated to America, settling in Boston in October 1683. His mother, Josiah's second wife, was Abiah ("Jane") Folger, daughter of Peter Folger of Nantucket, a weaver, schoolmaster, miller, and writer of verses. On both sides of the family Franklin had forebears skilled in the use of their hands and with literary or intellectual gifts.

Franklin relates in his autobiography that he "was put to the Grammar School at eight years of Age," but remained "not quite one Year." His father then sent him "to a School for Writing and Arithmetic." Although Franklin by his own admission failed arithmetic, he later repaired this deficiency. In midlife, he took up "making magic Squares, or Circles," some of which were very complex and obviously required skill in computation. Published in England and in France from 1767 to 1773, they have attracted much attention and comment ever since.

At ten years of age, Franklin was taken home from school to assist his father, a tallow chandler and soap boiler. Since he was fond of reading and had in fact spent on books "all the little Money that came into . . . [his] Hands," it was decided that Benjamin should become a printer. He was, accordingly, at age twelve indentured to "Brother James." Within a few years he was able to break the indenture and secure his freedom. He left Boston to seek his fortune, first in New York (briefly and unsuccessfully) and then in Philadelphia.

Franklin had immediate success in Philadelphia. Before long he came to the attention of Governor Keith, who offered to subsidize him—although he was only eighteen—in the printing business. Franklin was sent to London to select types and presses and to make useful business contacts. Once at sea, Franklin discovered that the governor had sent him off without any letter of introduction and without funds for purchasing the printing equipment—indeed, that the governor had merely been "playing . . . pitiful Tricks . . . on a poor ignorant Boy!" On arrival, Franklin found work in Samuel Palmer's printing house, where he set type for William Wollaston's *The Religion of Nature Delineated.*

After two years away from Philadelphia (from November 1724 to October 1726) Franklin returned to his adopted city, skilled in the various aspects of the printing craft. He soon had his own shop and before long became a major figure in the town and, eventually, in the colony. With a partner, he published the *Pennsylvania Gazette;* when the partnership was dissolved in 1730, Franklin kept the newspaper and shortly began publication of *Poor Richard: An Almanack* (1733). He was Clerk of the Assembly, postmaster of Philadelphia (1737–1753), and publisher (1741) of the *General Magazine.* He was an organizer of the Library Company (1731), and the Union Fire Company (1736), and was a promoter of the Academy of Philadelphia (later the College and Academy of Philadelphia and now the University of Pennsylvania), of which he became president of the trustees (1749).

As he became more deeply concerned with civic affairs and public life, Franklin retired from active business (1748), setting up what would become an eighteen-year partnership with David Hall, his printing house foreman. He was elected a member of the Pennsylvania Assembly (1751) and alderman of Philadelphia and was appointed a deputy postmaster-general for the British colonies in North America (1753–1774). He was sent to England in 1757 and remained until 1762 as the Assembly's agent.

Preparation for Scientific Research

When, in 1757, Franklin sailed for England for the second time, he had already won a high place in world science. He had published articles in the world's leading scientific journal, the *Philosophical Transactions of the Royal Society,* and was a fellow of that society (elected 29 May 1756). For his research in electricity the Society had conferred upon him (on 30 November 1753) one of their highest awards—the Copley Medal. He had received honorary degrees from Harvard (1753), Yale (later in 1753), and William and Mary (1756). His book on electricity had already appeared in three editions in England and two in France, and one of his experiments—"proving the sameness of Lightning and Electricity"—was world-famous. Franklin was largely self-taught in science—as he was in other subjects—but this does not mean that he was uneducated. He had rigorously studied the science of his day in the writings of the best masters available.

In 1744 Franklin sponsored Adam Spencer's lectures on experimental science in Philadelphia and purchased his apparatus; he had previously attended Spencer's lectures in Boston. Also in 1744 Franklin published a pamphlet on the stove he had invented; in it he refers to, and quotes from, certain great masters of experimental science whose works he knew, including Boerhaave, Desaguliers, 'sGravesande, and Hales. He was also familiar with the writings of Robert Boyle and knew well the major treatise on experimental physics of the age, Newton's *Opticks.* He had also encountered expositions of the Newtonian natural philosophy in the published Boyle lectures, a series which included books by Samuel Clarke and William Derham. Having known Pemberton in London, he no doubt would have read Pemberton's *View of Sir Isaac Newton's Philosophy,* of which Peter Collinson had sent a copy to the Library Company in 1732. Thus, even though Franklin may have had no formal training, he was well educated in Newtonian experimental science.

Gadgets and Inventions

Benjamin Franklin's reputation in science was made by his experiments and the theories he conceived or modified to explain his results. The experimental scientist of Franklin's day had not only to be able to design but also to construct the devices he needed. Franklin the artisan had no aversion to manual labor and operations. A gifted gadgeteer and inventor, he was not only able to make the devices he conceived but he could also think in terms of the potential of gadgets and instruments in relation to the development of his ideas: a significant ability, since usually the conception of an experimental problem cannot be separated from the means of exploring or solving it.

Throughout his life Franklin found it (as he writes in his autobiography) a source of "Pleasure . . . to see good Workmen handle their Tools." He was aware of the great advantage to his research in being able "to construct little Machines for my Experiments while the Intention of making the Experiment was fresh and warm in my Mind." This aspect of Franklin's research was especially noted by William Watson in his review of Franklin's book on electricity (*Philosophical Transactions,* 1752); Franklin, the reviewer said, has both "a head to conceive" and "a hand to carry into execution" whatever he considers "may conduce to enlighten the subject-matter."

Among Franklin's notable inventions and gadgets are the rocking chair, bifocal glasses, and the Pennsylvania fireplace, or Franklin stove. He also conceived the idea of "summer time," or daylight saving time. His most important invention, the lightning conductor or lightning rod, is, however, in a different category altogether, an application to human needs (in the Baconian sense) of recent discoveries in pure science.

First Researches in Electricity

In the early 1740's Franklin encountered the new electrical experiments in at least two ways. He saw some experiments performed by Adam Spencer in Boston in 1743 and again in Philadephia in 1744. Then, in 1745 (or possibly 1746) the Library Company of Philadelphia received "from Mr. Peter Collinson, F.R.S., of London, a Present of a Glass Tube, with some Account of the Use of it in making such electrical Experiments." Franklin records that he "eagerly seized the Opportunity of repeating what I had seen in Boston, and by much Practice acquir'd great Readiness in performing those also which we had an account of from England, adding a Number of new Ones."

The first researches in electricity at Philadephia were made by a group of four experimenters: Franklin, Philip Syng, Thomas Hopkinson, and Ebenezer Kinnersley, who was Franklin's principal coexperimenter. One of Franklin's first recorded discoveries was the action of pointed bodies. A grounded pointed conductor, he found, could cause a charged, insulated conducting body to lose its charge when the point was six to eight inches away; but a blunt conductor would not produce such a discharge until it was an inch or so away, and then there would be an accompanying spark. A companion discovery was made by Hopkinson: a needle placed on top of a suspended iron rod would prevent it from becoming charged, the electrical fire "continually runing out silently at the point" as fast as it was accumulated; this discovery had been anticipated by William Watson.

Other discoveries led Franklin and his coexperimenters to the concept that "the electrical fire is a real element, or species of matter, not created by the friction, but *collected* only." Thus all kinds of electrification, or changes in electrification, were to be explained by the transfer of "electrical fire," which was "really an element diffused among, and attracted by other matter, particularly by water and metals." Each body has a "natural" quantity of "electrical fire"; if it loses some, Franklin would call it electrically negative, or minus; if it gains some and therefore has a "superabundance" of "electrical fire," it would be positive, or plus. "To electrise *plus* or *minus,*" Franklin wrote in a letter to Collinson of 25 May 1747, "no more needs to be known than this, that the parts of the tube or sphere that are rubbed, do, in the instant of the friction, attract the electrical fire, and therefore take it from the thing rubbing." In short, since one or more bodies must gain the "electrical fire" that a given body loses, plus and minus charges or states of electrification must occur in exactly equal amounts. This quantitative principle is known today as the law of conservation of charge. It is still fundamental to all science, from microphysics to the electrification of gross bodies.

The Analysis of the Leyden Jar

One of the earliest and most significant results of the new Franklinian theory was the successful analysis of the Leyden jar, a topic introduced in a letter to Collinson, sent sometime prior to 28 July 1747. The Leyden jar, a form of condenser, or capacitor, was discovered or invented in the 1740's and was named after one of the several claimants to the discovery, Musschenbroek of Leyden; Franklin knew the device as Musschenbroek's "wonderful bottle." Essentially the device was a nonconductor (glass) with a conductor on each side; before long it was used with the inside filled with water or metal shot, and the outside coated with metal. Electrical contact was made with the water or metal shot by means of a wire running through an insulating cork stuck into the neck of the bottle. When the outer coating was grounded, as by being held in the hands of an experimenter, and the wire was brought to a charged body, the jar seemed capable of "accumulating" and "holding" a vast amount of "electricity."

The first observation made by Franklin was that if the wire and water inside the bottle are "electrised *positively* or *plus,*" then the outer coating is simultaneously "electrised *negatively* or *minus* in exact proportion." The equilibrium could not be restored through the glass of the bottle unless a conducting material simultaneously made contact with the outer coating and with the wire connected to the water or inner conducting material. He was astonished at the "wonderful" way in which "these two states of Electricity, the *plus* and *minus*" are "combined and balanced in this miraculous bottle."

In a letter of 29 April 1748, containing "Farther Experiments and Observations in Electricity," Franklin described some new experiments showing that a charged Leyden jar always has charges of opposite signs on the two conductors and that the charges are of the same magnitude. Clearly, he concluded, the "terms of *charging* and *discharging*" a Leyden jar are misleading, since "there is really no more electrical fire in the phial after what is called its *charging,* than before, nor less after its *discharging. . . .*"

Franklin then announced the most astonishing discovery of all, that in the Leyden jar "the whole force of the bottle, and power of giving a shock, is in the GLASS ITSELF." He reached this conclusion by a series of ingenious experiments, which are known today as the Franklin experiments on "the dissectible condenser." A Leyden jar with a loosely fitting cork was charged in the usual way and then placed on a glass insulator. The cork was carefully removed, together with the wire that hung down into the water; it was then found that the jar could be discharged as before by an experimenter's putting one hand around the outside of the jar while bringing a finger of the other hand to the jar's mouth so as to reach the water. Thus, the "force" was not "in the wire." Next, a test was made to determine whether the force "resided in the water" and was "condensed in it." A jar was charged as before, set on glass, and the cork and wire removed. The water was then carefully decanted into an empty, uncharged jar resting on glass; this second jar showed no evidence whatever of being charged. Either the "force" must have been lost during the decanting, or it must have remained behind in the glass. The latter was shown to be the case by refilling the first bottle with "unelectrified water," whereupon it gave the shock as usual.

In the next stage Franklin looked into the question of whether this property of glass came from the nature of its substance, or whether it was related to shape—a relevant question, since Franklin had pioneered in studying the effect of shape in the action of pointed and blunt conductors. In this inquiry he constructed a parallel-plate condenser (or capacitor) consisting of two parallel lead plates separated by a flat pane of sash glass. This condenser produced the same electrical effects as a Leyden jar, thus demonstrating that the "force" is a property of the glass as glass and is not related to shape. Franklin ingeniously joined together a number of such parallel-plate condensers to make "what we called an *electrical-battery*" consisting of eleven panes of glass, each "armed" with lead plates pasted on both sides, hooked together in series by wire and chain; the battery could be discharged by a special contrivance.

Full Statement of the Mature Theory

On 29 July 1750, Franklin sent Collinson his "Opinions and Conjectures concerning the Properties and Effects of the electrical Matter, arising from Experiments and Observations, made at Philadelphia, 1749." This paper began with the proposition that the electrical matter consists of "extremely subtile" particles, since it can easily permeate all common matter, even metals, without "any perceptible resistance." Here Franklin used the term "electrical matter" for the first time. Although he indicated a cause for belief in its "subtility," he took its atomicity or particulate composition for granted. The difference between electrical matter and "common matter" lies in the mutual attraction of the particles of the latter and the mutual repulsion of the particles of the former (which causes "the appearing divergency in a stream of electrified effluvia"). In eighteenth-century terms, such electrical matter constitutes a particulate, subtle, elastic fluid. The particles of electrical matter, although mutually repellent, are attracted strongly by "all other matter." Therefore, if a quantity of electrical matter be applied to a mass of common matter, it will be "immediately and equally diffused through the whole." In other words, common matter is "a kind of spunge" to the electric fluid. Generally, in common matter there is as much electrical matter as it can contain; if more be added, it cannot enter the body but collects on its surface to form an "electrical atmosphere," in which case the body "is said to be electrified." All bodies, however, do not "attract and retain" electrical matter "with equal strength and force"; those called electrics per se (or non-conductors) "attract and retain it strongest, and contain the greatest quantity." That common matter always contains electrical fluid is demonstrated by the fact of experience that a rubbed globe or tube enables us to pump some out.

The "electrical atmospheres" said to surround charged bodies are a means for explaining the observed repulsion between them, but this explanation takes cognizance only of the repulsion between positively charged bodies (that is, those which have gained an excess of fluid over their normal quantity). It offers no aid whatever in understanding the repulsion between negatively charged bodies—a phenomenon that had been observed by Franklin and his colleagues and reported by him in an earlier paper.

The concept of "electrical atmospheres" was not wholly novel with Franklin. Franklin's original contribution lay in the particular use he gave to this concept in his theory of electrical action. For example, Franklin stated that it takes the "form . . . of the body it surrounds." A sphere will thus have a spherical atmosphere and a cylinder a cylindrical one. Others had supposed that both would have a sphere of effluvia.

Franklin's concept of "electrical atmospheres" was based on the idea that an uncharged body must have its "normal" quantity of electrical matter or fluid and that, therefore, any further electrical matter or fluid added to it will collect around the outside, like a cloud. If two such charged bodies came near one another, these two clouds would produce repulsion, since the particles of which they are made tend to repel one another. Similarly, a body that has lost some of its normal quantity of electrical matter or fluid will attract the particles in the electric atmosphere of a positively charged body, until the two draw together and make contact. Franklin applied the concept of "electrical atmospheres" to explain the unequal distribution of charge in bodies that were not completely symmetrical, such as those which might be pointed or pear-shaped. These explanations were qualitatively successful, but they do not always appear convincing and certainly constitute one of the weakest and least satisfactory parts of the theory. Even more important, the doctrine of "electric atmospheres" could not contribute to the solution of one outstanding unsolved problem in the Franklinian explanation of electrical phenomena: the "apparent" repulsion between negatively charged bodies. We shall see below that this major defect in the theory was remedied by the addition of a new and very radical postulate by Aepinus.

One of the major advantages of the Franklinian theory was that it enabled "electricians" to distinguish clearly between the concept of a "repelling force" which could act even through a sheet of glass, although the electric fluid itself does not penetrate through glass. This basic concept was used in the explanation of the action of the condenser, wherein Franklin explained clearly—for what was, so far as I know, the first time—the mechanism of induced charges, the phenomenon of a negative charge being induced on a grounded conductor when a positively charged conductor is brought near it, or when a nearby conductor acquires a positive charge.

In the Leyden jar, according to Franklin's doctrine, the application of a positive charge to the conductor on one side of the glass will not cause the jar to be charged until or unless the conductor on the other side can lose some of its normal electric fluid, that is, until or unless it is grounded. Then and only then will electric fluid move away from that grounded conductor, leaving it negatively charged. Franklin thus naturally predicted, and proved by experiment, that the jar could be charged through its outer coating when the wire leading into the water is grounded, just as easily as in the normal manner—when a positive charge is applied to the inner conductor (water and wire) and the outside is grounded.

Later, in a famous series of experiments and explanations based upon some earlier ones made by John Canton, Franklin developed more fully this explanation of what we call today induced charges, or the phenomenon of charging by (electrostatic) induction. There is no doubt that it was Franklin's clear understanding of this process that caused his theory to be so highly valued in the eighteenth century. The theory is still used, with slight modifications, in all laboratory circumstances when charged objects are moved in the neighborhood of conductors which may be grounded or insulated or which can undergo a change in their condition of grounding or insulation. Only Franklin, and those who accepted his doctrine, could easily explain such phenomena as this: A positively charged body is brought near a conducting metal object placed on an insulating base and temporarily grounded; then the grounding is interrupted before the charged body is removed; the effect will be to induce in that object a negative charge. Now let the second object be an insulated cylinder; it will plainly display an unequal charge distribution, the end near the first body becoming negative and the far end positive; when the first body is withdrawn, the cylinder returns to its normal state and no longer shows any indication of charge. In the eighteenth century many scientists adduced this feature of the Franklinian theory (its ability to predict exactly the outcome of such experiments) as its major asset. In our own time J. J. Thomson has explained that the service of the one-fluid theory "to the science of electricity, by suggesting and co-ordinating researches, can hardly be overestimated." We still use this theory in the laboratory, Thomson said: "If we move a piece of brass and want to know whether that will increase or decrease the effect we are observing, we do not fly to the higher mathematics, but use the simple conception of the electric fluid which would tell us as much as we wanted to know in a few seconds" (in *Recollections and Reflections* [London, 1936], p. 252).

Dissemination of Experiments and Theories

Franklin's experiments on pointed conductors, grounding, the Leyden jar, and the conservation of charge, together with the statement of his theory of electrical action, based on the principle of conservation of charge, were all assembled by Collinson into a ninety-page book issued by E. Cave of London in 1751, with an unsigned preface written by Dr. John Fothergill. Buffon, who had recently stated that in electrical phenomena there seemed to be no one law governing the outcome of experiments, and that indeed the subject was characterized more by "bizzareries" than by regularities, came upon the book and had it translated into French in the following year; the French version was done by the naturalist Dalibard.

Thus, within two years Franklin's concepts and experiments were available to "electricians" on both sides of the Channel and—but for a number of minor revisions and extensions to new phenomena—all the main elements of Franklin's contributions to electrical theory had appeared in print.

One of the most challenging parts of Franklin's book was his discussion of thunder, lightning, and the formation of clouds. In a letter addressed to John Mitchel in London, dated 29 April 1749, Franklin wrote out some "Observations and Suppositions" that had led him to the hypothesis that clouds tend to become electrified through the vaporization effect on water of "common fire" (or ordinary heat) and "electrical fire." Rain, dew, and flashes of lightning between land clouds and sea clouds formed part of Franklin's suppositions, but six years later he freely admitted that he was "still at a loss" about the actual process by which clouds "become charged with electricity; no hypothesis I have yet formed perfectly satisfying me." Nevertheless, before April 1749 Franklin had assumed that clouds are electrified and that the lightning discharge is a rapid release of electric fluid from clouds.

On 7 November 1749, Franklin drew up a list of twelve observable similarities between the lightning discharge and the ordinary spark discharges produced in the laboratory. Notably, he concluded that since the "electric fluid is attracted by points," we might find out "whether this property is in lightning . . . . Let the experiment be made." But even before this experiment could be performed, Franklin assumed a favorable outcome. Convinced that lightning must be an electrical phenomenon, he warned his readers that high hills, trees, towers, spires, masts, and chimneys will act "as so many prominencies and points" and so will "draw the electrical fire" as a "whole cloud discharges there." He therefore advised his readers never "to take shelter under a tree, during a thunder gust."

In the paper entitled "Opinions and Conjectures," sent to Collinson in July of 1750 (containing the full statement of his theory of electrical action), Franklin also discussed the possible electrification of clouds and the nature of the lightning discharge. Immediately following the presentation of the property of pointed bodies to "draw on" and "throw off" the electric fluid at great distances, Franklin indicated that this knowledge of the "power of points may possibly be of some use to mankind, though we should never be able to explain it." Just as a grounded needle with its point upright could discharge a charged body and prevent a "stroke" to another nearby body, so Franklin argued that sharpened upright rods of iron, gilded to prevent rusting, fixed "on the highest parts of . . . edifices" and run down the outside of a building into the ground, or down "one of the shrouds of a ship" into the water, would "probably draw the electrical fire silently out of a cloud before it came nigh enough to strike, and thereby secure us from that most sudden and terrible mischief." Later, when the experiments were made, Franklin found that another function of the lightning rod, apart from "disarming" a passing cloud, would be to conduct a lightning stroke safely into the ground.

The experiment that Franklin devised required a sentry box large enough to contain a man and "an electrical [insulating] stand." The sentry box was to be placed on a high building; a long, pointed rod was to rise out through the door, extending twenty or thirty feet in the air, terminating in a point. This rod was to be affixed to the middle of the insulated stand, which was to be kept clean and dry so as to remain an insulator. Then when clouds, possibly electrified, would pass low, the rod "might be electrified and afford sparks, the rod drawing fire to" the experimenter, "from a cloud." To avoid danger, Franklin advised the man to be well insulated and to hold in his hand a wax handle affixed to a "loop of a wire" attached to the ground; he could bring the loop to the rod so that "the sparks, if the rod is electrified, will strike from the rod to the wire, and not affect him." Some years later, when Richmann performed this experiment in St. Petersburg, he did not fully observe all of Franklin's warnings and was electrocuted.

The sentry-box experiment was first performed at Marly, France, in May 1752. After Franklin's book had appeared in a French translation in 1752, the experiments he described were performed for the king and court; Buffon, Dalibard, and De Lor were then inspired to test Franklin's conjectures "upon the analogy of thunder and electricity." On 13 May 1752 Dalibard reported to the Paris Academy of Sciences: "In following the path that Mr. Franklin has traced for us, I have obtained complete satisfaction."

The account of this experiment was printed in the second French edition of Franklin's book on electricity and was later included in the English editions. A letter addressed from France to Stephen Hales, describing both the presentation of the Philadelphia experiments to the king of France and the success of the sentry-box experiment, was published in the *Philosophical Transactions* and was also reprinted in Franklin's book. Soon the lightning experiments were repeated by others in France, Germany, and England; and Franklin had the satisfaction of achieving an immediate and widespread international renown.

Later, Franklin devised a second experiment to test the electrification of clouds, one which has become more popularly known: the lightning kite. Franklin reported this experiment to Collinson in a letter of 1 October 1752, written after Franklin had read "in the publick papers from Europe, of the success of the *Philadelphia-Experiment* for drawing the electrick fire from clouds by means of pointed rods of iron erected on high buildings . . . ." Actually, Franklin appears to have flown his electrical kite prior to having learned of Dalibard's successful execution of the sentry-box experiment. The kite letter, published in the *Philosophical Transactions,* referred to the erection of lightning rods on public buildings in Philadelphia.

The lightning experiments caused Franklin's name to become known throughout Europe to the public at large and not merely to men of science. Joseph Priestley, in his *History . . . of Electricity,* characterized the experimental discovery that the lightning discharge is an electrical phenomenon as "the greatest, perhaps, since the time of Sir Isaac Newton." Of course, one reason for satisfaction in this discovery was that it subjected one of the most mysterious and frightening natural phenomena to rational explanation. It also proved that Bacon had been right in asserting that a knowledge of how nature really works might lead to a better control of nature itself: that valuable practical innovations might be the fruit of pure disinterested scientific research.

No doubt the most important effect of the lightning experiments was to show that the laboratory phenomena in which rods or globes of glass were rubbed, to the accompaniment of sparks, and induced charges and electrical shocks, belong to a class of phenomena occurring naturally. Franklin's experiments thus proved that electrical effects do not result exclusively from man's artifice, from his intervention in phenomena, but are in fact part of the routine operations of nature. And every "electrician" learned that experiments performed with little toys in the laboratory could reveal new aspects of one of the most dramatic of nature's catastrophic forces. "The discoveries made in the summer of the year 1752 will make it memorable in the history of electricity," William Watson wrote in 1753. "These have opened a new field to philosophers, and have given them room to hope, that what they have learned before in their museums, they may apply, with more propriety than they hitherto could have done, in illustrating the nature and effects of thunder; a phaenomenon hitherto almost inaccessible to their inquiries."

Franklin's achievement of a highly successful career wholly in the field of electricity marked the coming of age of electrical science and the full acceptance of the new field of specialization. On 30 November 1753, awarding Franklin the Royal Society's Sir Godfrey Copley gold medal for his discoveries in electricity, the earl of Macclesfield emphasized this very point: "Electricity is a neglected subject," he said, "which not many years since was thought to be of little importance, and was at that time only applied to illustrate the nature of attraction and repulsion; nor was anything worth much notice expected to ensue from it." But now, thanks to the labors of Franklin, it "appears to have a most surprising share of power in nature."

Some Later Contributions to Electricity

Spurred on by the success of the sentry-box and kite experiments, Franklin continued to make investigations of the lightning discharge and the electrification of clouds. He erected a test rod on his house, so as to make experiments and observations on clouds passing overhead. One of the results was most interesting, because he discovered: *"That the clouds of a thunder-gust are most commonly in a negative state of electricity, but sometimes in a positive state."* This statement led him to the following astonishing conclusion: "So that, for the most part, in thunderstrokes, *it is the earth that strikes into the clouds, and not the clouds that strike into the earth.*" Of course, this discovery did not alter the theory or practice of lightning rods, which Franklin found perform two separate functions. One is to disarm a cloud and to prevent a stroke, while the other is to conduct a stroke safely to the ground. His theory of the direction of the stroke (from clouds to earth or from earth to clouds) depends upon the identification of vitreous electrification (glass rubbed with silk) with the positive state and of resinous electrification (amber rubbed with wool or fur) with the negative. Franklin was aware that he had no definitive evidence for this identification, and hoped that others might provide a crucial experimental test.

To this day one still talks of a "Franklinian" fictitious "positive" current in circuit theory, and also thinks physically of a flow of electrons in the opposite direction.

One question of great interest to Franklin was whether the gross dimensions or the mass of a body may be the determining factor in the amount of "electric fluid" it can acquire. He discovered that an "increase of surface" makes a given mass or quantity of matter "capable of receiving a greater amount of charge." The surface is what counts, not the mass. As usual, Franklin had a pretty experiment to support his conclusion. In this case he used a small silver can on an insulating wine glass; in the can there were three yards of brass chain, one end of which was attached to a long silk thread that went over a pulley in the ceiling so that the chain could be drawn partly or completely out, thereby increasing the "surface" and making the body (can and chain) capable of receiving an additional charge.

In a closely related experiment Franklin studied the distribution of charge on a metal can placed on an insulated base. He showed that the charge "resides" wholly on the outside of the can; that there is no charge inside. He did not know the reason at first, but he later concluded that the symmetry of the situation produced mutual repulsion that drove any charge from the inside surface of the can to the outer one. Joseph Priestley, arguing from the analogy of a cylinder to a sphere, showed that by the reasoning of Isaac Newton's *Principia,* it would be possible for one to conclude that the law of electrical force must, like gravitation, be a law of the inverse square of the distance.

A Major Defect Remedied by Aepinus

Franklin's theory failed to give a satisfactory explanation of the observed phenomenon of the mutual repulsion of two negatively charged bodies. This defect was remedied by Franz Aepinus. Perplexed by the difficulties in explaining repulsion, Kinnersley thought that perhaps one could get rid of the doctrine of repulsion altogether. Franklin disagreed, putting forth the argument that repulsion occurs "in other parts of nature."

Aepinus, who altered Franklin's system, was an ardent Franklinian and a teacher of and collaborator with J. C. Wilcke, who translated Franklin's book on electricity into German. Wilcke made the first major table of what we would call today a triboelectric series, thus accounting for the production of joint negative and positive charges in different combinations of two materials.

Aepinus aimed to establish a theory of magnetic phenomena based upon "principles extremely similar to those on which the Franklinian electric theory is built," that is, using the concept of a magnetic fluid, with laws of action much like those of Franklin's electric theory. To complete his analogy, however, Aepinus introduced the revolutionary idea that in solids, liquids, and gases the particles that Franklin called "common matter" would—in the pure state—repel one another just as the particles of the electric fluid did. Aepinus' revision introduced a complete duality, the particles of common matter and the particles of electric matter each having the property of repelling particles of their own kind while having the additional property of attracting particles of the other kind. Normally one does not encounter particles of pure matter repelling one another, because their natural repulsion is reduced to zero by the presence of the magnetic or the electric fluid in the normal state of bodies. Hence, the Newtonian universal gravitation remains unaffected by the new postulate. Repulsion exists only when we deprive bodies of a part of their normal complement of either electric fluid or magnetic fluid.

Furthermore, certain experiments devised by Aepinus and Wilcke, using condensers separated by air instead of glass, showed that the Franklin doctrine of "atmospheres" could not exist in a physical sense. This was a position that Franklin himself had eventually more or less adopted, coming to conceive that the concept of "electrical atmospheres" was no more than a way of describing collections or distributions of electric charge whose parts have repulsive forces acting at a distance.

In one set of experiments to test the effect of "electrical atmospheres," Aepinus blew a stream of dry air on a charged body and found, just as Franklin had, that the charge of the body was not diminished. Franklin had then assumed that such experiments indicated only that the "atmosphere" of a charged body is an integral part of it, and he even thought to make the atmosphere "visible" by dropping rosin on a hot piece of iron near a charged body. Aepinus carried the matter through to its logical conclusion, saying that by "electrical atmosphere" one intended only to denote the "sphere of action" of the electrical charge on a body. Franklin, in commenting on Aepinus' book, expressed admiration for the magnetic theory which Aepinus had constructed along lines analogous to his own electrical theory, and he himself began to write of a magnetic fluid in the terms introduced by Aepinus. We do not know whether Franklin read the book very thoroughly, since he never referred to the great revision of his theory which Aepinus introduced. Indeed, by the time Aepinus' book (1759) reached him, Franklin was no longer actively pursuing his researches into electricity.

Gulf Stream, Convection Currents, and Storms

From his boyhood days Franklin had a passion for the sea. In his eight crossings of the Atlantic, he was always fascinated by problems of seamanship, ship design, and the science of the seas; and he made careful observations of all sorts of marine phenomena. He made experiments to see if oil spread on the waters would still the waves, and he put on a spectacular exhibition of this phenomenon for a group of fellows of the Royal Society in Portsmouth harbor.

Franklin's name is associated with the Gulf Stream, of which he printed the first chart. His interest in this subject began about 1770, when the Board of Customs at Boston complained that it seemed to require two weeks more for mail packets to make the voyage to New England from England than the time of voyage for merchant ships. Franklin, then still postmaster general, discussed the matter with a Nantucket sea captain, who explained that the Nantucketers were "well acquainted with the Stream, because in our pursuit of whales, which keep to the sides of it but are not met within it, we run along the side and frequently cross it to change our side, and in crossing it have sometimes met and spoke with those packets who are in the middle of it and stemming it." Franklin asked the captain, Timothy Folger, to plot the course of the Gulf Stream; this was the basis of the chart he had engraved and printed by the General Post Office. As early as 1775 Franklin had conceived of using a thermometer as an instrument of navigation in relation to the Gulf Stream, and he made several series of surface temperature measurements during the Atlantic crossings. In 1785, on his last return voyage from France, Franklin devised a special instrument to attempt to measure temperatures below the surface to a depth of 100 feet.

Franklin's studies of cloud formation and the electrification of clouds constitute a major contribution to the science of meteorology. He appears to have been the earliest observer to report that northeast storms move toward the southwest. He is also the first to have observed the phenomenon of convection in air.

Heat and Light

Franklin rejected the currently accepted corpuscular theory of light because of a mechanical argument. If "particles of matter called light" be ever so small, he wrote, their momentum would nevertheless be enormous, "exceeding that of a twenty-four pounder, discharged from a cannon." And yet, despite such "amazing" momentum, these supposed particles "will not drive before them, or remove, the least and lightest dust they meet with." The sun does not give evidence of a copious discharge of mass, since its gravitational force on the planets is not constantly decreasing.

Franklin's arguments were long considered the primary statement of the mechanical inadequacy of the "emission" theory and were still cited in 1835 in Humphrey Lloyd's report on optical theories to the British Association. Bishop Horsley, editor of Newton's *Opera,* made the official Newtonian reply in the *Philosophical Transactions* in 1770, noting that: "Dr. Franklin's questions are of some importance, and deserve a strict discussion." And when Thomas Young revived the wave theory toward the beginning of the nineteenth century, he cited Franklin as one of those predecessors who had believed in the wave theory: "The opinion of Franklin adds perhaps little weight to a mathematical question, but it may tend to assist in lessening the repugnance which every true philosopher must feel, to the necessity of embracing a physical theory different from that of Newton."

Franklin was perhaps more successful in his doctrine of fire. Here he tried to apply the principle of conservation to heat, assuming that there is a constant amount of heat, which is simply distributed, redistributed, conducted, or nonconducted, according to the kind of material in question. Interested in problems of heat conductivity, he designed a famous experiment, still performed in most introductory courses, in which a number of rods of different metals are joined together at one end and fanned out at the other, with little wax rings placed on them at regular intervals. The ends that are joined together are placed in the flame, and the "conductivity" is indicated by the relative speeds with which the wax rings melt and fall off. Franklin (in France) never had the occasion to perform the experiment, although he did obtain the necessary materials for doing so, and he suggested that Ingenhousz and he might do the experiment together. Ingenhousz, however, did it on his own. Franklin's experiments on heat were not fully understood until Joseph Black introduced the concepts of specific heat and latent heat.

Franklin's only major contribution to the theory of heat is in the specific area of differential thermal conduction. The success of his fluid theory of electricity, and his writings on heat as a fluid, did, however influence the later development of the concept of "caloric." Lavoisier wrote in 1777 that if he were to be asked what he understood by "matter of fire," he would reply, "with Franklin, Boerhaave, and some of the olden philosophers, that the matter of fire or of light is a very subtle and very elastic fluid. . . ."

Medicine and Hospitals

Throughout his life Franklin had a passion for exercise (notably swimming), for which he was an active propagandist. He was always an advocate of fresh air and had many arguments in France with those who held the night air to be bad for health and who believed—then as now—in the evil effects of drafts. I have referred to his invention of bifocal glasses; he also designed a flexible catheter. He wrote on a variety of medical subjects: lead poisoning, gout, the heat of the blood, the physiology of sleep, deafness, nyctalopia, infection from dead bodies, infant mortality, and medical education.

Although Franklin at one time had opposed the practice of inoculation, he later regretted his action and lamented the death of his own son from smallpox—which he publicly admitted might have been prevented by inoculation. He gathered a set of impressive statistics in favor of the practice, which were published in a pamphlet (London, 1759) on the benefits of inoculation against smallpox, accompanying William Heberden's instructions on inoculation.

Like others of his day, Franklin gave electric shocks in the treatment of paralysis. He concluded from his experiences that "I never knew any advantage from electricity in palsies that was permanent." He would not "pretend to say" whether—or to what degree—

there might have been an "apparent temporary advantage" due to "the exercise in the patients' journey, and coming daily to my house" or even—we may note with special interest today—the "spirits given by the hope of success, enabling them to exert more strength in moving their limbs."

Franklin's opinion that the beneficial effects of electrotherapy might derive more from the patient's belief in the efficacy of the cure than from any true curative powers of electricity is very much like one of the conclusions of the royal commission appointed in 1784 to investigate mesmerism, of which he was a member. This Commission was composed of four prominent members of the faculty of medicine and five members of the Royal Academy of Sciences (Paris), including Franklin, Bailly, and Lavoisier. Its report gave the death blow to mesmerism, and Mesmer had to leave Paris. The commission, apparently, did not see the psychological significance of their finding that "The imagination does everything, the magnetism nothing."

Later Life and Career

In spite of his extraordinary scientific accomplishments, the public at large knows of Franklin primarily as a statesman and public figure, and as an inventor rather than as a scientist—possibly because he devoted only a small portion of his creative life to scientific research. One of the three authors (along with Thomas Jefferson and John Adams) of the Declaration of Independence, he was a member of the Second Continental Congress and drew up a plan of union for the colonies. Sent to Paris in 1776 as one of three commissioners to negotiate a treaty, his fame preceded him, both for his personification of many ideas cherished in the Age of Enlightenment and for his great reputation in electricity; in 1773 he had been elected one of the eight foreign associates of the Royal Academy of Sciences. To many Frenchmen, his simplicity of dress, his native wit and wisdom, and his gentle manners without affectation seemed to indicate the virtues of a "natural man." In September 1778 he was appointed sole plenipotentiary, and in 1781 he was one of three commissioners to negotiate the final peace with Great Britain.

In France, Franklin enjoyed contact with many scientists and made the acquaintance of Volta, a strong supporter of Franklin's one-fluid theory; Volta began the next stage of electrical science with his invention of the battery, which made possible the production of a continuous electric current. Franklin appears to have been the first international statesman of note whose international reputation was gained in scientific activity.

Franklin returned to America in 1785, served the state of Pennsylvania, and was a member of the Constitutional Convention. He died on 17 April 1790 and was buried in Christ Church burial ground, Philadelphia.

BIBLIOGRAPHY

I. ORIGINAL WORKS. Franklin's scientific communications consist of pamphlets, reports, articles, and letters, published separately or in journals, especially *Gentleman's Magazine* and *Philosophical Transactions of the Royal Society.* His major scientific publication, *Experiments and Observations on Electricity, made at Philadelphia in America,* was assembled by his chief correspondent, Peter Collinson, and published with an unsigned preface by John Fothergill (London, 1751); supps. are *Supplemental Experiments and Observations . . .* (London, 1753) and *New Experiments and Observations . . .* (London, 1754), the latter with a paper by John Canton and a "Defence of Mr Franklin against the Abbe Nollet" by D. Colden. Subsequent eds. are described in *Benjamin Franklin's Experiments: A New Edition of Franklin's Experiments and Observations on Electricity,* ed., with a critical and historical intro., by I. Bernard Cohen (Cambridge, Mass., 1941). In addition to five eds. in English (1753–1774), translations appeared in French (1752, 1756, 1773), German (1758), and Italian (1774). See, further, Paul Leicester Ford, *Franklin Bibliography: A List of Books Written by, or Relating to Benjamin Franklin* (Brooklyn, N.Y., 1889), a work that is useful as a guide, although incomplete.

Franklin's complete writings and correspondence are in publication as *The Papers of Benjamin Franklin,* Leonard W. Labaree, inaugural ed. (New Haven, Conn., 1959–). Three earlier eds. of Franklin's works may be noted: Jared Sparks, *The Works of Benjamin Franklin . . .,* 10 vols. (Boston, 1836–1840); John Bigelow, *The Complete Works of Benjamin Franklin,* 10 vols. (New York–London, 1887–1888; a "Federal Edition" in 12 vols., 1904); and Albert Henry Smyth, *The Writings of Benjamin Franklin,* 10 vols. (New York, 1905–1907).

Information on Franklin MSS is available in Henry Stevens, *Benjamin Franklin's Life and Writings: A Bibliographical Essay on the Stevens' Collection of Books and Manuscripts Relating to Doctor Franklin* (London, 1881); Worthington C. Ford, *List of the Benjamin Franklin Papers in the Library of Congress* (Washington, D.C., 1905); and I. Minis Hays, *Calendar of the Papers of Benjamin Franklin in the Library of the American Philosophical Society* [and University of Pennsylvania], 5 vols. (Philadelphia, 1908). See also Francis S. Philbrick, "Notes on Early Editions and Editors of Franklin," in *Proceedings of the American Philosophical Society,* **97** (1953), 525–564.

Selections from Franklin's writings include Nathan G. Goodman, *The Ingenious Dr. Franklin, Selected Scientific Letters of Benjamin Franklin* (Philadelphia, 1931); Carl Van Doren, *Benjamin Franklin's Autobiographical Writings* (New York, 1945); and I. Bernard Cohen, *Benjamin Franklin: His Contribution to the American Tradition* (Indianapolis–New

York, 1953). See also *The Complete Poor Richard Almanacks Published by Benjamin Franklin, Reproduced in Facsimile,* intro. by Whitfield J. Bell, Jr., 2 vols. (Barre, Mass., 1970).

A parallel text ed. of Franklin's autobiographical writings, containing the text of the original MS, is Max Farrand, *Benjamin Franklin's Memoirs* (Berkeley–Los Angeles, 1949); the most recent and scholarly ed. based on MS sources is Leonard W. Labaree, Ralph L. Ketcham, Helen C. Boatfield, and Helene H. Fineman, eds., *The Autobiography of Benjamin Franklin* (New Haven–London, 1964).

I. Bernard Cohen has published, with an intro., a facs. ed. of Franklin's *Some Account of the Pennsylvania Hospital* (Baltimore, 1954).

II. Secondary Literature. The standard biography is Carl Van Doren, *Benjamin Franklin* (New York, 1938), possibly the best biography of a scientist in English. An admirable shorter biography is Verner W. Crane, *Benjamin Franklin and a Rising People* (Boston, 1954). Paul Leicester Ford, *The Many-sided Franklin* (New York, 1899) is still useful, esp. ch. 9, "The Scientist"; Bernard Faÿ, *Franklin, the Apostle of Modern Times* (Boston, 1929), lacks the valuable "Bibliographie et étude sur les sources historiques relatives à sa vie" included in vol. III of the French ed. (Paris, 1929–1931).

On Franklin in Europe, see Alfred Owen Aldridge, *Franklin and his French Contemporaries* (New York, 1957); Edward E. Hale and Edward E. Hale, Jr., *Franklin in France,* 2 vols. (Boston, 1888); and Antonio Pace, *Benjamin Franklin and Italy* (Philadelphia, 1958).

On Franklin and medicine, see Theodore Diller, *Franklin's Contribution to Medicine* (Brooklyn, N.Y., 1912); and William Pepper, *The Medical Side of Benjamin Franklin* (Philadelphia, 1911).

On lightning rods, see I. B. Cohen, "Prejudice Against the Introduction of Lightning Rods," in *Journal of the Franklin Institute,* **253** (1952), 393–440; "Did Diviš Erect the First European Protective Lightning Rod, and Was His Invention Independent?," in *Isis,* **43** (1952), 358–364, written with Robert E. Scholfield; and "The Two Hundredth Anniversary of Benjamin Franklin's Two Lightning Experiments and the Introduction of the Lightning Rod," in *Proceedings of the American Philosophical Society,* **96** (1952), 331–366.

Some other specialized studies of value are Cleveland Abbe, "Benjamin Franklin as Meteorologist," in *Proceedings of the American Philosophical Society,* **45** (1906), 117–128; Lloyd A. Brown, "The River in the Ocean," in *Essays Honoring Lawrence C. Wroth* (Portland, Me., 1951), pp. 69–84; N. H. de V. Heathcote, "Franklin's Introduction to Electricity," in *Isis,* **46** (1955), 29–35; Edwin J. Houston, "Franklin as a Man of Science and an Inventor," in *Journal of the Franklin Institute,* **161** (1906), 241–316, 321–383; Henry Stommel, *The Gulf Stream* (Berkeley–Los Angeles, 1958), ch. 1, "Historical Introduction"; Francis Newton Thorpe, *Benjamin Franklin and the University of Pennsylvania* (Washington, D.C., 1893); and Conway Zirkle, "Benjamin Franklin, Thomas Malthus and the United States Census," in *Isis,* **48** (1957), 58–62.

A bibliography up to 1956 may be found in I. Bernard Cohen, *Franklin and Newton, an Inquiry Into Speculative Newtonian Experimental Science and Franklin's Work in Electricity as an Example Thereof* (Philadelphia, 1956; Cambridge, Mass., 1966; rev. repr. 1972).

I. Bernard Cohen

FRANKLIN, ROSALIND ELSIE (*b.* London, England, 25 July 1920; *d.* London, 16 April 1958), *physical chemistry, molecular biology.*

The daughter of a banking and artistic family previously unconnected with science, Rosalind Franklin was a foundation scholar at St. Paul's Girls' School, London, from which she won an exhibition to Newnham College, Cambridge, in 1938. After graduating in 1941 she stayed on to investigate gas-phase chromatography under Ronald Norrish. In 1942 she joined the British Coal Utilisation Research Association where, under D. H. Bangham, she applied her expertise in physical chemistry to the problem of the physical structure of coals and carbonized coals. From 1947 to 1950 Franklin worked under Jacques Méring at the Laboratoire Central des Services Chimiques de l'État, Paris, where she developed her skill in X-ray diffraction techniques and applied them to a detailed and illuminating study of carbons and of the structural changes accompanying graphitization. In 1951 she joined Sir John Randall's Medical Research Council unit at King's College, London, to apply these techniques to the problems of the structure of DNA, and in 1953 she moved to Birkbeck College, London, to work similarly on the even more exacting problems of virus structure.

At the British Coal Utilisation Research Association, Franklin developed, with Bangham and other workers, a hypothesis of the micellar organization of coals which provided a satisfactory explanation of their absorptive behavior toward liquids and gases and their thermal expansion. From her study of the fine porosity of a range of coals, by measurements of true and apparent densities, Franklin concluded that their structure was best represented by a model with pore constrictions which gave coals the properties of molecular sieves. In Paris she turned her attention to the application of X-ray diffraction methods to the problems of carbon structure and developed a procedure for the detailed interpretation of the diffuse X-ray diagram of carbons. This allowed her to describe the structure in more precise quantitative terms than had been possible, and she made use of it to study in detail the structural changes that accompanied the formation of graphite when these carbons were heated to high temperatures.

In the course of this work Franklin developed a

relation between the apparent interlayer spacing of the partially graphitized carbons and the proportion of disoriented layers, which has proved of considerable value in the industrial study of carbons. In addition, by studying the changes in structure that chars of different origin underwent on heating, she established that there are two distinct classes of carbons—those which form graphite on heating to high temperatures (the graphitizing carbons) and those which do not (the nongraphitizing carbons)—and related these differences in behavior to structural differences in the parent chars. She showed, in particular, that the graphitizability increases with the fine-structure porosity and this, in turn, she believed to be related to the cross-linking between the crystallites.

Franklin's work on coals brought her into contact with Charles Coulson, through whom she was introduced to Randall, and with the award of a Turner Newall Fellowship she went to work in the King's College Medical Research Council Biophysics Unit. At that time (January 1951) Raymond Gosling, under M. H. F. Wilkins' direction, had obtained diffraction pictures of DNA showing a high degree of crystallinity; sharper pictures were obtained with higher ambient humidity.

Franklin and Gosling conducted a systematic study of the effect of humidity on the X-ray pattern produced. Using salt solutions to control humidity, they showed that there are two distinct intramolecular patterns, which they found to be producible from the same specimen: the crystalline "A" pattern at 75 percent relative humidity and a new "wet" paracrystalline pattern at 95 percent relative humidity. In a report which Franklin gave on this work in November 1951, she described this discovery and went on to show, as Wilkins had a year before in Cambridge, that the patterns were consistent with a helical conformation. She discussed how the $A \rightleftharpoons B$ transformation takes place and suggested, quite correctly, that the phosphates are on the outside of the helices and in the "A" form are held parallel to each other by electrostatic attraction between O^- and Na^+. When water is added, it penetrates between the helices, thus destroying the electrostatic attraction which holds them in parallel alignment. She said little about the forces operating inside the helices but mentioned hydrogen bonding between keto and amino groups of the bases.

Despite this promising beginning Franklin was too professional a crystallographer to proceed further in this way. Instead, she thought to solve the structure of DNA in an inductive manner by using Patterson functions and superposition. While publicly she heaped scorn on those who were convinced that DNA is helical, in her unpublished reports she stated that such a conformation is probable for the B form and not inconsistent with the A form. A spurious case of double orientation encountered in April 1952, which when indexed showed marked radial asymmetry (all left-hand reflections were indexed *hkl* and all right-hand ones $hk\bar{l}$), led her to seek nonhelical structures for the A form. Earlier ambiguities in the indexing of the A diagram had led Franklin to embark on a Patterson analysis. This helped her to obtain accurate parameters for the unit cell. Yet the cylindrical Patterson function obtained by Gosling in July 1952 strengthened her antihelical views, although the arrangement of peaks was consistent with a helix. She was misled, by what appeared to be clear evidence of a structural repeat at half the height of the unit cell, into ruling out helices for the A form, since no DNA chain could possibly be folded into a helix with a pitch equal to half the height of the unit cell (fourteen Å.).

At this time Franklin was thinking in terms of antiparallel rods in pairs back-to-back, forming a double sheet structure. Then she investigated diagonal rod structures such as would simulate the diffraction pattern of a helix, but by January 1953, when she started model building, she found such structures impossible to build. Still rejecting single- or multistrand helices, she investigated a figure-eight structure in which a single chain formed a long column of repeating eights. This, she believed, would account for the halving of the unit cell in the cylindrical Patterson function and clearly provided a form of tight packing which could be unfolded to give the dramatic increase in length (30 percent) when structure A changes to structure B. She knew that the helix in the extended B form is close-packed and was doubtful that the same type of structure could pack down even more densely.

At the end of February 1953 Franklin turned to the B pattern, and for two weeks she weighed the merits of single and multiple helices. In a paper dated 17 March which she wrote with Gosling, she ruled out triple-strand and equally spaced double-strand helices and stated that "if there are two non-equivalent, i.e., unequally spaced coaxial chains these are separated by 3/8th. of the fibre axis period." This is the conformation of the sugar-phosphate backbones as found in the Watson-Crick model. On the following day Franklin returned to the Patterson function of the A form, only to learn that Watson and Crick had solved the structure of the B form. She and Gosling quickly expanded and rearranged their draft paper of 17 March in the light of the Cambridge discovery so that it could appear in the 25 April issue of *Nature,* which contains Watson and Crick's paper on their model.

Franklin deserves credit for having discovered the A ⇌ B transformation and characterized the diffraction patterns of these forms of DNA; for providing Watson and Crick with vital data, in particular the parameters of the unit cell; for exposing the errors in their first unpublished model; and for marshaling the evidence in favor of the phosphates being on the outside of the helix. It was also she who, with the aid of the special tilting camera built by Gosling, discovered the meridional reflection on the eleventh layer line in the A pattern and was the first to show how the B form can pack down more tightly to give the A form with eleven residues in one turn of the helix. Although she had been misled by the cylindrical Patterson function, this did provide the most refined evidence in favor of the Watson-Crick model at the time of its discovery in 1953. Franklin and Gosling's rarely cited paper on this subject appeared in *Nature* on 25 July 1953.

For the last five years of her life Franklin worked in the Crystallography Laboratory of Birkbeck College, London, supported first by the Agricultural Research Council and later by the U.S. Department of Health. There she continued to publish on her earlier work on coals, completed the writing up of her DNA work, and took up the structure of tobacco mosaic virus (TMV). By 1956 she had greatly improved on J. D. Watson's X-ray pictures of 1954. With the aid of material supplied by Heinz Fraenkel-Conrat and by Gerhard Schramm, Franklin and her co-workers, A. Klug and K. C. Holmes, were able to reject the picture of TMV as a solid cylinder with the RNA in the center and the protein subunits, possibly of two types, on the outside. They showed that the particles are hollow, that the protein subunits are structurally of one type only, and that forty-nine such units are packed in helical array around the axis in the axial repeat period of sixty-nine Å. The greatest achievement of the Franklin team was the location of the RNA helix embedded within the protein fraction at a radial distance of forty Å. from the axis. From a study of the X-ray diagram of TMV, Franklin and Klug resolved the discrepancy between estimates of the maximum radius and the packing radius by postulating the morphology of the protein as "a helical array of knobs, one knob for each sub-unit." Shortly before her death from cancer, Franklin instituted work which was later to justify her conclusion that the RNA in TMV is present in the form of a single-strand helix.

Franklin was a deft experimentalist, keenly observant and with immense capacity for taking pains. As a result she was able with difficult material to achieve a remarkable standard of resolution in her X-ray diagrams. Although a bold experimentalist, she was critical of speculation, favoring an inductive approach which proved very successful in her work on coals and TMV but which allowed others to get ahead of her in her work on DNA. Where those with a more intuitive approach rejected antihelical data as spurious, Franklin felt obliged to invent other conformations which might yield a helical-type pattern. She would not trust to the principle of exclusion, nor was she confident of the "obvious" deductions dictated by physical intuition. Hence her work was not marked by great originality of thought. Her theory of graphitization, for instance, although the best of its day, was traditional in character and belongs to what is now regarded as the "classical" period. Her great strength lay in her technical innovations and her employment of precise techniques on difficult macromolecules. When she died at the age of thirty-seven, she had won international recognition both as an industrial chemist and as a molecular biologist.

BIBLIOGRAPHY

I. Original Works. Franklin and her co-workers published about forty papers. A complete list of her publications on the structure of viruses is in her paper written with D. L. D. Casper and A. Klug, "The Structure of Viruses as Determined by X-Ray Diffraction," in C. S. Holton *et al.*, eds., *Plant Pathology: Problems and Progress, 1908–1958* (Madison, Wis., 1959), pp. 447–461. This paper provides a broad review of Franklin's work and contains a tribute to her by W. M. Stanley.

Of her other papers the following appeared in *Acta crystallographica:* "The Interpretation of Diffuse X-Ray Diagrams of Carbon," **3** (1950), 107–117; "A Rapid Approximate Method for Correcting Low-Angle Scattering Measurements for the Influence of the Finite Height of the X-Ray Beam," *ibid.,* 158–159; "The Structure of Graphitic Carbons," **4** (1951), 253–261; "The *a* Dimension of Graphite," *ibid.,* 561; and "The Structure of Sodium Thymonucleate Fibres. I, II, & III," **6** (1953), 673–677, 678–685; **8** (1955), 151–156.

Other important papers are "A Note on the True Density, Chemical Composition and Structure of Coals and Carbonized Coals," in *Fuel,* **27** (1948), 46–49; "A Study of the Fine-Structure of Carbonaceous Solids by Measurements of True and Apparent Densities. Part I. Coals. Part II. Carbonized Coals," in *Transactions of the Faraday Society,* **45** (1949), 274–286, 668–682; "Crystallite Growth in Graphitizing and Nongraphitizing Carbons," in *Proceedings of the Royal Society,* **209A** (1951), 196–218; "Molecular Configuration in Sodium Thymonucleate," in *Nature,* **171** (1953), 740–741; and "Evidence for 2-Chain Helix in

Crystalline Structure of Sodium Deoxyribonucleate," *ibid.,* **172** (1953), 156–157.

Her last paper, written with A. Klug, was published after her death: "Order-Disorder Transitions in Structures Containing Helical Molecules," in *Discussions of the Faraday Society,* **25** (1958), 104–110.

II. SECONDARY LITERATURE. Obituary notices appeared in *The Times* (19 Apr. 1958), p. 3; and *Nature,* **182** (1958), 154.

For two very different accounts of Franklin's work on DNA, see J. D. Watson, *The Double Helix* (New York, 1968), *passim;* and A. Klug, "Rosalind Franklin and the Discovery of the Structure of DNA," in *Nature,* **219** (1968), 808–810, 843–844; *corrigenda,* 879, 1192; correspondence, 880.

ROBERT OLBY

FRAUNHOFER, JOSEPH (*b.* Straubing, Germany, 6 March 1787; *d.* Munich, Germany, 7 June 1826), *optics, optical instrumentation.*

Fraunhofer represents the highest order of the union of the craftsman and the theoretician. His family and early acquaintances were closely associated with the skilled craft tradition and particularly concerned with the glass and optical trades. As he acquired mastery of lens grinding, lens design, and glassmaking—through apprenticeship and independent study of optical books—Fraunhofer sought not merely to produce lenses which surpassed the best on the market but also to design and produce lenses which approached the optical ideal. In this pursuit he turned to the theoretical study of optics and light, a study which, when combined with his practical experience and understanding, ultimately made him the master theoretical optician of Europe and, as a by-product, led him to make numerous significant contributions to science.

Fraunhofer was the eleventh and last child of a poor master glazier, Franz Xaver Fraunhofer, and Maria Anna Fröhlich. After receiving only a limited elementary education, he entered his father's workshop. In November 1798, following the death of his parents, Fraunhofer's guardian apprenticed him to Philipp A. Weichselberger, a dull, unintellectual Munich master mirror-maker and glass cutter. Fraunhofer found his apprenticeship degrading and miserable, as his master discouraged further schooling and isolated him from his peers. Nevertheless, he maintained his goal of becoming a spectacles maker.

The fortunes of the sickly boy took an ironic turn for the better when, on 21 July 1801, the workshop-house collapsed, pinning him under the wreckage for some time. Elector Maximilian Joseph heard of the accident and presented him with the handsome sum of eighteen ducats. With the money Fraunhofer purchased a glass-working machine, books on optics, and release from the last six months of his six-year apprenticeship.

After a short, abortive business venture (producing engraving plates for visiting cards), Fraunhofer returned in November 1804 to work as a journeyman for Weichselberger until May 1806, when he entered the optical shop of the Munich philosophical (scientific) instrument company founded in 1802 by Joseph von Utzschneider, Georg von Reichenbach, and Joseph Liebherr.

Influenced by Ulrich Schiegg, a trained astronomer, and by Josef Niggl, the optics master under whom he served as a journeyman, Fraunhofer developed expertise in practical optics and acquired an interest in and a knowledge of mathematics and optical science. In 1809, in accordance with a contract negotiated between Utzschneider and Pierre Louis Guinand, Utzschneider designated Fraunhofer, who had criticized the available optical glass, to receive from Guinand instruction in his closely kept secrets of glassmaking. Guinand had moved from Switzerland to Bavaria in 1805 at the initiative of Utzschneider in order to supply the optical firm with glass; his tutelage allowed Fraunhofer to combine his understanding of optics with the practical knowledge of glassmaking. This instruction led to a two-year collaboration between Fraunhofer and Guinand that resulted in substantial increases in the size of glass blanks for lenses. Fraunhofer's advance in the firm—from journeyman in 1806, to manager of the optical workshop in 1809, to business partner with Utzschneider and director of the glassmaking (over Guinand) in 1811—was a reflection of his quick grasp of and original contributions to optical science, practical optical work, and glassmaking.

From 1819, when the optical workshop was returned to Munich from Benediktbeuern, he participated actively in the affairs of the Bavarian Academy of Sciences in Munich. In 1823, while still maintaining his active business schedule, he accepted the post of director of the Physics Museum of the academy and received the honorary title royal Bavarian professor. Fraunhofer initiated lectures on physical and geometrical optics shortly thereafter but had to discontinue them because of his frail health. Although he enjoyed neighborhood walks, he had little time for relaxation. Late in 1825 the lifelong bachelor contracted tuberculosis, from which he never recovered. During the last few years of his life Fraunhofer was elected to several foreign societies, including the Society of Arts in England, and received state honors from Denmark and his native Bavaria. The University of Erlangen conferred upon him the title of doctor of philosophy.

Fraunhofer was a blend of mathematically inclined natural philosopher, optical technician, and glassmaker. Although he had little formal education, he sought to understand optical theory and apply it to the practical work of constructing aberration-minimizing lens combinations. At the time he entered Utzschneider's instrument shop, the optical trade of Europe centered in London, where the leading names were Dollond and Ramsden. Yet even in London the lack of large blanks of homogeneous, striae-free crown and flint glass and the comparatively crude determinations of the optical constants of the glass limited the size and quality of lenses and restricted opticians to trial-and-error methods of optical construction.

Early in the nineteenth century the Munich firm that Fraunhofer joined took the lead in Germany in the manufacture of precision optical instruments and gained a gradual advantage over the London opticians, initially by obtaining the services of Guinand, who improved the making of optical glass. Later, Guinand and Fraunhofer, working together from 1809 to 1813, further improved the homogeneity of optical glass and increased the size of the striae-free blanks, so that large-diameter lenses could be made. Fraunhofer also sought to determine, with significantly greater precision than before, the dispersion and refractive index for different kinds of optical glass, so that he could abandon the traditional trial-and-error methods and approach lensmaking according to optical theory and calculation.

In order to determine precisely the optical constants of glass, Fraunhofer in 1814 used the two bright-yellow lines in flame spectra as a source of monochromatic light. With improved values for optical constants, he hoped to design and construct lens combinations in which the spherical aberration and coma could be eliminated. While conducting these tests, he observed the effect of the refracting medium on light, comparing the effect of light from flames with light from the sun, and found that the solar spectrum was crossed with many fine dark lines, a few of which William Hyde Wollaston had observed and reported upon in 1802. Designating the more distinct lines with capital letters ($A, B, C, D, \cdots, I$), he mapped many of the 574 lines that he observed between B on the red end and H on the violet end of the spectrum. Somewhat later he noted that some of these lines appeared to correspond to the bright doublet of lines in many flame spectra; yet he noted further that while the pattern observed for the sun and planets appeared identical, the patterns for the sun, Sirius, and other bright stars differed from one another. These observations stimulated considerable interest for the next half-century among natural philosophers, whose speculations culminated in the classical explanation of absorption and emission spectra made by Kirchhoff and Bunsen in 1859. For Fraunhofer, however, these observations were primarily of importance in his efforts to perfect the achromatic telescope.

In 1821 and 1823, shortly after Fresnel's studies of interference phenomena had received general attention, Fraunhofer published two papers in which he observed and analyzed certain diffraction phenomena and interpreted them in terms of a wave theory of light. In the 1821 paper he discussed his examination of the spectra resulting from light diffracted through a single narrow slit and quantitatively related the width of the slit to the angles of dispersion of the different orders of spectra. Extending his observations to diffraction resulting from a large number of slits, he constructed a grating with 260 parallel wires.

Although David Rittenhouse and Thomas Young had previously noted some effects of crude diffraction gratings, Fraunhofer made the first quantitative study of the phenomena. The presence of the solar dark lines enabled him to note that the dispersion of the spectra was greater with his grating than with his prism. Hence, he examined the relationship between dispersion and the separation of wires in the grating. Utilizing the dark lines as bench marks in the spectrum for his dispersion determinations, he concluded that the dispersion was inversely related to the distance between successive slits in the grating. From the same study Fraunhofer was able to determine the wavelengths of specific colors of light. Somewhat later he also constructed a grating by ruling lines on glass covered by gold foil and, even later, constructed a reflecting grating. The latter prompted him to consider the effects of light obliquely incident to the grating.

In the paper prepared in 1823, Fraunhofer revealed his continued investigation of diffraction gratings. Using a diamond point, he could rule up to 3,200 lines per Paris inch. He continued his study of the effect of oblique rays, developed formulations based on a wave conception, and calculated a revised set of wavelengths for the major spectral lines. Thus, his earlier observations of the dark lines in the solar spectrum enabled him to make the highly precise measurements of dispersion; then his use of the wave theory of light allowed him to derive, with suitable simplifications, the general formulation of the grating equation still in use today. His other papers focused principally upon the design and construction of new instruments, and one paper examined atmospheric light phenomena.

Fraunhofer's scientific studies were intimately related to his professional object: the design and production of the finest possible optical and mechanical instruments. Utilizing the lines in the solar spectrum as bench marks, he determined with unprecedented precision the optical constants of various kinds of glass. The combination of superior optical glass, the theoretical design and calculation of lens systems, the accurate determination of optical constants, and the use of Newton's rings for testing of lens surfaces enabled the Utzschneider-Fraunhofer shop in Munich to wrest leadership in the production of optical instruments from the London opticians during the first quarter of the century.

Although Fraunhofer openly published his observations of the spectral lines and his interpretation of diffraction spectra, he retained as trade secrets his knowledge of optical glassmaking and his methods of calculating and testing lenses. Among his most famous instruments were the nine-and-a-half-inch Dorpat refracting telescope and equatorial mounting used by Wilhelm Struve and the six-and-a-quarter-inch Königsberg heliometer with which Friedrich Bessel measured the parallax of 61 Cygni in 1838. Such a detection and measurement of parallax had been sought unsuccessfully since antiquity.

After Fraunhofer's death, Utzschneider and, later, Siegmund Merz continued the Munich business, actively participating in the movement initiated by Fraunhofer to replace the large reflecting telescopes with the large refractors. Although his Munich optical shop did not continue to lead in innovation during its remaining half-century of existence, Fraunhofer's approach of combining practical with theoretical knowledge and an understanding of both optics and glassmaking had not only made the German optical industry the leading one in the world but also continued to inspire generations of German optical scientists and industrialists. Fraunhofer's direct successors in the nineteenth century thus included Josef Max Petzval; Johann Friedrich Voigtländer, Peter Friedrich Voigtländer, and Friedrich von Voigtländer; Carl August Steinheil and Adolph Steinheil; Philipp L. Seidel; Carl Zeiss; Ernst Abbe; and Otto Schott.

BIBLIOGRAPHY

I. Original Works. Fraunhofer's published works were collected in Eugen C. J. Lommel, ed., *Joseph von Fraunhofer's gesammelte Schriften* (Munich, 1888). A review of an unpublished 1807 paper appears in *Forschungen zur Geschichte der Optik,* **1** (May 1929), 42–51.

II. Secondary Literature. Two important nineteenth-century studies are Joseph von Utzschneider, "Kurzer Umriss der Lebens-Geschichte des Herrn . . . Fraunhofer," in *Dinglers polytechnisches Journal,* **21** (1826), 161–181; and Siegmund Merz, *Fraunhofer's Leben und Wirken . . .* (Landshut, 1865). Two twentieth-century works have provided the bases for all subsequent studies: the most comprehensive biographical study, by the outstanding Zeiss historian of optics, Moritz von Rohr, *Joseph Fraunhofers Leben, Leistungen und Wirksamkeit* (Leipzig, 1929); and A. Seitz, *Josef Fraunhofer und sein optisches Institut* (Berlin, 1926). Upon the centennial of Fraunhofer's death, *Naturwissenschaften,* **14** (1926), 522–554, was devoted to an evaluation of his work. More recent studies include H. Jebsen-Marwedel, *Joseph von Fraunhofer und die Glashütte in Benediktbeuern* (1963); and W. Gerlach, "Joseph Fraunhofer und seine Stellung in der Geschichte der Optik," in *Optik,* **20** (1963), 279–292. Twentieth-century literature in English on Fraunhofer is very limited and mostly derived from the works of Rohr and Seitz: Moritz von Rohr, "Fraunhofer's Work and Its Present Day Significance," in *Transactions of the Optical Society,* **27** (1926), 277–294; W. H. S. Chance, "The Optical Glassworks at Benediktbeuern," in *Proceedings of the Physical Society,* **49** (1937), 433–443; and Henry C. King, *The History of the Telescope* (Cambridge, Mass., 1955), *passim.*

Reese V. Jenkins

FRAZER, JAMES GEORGE (*b.* Glasgow, Scotland, 1 January 1854; *d.* Cambridge, England, 7 May 1941), *anthropology.*

Frazer, the elder son of Daniel F. Frazer and his wife, Katherine Brown, grew up in Helensburgh, near Glasgow, in an educated Presbyterian household. He attended Springfield Academy, Larchfield Academy, and the University of Glasgow, graduating in 1874 after following a broadly based curriculum which included mathematics, physics, logic, moral philosophy, and English literature as well as the classics, which were his main interest. He then went to Trinity College, Cambridge, on a scholarship, took the classical tripos in 1878, and in 1879, following research on Plato's theory of Ideas, was elected to a fellowship at the college, which was renewed for the rest of his life. Frazer maintained his interest in the classics, and his only original research was some archaeological fieldwork undertaken for his translation of Pausanius' *Description of Greece,* published in 1898: his anthropological work was deeply rooted in his classical studies.

In 1883 William Robertson Smith came to Cambridge as professor of Arabic and aroused Frazer's interest in anthropology. He was also editor of the *Encyclopaedia Britannica* and asked Frazer to write a number of articles, first on classical subjects and later, after Frazer had read E. B. Tylor's *Primitive Culture* (1871), on "Totem" and "Taboo," both published in 1888; these were later expanded into the four-volume work *Totemism and Exogamy* (1910). As early as 1885 Frazer read to the Anthropological Institute a paper on burial customs which clearly showed the influence of Tylor, and in 1890 he published the first edition of *The Golden Bough.* This title was taken from book VI of the *Aeneid,* and the work started as an investigation of the rites surrounding the priest at the Grove of Diana in Aricia. But in the process of compilation, it was expanded into a detailed comparative study similar to *Primitive Culture* but was better documented and included more material on rites and practices in European countries which appeared similar to those of more primitive societies. This was extended further into a work of twelve volumes (1911–1915) and an appendix (1936); volume XII was an alphabetical bibliography of some 5,000 items in most European languages, of which less than 1 percent were asterisked to indicate that Frazer had not seen them himself.

Frazer was invited to Liverpool to occupy the first post of professor of social anthropology in any university, which he held for one year (1907–1908), giving an inaugural lecture entitled "The Scope of Social Anthropology." But he was not happy away from Cambridge and his library; and although he gave the Gifford lectures in 1924 and 1925, he did not like lecturing, any form of teaching, or even controversial discussion with professional anthropologists. Frazer was knighted in 1914, was elected a fellow of the Royal Society in 1920 under the statute governing special elections on grounds of "conspicuous service to the cause of science," was made a member of the Order of Merit in 1924, and received other honors, both British and foreign; in 1905 he was granted a Civil List pension. He married a Frenchwoman, Mrs. Lilly Grove, in 1896, and she energetically assisted him in his work and in ensuring its public recognition: she translated several of his works into French and worked on the abridgment of *The Golden Bough* published in 1922. Both died on 7 May 1941.

Frazer made no original observations in anthropology and is widely criticized for having little or no direct contact with the "savages" he wrote about. Lienhardt attributes some of his popular success to the simplifications encouraged by lack of personal experience. His method was to read the published literature, often for twelve to fifteen hours a day, and to make notes which he later classified, assembled in groups showing the relationships of practices from different parts of the world, and discussed. Leach has shown that his desire to present an elegant prose sometimes led him to distort the original report. Frazer also corresponded with fieldworkers, who valued his stimulating questions and comments, as shown by Bronislaw Malinowski and Sir Baldwin Spencer's *Scientific Correspondence.* He compiled a list of questions for fieldworkers, with advice on collecting data, clearly aimed at the amateur, which was published first in 1887 and in its final form in 1907. Many of his correspondents were missionaries and administrators, and although he collected a large number of letters, now at Trinity College, he rarely cited information from them.

The development of Frazer's work shows both the strengths and the weaknesses of the inductive method. No one before or since has brought together such a volume of data on customs and beliefs, classified and documented to stimulate other workers; yet most of his theories, arising from cogitation in a library on secondhand data, have been modified or superseded, particularly his conception of the evolutionary succession of magic, religion, and science in culture. His analysis of magic into sympathetic and contagious types still has some validity, and Frazer himself never maintained that his own theories were more than transitory and propounded to be superseded: "After all, what we call truth is only the hypothesis which is found to work best." He also believed that if his writings survived, it would be "less for the sake of the theories they propound than for the sake of the facts they record."

Although Frazer was unwilling to meet or discuss with anthropologists who did not agree with him, a generation of fieldworkers, of whom Malinowski is probably the best-known, were drawn to the subject by his inspiration, and it developed quickly. His other main importance in his time was simply the popularization of comparative anthropology and the beginning of acceptance of his thesis that mankind is one and that "when all is said and done our resemblances to the savage are still far more numerous than our differences from him." The prose style, consciously modeled on that of the eighteenth century, was attractive enough to be widely read, and his demonstration of numerous myths strikingly similar to the Christian stories undermined some conventional religious beliefs, a point picked up by the historian Arnold Toynbee.

Frazer's later influence was probably greatest on literature: T. S. Eliot acknowledged a debt to him, while Ezra Pound, D. H. Lawrence, and others probably were influenced. In his *Totem and Taboo* (1913) Freud quotes data from Frazer, often approving his conclusions. Although Frazer remarked that "the sexual instinct has moulded the religious consciousness of our race," he always refused to read Freud. He was, nevertheless, well aware of discrepancies between acts and the explanations given for them, and that motives are not always those men are conscious of; and he came near to an appreciation of the unconscious.

More recent reappraisals (beginning with the centenary of Frazer's birth in 1954) have been critical of his academic integrity as an anthropologist and have valued him predominantly as a literary figure: his work is, nevertheless, still read and referred to.

BIBLIOGRAPHY

I. Original Works. The most comprehensive bibliography is T. Besterman, *A Bibliography of Sir James George Frazer* (London, 1934); it is arranged chronologically and contains 266 items, together with a note by Frazer on his own notebooks. The originals of the notebooks are now in the British Museum, and the contents of many were published as *Anthologia anthropologica,* R. A. Downie, ed., 4 vols. (London, 1938–1939): they comprise extracts from material already published but not previously quoted by Frazer and are arranged alphabetically with indexes.

Editions of *The Golden Bough* in Frazer's lifetime are detailed by Besterman. In 1957, Macmillan, the original publishers, issued a two-volume paperback edition in their St. Martin's Library. Subsequently T. H. Gaster edited *The New Golden Bough* (New York, 1959), which gives a new abridgment of Frazer's work, including selections from the appendix *Aftermath,* and attempts by excision and rearrangement to bring the text up to date; it is the only short edition to contain references, and it also includes the editor's additional notes, with references, and a sizable index.

Frazer's first publication on anthropology, already profusely documented, was "On Certain Burial Customs as Illustrative of the Primitive Theory of the Soul," followed by discussion, in *Journal of the Anthropological Institute,* **15** (1885), 64–104. The last edition of his questions was issued as *Questions on the Customs, Beliefs, and Languages of Savages* (Cambridge, 1907). His letters to Spencer are in Sir Baldwin Spencer, *Spencer's Scientific Correspondence With Sir J. G. Frazer and Others,* R. R. Marett and T. K. Penniman, eds. (Oxford, 1932).

II. Secondary Literature. The only full-scale biography is by his assistant, R. A. Downie: *James George Frazer: The Portrait of a Scholar* (London, 1940); the actual biographical section is short and the evaluation appreciative, but the main body of the work is a useful summary of the contents of Frazer's various works. B. Malinowski, "Sir James George Frazer: A Biographical Appreciation," in his *A Scientific Theory of Culture and Other Essays* (Chapel Hill, N.C., 1944), pp. 177–221, is a professional appraisal. There is an article by E. O. James in the *Dictionary of National Biography, Supplement 1941–1950* (Oxford, 1959), pp. 272–278; and obituaries by H. J. Fleur in *Obituary Notices of Fellows of the Royal Society of London,* **3** (1939–1941), 897–914; by R. Marett in *Proceedings of the British Academy,* **27** (1941), 377–391; and three by Cambridge friends in *Cambridge Review,* **62** (1941), 439–440, 457.

More recent evaluations are R. G. Lienhardt, "James George Frazer," in *International Encyclopedia of the Social Sciences,* D. L. Sills, ed., V (New York, 1968), 550–553; J. B. Vickery, "The Golden Bough: Impact and Archetype," in *Virginia Quarterly Review,* **39** (1963), 37–57; T. H. Breen, "The Conflict in the Golden Bough: Frazer's Two Images of Man," in *South Atlantic Quarterly,* **66** (1967), 179–194; A. Kardiner and E. Preble, "James Frazer: Labor Disguised as Ease," in *They Studied Man* (London, 1962), pp. 78–197; A. Goldenweiser, "Sir James Frazer's Theories," in his *History, Psychology and Culture* (London, 1933), pt. II, ch. 2, pp. 167–176; and three articles in *The Listener,* **51** (1954), for the centenary: Gilbert Murray, pp. 13–14; V. White, pp. 137–139; and A. Macbeath, pp. 217–218.

Early criticism came from Sir William Ridgeway, "The Methods of Mannhardt and Sir J. G. Frazer . . .," in *Proceedings of the Cambridge Philological Society,* nos. 124–126 (1924), 6–19. Later criticism is F. Huxley, "Frazer With the Bloody Wood," in *New Statesman and Nation,* **59** (1960), 561–562.

Radical criticism by E. R. Leach began with his "Golden Bough or Gilded Twig?," in *Daedalus,* **90** (1959), 371–387; this was in their series "Reputations" and was followed by H. Weisinger, "The Branch That Grew Full Straight," *ibid.,* 388–399. Leach continued with a review of I. C. Jarvie, *The Revolution in Anthropology* (London, 1964), of which sec. VI, ch. 1, was entitled "Back to Frazer." There was an exchange between Leach and Jarvie in *Encounter,* **25** (1965), 24–36; **26,** (1966), 53–56, 92–93; it was conveniently reprinted as a discussion, with additional comments by other anthropologists and a full bibliography of relevant material, in *Current Anthropology,* **7** (1966), 560–576.

Diana M. Simpkins

FREDERICK II OF HOHENSTAUFEN (*b.* Iesi, Italy, 26 December 1194; *d.* Castelfiorentino, Italy, 13 December 1250), *natural sciences.*

Frederick II was the son of Emperor Henry VI and Constance of Sicily and was thus the grandson of both Frederick Barbarossa and Roger II of Sicily. He was crowned king of Sicily at Palermo in May 1198, following his father's death in 1197. Upon his mother's death six months later, Pope Innocent III became Frederick's guardian and regent of Sicily, a situation not ended until 1208, when Frederick came of age. In 1210 Emperor Otto IV invaded Sicily; the young Frederick in turn challenged Otto's rule in Germany the next year. The victory of his ally Philip II of France at Bouvines (1214) strengthened his position, and at Otto's death in 1218 Frederick was left unchallenged in Germany and northern Italy; he was crowned Holy Roman emperor in 1220. Thereupon Frederick turned to the restoration of order in Sicily, a process finally completed with the promulgation of the Constitutions of Melfi (*Liber Augustalis*) in 1231. If taxation in the resulting nonfeudal, centralized state was high, the coinage was stable and justice relatively easy to obtain; with the creation of the University of Naples in 1224 the emperor sought to bring even professional education under his control.

A struggle between Frederick and the papacy was now inevitable: Rome was caught between the empire to the north and Sicily to the south and was threatened by their possible union. The conflict broke out first in 1227, when Gregory IX excommunicated Frederick as the latter was setting out on crusade; the pope was forced to release him in 1230, after he had returned from the East with possession of Jerusalem secured by negotiation. Frederick now momentarily favored the restoration of the German princes' privileges, hoping to use the princes against the increasingly powerful Lombard cities. By 1239 Gregory IX had allied with the Lombard League and excommunicated the emperor once again. This time the conflict did not die away; war became general between imperial and papal factions, Ghibelline and Guelf, in Germany and Italy. The imperial position was severely weakened by the emperor's defeat before Parma in 1248, but Frederick had begun to regain the advantage when he died of a sudden fever in 1250.

What immediately strikes anyone attempting to understand Frederick II is his intense curiosity about the particulars of nature, most unusual in an age that was forever seeking universals. His contemporaries were struck by this too, as the famous stories recounted by the monk Salimbene show—the story, for example, that Frederick once disemboweled two men after giving them a hearty meal in order to determine the relative effects of sleep and exercise (he had sent one hunting) upon digestion. True or not—Salimbene was a Guelf partisan—the tale shows how people expected the emperor to behave. Anecdotes like this were of a piece with others about the exotic menagerie (which at one time or another actually included monkeys, camels, a giraffe, and an elephant) that moved with him in Italy and Germany.

That a serious spirit of inquiry was behind all this show is easily seen in the "many-sided patronage of learning" so prominent at Frederick's court. His kingdom of Sicily, heir to both the Greek and the Islamic cultures, had been a center of science and translation in the twelfth century under his grandfather, Roger II. Frederick continued this tradition, drawing scholars of widely different backgrounds and interests to his court. Two seem to have been of particular importance as advisers: the famous Michael Scot (from *ca.* 1228 until his death, *ca.* 1236) and a Master Theodore (*ca.* 1235–1250). The mathematician Leonardo Fibonacci, although not attached to the court, was well known there; the revised version of his *Liber abaci* is dedicated to Michael Scot, and the *Liber quadratorum* to Frederick himself. In addition, Frederick was in communication with other scholars—Christian, Jewish, and Muslim—far from court.

The court philosophers were regularly called upon to satisfy Frederick's curiosity. Michael Scot has left us a questionnaire put to him by the emperor, containing a wide range of problems: Precisely where are heaven, hell, purgatory, and the several abysses in relation to the earth and to each other? Why are there both sweet and salt waters on the earth, and whence do they arise? What gives rise to volcanic fire and smoke? We know of still other questions—metaphysical, mathematical, and optical (why do objects partly immersed in water appear bent?)—sent to Muslim and Jewish philosophers in Spain and Egypt. No program lay behind these questions; it was simply that the accepted commonplaces of experience regularly stirred Frederick to inquiry.

Such questions may show the breadth of Frederick's interests but not the depth of his own knowledge; the latter is fully revealed only in the famous *De arte venandi cum avibus,* a composition developed by Frederick over some thirty years, that we possess in a draft completed *ca.* 1244–1248, in part later emended by his son Manfred. (A finished version has apparently been lost, probably at Parma.) The first of the extant six books, which was conceived by Frederick as a necessary preliminary to the technical substance of falconry, is a remarkable survey of general ornithology: it moves from the classification of birds to their feeding habits, migration, mating, nesting, anatomy and physiology, flight, and molting. As impressive as the collected material is the systematic personal observation on which it is obviously based; Frederick describes his experimental determination that vultures locate their food by sight rather than by smell (ch. 10) and tells of his successful efforts to duplicate in Apulia the artificial incubation of eggs by sunlight that he had observed in Egypt (ch. 23). The later books are more technical and specialized, treating the training and rearing of falcons (book II), the use of the lure (book III), and the techniques of hawking with various birds (books IV–VI). But still they rest upon the emperor's own experience. His passion for the sport is apparent even in what survives of his correspondence, which shows him turning all his administrative resources to the instruction and supervision of his falconers. He was in fact away hawking at the moment when his siege of Parma was so disastrously broken.

Frederick's attitude in *De arte venandi* toward Aristotle as zoologist is of some interest and might be likened to that of a field naturalist toward a research biologist: critical if sometimes grudgingly respectful of the other's specialized knowledge. He points out that experience shows that Aristotle's deductions cannot always be relied upon and notes regretfully that "he was ignorant of the practice of falconry," but he refers his readers for supplementary taxonomic and embryological detail to Aristotle's *Historia animalium* (which had been translated from Arabic by Michael Scot at least a decade before his arrival at Frederick's court, and included the *De animalibus, De partibus animalium,* and *De generatione animalium*). At one point (book I, ch. 27) he even draws upon the (pseudo-) Aristotelian *Mechanica* to argue that the primary wing feathers must have the greatest power to carry a bird forward in flight. It remains characteristic of the emperor that he would disdain no source of knowledge, as long as it could be controlled by his own experience and judgment.

BIBLIOGRAPHY

I. ORIGINAL WORKS. The *De arte venandi cum avibus* exists in MS in two traditions, one including only the first two books, the other including all six. The two earliest MSS of the former tradition (MS Vat. Pal. Lat. 1071, copied perhaps as early as 1260, and MS Paris BN Fr. 12400, probably copied from the Vatican MS *ca.* 1310) are illustrated with a series of remarkable miniatures that presumably reflect Frederick's archetype; Haskins considered that the emperor himself had given the directions for these illustrations, which in the Vatican MS are strikingly faithful to nature. This two-book tradition has been twice edited, by Johann Velser (Augsburg, 1596) and by Johann Gottlieb Schneider (Leipzig, 1788–1789); the six-book version has been published (although without editorial remarks of any sort) by Karl Arnold Willemsen, 2 vols. (Leipzig, 1942). Willemsen has also reproduced many of the illustrations accompanying the *De arte venandi* in the Paris MS under the title *Die Falkenjagd. Bilder aus dem Falkenbuch Kaiser Friedrichs II* (Leipzig, 1943). An English trans. of all six books of Frederick's work has been published by Casey A. Wood and F. Marjorie Fyfe (Stanford, 1943); on pp. lvii–lxxxvii the editors examine the known MSS of the *De arte venandi* and cite two German trans. (of 1756 and 1896) of the two-book tradition besides the Velser and Schneider eds. C. H. Haskins' article "The *De arte* . . .," referred to below, also discusses the MS tradition of the work and forms the basis of the Wood-Fyfe treatment.

II. SECONDARY LITERATURE. A full if somewhat overly romantic study of Frederick's life and thought is Ernst Kantorowicz, *Kaiser Friedrich der Zweite,* 2 vols. (Berlin, 1927; repr. Düsseldorf–Munich, 1963); an English trans. by E. O. Lorimer, *Frederick the Second, 1194–1250* (London, 1931; repr. New York, 1957), omits the original's bibliography and footnotes. Kantorowicz treats Frederick's attitude toward science and the natural world with considerable insight on pp. 308–327 of the German version (pp. 334–365 of the English version). His treatment owes a great debt to the still fundamental articles of Charles Homer Haskins: "Science at the Court of the Emperor Frederick II," "Michael Scot," and "The *De arte venandi cum avibus* of Frederick II," collected in his *Studies in the History of Mediaeval Science* (Cambridge, Mass., 1924; repr. New York, 1960), pp. 242–326. A number of more recent special studies have been brought together in Gunther Wolf, ed., *Stupor mundi. Zur Geschichte Friedrichs II. von Hohenstaufen,* vol. CI of *Wege der Forschung* (Darmstadt, 1966), which includes a considerable extract from Martin Grabmann's *Mittelalterliches Geistesleben,* "Kaiser Friedrich II. und sein Verhältnis zur aristotelischen und arabischen Philosophie" (pp. 134–177 of *Stupor mundi*). The question of Frederick's knowledge and use of contemporary medical and natural-philosophical doctrine has been further studied in two articles by Johannes Zahlten: "Medizinische Vorstellungen im Falkenbuch Kaiser Friedrichs II.," in *Sudhoffs Archiv für Geschichte der Medezin und der Naturwissenschaften,* **54** (1970), 49–103; and "Zur Abhängigkeit der naturwissenschaftlichen Vorstellungen Kaiser Friedrichs II. von der Medizinschule zu Salerno," *ibid.,* 173–210.

MICHAEL MCVAUGH

FREDERICQ, LÉON (*b.* Ghent, Belgium, 24 August 1851; *d.* Liège, Belgium, 2 September 1935), *physiology.*

After his secondary studies in Ghent, Fredericq entered the University of Ghent in October 1868. His vocation was clearly defined: he intended to study natural sciences. After obtaining his doctor's degree in 1871 he became *préparateur* for the physiology course at the Faculty of Medicine and at the same time followed the medical curriculum. After receiving his M.D. in 1875, Fredericq went to Paris, where he attended the lectures of Ranvier and G. Pouchet, and to Strasbourg, where he attended the lectures of Waldeyer, E. Tiegel, A. Kundt, and especially Hoppe-Seyler, professor of biochemistry, who allowed him to spend the afternoons in his laboratory to learn biochemical techniques. In the summer of 1876 he went to the marine biological laboratory at Roscoff, where, under Lacaze-Duthiers, he studied the nervous physiology of sea urchins.

Back in Ghent in October 1876, Fredericq began

his classic work on blood coagulation. In December he moved to the laboratory of Paul Bert in Paris, where he learned the techniques of blood-gas analysis. There he completed his first classic experiments comparing the distribution of carbon dioxide between blood cells and blood plasma. These experiments were continued in Ghent, to which he returned in March 1877. During the summer of the same year he went again to Hoppe-Seyler's laboratory in Strasbourg and began a study of digestion in invertebrates, which he continued in Ghent during that autumn and winter. In April 1878, in order to obtain the degree of *docteur spécial* in physiology, he presented an important paper on his work on blood coagulation and on blood gases. In this paper Fredericq defined the coagulable protein of the plasma, fibrinogen, after its isolation by heat coagulation at 56°C. In horse plasma he distinguished three protein entities: fibrinogen, paralbumin (now called serum globulin), and serum albumin. He showed that in the lungs, the exchanges of oxygen and carbon dioxide are controlled by simple diffusion. Regarding the transport of carbon dioxide from the tissues to the lungs, Fredericq compared the distribution of the gas between plasma and cells at different partial pressures of carbon dioxide, thus beginning the series of investigations leading to our present knowledge of the transport of carbon dioxide.

During the summer of 1878 Fredericq was again in Roscoff and within a short period completed a masterly study of the physiology of the octopus, in which he described and named the copper-containing oxygen carrier hemocyanin. In December 1878 he worked in Marey's laboratory in Paris on respiratory innervation. He subsequently returned to Ghent, where he and G. Vandevelde began a study on the speed of nerve impulse in lobster nerves which was completed at Roscoff during the summer of 1879.

In October 1879 Fredericq was appointed professor of physiology at the University of Liège, succeeding Theodor Schwann, originator of the cell theory. In order to prepare plans for a new physiological institute, Fredericq visited Emil du Bois-Reymond in Berlin, where he came under the lasting influence of the great physiologist. In the first days of 1880 Fredericq settled in Liège; there, in September 1881, he married Bertha Spring, a sister of the chemist Walthère Spring.

In 1882, while at the North Sea, Fredericq tasted the blood of a lobster and of other marine invertebrates and found it as salty as seawater. He then tasted the blood of a number of saltwater fishes but found them not as salty as seawater, or about as salty as the blood of freshwater fishes, which are in turn more salty than fresh water itself. Moreover, while cutting the legs off crabs in order to obtain the blood, Fredericq discovered the phenomenon he called autotomy, the reflex casting off of a part of the body when an animal is attacked, the mechanism of which he explained later. In his blood-tasting experiments, Fredericq discovered the equal salinity of the internal and external media of marine invertebrates, while the blood salinity of bony fishes was found to be independent of their external medium.

During the following years Fredericq continued experiments on osmoregulation and in 1901, at the marine station in Naples, he used cryoscopy to determine the lowering of the freezing point of the bloods and of the juices extracted from the tissues of several animals. He also determined the amount of ash in the two series of samples and accounted for the difference in molecular concentration resulting from the cryoscopy experiments and the weighing of the ash by postulating the existence of important amounts of small organic molecules in the tissues of marine invertebrates and in the blood and tissues of Elasmobranchs. Urea was identified later by E. Rodier (1900) in elasmobranchs, but the intracellular organic components of the marine invertebrates, which compensate for the lack of a high concentration of inorganic constituents in their blood, despite the fact that they must maintain osmotic equilibrium with seawater, were identified only recently as amino acids (M. C. Camien, H. Sarlet, G. Duchâteau, and M. Florkin, 1951).

In March 1882, Fredericq began a series of experiments on the regulation of temperature in mammals. For these studies, he devised a respiratory apparatus which allowed the estimation of the oxygen used by a simple volume determination, without a gas analysis. This apparatus was the ancestor of all devices used for the indirect measurement of metabolism in man. With the help of this apparatus Fredericq showed, among other things, that the curves of heat production and of oxygen consumption both show a minimum, the point of thermic neutrality. He also showed that homoiotherms resist an increase or a decrease in temperature by different mechanisms. The memorable experiments of Legallois, carried out in 1812, had led to the conclusion that the respiratory center must be located in the medulla oblongata. Several physiologists had been reluctant to accept this conclusion. By progressive cooling, Fredericq recorded a number of facts which strengthened the notion that the respiratory center is located in the medulla. This localization was also supported by his cross-circulation experiments, carried out from 1887, in which the blood from the carotid artery of one dog, A, goes to the head of another dog, B, and the head of the latter receives blood only from the first dog. If dog A inspires air poor in oxygen, it is dog B who shows the symptoms of dyspnea. The method of cross circulation has since been used in a great deal of important experimental research.

Research pursued in Pflüger's laboratory had been interpreted as showing that oxygen and carbon dioxide move from a higher-pressure region to a lower-pressure one, in accordance with the laws of diffusion. On the other hand, in 1888 and 1891, Christian Bohr had published a series of results which tended to show that the lung plays a secretory role in the absorption of oxygen and the elimination of carbon dioxide, both moving in a direction contrary to that which would agree with the laws of diffusion. Fredericq built an aerotonometer more exact than those of his predecessors and, in 1895, showed clearly that gas exchanges obey the laws of diffusion in the gills of aquatic animals as well as in the lungs of air-breathing animals.

The first topic studied by Fredericq in the field of circulation physiology concerned the oscillations of blood pressure. He defined three categories of these oscillations: small, numerous ones corresponding to cardiac beats; less frequent oscillations related to the respiratory movement (Traube-Hering curves); and vasomotor oscillations (Sigmund Mayer's curves).

Fredericq is one of the physiologists who has made the greatest contributions to the interpretation of the mechanisms of heart contraction. He recognized that a pulsation starts in the right auricle and spreads rapidly to both auricles, then travels slowly to the bundle of His to radiate through the muscle of both ventricles (1906). Fredericq also studied the phenomenon of fibrillation, described by Ludwig and M. Hoffa in 1850. He demonstrated that ventricular fibrillation has no effect on the auricles and does not cross the bundle of His, while auricular fibrillation, through irregular stimulations through the bundle of His, is the cause of ventricular arrhythmia.

Fredericq's work remains typical of the classical period of physiology. Centered on such topics as heat regulation, respiration, the heart, and circulation, it has played an important role in laying the bases of experimental medicine.

Fredericq was a man of many talents. An excellent draftsman and watercolorist, a great traveler, a botanist, and an entomologist, he devoted a large part of his activities after retirement to an extensive study of the subalpine region of the Hautes Fagnes in the Ardennes. There he established a scientific station, and a museum of the fauna, flora, and geology of the region bears his name.

Albert I, king of the Belgians, recognized Fredericq's outstanding merits by making him a baron in 1931.

BIBLIOGRAPHY

A complete list of Fredericq's publications is in his biography by Marcel Florkin, cited below (1943).

On Fredericq and his work, see M. Florkin, *Léon Fredericq et les débuts de la physiologie en Belgique* (Brussels, 1943); "Emil du Bois-Reymond et Léon Fredericq," in *Chronique de l'Université de Liège* (Liège, 1967), pp. 181-198; and "Léon Fredericq, 1851-1935," in *Florilège des sciences en Belgique* (Brussels, 1967), pp. 1015-1034; M. Florkin and Z. M. Bacq, *Un pionnier de la physiologie. Léon Fredericq* (Liège, 1953), a collection of extracts from Fredericq's works; and P. Nolf, "Léon Fredericq," in *Annuaire de l'Académie royale de Belgique* (1937), pp. 47-100.

MARCEL FLORKIN

FREDHOLM, (ERIK) IVAR (*b.* Stockholm, Sweden, 7 April 1866; *d.* Stockholm, 17 August 1927), *applied mathematics.*

Ivar Fredholm's small but pithy output was concentrated in the area of the equations of mathematical physics. Most significantly, he solved, under quite broad hypotheses, a very general class of integral equations that had been the subject of extensive research for almost a century. His work led indirectly to the development of Hilbert spaces and so to other more general function spaces.

Fredholm was born into an upper-middle-class family; his father was a wealthy merchant and his mother, née Stenberg, was from a cultured family. His early education was the best obtainable, and he soon showed his brilliance. After passing his baccalaureate examination in 1885, he studied for a year at the Polytechnic Institute in Stockholm. During this single year he developed an interest in the technical problems of practical mechanics that was to last all his life and that accounted for his continuing interest in applied mathematics. In 1886 Fredholm enrolled at the University of Uppsala—the only institution in Sweden granting doctorates at that time—from which he received the Bachelor of Science in 1888 and the Doctor of Science in 1898. Because of the superior instruction available at the University of Stockholm, Fredholm also studied there from 1888, becoming a student of the illustrious Mittag-Leffler. He remained at the University of Stockholm the rest of his life, receiving an appointment as lecturer in mathematical physics in 1898 and in 1906 becoming professor of rational mechanics and mathematical physics.

Fredholm's first major work was in partial differential equations. His doctoral thesis, written in

1898 and published in 1900, involved the study of the equation—written in Fredholm's own operator notation—

$$f\left(\frac{\partial}{\partial x_1}, \frac{\partial}{\partial x_2}, \frac{\partial}{\partial x_3}\right) u = 0,$$

where $f(\xi,\eta,\zeta)$ is a definite homogeneous form. This equation is significant because it occurs in the study of deformation of anisotropic media (such as crystals) subjected to interior or exterior forces. Initially, Fredholm solved only the particular equations associated with the physical problem; in 1908 he completed this work by finding the fundamental solution to the general elliptical partial differential equations with constant coefficients.

Fredholm's monument is the general solution to the integral equation that bears his name:

$$(1) \qquad \phi(x) + \int_0^1 f(x,y)\phi(y)\, dy = \psi(x).$$

In this equation the functions f (called the kernel) and ψ are supposed to be known continuous functions, and ϕ is the unknown function to be found. This type of equation has wide application in physics; for example, it can be shown that solving a particular case of (1) is equivalent to solving $\Delta u + \lambda u = 0$ for u, an equation that arises in the study of the vibrating membrane.

Equation (1) had long been under investigation, but only partial results had been obtained. In 1823, Niels Abel had solved a different form of (1) that also had a particular kernel. Carl Neuman had obtained, in 1884, a partial solution for (1) by use of an iteration scheme, but he had to impose certain convexity conditions to ensure convergence of his solution. By 1897 Vito Volterra had found a convergent iteration scheme in the case where f has the property that $f(x,y) = 0$ for $y > x$.

Fredholm began work on equation (1) during a trip to Paris in 1899, published a preliminary report in 1900, and presented the complete solution in 1903. His approach to this equation was ingenious and unique. Fredholm recognized the analogy between equation (1) and the linear matrix-vector equation of the form $(I + F)U = V$. He defined

$$D_f = 1 + \sum_{n=1}^{\infty} \frac{1}{n!} \int_0^1 \int_0^1 \cdots \int_0^1 [f(x_i,x_j)] dx_1\, dx_2 \cdots dx_n,$$

where $[f(x_i,y_j)]$ is the determinant of the $n \times n$ matrix whose ij^{th} component is $f(x_i,x_j)$. The quantity D_f, Fredholm showed, plays the same role in equation (1) that the determinant of $I + F$ plays in the matrix equation; that is, there is a unique solution ϕ of equation (1) for every continuous function ψ whenever D_f is not zero. Furthermore, he proved that the homogeneous equation associated with equation (1),

$$(2) \qquad \phi(x) + \int_0^1 f(x,y)\phi(x)\, dy = 0,$$

has a nontrivial solution (that is, one not identically zero) if and only if $D_f = 0$.

The analogy between the matrix and integral equations was further pointed up by Fredholm when he defined the nth order minor of f—denoted by $D_f\begin{pmatrix}\xi_1, \xi_2, \cdots, \xi_n \\ \eta_1, \eta_2, \cdots, \eta_n\end{pmatrix}$—by an expression similar to that for D_f. Then he showed that if D_f is not zero, an explicit representation for the solution of equation (1) similar to Cramer's rule was given by

$$\phi(x) = \psi(x) - \int_0^1 \frac{D_f\begin{pmatrix}x \\ y\end{pmatrix}}{D_f} \psi(y)\, dy.$$

Fredholm then went on to show that if D_f is equal to zero, the dimension of the null space (the vector space of the set of solutions) of equation (2) is finite dimensional. He did this by setting

$$\Phi_i(x) = \frac{D_f\begin{pmatrix}\xi_1, \xi_2, \cdots, \hat{\xi}_i, \cdots, \xi_n \\ \eta_1, \eta_2, \quad \cdots, \quad \eta_n\end{pmatrix}}{D_f\begin{pmatrix}\xi_1, \xi_2, \cdots, \xi_n \\ \eta_1, \eta_2, \cdots, \eta_n\end{pmatrix}}, \quad i = 1, 2, \cdots n,$$

where the denominator is a nonvanishing minor of least nth (finite) order (which he showed always exists) and where the same minor is denoted in the numerator, but with $\hat{\xi}_i$ replaced by the variable x. Then he proved the set $\{\Phi_i : i = 1,2,\cdots,n\}$ to be a basis for the null space of equation (2). Finally, to solve equation (1) in the case $D_f = 0$, Fredholm first showed that a solution will exist when and only when $\psi(x)$ is orthogonal to the null space of the transposed homogeneous equation—or, equivalently, when

$$\int_0^1 \psi(x)\Psi_i(x)\, dx = 0 \ (i = 1,2, \cdots, n),$$

where $\{\Psi_i : i = 1,2, \cdots, n\}$ is a basis for the null space of the equation

$$\phi(x) + \int_0^1 f(y,x)\phi(y)\, dy = 0.$$

In this case, the solutions are not unique but can be represented by

$$\phi(x) = \psi(x) + \int_0^1 g(x,y)\psi(y)\, dy + \sum_{i=1}^{n} a_i\Phi_i,$$

$$\text{where}\quad g(x,y) = \frac{-D_f\begin{pmatrix} x & \xi_1, & \xi_2, & \cdots, & \xi_n \\ y & \eta_1, & \eta_2, & \cdots, & \eta_n \end{pmatrix}}{D_f\begin{pmatrix} \xi_1, & \xi_2, & \cdots, & \xi_n \\ \eta_1, & \eta_2, & \cdots, & \eta_n \end{pmatrix}}$$

and $\{a_i : i = 1,2, \cdots, n\}$ is a set of arbitrary constants.

Thus, Fredholm proved that the analogy between the matrix equation $(I + F)U = V$ and equation (1) was complete and even included an alternative theorem for the integral equation. Yet he showed more. His result meant that the solution $\phi(x)$ for equation (1) could be developed in a power series in the complex variable λ

$$\phi(x) = \psi(x) + \sum_{p=1}^{\infty} \psi_p(x)\lambda^p$$

which is a meromorphic function of λ for every λ satisfying $D_{\lambda f} \neq 0$. (To see this, replace $f(x,y)$ with $\lambda f(x,y)$ in equation [1].) This result was so important that, unable to prove it, Henri Poincaré was forced to assume it in 1895–1896 in connection with his studies of the partial differential equation $\Delta u + \lambda u = h(x,y)$.

Fredholm's work did not represent a dead end. His colleague Erik Holmgren carried Fredholm's discovery to Göttingen in 1901. There David Hilbert was inspired to take up the study; he extended Fredholm's results to include a complete eigenvalue theory for equation (1). In the process he used techniques that led to the discovery of Hilbert spaces.

BIBLIOGRAPHY

The *Oeuvres complètes de Ivar Fredholm* (Malmö, 1955) includes an excellent obituary by Nils Zeilon.

Ernst Hellinger and Otto Toeplitz, "Integralgleichungen und Gleichungen mit unendlichvielen Unbekannten," in *Encyklopädie der mathematische Wissenschaften,* (Leipzig, 1923–1927), pt. 2, vol. III, art. 13, 1335–1602, was also published separately (Leipzig–Berlin, 1928). It presents an excellent historical perspective of Fredholm's work and the details of his technique; it also contains an excellent bibliography.

M. BERNKOPF

FREGE, FRIEDRICH LUDWIG GOTTLOB (*b.* Wismar, Germany, 8 November 1848; *d.* Bad Kleinen, Germany, 26 July 1925), *logic, foundations of mathematics.*

Gottlob Frege was a son of Alexander Frege, principal of a girl's high school, and of Auguste Bialloblotzky. He attended the Gymnasium in Wismar, and from 1869 to 1871 he was a student at Jena. He then went to Göttingen and took courses in mathematics, physics, chemistry, and philosophy for five semesters. In 1873 Frege received his doctorate in philosophy at Göttingen with the thesis, *Ueber eine geometrische Darstellung der imäginaren Gebilde in der Ebene.* The following year at Jena he obtained the *venia docendi* in the Faculty of Philosophy with a dissertation entitled "Rechungsmethoden, die sich auf eine Erweitung des Grössenbegriffes gründen," which concerns one-parameter groups of functions and was motivated by his intention to give such a definition of quantity as gives maximal extension to the applicability of the arithmetic based upon it. The idea presented in the dissertation of viewing the system of an operation f and its iterates as a system of quantities, which in the introduction to his *Grundlagen der Arithmetik* (1884) Frege essentially ascribes to Herbart, hints at the notion of f-sequence expounded in his *Begriffschrift* (1879).

After the publication of the *Begriffschrift,* Frege was appointed extraordinary professor at Jena in 1879 and honorary professor in 1896. His stubborn work toward his goal—the logical foundation of arithmetic—resulted in his two-volume *Grundgesetze der Arithmetik* (1893–1903). Shortly before publication of the second volume Bertrand Russell pointed out in 1902, in a letter to Frege, that his system involved a contradiction. This observation by Russell destroyed Frege's theory of arithmetic, and he saw no way out. Frege's scientific activity in the period after 1903 cannot be compared with that before 1903 and was mainly in reaction to the new developments in mathematics and its foundations, especially to Hilbert's axiomatics. In 1917 he retired. His *Logische Untersuchungen,* written in the period 1918–1923, is an extension of his earlier work.

In his attempt to give a satisfactory definition of number and a rigorous foundation to arithmetic, Frege found ordinary language insufficient. To overcome the difficulties involved, he devised his *Begriffschrift* as a tool for analyzing and representing mathematical proofs completely and adequately. This tool has gradually developed into modern mathematical logic, of which Frege may justly be considered the creator.

The *Begriffschrift* was intended to be a formula language for pure thought, written with specific symbols and modeled upon that of arithmetic (i.e., it develops according to definite rules). This is an essential difference between Frege's calculus and, for example, Boole's or Peano's, which do not formalize mathematical proofs but are more flexible in expressing the logical structure of concepts.

One of Frege's special symbols is the assertion sign $\vdash$— (properly only the vertical stroke), which is interpreted if followed by a symbol with judgeable content. The interpretation of $\vdash\!\!\!-\!\!\!-\; A$ is "*A* is a fact." Another symbol is the conditional $\begin{array}{l}\top\\ \llcorner\end{array}$, and $\begin{array}{l}\top\!\!-\; A\\ \llcorner\!\!-\; B\end{array}$ is to be read as "*B* implies *A*." The assertion $\begin{array}{l}\vdash\!\!\top\!\!-\; A\\ \;\;\llcorner\!\!-\; B\end{array}$ is justified in the following cases: (1) *A* and *B* are true; (2) *A* is true and *B* is false; (3) *A* and *B* are false.

Frege uses only one deduction rule, which consists in passing from $\vdash\!\!\!-\!\!\!-\; B$ and $\begin{array}{l}\vdash\!\!\top\!\!-\; A\\ \;\;\llcorner\!\!-\; B\end{array}$ to $\vdash\!\!\!-\!\!\!-\; A$. The assertion that *A* is not a fact is expressed by $\vdash\!\!\!\top\!\!\!-\; A$, i.e., the small vertical stroke is used for negation. Frege showed that the other propositional connectives, "and" and "or," are expressible by means of negation and implication, and in fact developed propositional logic on the basis of a few axioms, some of which have been preserved in modern presentations of logic. Yet he did not stop at propositional logic but also developed quantification theory, which was possible because of his general notion of function. If in an expression a symbol was considered to be replaceable, in all or in some of its occurrences, then Frege calls the invariant part of the expression a function and the replaceable part its argument. He chose the expression Φ(*A*) for a function and, for functions of more than one argument, Ψ(*A,B*). Since the Φ in Φ(*A*) also may be considered to be the replaceable part, Φ(*A*) may be viewed as a function of the argument Φ. This stipulation proved to be the weak point in Frege's system, as Russell showed in 1902.

Generality was expressed by

$$\vdash\!\smile^{\!\!\!\!\mathfrak{a}}\!\!-\; \Phi(\mathfrak{a})$$

which means that Φ(*a*) is a fact, whatever may be chosen for the argument. Frege explains the notion of the scope of a quantifier and notes the allowable transition from $\vdash\!\!\!-\!\!\!-\; X(a)$ to $\vdash\!\smile^{\!\!\!\!\mathfrak{a}}\!\!-\; X(\mathfrak{a})$, where *a* occurs only as argument of *X*(*a*), and from $\begin{array}{l}\vdash\!\!\top\!\!-\; \Phi(a)\\ \;\;\llcorner\!\!-\; A\end{array}$ to $\begin{array}{l}\vdash\!\!\top\!\smile^{\!\!\!\!\mathfrak{a}}\!\!-\; \Phi(\mathfrak{a})\\ \;\;\llcorner\!\!-\!\!-\!\!-\; A\end{array}$, where *a* does not occur in *A* and in Φ(*a*) occurs only in the argument places.

Existence was expressed by $\vdash\!\!\top\!\smile^{\!\!\!\!\mathfrak{a}}\!\!\top\!\!-\Lambda(\mathfrak{a})$. There was no explicitly stated rule of substitution.

It should be observed that Frege did not construct his system for expressing pure thought as a formal system and therefore did not raise questions of completeness or consistency. Frege applied his *Begriffschrift* to a general theory of sequences, and in part III he defines the ancestral relation on which he founded mathematical induction. This relation was afterward introduced informally by Dedekind and formally by Whitehead and Russell in *Principia mathematica.*

The *Begriffschrift* essentially underlies Frege's definition of number in *Grundlagen der Arithmetik* (1884), although it was not used explicitly. The greater part of this work is devoted to a severe and effective criticism of existing theories of number. Frege argues that number is something connected with an assertion concerning a concept; and essential for the notion of number is that of equality of number (i.e., he has to explain the sentence "The number which belongs to the concept *F* is the same as that which belongs to *G.*"). He settled on the definition "The number which belongs to the concept *F* is the extension of the concept of being equal to the concept *F,*" where equality of concepts is understood as the existence of a one-to-one correspondence between their extensions. The number zero is that belonging to a concept with void extension, and the number one is that which belongs to the concept equal to zero. Using the notion of *f*-sequence, natural numbers are defined, with ∞ the number belonging to the notion of being a natural number.[1]

Frege's theories, as well as his criticisms in the *Begriffschrift* and the *Grundlagen,* were extended and refined in his *Grundgesetze,* in which he incorporated the essential improvements on his *Begriffschrift* that had been expounded in the three important papers "Funktion und Begriff" (1891), "Über Sinn und Bedeutung" (1892), and "Über Begriff und Gegenstand" (1892). In particular, "Über Sinn und Bedeutung" is an essential complement to his *Begriffschrift.* In addition, it has had a great influence on philosophical discussion, specifically on the development of Wittgenstein's philosophy. Nevertheless, the philosophical implications of the acceptance of Frege's doctrine have proved troublesome.

An analysis of the identity relation led Frege to the distinction between the sense of an expression and its denotation. If *a* and *b* are different names of the same object (refer to or denote the same object), we can legitimately express this by *a* = *b,* but = cannot be considered to be a relation between the objects themselves.

Frege therefore distinguishes two aspects of an expression: its denotation, which is the object to which it refers, and its sense, which is roughly the thought expressed by it. Every expression expresses its sense. An unsaturated expression (a function) has no denotation.

These considerations led Frege to the conviction that a sentence denotes its truth-value; all true sentences denote the True and all false sentences denote the False—in other words, are names of the True and the False, respectively. The True and the False are to be treated as objects. The consequences of this distinction are further investigated in "Über Begriff und Gegenstand." There Frege admits that he has not given a definition of concept and doubts whether this can be done, but he emphasizes that concept has to be kept carefully apart from object. More interesting developments are contained in his "Funktion und Begriff." First, there is the general notion of function already briefly mentioned in the *Grundlagen,* and second, with every function there is associated an object, the so-called *Wertverlauf,* which he used essentially in his *Grundgesetze der Arithmetik.*

Since a function is expressed by an unsaturated expression $f(x)$, which denotes an object if x in it is replaced by an object, there arises the possibility of extending the notion of function because sentences denote objects (the True [T] and the False [F]), and one arrives at the conclusion that, e.g., $(x^2 = 4) = (x > 1)$ is a function. If one replaces x by 1, then, because $1^2 = 4$ denotes F, as does $1 > 1$, it follows that $(1^2 = 4) = (1 > 1)$ denotes T.

Frege distinguishes between first-level functions, with objects as argument, and second-level functions, with first-level functions as arguments, and notes that there are more possibilities. For Frege an object is anything which is not a function, but he admits that the notion of object cannot be logically defined. It is characteristic of Frege that he could not take the step of simply postulating a class of objects without entering into the question of their nature. This would have taken him in the direction of a formalistic attitude, to which he was fiercely opposed. In fact, at that time formalism was in a bad state and rather incoherently maintained. Besides, Frege was not creating objects but was concerned mainly with logical characterizations. This in a certain sense also holds true for Frege's introduction of the *Wertverlauf,* which he believed to be something already there and which had to be characterized logically.

In considering two functions, e.g., $x^2 - 4x$ and $x(x - 4)$, one may observe that they have the same value for the same argument. Therefore their graphs are the same. This situation is expressed by Frege true for Frege's introduction of the *Wertverlauf,* as $x^2 - 4x$." Without any further ado he goes on to speak of the *Wertverlauf* of a function as being something already there, and introduced a name for it. The *Wertverläufe* of the above mentioned functions $x(x - 4)$ and $x^2 - 4x$ are denoted by $\grave{\alpha}(\alpha - 4)$ and $\grave{\epsilon}(\epsilon^2 - 4\epsilon)$ respectively, and in general $\grave{\epsilon}f(\epsilon)$ is used to denote the *Wertverlauf* of function $f(\xi)$. This *Wertverlauf* is taken to be an object, and Frege assumes the basic logical law characterizing equality of *Wertverläufe:*

$$(\grave{\epsilon}f(\epsilon) = \grave{\alpha}\, g(\alpha)) = (-\!\!\smile^{\mathfrak{a}}\!\!-\, f(\mathfrak{a}) = g(\mathfrak{a})).$$

Frege extends this to logical functions (i.e., concepts), which are conceived of as functions whose values are truth-values, and thus extension of a concept may be identified with the *Wertverlauf* of a function assuming only truth-values. Therefore, e.g., $\grave{\epsilon}(\epsilon^2 = 1) = \grave{\alpha}(\alpha + 1)^2 = 2(\alpha + 1)$.

In the appendix to volume II of his *Grundgesetze,* Frege derives Russell's paradox in his system with the help of the above basic logical law. Russell later succeeded in eliminating his paradox by assuming the theory of types.

It is curious that the man who laid the most suitable foundation for formal logic was so strongly opposed to formalism. In volume II of the *Grundgesetze,* where he discusses formal arithmetic at length, Frege proves to have a far better insight than its exponents and justly emphasizes the necessity of a consistency proof to justify creative definitions. He is aware that because of the introduction of the *Wertverläufe* he may be accused of doing what he is criticizing. Nevertheless, he argues that he is not, because of his logical law concerning *Wertverläufe* (which proved untenable).

When Hilbert took the axiomatic method a decisive step further, Frege failed to grasp his point and attacked him for his imprecise terminology. Frege insisted on definitions in the classic sense and rejected Hilbert's "definition" of a betweenness relation and his use of the term "point." For Frege geometry was still the theory of space. But even before 1814 Bolzano had already reached the conclusion that for an abstract theory of space, one may be obliged to assume the term point as a primitive notion capable of various interpretations. Hilbert's answer to Frege's objections was quite satisfactory, although it did not convince Frege.

BIBLIOGRAPHY

I. Original Works. Frege's writing includes *Ueber eine geometrische Darstellung der imaginären Gebilde in der Ebene,* his inaugural diss. to the Faculty of Philosophy at Göttingen (Jena, 1873); *Begriffschrift, eine der arithmetischen nachgebildete Formelsprache des reinen Denkens* (Halle, 1879), 2nd ed., I. Angelelli, ed. (Hildesheim, 1964), English trans. in J. van Heijenoort, *From Frege to Godel* (Cambridge, 1967), pp. 1–82; *Die Grundlagen der Arithmetik* (Breslau, 1884), trans. with German text by J. L. Austin (Oxford, 1950; 2nd rev. ed. 1953), repr. as *The Foundations of Arithmetic* (Oxford, 1959); *Function und Begriff* (Jena, 1891), English trans. in P. Geach and M. Black, pp. 21–41 (see below); "Über Sinn und Bedeutung," in *Zeitschrift für Philosophie und philosophische Kritik,* n.s. **100** (1892), 25–50, English trans. in P. Geach and M. Black, pp. 56–78 (see below); "Über Begriff und Gegenstand," in *Vierteljahrschrift für wissenschaftliche Philosophie,* **16** (1892), 192–205, English trans. in P. Geach and M. Black, pp. 42–55 (see below); *Grundgesetze der Arithmetik,* 2 vols. (Jena, 1893–1903), repr. in 1 vol. (Hildesheim, 1962); and "Über die Grundlagen der Geometrie," in *Jahresbericht der Deutschen Mathematikervereinigung,* **12** (1903), 319–324, 368–375; **15** (1906), 293–309, 377–403, 423–430.

II. SECONDARY LITERATURE. On Frege and his work, see I. Angelelli, *Studies on Gottlob Frege and Traditional Philosophy* (Dordrecht, 1967); P. Geach and M. Black, *Translation of the Philosophical Writings of Gottlob Frege,* 2nd ed. (Oxford, 1960); H. Hermes, *et al., Gottlob Frege, Nachgelassene Schriften* (Hamburg, 1969); J. van Heijenoort, *From Frege to Godel* (Cambridge, 1967); P. E. B. Jourdain, "The Development of the Theories of Mathematical Logic and the Principles of Mathematics. Gottlob Frege," in *Quarterly Journal of Pure and Applied Mathematics,* **43** (1912), 237–269; W. Kneale and Martha Kneale, *The Development of Logic* (Oxford, 1962) pp. 435–512; J. Largeault, *Logique et philosophie chez Frege* (Paris–Louvain, 1970); C. Parsons, "Frege's Theory of Number," in M. Black, ed., *Philosophy in America* (London, 1965), pp. 180–203; G. Patzig, *Gottlob Frege, Funktion, Begriff, Bedeutung* (Göttingen, 1966); and *Gottlob Frege, Logische Untersuchungen* (Göttingen, 1966); B. Russell, *The Principles of Mathematics* (Cambridge, 1903), Appendix A, "The Logical and Arithmetical Doctrines of Frege"; M. Steck, "Ein unbekannter Brief von Gottlob Frege über Hilberts erste Vorlesung über die Grundlagen der Geometrie," in *Sitzungsberichte der Heidelberger Akademie der Wissenschaften,* Abhandlung 6 (1940); and "Unbekannte Briefe Frege's über die Grundlagen der Geometrie und Antwortbrief Hilbert's an Frege," *ibid.,* Abhandlung 2 (1941); H. G. Steiner, "Frege und die Grundlagen der Geometrie I, II," in *Mathematische-physikalische Semesterberichte,* n.s. **10** (1963), 175–186, and **11** (1964), 35–47; and J. D. B. Walker, *A Study of Frege* (Oxford, 1965).

B. VAN ROOTSELAAR

FREIESLEBEN, JOHANN KARL (*b.* Freiberg, Saxony, Germany, 14 June 1774; *d.* Nieder-Auerbach, Saxony, Germany, 20 March 1846), *geology, mineralogy, mining.*

Freiesleben came from an old Freiberg mining family. This circumstance, coupled with the active, centuries-old mining industry in the vicinity of Freiberg, determined his choice of mining science as his profession. While still a secondary school student he worked as a miner in pits and galleries. Freiesleben attended the Mining Academy in Freiberg from 1790 to 1792, and there he found a patron in Abraham Gottlob Werner, professor of geology and mineralogy. When Leopold von Buch and Alexander von Humboldt came to Freiberg in order to study under Werner, Freiesleben became friendly with both of them. He made his first scientific journey through Saxony and Thuringia with Buch, and with his friend E. F. von Schlotheim he explored the Thuringian Forest. With Humboldt he journeyed to Bohemia, and in 1795 they traveled in the Swiss Jura, the Alps, and Savoy. A lasting friendship developed between the two men. From 1792 to 1795 Freiesleben studied jurisprudence in Leipzig and often visited the Harz Mountains.

Upon returning from the journey to Switzerland, Freiesleben obtained a position as a mining official in Marienberg and Johanngeorgenstadt. In the latter city he married Marianne Caroline Beyer, the daughter of a clergyman, in 1800. In the same year he became director of the copper and silver mines in Eisleben. In this capacity he did much work in the technical aspects of mining and in science. He returned to Freiberg in 1808. There he joined the Bureau of Mines and was entrusted with the management of various governmental and corporate mines and metallurgical works. In 1838 he was placed in charge of all Saxon mining operations. He was pensioned in 1842. He died in 1846 after a short illness, while on an official tour.

Freiesleben was awarded a doctorate by the University of Marburg in 1817, and in 1828 he became a member of the Prussian Academy of Sciences in Berlin. He was a loyal friend and an adviser and benefactor to the lonely and needy; he was, moreover, closely bound to his family.

A product of Freiesleben's trips to the Harz Mountains was one of his first major works: *Bemerkungen über den Harz* (1795), in which mineralogical and technical mining observations and descriptions stand out. Freiesleben completed his most important work, *Beitrag zur Kenntniss des Kupferschiefergebirges* (1807–1815), during his stay in Eisleben. In this he presents a painstaking and detailed description of the Permian Kupferschiefer and of the accompanying formations of the Zechstein and the Lower Permian Rotliegend, as well as of the Triassic. For decades this work remained indispensable to science and technology. Only when he attempted to trace individual formations into neighboring regions did he make errors. Thus he equated the limestone in the Swiss Jura and the Swabian Alb (now known as Malm) with the similar-appearing dolomite of the Zechstein (Upper Permian) in Thuringia and Saxony because of its many caverns. He also compared the Cretaceous Alpine limestone with the Upper Permian limestone, and the Cretaceous Quadersandstein of the northern edge of the Harz with the Triassic Bunter sandstone of Saxony.

Beginning in 1820 Freiesleben published the *Magazin für die Oryktographie von Sachsen.* It consisted of individual volumes written by him and formed one of the most important sources of information about mineral occurrence in Saxony. Freiesleben himself composed twelve consecutive volumes and three special volumes; the remaining four volumes were published after his death. Of particular importance in this series is his work on the ore veins in Saxony (1843–1845). In this journal there are also descriptions of sediments and proof of the occurrence of fossil mammalian bones and teeth in Saxony (**7**, 1836).

Along with his scientific publications, Freiesleben was occupied with the administrative, technical, and mining matters connected with his official duties. He devised a series of technical improvements in mining and metallurgy, primarily in the mining of the Kupferschiefer in Eisleben and Mansfeld. He also found time to prepare for publication the extensive group of works on mineralogy, geology, and mining that he wrote while in office. Furthermore, during his years in Freiberg he maintained a constant interest in the administration and the social problems of his native city and was actively involved in them.

Freiesleben was one of the most gifted and most learned students of Werner, the leading geologist of the time in Europe. In his writings he helped to apply the theories of his teacher and to make them more widely known. Through his exact and reliable descriptions of the Permian and Triassic sedimentary formations in Saxony and Thuringia he pushed beyond Werner to a greater knowledge of the stratigraphic relationships of these periods in central Germany and helped to create the basis for stratigraphic comparisons with neighboring regions. His painstaking and accurate data on mining in Saxony and on the occurrence of minerals there are still valuable for historical purposes.

BIBLIOGRAPHY

I. Original Works. Freiesleben's writings include "Geognostisch-bergmännische Beobachtungen auf einer Reise durch Saalfeld, Camsdorf und einen Theil Thüringens," in *Lempe's Magazin für Bergbaukunde,* **10** (1793), 3–114; *Bemerkungen über den Harz,* 2 vols. (Leipzig, 1795); *Geognostischer Beitrag zur Kenntniss des Kupferschiefergebirges mit besonderer Hinsicht auf einen Theil der Grafschaft Mansfeld und Thüringens,* 4 vols. (Freiberg, 1807–1815); *Beyträge zur mineralogischen Kenntniss von Sachsen,* 2 vols. (Freiberg, 1817); and *Magazin für die Oryktographie von Sachsen,* **1–12** and 3 spec. vols. published by Freiesleben; **13–15** and spec. vol. 4 published after his death by C. H. Müller (Freiberg, 1820–1848).

II. Secondary Literature. On Freiesleben or his work, see H. Claus, "Beiträge zur Geschichte der geologischen Forschung in Thüringen," in *Beiträge zur Geologie von Thüringen,* I (Jena, 1927), 9–10; B. von Freyberg, *Die geologische Erforschung Thüringens in älterer Zeit* (Berlin, 1932), pp. 25, 29, 32, 36, 41, 51, 59, 71, 82, 83, 88, 89, 90, 94, 101, 102, 106, 109; C. W. von Gümbel, "Freiesleben, Johann Karl," in *Allgemeine deutsche Biographie,* VII (Leipzig, 1878), 339–340, with bibliography; B. F. Voigt, "Johann Karl Freiesleben," no. 52 in *Neuer Nekrolog der Deutschen,* XXIV, pt. 1 (Weimar, 1848), 191–196, with bibliography; and K. A. von Zittel, *Geschichte der Geologie und Paläontologie bis Ende des 19. Jahrhunderts* (Munich–Leipzig, 1899), pp. 120–121, also pp. 93, 268, 494, 500, 608, 609.

Heinz Tobien

FREIND, JOHN (*b.* Croughton, Northamptonshire, England, 1675; *d.* London, England, 26 July 1728), *chemistry, medicine.*

Freind's father, William, rector of Croughton, sent his three sons to Westminster School and Christ Church, Oxford, to follow in his footsteps. Freind's latinity attracted the favorable notice of Dean Henry Aldrich and led to his first publication of Latin translations. At Oxford he met Francis Atterbury, then a tutor and later bishop of Rochester, with whom he was to be associated politically. Freind was B.A. (1698), M.A. (1701), M.B. (1703), and, by diploma, M.D. (1707). In 1704 he gave, by invitation, nine lectures on chemistry at the Ashmolean Museum, later published as *Praelectiones chymicae.* These are notable for Freind's adoption of the principles of Newtonian attraction (which he derived from the lectures given by John Keill), in an attempt to make chemistry truly mechanical. He tried to estimate quantitatively the relative forces operating between particles in order to explain association, dissociation, calcination, distillation, fermentation, and all other chemical processes. The publication of a second edition at Amsterdam in 1710 provoked an unfavorable review in the *Acta eruditorum,* to which Freind replied in the *Philosophical Transactions of the Royal Society* for 1712. The Leipzig attack was part of the Leibniz–Newton polemic, and the criticism was based not upon Freind's chemistry but upon his Newtonianism, and was so regarded by Newton's friends (Arnold Thackray, "Matter in a Nutshell," in *Ambix,* **15** [1968], 35–36). Ironically, this may have assisted Freind's election as a fellow of the Royal Society in March 1712.

Freind had already left Oxford and begun his medical career, first as physician to the English forces in the 1705 campaign under the earl of Peterborough, whose defense he was soon to write, then in Italy and later in Flanders as physician to the duke of Ormonde. He married Anne Morice in 1709 and soon returned to London, where he practiced very successfully. In 1716 Freind became a fellow of the Royal College of Physicians, in whose affairs he was subsequently active, and he began to write on medical topics. *Emmenologia* (1717) displays a leaning toward mechanistic physiology, but most of his other medical works are concerned with therapeutics.

In 1722, having weathered the storm of controversy arising from his association with Peterborough, Freind became M.P. for Launceston and, having strong Jacobite leanings, became involved in Atterbury's plot and was for some months confined to the Tower on a charge of high treason. From the Tower he wrote to his friend Richard Mead—who was subsequently to secure his release—a letter on smallpox and also sent him his *History of Physick.* (Mead had sent him a copy of Daniel Leclerc's *Histoire de la médecine.*) This was long regarded as an authoritative work, especially on English medieval and Renaissance medicine, although the first volume is concerned entirely with post-Galenic Greek writers, and much of the second with Islamic physicians; it is especially strong on medical treatment. Soon after his release Freind was appointed physician to the royal children and in 1727 to Queen Caroline.

BIBLIOGRAPHY

I. Original Works. *Opera omnia medica,* John Wigan, ed. (London, 1733; Venice, 1733; Paris, 1735), contains all Freind's major scientific and medical writings: *Praelectiones chymicae* (London, 1709; Amsterdam, 1710), English trans. by "J. M." as *Chymical Lectures,* with app. (London, 1712); *Emmenologia, in qua fluxus mulieribus menstrui phaenomena . . . ad rationes mechanicas exiguntur* (Oxford, 1703; 2nd ed., London, 1717; Paris, 1727), English trans. by T. Dale (London, 1729), also a French trans. (Paris, 1730); Freind's revised version, with extensive commentary, of *Hippocratis de morbis popularibus liber primus et tertius* (London, 1717); *J. F. de purgantibus, in secunda variolarum confluentium febre adhibendis, epistola* (London, 1719), English trans. by T. Dale, with the commentaries on Hippocrates (London, 1730); *J. F. ad R. Mead de quibusdam variolarum generibus epistola* (London, 1723), English trans. by T. Dale (London, 1730); "Oratio anniversaria ex Harvaio instituto," delivered to the College of Physicians in 1720; and *Historia medicinae,* a Latin trans. by John Wigan of *The History of Physick; From the Time of Galen to the Beginning of the Sixteenth Century* (London, 1725, 1726; 2nd ed., London, 1727; 5th ed., 1758), French trans. by Stephen Coulot (Leiden, 1727). He also published three papers in the *Philosophical Transactions of the Royal Society:* "Concerning a Hydrocephalus," no. 256 (1699), 318–322; "A Case of an Extraordinary Cramp," no. 270 (1701), 799–804; and "A Vindication of His Chymical Lectures" [against the attack in *Acta eruditorum,* Leipzig, 1710], no. 331 (1712), 330–342, which is printed in English in the 1712 ed. of *Chymical Lectures.*

Freind's undergraduate eds. of Aeschines the Orator and of Ovid's *Metamorphoses* were published at Oxford in 1696. *An Account of the Earl of Peterborow's Conduct in Spain* (London, 1706, 1707, 1708) provoked considerable controversy and a number of replies.

There is a portrait of Freind in the Royal College of Physicians, an engraved portrait frontispiece to the *Opera omnia,* and a medal with his portrait executed by Saint Urbain. There is a contemporary monument in Westminster Abbey.

II. Secondary Literature. There is a short biography in the preface to the *Opera omnia* by John Wigan (in Latin). A much better account is in the abridgment of the *Philosophical Transactions* by Charles Hutton, George Shaw, and Richard Pearson (London, 1809), IV, 423. There is a fair account in William Munk, *Roll of the Royal College of Physicians* (London, 1851), II, 441–450. The *Dictionary of National Biography* has a very full account of his political activities and a fair summary of his medical interests.

Marie Boas Hall

FRÉMY, EDMOND (*b.* Versailles, France, 28 February 1814; *d.* Paris, France, 2 February 1894), *chemistry.*

Frémy began his career at the École Polytechnique as assistant to Pelouze and succeeded him as professor in 1846. He also became professor at the Muséum d'Histoire Naturelle when Gay-Lussac died in 1850 and was elected its director after Chevreul retired in 1879.

Frémy's first project was to continue Pelouze's studies of iron oxides, and he expanded them to include oxides of chromium, tin, and antimony that form salts with alkalies in the same way as manganese. In 1835 he published a memoir in the *Annales de chimie* on the splitting of fats by sulfuric acid, a process that was adopted by French industry. From then on, Frémy pursued scientific investigations as professor and industrial work as consultant (later as administrator of the Compagnie de Saint-Gobin). He proposed improvements in the chamber process for making sulfuric acid (low temperature and ample air and water), and he introduced the residue from burning pyrites as the raw material for iron production. From research on the setting of hydraulic cement, Frémy proceeded to the synthesis of rubies by heating alumina with potassium chromate and barium fluoride.

At the museum, from 1850 until 1879, he sought to prove the transformation of plant materials, especially "vasculose" (cellulose), into coal by way of lignite and ulmic acid.

Together with Pelouze, Frémy published a textbook that saw several editions until 1865; then he organized the collaboration of professors and industrialists on a chemical encyclopedia, which appeared in ninety-one parts between 1882 and 1901.

Paul Dehérain, his biographer and former student, said of Frémy: "He disliked theories, did not know them well, and thought them dangerous."

BIBLIOGRAPHY

Frémy's main work was *Encyclopédie chimique, publiée sous la direction de M. Frémy . . . par une réunion d'anciens élèves de l'École Polytechnique, de professeurs et d'industriels,* 10 vols. (Paris, 1882–1901). He wrote the "Discours préliminaire" (1882) and chs. in several vols., especially vol. V, *Applications de chimie inorganique;* see "Généralités sur quelques industries chimiques" (1883), in vol. V, sec. 1, pt. 2, in which he summarizes much of his own work and emphasizes its originality. He was coauthor, with T. J. Pelouze, of *Traité de chimie générale,* 6 vols. (Paris, 1854–1857).

A biography is P.-P. Dehérain, "Edmond Frémy," in *Revue générale des sciences* (18 Feb. 1894), 20–31.

EDUARD FARBER

FRENET, JEAN-FRÉDÉRIC (*b.* Périgueux, France, 7 February 1816; *d.* Périgueux, 12 June 1900), *mathematics.*

Frenet was the son of Pierre Frenet, a *perruquier.* In 1840 he entered the École Normale Supérieure and later studied at the University of Toulouse, where he received the doctorate for the thesis *Sur les fonctions qui servent à déterminer l'attraction des sphéroïdes quelconques. Programme d'une thèse sur quelques propriétés des courbes à double courbure* (1847). The latter part of the thesis was subsequently published in the *Journal de mathématiques pures et appliquées* (1852) and contains what are known in the theory of space curves as the Frenet-Serret formulas. Frenet, however, presents only six formulas explicitly, whereas Serret presents all nine. Frenet subsequently explained the use of his formulas in "Théorèmes sur les courbes gauches" (1853).

After a period as a professor in Toulouse, Frenet went to Lyons, where in 1848 he became professor of mathematics at the university. He was also director of the astronomical observatory, where he conducted meteorological observations. He retired in 1868 with the title of honorary professor and settled at Bayot, a family estate in his native Périgueux. Unmarried, he lived quietly with a sister until his death.

Frenet's constantly revised and augmented *Recueil d'exercises sur le calcul infinitésimal* (1856) was popular for more than half a century. It contains problems with full solutions and often with historical remarks.

Frenet was a man of wide erudition and a classical scholar who was respected in this community, but his mathematical production was limited.

BIBLIOGRAPHY

Frenet's best-known works are *Sur les fonctions qui servent à déterminer l'attraction des sphéroïdes quelconques. Programme d'une thèse sur quelques propriétés des courbes à double courbure* (Toulouse, 1847); "Sur quelques propriétés des courbes à double courbure," in *Journal de mathématiques pures et appliquées,* **17** (1852), 437–447; "Théorèmes sur les courbes gauches," in *Nouvelles annales de mathématiques,* **12** (1853), 365–372; and *Recueil d'exercises sur le calcul infinitésimal* (Paris, 1856; 7th ed., 1917).

Minor mathematical papers are "Note sur un théorème de Descartes," in *Nouvelles annales de mathématiques,* **13** (1854), 299–301; "Sur une formule de Gauss," in *Mémoires de la Société des sciences physiques et naturelles de Bordeaux,* **6** (1868), 385–392. Meteorological observations are in *Mémoires de l'Académie impériale de Lyon, Classe des sciences,* **3** (1853), 177–225; **6** (1856), 263–326; and **8** (1858), 73–121, continued afterward by A. Drian.

An obituary of Frenet is in *L'avenir de Dordogne* (17 June 1900).

D. J. STRUIK

FRENICLE DE BESSY, BERNARD (*b.* Paris, France, *ca.* 1605; *d.* Paris, 17 January 1675), *mathematics, physics, astronomy.*

Frenicle was an accomplished amateur mathematician and held an official position as counselor at the Cour des Monnaies in Paris. In 1666 he was appointed member of the Academy of Sciences by Louis XIV. He maintained correspondence with the most important mathematicians of his time—we find his letters in the correspondence of Descartes, Fermat, Huygens, and Mersenne. In these letters he dealt mainly with questions concerning the theory of numbers, but he was also interested in other topics. In a letter to Mersenne, written at Dover on 7 June 1634, Frenicle described an experiment determining the trajectory of bodies falling from the mast of a moving ship. By calculating the value of g from Frenicle's data we obtain a value of 22.5 ft./sec.^{2}, which is not far from Mersenne's 25.6 ft./sec.^{2}. In addition, Frenicle seems to have been the author, or one of the authors, of a series of remarks on Galileo's *Dialogue.*

On 3 January 1657 Fermat proposed to mathematicians of Europe and England two problems:

FRENICLE DE BESSY

(1) Find a cube which, when increased by the sum of its aliquot parts, becomes a square; for example, $7^3 + (1 + 7 + 7^2) = 20^2$.

(2) Find a square which, when increased by the sum of its aliquot parts, becomes a cube.

In his letter of 1 August 1657 to Wallis, Digby says that Frenicle had immediately given to the conveyer of Fermat's problems four different solutions of the first problem and, the next day, six more. Frenicle gave solutions of both problems in his most important mathematical work, *Solutio duorum problematum circa numeros cubos et quadratos, quae tanquam insolubilia universis Europae mathematicis a clarissimo viro D. Fermat sunt proposita* (Paris, 1657), dedicated to Digby. Although it was assumed for a long time that the work was lost, four copies exist. In it Frenicle proposed four more problems: (3) Find a multiply perfect number x of multiplicity 5, provided that the sum of the aliquot parts (proper divisors) of $5x$ is $25x$. A multiply perfect number x of multiplicity 5 is one the sum of whose divisors, including x and 1, is $5x$. (4) Find a multiply perfect number x of multiplicity 7, provided that the sum of the aliquot divisors of $7x$ is $49x$. (5) Find a central hexagon equal to a cube. (6) Find r central hexagons, with consecutive sides, whose sum is a cube. By a central hexagon of n sides Frenicle meant the number

$$H_n = 1 + 6 + 2\cdot 6 + 3\cdot 6 + \cdots + (n-1)\cdot 6 = n^3 - (n-1)^3.$$

Probably in the middle of February 1657 Fermat proposed a new problem to Frenicle: Find a number x which will make $(ax^2 + 1)$ a square, where a is a (nonsquare) integer. We find equations of this kind for the first time in Greek mathematics, where the Pythagoreans were led to solutions of the equations $y^2 - 2x^2 = \pm 1$ in obtaining approximations to $\sqrt{2}$. Next the Hindus Brahmagupta and Bhaskara II gave the method for finding particular solutions of the equation $y^2 - ax^2 = 1$ for $a = 8$, 61, 67, and 92. Within a very short time Frenicle found solutions of the problem. In the second part of the *Solutio* (pp. 18–30) he cited his table of solutions for all values of a up to 150 and explained his method of solution. Fermat stated in his letter to Carcavi of August 1659 that he had proved the existence of an infinitude of solutions of the equation by the method of descent. He admitted that Frenicle and Wallis had given various special solutions, although not a proof and general construction. After noting in the first part of the *Solutio* (pp. 1–17) that he had made a fruitless attempt to prove that problem (1) is unsolvable for a prime x greater than 7, Frenicle investigated solutions of the problem for values of x that are either primes or powers of primes. At the end of this part he made some remarks about solutions of the equations $\sigma(x^3) = ky^2$ and $\sigma(x^2) = ky^3$, where $\sigma(x)$ is the sum of the divisors (including 1 and x) of x.

Also in 1657 Fermat proposed to Brouncker, Wallis, and Frenicle the problem: Given a number composed of two cubes, to divide it into two other cubes. For finding solutions of this problem Frenicle used the so-called secant transformation, which can be represented as

$$x_3 = x_1 + t(x_2 - x_1); \qquad y_3 = y_1 + t(y_2 - y_1).$$

Although Lagrange is usually considered the inventor of this transformation, it seems that Frenicle was first. Other works by Frenicle were published in the *Mémoires de l'Académie royale des sciences.* In the first of these, "Méthode pour trouver la solution des problèmes par les exclusions," Frenicle says that in his opinion, arithmetic has as its object the finding of solutions in integers of indeterminate problems. He applied his method of exclusion to problems concerning rational right triangles, e.g., he discussed right triangles, the difference or sum of whose legs is given. He proceeded to study these figures in his *Traité des triangles rectangles en nombres,* in which he established some important properties. He proved, e.g., the theorem proposed by Fermat to André Jumeau, prior of Sainte-Croix, in September 1636, to Frenicle in May (?) 1640, and to Wallis on 7 April 1658: If the integers a, b, c represent the sides of a right triangle, then its area, $bc/2$, cannot be a square number. He also proved that no right triangle has each leg a square, and hence the area of a right triangle is never the double of a square. Frenicle's "Abrégé des combinaisons" contained essentially no new things either as to the theoretical part or in the applications. The most important of these works by Frenicle is the treatise "Des quarrez ou tables magiques." These squares, which are of Chinese origin and to which the Arabs were so partial, reached the Occident not later than the fifteenth century. Frenicle pointed out that the number of magic squares increased enormously with the order by writing down 880 magic squares of the fourth order, and gave a process for writing down magic squares of even order. In his *Problèmes plaisants et délectables* (1612), Bachet de Méziriac had given a rule "des terrasses" for those of odd order.

BIBLIOGRAPHY

I. ORIGINAL WORKS. Copies of the *Solutio* are in the Bibliothèque Nationale, Paris: V 12134 and Vz 1136; in the library of Clermont-Ferrand: B.5568.R; and in the Preussische Staatsbibliothek, Berlin: Ob 4569. Pt. 1 of the *Traité des triangles rectangles en nombres* was printed at Paris in 1676 and reprinted with pt. 2 in 1677. Both pts. are in *Mémoires de l'Académie royale des sciences,* **5** (1729), 127–208; this vol. also contains "Méthode pour trouver la solution des problèmes par les exclusions," pp. 1–86; "Abrégé des combinaisons," pp. 87–126; "Des quarrez ou tables magiques," pp. 209–302; and "Table générale des quarrez magiques de quatres côtez," pp. 303–374, which were published by the Academy of Sciences in *Divers ouvrages de mathématique et de physique* (Paris, 1693).

II. SECONDARY LITERATURE. There is no biography of Frenicle. Some information on his work may be found in A. G. Debus, "Pierre Gassendi and His 'Scientific Expedition' of 1640," in *Archives internationales d'histoire des sciences,* **63** (1963), 133–134; L. E. Dickson, *History of the Theory of Numbers* (Washington, D.C., 1919–1927), II, *passim;* C. Henry, "Recherches sur les manuscrits de Pierre de Fermat suivies de fragments inédits de Bachet et de Malebranche," in *Bullettino di bibliografia e di storia delle scienze matematiche e fisiche,* **12** (1870), 691–692; and J. E. Hofmann, "Neues über Fermats zahlentheoretische Herausforderungen von 1657," in *Abhandlungen der Preussischen Akademie der Wissenschaften,* Math.-naturwiss. Klasse, Jahrgang 1943, no. 9 (1944); and "Zur Frühgeschichte des Vierkubenproblems," in *Archives internationales d'histoire des sciences,* **54–55** (1961), 36–63.

H. L. L. BUSARD

FRENKEL, YAKOV ILYICH (*b.* Rostov, Russia, 10 February 1894; *d.* Leningrad, U.S.S.R., 23 January 1954), *physics.*

As a child Frenkel exhibited both interest and ability in music and painting; but later, in school, he was attracted to mathematics and physics. In 1911 he completed his first independent mathematical paper, in which he created a new type of calculus—but it proved to be already known under the name calculus of finite differences. In 1912 he independently developed a physical theory which he showed to A. F. Joffe, with whom he established a close relationship. In 1913 Frenkel entered the Physics and Mathematics Faculty of St. Petersburg University, from which he graduated with honors in 1916. In 1916–1917 he participated in a seminar led by Joffe at the Petrograd Polytechnic Institute, and in 1918 he taught at the newly created Tavrida University in Simferopol. Frenkel returned to Petrograd (Leningrad) in 1921 and worked at the Physico-Technical Institute, which was directed by Joffe, for the rest of his life; he also taught theoretical physics at Leningrad Polytechnic Institute. In 1929 Frenkel was elected an associate member of the Academy of Sciences of the U.S.S.R. He spent 1930–1931 in the United States, where he lectured at the University of Minnesota.

Frenkel published many scientific books and journal articles, and his research encompassed extremely varied fields of theoretical physics. He was one of the founders of the modern atomic theory of solids (metals, dielectrics, and semiconductors). In 1916 he conceived, on the basis of the Bohr model of the atom, the theory of the double electric layer on the surface of metals, which permitted the first evaluations of the surface tensions of metals and of the contact potential. In 1924, on the basis of virial theory, Frenkel demonstrated that during the condensation of a metal from vapor the valence electrons of the atoms must become itinerant, moving at a speed comparable to the rate of intra-atomic motion. This was a noteworthy contribution to the problem of the heat capacity of electrons in metals, which had been blocking progress of the theory.

In 1927 Frenkel became the first to attempt to construct a theory of metals based on the representations of quantum wave mechanics and was able to explain quantitatively the large mean free paths of electrons in metals. In 1928 he developed a simple, elegant deduction of the Pauli theory of the paramagnetism of electrons in metals, used in the majority of textbooks. He also offered in that year the first quantum mechanical explanation of the nature of ferromagnetism, which was independently developed somewhat later in Werner Heisenberg's theory. He simultaneously offered the theory of coercive force in metals.

Using the virial theorem, Frenkel established the connection between the electron theory of metals, the Thomas-Fermi atomic model, as well as the theory of the nucleus and high-density stars. The general fundamental questions first raised in these works have not lost their significance. In 1930 Frenkel and J. G. Dorfman offered the first theoretical substantiation of the breakup of a ferromagnetic substance into separate domains and predicted the existence of single-domain particles.

In 1930–1931 Frenkel made a detailed study of the absorption of light in solid dielectrics and semiconductors. He pointed out the possibility of the emergence of two different forms of excitation in a crystal. When light is absorbed, an excitation state without ionization may appear. Frenkel called this excitation state "exciton," since such a state has the properties of a quasi particle distributed inside the dielectric or semiconductor. The second type of excitation generated by light in solid bodies, according to Frenkel's theory, is associated with ionization, i.e., with formation of a free electron and a free hole.

When bound together the electron and hole form a unique neutral system that possesses a discrete energy spectrum; this system is called Frenkel's exciton.

Frenkel's work on the theory of electric breakdown in dielectrics and semiconductors (1938) has great significance. As early as 1926, in his work on thermal motion in solid and liquid bodies, Frenkel was the first to work out a model of a real crystal, in which a fraction of the molecules or ions oscillate around temporary equilibrium positions which are intermediate between lattice points and in which a fraction of the lattice points are correspondingly free; the vacancies thus formed (Frenkel's defects) migrate throughout the crystal.

In distinction to the generally held representation of the closeness of the liquid state to the gaseous, Frenkel put forward the new idea of an analogy between a liquid and a solid body. He considered a liquid to be a body possessing short-range but not long-range order. Frenkel's theory of diffusion and viscosity, which was built on this model, proved to be exceedingly fruitful. Frenkel systematically developed his thory of the liquid state in the monograph *Kineticheskaya teoria zhidkostey* ("The Kinetic Theory of Liquids," 1945), which earned him the first-degree State Prize in 1947.

Frenkel paid considerable attention to the theory of the mechanical properties of solid bodies. In papers published in conjunction with T. A. Kontorova (1937, 1938) it was first demonstrated theoretically that in distortion-free lattices a special form of particle motion is possible—a gradual, mutually concordant shift from certain equilibrium positions to others, which leads to a gradual, mutual displacement of the rows of atoms. This theory permitted the explanation of several specific particulars of the plastic deformation and twinning of crystals. The theory of the elasticity of rubbery substances, developed by Frenkel and S. E. Bresler in 1939, proved to be in good agreement with experimental data.

Frenkel's research had an essential influence on the development of electrodynamics and the theory of electrons, as well as the theory of atomic nuclei. His 1926 study served as the basis for the investigation of many questions concerning the dynamics of a spinning electron before the appearance, in 1928, of Dirac's theory of relativistic quantum mechanics. In *Elektrodinamika,* published by Frenkel in 1928, questions of classical electrodynamics were examined from a completely new point of view. In 1936 he was the first to attempt the construction of a statistical theory of heavy nuclei, considering the nucleus as a solid body and setting aside the individual motion of nucleons. In 1939, shortly after the discovery of the splitting of heavy nuclei by Otto Hahn and Fritz Strassman, Frenkel developed (independently of Bohr and J. A. Wheeler) a theory which explains the process of splitting as the result of the electrocapillary oscillation of electrically charged drops of nucleic liquid.

Frenkel also solved many problems in meteorology and geophysics. Between 1944 and 1949 he proposed the theory of atmospheric electrification in which the close connection between the electrification of clouds and the existence of fields in cloudless atmosphere was established. In 1945 he formulated a new theory of geomagnetism.

BIBLIOGRAPHY

I. Original Works. Frenkel's writings include *Lehrbuch der Elektrodynamik,* 2 vols. (Berlin, 1926–1928); *Kinetic Theory of Liquids* (Oxford, 1946); *Wave Mechanics. Elementary Theory* (New York, 1950); *Wave Mechanics. Advanced General Theory* (New York, 1950); *Sobranie izbrannykh trudov* ("Collection of Selected Works"), 3 vols. (Moscow–Leningrad, 1956–1958); *Prinzipien der Theorie der Atomkerne* (Berlin, 1957); and *Statistische Physik* (Berlin, 1957).

II. Secondary Literature. Articles and books on Frenkel and his work (in Russian) are A. I. Anselm, "Yakov Ilyich Frenkel," in *Uspekhi fizicheskikh nauk,* **47,** pt. 3 (1952), 470; J. G. Dorfman, "Yakov Ilyich Frenkel," in Frenkel's *Sobranie izbrannykh trudov,* II (Moscow–Leningrad, 1958), 3–15; V. Y. Frenkel, *Yakov Ilyich Frenkel* (Moscow–Leningrad, 1966); and I. E. Tamm, "Yakov Ilyich Frenkel," in *Uspekhi fizicheskikh nauk,* **76,** pt. 3 (1962), 327.

J. G. Dorfman

FRENZEL, FRIEDRICH AUGUST (*b.* Freiberg, Germany, 24 May 1842; *d.* Freiberg, 27 August 1902), *mineralogy.*

Frenzel was a member of a family of miners and from 1861 to 1865 studied at a mining school in Freiberg, graduating with the title of mine inspector. He then worked as timberman in a prospecting mine and simultaneously attended lectures and laboratory courses at the Mining Academy; he was permitted to do so because he had graduated from mining school with excellent marks. During this period Frenzel also gave lessons in mineralogy and chemistry to foreigners studying in Freiberg. In 1868 he became an employee of the state mines and in 1874 was promoted to mine chemist. He held this post for over a quarter of a century and, beginning in 1883, lectured also in mineralogy and geognosy at the Royal Mining School. Early in 1902 he became head of the laboratory of the main mining administration.

While studying at the Mining Academy, Frenzel attended lectures by prominent scientists: the chemist-mineralogist A. Breithaupt, the geologist Bernhard Cotta, the chemist Theodor Scheerer, and the mineralogist Theodor Richter, who influenced the formation of his interests. Decisive for all of Frenzel's subsequent scientific activity was Breithaupt's trusting him with technical work and, later, with scientific research as well.

In a short time Frenzel became a qualified specialist noted for the exceptional carefulness of his determinations. Beginning in 1870, he published articles on the description of individual minerals.

In 1871, while studying rocks from the Pucher mine in Saxony, Frenzel discovered a previously unknown bismuth vanadate and named the new mineral pucherite. A year later he described two other new minerals: miriquidite (arsenate and phosphate of lead and iron) and heterogenite (hydrous oxide of cobalt containing an admixture of copper).

In 1874 Frenzel's *Mineralogisches Lexikon für das Königreich Sachsen* was published at Leipzig. It contained descriptions of 723 minerals that gave their physical properties and chemical composition. This handbook became very popular among geologists and brought widespread recognition to its author.

During the next few years Frenzel discovered five more minerals: in 1881, lautite (CuAsS), named for the Lauta deposit in Saxony; in 1882, rezbanyite, a complex compound of copper, lead, and bismuth found in the ores of Rézbánya deposit in Hungary (now Băiţa, Rumania); in 1888, amarantite and hohmannite, iron sulfates from Ehrenfriedersdorf, that were of similar composition; and in 1893, cylindrite, a sulfostannate of lead and antimony found in silver-tin veins. He also described several other minerals which he thought were new species but which later proved to have been previously described. Frenzel published some fifty mineralogical papers, the majority of which are still valuable as references.

Frenzel was in constant contact with a number of prominent scientists of his time. He was especially friendly with the German mineralogists Gerhard vom Rath and Carl Hintze and the Russian geochemist-mineralogist Andreas Arzruni. He was a foreign member of the American Institute of Mining Engineers (1873) and a member of the German Geological Society (1875).

As a long-time officer of the Naturalists' Society of Freiberg he sought to arouse interest in research on natural history. A great help in this respect was his ability as a lecturer. A passionate collector, Frenzel assembled two large collections of minerals. He was also interested in ornithology; he wrote and edited numerous articles for the monthly publication of the German Society for the Protection of Birds.

BIBLIOGRAPHY

Frenzel's papers include "Pucherit," in *Journal für praktische Chemie,* **4** (1871), 227–231, 361–362; "Heterogenit," *ibid.,* **5** (1872), 401–408; "Miriquidit," in *Neues Jahrbuch für Mineralogie, Geologie und Paläontologie* (Stuttgart, 1874), 673–687; "Über Lautit und Trichlorit," in *Tschermaks mineralogische und petrographische Mitteilungen,* **4** (1882), 97; "Rezbanyit," *ibid.,* **5** (1883), 178–188; "Hohmannit und Amarantit," *ibid.,* **9** (1888), 397–400; and "Über den Kylindrit," in *Neues Jahrbuch für Mineralogie, Geologie und Paläontologie,* pt. 2 (1893), 125–128.

An obituary is R. Beck, "Friedrich August Frenzel. Nekrolog," in *Zentralblatt für Mineralogie, Geologie und Paläontologie* (1902), 641–646, which includes a bibliography of forty-six titles.

V. V. TIKHOMIROV
T. A. SOFIANO

FRERE, JOHN (*b.* Westhorpe, Suffolk, England, 10 August 1740; *d.* East Dereham, Norfolk, England, 12 July 1807), *archaeology.*

Frere was the son of a country gentleman, Sheppard Frere, and of Susanna Hatley. He was privately educated near his home before entering Gonville and Caius College, Cambridge, in 1758. He graduated with a B.A. in 1763 and was second wrangler; he took his M.A. in 1766 and was a junior fellow from 1766 to 1768. Frere's professional career was in law and politics: he was admitted to the Middle Temple in 1761, became high sheriff of Suffolk in 1766, and Member of Parliament for Norwich in 1799. In 1768 he married Jane Hookham and lived at the family seat, Roydon Hall. They had seven sons.

Frere's scientific work was mainly a hobby, and his election as a fellow of the Royal Society in 1771 was indicative of his general interest in science rather than of a distinction already achieved. He is said to have been active in the Royal Society, but there is little record of this. The only substantial publication is a two-page letter to the secretary of the Society of Antiquaries of London, that was read to the society on 22 June 1797 and published in *Archaeologia* in 1800. In this Frere records his discovery, at a brickyard near Hoxne, of shaped flints which were "evidently weapons of war, fabricated and used by a people who had not the use of metals." A careful examination of the strata showed that the gravel in which the flints were found had been covered for a very long period. He also heard of, but was not able to see, a very large jawbone which had been found in the same stratum, and concluded that the deposit was "of a very remote period indeed." Finally, Frere discovered from workmen on the site that they had already disposed of numerous such flints, and he presumed that this was "a place of their manufacture and not of their accidental deposit."

The discovery aroused little or no interest at the time, and it was not until 1840, when Boucher de Perthes made news by finding similar implements in the Somme, that Frere's perceptiveness was appreciated. These flints probably exhibited the best known workmanship of the lower Paleolithic period, and further excavations were made later in late Acheulean deposits at Hoxne. The weapons discovered by Frere are in the possession of the Society of Antiquaries of London and are deposited in the British Museum.

BIBLIOGRAPHY

Frere's "Account of Flint Weapons Discovered at Hoxne in Suffolk" was published in *Archaeologia,* **13** (1800), 204–205; there was a 2nd ed. of this volume in 1807. The paper was reprinted verbatim, with a discussion of Frere's work, by J. Reid Moir in his "A Pioneer in Palaeolithic Discovery," in *Notes and Records. Royal Society of London,* **2** (1939), 28–31, with portrait; and by Glyn Daniel, in *Origins and Growth of Archaeology* (London, 1967), pp. 57–58.

The main biographical sources for Frere are the article by Warwick Wroth in *Dictionary of National Biography,* XX (London, 1889), 267–268, which includes additional references; the memoir on the life of his son in John Hookham Frere, *Works,* I (London, 1872), xii–xv; and the entry in J. Venn, *Biographical History of Gonville and Caius College,* II, *1713–1897* (Cambridge, 1898), 75.

Frere's work was also discussed in J. Prestwich, "On the Accounts of Flint Implements Associated With the Remains of Animals of Extinct Species in Beds of a Late Geological Period, in France, at Amiens, and Abbeville, and in England at Hoxne," in *Philosophical Transactions of the Royal Society,* **150** (1860), 277–317; and in J. Reid Moir, *The Antiquity of Man in East Anglia* (Cambridge, 1927), p. 59.

DIANA M. SIMPKINS

FRESENIUS, CARL REMIGIUS (*b.* Frankfurt am Main, Germany, 20 December 1818; *d.* Wiesbaden, Germany, 11 June 1897), *analytical chemistry.*

Fresenius' father, Jakob Heinrich Fresenius, was a notary; his mother was Maria Veronika Finger. Until the Thirty Years' War most of his male ancestors had been Protestant ministers. After attending elementary and secondary school in Frankfurt and in Weinheim, Fresenius was apprenticed to an apothecary. He frequently attended the public science lectures at the Physical Society and other institutions, and in 1840 he entered the University of Bonn, where he studied science, history, and philosophy. In those days very few institutions of higher learning afforded any opportunity for practical experimentation. Bonn was not one of them, so Fresenius tested his newly acquired knowledge in the private laboratory of Ludwig Marquart. The principal aim of his experiments was identification of the different elements through qualitative analysis by the wet method.

When Fresenius began to conduct his own laboratory experiments with qualitative reactions, he was faced with a problem then doubtless confronting all young chemists: the lack of any guidelines for systematic qualitative analysis or any coherent sources from which the art could be learned. Older books on analytical chemistry dealt with the subject only from the standpoint of elements, which they listed in the order of their behavior in the presence of various reagents, but gave no systematic methods for identifying the constituents of a mixture of unknown substances. He therefore devised a method of his own for systematic identification and separation of the individual metals (cations) and nonmetals (anions), selecting from the great multitude of reactions those which struck him as most suitable. His system worked so well that, at Marquart's suggestion, he expanded it into a book, published in 1841 under the title *Anleitung zur qualitativen chemischen Analyse.*

By this time Fresenius was in Giessen to continue his chemical studies under the direction of Justus Liebig. In addition to Liebig's lectures, he attended those of Heinrich Buff and Hermann Kopp. The second edition of his *Anleitung,* with a preface by Liebig, appeared in 1842. It states that as early as 1841 inorganic analytical chemistry was being done according to the Fresenius text in Liebig's laboratory. The book gained Fresenius his doctorate on 23 July 1842, and Liebig made him his assistant. The book was an unprecedented success. A third edition was published in 1844 and a fourth in 1846. In a period of twenty years there were eleven German editions. By the time of Fresenius' death seventeen had appeared, each an improved and expanded version of the preceding one, incorporating the latest knowledge and results. The book was soon translated into English, French, Italian, Dutch, Russian, Spanish, Hungarian, and Chinese. The first English edition, translated by J. Lloyd Bullock, appeared in 1841 under the title *Elementary Instruction in Qualitative Analysis.* Eight English editions were published. This enormous success clearly shows the magnitude of the gap in scientific knowledge which the Fresenius system of qualitative analysis filled. The system was taught for a century in all colleges and universities, and while qualitative analysis by the wet method on a macroscopic scale has lost much of its practical importance in recent times, it is still regarded as a valuable instruction tool and continues to be taught in many places.

The Fresenius system is oviously based on Heinrich Rose's separation method. Fresenius divided the cations (or metal oxides, as they were then called under Berzelius' dualistic theory) into six groups. Classed in the same group are cations that behave in the same way (precipitate or, less frequently, dissolve) in the presence of a given reagent under specific experimental conditions. The basic reagent used was hydrogen sulfide; the determining property, the behavior of the various metallic sulfides in different situations. The breakdown was as follows:

Group 6—metals which form a precipitate with hydrogen sulfide in acid or alkaline solution: mercury (+1, +2), lead, bismuth, silver, copper, and cadmium. Silver, mercury (+1), and lead are precipitable with hydrochloric acid.

Group 5—gold, platinum, antimony, tin (+4, +2), arsenic (+3, +5), whose sulfides are soluble in ammonium sulfide.

Group 4—metals whose sulfides are precipitable only in alkaline or neutral solution: zinc, manganese, nickel, cobalt, and iron (+3, +2).

Group 3—metals whose sulfides are soluble and whose hydroxides are precipitable with ammonium sulfide: aluminum and chromium.

Group 2—metals whose sulfides are soluble and are precipitated with alkali carbonates and alkali phosphates: barium, strontium, calcium, and magnesium.

Group 1—both the sulfides and carbonates are soluble: sodium, potassium, and ammonium.

This classification matches exactly the one still in use today, except that Groups 4 and 3 were subsequently merged and the numeration was reversed, Fresenius' Group 6 becoming Class 1, etc. Fresenius did not content himself with the separation into groups but, through treatment with other suitable reagents, broke down each group into its individual member elements. He never used the blowpipe. The number of reagents that he employed was relatively small, which made his system simple and easy to learn.

Fresenius married his cousin Charlotte Rumpf in 1845. They had four daughters and three sons, two of whom, Heinrich and Wilhelm, became chemists and continued operation of the Fresenius Training and Research Institute and publication of the *Zeitschrift für analytische Chemie.* After more than twenty-five years of marriage Fresenius' wife died, and Fresenius married Auguste Fritze, a friend of his deceased wife.

In 1845 the Wiesbaden Agricultural College in the duchy of Nassau offered Fresenius a position as professor of chemistry, physics, and engineering. He accepted and moved to Wiesbaden. The college was very poorly equipped, and Fresenius had no laboratory for teaching or for his own experimental work. He decided to establish one. With a modest subsidy from the duchy, he bought a building and equipped it. This laboratory, which opened in 1848, served several purposes. It offered training in practical chemistry, especially analytic procedures. When it opened, five students started work there under the direction of an instructor, Emil Erlenmeyer, later professor of chemistry at the University of Munich. By 1854–1855 there were thirty-eight students and three instructors. A school of pharmacy was subsequently added. The duchy of Nassau allowed college credit for study at Fresenius' laboratory, but this was discontinued after Nassau was annexed to Prussia. The laboratory then switched to training food chemists and public health personnel. As the role of practical education began to increase at the universities, the laboratory turned more and more to the training of laboratory technicians. It also conducted analyses for industry, soon acquiring an international reputation in this field. Its arbitrational analyses settled many disputes in foreign countries. Fresenius ran the enterprise until his death, and his research institute still operates under the direction of the Fresenius family.

In 1845 Fresenius also published his *Anleitung zur quantitativen chemischen Analyse.* Although this book had had six printings by the time of his death, it is of less importance than his work on qualitative analysis. After describing the analytic operations, the book discusses the forms in which the individual elements can be determined. It then deals with the separations but fails to offer any particularly coherent system (which so far no one else has done). It is also noteworthy that the book does describe many examples of indirect analysis. In many places, too, Fresenius' book touches upon the thermal behavior of analytic precipitates, indicating their thermal stability and discussing the nature of thermal decomposition processes. He can therefore rightly be regarded as one of the pioneers of thermal analysis.

In 1862 Fresenius founded the journal *Zeitschrift für analytische Chemie.* The earliest chemical journals date from the last two decades of the eighteenth century. For almost a century, though, there was no differentiation within the general field of chemistry. The founding of the *Zeitschrift für analytische Chemie* marked the beginning of specialization.

In a special announcement, Fresenius explained his intention in publishing the journal:

> It is readily provable that all great advances in chemistry have been more or less directly related to new or improved analytic methods. The first usable procedures for analyzing the salts were followed by our discovery of the stoichiometric relationships; the progress in analysis of inorganic substances yielded ever more precise equivalent weights; the methods for exact determination of the elements in organic substances gave unexpected impetus to the development of organic chemistry. . . . In truth, therefore, our methods of analysis represent a great achievement in themselves, an important scientific treasure.

The nature of an independent science of analytical chemistry was thus proclaimed. The journal, consisting of original writings on all aspects of analytical chemistry and of systematically arranged reports, still appears regularly. Fresenius himself published many papers on the results of his experimental research. While all of them were scientifically precise, they dealt mostly with special cases and, as regards methodology, contained nothing remotely comparable in significance to his qualitative system. He reported his analyses of numerous mineral waters and explored in detail the possible analytic uses of potassium cyanide; and he was concerned with the detection and quantitative determination of arsenic in cases of poisoning and with the testing of potash, soda, acids, and pyrolusite. He reported also on the determination of nitric acid, lithium, a great many metal alloys, sulfuric acid, metal ores, and boric acid, and the separation of the salts of the alkaline earth metals. Most of those studies consisted of experimental and critical testing of existing methods and of selection of the most favorable operating conditions rather than of a quest for new methods and forms of analysis. To render the analytic process more precise and refine its methods, Fresenius determined the solubility of many analytic precipitates and, on the basis of those tests, recommended correction values for analytic calculations. He also engaged in food research, primarily in analysis of fruit and wine.

Fresenius was active in that period when analytical chemistry was serving not only to increase man's knowledge of the constituents of his environment but also was being increasingly used for day-to-day control of industrial products. Analytic laboratories became the natural and indispensable adjuncts of factories in which chemical analyses were an everyday routine. These laboratories required trained personnel, reliable and fast analytic techniques, and an expedient way to prepare information for the analytical literature. Fresenius recognized that chemical analysis had ceased to be a scholarly preoccupation of the few and had become the daily occupation of the many, and he made it his job to help satisfy those needs. This was the aim of his school, his analytic research institute, and his journal. Even most of his own scientific writings were oriented toward the practical and the industrial. This, in fact, was his second greatest accomplishment: he played a large role in shaping the science of chemical analysis to meet the requirements of an industrial age.

Fresenius' work gained him public recognition, and many honors were bestowed upon him. He was several times president of the Versammlung Deutscher Naturforscher und Ärzte and honorary member of the Gesellschaft Deutscher Chemiker. Contemporaries characterized him as a deeply religious man, with an excellent sense of humor, and an exemplary father. He loved hunting. In 1961 the Gesellschaft Deutscher Chemiker established a Fresenius Prize for outstanding achievement in the field of analytical chemistry.

BIBLIOGRAPHY

I. Original Works. Fresenius' writings include *Anleitung zur qualitativen chemischen Analyse* (Bonn, 1841; 2nd–17th eds., Brunswick, 1842–1896); *Anleitung zur quantitativen chemischen Analyse* (Brunswick, 1845; 2nd–6th eds., 1847–1887); many of his chief analytical works were published in *Justus Liebigs Annalen der Chemie* and in *Zeitschrift für analytische Chemie* and are listed in Poggendorff.

II. Secondary Literature. Works on Fresenius are E. Fischer, "Carl Remigius Fresenius," in *Zeitschrift für angewandte Chemie,* **10** (1897), 520; H. Fresenius, "Zur Erinnerung an Remigius Fresenius," in *Zeitschrift für analytische Chemie,* **36** (1897), 10; R. Fresenius, "Fresenius, Carl Remigius (1818–1897)," in *Nassauische Lebensbilder,* vol. I (Wiesbaden, 1940); W. Fresenius, "Remigius Fresenius," in *Zeitschrift für analytische Chemie,* **192** (1963), 3; A. J. Ihde, *The Development of Modern Chemistry* (New York–London, 1964), pp. 278–280; F. Szabadváry, *History of Analytical Chemistry* (New York–Oxford, 1966), pp. 161–172, 176–181; and *Geschichte der analytischen Chemie* (Brunswick, 1966), pp. 185–192, 196–200.

Ferenc Szabadváry

FRESNEL, AUGUSTIN JEAN (*b.* Broglie, France, 10 May 1788; *d.* Ville-d'Avray, France, 14 July 1827), *optics.*

Fresnel's father, Jacques, was a successful Norman architect and building contractor. In 1785, while directing improvements on the château of the maréchal de Broglie, he married Augustine Mérimée, the pious, well-educated daughter of the estate's overseer. Subsequently he was employed on the harbor construction project at Cherbourg; and when this work was interrupted by the Revolution in 1794, he retired with his family to Mathieu, north of Caen. Here Augustin spent the remainder of his childhood, deeply influenced by the home. In an atmosphere heavy with the values of a stern Jansenism his parents provided him with an elementary education. At twelve, undistinguished except for his practical ingenuity and mechanical talents, he entered the École Centrale in Caen. The school's progressive curriculum afforded Fresnel an introduction to science, and two of his masters made a lasting impression: F. J. Quesnot, the mathematics teacher, and P. F. T. Delarivière, the grammar instructor, whose course imparted the elements of *Idéologie.*

Intending a career in engineering, Fresnel was admitted to the École Polytechnique in Paris in 1804. For two years he benefited from the school's high-level scientific instruction. After an additional three years of technical courses and practical engineering experience at the École des Ponts et Chaussées, he completed his formal training and entered government service as a civil engineer. The Corps des Ponts et Chaussées first assigned him to Vendée, where he worked on the roads linking the department with its new *chef-lieu* at La Roche-sur-Yon. About 1812 he was sent to Nyon, France, to assist with the imperial highway which was to connect Spain with Italy through the Alpine pass at Col Montgenèvre. In moments snatched from his professional duties Fresnel diverted himself with a series of philosophical, technical, and scientific concerns.

By mid-1814 Fresnel had turned to optics and had begun to consider the claims of the wave or pulse hypothesis of light. This inquiry, barely begun, was suddenly thrust aside the following year. Seeing Napoleon's return from Elba as "an attack on civilization," Fresnel deserted his post and offered his services to the Royalist forces. With the reestablishment of the empire he found himself suspended from his duties and put under police surveillance. Returning home to Mathieu, he devoted his enforced leisure to optics, undertaking experiments on diffraction. These confirmed his belief in the wave nature of light and started him on a decade of research aimed at developing his hypothesis into a comprehensive mathematical theory. With the Second Restoration, Fresnel was reactivated by the Corps des Ponts et Chaussées and thereafter was forced to restrict his investigations to periods of leave. Through the intervention of such influential friends as François Arago, these were not infrequent. From the spring of 1818 his scientific work was made easier by assignments in Paris, and intensive research over the next few years produced important results. After 1824 his efforts slackened. Work with the Lighthouse Commission, including the development of his new "echelon" lenses, put severe demands on his time, and faltering health sapped his energy.

Tuberculosis, the cause of his early death, cast a shadow over Fresnel's entire career. Plagued continually by ill health, he sought consolation in a religious faith which offered belief in Divine Providence and the hope of an afterlife. But this was no theology of resignation. Summoning the will to struggle against bodily suffering and fatigue, Fresnel threw himself into difficult tasks. Behind his remarkable determination was a severe Puritan, middle-class outlook which saw the highest merit in personal achievement, performance of duty, and service to society. Serious, intent, haunted by thoughts of an early grave, Fresnel bound himself closely to these ideals, shunning pleasures and amusements and working to the point of exhaustion. Despite the urgency of everything he attempted, Fresnel was always attentive to detail, systematic, and thorough. In science no less than in politics he held tenaciously to his convictions and defended them with courage and vigor. As a functionary he voiced outrage when the behavior of others fell short of his own high ethical standards. At times this approached a rankling self-righteousness, but generally his contemporaries saw him as reserved, gentle, and charitable.

For his scientific achievements Fresnel received several important honors. In 1823 the Académie des Sciences elected him to membership by unanimous vote. He was a foreign associate of the Société de Physique et d'Histoire Naturelle of Geneva and a corresponding member of the Royal Society of London. In the last month of his life he received the Royal Society's Rumford Medal.

Confined almost exclusively to optics, Fresnel's scientific work shows an essential unity. Above all, his research found its motivation and direction in an attempt to demonstrate that light is undulatory and not corpuscular. Challenging the prevailing Newtonian view, he undertook a series of brilliant investigations which systematically elaborated the wave concept and established its conformity with experience. Fresnel brought to his research an ingenious mind, deft hands, and the discipline of an excellent scientific education. He was equally proficient in experiment and mathematics and effectively combined the two. Characteristically, he initiated his investigations with experiments and proceeded, via analysis, to theory. He set as his goal mathematical theories from which precise consequences could be deduced and tested by further experiments. For Fresnel a true theory was one that predicts experience and rests on a simple conceptual basis, free of all auxiliary hypotheses. The simplicity requirement, which served Fresnel as a constant guide in his theoretical formulations, was grounded on a deep-seated belief that nature aims at the production of the most numerous and varied effects by the fewest and most general causes. This is the meaning of the epigram placed at the head of his prize essay on diffraction: "Natura simplex et fecunda." The idea of the underlying unity of natural processes doubtless found a guarantee in Fresnel's Providentialism. A consideration of his close relationship with Ampère and others in the circle of Maine de Biran might also disclose certain philosophical influences contributing to this viewpoint.

It was Fresnel's belief in the essential unity and simplicity of nature that conditioned his preference for a wave conception of light. His earliest statement in favor of light as a form of motion (in a letter of 5 July 1814) envisioned the possibility of referring heat, light, and electricity to the modifications of a single, universal fluid. Apparently, then, he regarded the whole Newtonian scheme of imponderables with its multiple fluids as suspect from the very start. But within this general scheme the corpuscular theory of light had its own special burden of complexity. Ignorant of the elaborations of the theory undertaken to accommodate polarization, Fresnel was not yet aware of how complex corpuscular optics had become. His determination to overhaul optical theory was sparked by a dissatisfaction with the caloric view of heat and an appreciation of the analogies between heat and light. But after he learned of Biot's work, he regularly assailed the corpuscular theory for its lack of unity and simplicity.

Rejecting corpuscular optics, Fresnel was poorly acquainted with earlier theories that conceived light as waves or pulses. In France, as elsewhere, the views of Huygens and Euler had no following and were hardly discussed. Physics textbooks of the period took note of the "Cartesian" hypothesis but dismissed it in a few lines. Apparently it was only with the most general knowledge of the work of his predecessors that Fresnel began to construct his theory. If he knew of Huygens' principle when he undertook his first investigations, he did not reveal it. From the start, however, he possessed another important concept, which made his theory, unlike that of Huygens, a true wave theory. This was the idea that the pulses constituting light succeed one another at regular intervals. Fresnel may have taken the idea from Euler, but it is more probable that he hit upon it independently. Nor was he aided by the work of Thomas Young. He became familiar with Young's contributions to wave optics only after he was well into his own experiments.

Fresnel's first experimental investigation, a study of diffraction, gave him a firm foothold in undulatory optics and started him down a profitable path. By studying diffraction effects—the shadow and associated bands of color produced when a hair or other thin object is illuminated by a narrow beam—he hoped to counter objections to the wave hypothesis based on the apparent rectilinearity of the propagation of light and, if possible, to find positive support for the view of light as vibrations. The key to success was found in an application of the principle of interference, a concept drawn from acoustical theory. Attaching a slip of black paper to one edge of a diffracter, Fresnel observed that the bands of light within the shadow disappeared. By "a mere translation of the phenomenon" he concluded that the internal bands depend upon a crossing of rays inflected into the shadow from both edges of the diffracter. Since the bands outside the shadow on the side opposite the attached paper remained, the external bands appeared to arise from a crossing of rays proceeding directly from the light source and by reflection from one edge of the diffracter. Referred to the mechanical level, these effects seemed explicable only if light were undulatory. Bright bands would occur where the vibrations constituting light are in phase and reinforce one another. Intervening bands of darkness would correspond to places where the vibrations are out of phase by some odd number of half wavelengths and cancel one another.

To put the concept of constructive and destructive interference to the test, Fresnel worked out simple algebraic formulas correlating the positions of the bands with factors determining the occurrence of interference—the path differences of the intersecting rays and the wavelength of the light. Performing the experiment with monochromatic red light and gauging the positions of the bands for various intervals between the light source, the diffracter, and the receiving screen (or plane of observation, since it proved equally effective and more convenient to dispense with the screen and view the bands directly with a lens), he found a close correspondence between actual values and those predicted by his formulas.

Although a paper of October 1815, embodying these results, won Arago to the cause of wave optics and made a favorable impression on the Institut de France, Fresnel was still far from a complete theory of diffraction. His indiscriminate use of the terms "rays," "vibrations," "inflection," and "diffraction" bespoke a residue of corpuscular influences and was symptomatic of a lack of precision in his formulation. The mirror experiment, demonstrating interference in circumstances where the attractive forces of inflection could not be invoked to explain its effects, marked an important step forward. In front of two mirrors arranged end to end at an angle slightly less than 180° Fresnel set a minute light source. After the necessary adjustments to obtain precisely the right conditions, he saw bands of color produced as the rays reflected from one of the mirrors intersected and interfered with rays reflected from the other. The interpretation of the bands in terms of interference seemed all the more certain since band positions corresponded to theoretical values obtained by adapting the diffraction formulas.

Although inflection was thus effectively discredited, Fresnel saw the need for further refinements. His formulas, positing rectilinear "rays" and referring path measurements to the very edge of the diffracter, predicted band positions only if it were assumed that the rays turned aside at the diffracter lost half a wavelength. Otherwise there was an inexplicable reversal, the bright bands occurring where dark ones were predicted and vice versa. Spurred by a desire to eliminate the ad hoc hypothesis, Fresnel undertook to reconstruct his theory on a new basis, a step carrying him, for the first time, beyond Young. Boldly he conceived the idea of combining Huygens' principle with the principle of interference. Applying the idea to diffraction, he supposed that elementary waves arise at every point along the arc of the wave front passing the diffracter and mutually interfere. The problem was to determine the resultant vibration produced by all the wavelets reaching any point behind the diffracter. The mathematical difficulties were formidable, and a solution was to require many months of effort. In the first attempt, fashioned around the concept of "efficacious rays," Fresnel succeeded in reducing the discrepancy between theory and fact by half, and in a paper of 15 July 1816 that reported the investigation, he begged critics at the Institut de France to treat with indulgence "his essays in such a difficult theory."

Not until the spring of 1818 was Fresnel able to reach his goal. Restored to active service in the Corps des Ponts et Chaussées and assigned to Rennes, he bore heavily the yoke of his engineering duties and continually badgered his superiors for leave. Whenever possible he returned to Paris to pick up the thread of his research. Throughout 1817 he concerned himself with polarization, but the need to cope with the periodic effects of chromatic polarization immediately reintroduced the basic mathematical problem carried over from the study of diffraction: that of "calculating the influence of any number of systems of luminous waves on one another." Fresnel took a decisive step toward the solution when, aided by an analogy between the oscillations of an ether molecule and those of a pendulum, he derived a general expression for the velocity of ether molecules put into motion by a wave.

Considering next the combined effect of multiple waves, Fresnel worked through to an important result. Just as a force can be resolved into perpendicular components, so the amplitude of the oscillations imparted by any wave can be reduced to the amplitudes of two concurring waves following one another at an interval of a quarter wavelength. To find the net effect of multiple waves, then, it was sufficient to reduce each to its two components, add like components, and recombine the sums. Temporarily setting polarization aside, Fresnel hastened to apply this result to diffraction. Urgency was called for, because the Académie des Sciences had announced that diffraction would be the subject of its competition for 1819. Looking beyond the prize to the scientific "revolution" he hoped to effect, Fresnel was anxious to enter the contest. Not long before the closing date he put the final touches to his theory. Without any gratuitous hypotheses he could now calculate the light intensity at any point behind a diffracter.

In Figure 1 *P* is the point, *AG* the diffracter, *C* the light source, and *AMI* a partially intercepted wave

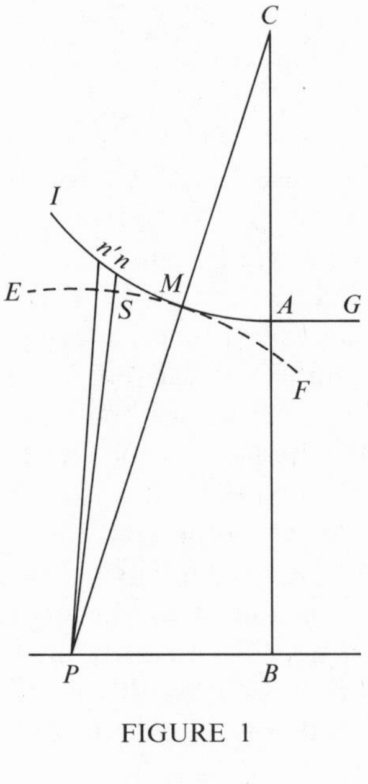

FIGURE 1

front. One of the infinitesimally small arcs into which AMI may be divided is shown as $n'n$. From each of these elements a train of wavelets is assumed to arise, and the problem is to determine the composite effect of all the wavelets at P. The procedure takes the form indicated above, the wavelets being related to a wave emanating from the point M on the line CP and to another wave differing in phase by a quarter undulation. Considering the effect at P produced by a wavelet proceeding from $n'n$, Fresnel represents this small portion of the original wave front as dz and specifies its distance to M as z. The interval nS between the wave AMI and the tangent arc drawn around P is determined to be $1/2\, z^2(a + b/ab)$, a and b representing the distances CA and AB. Substituting into the appropriate expression supplied by his general mathematical investigation, Fresnel wrote the component of the wavelet relative to the wave emanating from M as

$$dz \cos\left(\pi \frac{z^2(a + b)}{ab\lambda}\right),$$

λ representing the wavelength. The other component relative to a wave separated from the first by a quarter wavelength is

$$dz \sin\left(\pi \frac{z^2(a + b)}{ab\lambda}\right).$$

The sum of similar components of all the wavelets is then

$$\int dz \cos\left(\pi \frac{z^2(a + b)}{ab\lambda}\right) \text{ and } \int dz \sin\left(\pi \frac{z^2(a + b)}{ab\lambda}\right).$$

These expressions later passed into the textbooks as "Fresnel's integrals." The square root of the sum of their squares gives the amplitude of the resultant vibration at P, while the sum of their squares measures the observable light intensity at the point. Tested and strikingly corroborated by experiment, the new theory served as Fresnel's entry to the competition and was awarded the prize. During the judging it received a dramatic and unexpected confirmation. One of the commissioners, Poisson, had perceived in Fresnel's mathematics the seemingly improbable consequence that the center of the shadow of a small disk used as a diffracter would be brightly illuminated. An experiment performed to test the calculation confirmed it exactly.

That light under certain circumstances displays an asymmetric aspect remained the most serious challenge for the undulatory conception of light. Particles might have "sides," but longitudinal waves could not. Understandably, Young experienced "a descent from conviction to hesitation" when informed of Malus' discovery of polarization by reflection. With Fresnel, however, it was otherwise. Undaunted, he set out early in his investigations to find an accommodation between the asymmetry of light and the wave hypothesis. For clues about the nature of polarization his first tack was to pursue a comparative approach in which the effects of polarized light would be juxtaposed against the known characteristics of ordinary light. Specifically, he decided to substitute polarized light for ordinary light under conditions producing interference. Initial experiments carried out jointly with Arago early in 1816 afforded no new insights. Polarized light gave the same effects as ordinary light. Fresnel questioned the adequacy of these hasty tests, and several months later undertook new experiments, obtaining results that were quite different. Aided further by Arago, he showed convincingly that in circumstances where ordinary light would interfere, rays polarized in mutually perpendicular planes have no effect on one another.

The theoretical implications were puzzling. In a note to a preliminary draft of the paper reporting the investigation, Fresnel offered two hypotheses accounting for his findings, one his own and the other elicited from Ampère. The noninterference of rays polarized in mutually perpendicular planes suggested that the vibrations constituting light are either transverse or a combination of longitudinal and transverse motions. Neither hypothesis appeared tenable. Transverse waves, the prevailing theory of elasticity held, are possible only in a solid medium; but an all-pervading solid ether could not be reconciled with the free, unimpeded movements of the planets demonstrated by astronomy. When he submitted his paper to the Académie des Sciences, Fresnel deleted the note, and Arago's account of the investigation published in 1818 scrupulously avoided all theoretical considerations.

Lacking any alternative hypotheses, Fresnel continued his inquiry. On the basis of the recent experimental findings he next worked out a detailed explanation of chromatic polarization. But, as with diffraction, the calculation of precise theoretical values and full confirmation had to await the "general law of the reciprocal influence of luminous waves," available only at the beginning of 1818. Although it extended the sway of interference as an explanatory concept, the study of chromatic polarization disclosed nothing new about the basis of polarization.

In search of further clues, Fresnel turned his attention to the influence of reflection on polarized light. His first efforts, summarized in a paper of November 1817, resulted in the discovery of an unusual modification of light, later designated "circular polarization." The novel light appeared to be symmetric about an axis drawn in the direction of its motion, but in other respects it behaved like polarized light. Fresnel determined that these characteristics would follow if the light were supposed to consist of two components with mutually perpendicular planes of polarization and a phase difference of a quarter undulation. Yet for the moment he saw no way to translate this into a satisfactory mechanical hypothesis. Another important investigation, completed in March 1818, showed that the rotation of the plane of polarization associated with the passage of light through quartz and certain liquids depends upon a weak double refraction and the superposition of two circularly polarized rays.

As he weighed the implications of these studies, Fresnel was gradually brought to the realization that the vibrations constituting light could only be transverse. Consistently the characteristics of polarized light testified to forces acting at right angles to the rays, and finally the conclusion became inescapable. In an article appearing in the *Annales de chimie et de physique* in 1821, Fresnel publicly committed himself to the view that light waves are exclusively transverse. Attempting a mechanical rationale, he offered a brief account of a hypothetical ether that would lend itself to transverse vibrations and yet retain the essential properties of a fluid. He then proceeded to an interpretation of polarization. Ostensibly, polarized light had its basis in ether vibrations executed in a definite, fixed plane at right angles to the direction of the wave. As for ordinary light, it could be considered "the union, or more exactly, the rapid succession, of systems of waves polarized in all directions." For Fresnel the major support for this conception of the nature of light was that it gave meaning and order to his empirical findings. His essay into ether mechanics was weak and was intended only as a demonstration of the physical possibility of transverse waves. The proof came from all the indications of experience, and a rigorous mechanical justification, however desirable, seemed unnecessary. Few among Fresnel's contemporaries agreed. Even Arago, who gave his faithful support in everything else, deserted him here.

Fresnel found an effective answer to his critics in a successful application of the concept of transverse waves to double refraction. A start was made in the article of 1821, when he suggested that the two rays of double refraction correspond to perpendicular components of the vibrations of the ray incident on the doubling crystal. From this simple idea he rapidly traversed an arduous course to a full-blown mathematical theory. As usual, his approach was to work back from experience. Availing himself of the law of refraction and Huygens' law of extraordinary refraction, he proceeded to develop a series of unified constructions specifying the velocities of both the rays of double refraction. Initially he found that the velocities could be accurately represented by the semi-axes of the intersection of the wave surface with an ellipsoid of revolution. This sufficed for double refraction in uniaxial crystals, but a more general construction was needed to provide for the refracting characteristics of biaxial crystals. By substituting an ellipsoid with three unequal axes for the ellipsoid of revolution, Fresnel had the solution, or at least a partial solution.

In one crucial respect the new construction fell short of full generality. It proved valid for most doubling crystals, which show weak double refraction, but it was not adequate for those like Iceland spar, in which the separation of the rays is considerable. The final construction, in the form of an equation of the fourth degree, followed only a week after the paper of 19 November 1821, which recounted the previous results. Although he now had a general law of double refraction meeting every test of experience, Fresnel pressed on. As in the study of polarization, he was reluctant to end his investigation without showing the mechanical plausibility of his results. In two supplements to the November memoir he concerned himself with this problem. When later he prepared an account of the investigation for publication, the mechanical considerations were emphasized, and the law of double refraction was represented as a deduction from the general properties of an elastic fluid. That this obscured the actual route of discovery is unimportant. Fresnel's treatment of double refraction was an impressive synthesis, and while transverse wave motion may not have been rendered more acceptable, successful applications of the new theory built around it soon made it indispensable.

The study of double refraction was Fresnel's last major contribution to wave optics. Thereafter his responsibilities on the Lighthouse Commission absorbed the bulk of his energies. To the problems encountered here—the improvement of lenses and the design, construction, and location of the lighthouses—he brought the same inventiveness, concentration, and perseverance previously manifest in his scientific work. Yet science was not entirely forgotten in these later years. Fresnel found the time to carry out an investigation of partial reflection, to make a beginning toward a mathematical theory of dispersion, and to act as chief propagandist for the wave theory. In occasional notes and academic reports he addressed himself to topics outside of optics. Most noteworthy was his contribution to Ampère's electrodynamic molecular model. It is tempting to think that, given more time, he might have pursued further his youthful vision of restoring heat, light, and electricity to a common basis in the motions of a universal ether.

As it was, Fresnel succeeded fully in attaining his explicit goal, the establishment of the wave conception of light. Not long after his death scientific opinion definitely shifted in favor of waves and opened up the pathway leading to the deeper insights of Maxwell. In broad context Fresnel's work can be viewed as the first successful assault on the theory of imponderables and a major influence on the development of nineteenth-century energetics.

BIBLIOGRAPHY

I. Original Works. Fresnel's writings were collected in *Oeuvres complètes d'Augustin Fresnel,* Henri de Senaramont, Émile Verdet, and Léonor Fresnel, eds., 3 vols. (Paris, 1866–1870). Provided with a detailed analytical table of contents, this comprehensive edition lacks only the important notes on electrodynamics addressed to Ampère. For these, see *Mémoires sur l'électrodynamique,* Société Française de Physique, ed., 2 vols. (Paris, 1885–1887), I, 141–147.

II. Secondary Literature. The details of Fresnel's life are poorly known, and no full-length biography has been published. The most detailed account is François Arago's "Éloge historique," in Fresnel's *Oeuvres complètes,* III, 475–526. Other contemporary sources are A. J. C. Duleau, *Notice sur A. Fresnel* (Paris, 1827); an anonymous account in Vielh de Boisjoslin, ed., *Biographie universelle et portative des contemporains,* 4 vols. (Paris, 1830), II, 1770–1775; A. Marc, *Notice sur A. J. Fresnel* (Caen, 1845); and Léon Puiseux, "Fresnel," in *Notices sur Malherbe, La Place, Varignon, Rouelle, Vauquelin, Descotils, Fresnel et Dumont-d'Urville* (Caen, 1847).

Among recent accounts with biographical interest the most noteworthy are Charles Fabry, "La vie et l'oeuvre scientifique d'Augustin Fresnel," in *Revue internationale de l'enseignement,* **47** (1927), 321–345; G. A. Boutry, "Augustin Fresnel: His Time, Life and Work, 1788–1827," in *Science Progress,* **36** (1948), 587–604; and Pierre Speziali, "Augustin Fresnel et les savants genevois," in *Revue d'histoire des sciences et de leurs applications,* **10** (1957), 255–259.

The *Revue d'optique,* **6** (1927), is a centennial issue devoted entirely to Fresnel. The best starting point for an assessment of his scientific work is Verdet's introduction to the *Oeuvres complètes.* Brief but authoritative is the discussion in Vasco Ronchi, *Histoire de la lumière* (Paris, 1956), pp. 242–261. Fresnel's investigations leading to the recognition of transverse wave motion are analyzed in detail in André Chappert, "L'introduction de l'hypothèse des vibrations transversales dans l'oeuvre de Fresnel," an unpublished study done for the Diplôme d'Études Supérieures de Philosophie at the University of Paris. See also R. Silliman, "Augustin Fresnel (1788–1827) and the Establishment of the Wave Theory of Light" (thesis, Princeton University, 1968).

Robert H. Silliman

FREUD, SIGMUND (*b.* Freiberg, Moravia [now Příbor, Czechoslovakia], 6 May 1856; *d.* London, England, 23 September 1939), *psychology.*

Freud's father, Jakob, was a wool merchant in Freiberg. His mother, Amalie Nathanson, was Jakob's second wife and twenty years younger than he. Freud was the oldest child in the father's second family. An older half brother, about the age of Freud's mother and with a child of his own about Freud's age, lived nearby. Freud was to write that the confusion all this caused him as an infant sharpened his intellect and his curiosity. He also wrote of himself: "A man who has been the indisputable favorite of his mother keeps for life the feeling of a conqueror, that confidence of success that often induces real success."[1] The wool trade in Freiberg, which had made Jakob mildly prosperous, collapsed, and the family moved to Vienna in 1860. For the rest of his long life Jakob was often unemployed, and the family was at times on the brink of poverty. In this respect, Jakob provided an unheroic ideal for his son. The family was Jewish and kept to Jewish society and customs, but they were not strongly religious. The father was something of a freethinker, and the son had lost any religious beliefs by his adolescence. Freud attended Sperl Gymnasium in Vienna from the age of nine to the age of seventeen, graduating with distinction in 1873. The curriculum emphasized modern and classical languages and included mathematics. Freud was studious and was encouraged in this by his parents, who made considerable financial sacrifice for his education. They anticipated a distinguished career for their son, which anticipation he shared. Freud's unusual degree of ambition lasted well into his middle years.

In 1873 Freud entered the University of Vienna to study medicine. He chose medicine, not out of a desire to practice it, but with a vague intention of studying the human condition with scientific rigor. In choosing his career—and throughout his life—Freud placed a high ethical value on the physical sciences. He took Ernst von Brücke, professor of physiology at Vienna, as a model. Brücke was one of the founders of the Helmholtz school of German physiologists, who had accelerated the progress of that science with their own work and teaching. Freud spent three years more than was necessary in qualifying for his medical degree, which he finally received in 1881. This delay resulted from starting what he intended to be a career in biological research. He spent an increasing amount of time in Brücke's Physiological Institute from 1876 through 1882. His first studies were on the connections of a large nerve cell (Reissner's cell) that had been discovered in the spinal cord of a primitive genus of fish, and his observations made it possible to fit these cells into an evolutionary scheme. He also studied the structure of nerve fibers in living crayfish and devoted some time to the anatomy of the human brain. He had made a successful start on a research career when the poor economic prospects of his position forced him to change his plans. Brücke's two assistant professors were only ten years older than Freud, so the chance for moving up to a position with an adequate salary seemed remote. Freud met his future wife in 1882 and had to face the fact that he could not continue at the institute and support a wife. He decided to obtain the clinical experience that would gain him respectable status as a practitioner. He joined the resident staff of the Vienna General Hospital in July 1882 and remained there until August 1885, working in the various clinical departments of the hospital for short periods of time. He stayed fourteen months in the department of nervous diseases because he wished to specialize in neuropathology.

Freud did not limit his activities to training in clinical medicine while at the Vienna General Hospital. He found time to continue his anatomical research on the human brain, tracing the course of nerve tracts in the medulla oblongata. He also began a series of studies in clinical neurology. This work was in the tradition of patient investigation that he had learned at Brücke's institute, in contrast with his research on the therapeutic use of cocaine, which he began in 1884. He used the drug himself, finding it made him euphoric and able to work well. His letters to his fiancée show high hopes that the research would bring quick recognition and would enable him to afford marriage sooner. He published two articles on the use of cocaine as a stimulant, as an analgesic, and as an aid in withdrawal from morphine addiction. Within two years there were reports of cocaine addiction, and Freud's reputation was clouded. Freud spent four months studying with J. M. Charcot, the foremost French neurologist, after leaving the Vienna General Hospital.

Freud set up practice as a neuropathologist on his return from Paris and was soon married. His bride was Martha Bernays, the daughter of an intellectually distinguished German Jewish family. It had taken four years from his decision to give up a research career for marriage to become a financial possibility. His prolonged engagement had been full of near breakups and reconciliations. Freud had been extremely jealous of anyone for whom Martha showed any affection, including her mother. Since Martha was in Hamburg for much of their engagement, they left a vivid record of this tempestuous period in their letters. Freud was thirty at his marriage (1886); Martha was twenty-five. In the first decade of their marriage the couple had three sons and three daughters. Freud's professional offices were adjacent to the living quarters in their first and subsequent apartments. After he married, Freud's practice, home, family, and extensive writing occupied most of his time. In the early years of his practice he went several times a week to Kassowitz's Children's Clinic, where he headed the department of neurology. Throughout his career he was on the faculty (without chaired appointments) of the University of Vienna, where he lectured, first on neuropathology and then on psychoanalysis.

Freud's psychological life was not as smooth as the description of his everyday life might imply. Psychoanalysts have found a search for a father figure important in Freud's psychological history, his own father not having provided an adequate model. At least it is clear that he sought authoritative approbation of his career. Yet he was not swayed from a self-determined course by the successive candidates for father figure, most prominently Brücke, Josef Breuer, and Wilhelm Fliess. Brücke remained a loyal friend after Freud gave up his research career, but Freud's career was diverging too far from Brücke's for Freud to seek sanction from him. Breuer was fourteen years older than Freud, had made signal contributions to neurophysiology in his younger years, and was a distinguished physician. They culminated a decade of collaboration with their joint publication of *Studies in Hysteria* (1895), which described the clinical experience that was one of Freud's bases for psychoanalysis. Breuer was unwilling to join Freud in the radical innovations of psychoanalysis; he was dubious about the emphasis on sex that developed and, being established, did not share Freud's driving ambition. The publication of their joint work came near the end of their collaboration. Freud harshly criticized Breuer's personality in later years.

Fliess was a Berlin physician with whom Freud corresponded regularly from 1893 until 1900. During this period Freud was conducting his self-analysis and rapidly developing his psychoanalytic theories, the two being aspects of a single venture. His letters to Fliess rather fully disclose his thoughts during this crucial phase. Fliess also was developing radical theories on the periodicity of biological events (which have never appeared to have any validity). While there seems to have been little significant mutual influence, each provided the other an audience. Fliess took Breuer's place as someone who apparently could understand and who approved of Freud's ideas. Fliess broke with Freud in 1900 over a trivial matter. There is no equivalent of the Fliess correspondence, which exhibits Freud's bitterness toward Breuer, after their professional estrangement. Perhaps Freud was then intellectually more self-confident. In any event, he was soon to become the intellectual father figure of the psychoanalytic movement. The meetings of his followers began at Freud's house in 1902.

Freud was in robust health into his late sixties. He was bothered, but never disabled, by a number of afflictions, including some intestinal problems that he considered psychosomatic. World War I was difficult for the Viennese, with food and fuel in short supply. There was the stress of having two sons in combat. The shortage of cigars was also an affliction for Freud, who had been accustomed to smoking fifteen to twenty each day, preferably Schimmelpenninck cigars from Holland. It was a sign of Freud's vigor that he came through all this without a decline in health. In 1923 cancer of the jaw, the disease that led to his death, was detected. From then on, he had repeated operations, metal appliances were put in his jaw to replace the bone removed, and he was frequently in pain. He preferred to remain mentally alert rather than take pain-killing drugs. After 1923 he wrote three books and many articles, and continued his practice and his extensive correspondence.

Freud remained in Vienna even though he was well aware of the impending danger from the Nazis. He was offered foreign asylum in 1936 and 1937 but, partly out of his identification with less fortunate Jews, remained until June 1938, three months after the Nazis gained control in Austria. He was allowed to go to England after Ernest Jones managed some complicated diplomatic maneuvering and the payment of a ransom, and he died in London in September 1939.

Freud made a solid contribution to conventional neuropathology. His first book was *Aphasia,* published in 1891. It was a masterly review and critique of the literature on the subject and presented a synthetic view of the condition. Freud refuted the view, prevalent among German-speaking neurologists, that the losses of function in aphasia were due to lesions in anatomically circumscribed centers corresponding to the various functions involved in language. He demonstrated that the anatomical postulates would not fit with specific case studies and that it was necessary to assume that the cerebral areas involved in language were less circumscribed. Freud also incorporated into his synthesis the view that function could be reduced in an area, not simply canceled, by the disease. Here he relied on John Hughlings Jackson, the English neurologist. Hughlings Jackson used the term "disinvolution" to describe the lesser vulnerability to pathological weakening of cortical complexes acquired earlier in the life of the individual. Freud's book had little immediate impact, perhaps because it contained no new case material. Part of his motivation to write it must have been the desire to get at the neurological events underlying complex psychological processes. In this it foreshadowed his *Psychology for Neurologists,* which he wrote in 1895. Freud's three works on cerebral paralysis in children, published in 1891, 1893, and 1897, were immediately recognized as definitive works on the subject and have remained so valued. In them he presented his own cases from the Kassowitz clinic, as well as a review of the literature. His studies brought order out of a confusing array of paralyses.

The development of Freud's psychoanalytic thought can usefully be described as occurring in three phases. In the first phase he gradually developed his ideas during his experience in the therapy of hysteria. Breuer had some part—just how much is impossible to determine—in the formation of the ideas, and certainly held Freud back from making the large speculations that characterized the second phase. In the second phase, in the middle of the 1890's, Freud developed his ideas more rapidly and with less reference to clinical experience than he had before and would later. He formed a comprehensive theory of the determinants of human thought and behavior, which became his metapsychology. This was in large part based on previous theories. During this phase Freud had only Fliess for his critical audience. In the third phase, which lasted from the late 1890's until the end of his career, Freud elaborated greatly on the ideas developed during the first two phases. There was again much reference to his clinical experience, but it was often interpreted so that it fit his previous ideas.

The first phase of Freud's intellectual development occurred during his first years of treating hysteria. Although at the Kassowitz clinic he saw patients assumed to have definite physical damage to the nervous system, most of the patients who came to his office he considered hysterics. Hysteria was considered to have both physical and psychological causes. Most theories emphasized hereditary weakness of the nervous system as the physical cause. It was commonly considered that a psychologically traumatic event, with this background of a weak nervous system, brought on the condition. Physicians usually tried physical therapeutic approaches. In the first years of his practice Freud used bed rest and low-voltage stimulation to paralyzed limbs of hysteric patients. He had begun his practice with some knowledge of psychological therapy for hysteria; Breuer had told him in 1882 about what was to become known as the "case of Anna O." Breuer treated the patient, whom he considered a hysteric, from 1880 to 1882. Her symptoms included an intermittent paralysis of the limbs and severe speech and visual disturbances. Breuer found, rather by accident, that if the patient described in detail the manifestations of a symptom, it was relieved for a time. Breuer called this method "catharsis."

Breuer also used hypnotic suggestion with Anna O. and with other patients. He told the hypnotized patient that such-and-such a symptom would disappear and found that the symptom disappeared, at least temporarily. Hypnotic suggestion had been used for years by Liébeault and Bernheim at Nancy, and a few other physicians in Vienna were using it. When Freud left the Vienna General Hospital in 1885, he received a traveling grant to study in Paris with Charcot, who was then making hysteria the focus of his attention. He maintained that the manifestations of hysteria were regular and that the common medical opinion (prevalent in Vienna) that they were feigned by hysterics was therefore erroneous. Freud never accepted Charcot's elaborate systematization, but his reputation sanctioned Freud's taking the condition seriously, as deserving of scientific study, and his considering its psychological as well as physical aspects. Freud's growing doubt as to the efficacy of electric stimulation and other physical therapeutic techniques led him to employ Breuer's method of hypnotic suggestion. He considered the method useful and became an advocate of it in Vienna.

In 1889 Freud was using Breuer's carthartic method in conjunction with hypnosis. This gradually developed into the free association method. Instead of leading the patient to talk about the first occurrence of a symptom, he encouraged the patient to say whatever came into his mind, without exercising any conscious control over it. Freud believed that the patient exhibited parts of the network of associated ideas which had already been established during his life. The therapist could surmise those ideas which made up the neurosis from those which the patient disclosed in free association. Freud formed the essentials of his concepts of the unconscious, of repression, and of transference during the development of the free association method. Parts of the complex of associated ideas, unacceptable in the conscious thought of the patient, were repressed. They remained in the unconscious, influencing what came into consciousness, but never themselves came into consciousness. Freud made great progress in technique and concept with the case of Elizabeth von R., which he probably began in 1892. The patient could not accept her love for her brother-in-law, especially after the untimely death of her sister, repressed it, and developed hysteria. Using free association, Freud interpreted the unconscious ideas, related them to the patient, and gradually got her to accept the situation in her conscious thought. Freud found transference, the basically erotic feeling of the patient for the therapist, to be a regular development in an analysis and necessary for its success.

Freud wrote the crucial document of the second phase of the development of his psychoanalytic ideas in 1895. The "Project for a Scientific Psychology" was a comprehensive theory of the neurological events underlying human thought and behavior. The essentials of some of his central psychoanalytic concepts were in it, to be elaborated in his later writings. Freud did not publish it (it first appeared in 1954) but sent it to Fliess and discussed and revised it in their correspondence for several years. To attempt to explain human thought and behavior in terms of the structure and function of the nervous system was not unusual; an enthusiasm for physical science and a confidence in its methods for dealing with complex phenomena permeated German medicine. More specifically, two men with whom Freud was in close and frequent contact had made this attempt. Freud's professor of psychiatry at Vienna was Theodor Meynert, and he continued to work with Meynert while at the Vienna General Hospital. Meynert and Sigmund Exner, one of Brücke's two assistants at the Physiological Institute, both wrote large works correlating neurology with thought and behavior. These works resemble Freud's "Project" in their basic theories.

In the view of Meynert, Exner, and Freud, all nervous system function consisted of reflexes of a certain type. There was an analogy—sometimes implicit, sometimes explicit—between the flow of an electric current through a network of wires and the passage of nerve impulses through nervous pathways. A quantitative phenomenon (called excitation, nerve energy, or quantity in the "Project") flowed through the pathways with an unspecified force, tending to make it flow from the sensory periphery to the motor periphery of the system. The force was generated by the sense organs when they were stimulated, in proportion to the intensity and duration of the stimulation. The excitation was discharged at the motor periphery of the nervous system, primarily in triggering the contraction of muscles. Excitation was neither added nor lost during its passage through the system, so that the amount of motor activity was proportional to the amount of stimulation. There was ample evidence from neurological experiments that reflex contractions were, in general, proportional to the amount of stimulation. Since the middle of the eighteenth century, scientists had noted that the more painful the stimulation of a limb of an experimental animal, the greater the reflex flection of the limb. When Freud was at Brücke's institute, electrical recordings from nerve tracts were interpreted as supporting this view. An increase in voltage was recorded from sensory nerve tracts when the intensity of the stimulus increased. That this increase resulted from bringing into function more channels, or nerve cells, was not recognized. Experimentally based observations of spinal reflexes and the anatomical evidence that the gray matter of the brain was histologically similar to the gray matter of the spinal cord had led to the doctrine that the entire system functioned reflexly. It was assumed that food-seeking in response to somatic stimuli was a reflex response, with the central transfer of excitation taking place through brain pathways. Consciousness occurred when the excitation, on its way from sense organs to motor organs, passed through the cerebral cortex. In spinal reflexes, excitation passed through innately determined pathways. The reflex ended in a motor act, which brought about the end of the stimulation of the sense organ. The painfully stimulated limb was flexed and withdrawn. In the cortex, pathways were put into function during the life of the individual; this was the neurological event resulting in learning. The coming into function of new pathways took place when the innately determined pathways did not serve to end the excitation from the sense organs.

Freud followed Meynert in taking a baby's learning to nurse as a paradigm of the opening up of cortical pathways. Freud did so in the "Project" and in his two most important published works, *The Interpretation of Dreams* and *Three Essays on the Theory of Sexuality.* When excitation entered the infant's nervous system—the concomitant of hunger—it was first channeled through innately determined pathways. The baby kicked and screamed, which was to no avail in bringing about the ending of the influx of excitation from the somatic sense organs. Then the mother turned the baby's mouth to her nipple, the baby sucked, and the inflow from the sense organs ceased. The next time the baby was hungry, the excitation passed through the cortical pathways that had been opened up, those which served the sight of the nipple and the turning of the baby's head to the nipple. The nervous system did not transfer excitation through innate pathways or those serving learning until the sense organs were stimulated. There was no nervous function without stimulation. Meynert put it thus: "The brain . . . does not radiate its own heat; it obtains the energy underlying all cerebral phenomena from the world beyond it."[2] In the terminology of Freud's metapsychology, this became the pleasure principle, the tendency of the psychic apparatus to function so as to discharge the excitation that impinged upon it.

The outline of the distinction between the ego and the id is in the "Project." Freud defined the ego as that complex of cortical pathways that were put into function during the baby's learning to turn to the nipple and in other learning experiences. This was a term common in psychology. When the ego was again subject to the inflow of excitation, the correlate of hunger, the baby carried out the same motor acts that had previously ended the inflow. This reusing of pathways, without alteration of the pattern of transmission of excitation and without any change in the resulting behavior, Freud called the primary process in the ego. When the baby was hungry at a later time, part of the current stimuli to the sense organs was not the same as it had been when the pathways serving the primary process were put into function. For example, if the mother presented her other breast to the baby, the stimulation of the eyes would be different. To cover this situation, Freud postulated an inhibiting ego that did not allow discharge over the primary process pathways, which would result in an exact repetition of the first turning to the breast, but compared current perceptions with those making up the pathways serving the primary process. By a complex process, which Freud did not succeed in reducing to plausible mechanical terms, the necessary change in the motor act was determined by the inhibiting ego. In Freud's later formulation, the ego became roughly the equivalent of the inhibiting ego, while that part of the ego not under the control of the inhibiting ego became the id, the part of the psychic apparatus that mediated primary processes.

The whole construct depended to a large extent on certain ideas that were proper to psychology rather than neurology. Meynert and Freud accepted association psychology as an adequate statement of the determinants of human thought and behavior. For example, a law of association psychology—that simultaneous or temporally contiguous sense perceptions become associated, so that they tend to be recalled jointly—provided the background for their assumption that the sight of the nipple, the perception of hunger, etc. would have their nervous concomitants connected in the pathways of the primary process. There was of course no neurological evidence that the cortical pathways serving a visual perception and those serving the perception of a somatic state, when both had nervous excitation transmitted to them, would come into functional connection. The evidence was first behavioral, then incorporated into association psychology. German association psychology, which Freud had studied, also included the concept of affect as a quantitative entity attached to ideas. This agreed with the concept that the cortical pathway serving an idea has excitation passing through it. This association psychology was commonly described in mechanical terms and lent itself to theories of brain function.

Freud was led to his concept of the sexual origin of neuroses by this view of the function of the nervous system. In *Studies in Hysteria,* he and Breuer (Breuer is listed as the author of the theoretical section, but Freud took an equal—if not major—part in developing the ideas in it) wrote that the intense and long-lasting nervous and mental activity manifested in hysteria resulted from excitation impinging from the sex organs. The primary causes of the increase of excitation were the need for oxygen, food, and water. However, their patients were not deprived of oxygen, food, or water, so that the sex organs were "undoubtedly the most powerful source of persisting increases of excitation (and consequently of neuroses)."[3] Excitation was passing through the nervous pathways in quantity, the theory of nervous function required a sensory source for it, and the sex organs were the obvious choice. Certainly Freud's and Breuer's patients had disturbances in their sexual lives; it would be expected in lives so generally disordered. Yet the theory of nervous function led to selection of such disturbances as the essential etiology of neuroses.

Freud's idea that dreams are wish-fulfillment processes was a special instance of his view that all mental processes were wish-fufillment processes, which in turn followed from the theory of nervous function. He stated in the "Project" that by "wish" he meant the cortical pathway which had previously been opened up to discharge excitation impinging from the sense organs. The hungry baby wished for the mother's nipple because a cortical pathway representing the nipple had been part of the complex of channels put into function when the baby had first stopped the inflow of hunger excitation. In the simplest type of dream, a slightly hungry baby would dream of the nipple because there was a slight inflow of excitation from the sense organs serving hunger. If there was too much excitation flowing, the baby would wake up. Freud thought that excitation impingement of low quantity was a condition of sleep. He had not given much attention to the interpretation of dreams until after he had arrived at the theory of their wish-fulfillment nature. He made this momentous theoretical advance while he was writing the "Project" in the summer of 1895. The first dream he interpreted in detail was one he had during that summer and reported in the "Project." Thereafter he interpreted many of his own dreams as part of his regular self-analysis, using the wish-fulfillment theory as the essential interpretive tool.

Freud's observations and interpretations of his own mental states during the second phase of the development of his psychoanalytic thought were as important as all his case studies taken together. His wish-fulfillment theory was formed after the dream (which has become known as that of "Irma's injection") he had while writing the "Project." In July 1897, Freud began a regular analysis of himself, devoting some time to it each day, with the definite aim of unearthing the roots of his own character. In the fall of the same year, he reached his concept of infantile sexuality after interpreting his own dreams. The crucial phase of his self-analysis seems to have ended by 1900, but he continued it, on a regular basis, for the rest of his life.

Freud's theory of infantile sexuality was a momentous step forward in the understanding of human psychology. The theory was shaped by the "Project" and by Freud's powerfully working intuition. The influence of the "Project" can be traced, while only its results give evidence of his intuition. Freud's interpretation of his dreams was the central part of his accelerated self-analysis in 1897. Using the wish-fulfillment concept, he found evidence of intense mental activity, with an erotic content, in his own infancy. There is no detailed record of these dream interpretations, but the results of them are in his letters to Fliess. In October 1897, he wrote that when he was two, "*Libido* towards *matrem* was aroused; the occasion must have been the journey with her from Leipzig to Vienna, during which we spent the night together and I must have had the opportunity of seeing her *nudam.*" Libido was intended in the sense he used it later, where he described it as the sexual counterpart of hunger. In his next letter Freud described his love of his mother and jealousy of his father, stated that this was a general occurrence in early childhood, and related it to the Oedipus legend. The next letter after that described infants' desire for "sexual experiences" they had already known.

Because he held the idea of the nervous reflex as a transfer of a quantity of excitation originating at the sensory periphery, Freud had to assume that the infant must have a source of considerable excitation in order to have aroused libido and "sexual experiences." By the next month, November 1897, Freud had taken this step. He wrote to Fliess: "We must suppose that in infancy sexual release is not so much localized as it becomes later, so that zones which are later abandoned (and possibly the whole surface of the body) stimulate to some extent the production of something that is analogous to the later release of sexuality."[4] The occurrence of sexual dreams implied the existence of previous sexual experiences. The theory of nervous function implied that excitation from the sense organs had been discharged over pathways opened up during these experiences; this in turn necessitated sense-organ sources of this excitation. Freud did not need to suppose anything about sources of excitation to make the generalization that infants have mental activity that becomes related to adult sexuality. But to save his comprehensive theory he needed to postulate infantile erogenous zones. His developed theory of psychosexual development, in *Three Essays on the Theory of Sexuality,* is a great elaboration of the ideas he presented to Fliess. His later ideas are elaborations of the 1897 concept that infantile sexual experiences are shaped by the character of inflows of excitation from the sense organs.

The third phase of the development of Freud's ideas is marked by the elaboration, in terms of a wealth of clinical experience, of the ideas he pioneered in the first two phases. He also applied his psychoanalytic understanding to social theory. The pace of development was slower, but his publications from this period (after 1900) fill nineteen volumes in his collected works. The work published previously and judged psychoanalytic by the editors of the *Standard Edition* of his writings fill four volumes. His writings in neuropathology, if similarly collected, would fill an additional three or four volumes.

The Interpretation of Dreams, published in 1901, has usually been considered Freud's most important work. In the famous seventh chapter he published for the first time much of the general theory he had formulated in the "Project" in 1895. He remarked that the book had been essentially finished in 1895, but not "written down" until the summer of 1899.[5] In the seventh chapter the brain becomes the "psychic apparatus," and most other neurological terms are replaced by psychological and psychoanalytic terms (but not all terms are replaced; the basic mode of function is still called the reflex). The volume contains many detailed accounts of dreams and many interpretations, primarily of his own dreams following his formulation of the wish-fulfillment theory. In carrying out these interpretations, Freud refined his understanding of the mode of operation of the unconscious. He discussed displacement, the transfer of hate or love from one person to another, when the transfer makes the resulting conscious emotion acceptable to the ego. For example, sexual desire for the mother might be transferred to another woman. He pointed to the extensive appearance in conscious thought of symbols for repressed thought. The consciously desired woman might be wearing shoes such as the unconsciously desired mother had worn. Regression, the tendency to think in a manner that was appropriate in the earlier life of the individual, was the neurotic equivalent of earlier thought patterns in dream consciousness.

Freud published *Three Essays on the Theory of Sexuality,* the second in importance of his books, in 1905. This and *The Interpretation of Dreams* were the only two of his books that he continually revised for succeeding editions. The same concern with the quantity of excitation, its origin, and the time of its impingement that led Freud to postulate infantile sources of sexual excitation in 1897 shaped his elaboration of infantile psychosexual development in this book. The paradigm of the infant learning to suck was, with additions, used in describing the oral stage of development. The lips were an erogenous zone which originated excitation (now libido). The baby did not know (there were no innate processes) how to end this inflow of excitation any more than he knew how to end the inflow of excitation caused by hunger. The inflow of excitation from the lips was ended by the act of sucking. Freud had to make all the erogenous zones consistent with the obvious model of the genitals, which cease to originate excitation after "some kind of manipulation that is analogous to sucking."[6] The child's dependence on the mother for stopping the inflow of excitation, or pleasure, resulted in a psychological makeup marked by receptive dependency.

In the anal phase of infantile development the source of excitation was the anus, and the inflow of excitation was brought to an end by the passage of feces. The child might retain feces so that there would be greater mechanical effect on the anus when the feces was passed or might manipulate the anus. Toilet training interfered with the child's management of excretion for his pleasure. The psychology of this phase is dominated by obstinacy and retentiveness, with toilet training imparting defensive prohibitions, such as disgust and cleanliness, against manipulating the anus. The phallic phase foreshadows adult sexuality, with the genitals the source of excitation and infantile masturbation the means of ending the inflow. The psychology of this phase is dominated by the Oedipus complex and its derivative competitiveness. Sexual maturity, or the genital phase, had of course the same source of excitation as the phallic phase, but with ego mastery of the drives that dominated the earlier phases.

Passage through the successive stages of psychosexual development influenced the behavior of the adult. In some individuals, the psychological patterns appropriate to infantile stages were dominant in their adult life. The traits associated with the successive phases were not as tidily stated as this summary implies. It was left to Karl Abraham, one of Freud's most capable followers, to work out the character types associated with the dominance of thought patterns appropriate to each stage of psychosexual development.

The Interpretation of Dreams and *Three Essays* made evident a novel feature of Freud's thought: his emphasis on the similarity between normal and abnormal thought and behavior. Dream consciousness was very much like neurotic thought processes. The difference between normal and neurotic sexual behavior could be only a matter of the relative strength of the processes established during the individual's passage through oral, anal, and phallic phases. That normal and abnormal phenomena were so similar was by no means a new idea, but the theorists of the dominant association psychology, psychiatrists, and theorists in neurology such as Meynert had made only trivial use of the idea.

Freud's last major contribution to psychoanalytic theory was *The Ego and the Id,* published in 1923, in which he elaborated on the concept of the superego. In the "Project" he had assumed that ego (then called inhibiting ego) processes were conscious and that those of the id (a term introduced later) were unconscious. The superego was a part of the ego that did not involve consciousness. In what Freud regarded as normal development, the infant first took his mother as the desired sexual object. Oedipal fear of the father (essentially fear of castration by the father) led the infant to give up this object. Fear preventing the mother from being the object of libido, she was replaced with the mental representation of the person himself. The discharge of excitation (now libido) could take place through acts that were in accord with parental commands and therefore did not produce fear. The superego, the result of parental criticism and prohibitions, was Freud's version of conscience. Two years later Freud wrote in *Inhibitions, Symptoms and Anxiety* that guilt feelings are the result of thoughts or acts not in accord with the superego, the internal representation of the parents. In the new scheme the aim of therapy remained the same: bringing unconscious processes under the control of the conscious ego. But it was now necessary to analyze not only the relatively simple unconscious processes in the id but also the more complex processes in the superego. Freud's beginning in ego analysis was advanced especially by his daughter Anna.

The focuses in Freud's writings fit with his view on the use of psychoanalysis. He regarded psychoanalysis as important primarily as a research tool and a theory of the determinants of human thought and behavior based on his research. The therapeutic usefulness of the method and theory he considered quite secondary. He did not believe psychoanalytic therapy was efficacious except in cases of hysteria and obsessional neuroses provided that the patient was relatively young and intelligent. In keeping with this view, he wrote only four detailed case studies after *Studies in Hysteria* (1895). He used fragments of cases in the rest of his publications to advance and buttress his theoretical expositions. The elaboration of his ideas in the third phase required that the therapist interpret clinical data differently, but there is little discussion in Freud's work on how to get at clinical data or how to impart interpretations to the patient so that the patient can bring the unconscious material under the control of his ego.

Totem and Taboo, published in 1913, was Freud's first and most important volume on social theory. He took cues from Darwin's theory that the first human society consisted of a horde of brothers led by a strong father and from Sir James Frazer's *Golden Bough,* which described a universal taboo against incest and against killing the totem animal. The sons, driven by their Oedipal urges, killed the father and became leaderless. Their need for a strong leader led them to deify the totem animal, thus establishing the forerunner of religious systems. Social development depended on overcoming, with institutions which forbade incest, the Oedipal desire for the mother. Freud emphasized the continuance of hostile impulses within developed societies in *Civilization and Its Discontents* (1927). Aggression against the father was repressed by the incorporated parental image, the superego. This repression was institutionalized in social justice. Discontent was an inevitable aspect of civilization because, even though Oedipal aggression had been repressed, the wish had not; and the wish had the same power to produce guilt that the act did.

The dispersion of Freud's thought in Europe centered in the psychoanalytic movement. The weekly meetings that began at Freud's house in 1902 developed into the International Psychoanalytic Association, established at Nuremberg in 1910. Swiss participants, including Carl Jung, and of course the

Viennese, including Alfred Adler and Sándor Ferenczi, were dominant. At this meeting Ferenczi, with Freud's encouragement, proposed an authoritarian structure, with an elite determining proper psychoanalytic doctrine. Freud's attitude was expressed in a statement he made about succession: "When the empire I founded is orphaned, no one but Jung must inherit the whole thing."[7] This aspect of the organization led to the resignation of Eugen Bleuler, professor of psychiatry in Switzerland and the only European member of the association with solid academic credentials in psychiatry. This was the first instance of a failure by the psychoanalytic movement to keep open the lines of communication with European academic psychiatry, and of course it decreased the European influences of Freud's ideas. Those who were not willing to subordinate their intellects to that of Freud left the association. Alfred Adler disagreed with Freud over the importance of the Oedipus complex and left in 1911. Jung departed in 1914 over differences on the importance of sexuality and also because of personal conflicts with Freud.

The response to the developing threat of Jung's schism was the formation of the Committee, a permanent elite to guarantee the maintenance of what had already become an orthodoxy. The members of the committee agreed that if any of them wished to depart from any of "the fundamental tenets of psychoanalytical theory—for example, the conception of repression, of the unconscious, of infantile sexuality—he would promise not to do so publicly before first discussing his views with the rest."[8] The founder and for many years chairman of the committee was Ernest Jones; the other members were Abraham, Hanns Sachs, Ferenczi, Otto Rank, and, later, Max Eitingon. Freud had passed from seeking to being an intellectual father figure: Breuer was fifteen years older than Freud, Fliess a year younger, and the members of the committee were between sixteen and twenty-nine years younger than Freud. All remained loyal except Rank, who broke with Freud in 1929 after several years of agonizing over the departure from his mentor. The committee had at least equal responsibility with Freud for the authoritarian nature of the movement. In the case of Rank, Freud first welcomed Rank's radical departure from his theory of psychosexual development, in which Rank made the birth trauma crucial, but was influenced by the committee not to accept this novelty. Freud became convinced that Rank's own neurotic psychology led to his revisionism, a reason too often used by Freud and his followers to explain objections to Freud's ideas.

The cultish aspect of the European psychoanalytic movement was one of the reasons for the relatively small influence of Freud's views there. (More important reasons will emerge in the discussion below of his far greater influence in America.) Most important was that their opportunity to influence was blocked when the Nazis came to power in the early 1930's. They regarded psychoanalysis as a Jewish doctrine, proscribed it, and forced many of its adherents, the majority of whom were Jewish, to flee. Often they went first to England, where psychoanalysis was more accepted than in any country except America. With appropriate employment limited in England, many came to America, where they greatly augmented the influence of Freud's ideas.

The United States has given Freud his stature in the history of thought. Long before he was accorded any equivalent honor in Europe, he was invited to give a series of lectures at Clark University in Worcester, Massachusetts, to mark its twentieth anniversary. G. Stanley Hall, a prominent psychologist and president of Clark, extended the invitation. Freud was enthusiastically received by James Putnam, professor of neurology at Harvard, who was to become president of the new American Psychoanalytic Society in 1910. Reputable American journals were open to Freud and his followers, while in Europe they published mostly in journals that they themselves had established. American physicians were the central element in the transmission of Freud's thought. From its beginnings, they dominated the American Psychoanalytic Association. (This led to the break of this association with the International Psychoanalytic Association over the question of whether psychoanalysts should be physicians in addition to having analytic training under the supervision of the psychoanalytic organization. In 1938 the American association, opting for medical qualification, separated from the international association. Freud had repeatedly stated that medical training was not of value to psychoanalysts.) The physicians' dominance of organized psychoanalysis, and the acceptance of parts of Freud's thought by physicians outside organized psychoanalysis, led American laymen, with their general respect for physicians, to respect psychoanalysis. Only the influence on American medicine will be outlined here, the rationale being that while Freud's thought affected all Americans who studied human thought and behavior, the influence on physicians was crucial for the general acceptance of Freud and the content of the influence tended to be the same for an anthropologist or a literary critic as it did for a physician.

By 1920 most American physicians interested in neurology and psychiatry had taken some account of Freud's theories. They prided themselves on their eclecticism, and many of them had accepted part of his thought. An important reason for this was that they were familiar with psychological therapies for illnesses assumed to have important, if not exclusively, psychological causes. Adolf Meyer had emphasized the patient's specific psychological history, as Freud did, and had used counseling as therapy. William A. White was ready to include a discussion of Freud's thought in a textbook of psychiatry he published in 1909, because his own dynamic psychiatry had prepared him to accept much of Freud's work as soon as he became familiar with it. Many American physicians had begun using psychotherapeutic techniques, two variants being called persuasion and reeducation, in the first decade of the twentieth century. These methods did not carry with them the theoretical luggage that Freud's free association method did. The Americans did or did not use such methods according to each physician's estimate of their efficacy; they approached psychoanalysis in the same pragmatic way. They thus reversed Freud's position that psychoanalysis was valuable chiefly as a theory and a research method to advance the theory and only secondarily as a means of therapy. There was an open-mindedness among American physicians not evident in Europe. A. A. Brill, the most energetic advocate of Freud in the United States, had patients referred to him by physicians who were opposed to Freud's thought. They apparently acted on the assumption that for these particular cases it might work, and they did not isolate Brill for his opinions. Psychoanalysts remained part of the medical establishment, albeit a small part.

Freud's name became the one most often associated with psychotherapy in general, and the distinction between the Freudian approach and any psychotherapy was blurred for many physicians. Nevertheless, there were influences more specific than Freud's furthering of psychotherapy in general. His thought brought about a greater emphasis on early childhood and on the sexual determinants of behavior. Psychotherapy used more exploratory techniques, in an attempt to reconstruct the etiology of a disease, and less exhortation to the patient to change himself. The few members of the American Psychoanalytic Association were of course more conversant with Freud's thought, and most of them used free association in relatively pure form.

The culmination of Freud's influence on American medicine came after World War II. From 1920 until the late 1930's the number of psychoanalysts in the United States did not greatly increase. The European refugees increased their numbers in the 1930's, but it was one small group joining another. In the late 1940's and 1950's there was a rapid increase in their number. Psychiatry shared in the great increase of federal funds available for medical research and education, and the disbursement of these funds was often controlled by people strongly inclined toward a Freudian approach. Federal funds after the war financed research and academic positions that were most often filled with psychoanalysts or with men who had indicated their acceptance of analysis by undergoing analysis themselves. Nearly all the chairmen of psychiatry departments since 1946 have been psychoanalyzed. Psychoanalysis became entrenched in the medical school curriculum, often being the core of the basic course in psychiatry. The general increase in prosperity in the United States was also essential to the increased number of psychoanalysts. Psychoanalysis required far more time from the physician than any other therapy, psychological or physical, and was therefore costly. Only an affluent people could afford psychoanalysis. The sponsorship of Freud's thought by the medical establishment was an important part of the context in which one implication of his thought became influential—an implication he never intended. He had emphasized the similarity of normal and abnormal behavior. Especially in his writing on social theory, he had found aspects of mental illness manifest in society at large. An extension of this emphasis was a radical redefinition of mental illness. Mental illness had been that which was marked by bizarre symptoms. Freud's patients, for example, had psychogenic paralyses, were unable to go out into the street, or repeatedly washed their hands. American psychoanalysts only rarely saw such cases. Their patients typically had an inability to form adequate personal relationships. Such inabilities were explicable in terms of Freud's thought, but he never proposed devoting most of the resources of psychiatry to curing them. The other side of this coin was a neglect of the mentally ill who did have bizarre symptoms, mainly those in institutions, in a period in which psychiatry had far more financial support than it had ever had before.

Psychoanalysis was no longer equated with Freud's thought, but his influence remained. The libidinous inflow of excitation was no longer taken as the sole motive power for the symptoms of mental illness but was one among several drives given equal theoretical status. Yet much of Freud's description of infantile psychosexual development as the primary determinant of adult psychology was incorporated into more complex theories. Above all, his general view of the unconscious remained influential. Most psychoanalytic theories included the unconscious as the sum of processes that, while not observable consciously, determine conscious thought and are organized so as to satisfy needs, although the needs are not necessarily consciously recognized. While the psychoanalytic hegemony over American psychiatry and the medical hegemony over psychotherapy began to break up in the 1960's, there was by 1970 no clear indication of how this would affect the influence of Freud's thought.

NOTES

1. Jones, I, 5.
2. Amacher, p. 24.
3. *Studies in Hysteria,* in *Standard Edition,* II, 199–200.
4. *The Origins of Psychoanalysis,* pp. 215–232.
5. Jones, I, 351.
6. *Three Essays,* in *Standard Edition,* VII, 184.
7. Ludwig Binswanger, *Sigmund Freud: Reminiscences of a Friendship* (New York, 1957), p. 31.
8. Jones, II, 152.

BIBLIOGRAPHY

I. ORIGINAL WORKS. The definitive ed. of Freud's work is in English: *Standard Edition of the Complete Psychological Works of Sigmund Freud,* James Strachey, ed., 23 vols. (London, 1953–1966), vol. XXIV in preparation. This is a magnificently edited work, with many annotations giving both details and interpretations. It is a variorum edition and includes with each article or book a bibliography of earlier eds. in German and English. Vol. XXIV will contain a full bibliography and an index to the entire work. Freud's neurological writings (and an incomplete bibliography of his works) are listed in *The Origins of Psychoanalysis: Letters to Wilhelm Fliess, Drafts and Notes: 1887–1902,* Marie Bonaparte, Anna Freud, and Ernst Kris, eds. (New York, 1954). This includes an annotated English trans. of the "Project for a Scientific Psychology" (also in vol. I of the *Standard Edition*). An incomplete listing of the various eds. of Freud's works and of secondary works on Freud is in Alexander Grinstein, ed., *The Index of Psychoanalytic Writings,* 9 vols. (New York, 1956–1966). These vols. list works published through 1960; vols. in preparation will list works published through 1968.

II. SECONDARY LITERATURE. The standard biography of Freud remains Ernest Jones, *The Life and Work of Sigmund Freud,* 3 vols. (New York, 1953–1957). This must be used with caution regarding two of its aspects. Jones brought together a great deal of material, but he was not consistently accurate in his use of it and was too much the disciple of Freud to make very critical interpretations. For Freud's life, a recent book by Paul Roazen is somewhat corrective to Jones and otherwise useful: *Brother Animal* (New York, 1969). It has valuable biographical information on Freud, references to material not available to Jones, and discussions of the tendentious editing for publication of Freud's letters by his followers.

The Freud Archive in the Library of Congress apparently contains most of the unpublished material relevant to Freud. The largest part of it was not to be used for fifty years, but this restriction has not been applied consistently. Serious scholars should consult the library as to the possibility of using the archive. The present study is in part based on the author's *Freud's Neurological Education and Its Influence on Psychoanalytic Theory,* Psychological Issues Monograph no. 16 (New York, 1965). The discussion of Freud's American influence relies heavily on John Chynoweth Burnham, *Psychoanalysis and American Medicine, 1894–1918: Medicine, Science, and Culture,* Psychological Issues Monograph no. 20 (New York, 1967). This work and David Shakow and David Rapaport, *The Influence of Freud on American Psychology,* Psychological Issues Monograph no. 13 (New York, 1964), are unusual in their careful analyses of Freud's influence.

PETER AMACHER

FREUNDLICH, ERWIN FINLAY (*b.* Biebrich, Germany, 29 May 1885; *d.* Wiesbaden, Germany, 24 July 1964), *astronomy.*

Freundlich was the son of a German businessman, E. Philip Freundlich, and his British wife, Ellen Elisabeth Finlayson. He had four brothers and two sisters. Like his brothers he received his primary schooling in Biebrich and completed a classical education at the Dilthey School in the neighboring and larger town of Wiesbaden. After leaving this school in 1903, Freundlich worked at the dockyard in Stettin before beginning a course in naval architecture at the Technical University of Charlottenburg. After a heart condition forced him to discontinue this course for about a year, he decided to begin anew and went to Göttingen to study mathematics, physics, and astronomy. With the exception of the winter semester 1905–1906, which he spent as a student in Leipzig, the rest of his higher education was confined to Göttingen University, from which he obtained his Ph.D. in 1910 with a thesis entitled "Analytische Funktionen mit beliebig vorgeschriebenem unendlich viel blättrigem Existenzbereiche."

At the suggestion of his tutor, Felix Klein, Freundlich applied for the post of assistant at the Royal Observatory in Berlin and was appointed on 1 July 1910. In the following year Albert Einstein, having heard that Freundlich was investigating the possibility of gravitational absorption, requested Freundlich's cooperation in observing the motion of the planet Mercury. Einstein himself had his own reasons for doubting that its position would coincide with that predicted on the basis of Newtonian mechanics. Freundlich's observations fully confirmed earlier evidence for such a discrepancy, and he insisted on publishing that discovery in 1913, against the wishes of the director of the Berlin observatory. That same year he married Käte Hirschberg in a civil ceremony in the Herder House in Weimar, and a small house was built for the couple at the Berlin observatory's new site in Neubabelsberg (Berlin). The German chemist Emil Fischer, impressed by Freundlich's insistence on the validity of his revolutionary conclusion, introduced him to his wealthy friend Gustav Krupp von Bohlen und Halbach, who financed Freundlich's first solar eclipse expedition to Feodosiya in the Crimea in 1914, which unfortunately had to be abandoned owing to the outbreak of World War I. Freundlich was interned for a short time before being allowed to return to Berlin.

The object of the expedition was to test the validity of a prediction of Einstein's still incomplete theory of general relativity relating to the deflection of a ray of light from a star by the sun's gravitational field, to which Freundlich drew attention in an article published in 1914. A further prediction, also mentioned in that article, which followed from the application of Einstein's principle of equivalence to light rays, was that the wavelength of light should be increased in the presence of a strong gravitational field such as the sun's; but Freundlich was obliged to conclude that the well-known phenomenon of the solar red shift could not be regarded as constituting a decisive verification of the theory.

Not having the necessary facilities at his disposal for making new reliable observations of the solar red shift, Freundlich turned his attention to the measurement of wavelength shifts in the spectra of stars in various star systems but obtained inconclusive results because so little was known about stellar masses. He later tried to reduce this deficiency by researches on the distribution of stars in globular star clusters. An increasing amount of attention was focused on Freundlich's work after Einstein's publication of 1916 had revealed the immense significance of his theory of general relativity for the future development of physics, and after Freundlich had discussed the means of testing it in his first book, *Die Grundlagen der Einsteinschen Gravitationstheorie* (Berlin, 1916). An article by him on this subject appeared in *Naturwissenschaften* (1917), and a second edition of his book was published at Leipzig in 1920. Freundlich resigned his post in 1918 to work full-time with Einstein, financed by the Kaiser Wilhelm Gesellschaft. He always modestly regarded himself as less of a collaborator with Einstein than as a butt for the latter's highly original ideas. His occasional inability to comprehend these ideas had the salutary effect of making Einstein seek to simplify their mathematical formulation, for if one of Felix Klein's pupils could not make sense of his equations who could? Through his intimate contact with Einstein, Freundlich was the first to become thoroughly acquainted with the fundamental principles of the new gravitational theory and, as Einstein himself remarks in the foreword of Freundlich's book, he was particularly well qualified as its exponent because he had been the first to attempt to put it to the test.

After Arthur Eddington confirmed that Einstein's theory accounted quantitatively for the discrepancy in the position of the planet Mercury, on whose reality Freundlich had boldly insisted in 1913, the validity of the principle of relativity itself could no longer be doubted and Freundlich's scientific reputation was fully vindicated. Thus, in 1920, the Prussian Ministry of Culture decided to support the creation of the Einstein Institute at the Astrophysical Observatory, Potsdam; Freundlich was appointed observer in 1921 and later chief observer and professor of astrophysics. This institute was designed specifically to strengthen the empirical foundations of Einstein's gravitational theory and was equipped with an astrophysical laboratory and a powerful tower telescope for solar work, the *Einsteinturm*. Here, from 1921 to 1933, Freundlich encouraged his co-workers to tackle problems that appeared at the time to be of particular significance in the solution of the solar red-shift problem, such as the origin of the ultraviolet cyanogen bands (1924) and the measurement of the center-to-limb variation in wavelength along different radii on the solar disk (1930). Simultaneously he was supervising the construction of specially designed equipment for observing light deflection; and he planned three further eclipse expeditions, two of which (in 1922 and 1926) were unsuccessful because of bad weather conditions. The third (to Sumatra in 1929) was a complete success—even though the final result proved to be significantly in excess of what Einstein's theory had predicted.

It was typical of Freundlich that he was less concerned about the negative role of this discrepancy in casting doubt upon Einstein's assumption that the laws of motion for matter are also valid for the energy contained in a light ray than about the positive and exciting possibility that its very existence might hold the key to the still unexplained rift between relativity theory and quantum mechanics, and thereby assist the unification of the macroscopic and microscopic patterns of nature. To say that Freundlich wished to disprove Einstein is to mistake entirely the motivation which caused him in later years continually to stress the excess of his observed value for the light-deflection over that predicted by general relativity theory—a fact, incidentally, which subsequent independent eclipse experiments have served only to confirm, and for which no satisfactory interpretation has as yet been forthcoming.

When Hitler came to power in 1933, Freundlich reluctantly resigned his post in Potsdam and emigrated to Turkey, a decision partially determined by the fact that his wife's sister had died earlier that year and he had assumed the guardianship of her two young children, whose lives he considered—with some justification—to be in danger.

From 1933 to 1937 Freundlich helped to reorganize the University of Istanbul and to create a modern observatory. He also wrote, for translation into Turkish, the first astronomical textbook published in that language (1937). He left Turkey for an appointment as professor of astronomy at Charles University in Prague, but Hitler's policy toward Czechoslovakia forced him to leave this post in January 1939. One month later, in Holland, he received an offer from Sir James Irvine, principal of St. Andrews University, of a lectureship there, on the understanding that he would be encouraged to build an observatory and create a new department of astronomy. The St. Andrews University Observatory was completed in 1940. In the following year Freundlich—or Finlay-Freundlich, as he preferred to call himself since he was now resident in Scotland—was elected a fellow of the Royal Society of Edinburgh. During the rest of World War II he lectured on astronomy to undergraduate students and taught celestial navigation to Air Ministry cadets who were taking special short courses at St. Andrews as part of their basic training.

Although useful for demonstration purposes, the instruments at Freundlich's observatory scarcely constituted the basis for observational research in a rapidly expanding and increasingly competitive field, so he had the inspiration to construct the first Schmidt-Cassegrain telescope, which reduces the spherical aberration and length of tube from those of the conventional Cassegrain type and gives a plane image conveniently located just outside the back of the main mirror. It is undoubtedly more than a mere coincidence that about this time Freundlich was occupied with further studies on the structure of globular star clusters, since the Schmidt-Cassegrain arrangement is eminently suited for astrographic work. An eighteen-inch-aperture pilot model was constructed under Freundlich's supervision in the workshops of the St. Andrews University Observatory and was mounted at the Mills Observatory, Dundee, in 1949. Theoretical calculations on the design of this new telescope were carried out by E. H. Linfoot of Cambridge University. The results of tests made with this pilot model in February 1950 proved to be so encouraging that work was begun on a larger-scale telescope thirty-seven inches in diameter. Experimental researches on the preparation of multilayer coatings for interferometer plates were simultaneously being carried out at the observatory by Alan Jarrett; these led to a long and fruitful program of research on the aurora borealis, resulting in the observation of certain emission lines of the solar corona with the aid of a Fabry-Pérot interferometer by Jarrett and H. von Klüber during the total solar eclipses of 1954, 1955, and 1958. Bad weather conditions during the eclipses in 1954 and 1955 foiled Freundlich's own attempts to repeat his light-deflection experiment with the instruments he had used in 1929.

On 1 January 1951, Freundlich became the first Napier professor of astronomy at St. Andrews University. In his inaugural lecture, delivered just over a year later, he characteristically stressed the broad cultural value of the study of astronomy as well as the more specialized aims of that science and again made reference to the importance of the light-deflection experiment as a means of verifying the fundamental principles of Einstein's theory. The related problem of interpreting the nonkinematic red shifts observed in solar, stellar, and galactic spectra was one that he began to reconsider seriously during his recovery from a heart attack in 1953; and his researches led him to jeopardize his scientific reputation once again by proposing the revolutionary hypothesis that the entire range of unexplained astrophysical data could be comprehended by an empirical formula relating the red shifts to the temperature of the radiation field and the distance through it which a ray of light would have to traverse before reaching a terrestrial observer.

Apart from the objection that this interpretation denied the existence of the gravitational red shift predicted from the general relativity theory, the majority of the criticisms which were immediately raised against Freundlich's red-shift formula centered on the unreliability of the observational data that he had cited in support of it. This led him to concentrate his attention on the particular problem of the solar red shift, for which reliable measurements could be made (at any rate, in principle); and he engaged a research assistant to examine whether or not the gravitational red shift was implicit in observations of this phenomenon. The initial aim of this research was inverted by the results of independent experiments in nuclear physics using gamma rays and the earth's gravitational field instead of light rays and the sun's gravitational field, which seemed to confirm the quantitative value of Einstein's prediction. Nevertheless it served to show that Freundlich's formula is merely an alternative empirical expression of the so-called relativity-radial current interpretation of the solar red shifts; moreover, it is one that is restricted to Fraunhofer lines of moderate intensity, for which the Doppler effects associated with the solar granulation are determinative in producing the observed shifts. This conclusion, derived from an analysis only of solar observations, would appear to imply that Freundlich's hypothesis is invalid as the basis of a general interpretation of the still unexplained red shifts of stars and galaxies; but this is an inference that Freundlich himself was not prepared to draw, as is evident from his last paper on the subject (1963).

Freundlich continued to act as director of the St. Andrews observatory until he resigned his chair in 1959. In the latter half of the 1950's he composed his book *Celestial Mechanics* (1958) and made plans for his retirement to Wiesbaden.

The closing years of Freundlich's life were marred by incidents arising out of the reluctance of his successor, D. W. N. Stibbs, to grant him open access to the St. Andrews observatory in order to witness the final stages of the work on the thirty-seven-inch Schmidt-Cassegrain telescope. The tensions that thus arose occasioned, *inter alia,* the resignation of his highly skilled technician, Robert L. Waland, before the optical components were satisfactorily completed and adjusted, and partly explain why that instrument has never yielded the results of which it might otherwise have been capable. At the time of his death Freundlich was an honorary professor at the University of Mainz.

BIBLIOGRAPHY

A complete list of Freundlich's publications, collated by Tadeusz B. Slebarski, is in an obituary notice by H. von Klüber in *Astronomische Nachrichten,* **288** (May 1964–December 1965), 281–286. A less detailed obituary by the same author is in *Quarterly Journal of the Royal Astronomical Society,* **6** (Mar. 1965), 82–84. *The Alumnus Chronicle* (University of St. Andrews), no. 36 (June 1951), 23–28, contains Freundlich's article "The Schmidt-Cassegrain Telescope"; and no. 40 (June 1953), 2–14, his inaugural address, "The Educational Value of the Study of Astronomy." A detailed account of researches on the solar red-shift problem, which gives due weight to Freundlich's contributions, is Eric G. Forbes, "A History of the Solar Red Shift Problem," in *Annals of Science,* **17** (1961), 129–164.

ERIC G. FORBES

FREY, MAXIMILIAN RUPPERT FRANZ VON (*b.* Salzburg, Austria, 16 November 1852; *d.* Würzburg, Germany, 25 January 1932), *physiology.*

Frey's father, Carl, was a well-to-do merchant in Salzburg. His mother, Anna Gugg, was the daughter of a high-ranking Austrian official. Frey began his studies in medicine at Vienna, where Ernst Brücke was then teaching physiology. From there he went to Leipzig and Freiburg. As early as 1876, in Carl Ludwig's physiology laboratory at Leipzig, he began examining the functioning of the vasodilating and vasoconstrictive nerves in the salivary glands. In 1877 he graduated from Leipzig. Frey returned in 1880 to Ludwig's laboratory and remained there until 1897. He became a lecturer in physiology at Leipzig in 1882 and in 1891 was made associate professor. In 1897 he accepted a professorship of physiology at Zurich and in 1899 at Würzburg, where he remained until his death.

Frey was charming but reserved and modest and of a critical temperament. He was musical (he played the flute) and loved the Alps. He possessed tremendous scientific imagination and great ingenuity in the techniques and variation of physiological experiments.

During the first period of his career (1880–1888) Frey was concerned primarily with muscle physiology; during the second period (1889–1892) with the mechanics of circulation, e.g., through analysis of pulse and blood pressure; and during the third period (1892–1932) he became a pioneer in the investigation of the "lower senses," i.e., the sensory organs of the skin and "deep sensibility."

In muscle physiology he worked on, among other things, a comparison of the extent of a single contraction and of tetanus, including when under a load. Together with Max Gruber, Frey discovered the increased oxygen consumption of muscle in the recovery phase (1880). He investigated the role of lactic acid in muscle metabolism, the influence of inorganic ions on muscle contraction and membrane permeability, and heat production in muscle. He built an interesting apparatus (1885) for perfusing a surviving, isolated muscle.

In circulatory physiology Frey developed distortion-free recording and measuring units which helped him to answer questions concerning the course of pulse curves, reflection phenomena, and the inertia of recording levers.

From 1894 Frey was particularly preoccupied with the physiology of the skin senses and found, identified, and localized the pressure points and sensory organs for heat and cold, using appropriate methods and working on a quantitative basis (irritating hair, prickling bristle). He examined the thresholds, the summation, the adequate and inadequate stimulation of the sensory receptors, the nature of itching, the sensation of vibration (1915), and tickling (1922).

Frey proved the existence of sensory muscle receptors for the development of strength and the changing of the muscle length, thus laying the foundations for the understanding of the so-called deep sensibility (from 1913).

His laboratory produced outstanding clinicians and researchers, such as L. Krehl, P. Hoffmann, H. Rein, H. Schriever, E. Wöhlisch, H. Strughold, and F. Schellong.

BIBLIOGRAPHY

I. Original Works. Among Frey's writings are *Die Untersuchung des Pulses und ihre Ergebnisse in gesunden und kranken Zuständen* (Berlin, 1892); "Physiologie der Haut," in E. Lesser, ed., *Enzyklopädie der Haut- und Geschlechtskrankheiten* (Leipzig, 1900), pp. 387-392; *Vorlesungen über Physiologie* (Berlin, 1904); "Allgemeine Physiologie der quergestreiften Muskeln," in *Nagels Handbuch der Physiologie,* IV (Brunswick, 1909), 427-543; "Allgemeine Muskelmechanik," in R. A. Tigerstedt, ed., *Handbuch der physiologischen Methodik,* II, pt. 3 (Leipzig, 1911), 87-119; "Physiologie der Sinnesorgane der menschlichen Haut," in *Ergebnisse der Physiologie,* **9** (1910), 351-368; "Die sensorischen Funktionen der Haut und der Bewegungsorgane," in R. A. Tigerstedt, ed., *Handbuch der physiologischen Methodik,* III, pt. 1 (Leipzig, 1914), 1-45; and "Physiologie der Haut," in *J. Jadassohns Handbuch der Haut- und Geschlechtskrankheiten,* I, pt. 2 (Berlin, 1929), 1-160, written with H. Rein.

II. Secondary Literature. See P. Hoffmann, "Die wissenschaftliche Persönlichkeit Max von Freys," in *Verhandlungen der Physikalisch-medizinischen Gesellschaft zu Würzburg,* n.s. **57** (1932), 56-66. Obituaries are in *Zeitschrift für Biologie,* **92** (1932), i-v; *Münchener medizinische Wochenschrift,* **79** (1932), 315-316; E. Wöhlisch, in *Verhandlungen der Physikalisch-medizinischen Gesellschaft zu Würzburg,* n.s. **57** (1932), 52-56; H. Rein, in *Klinische Wochenschrift,* **11** (1932), 439; and in *Ergebnisse der Physiologie,* **35** (1933), 1-9, with inaccurate bibliography.

Assessments are H. Schriever, in *Neue deutsche Biographie,* V (Berlin, 1961), 419-420; K. E. Rothschuh, in *Geschichte der Physiologie* (Gottingen-Berlin-Heidelberg, 1953), pp. 156-157, with portrait; and I. Fischer, *Biographisches Lexikon der hervorragenden Ärzte der letzten 50 Jahre,* I (Berlin-Vienna, 1932), 448.

K. E. Rothschuh

FRIBERGIUS, KALBIUS. *See* **Rülein von Calw, Ulrich.**

FRIEDEL, GEORGES (*b.* Mulhouse, France, 19 July 1865; *d.* Strasbourg, France, 11 December 1933), *crystallography.*

Georges Friedel was the son of the famous chemist Charles Friedel (1832-1899), who taught mineralogy and organic chemistry at the University of Paris and was, at the same time, the curator of the mineralogical collections of the School of Mines. Charles's father was a banker in Strasbourg; his maternal grandfather was Georges Duvernoy, a co-worker of Cuvier and his successor at the Collège de France. The Friedel family had left their Alsatian home before the Franco-Prussian War. Georges spent his childhood, until the age of fifteen, in Paris, where his parents' apartment was in the building of the School of Mines. This school was to exert a profound influence on his career. He entered the École Polytechnique in 1885, having placed first in the competitive entrance examination. Upon graduation he returned to the School of Mines for a three-year course (1887-1890). Mallard was his professor of mineralogy, and his father introduced him to research in mineral synthesis. He married Hélène Berger-Levrault (1888) while still in graduate school.

As a mining engineer Friedel received an appointment in the French civil service (1891) and was put in charge of the Moulins district. In 1893 he entered the School of Mines at Saint-Étienne, where he taught courses in assaying, ferrous metallurgy, physics, mineralogy, geology, and the applications of electricity to mining. From 1899 he lectured only on geology and mineralogy, and after he became director (1907), he limited himself to mineralogy. Friedel felt strong ties to the Saint-Étienne school and declined several calls from the School of Mines in Paris. But, after World War I, he did accept the chairmanship of the Institute of Geological Sciences at the newly reopened French University of Strasbourg, where his great-grandfather Duvernoy had been the dean of the Faculty of Sciences some eighty-five years before. The return to his liberated Alsace was one of the great joys of his life. For some time before his retirement in 1930, a painful illness prevented Friedel from giving his courses, and his son Edmond substituted for him. He was confined to his room, and one of his daughters, Marie, nursed him with great devotion. His wife had died in 1920. Racked with great physical suffering, he kept his intellectual curiosity and marvelous lucidity to the end.

The work of Friedel is remarkable for its diversity. It is essentially crystallographic and mineralogical, but it deals also with petrology, geology, and even engineering and pedagogy.

Jointly with his father, Friedel first published accounts of a number of syntheses produced in a steel tube lined with platinum, at about 500°C. and under high pressure. Synthetic minerals were prepared by letting group I hydroxides and silicates or salt solutions act on mica. Among nonminerals he obtained tricalcium aluminum hexahydroxytrichloride dihydrate (1897) and a calcium aluminate (1903), both known for their twinning, and lithium metasilicate (Li_2SiO_3), which syncrystallizes with beryllium orthosilicate (Be_2SiO_4). With François Grandjean, Friedel synthesized chlorites by attacking pyroxene with alkali solutions (1909). By preparing potassium nepheline (1912) he settled the question of "excess silica" in the nepheline formula.

Friedel's work (1896–1899) established the interstitial nature of zeolitic water, which can be replaced by many liquids and gases in the zeolitic "sponge." He found zeolitic water in compounds other than zeolites.

In 1893 Friedel developed a method for the accurate measurement of path-difference that is based on the restoration of elliptically polarized light to plane polarized light. This method was later applied to the study of stressed glass by R. W. Goranson and L. H. Adams.

In 1904 the law of Bravais, based as it was on speculative considerations, was far from being generally accepted. Friedel established its validity as a law of observation, regardless of theory. In this sense the law of Bravais is truly Friedel's: given any crystalline species with sufficient morphological development, it is always possible (and herein lies the law) to find a lattice such that the spacing $d(hkl)$ of a family of parallel nets is, to a first approximation, a measure of the frequency of occurrence of the corresponding form $\{hkl\}$. Friedel determined this unique morphological lattice for hundreds of substances, thereby removing the arbitrariness of the unit lengths chosen in accordance with the law of simple indices.

Another empirical law enunciated by Friedel, and shown by Alfred Liénard to be a consequence of the law of Bravais, is the law of mean indices (1908): the cell edges, a, b, c, are roughly proportional to the sums, Σh, Σk, Σl, of the absolute values of the indices of the observed forms. After 1912, when the structural lattice, which expresses the periodicity of the crystal structure, could be determined by X-ray diffraction, Friedel noted that in many instances it did not coincide with his morphological lattice. This discrepancy, he pointed out, does not diminish but, rather, enhances the value of the morphological lattice, which remains the expression of duly observed facts. Final confirmation of the law of Bravais came with its generalization by J. D. H. Donnay and D. Harker in 1937, after Friedel's death, when it was found that the effective interplanar spacings depend not only on the lattice mode but also on the glide planes and screw axes in the space group.

In 1905 the Bravais lattice was, structurally speaking, only a hypothesis. Friedel proved its physical reality by noting that irrational threefold axes (compatible with the law of rationality but impossible in a lattice) had never been found in crystals. This fundamental observation is known as Friedel's law of rational symmetric intercepts.

Bravais and Mallard had begun the theory of twinning. In 1904 Friedel completed it and stated the general law that governs all twins: a lattice, the "twin lattice," extends through the whole crystalline edifice; it is the crystal lattice itself or one of its superlattices; its prolongation from one of the twinned crystals to another can be exact or approximate. Hence the four possibilities and the classification of twins into four classes. The theory accounted for all known twins but one: the Zinnwald twin in quartz. Friedel's very last paper (1933), correlating observations of J. Drugman and results of M. Schaskolsky and A. Schubnikow on alum, explains the exception: two pre-existing crystals unite during growth, one face of the smaller adhering to another face of the larger, in such an orientation as to have a lattice row in common. The theory was thus generalized: in addition to the four classes of triperiodic twins, monoperiodic twins, such as the Zinnwald twin, must be recognized; diperiodic ones, in which the twinned crystals would have a net in common (as in epitaxy), should also be possible.

Lehmann's so-called liquid crystals were thoroughly investigated by Friedel and his co-workers François Grandjean, Louis Royer, and his son Edmond from 1907 to 1931. Two new stases (structural types of matter), the nematic and the smectic, were found to exist between the amorphous and the crystalline. (Cholesteric substances belong to the nematic stasis.) The four stases are separated by discontinuous transformations, which justify the classification. A treatment in English is available in J. Alexander's *Colloid Chemistry* (1926); it summarizes the detailed review paper of 1922, which to this day remains the indispensable introduction to the field. Friedel's work on the mesomorphous stases is perhaps the most important of all his contributions: its many new observations and interpretations opened up most of the lines of research now pursued in this field, where it remains the basic reference.

Friedel took an immediate, although theoretical, interest in Laue's discovery of X-ray diffraction by crystals (1912). As early as 1913 he enumerated the eleven centrosymmetries that can be determined by X rays (Friedel's law, to X-ray diffractionists). Other papers deal with the role of the length of the X-ray wave train (1913), the calculation of intensities (1919), and diffraction by solid solutions (1926).

Friedel was responsible for a theory of crystal growth (1924–1927) that brings out the similarity of crystal corrosion by a slightly undersaturated solution and crystal growth in a slightly supersaturated one. The two phenomena are symmetrical with respect to the saturation point. The theory thus explains negative crystals. Curved faces are accounted for by convergent and divergent diffusion (angle effect, edge effect).

Friedel pointed out that a holoaxial hemihedry may be simulated by a holohedral crystal grown in an optically active medium. He also studied diamond, clarified its holohedry, discussed its inclusions, ascribed its birefringence to strain, and (with Ribaud, 1924) on rapid heating to 1885°C., found a new allotropic form, still unconfirmed but possibly the "white carbon" described by A. El Goresy and G. Donnay ("A New Allotropic Form of Carbon From the Ries Crater," in *Science,* **161** [1968], 363–364).

Friedel's chief geological contribution was the recognition of the first mylonite in France (with Pierre Termier, 1906). In 1907 he was awarded the Prix Joseph Labbé of the French Academy in recognition of the part he had played in the discovery of a new coalfield.

As a school administrator at Saint-Étienne, Friedel stressed laboratory work and introduced new courses in statistics, foreign languages, economics, and industrial hygiene; at Strasbourg, he planned the scientific training of geological engineers and was one of the founders of the Petroleum Institute. As a teacher he exerted an enormous influence, which is still felt: his admirable textbook *Leçons de cristallographie* (1926) was reprinted in 1964. Its often quoted preface, entitled "A Warning," is a sort of scientific testament, stressing the importance of meticulous observation and scrupulous acceptance of well-established facts.

BIBLIOGRAPHY

I. Original Works. For a complete list of Friedel's works, see Grandjean's article. Among his writings note especially "Les états mésomorphes de la matière," in *Annales de physique,* **18** (1922), 273–474; "The Mesomorphic States of Matter," in J. Alexander, *Colloid Chemistry,* I (New York, 1926), 102–136; and *Leçons de cristallographie professées à la Faculté des sciences de Strasbourg* (Paris, 1926; repr. 1964).

II. Secondary Literature. On Friedel or his work, see J. D. H. Donnay, "Memorial of Georges Friedel," in *American Mineralogist,* **19** (1934), 329–335, with condensed bibliography; F. Grandjean, "Georges Friedel 1865–1933," in *Bulletin de la Société française de minéralogie,* **57** (1934), 144–171, with bibliography, 172–183; *Memorial Volume. Georges Friedel 1865–1933* (Strasbourg–Paris, 1939), a limited ed. of 1,000 numbered copies; and A. F. Rogers, "Friedel's Law of Rational Symmetric Intercepts, With Bibliography of Irrational Three-Fold Axes of Symmetry," in *American Mineralogist,* **10** (1925), 181–187.

J. D. H. Donnay

FRIEDMANN, ALEKSANDR ALEKSANDROVICH (*b.* St. Petersburg, Russia, 29 June 1888; *d.* Leningrad, U. S. S. R., 16 September 1925), *mathematics, physics, mechanics.*

Friedmann was born into a musical family—his father, Aleksandr Friedmann, being a composer and his mother, Ludmila Vojáčka, the daughter of the Czech composer Hynek Vojáček.

In 1906 Friedmann graduated from the Gymnasium with the gold medal and immediately enrolled in the mathematics section of the department of physics and mathematics of St. Petersburg University. While still a student, he wrote a number of unpublished scientific papers, one of which, "Issledovanie neopredelennykh uravneny vtoroy stepeni" ("An Investigation of Second-degree Indeterminate Equations," 1909), was awarded a gold medal by the department. After graduation from the university in 1910, Friedmann was retained in the department to prepare for the teaching profession.

At the beginning of 1913, Friedmann began work at the aerological observatory located in Pavlovsk, near St. Petersburg. There he immersed himself in a study of the means of observing the atmosphere. In addition to synoptic and dynamic meteorology, he familiarized himself with the theory of the earth's magnetism and quickly became a prominent specialist in meteorology and related fields.

The year 1914 was marked for Friedmann by two important events: he passed the examinations for the degree of master of pure and applied mathematics at St. Petersburg University and he published in the *Geofizichesky sbornik* an important paper, "O raspredelenii temperatury vozdukha s vysotoyu" ("On the Relationship of Air Temperature to Altitude"). In this paper he examined theoretically the question of the existence of an upper temperature inversion point in the stratosphere.

In the fall of 1914, Friedmann volunteered for service in an aviation detachment, in which he worked, first on the northern front and later on other fronts, to organize aerologic and aeronavigational services. While at the front, Friedmann often participated in military flights as an aircraft observer. In the summer of 1917 he was appointed a section chief in Russia's first factory for the manufacture of measuring instruments used in aviation; he later became director of the factory. Friedmann had to relinquish this post because of the onset of heart disease. From 1918 until 1920, he was professor in the department of theoretical mechanics of Perm University.

In 1920 he returned to Petrograd and worked at the main physics observatory of the Academy of Sciences, first as head of the mathematical department and later, shortly before his death, as director of the observatory.

Friedmann's creative thought penetrated into every area of his knowledge and illuminated it with the brilliance of his disciplined mind and creative imagination. His scientific activity was concentrated in the areas of theoretical meteorology and hydromechanics. Here were manifested his mathematical talent and his unwavering striving for, and ability to attain, the concrete, practical application of solutions to theoretical problems.

Friedmann was one of the founders of dynamic meteorology. To him belong fundamental works in such areas as the theory of atmospheric vortices and vertical air fluxes. He also studied the problems of applying to aeronautics the theory of physical processes that occur in the atmosphere.

Friedmann's most important work in hydromechanics is *Opyt gidromekhaniki szhimaemoy zhidkosti* (1922). In this work he gave the fullest theory of vortical motion in a fluid and examined—and in a number of cases solved—the important problem of the possible motions of a compressible fluid under the influence of given forces.

Friedmann made a valuable contribution to Einstein's general theory of relativity. As always, his interest was not limited simply to familiarizing himself with this new field of science but led to his own remarkable investigations. Friedmann's work on the theory of relativity dealt with one of its most difficult questions, the cosmological problem. In his paper "Über die Krümmung des Raumes" (1922), he outlined the fundamental ideas of his cosmology: the supposition concerning the homogeneity of the distribution of matter in space and the consequent homogeneity and isotropy of space-time; that is, the existence of "world" time, for which, at any moment in time, the metrics of space will be identical at all points and in all directions. This theory is especially important because it leads to a sufficiently correct explanation of the fundamental phenomenon known as the "red shift." This solution of the Einstein field equations, obtained from the above propositions, is the model for any homogeneous and isotropic cosmological theory. It is interesting to note that Einstein thought that the cosmological solution to the equations of a field had to be static and had to lead to a closed model of the universe. Friedmann discarded both conditions and arrived at an independent solution. Einstein welcomed Friedmann's results because they showed the dispensability of the ad hoc cosmological term Einstein had been forced to introduce into the basic field equation of general relativity. Friedmann's interest in the theory of relativity was by no means a passing fancy. In the last years of his life, together with V. K. Frederiks, he began work on a multivolume text on modern physics. The first book, *The World as Space and Time,* is devoted to the theory of relativity, knowledge of which Friedmann considered one of the cornerstones of an education in physics.

In addition to his scientific work, Friedmann for several years taught courses in higher mathematics and theoretical mechanics at various colleges in Petrograd (the Polytechnical Institute, the Institute of Ways and Means of Communication, and the Military Naval Academy). He found time to create new and original courses, brilliant in their form and exceedingly varied in their content, which covered approximation and solution of numerical equations, differential geometry and tensor analysis, hydromechanics, applied aerodynamics, and theoretical mechanics. Friedmann's unique course in theoretical mechanics combined mathematical precision and logical continuity with original procedural and physical trends. He is rightfully considered a distinguished representative of a renowned pleiad of Russian students of mechanics to which also belonged such leading figures as Zhukovsky, Chaplygin, Krylov, and Kochin.

Friedmann died of typhoid fever at the age of thirty-seven. In 1931, he was posthumously awarded the Lenin Prize for his outstanding scientific work.

BIBLIOGRAPHY

I. Original Works. Friedmann's most important works include "Zur Theorie der Vertikaltemperaturverteilung," in *Meteorologische Zeitschrift,* **31,** no. 3 (1914), 154–156; "O raspredelenii temperatury vozdukha s vysotoyu" ("On the Relationship of Air Temperature to Altitude"), in *Geofizichesky sbornik,* **1,** pt. 1 (1914), 35–55; "Sur les tourbillons dans un liquide à température variable," in *Comptes* *rendus hebdomadaires des séances de l'Académie des sciences,* **163,** no. 9 (1916), 219–222; "O vikhryakh v zhidkosti s menyayushcheysya temperaturoy" ("On Whirlpools in a Liquid With Changing Temperature"), in *Soobshcheniya i protokoly Kharkovskago matematicheskago obshchestva,* 2nd ser., **15,** no. 4 (1917), 173–176; "Die Grössenordnung der meteorologischen Elemente und ihrer räumlichen und zeitlichen Abteilungen," in *Veröffentlichungen des Geophysikalischen Instituts der Universität Leipzig,* 2nd ser., no. 10 (1914), written with K. G. Hesselberg; "O vertikalnykh techeniakh v atmosfere" ("On Vertical Fluxes in the Atmosphere"), in *Zhurnal fiziko-matematicheskogo obshchestva pri Permskom gosudarstvennom universitete,* pt. 2 (1919), pp. 67–104; "O raspredelenii temperatury s vysotoy pri nalichnosti luchistogo teploobmena Zemli i Solntsa" ("On the Relation of Temperature to Altitude in the Presence of Radiation Heat Exchange Between the Earth and Sun"), in *Izvestiya Glavnoi geofizicheskoi observatorii,* no. 2 (1920), pp. 42–44; "O vertikalnykh i gorizontalnykh atmosfernykh vikhrvakh" ("On Vertical and Horizontal Atmospheric Whirlwinds"), *ibid.,* no. 3 (1921), pp. 3–4; *Opyt gidromekhaniki szhimaemoy zhidkosti* (Petrograd, 1922); "Über die Krümmung des Raumes," in *Zeitschrift für Physik,* **10,** no. 6 (1922), 377–386; *Mir kak prostranstvo i vremya* ("The World as Space and Time," Petrograd, 1923; 2nd ed., Moscow, 1965), written with V. K. Frederiks; "O dvizhenii szhimaemoy zhidkosti" ("On the Motion of a Compressible Liquid"), in *Izvestiya gidrologicheskogo instituta,* no. 7 (1923), pp. 21–28; "Über die Möglichkeit einer Welt mit konstanter negativer Krümmung des Raumes," in *Zeitschrift für Physik,* **21** (1924), 326–332; "O rasprostranenii preryvistosti v szhimaemoy zhidkosti" ("On the Extent of Discontinuity in a Compressible Liquid"), in *Zhurnal Russkago fiziko-khimicheskago obshchestva,* **56,** no. 1 (1924), 40–58; "O krivizne prostranstva" ("On the Curvature of Space"), *ibid.* (1924), 59–68; and "Théorie du mouvement d'un fluide compressible," in *Geographische Zeitschrift* (1924).

II. SECONDARY LITERATURE. On Friedmann and his work, see (in chronological order), A. F. Vangengeim, "A. A. Friedman," in *Klimat i pogoda,* nos. 2–3 (1925), pp. 5–7, an obituary; N. M. Gyunter, "Nauchnie trudy A. A. Freidmana" ("The Scientific Works of A. A. Friedmann"), in *Zhurnal Leningradskogo fiziko-matematicheskogo obshchestva,* **1,** no. 1 (1926), 5–11; and A. F. Gavrilov, "Pamyati A. A. Friedmanna" ("In Memory of A. S. Friedmann"), in *Uspekhi fizicheskikh nauk,* **6,** no. 1 (1926), 73–75.

See also *Geofizichesky sbornik* (Leningrad, 1927), V, pt. 1, which contains, in addition to an obituary by V. A. Steklov, E. P. Friedmann, "Pamyati A. A. Friedmanna" ("In Memory of A. A. Friedmann"), pp. 9–10; I. V. Meshchersky, "Trudy A. A. Friedmanna po gidromekhanike" ("A. A. Friedmann's Works on Hydromechanics"), pp. 57–60; and M. A. Loris-Melikov, "Raboty Friedmanna po teorii otnositelnosti" ("Friedmann's Works on the Theory of Relativity"), pp. 61–63.

Also useful is L. G. Loytsyansky and A. I. Lurie, "A. A. Friedmann," in *Trudy Leningradskogo politekhnicheskogo instituta imeni M. I. Kalinina,* no. 1 (1949), pp. 83–86.

A. T. GRIGORIAN

FRIEND, JOHN ALBERT NEWTON (*b.* Newton Abbot, Devonshire, England, 20 July 1881; *d.* Birmingham, England, 15 April 1966), *chemistry.*

The son of the Reverend Hilderic Friend, a Wesleyan missionary minister, Friend moved with his family every two or three years into a fresh circuit and consequently attended a number of schools. In 1890 the family moved to Idle-Eye Dale, near Bradford, Yorkshire. In 1896 the family moved to Ocker Hill, Tipton, Staffordshire, where he passed the examination admitting him to King Edward's High School in Birmingham. There he won a Foundation scholarship and passed the London matriculation examination in 1899 and, the following year, the London intermediate examination which qualified him to study for the B.Sc. The school awarded Friend a leaving exhibition which enabled him to proceed to Masons Science College, which had only recently become Birmingham University. There he studied chemistry under Percy Frankland and physics under J. H. Poynting. In 1902 he graduated with a B.Sc. degree with honors.

After receiving the Priestley scholarship, Friend spent a year carrying out research on Caro's permonosulfuric acid and was awarded the M.Sc. in 1903; he then became assistant science master at the Dual Watford Grammar Schools, where he taught chemistry and physics. Soon thereafter he began his researches on the corrosion of metals for which he was awarded the Carnegie Gold Medal by the Iron and Steel Institute in 1913. He demonstrated that the resistance of steel to neutral corroding media rises with increasing chromium content.

By living frugally and earning extra money from private pupils and evening classes, Friend was able to save enough to enroll in 1906 at the University of Würzburg. There under Wilhelm Manchot he carried out research on carbonyl derivatives of cuprous salts, for which he was awarded the Ph.D. in 1908.

In September 1908 Friend was appointed lecturer in chemistry at the Darlington Technical College. In October 1909 he began classes in the chemistry of paints, the first on the subject to be held outside London, and in 1910 he was awarded the D.Sc. by Birmingham University. Friend left Darlington for Worcester in 1912, to become head of the Victoria Institute Science and Technical Schools. In 1915 he became a fellow of the Institute of Chemistry, now the Royal Institute of Chemistry. The following year, in London, he was appointed lieutenant in the Anti-Gas Section of the Royal Army Medical Corps (later taken over by the Royal Engineers). In 1917 Friend was invited to act as scientific adviser to the Sea Action Committee of the Institution of Civil Engineers and carried out valuable researches on corrosion by seawater. He also conducted experiments at Southampton and Weston-super-Mare to compare the protective efficiencies of various paint coatings on steel plates exposed to similar corrosive influences.

At the end of World War I, Friend returned to his post at Worcester. In 1919 he was elected an honorary member of the Oil and Colour Chemists' Association and from 1922 to 1924 served as its honorary president. The following year (1920) he became head of the chemistry department at the Birmingham College of Advanced Technology, which in 1965 became the University of Aston in Birmingham. He was elected an honorary member of the British Association of Chemists in 1924 and, in 1958, an honorary life member of the Birmingham University Chemical Society.

After the outbreak of World War II in 1939, Friend joined the Local Defense Volunteers (later the Home Guard) and founded a chemical defense school, which was responsible for training some 50,000 Home Guard personnel in antigas measures. In 1946, having reached the age limit of sixty-five, he retired from Birmingham and was appointed lecturer in science in the service of the Central Advisory Council for Adult Education in His Majesty's Forces, in which capacity he lectured at camps in Europe, Africa, and the Near East. He returned to England in 1950 and began to lecture at various military camps in the Midlands for the Birmingham University Extra Mural Department, an activity which advancing age forced him to relinquish in 1958.

Friend's research activities constitute an unusual blend of pure and applied topics. Best known as a distinguished teacher and author, he vigorously pursued research on valence theory, persulfates, metallic corrosion, paints, linseed oil, rare earths, solubilities of salts, viscosities of organic liquids, analysis of ancient artifacts, and the history of science. Foremost among his twenty-four books is the *Textbook of Inorganic Chemistry,* of which he was editor and part author. The work, which began in 1914 and ultimately comprised twenty-two volumes, was not completed until 1930. Although most of his books deal with chemistry and related subjects, his volumes on iron in antiquity, mathematical puzzles, demonology, sympathetic magic, and witchcraft testify to the breadth of his interests.

BIBLIOGRAPHY

I. ORIGINAL WORKS. Friend's books include *The Theory of Valency* (1909); *An Introduction to the Chemistry of Paints* (London, 1910); *Elementary Domestic Chemistry* (London, 1911); *The Corrosion of Iron and Steel* (London, 1911); *Textbook of Inorganic Chemistry,* 22 vols. (London, 1914–1930); *The Chemistry of Linseed Oil* (London, 1917); *The Chemistry of Combustion* (London, 1922); *Iron in Antiquity* (London, 1926); *A Textbook of Physical Chemistry,* 2 vols. (London, 1932–1935; rev. in 1 vol., 1948); *Man and the Chemical Elements* (London, 1951); *Numbers: Fun and Facts* (New York, 1954; 2nd ed., 1957); *Words: Tricks and Traditions* (New York, 1957); *Science Data* (London, 1960); *More Numbers: Fun and Facts* (New York, 1961); *Demonology, Sympathetic Magic and Witchcraft* (London, 1961); and *Still More Numbers: Fun and Facts* (New York, 1964).

II. SECONDARY LITERATURE. G. B. Kauffman, ed., *Classics in Coordination Chemistry,* II: *Selected Papers (1798–1935)* (New York, in press), contains a short biography as well as annotated versions of two of Friend's papers on valency: "A Criticism of Werner's Theory and the Constitution of Complex Salts," in *Journal of the Chemical Society,* **93** (1908), 1006–1010, and "A Cyclic Theory of the Constitution of Metalammines and of Ferro- and Ferricyanides," *ibid.,* **109** (1916), 715–722.

GEORGE B. KAUFFMAN

FRIES, ELIAS MAGNUS (*b.* Femsjö, Sweden 15 August 1794; *d.* Uppsala, Sweden, 8 February 1878), *botany.*

Fries was born in a parsonage in the southwestern part of the province of Småland, in southern Sweden. His father was interested in natural history and inspired the same interest in his son. The area is poor in phanerogams but extremely rich in fungi, which may have contributed to Fries's becoming, even in his teens, an advanced mycologist. He graduated from the Gymnasium in Växjö and in 1811 he enrolled at the University of Lund. There his botanical interest took on a more serious character and was guided principally by the professor of botany, C. A. Agardh. Under Agardh, Fries took his degree in philosophy (*filosofie magister*) in 1814, having defended the first part of his dissertation "Novitiae florae Suecicae." From then until his death Fries was totally devoted to botany. He became a docent at the university, which gave him the right to teach there without salary. In 1819 he advanced to adjunct, which brought him a small income, and in 1828 he became *botanices demonstrator,* a slightly more lucrative post. All this time he had to depend upon his father for his living.

During his first ten years at the university Fries devoted most of his studies to mycology, soon acquiring an international reputation. In 1815 he published the first volume of his first important work in mycological systematics, *Observationes mycologicae* (2 vols., Copenhagen, 1815–1818); and in 1821, when he was only twenty-seven he began publishing his *Systema mycologicum,* the great work which, more than anything else he wrote, brought him his fame (3 vols.: I, Lund, 1821; II, in 2 pts., Lund, 1822–1823; III, 2 pts., Greifswald, 1829–1832).

For the lichens, then regarded as a natural class or order, Fries worked out a general systematics in his *Lichenum dianome nova* (Lund, 1817), partly inspired by the great Swedish lichenologist Acharius. In the second half of his twenties he was intensely absorbed by the lichens, and with his friend Christian Stenhammar, a vicar and naturalist, he published *Lichenes Sueciae exsiccati* (Lund, 1824–1827), which consisted of dried specimens of lichens and an accompanying text. His lichenological studies were crowned by his authoritative *Lichenographia Europaea reformata* (Lund, 1831), containing a survey of all known lichens of Europe and information on their distribution.

From 1835 Fries was professor of botany at Uppsala. He soon rose to a central position in Swedish botany and was regarded as its unrivaled leader. Throughout his life he was an extremely prolific writer. He strengthened his international position in mycology through a number of works, such as *Epicrisis systematis mycologici,* 2 vols. (Uppsala, 1836–1838; new ed. with the title *Hymenomycetes Europaei,* Uppsala, 1874); *Monographia hymenomycetum Sueciae,* 2 vols. (Uppsala 1857–1863), which appeared both as a series of academic dissertations and as a separate work, *Sveriges ätliga och giftiga svampar,* 10 pts. (Stockholm, 1860–1866); and *Icones selectae hymenomycetum nondum delineatorum* (I, Stockholm, 1867–1875; II, Stockholm–Uppsala, 1877–1884), the second volume of which was published, following his wishes, by his sons Thore and Robert. Among the phanerogams such critical genera as *Hieracium* (*Epicrisis generis Hieraciorum,* Uppsala, 1862), *Salix,* and *Carex* were his favorites. His long floristic experience in Skåne was summarized in his *Flora Scanica* (Uppsala, 1835).

Fries's foremost accomplishment in botany was in systematics. Almost from the beginning he showed a passion for understanding the underlying principles of this discipline and for tackling the questions concerning the real and natural relationship between plants and plant groups—all problems of great difficulty in the age before Darwin. A factor that proved critical for all his work was his encounter with the romantic German *Naturphilosophie* in the years after 1810. During his first decade as a systematist he admired Lorenz Oken and his extremely speculative system of nature, as presented in Oken's *Lehrbuch der Naturphilosophie* (1809–1811). Oken conceived of the universe as built of spiritual principles, the four "elements," which in diverse combinations and refinements constitute animals and plants. At the same time the different classes of plants reflect in different degrees the main organs of an individual plant: the root, the stem, the flower, and the fruit. In *Systema mycologicum* Fries sought to apply Oken's principles to fungus systematics. His four main groups of fungi—Coniomycetes, Hyphomycetes, Gasteromycetes, and Hymenomycetes—were thus considered as expressing diverse "cosmic moments," very reminiscent of Oken's "elements." In this work Fries also took up ideas from Oken's friend C. G. Nees von Esenbeck, whose highly romantic *System der Pilze und Schwämme* had been published in 1817. Nees argued that the fungi represent a special aspect of the vegetable world, its negative pole and autumn side, manifested in their conspicuous fruit bodies (spore organs), which seemed to dominate their vegetable parts. In the same vein Fries spoke about a *nisus reproductivus* among the fungi, which separated this plant group from all other vegetables.

Already in *Systema orbis vegetabilis* (1825) Fries had to a great extent freed himself from the influence of Oken and Nees. Yet his views still reflected the same visionary and speculative romanticism, his conviction of nature's inner spirituality and unity. He expressed his belief in a close relationship between human logic and nature's way of separating the organisms into classes, orders, genera, and species. In every taxon he found four subdivisions, which in their turn could be divided in four units of lower degree. He called this consequent quartering a double dichotomy, reflecting the dichotomous method of ordinary logical division. Thus he divided the whole plant kingdom into the four groups Dicotyledoneae, Monocotyledoneae, Heteronemeae (ferns and mosses), and Homonemeae (algae and fungi).

Later, Fries gradually turned away from the extravagant speculation of his youth. More and more he became convinced that human reason could not grasp the great scheme according to which the Creator had distributed his creatures in systematic groups. Instead, he stated that one can trace the true relationships only through painstaking observation of the different species in their natural surroundings. In this context his vitalism became more and more apparent; life represents a secret and divine force, which determines the essence of each species, and the true characteristics of species can be determined only through empirical observation of the living specimens.

Yet Fries never completely abandoned his vision of a great natural system that would cover all of the vegetable kingdom in some detail. This was to a certain degree realized in 1835 in his *Flora scanica,* and even there one could retrace fundamental points of view which had their origin in German romantic philosophy.

Three characteristics of Fries's systematics are of special importance:

1. His idealistic conception of natural relationships. He thought that all organisms were related to certain types or ideas, which they expressed and resembled in a higher or lower degree, belonging to such a type being the basis for their true affinity. In his vision the taxa constituted "spheres"; the type was in the "center" and the other members of the taxon on the "radii" at different distances from the center and facing in different directions toward other groups.

2. The distinction he drew between affinity and analogy. By "analogy" he meant a kind of similarity in the outer appearance of two or more organisms which have no inner relationship or affinity. In his terminology this meant that the analogous forms are related to different types, belong to different spheres, but are situated at the same distance from the center of their respective spheres. These concepts found their way to British biologists through William Sharp MacLeay's article "Remarks on the Identity of Certain General Laws Which Have Been Lately Observed to Regulate the Natural Distribution of Insects and Fungi" (*Transactions of the Linnean Society,* **14** [1823]).

3. His ideas on evolution. Since the 1820's Fries had been convinced that evolutionary processes had taken place within the organic world and that through the ages the organisms had passed from more primitive to more perfect stages. But for a long while he could not accept any theory of descent. Thus, according to him, all species had existed from the beginning, rude and primitive but definitely different from each other. Through the ages they had separately and gradually reached their present forms. Later, Fries had to concede that not all species had an evolutionary history separate from all other species. He began to believe that all forms within a genus had only one common ancestor and that the different species now existing within it were *temporis filiae,* daughters of time. He considered that the driving force behind this evolution was mainly a tendency within the organisms to strive toward the perfect state of the respective types or ideas, a reflection of his basically romantic vision. When, in old age, Fries had read Darwin's *Origin of Species,* he could agree with the general theory of evolution, but he hesitated before the idea of the descent of nearly all organisms from one or a few original forms. And he absolutely could not accept the mechanism of "struggle for existence" and natural selection as the main force acting in evolution.

Today Fries's renown is based primarily upon his mycological work. His views on the large taxa, e.g., the "classes" within which he ordered the fungi, certainly are obsolete. He could never admit the importance of those microscopic characters which were detected with the new and better instruments available from the 1830's. Therefore he hesitated too long when confronted with the discovery of basidia and asci (reported to him in the 1830's by the British mycologist Miles Berkeley), fundamental for the modern grouping of the main categories of fungi. Yet his distinction of different spore colors still has important taxonomic value, and he is especially remembered for his ability to describe species. In fact, according to a decree of the Seventh International Botanical Congress (Stockholm, 1950), *Systema mycologicum* forms the basis for the nomenclature within all groups of fungi except Uredinales, Ustilaginales, and Gasteromycetes.

BIBLIOGRAPHY

I. Original Works. Fries's most important works are mentioned in the text. For a detailed bibliography, see T. O. B. N. Krok, *Bibliotheca botanica Suecana* (Uppsala–Stockholm, 1925), pp. 199–215. There are facsimiles of *Systema mycologicum* and *Elenchus fugorum* (New York, 1952; Weinheim-Bergstrasse, 1960); *Monographia hymenomycetum Sueciae* (Amsterdam, 1963); and *Hymenomycetes Europaei* (Leipzig, 1937; Amsterdam, 1963).

Unpublished correspondence is in the Uppsala University library and a number of other Swedish libraries (see *Svenskt biografiskt lexikon,* XVI [Stockholm, 1965], 526); the Botanisk Centralbibliotek, Copenhagen; the Muséum National d'Histoire Naturelle, Paris; the British Museum (Natural History), London; and the Arnold Arboretum and Gray Herbarium of Harvard University.

II. Secondary Literature. On his life and work, see J. Arrhenius, "Elias Magnus Fries," in *Levnadsteckningar över K. Svenska Vetenskapsakademiens ledamöter,* II (Stockholm, 1878–1885), 195–226; Gunnar Eriksson, *Elias Fries och den romantiska biologin* (Uppsala, 1952), with a summary in English, pp. 457–462; and *Svenski biografiskt lexikon,* XVI, 522–526; and R. Fries, "Elias Fries," in *Swedish Men of Science* (Stockholm, 1952), 178–185.

Gunnar Eriksson

FRIES, JAKOB FRIEDRICH (*b.* Barby, Germany, 23 August 1773; *d.* Jena, Germany, 10 August 1843), *philosophy, physics, mathematics.*

Fries was educated in Niesky at the Moravian

Academy of the United Brethren of Herrenhut. This upbringing had a lasting influence upon him, even though he early freed himself from the religious dogmas learned in his theological studies there. In 1795 Fries went to Leipzig to study philosophy and in 1797 he transferred to Jena to study with Fichte. By 1798 he had published five essays on the relation of metaphysics to psychology. Having completed his course at Jena, he spent a year as a private tutor in Switzerland. At the same time he worked to finish his thesis, "De intuitu intellectuali," with which he qualified as docent at Jena in 1801.

In 1805 Fries was called to become an assistant professor of philosophy and elementary mathematics at Heidelberg. In 1816 he returned to Jena as full professor of theoretical philosophy. He was suspended because of political pressures following his participation in the Wartburgfest, a demonstration by liberal students in October 1817. Fries did not obtain permission to teach again at Jena until 1824, when he received a professorship of physics and mathematics. In 1825 he became professor of philosophy, a post he held for the rest of his life.

Fries considered himself Kant's most loyal disciple. He believed that Kant had finished the philosopher's task for all time and that only individual elements of his doctrine were susceptible to correction. Despite this belief Fries himself decisively altered the Kantian formulation by psychologizing Kant's transcendental idealism in his major book, *Neue oder anthropologische Kritik der Vernunft* (Heidelberg, 1807). He was opposed to all contemporary speculative systems and considered the Romantic interpretation of nature good only for aesthetics. In opposition to Schelling and his school, he went back to the attitude of critical Kantianism that held *Naturphilosophie* to be the philosophy of exact sciences (see, for example, his *Die mathematische Naturphilosophie* [Heidelberg, 1822]).

Fries also spoke for contemporary positive scientific research, for which he gained authority from his works on physiological optics and the theory of probabilities, as well as from his textbook on experimental physics. With Kant he asserted the possibility of an a priori natural science, designed to show how the categories are applicable to experience as determinations of time through universal mathematical schema and how a system of universal laws of nature arises from this union. This system encompasses the theory of pure motion, which unites Newton's mathematical approach with Kantian philosophy. (Fries's interpretation of Newton was strongly influenced by the commentary of Le Seur and Jacquier to their four-volume 1739 edition of the *Principia,* which contains the development of those mathematical propositions that Fries presented in detail in his own *Die mathematische Naturphilosophie.*)

Fries's system almost yields the philosophy of applied mathematics, although there remains the field of derivable statements a priori. Among them Fries considers the Newtonian axioms to be foremost. On the other hand, attraction and its lawfulness cannot be deduced a priori. While Fries took over Kant's classification of natural knowledge into the four disciplines of phoronomy, dynamics, mechanics, and phenomenology, he added two new ones that he designated stochiology and morphology. Stochiology treats dynamics from a comprehensive viewpoint and attempts to establish a dynamic explanation of heat and light, as well as electrical and chemical phenomena.

Whereas Fries, like Kant, explained matter dynamically—and indeed he was much more sharply opposed to the atomists than was Kant—he deviated from him considerably with regard to dynamics itself. This is illustrated particularly by his rejection of apriorism in the concrete determination of the degree of force with which masses act upon each other. In further opposition to Kant, Fries posited four types of fundamental force in the constitution of matter: attractive and repulsive forces acting at a distance as well as attractive and repulsive contact forces. For the first two types of force the simplest mode of action is given by their proportionality to $1/v^2$, for the latter two, by the proportionality

$$k = \frac{\text{density}}{mv}.$$

Fries took a final important step beyond Kant in the introduction of the organic into his system of nature through the supposition of natural instincts. This doctrine of the instincts stated that along with the determination of the forms of interaction, the law of the counteraction of the fundamental forces (that is, the behavior of the moved mass in space) must also be considered. According to Fries, the succession of appearances is caused by such instincts, which display complete forms of reciprocal action. They alone, rather than particular materials and forces, provide the explanation of physical phenomena and processes.

Physical processes may be divided into four types: gravitational (heavy masses acting at a distance); chemical (heavy masses in admixtures and dissociations with contact action); phlogistic (in which the counteraction is determined by caloric); and morphotic (in which the counteraction is determined primarily by the rigidity of the moving forces). The instincts on which these processes are based may be further divided into two classes—instincts of mechanisms and instincts of organisms. In Fries's view, all processes that are freely determined by uniformly accelerating attractive forces must be attributed to organic instincts; and all processes that are determined by attraction of bodies in contact without acceleration, and are thus reaching a state of rest in reestablished equilibrium, must be attributed to mechanical instincts.

Planetary orbits and pendulum motion may, if air resistance and friction are ignored, serve as examples of the action of organic instincts. Organizing instincts here predominate over mechanical ones, since otherwise the world, beginning in chaos, would attain motionless equilibrium in finite time. The prevalence of organizing instincts is necessary to the closed system of periodic recurrence of events required for a world without beginning and without end. Lesser cycles of events are the only ones that can be altered from the outside alone. If one supposes these comprised in greater cycles of events in which, again, the organic force predominates, and then supposes these greater cycles included in still greater ones, and so on, a lack of exact periodicity in the whole is understandable.

The distinction between organic and mechanical instincts makes it possible to distinguish between organic and inorganic nature. An inorganic (dead) body, or mechanical formation, is any that is formed according to the law of equilibrium; a living body obeys the law of self-preservation of its motion—this principle of self-preservation is the corporeal soul. The corporeal soul itself exhibits only the form of the interaction of the corporeal parts. This definition reflects Kant's determination of the organism as the *causalitas mutua* of its parts.

According to Fries's speculative natural history, the cosmos is constructed out of three elements—earth, water, and air—according to weight. In the solid core of the earth the forces have long maintained themselves in equilibrium. Above the earth, in the water and air, the equilibrium is preserved by the action of sunlight, the daily and yearly motion of the earth, and the electrical reaction of the atmosphere to daily and annual heating and cooling cycles. In addition, the vigor of the life-movements and the circulation of life as the basic vital principle also depend upon thermal-electrical relationships. "All morphotic processes are dominated by the formative instincts [*Bildungstrieben*], and specifically the mineral and the two organic instincts," Fries wrote.

The laws of crystallization display the true morphotic principle. Without denying the differences between crystal and organism (including the difference in mode of growth, namely apposition as opposed to intussusception), Fries maintained that these laws are crucial to an understanding of organic form. Indeed, organic formation to the extent that it represents a higher, correspondingly altered process, is to be understood only on the basis of crystallization. Fries called for a theory of free crystallization to expedite a theory of organic formation; he thereby thought to explain a self-maintaining organic process by means of the circuit law of the voltaic cell. It is necessary to this hypothesis, however, that the electrical currents that arise in the play of chemical combinations and dissociations flow in such a way as to transform the oxides emerging from contact with the conductor of the second class, so that the material of this conductor be replaced. Fries could thus ask if a plant might be a self-maintaining open voltaic chain whose root acts as a negative conductor while the opposite pole puts forth leaves and flowers, or if an animal might be a self-maintaining closed voltaic chain that therefore also possesses its own inherent magnetism.

Fries devised a diagram

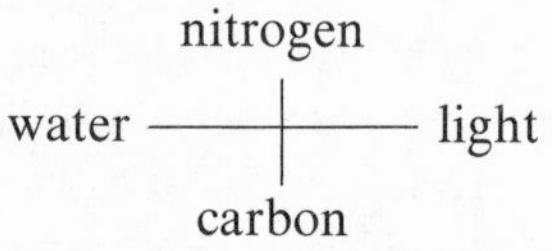

to represent the bases of all empirical theories of formation and dissolution in the three natural kingdoms. His representation combined the two polar principles of electrical and material opposition. In this system electrical opposition emerged as the principle of all animation through the activity of sunlight on water, while the differences between chemical materials, represented by the original opposition of carbon and nitrogen, is the principle of all production of form. The effect of these two original polarities on each other allowed the reconciliation of the three natural instincts posited by Fries. Specifically, the water-light polarity reconciled the mechanical-mineral instinct; the open circuit between water, carbon, and nitrogen, the vegetative one; and the closed circuit between nitrogen, light, carbon, and water (which encompasses the whole of nature), the animal instinct.

Fries's doctrine of nature thus can be understood only in connection with romantic *Naturphilosophie,* in which the idea of polarity and the importance of magnetism and galvanism were employed to account for far more than just physical events. Fries's doctrine of nature, however, employed the natural science available at the time in a serious attempt to overcome Kant's vitalism, which even a Newton of the grass-blades would not accept. Indeed, his speculations in natural philosophy were actually fruitful for the development of modern biology through the work of his student Matthias Schleiden, who sought to put into practice the idea of the reduction of the organic to crystallization processes and thereby became the founder of modern cytology.

BIBLIOGRAPHY

I. ORIGINAL WORKS. Fries's principal work is *Neue oder anthropologische Kritik der Vernunft,* 3 vols. (Heidelberg, 1807; 2nd ed. 1828–1831). His other scientific works include *Entwurf eines Systems der theoretischen Physik* (1813); *Die mathematische Naturphilosophie nach philosophischer Methode bearbeitet* (Heidelberg, 1822); and *Versuch einer Kritik der Prinzipien der Wahrscheinlichkeitsrechnung* (Brunswick, 1842). A detailed bibliography of his books and essays is contained in the biography written by his son-in-law Henke, pp. 379 ff.

A 26-vol. ed. of Fries's collected works, ed. and with intro. and index by Gert Koenig and Lutz Geldsetzer, is in publication (Aalen, 1969–).

II. SECONDARY LITERATURE. Works about Fries include T. Elsenhaus, *Fries und Kant. Ein Beitrag zur systematischen Grundlegung der Erkenntnistheorie,* 2 vols. (Giessen, 1906); Kuno Fischer, *Die beiden Kantischen Schulen in Jena,* Akademische Reden no. 2 (Stuttgart, 1862); M. Hasselblatt, *J. Fr. Fries, Seine Philosophie und seine Persoenlichkeit* (Munich, 1922); E. L. T. Henke, *J. Fr. Fries; Aus seinem handschriftlichen Nachlass dargestellt* (Leipzig, 1867); J. G. Meusel, in *Das gelehrte Teuschland oder Lexicon der jetzt lebenden teuschen Schriftsteller,* vol. II, and also in *Neuer Nekrolog der Deutschen Jgg.* (1823–1853), *Conversations-lexicon,* vol. X–A (Leipzig, 1851–1855); and C. Siegel, "Fries, Fortbildung der Kantischen Naturphilosophie," in *Geschichte der deutschen Naturphilosophie* (Leipzig, 1913), pp. 119–130.

H. M. NOBIS

FRISI, PAOLO (*b.* Milan, Italy, 13 April 1728; *d.* Milan, 22 November 1784), *mathematics, physics, astronomy.*

Frisi was a member of the Barnabite order. In physics his research must be evaluated in relation to the concepts dominant in his time, which led him to justify and interpret certain phenomena of light and aspects of electricity, referring to the vibratory motion of ether and other properties attributed to it.

As an astronomer he concerned himself with the daily movement of the earth (in *De motu diurno terrae,* awarded a prize by the Berlin Academy), the obliquity of the ecliptic, the movement of the moon, the determination of the meridian circle, and matters concerning gravity in relation to Newton's general theories.

His mathematical activity included studies on kinematics (composition of rotatory movements, etc.) and, notably, on isoperimetry. He also did work in hydraulics and was called upon to plan works for the regulation of rivers and canals in various parts of northern Italy. He was responsible for laying out the canal built in 1819 between Milan and Pavia.

Frisi wrote critical notes in honor of Galileo, Cavalieri, Newton, and d'Alembert, illustrating the contributions each had made to science and the influence each had exerted. In Italy during his lifetime he was considered a scientific authority and was also well known abroad, so much so that his major works (which he wrote in Latin) were translated into French and English. *Algebra e geometria analitica* (1782), *Meccanica* (1783), and *Cosmografia* (1785), in which he brought together the best of his work, were, for that era, very up-to-date. Frisi was an editor of *Il caffè,* a newspaper that was influenced by the thought of the French Illuminati and that exerted a notable influence on the cultural, social, and political life of Milan in the second half of the eighteenth century.

BIBLIOGRAPHY

I. ORIGINAL WORKS. Among Frisi's works are *Disquisitio mathematica in causam physicam figurae* (Milan, 1751); *De methodo fluxionum geometricarum* (Milan, 1753); *Nova electricitas theoria* (Milan, 1755); *De motu diurno terrae dissertatio* (Pisa, 1756); *Piano de' lavori da farsi per liberare* (Lucca, 1761); *Del modo di regolare i fiumi, e i torrenti* (Lucca, 1762); *De gravitate universali corporum* (Milan, 1768); *Danielis Melandri et Paulli Frisii alterius ad alterum de theoria lunae commentaria* (Parma, 1769); *Opuscoli filosofici* (Milan, 1781); *Opera,* 3 vols. (Milan, 1782–1785); and *Operette scelte* (Milan, 1825).

His many papers include "Dell'equilibrio delle cupole e delle volte," in *Atti della Società patriotica di Milano,* **1** (1773), 222 ff.; and "Dissertatio de quantitatibus maximis et minimis isoperimetricis," in *Atti dell'Accademia dei fisiocritici di Siena,* **6** (1781), 121 ff.

II. SECONDARY LITERATURE. On Frisi and his work, see Girolamo Boccardo, in *Nuova enciclopedia italiana* (Turin, 1875–1888), IX, 1005–1006; Francesco Jacquier, *Elogio accademico* (Venice, 1786); Pietro Riccardi, *Biblioteca matematica italiana dall'origine della stampe . . .* (Modena, 1870; 7th ed., 1928); and Pietro Verri, *Memorie appartenenti alla vita ed agli studi del sig. D. Paolo Frisi* (Milan, 1784), which is reprinted in *Operette scelte.*

LUIGI CAMPEDELLI

FRISIUS, GEMMA. See **Gemma Frisius, Reiner.**

FRITSCH, GUSTAV THEODOR (*b.* Cottbus, Germany, 5 March 1838; *d.* Berlin, Germany, 12 June

1927), *anatomy, physiology, zoology, anthropology, photography.*

Fritsch was the son of the royal Prussian inspector of buildings; his maternal grandfather was a well-known Silesian industrialist named Kramsta. After his Gymnasium education in Breslau he decided to work at Berlin under the physiologist Johannes Müller, whose early death prevented any personal association. After serving in a guards regiment, Fritsch began to study medicine and science at the University of Berlin and later attended the medical schools of Breslau and Heidelberg; at these schools he met Hermann von Helmholtz, Ludwig Traube, Friedrich von Frerichs, and Bernhard von Langenbeck. On 9 August 1862 he received the M.D. with a thesis on spinal cord structure. In the following year he received his medical license and, after a three-year visit to South Africa (1863–1866), during which he indulged in anthropological and geographical investigations, worked as an assistant to the Berlin anatomist Karl B. Reichert. Fritsch passed his habilitation in anatomy in 1869. In the meantime he had accompanied the Prussian solar eclipse expedition to Aden and had made a tour of Egypt. His photographic skill was valuable on these expeditions, and in Egypt he studied electric fishes.

After serving in the army during the Franco-Prussian War and winning the Iron Cross, Fritsch was appointed extraordinary professor of comparative anatomy under Reichert in 1874 but soon left to join the Prussian Venus expedition to Isfahan, Persia; he also visited Smyrna, where he made a comparative study of the fish brain, published in 1878. He now found working space in the Institute of Pathology, and Emil du Bois-Reymond created a position for him as chief of histology and photography in the department of physiology. Du Bois-Reymond revived Fritsch's interest in electric fishes, and these studies took him again to Africa.

After du Bois-Reymond retired, Fritsch worked under his successor, Theodor Wilhelm Engelmann; now, however, his interests changed to physical anthropology, in which field he again exploited his ability as a photographer. When Engelmann retired, the new director, Max Rubner, also had interests which did not coincide with Fritsch's. His friends Wilhelm Waldeyer and Adolf Fick gave him working accommodations in the Anatomy Institute. Fritsch retired in 1921, and before his death his vision became impaired by chemical trauma. In 1893 he had been made a member of the medical privy council and in 1899 an honorary ordinary professor.

Fritsch married the daughter of the University of Breslau's publisher, Ferdinand Hirt, in 1871. His financial independence, partly the result of this union, allowed him to indulge in activities which would otherwise have been impossible for him.

As Haller has pointed out, Fritsch belonged to the Kretschmer cyclothymic personality group. He demonstrated the many-sidedness of his character and his mental agility by working in several areas of science as well as having interests outside science. He had the characteristic tendency to collect data omnivorously and multisensorily but also a strong dislike of systematized and nonempirical methods. Philosophical and metaphysical subjects were avoided, and he preferred to deal with practical rather than theoretical issues. Fritsch's energy was immense, and he was happy only when active. This urge to create and to act, together with his independence of mind, made it difficult for him to accept the fact that his academic advancement had not gone beyond the level of extraordinary professor.

Fritsch's most important contribution to the medical sciences was his study of the electrophysiology of the brain. With Eduard Hitzig he published an epochal paper that established the existence of functional localization in the cerebral cortex of the dog (1870). Although the phrenologists had made similar claims at the beginning of the nineteenth century and such clinicians as Jean-Baptiste Bouillaud, Pierre-Paul Broca, and J. Hughlings Jackson had supported the concept of cerebral localization in the 1860's, Fritsch and Hitzig provided the first incontrovertible experimental evidence for it. They opened up a vast new field of cerebral physiology which is still being studied. Hitzig continued his interest in this subject but Fritsch did not, although his work on the electric fish contributed to the growing knowledge of electrophysiology.

Fritsch was a pioneer in photography, and throughout his life was a keen and able photographer. He applied his skill to photomicrography and stereoscopy in microscopic anatomy and also to other aspects of his medical and anthropological work; he was much interested in the artistic concept of the human figure. Fritsch was also a coeditor of the periodical *Internationale photographische Monatsschrift für Medizin und Naturwissenschaften,* which began publication at Leipzig in 1896.

Much of his work in anthropology and ethnology revolved about the concept of racial dominance. Fritsch believed that racial variations in visual acuity existed, and his 1908 book dealt with the "fovea" or "area centralis" (his terms). He also wrote a book on human anatomy for the anthropologist, as well as one on the physical features of the modern Egyptian. His last major publication, which appeared in 1912, dealt with the anthropological significance of scalp hair.

BIBLIOGRAPHY

I. ORIGINAL WORKS. Fritsch's work in physiology includes "Ueber die elektrische Erregbarkeit des Grosshirns," in *Archiv für Anatomie und Physiologie,* **1** (1870), 300–332, written with Eduard Hitzig, English trans. in G. Von Bonin, *The Cerebral Cortex* (Springfield, Ill., 1960), pp. 72–96.

On anatomy and zoology he wrote *De medulla spinalis textura* (Berlin, 1862), his M.D. inaugural dissertation (not seen); "Zur vergleichenden Anatomie der Amphibienherzen," in *Archiv für Anatomie und Physiologie,* **1** (1869), 654–758, his *Habilitationsschrift; Ueber das stereoskopische Sehen im Mikrotypien auf photographischen Wege* (Breslau, 1872); and *Untersuchungen über den feinern Bau des Fischgehirns, mit besonderer Berücksichtigung der Homologien bei anderen Wirbelthierklassen* (Berlin, 1878) were on his work carried out in Smyrna. See Herrick (1892), below, for titles of other publications in several fields.

Electric fish are the subject of "Vorläufiger Bericht über die von Prof. Gustav Fritsch in Aegypten angestellten neuen Untersuchungen an elektrischen Fischen," in *Archiv für Anatomie und Physiologie,* Physiologische Abteilung, **2** (1882), 61–75, 307–413, based on letters from South Africa; *Die elektrische Fische im Lichte der Descendenslehre* (Berlin, 1884); *Sitzungsberichte der K. Preussischen Akademie der Wissenschaften zu Berlin* (1885), no. 1, 119–129, and (1891), no. 2, 941–970, reports from Africa on electric fish; *Die elektrische Fische: I. Malapterurus* (Leipzig, 1887); and *Die elektrische Fische. II. Torpede* (Leipzig, 1890).

Books on anthropology are *Drei Jahre in Südafrika* (Breslau, 1868), his first book on Africa, which included anthropology, zoology, and botany; *Die Eingeborenen Südafrika's ethnologisch und anatomisch beschrieben* (Breslau), an account of native races of South Africa with numerous portraits and color plates; *Süd-Afrika bis zum Zambesi* (Leipzig, 1885); *Die Gestalt des Menschen* (Stuttgart, 1893; 2nd ed., 1905), human anatomy for anthropologists; *Aegyptische Volkstypen der Jetztzeit* (Wiesbaden, 1904); *Ueber Bau und Bedeutung der Area centralis des Menschen* (Berlin, 1908); and *Die Haupthaar und seine Bildungstätte bei den Rassen des Menschen* (Berlin, 1912).

II. SECONDARY LITERATURE. The best biography of Fritsch is Graf Haller, "Gustav Fritsch zum Gedächtnis," in *Anatomischer Anzeiger,* **64** (1927), 257–269. See also "Neurologists and Neurological Laboratories—No. 1. Professor Gustav Fritsch," in *Journal of Comparative Neurology,* **2** (1892), 84–88, probably by C. L. Herrick; C. Benda, "Gustav Fritsch zum 70. Geburtstage," in *Deutsche medizinische Wochenschrift,* **34** (1908), 605–606; and "Gustav Fritsch †," *ibid.,* **53** (1927), 1273, with portrait; "Death of Gustav Fritsch," in *Journal of the American Medical Association,* **89** (1927), 635; R. du Bois-Reymond, "Nachruf auf Gustav Fritsch," in *Medizinische Klinik,* **23** (1927), 1047–1048; and H. Grundfest, "The Different Careers of Gustav Fritsch (1838–1927)," in *Journal of the History of Medicine,* **18** (1963), 125–129 (with portrait), which contains several errors.

EDWIN CLARKE

FRITZSCHE, CARL JULIUS (*b.* Neustadt, Saxony, Germany, 29 October 1808; *d.* Dresden, Germany, 20 June 1871), *chemistry.*

Fritzsche was originally a pharmacist, served as assistant to the chemist Mitscherlich, and obtained the doctorate in botany at Berlin in 1833. He immigrated to Russia in 1834 and became manager of H. W. Struve's mineral-water works in St. Petersburg. He was elected a member of the Academy of Sciences in 1838, an associate in 1844, and full academician in 1852.

Fritzsche began a long series of researches on indigo in 1839 when he observed the action of nitric acid on indigo. In 1840 he distilled a mixture of indigo and potassium hydroxide; he correctly analyzed the base that he obtained and named it *Anilin* after the Spanish word for indigo, *añil,* derived in turn from the Arabic *an-nil.* Erdmann, editor of the *Journal für praktische Chemie,* recognized that Fritzsche's aniline was identical to *Krystallin,* which Unverdorben had prepared from indigo in 1826. Fritzsche began an association with Zinin of the University of Kazan—ultimately resulting in their sharing a laboratory at the St. Petersburg Academy—when he demonstrated in 1842 that *Benzidam,* which Zinin had obtained by reducing Mitscherlich's nitrobenzene with ammonium sulfide, was identical to aniline. In his studies of coal tar, Hofmann showed that the compounds of Unverdorben, Fritzsche, and Zinin were identical to *Kyanol,* which Runge had found in coal tar in 1834. Hofmann preferred the name, aniline, and he introduced a new method in 1845 for preparing it by using zinc and hydrochloric acid in reducing nitrobenzene.

Fritzsche continued his work on indigo, isolating and naming crysanilic and anthranilic acids. He found that when anthranilic acid is heated above its melting point it decomposes quantitatively into aniline and carbon dioxide. He also investigated uric and purpuric acids; osmium, iridium, vanadium, and their compounds; potassium bromate; and nitrogen oxides. He discovered *ortho-* and *para*-nitrophenols; compounds of hydrocarbons and picric acid; and gray tin. Fritzsche, who never became a classroom teacher, devoted his life to research and travel. Although stricken with paralysis, he finished his investigation of the dimorphism of tin shortly before he returned to Germany, where he died.

BIBLIOGRAPHY

I. ORIGINAL WORKS. Fritzsche's first publication on indigo was "Vorläufige Notiz über ein neues Zersetzungsproduct des Indigo durch Salpetersäure," in *Journal für praktische Chemie,* **16** (1839), 507–508, and was followed by his announcement of the discovery of aniline in "Ueber das Anilin, ein neues Zersetzungsproduct des Indigo," *ibid.,* **20** (1840), 453–457. His discovery of crysanilic and anthranilic acids was reported in "Ueber die Producte der Einwirkung des Kali auf das Indigblau," *ibid.,* **23** (1841), 67–83. For lists of other important papers see the Butlerov and Sheibley articles listed below.

II. SECONDARY LITERATURE. For biographical details and discussions of Fritzsche's contributions to chemistry, see Alexander M. Butlerov, "Carl Julius Fritzsche," in *Berichte der Deutschen chemischen Gesellschaft,* **5** (1872), 132–136, also printed in *Journal of the Chemical Society,* **25** (1872), 245–248; Henry M. Leicester, "N. N. Zinin, An Early Russian Chemist," in *Journal of Chemical Education,* **17** (1940), 303–306; and Fred E. Sheibley, "Carl Julius Fritzsche and the Discovery of Anthranilic Acid, 1841," *ibid.,* **20** (1943), 115–117.

A. ALBERT BAKER, JR.

FROBENIUS, GEORG FERDINAND (*b.* Berlin, Germany, 26 October 1849; *d.* Charlottenburg, Berlin, Germany, 3 August 1917), *mathematics.*

Frobenius was the son of Christian Ferdinand Frobenius, a parson, and Christiane Elisabeth Friedrich. He attended the Joachimthal Gymnasium in Berlin and then began his mathematical studies at Göttingen in 1867, completing them with a doctorate at Berlin in 1870. In the latter year he taught at the Joachimthal Gymnasium and moved to the Sophienrealschule the following year. In 1874, on the basis of his mathematical papers, Frobenius was appointed assistant professor at the University of Berlin. The next year he was made a full professor at the Eidgenössische Polytechnikum in Zurich. In 1876 he married Auguste Lehmann. Frobenius returned permanently to the University of Berlin in 1892, as professor of mathematics. Important publications led to his election to membership in the Prussian Academy of Sciences at Berlin in 1893.

Frobenius wrote many papers, a number of them of decisive importance. Several were done with other prominent researchers, particularly with Ludwig Stickelberger and Issai Schur.

Frobenius' major achievements were in group theory, which in the 1870's and 1880's, through the joining of its three historical roots—the theory of solutions of algebraic equations (Galois theory, permutation groups), geometry (finite and infinite transformation groups, Lie theory), and number theory (composition of quadratic forms, modules)—produced the concept of the abstract group, the first abstract mathematical structure in the modern sense.

Frobenius, who had become acquainted with the idea of abstract algebra in Berlin, through Leopold Kronecker and Ernst Kummer, made fundamental contributions to the concept of the abstract group in "Ueber Gruppen von vertauschbaren Elementen" (1879), written with Stickelberger, and in "Über endliche Gruppen" (1895). He exerted even greater influence on the development of group theory by means of the theory of finite groups of linear substitutions of *n* variables. This theory, which he and Schur completed in all its essential aspects, was conceived from the beginning as a representation theory of abstract groups. Its nucleus is the theory of group characters. Among the relevant works on this topic are "Über die Gruppencharaktere" (1896), "Über die Darstellung der endlichen Gruppen durch lineare Substitutionen" (1897, 1899), "Über die Komposition der Charaktere einer Gruppe" (1899), and "Über die reellen Darstellungen der endlichen Gruppen" (1906), written with Schur.

The representation theory of finite groups through linear substitutions was later to offer the possibility of surprising and important applications to difficult questions in the theory of finite groups, properly speaking, and, in the 1920's and 1930's, to group-theory questions in quantum mechanics.

BIBLIOGRAPHY

I. ORIGINAL WORKS. Frobenius' writings were brought together in *Gesammelte Abhandlungen,* J. P. Serre, ed., 3 vols. (Berlin–Heidelberg–New York, 1968). Among his works are "Ueber Gruppen von vertauschbaren Elementen," in *Journal für die reine und angewandte Mathematik,* **86** (1879), 217–262, written with L. Stickelberger; "Über endliche Gruppen," in *Sitzungsberichte der Preussischen Akademie der Wissenschaften zu Berlin* (1895), 81–112; "Über die Darstellung der endlichen Gruppen durch lineare Substitutionen," in *Monatsberichte der Preussischen Akademie der Wissenschaften zu Berlin* (1897), 994–1015, (1899), 482–500; and "Über die reellen Darstellungen der endlichen Gruppen," *ibid.* (1906), 186–208, written with I. Schur.

II. SECONDARY LITERATURE. Frobenius' work is discussed in H. Wussing, *Die Genesis des abstrakten Gruppenbegriffes* (Berlin, 1969), pp. 182–184. A short biography is N. Stuloff, "G. F. Frobenius," in *Neue Deutsche Biographie,* V (1961), 641. There are also biographies and information on works in *Deutsches biographisches Jahrbuch* (1917–1920; 2nd ed., Berlin–Leipzig, 1928), p. 654; Poggendorff, III, 481; IV, 463–464; V, 399, and VI, pt. 2, 824; and *Vierteljahrsschrift der Naturforschenden Gesellschaft in Zürich,* **62** (1917), 719.

H. WUSSING

FROST, EDWIN BRANT (*b.* Brattleboro, Vermont, 14 July 1866; *d.* Chicago, Illinois, 14 May 1935), *astronomy.*

The second son of Carlton Pennington Frost and Eliza Ann DuBois, Frost spent most of his youth at Hanover, New Hampshire, where his father held a professorship in medicine at Dartmouth College and was later dean of the medical school. He was much influenced by the astronomer C. A. Young. Frost's early education was at home, his first experience of a formal classroom being at the age of eleven. He graduated from Dartmouth in 1886 with honors in physics. After remaining at Dartmouth a few months to do graduate work in chemistry, Frost taught for a term in Hancock, New Hampshire. He spent the spring of 1887 learning practical astronomy under Young at Princeton and in the autumn returned to Dartmouth as instructor in physics and astronomy. In 1890 he left for two years' study in Europe, first for a semester at the University of Strasbourg and then with H. C. Vogel at the Potsdam Observatory. Frost returned to Dartmouth as assistant professor in astronomy, being promoted to full professor in 1895. In 1896 he married Mary Elizabeth Hazard. In 1898 he became professor of astrophysics at the new Yerkes Observatory, although he continued to spend part of his time teaching at Dartmouth until 1902. He succeeded Hale as director of the Yerkes Observatory in 1905, a position he held until 1932.

In 1915, while observing with the forty-inch telescope at Yerkes, his right retina became detached, and vision with this eye was completely lost within a year. A cataract developed in his left eye, and a hemorrhage occurred a few years later. Almost total blindness was only a minor inconvenience to him; if he had not been so afflicted, he would probably not have discovered that one can determine the temperature (in degrees Fahrenheit) by counting the number of chirps of the snowy tree cricket (*Oecanthus niveus*) in thirteen seconds and adding forty-two.

It was during his stay at Potsdam that Frost became involved in stellar spectroscopy, and the appearance of the nova T Aurigae (1891) prompted him to obtain photographs of the spectrum of this and other stars. On returning to Dartmouth he published under the title *A Treatise on Astronomical Spectroscopy* (1894) a translation and revision of Scheiner's *Die Spectralanalyse der Gestirne;* this was a standard text for many years. He made routine solar, cometary, and meteorological observations and participated in some of the first X-ray experiments outside Europe; he also made a qualitative study of the spectrum of Beta Lyrae (1895). At the 1900 eclipse he obtained photographs of the flash spectrum and also of the spectrum of the corona. He secured spectrograms of Comet Morehouse 1908 III and nova DI Lacertae 1910. He edited the extensive series of solar observations by C. H. F. Peters (1906) and subsequently Barnard's micrometric measurements of star clusters (1931).

Frost's principal research field, however, was stellar spectroscopy, specifically the determination of radial velocities of stars and especially stars of early spectral type. By 1895 radial velocities had been determined for only fifty stars. Soon after arriving at Yerkes, Frost designed for the forty-inch refractor the Bruce spectrograph; it is in no small measure due to the observations by Frost and his colleagues with this instrument that the number of stars whose radial velocities were known increased more than a hundredfold during the following forty years. Frost was the first to realize that there are systematic differences between the velocities of stars of different spectral types. He early recognized the need for calibrating the results obtained with different instruments and by a variety of methods. A natural outcome of radial velocity studies is the discovery of spectroscopic binaries; this is particularly true for stars of early spectral type, of which Frost found and determined the orbits of a considerable number.

Frost received honorary D.Sc. degrees from Dartmouth (1911) and Cambridge (1912). He was an associate of several foreign astronomical societies. He served as an assistant editor of the *Astrophysical Journal* from its inception in 1895 and as an editor from 1902 until his death.

BIBLIOGRAPHY

I. ORIGINAL WORKS. Frost's works include *A Treatise on Astronomical Spectroscopy* (Boston, 1894), a trans. and rev. of J. Scheiner's *Die Spectralanalyse der Gestirne;* "Spectroscopic Observations of Standard Velocity Stars," in *Astrophysical Journal,* **18** (1903), 237–277, written with W. S. Adams; "Radial Velocities of Twenty Stars Having Spectra of the Orion Type," in *Publications of the Yerkes Observatory,* **2** (1904), 145–250, written with W. S. Adams; "Radial Velocities of 368 Helium Stars," in *Astrophysical Journal,* **64** (1926), 1–77, written with S. B. Barrett and O. Struve; "Radial Velocities of 500 Stars of Spectral Class A," in *Publications of the Yerkes Observatory,* **7** (1929), 1–79, written with S. B. Barrett and O. Struve; and *An Astronomer's Life* (Boston-New York, 1933).

II. SECONDARY LITERATURE. An obituary notice by P. Fox appeared in *Astrophysical Journal,* **83** (1936), 1–9.

BRIAN G. MARSDEN

FROUDE, WILLIAM (*b.* Dartington, Devonshire, England, 1810; *d.* Simonstown, Cape of Good Hope [now Union of South Africa], 4 May 1879), *ship hydrodynamics.*

Froude (pronounced Frude) was the sixth son of Archdeacon Richard Hurrell Froude, rector at Dartington, and Margaret Spedding of Cumberland. He studied seven years at Oriel College , Oxford, where he was tutored in mathematics by his oldest brother, Robert Hurrell. (The latter was also a leader of the Oxford Movement, and it is noteworthy that William was the only member of the family who did not follow Newman into Roman Catholicism.) While subsequently occupied as a civil engineer, Froude came under the influence of I. K. Brunel, builder of both railways and oceangoing steamships, who stimulated his interest in naval architecture.

Froude retired from active civil engineering practice at the age of thirty-six, but he continued to give attention to various aspects of ship behavior, both recreational (he was an avid yachtsman) and technical. At Brunel's request he undertook in 1856 a resistance and rolling study of the *Great Eastern,* and his analytical and experimental work on the subject, at full as well as reduced scale, extended to many ships over many years. Of even greater importance than his control of rolling by use of bilge keels was his promotion of resistance studies on scale models. His efforts to secure the support of the Admiralty for the construction of a model towing tank at first aroused the opposition of John Scott Russell and other members of the Institution of Naval Architects, and it was not till 1870 that the sum of £2,000 was granted for this purpose. The original tank, 250 feet in length, was built on Froude's own land at Torquay only eight years before his death; he was ably assisted by his son, Robert Edmund Froude, who later built the Admiralty tank at Haslar.

William Froude's great manual skill was of inestimable value in the construction and operation of the tank, and many of his model and prototype processes and instruments continue to be employed: the use of paraffin and waterline cutting machines for models; resistance recorders; governors; roll indicators; and propeller-engine dynamometers. Use of the scale model for resistance studies was based upon his hypothesis that the total resistance could be considered the sum of wave formation and skin friction and that each could be scaled independently. He showed that the wave effects would be similar in model and prototype if the velocity were reduced in proportion to the square root of the length. This is known as Froude's law of similarity, even though it had been published by Ferdinand Reech, a professor in the school of naval architecture at Paris, in 1852 and purportedly introduced in his lectures as early as 1831. Froude formulated the law of skin-friction similarity after towing streamlined catamaran planks of various lengths and surface finishes through water over a wide range of speeds. The resistance of the smooth surfaces was found to vary with no more than the 1.85 power of the velocity, and only for the roughest did the power reach 2.0. His perceptive understanding of the effect of surface length was in close accord with present-day boundary-layer theory.

Froude was elected a fellow of the Royal Society of London in 1870. In 1876 he received both the honorary degree of LL.D. from the University of Glasgow and a Royal Medal of the Royal Society. His many writings are to be found in the *Transactions of the Institution of Naval Architects* and in reports to the British Association for the Advancement of Science. Froude's last paper, published a year before his death, was on the subject of screw propulsion, one of his early interests. While on a holiday trip to the Cape in 1879 he succumbed to dysentery just before his scheduled return to England.

BIBLIOGRAPHY

I. ORIGINAL WORKS. Froude's writings include "Experiments on the Surface-friction Experienced by a Plane Moving Through Water," in *British Association for the Advancement of Science Report,* 42nd Meeting, 1872; and "On Experiments with H.M.S. *Greyhound,*" in *Transactions of the Institution of Naval Architects,* **16** (1874), 36–73.

II. SECONDARY LITERATURE. On Froude and his work, see "Memoir of the Late William Froude, LL.D., F.R.S.," in *Transactions of the Institution of Naval Architects,* **20** (1879), 264–269; W. Abell, "William Froude," in *Transactions of the Institution of Naval Architects,* **76** (1934), which quotes his 1868 request to the Admiralty; and H. Rouse and S. Ince, *History of Hydraulics* (New York, 1963), pp. 243–256.

HUNTER ROUSE

FUBINI, GUIDO (*b.* Venice, Italy, 19 January 1879; *d.* New York, N.Y., 6 June 1943), *mathematics.*

Fubini was the son of Lazzaro Fubini, who taught mathematics at the Scuola Macchinisti in Venice, and Zoraide Torre. At the age of seventeen, after brilliantly completing secondary studies in his native city, he entered the Scuola Normale Superiore di Pisa, where Dini and Bianchi were among his teachers. In 1900 he defended a thesis on Clifford's parallelism in elliptical spaces, the results of which rapidly became classic because of their inclusion in the 1902 edition of Luigi Bianchi's treatise on differential geometry. Fubini remained in Pisa for another year to complete work on the diploma allowing him to teach at the university level. The important memoir that he wrote in this connection deals with the fundamental principles of the theory of harmonic functions in spaces of constant curvature, a subject quite different from that of his doctoral thesis.

Placed in charge of a course at the University of Catania toward the end of 1901, Fubini soon won the competition for nomination as full professor. From Catania he went to the University of Genoa and then, in 1908, to the Politecnico in Turin. There he taught mathematical analysis, and at the same time, at the University of Turin, higher analysis. In 1938 Fubini was forced to retire under the racial laws promulgated by the Fascist government. The following year, at the invitation of the Institute for Advanced Study at Princeton, he immigrated to the United States and was welcomed among the institute's members. His prudent decision to seek voluntary exile was in part dictated by his concern for the future of his two sons, both engineers. Already in poor health, he continued to teach at New York University until he died of a heart ailment at the age of sixty-four.

A man of great cultivation, fundamentally honorable and kind, Fubini possessed unequaled pedagogic talents. His witty banter and social charm made him delightful company; he was small in stature, and his voice was vigorous and pleasant. Deeply imbued with a sense of family, he wished toward the end of his life legally to add Ghiron—the maiden name of his wife, whom he had married in 1910—to his own. Those works on mathematical subjects designed to be of use to engineers resulted from his own interest in watching over his sons' studies. With regard to Luigi Bianchi, Fubini's gratitude was the equal of his respect and admiration for Bianchi as a model for both his life and his work. Upon Bianchi's death in 1928, Fubini succeeded him as coeditor of the *Annali di matematica pura ed applicata,* a position that he held until 1938. A member of several Italian scientific academies, Fubini received the royal prize of the Lincei in 1919.

Fubini was one of Italy's most fecund and eclectic mathematicians. His contributions opened new paths for research in several areas of analysis, geometry, and mathematical physics. Guided by an ever-alert geometric intuition and possessed of an absolute mastery of all the techniques of calculation, he was able to follow leads that had barely been glimpsed. His technical mastery often permitted him to discover simpler demonstrations of such theorems as those of Bernstein and Pringsheim on the development of Taylor series.

In analysis Fubini did work on linear differential equations, partial differential equations, analytic functions of several complex variables, and monotonic functions. He also studied, in the calculus of variations, the reduction of Weierstrass' integral to a Lebesgue integral; the possibility of expressing every surface integral by two simple integrations, and the converse; and the manner of deducing from the existence of $\delta^n f/\delta x^n$ and $\delta^n f/\delta y^n$ the existence of lower-order derivatives of the function $f(x,y)$. In addition, Fubini determined, with regard to the minimum-value principle, the limit of a series of functions that take on given values on the contour of a domain, by supposing that the corresponding Dirichlet integrals tend toward their lower limit; he also indicated how his procedure could be applied to the calculus of variations. Finally, he investigated nonlinear integral equations and those with asymmetric kernels.

In the field of discontinuous groups, Fubini studied linear groups and groups of movement on a Riemannian variety in order to establish their criteria of discontinuity, as well as to prove the existence of fundamental domains and to indicate the method of constructing them. He examined functions admitting of such groups, as well as the automorphic harmonic functions in a space of n dimensions, in this way generalizing certain theorems of Weierstrass. For continuous groups, he established the conditions required in order to be able to attribute a metric to them.

In the field of non-Euclidean spaces Fubini, in his thesis on Clifford's notion of parallelism, introduced sliding parameters, which made possible the transposition to elliptical geometry of certain results of ordinary differential geometry, such as Frenet's formulas and the determination of couples of applicable surfaces. His work on the theory of harmonic functions in spaces of constant curvature contains an extension of the Neumann method and of the Appell and Mittag-Leffler theorems.

The most extensive field that Fubini cultivated was that of differential projective geometry, for which he elaborated general procedures of systematic study that still bear his name. The difficulties to be surmounted in order to pass from classical to projective differential geometry arise mainly from mathematical techniques and their use. To succeed in this endeavor, Fubini utilized absolute differential calculus and certain contravariant differentials. First he defined the local application of two varieties with respect to a Lie group; then he introduced the "projective linear element" as the quotient of two covariant differential forms and demonstrated that the necessary and sufficient condition for a projective application is the equality of these elements. He envisaged homogeneous coordinates normalized from a variable point on the surface or hypersurface, and he defined the "projective normals," the "projective geodesics," and the more general geodesics. In a Euclidean space the transformation by affinity of a surface of constant curvature is characterized by its second projective normal's being extended to infinity. These fundamental investigations of metric, or affine, geometry, which were pursued by other researchers, are collected in *Geometria proiettiva differenziale* and *Introduction à la géométrie projective différentielle des surfaces,* both written in collaboration with Eduard Čech.

Fubini's contributions to mathematical physics are varied. They began during World War I with theoretical studies on the accuracy of artillery fire and then turned to such problems in acoustics and electricity as anomalies in the propagation of acoustic waves of large amplitude, the pressure of acoustic radiation, and electric circuits containing rectifiers. Fubini was also interested in the equations of membranes and vibrating diaphragms. The mathematical aspects of the engineering sciences likewise occupied his attention. A work on engineering mathematics and its applications appeared posthumously in 1954. Finally, one must note his textbooks—courses in analysis and collections of problems which have been used by many generations of students—to appreciate fully the many-faceted work of Fubini, one of the most luminous and original minds in mathematics during the first half of the twentieth century.

BIBLIOGRAPHY

I. Original Works. Fubini's writings were brought together in *Opere scelte,* 3 vols. (Rome, 1957–1962).

Among his articles are "Di un metodo per l'integrazione e lo studio delle equazioni alle derivate parziali," in *Rendiconti del Circolo matematico di Palermo,* **17** (1903), 222–235; "Nuove ricerche intorno ad alcune classi di gruppi discontinui," *ibid.,* **21** (1906), 177–187, in which, in a note, Fubini mentions seven of his articles on the same subject; "Sul principio di Dirichlet," *ibid.,* **22** (1906), 383–386; "Il principio di minimo e i teoremi di esistenza per i problemi al contorno relativi alle equazioni alle derivate parziali di ordine pari," *ibid.,* **23** (1907), 58–84, 300–301; "Applicabilità proiettiva di due superficie," *ibid.,* **41** (1916), 135–162; "Su una classe di congruenze W di carattere proiettivo," in *Atti della R. Accademia nazionale dei Lincei. Rendiconti,* **25** (1916), 144–148; "Invarianti proiettivo-differenziali delle curve tracciate su una superficie e definizione proiettivo-differenziale di una superficie," in *Annali di matematica pura ed applicata,* **25** (1916), 229–252; "Fondamenti di geometria proiettivo-differenziale," in *Rendiconti del Circolo matematico di Palermo,* **43** (1918–1919), 1–46; "Su alcune classi di congruenze di rette e sulle trasformazioni delle superficie R," in *Annali di matematica pura ed applicata,* **58** (1924), 241–257; and "Luigi Bianchi e la sua opera scientifica," *ibid.,* **62** (1929), 45–81.

Fubini's books are *Introduzione alla teoria dei gruppi discontinui e delle funzioni automorfe* (Pisa, 1908); *Lezioni di analisi matematica* (Turin, 1913; 2nd ed., 1915); *Esercizi di analisi matematica (calcolo infinitesimale) con speciale riguardo alle applicazioni* (Turin, 1920), written with G. Vivanti; *Geometria proiettiva differenziale,* 2 vols. (Bologna, 1926–1927), written with E. Čech; *Introduction à la géométrie différentielle des surfaces* (Paris, 1931), written with E. Čech; *Anomalie nella propagazione di onde acustiche di grande ampiezza* (Milan, 1935); *Circuiti elettrici contenenti raddrizzatori* (Turin, 1936); *Acustica non lineare delle onde di ampiezza* (Milan, 1938); and *La matematica dell'ingegnere e le sue applicazioni* (Bologna, 1954), written with G. Albenga.

II. Secondary Literature. See the unsigned "Guido Fubini Ghiron," in *Annali di matematica pura ed applicata,* 4th ser., **25** (1946), ix–xii; and M. Picone, in *Bollettino dell'Unione matematica italiana,* 2nd ser., **1,** no. 1 (Dec., 1946), 56–58.

Pierre Speziali

FUCHS, JOHANN NEPOMUK VON (*b.* Mattenzell, Bavaria, Germany, 15 May 1774; *d.* Munich, Germany, 5 March 1856), *chemistry, mineralogy.*

Fuchs, the son of poor peasants, proved such an outstanding student in the convent school that he was sent on to the Gymnasium. Patrons enabled him to study medicine in Vienna. He graduated from the University of Heidelberg and passed the examinations for the physician's license in Munich. Under the influence of Jacquin, Fuchs became interested in chemistry and mineralogy. The Bavarian state, which was engaging chemists in the hope of promoting the chemical industry and of reviving interest in the University of Landshut, sent Fuchs on a fact-finding trip. He visited the Bergakademie in Freiburg and traveled to Berlin and Paris. He met with W. A. Lampadius, A. G. Werner, C. S. Weiss, Klaproth, V. Rose (the younger), Guyton de Morveau, Fourcroy, Berthollet, Vauquelin, and Haüy and widened his knowledge in the course of several mineralogical and geological field trips. Upon his return to Bavaria, he passed an examination before a commission of the Bavarian Academy of Sciences resulting in his appointment, in the fall of 1805, as lecturer at the University of Landshut; he received a full professorship in May 1807. In 1810 Fuchs married the daughter of a wealthy taverner named Fahrenbacher. In the fall of 1823 Fuchs went to Munich as a member of the Bavarian Academy of Sciences and curator of the state mineralogical collection. Following the transfer of the Ludwig-Maximilian University from Landshut to Munich in 1826, Fuchs rejoined its faculty as professor of mineralogy. From 1833 on, he served as chemist on the Obermedizinalausschuss and the Supreme School Board. In 1835 he was appointed Oberberg- und Salinenrat and served as president of the Polytechnischer Verein für das Königreich Bayern.

A devout Catholic, Fuchs was thrifty, kind, and helpful and abhorred scientific arguments. Although he had to regulate his living habits strictly after contracting a lung disease in 1805, he was able to carry on his scientific work until the age of eighty-two.

Fuchs was the first titular professor of chemistry at the Ludwig-Maximilian University, where chemistry was still considered a primitive empirical science even though its role as an auxiliary science in medicine, pharmacy, and economics was not to be gainsaid. Together with Stromeyer and Döbereiner, Fuchs was one of the first in Germany to introduce practical laboratory instruction at the university level. Under his guidance, advanced students were required to carry out mineral analyses.

Fuchs became, by royal appointment, a consultant to bleaching and dyeing enterprises, breweries, distillers, starch manufacturers, paper mills, and tobacco processors. He also introduced beet-sugar refining in Bavaria.

Fuchs's scientific work was directed mainly toward the practical and empirical. He improved the spirit lamp—important for the laboratory—and the soldering iron and developed a rapid beer-testing process, the hallymetric beer test. He was the first to produce water glass and tested its use in fire protection and as varnish. In the course of research on lime, mortar, and cement, he became the first to present a clear, scientific exposition of the process of hydraulic cement setting.

Fuchs continuously stressed the importance of chemistry in the study of mineralogy. By means of a great number of analyses he was able to determine the composition of many minerals and mineral waters used for medicinal purposes.

At a time when chemical formulas, quantitative analysis, and the theory of the atom were just beginning to become common knowledge, Fuchs endeavored to solve the mystery of the structure of minerals. He confirmed the stoichiometric laws, observed isomorphism—which he called *Varikierung* ("variation")—and the cation exchange of zeolites. Opal, quartz, diamond, and soot served as objects of study in his determination of the difference between crystalline and amorphous structures.

BIBLIOGRAPHY

I. Original Works. Fuchs's writings are collected in *Gesammelte Schriften des Johann Nep. von Fuchs,* edited and with an obituary by Cajetan Georg Kaiser (Munich, 1856). His *Naturgeschichte des Mineralreichs* was published as vol. III of *Handbuch der Naturgeschichte,* Johann Andreas Wagner, ed. (Kempten, Bavaria, 1842).

II. Secondary Literature. On Fuchs and his work, see Franz von Kobell, *Denkrede auf Johann Nepomuk von Fuchs vom 28. März 1856* (Munich, 1856); Wilhelm Prandtl, "Johann Nepomuk Fuchs," Ralph E. Oesper, trans., in *Journal of Chemical Education,* **28** (1951), 136–142; and Friedrich Quietmeyer, *Zur Geschichte der Erfindung des Portlandzementes* (Berlin, 1912), pp. 88–92.

Eberhard Schmauderer

FUCHS, IMMANUEL LAZARUS (*b.* Moschin, near Posen, Germany [now Poznan, Poland], 5 May 1833; *d.* Berlin, Germany, 26 April 1902), *mathematics.*

Fuchs was a gifted analyst whose works form a bridge between the fundamental researches of Cauchy, Riemann, Abel, and Gauss and the modern theory of differential equations discovered by Poincaré, Painlevé, and Picard.

By the time Fuchs was a student at the Friedrich Wilhelm Gymnasium, his unusual aptitude in mathematics had awakened a corresponding interest in the discipline. At the University of Berlin he studied with Ernst Eduard Kummer and Karl Weierstrass, and it was the latter who introduced him to function theory, an area that was to play an important role in his own researches. Fuchs received the doctorate from Berlin in 1858, then taught first at a Gymnasium and later at the Friedrich Werderschen Trade School. In 1865 he went to the University of Berlin as a *Privatdozent,* and there he began the study of regular singular points. In 1866 he became an extraordinary professor at the university. From 1867 to 1869 Fuchs was professor of mathematics at the Artillery and Engineering School and then went as ordinary professor to Greifswald. He remained there five years, spent one year at Göttingen and then, in 1875, went to Heidelberg. In 1882 Fuchs returned to Berlin, where he became professor of mathematics, associate director of the mathematics seminars, and a member of the Academy of Sciences. He remained at Berlin until his death. For the last ten years of his life he was editor of the *Journal für die reine und angewandte Mathematik.*

Except for a few early papers in higher geometry and number theory, all of Fuchs's efforts were devoted to differential equations.

In his monumental 1812 work, *Disquisitiones*

generales circa seriem infinitam, Gauss investigated the hypergeometric series and noted that, for appropriately chosen parameters, most known functions could find representation through this series. In 1857 Riemann conjectured that functions so expressed, which satisfy a homogeneous linear differential equation of the second order with rational coefficients, might be employed in the solution of any linear differential equation. This provided an alternate approach to the power series development which had been presented by Cauchy and extended by Briot and Bouquet. With Riemann's work as inspiration these methods were synthesized and extended by Fuchs in a series of papers that began to appear in 1865.

In the real domain the method of successive approximations was first applied by Liouville (1838) to homogeneous linear differential equations of the second order and later (1864) by M. J. Caqué to the nth-order case. A second method of proving the existence of solutions derives from a method suggested by Euler (1768), developed by Cauchy (1820–1830), and refined by Lipschitz in 1876.

For a first-order equation, $dw/dz = f(z,w)$, the Cauchy-Lipschitz method can be extended to the complex domain, as can the method of limits. It was Fuchs, however, who provided the proof of the existence of solutions, satisfying initial conditions for $z = z_0$, for the linear differential equation of order n. The general homogeneous linear differential equation of order n has the form

$$(1) \qquad \frac{d^n w}{dz^n} + p_1(z)\frac{d^{n-1}w}{dz^{n-1}} + \cdots + p_n(z)w = 0,$$

and it is assumed that the $p_i(z)$ are analytic throughout a domain D in the Z plane. With z_0 and z in D, c_r are chosen so that the Taylor series,

$$w(z) = \Sigma\, c_r(z - z_0)^r,$$

formally satisfies the differential equation. The c_r are shown to be finite as long as the initial values are finite. Furthermore, if M_ν is the upper bound of $|p_\nu(z)|$ on $|z - z_0| = a$, then $p_\nu^{(r)} \leqslant M_\nu/a^r$, so that if

$$P_\nu(z) = \frac{M_\nu}{1 - \dfrac{z - z_0}{a}},$$

then

$$|p_\nu(z)| \leq |P_\nu(z)|$$

within $|z - z_0| = a$ and on the circumference.

If now w is replaced by W in equation (1), where, as above,

$$W(z) = \Sigma C_r(z - z_0)^r$$

where $C_i = |c_i|$, then

$$|w^{(r)}(z_0)| \leq W^{(r)}(z_0)$$

and, hence,

$$\Sigma |c_r(z - z_0)^r| \leq \Sigma C_r(z - z_0)^r.$$

But the circle of convergence of the dominant series can, as Fuchs showed, be readily found to be $|z - z_0| = a$. Consequently there is a solution to the differential equation, satisfying the given initial conditions, when $z = z_0$, which is expressible by a Taylor series that is absolutely and uniformly convergent within any circle, that has its center at z_0, in which the $p_i(z)$ are analytic.

The singularities of the solution are precisely the singularities of equation (1), so that, because of the linearity of this equation, there are neither movable singularities nor movable poles. To determine whether the point at infinity is a singular point, it is necessary only to effect the substitution $z = 1/Z$ and reduce the equation to the form given by (1). If the equation in Z has singularities at the origin, then the equation in z has a singular point at infinity. Thus, in all cases the singular points can be found simply by inspecting the equation itself.

Fuchs introduced the term "fundamental system" to describe n linearly independent solutions of the linear differential equation $L(u) = 0$. It is clear that for any nonsingular point such a fundamental set of solutions exists. The so-called Fuchsian theory is concerned with the same existence question in relation to an arbitrarily given singular point and, once the existence problem is solved, an investigation of the behavior of the solutions in the neighborhood of the singular point.

BIBLIOGRAPHY

Fuchs's works were published as *Gesammelte mathematische Werke,* Richard Fuchs and Ludwig Schlesinger, eds., 3 vols. (Berlin, 1904–1909). His speech as rector, given 3 Aug. 1900, is *Rede zur Gedächtnissfeier des Stifters der Berliner Universität* (Berlin, 1900).

Obituaries include E. J. Wilczynski, in *Bulletin of the American Mathematical Society,* **9** (1902), 46–49; *Atti dell'Accademia nazionale dei Lincei. Rendiconti,* 5th ser., **11** (1902), 397–398; *Bibliotheca mathematica,* 3rd ser., **3** (1902), 334; and *Enseignement mathématique,* **4** (1902), 293–294.

See also Otto Biermann, *Zur Theorie Fuchs'schen Functionen* (Vienna, 1885), reprinted from *Sitzungsberichte der Wien Akademie der Wissenschaften,* **92** (1885).

JEROME H. MANHEIM

FÜCHSEL, GEORG CHRISTIAN (*b.* Ilmenau, Germany, 14 February 1722; *d.* Rudolstadt, Germany, 20 June 1773), *geology.*

Füchsel studied medicine at the University of Jena and medicine, natural sciences, and theology at the University of Leipzig. After settling in Rudolstadt, he engaged in the "salon" science of natural history cabinets and mineral collections. He served as town physician and later court physician to the princes of Schwarzburg-Rudolstadt. His major work, "Historia terrae et maris, ex historia Thuringiae, per montium descriptionem, eruta," appeared in 1761 in the *Acta* of the Erfurt Academy of Sciences. Although written in German, this work was published in a very defective Latin translation made by a friend of Füchsel. Its frequent unintelligibility perhaps accounts in part for the relative neglect of the "Historia."

Most eighteenth-century writings on geology tended to be either submerged in extended and superficial accounts of general natural history and in cosmological speculation, or limited to the most detailed sort of descriptions of individual occurrences: hot springs, fossil finds, strange crystals, erratic boulders, mines, caves, and quarries. In contrast with such works, Füchsel's "Historia" is unusual for its purely geological orientation. This book-length work contains the enunciation and substantiation of general principles of historical geology, an extensive description of all the stratified rocks of the Thüringer Wald used to illustrate the general principles, an explanation of the causes of dynamic changes in the earth's crust, and an explanation of the origin of veins and their minerals. An appendix ("Usus historiae . . .") furnishes an extended discussion of the applications of such geological knowledge.

Most noteworthy among Füchsel's principles of geology are his assumptions of a rigorous actualism and the fruitful concept of a formation (which he calls a *series montana* or *ein Geburge*). After a thorough account of all the formations of the Thüringer Wald (including data on lithology, notable minerals, fossil content, inclusion of foreign rocks, spatial orientation, and geographical extent for each formation), Füchsel's work proceeds to construct, by induction, a historical account of the region's geology founded on the assumption of a uniformity of natural processes through time. "In truth we must take as the norm in our explanation [of the earth's history] the manner in which nature acts and produces solids at the present time; we know no other way."[1] He distinguished a formation as those strata formed at the same time, of the same material, and in the same manner.[2] In establishing the history Füchsel also used the principle of superposition and the method of correlation by index fossils to reconstruct a complete stratigraphic sequence for Thüringen and to assimilate separated occurrences of the same formations to their proper place in the sequence. To illustrate the stratigraphic data of this history, Füchsel produced the first published geological map. Unlike previous soil maps (such as Christopher Packe's *Chart of East Kent*), Füchsel's map indicated not only the distribution of rocks but also their arrangement in relation to each other and their relative ages.

The *Acta* of the Erfurt Academy had only a limited circulation, and in his other major work, *Entwurf zu der ältesten Erd- und Menschengeschichte . . .*, which appeared anonymously in 1773, Füchsel complained that only a few scholars seemed to have given the "Historia" much attention. Nonetheless, his ideas did exert an influence on the geological literature of the time, probably through a long notice by J. S. Schröter in the popular *Journal für Liebhaber des Steinreichs*[3] and through the writings of J. K. W. Voigt, J. E. I. Walch, and Goethe. A. G. Werner's system seems to owe much to Füchsel, but the precise connections have not yet been fully documented.

NOTES

1. "Historia," pp. 81–82, sec. 43. "Praecedentes observationes tam inter se quam cum aliis, combinare, atque eventus seu historiam exinde deducere liceat. Modus vero quo natura hodierno adhuc tempore agit, et corpora producit, in hac explanatione pro norma assumendus est; alium non novimus."
2. *Ibid.*, p. 48, sec. 4. "Montes eiusdem situs, ab eadem massa, eodemque modo constructos seriem montanam (ein Geburge) nominare liceat." A similar definition is found in p. 25, sec. 39, of the *Entwurf.*
3. **2** (1775), 54–63.

BIBLIOGRAPHY

I. Original Works. *Acta Academiae electoralis moguntinae scientiarum utilium, quae Erfordiae est,* **2** (1761), contains both the "Historia terrae et maris . . .," 44–208, and the "Usus Historiae terrae et maris," 209–254. Füchsel also published "Ansicht des Erfurthischen Gebietes als eines Theils von Thüringen" in *Neue oekonomische Nachrichten* (Leipzig), **3** (1766), 359–390. His last work appeared anonymously as *Entwurf zu der ältesten Erd- und Menschengeschichte, nebst einem Versuch, den Ursprung der Sprache zu finden* (Frankfurt–Leipzig, 1773). An English trans. of the "Historia" is in preparation.

II. Secondary Literature. The excellent and comprehensive biography by Rudolf Möller, "Mitteilungen zur Biographie Georg Christian Füchsels," in *Freiberger Forschungshefte,* **D43** (Leipzig, 1963), includes references to Füchsel's other published articles, to pertinent archival materials, and to relevant secondary literature. For further analysis of Füchsel's ideas see T. E. Gumprecht, "Einige Beiträge zur Geschichte der Geognosie," in *Archiv für Mineralogie, Geognosie, Bergbau und Hüttenkunde,* **23** (1850), 468-576.

BERT HANSEN

FUETER, KARL RUDOLF (*b.* Basel, Switzerland, 30 June 1880; *d.* Brunnen, Switzerland, 9 August 1950), *mathematics.*

Fueter was the son of Eduard Rudolf Fueter, an architect, and Adèle Gelzer. In 1908 he married Amélie von Heusinger.

After receiving his early education in Basel, Fueter began to study mathematics at Göttingen in 1899 and graduated in 1903. Under the supervision of David Hilbert he presented a work dealing with the theory of quadratic number fields. After further study in Paris, Vienna, and London and teaching in Marburg and Clausthal (now Clausthal-Zellerfeld), Fueter became a professor of mathematics in Basel in 1908; he accepted the same post at the Technische Hochschule in Karlsruhe in 1913 and at the University of Zurich in 1916. His field of interest was the theory of numbers as presented in Hilbert's work. He derived the class formula for the entire group of Abelian number fields over an imaginary quadratic base field. He gave a summary of these in his *Vorlesungen über die singulären Moduln und die komplexe Multiplikation der elliptischen Funktionen* (1924–1927). Later he founded his own school of thought on the theory of functions of a quaternion variable.

Fueter was cofounder and president of the Swiss Mathematical Society, rector of the University of Zurich, and president of the Euler Commission of the Swiss Society of Sciences (editors of the *Opera Omnia Leonhardi Euleri*). He held the rank of colonel in the artillery of the Swiss militia, and at the outbreak of World War II he served in the Department of Press and Radio. In *Spying for Peace* (London, 1961), Jon Kimche states, "Fueter restated the democratic rights of the press in almost classical form. . . . In his report of April 10, 1940 . . . Fueter developed his argument more fully. 'It is the duty of our press to reject the domestic and foreign policies of the National Socialists both clearly and forcefully.' " Fueter was, therefore, particularly noted for his opposition to Nazism and to the spread of its policies within Switzerland.

BIBLIOGRAPHY

Fueter's major works are *Synthetische Zahlentheorie* (Berlin, 1917; 3rd ed., 1950); *Vorlesungen über die singulären Moduln und die komplexe Multiplikation der elliptischen Funktionen,* 2 vols. (Leipzig-Berlin, 1924–1927); and *Das mathematische Werkzeug des Chemikers, Biologen und Statistikers* (Zurich, 1926; 3rd ed., 1947).

A biography is A. Speiser, in *Elemente der Mathematik,* **5** (1950), published with Fueter's autobiographical notes.

J. J. BURCKHARDT

FUHLROTT, JOHANN KARL (*b.* Leinefelde, Germany, 1 January 1804; *d.* Elberfeld [now Wuppertal], Germany, 17 October 1877), *natural history, human paleontology.*

Fuhlrott obtained his doctorate from the University of Bonn in 1830 and went from there to Elberfeld, where he became a science teacher and subsequently vice-director of the Realschule. He won modest recognition as a naturalist, publishing geological descriptions of the hills and caves in the Rhineland region between Düsseldorf and the Wupper River.

In August 1856, Fuhlrott received an assortment of fossilized bones found by two quarry workers in the Feldhofer cave of the Neander Valley. These men had uncovered what they thought to be the skeleton of a cave bear and were carelessly discarding it when the quarry owner persuaded them to save some of the remains for the Elberfeld teacher. Portions of the skull and pelvis, along with the larger limb bones, were delivered to Fuhlrott.

He studied the specimens and began to suspect that they were not bear bones but the remains of an ancient and primitive form of human being. Its physical build smaller than that of modern man, this creature with low, retracted forehead had plodded along on bowed legs, its head and chest hunched forward. Fuhlrott recognized the importance of this find and rushed to the grottoes in time to retrieve some ribs, the right radius, the left ulna, and part of the right scapula—all that remained of the probably perfect skeleton.

At Fuhlrott's request Hermann Schaaffhausen of Bonn examined the fragments and confirmed his diagnosis of their antiquity. Schaaffhausen presented a preliminary description of the fossils at the Lower Rhine Medical and Natural History Society on 4 February 1857; Fuhlrott was invited to discuss them fully before the Natural History Society of the Prussian Rhineland and Westphalia on 2 June of that year. Addressing this august body at Bonn, Fuhlrott was dismayed at the reaction to his find. Rudolf Virchow and Carter Blake dismissed the bones as the remains of an idiot ravaged by rickets in youth and arthritis in later life. They refused to credit any great age to them.

Schaaffhausen alone defended Fuhlrott's position, saying,

> There is no reason whatever for regarding the unusual development of the frontal sinuses in the remarkable skull from the Neanderthal as an individual or pathological deformity: it is unquestionably a typical race characteristic and is physiologically connected with the uncommon thickness of the other bones of the skeleton, which exceeds by one-half the usual proportions [quoted in T. H. Huxley, *Collected Essays,* p. 176].

Reaction to his speech was hostile, but Fuhlrott and Schaaffhausen refused to quit their positions in the extensive controversy that ensued. They appealed to the public for support and managed to attract attention beyond the borders of Germany. They gained an important ally in Sir Charles Lyell, who journeyed from England in 1860 to investigate the discovery site of the disputed fossils. His visit to Fuhlrott convinced Lyell that the specimen was authentically human, *Homo neanderthalensis.* But it was not until after Fuhlrott's death and the discovery of fossil men at Spy, Belgium, and at Gibraltar that opposition to the notion of Neanderthal man was finally silenced.

BIBLIOGRAPHY

I. Original Works. Fuhlrott's main publication is *Der fossile Mensch aus dem Neanderthal und sein Verhältniss zum Alter des Menschengeschlects* (Duisburg, 1865). Also important is his "Über die Kalksteinschichten im Neanderthale, Worin 1856 der Homo Neanderthalensis gefunden Wurde," in *Correspondenzblatt des Naturhistorischen Vereins für Rheinland und Westphalen,* **25** (1868), 62–70. In the *Jahresberichte des Naturwissenschaftlichen Vereins von Elberfeld und Barmen, Nebst wissenschaftlichen Beilagen* are "Felsenmeer im Odenwald," **3** (1858), 75–79; "Das Wisperthal und der Wisperwind," **4** (1863), 11–18; "Grundzüge der Quellenkunde," *ibid.,* 129–150; and "Die erloschenen Vulcane am Rhein und in der Eifel," **5** (1878), 3–25. In the *Verhandlungen des Naturhistorischen Vereins der Preussischenen Rheinlande und Westphalens* (Bonn) are "Paläontologisches" (1859), 125–126; and "Menschliche Ueberreste aus einer Felsengrotte des Düsselthals," *ibid.,* 131–153. There are also "Die Kalksteinschichten der Feldhofer Grotte im Neanderthale," in *Zeitschrift für gesammten Naturwissenschaften,* **33** (1869), 275–277; and "Ueber eine neu endeckte Höhle bei Barmen," in *Sitzungsberichte der Niederrheinischen Gesellschaft für Natur- und Heikunde zu Bonn* (1870), 208–209.

II. Secondary Literature. See Aleš Hrdlička, *The Skeletal Remains of Early Man,* Smithsonian Miscellaneous Collections, **83** (Washington, D.C., 1930), 149–151. T. H. Huxley cites George Busk's trans. of Schaaffhausen's history of discovery and description of Neanderthal man in "Man's Place in Nature," in *Collected Essays,* **7** (New York, 1896; repr. 1968), 168–185. See also George Busk's trans. of Schaaffhausen's "On the Crania of the Most Ancient Races of Man," in *Natural History Review,* **1** (1861), 283.

Martha B. Kendall

FULTON, JOHN FARQUHAR (*b.* St. Paul, Minnesota, 1 November 1899; *d.* New Haven, Connecticut, 28 May 1960), *physiology, history of medicine.*

The son of an ophthalmologist who assisted in the founding of the University of Minnesota, Fulton graduated from St. Paul High School at the age of sixteen. His studies at the University of Minnesota were interrupted by a period of military service in World War I. Upon discharge he transferred to Harvard University, where he received the Bachelor of Science degree, *magna cum laude,* in 1921. That year, as a Rhodes Scholar, Fulton went to Oxford and was admitted to Magdalen College. There he met C. S. Sherrington, and in 1923, when he received an appointment as Christopher Welsh Scholar, he had the privilege of working in Sherrington's laboratory. In the same year he married Lucia Pickering Wheatland. Fulton's return to Harvard for medical training brought him into contact with Harvey Cushing, then at the zenith of his neurosurgical career. He was so attracted by Cushing's clinical acumen and devotion that he spent a year working with him. This experience alerted the brilliant young physiologist to the possibility of using modern surgical techniques in the physiology laboratory in the analysis of the functions of the nervous system.

As a result, when he was appointed professor of physiology at Yale Medical School in 1929, Fulton organized the first primate laboratory for experimental physiology in America. His aim was to produce and analyze in higher primates such neurological syndromes as hemiplegia and ataxia. In operating rooms modeled after clinical neurosurgical theaters, he used his superb surgical skill on chimpanzees and orangutans, so that he might study the function of brains most closely resembling that of man. Stimulated by his enlightening analyses of spasticity and paralysis, would-be neurosurgeons, neurologists, and physiologists sought his laboratory for training and later became professors in universities in the United States and abroad. Perhaps Fulton's major contribution to this program was his enthusiasm, which stimulated his associates to explore—from the historical, bibliographical, or investigational viewpoint—the mysteries of the nervous system. Frequently this work was carried out more with his blessing than with his supervision, yet he was always eager to discuss and to integrate findings into the current neurological thinking, for his goal was to "aid those whose ultimate objective is the study of Clinical Medicine." In spite of these activities Fulton found time to write the textbook, *The Physiology of the Nervous System,* which was translated into French, German, Portuguese, Spanish, Japanese, and Russian; and he founded, with J. G. Dusser de Barenne, the *Journal of Neurophysiology,* which he nurtured through its early years.

Early in his career Fulton became interested in the motor system. His contacts with Sherrington stimulated him to study the mechanisms of neuromuscular transmission, which he reported in a monograph entitled *Muscular Contraction and the Reflex Control of Movement* (1926). His subsequent investigations concerned the cortical and subcortical influence on the spinal motor pathways. He used the techniques of stimulation and ablation to demonstrate the changing role of the cerebrum in the ascending phylogenetic scale. Fulton showed the differential influence on movement of the postcentral, central, and precentral cortex. He believed that lesions of the motor cortex produced essentially a flaccid paresis and that the addition of premotor lesions introduced a spastic element. He showed that cerebellar hemispheral and vermal lesions had varying effects upon tone and motor performance, and demonstrated that the cerebral motor cortex compensated for cerebellar lesions.

With the outbreak of World War II, the activities of the primate laboratory at New Haven became centered on physiology, particularly in its medical applications to aviation. Fulton had a decompression chamber built in his laboratory and devoted much time to important research in this field.

Throughout his physiological career Fulton maintained a deep interest in the history of medicine. Perhaps this stemmed from his contacts at Oxford with Sherrington and the posthumous influence of William Osler and may have been fostered further by his close friendship with Harvey Cushing. Fulton was particularly interested in the lives of the men who developed new concepts in medicine. There is evidence of this fascination in the many biographical and bibliographical sketches he wrote. The culmination of this activity was his life of Harvey Cushing, which presents a well-documented and, in view of Fulton's intimacy with Cushing, surprisingly well-balanced account.

With the aid of Cushing and Arnold Klebs, Fulton was able to establish a historical library for the Yale School of Medicine. It was to house the large collections of Cushing and Klebs and his own library. As his energies lessened because of impaired health, Fulton devoted more time to this hobby and less to the physiological laboratory. In 1951 he resigned as Sterling professor of physiology to become Sterling professor of the history of medicine and chairman of a newly created department of the history of medicine at Yale Medical School. He entered this new office with enthusiasm and developed graduate programs in the history of science and medicine.

The impact of Fulton's contributions was recognized at home and abroad. For his scientific assistance in the Allied war effort, he received honors from the governments of France, Belgium, Rumania, and Cuba. He was also awarded honorary degrees by nine American and foreign universities.

BIBLIOGRAPHY

I. Original Works. Fulton's writings include *Muscular Contraction and the Reflex Control of Movement* (Baltimore, Md., 1926); *Selected Readings in the History of Physiology* (Springfield, Ill., 1930); *The Sign of Babinski. A Study of the Evolution of Cortical Dominance in Primates* (Springfield, Ill., 1932), written with A. D. Keller; *Physiology of the Nervous System* (New York, 1938); and *Harvey Cushing, A Biography* (Springfield, Ill., 1946).

II. Secondary Literature. See H. E. Hoff, "The Laboratory of Physiology," in *Yale Journal of Biology and Medicine,* **28** (1955–1956), 165–167, with Fulton's bibliography appended, 168–190. Obituaries are in *Journal of Neurophysiology,* **23** (1960), 347–349; *Journal of Neurosurgery,* **17** (1960), 1119–1123; *Bulletin of the History of Medicine,* **35** (1961), 81–86; and *New England Journal of Medicine,* **262** (1960), 1340–1341.

A. Earl Walker

FUNK, CASIMIR (*b.* Warsaw, Poland [then Russia], 23 February 1884; *d.* New York, N.Y., 20 November 1967), *biochemistry.*

Funk was the son of Jacques and Gustawa Zysan Funk. His father was a prominent dermatologist. In 1904 he received the Ph.D. in organic chemistry at the University of Bern, where he worked on the synthesis of stilbestrols. Following work at the Pasteur Institute, the Wiesbaden Municipal Hospital, and the University of Berlin, where he was an assistant to Emil Abderhalden, he took a post at the Lister Institute in London, where he was soon assigned to work on beriberi. In 1914 he married Denise Schneidesch of Brussels, by whom he had two children. In 1915 the Funks immigrated to New York, where he held several industrial and university positions. In 1920 he became a U.S. citizen. In 1923 the Rockefeller Foundation supported his return to Warsaw as chief of the biochemistry department in the State Institute of Hygiene, a post which he abandoned in 1927 because of political conditions in Poland. In Paris, from 1928 to 1939, Funk was consultant to a pharmaceutical firm and founder of the Casa Biochemica, a privately financed research institute. This was abandoned in the face of the German invasion, and Funk returned to New York as consultant to the U.S. Vitamin Corporation. From 1940 he was president of the Funk Foundation for Medical Research.

At the Lister Institute, Funk prepared a pyrimidine-related concentrate of rice polishings which was curative for beriberi in pigeons. In 1912 he proposed the term "vitamine" (for vital amine) for organic compounds responsible in trace amounts for the cure or prevention of beriberi, scurvy, rickets, and pellagra. His concentrates were primarily nicotinic acid (noneffective for beriberi but later shown by Elvehjem to be curative for pellagra) contaminated with the anti-beriberi vitamin. Besides his work on vitamins, Funk conducted extensive studies on animal hormones, particularly the male sex hormone, and on the biochemistry of cancer, ulcers, and diabetes. He theorized freely and saw close relationships between trace nutrients (vitamins and minerals), hormones, and enzymes. A number of substances developed in his laboratories were sold commercially in the pharmaceutical industry.

BIBLIOGRAPHY

I. Original Works. A comprehensive but incomplete bibliography of Funk's publications appears in Harrow's biography (see below). His first paper on the nature of the anti-beriberi substance is "On the Chemical Nature of the Substance Which Cures Polyneuritis in Birds Induced by a Diet of Polished Rice," in *Journal of Physiology,* **43** (1911), 395–400. The paper introducing the term "vitamine" is "The Etiology of Deficiency Diseases," in *Journal of State Medicine,* **20** (1912), 341–368. *Die Aetiologie der Avitaminosen mit besonderer Berücksichtigung der physiologischen Bedeutung der Vitamine* (Wiesbaden, 1914) was printed in several German eds. and in an English trans. by H. E. Dubin as *The Vitamins* (Baltimore, 1922). See also his *L'histoire de la découverte des vitamines* (Paris, 1924).

II. Secondary Literature. A popularized biography is Benjamin Harrow, *Casimir Funk, Pioneer in Vitamins and Hormones* (New York, 1955). An anonymous sketch of his life appeared in *Current Biography,* **6** (1945), 22–24; and an obituary notice appeared in the *New York Times* (21 Nov. 1967).

Aaron J. Ihde

FUSS, NICOLAUS (or **Nikolai Ivanovich Fus**), (*b.* Basel, Switzerland, 30 January 1755; *d.* St. Petersburg, Russia, 4 January 1826), *mathematics, astronomy.*

Fuss was born into a Swiss family of modest means. His mathematical abilities, which manifested themselves quite early, attracted the attention of a number of prominent scholars, including Daniel Bernoulli, who in 1772 recommended him to Euler, then living in Russia, as a secretary. Fuss arrived in St. Petersburg at the age of seventeen and spent the rest of his life in Russia.

Fuss wrote his first papers, which had purely practical goals, under Euler's direct guidance. These were *Instruction détaillée pour porter les lunettes*. . . (1774) and *Éclaircissemens sur les établissemens publics en faveur tant des veuves*. . . (1776). The latter concerns problems of the insurance business.

In January 1776, Fuss was selected as a junior scientific assistant of the St. Petersburg Academy of Sciences; in February 1783, he became an academician in higher mathematics; and from September 1800 until his death he was the academy's permanent secretary.

The majority of Fuss's writings contain solutions to problems raised in Euler's works. They deal with several branches of mathematics (spherical geometry, trigonometry, the theory of series, the geometry of curves, the integration of differential equations) and with mechanics, astronomy, and geodesy. From 1774—the year of his first published paper—more than 100 of his articles appeared in the publications of the St. Petersburg Academy of Sciences.

Fuss's best papers deal with spherical geometry, the problems of which he worked out with the St. Petersburg academicians A. J. Lexell and F. T. Schubert. In his first paper on spherical geometry, which was published in *Nova acta Academiae scientiarum imperialis Petropolitanae* (1788), he gave solutions to three new problems concerning spherical triangles which are constructed on a given base, between two given great circles, and satisfy certain extremal conditions. In another article (1788) the characteristics of a spherical ellipse, i.e., of the geometrical locus of the vertexes of spherical triangles with a given base and a sum of two other sides, are studied in detail.

Fuss was also responsible for new solutions to a number of difficult problems in elementary geometry. These included Apollonius' problem of constructing a circle tangent to three given circles (1790) and Cramer's problem—which generalizes Pappus' problem—of inscribing a triangle inside a given circle, such that the sides of the triangle, or their extensions, pass through three given points (1783).

In differential geometry Fuss solved a number of problems concerning the determination of the properties of curves which are defined by certain relationships between the radius of curvature, the radius vector, and the length of an arc (1789). These papers partially bordered on so-called intrinsic geometry, which was developed into an independent mathematical discipline by Ernesto Cesàro and others at the end of the nineteenth century.

Fuss was an honorary member of the Berlin, Swedish, and Danish academies. In 1778 the Paris Academy of Sciences awarded him a prize for his astronomical paper "Recherche sur le dérangement d'une comète qui passe près d'une planète" (*Mémoires des savants étrangers,* **10** [1785]). In 1798 a prize was awarded to him by the Danish Society of Sciences for his paper *Versuch einer Theorie des Widerstandes zwei-und vierrädiger Wagen usw.* (Copenhagen, 1798).

Fuss also did much in the field of education. He taught for many years at the military and naval cadet academies. At the beginning of the nineteenth century he was active in the reform of the Russian national education system. He compiled a number of textbooks, including *Leçons de géométrie à l'usage du Corps impérial des cadets . . .* (St. Petersburg, 1798), *Nachalnye osnovania ploskoy trigonometrii, vysshey geometrii i differentsialnogo ischislenia* ("Foundations of Plane Trigonometry, Higher Geometry, and Differential and Integral Calculus," 3 vols., St. Petersburg, 1804), and *Nachalnye osnovania chistoy matematiki* ("Fundamentals of Pure Mathematics," 3 vols., St. Petersburg, 1810–1812). These textbooks show the influence of all of Euler's work, especially his *Vollständige Anleitung zur Algebra* (2 vols., St. Petersburg, 1770), which Fuss used as a model in compiling a handbook for the cadet corps and the first algebra textbook for Russian Gymnasiums.

BIBLIOGRAPHY

I. ORIGINAL WORKS. Fuss's writings include *Instruction détaillée pour porter les lunettes de toutes les différentes espèces au plus haut degré de perfection . . . tirée de la théorie dioptrique de M. Euler . . .* (St. Petersburg, 1774); *Éclaircissemens sur les établissemens publics en faveur tant des veuves que des morts, avec la déscription d'une nouvelle espece de tontine. . . . Calculés sous la direction de Mr. Léonard Euler par Mr. N[icolaus] F[uss]* (St. Petersburg, 1776); "Solutio problematis geometrici Pappi Alexandrini," in *Acta Academiae Scientiarum imperialis Petropolitanae,* **4**, pt. 1 (1783), 97–104; "Problematum quorundam sphaericorum solutio," in *Nova Acta Academiae Scientiarum imperialis Petropolitanae,* **2** (1788), 67–80; "De proprietatibus quibusdam ellipseos in superficie sphaerica descriptae," *ibid.,* **3** (1788), 90–99; "Solutio problematis ex methodo tangentium inversa," *ibid.,* **4** (1789), 104–128; "Recherches sur un problème de mécanique," *ibid.,* **6** (1790), 172–184.

A full bibliography of Fuss's mathematical works can be found in the following publications: *Matematika v izdaniakh Akademii Nauk (1728–1935). Bibliografichesky Ukazatel* ("Mathematics in the Publications of the Academy of Sciences [1728–1935]. Bibliographic Index"), compiled by O. V. Dinze and K. I. Shafranovsky (Moscow–Leningrad, 1936), see index; F. A. Brokgauz and I. A. Efron, eds., *Entsiklopedichesky slovar* ("Encyclopedic Dictionary"), XXXVI A (St. Petersburg, 1902), 913–914; Poggendorff, I, 822–823; and M. Cantor, *Vorlesungen über die Geschichte der Mathematik,* 3rd ed., IV (Leipzig, 1913), see index.

II. SECONDARY LITERATURE. On Fuss or his work, see V. V. Bobynin, "Fuss, Nikolai," in F. A. Brokgauz and I. A. Efron, eds., *Entsiklopedichesky slovar,* XXXVI A (St. Petersburg, 1902), 913–914; V. I. Lysenko, "O rabotakh peterburgskikh akademikov A. I. Lekselya, N. I. Fussa i F. I. Shuberta po sfericheskoy geometrii i sfericheskoy trigonometrii" ("On the Works of the Petersburg Academicians A. J. Lexell, N. I. Fuss, and F. T. Schubert in Spherical Geometry and Spherical Trigonometry"), in *Trudy Instituta istorii estestvoznaniya i tekhniki. Akademiya nauk SSSR,* **34** (1960), 384–414, which examines several of Fuss's unpublished compositions, which are preserved in the archives of the Soviet Academy of Sciences; and "Iz istorii pervoy peterburgskoy matematicheskoy shkoly" ("From the History of the First Petersburg School of Mathematics"), *ibid.,* **43** (1961), 182–205.

See also A. P. Youschkevitch, "Matematika" ("Mathematics"), in *Istoria estestvoznania v Rossii* ("History of Natural Science in Russia"), I, pt. 1 (Moscow, 1957), 215–272; and "Matematika i mekhanika" ("Mathematics and Mechanics"), in *Istoria Akademii nauk SSSR* ("History of the USSR Academy of Sciences"), I (Moscow–Leningrad, 1958), 350–352.

A. I. VOLODARSKY

FYODOROV (or **FEDOROV**), **EVGRAF STEPANOVICH** (*b.* Orenburg, Russia [now Chkalov, U.S.S.R.], 22 December 1853; *d.* Petrograd [now Leningrad], U.S.S.R., 21 May 1919), *crystallography, geometry, petrography, mineralogy, geology.*

His father, Stepan Ivanovich Fyodorov, came from a peasant family and was a major-general in the Engineer Corps. He was noted for the sharpness of his disposition, which he evidently passed on to his son.

Fyodorov's mother, Yulia Gerasimovna Botvinko, the daughter of a procurator in Vilna, was a progressive and cultured woman. She gave her son the elements of a musical education and, in particular, imparted a love of reading and accustomed him to steady work and discipline. Fyodorov later said that he was wholly indebted to his mother for his exceptional capacity for work. She made him knit large tablecloths with intricate figures, which probably developed his feeling for symmetry.

Fyodorov's mathematical abilities appeared very

early; when he was five, he had already mastered the rules of arithmetic. At the age of seven he studied with fascination and finished in two days a textbook of elementary geometry. In his own words, the content of the first pages of the text evoked "a resonance in my psyche, so that I was literally carried away." At the age of ten Fyodorov entered the second class of Annensky College. After the death of his father in 1866, the straitened circumstances of his family forced him to transfer to the military Gymnasium, which he could attend at state expense. Here he joined a small group of friends who were studying natural science and philosophy intensively. At the same time Fyodorov independently immersed himself in the mathematical disciplines, which for him were always invested with an aura of special beauty. In 1869 he transferred to the Petersburg Military Engineering School. There he became an active member of an illegal group devoted to self-education, in which, under the influence of the literary critic, Dmitry Pisarev, the works of the materialist natural scientists were studied.

In 1872 Fyodorov graduated and went to Kiev with the rank of second lieutenant in a combat engineering battalion; the following year he returned to St. Petersburg, and in 1874 he retired completely from military service. As a result of his enthusiasm for natural sciences he became a free auditor at the Military Medical and Surgical Academy. Having passed the necessary examinations, Fyodorov entered the second-year course of the Technological Institute, where he concentrated on physics and chemistry. All his thoughts and interests were already directed toward theoretical mathematics, particularly geometry; this made possible the completion of his important monograph, *Nachala uchenia o figurakh,* which he had begun at the age of sixteen. In it he touched on symmetry and the theory of crystal structure and set forth the principles of contemporary theoretical crystallography. His work on the theory of mathematical polyhedrons brought Fyodorov to questions relating to natural polyhedrons—the crystals of minerals—and to geometric mineralogy.

Because of his enthusiasm for crystallography Fyodorov chose the specialty closest to this science and in 1880, at the age of twenty-seven, he entered the third-year course at the Mining Institute, where a general course in crystallography and related mineralogy was taught. After graduating from the Mining Institute in 1883 (his name was placed at the top of the list carved in marble), Fyodorov joined a Mining Department expedition to investigate the northern Urals.

Fyodorov married Ludmila Vasilievna Panyutina, a vivacious and purposeful girl who had come from Kungur in the Urals to study medicine in St. Petersburg. She selflessly helped him in his scientific and revolutionary work. Fyodorov's son, Evgraf Evgrafovich, was a specialist in climatology and later a corresponding member of the Soviet Academy of Sciences.

In childhood Fyodorov had been sickly; in his middle years he was extremely robust. He always worked a great deal and was extraordinarily precise in carrying out the life plan he had set for himself. He went on expeditions to the Urals and other regions, distinguishing himself on them because of his great endurance. Fyodorov traveled under conditions of great privation and worked to the point of exhaustion; on expeditions he was sunburned and thin but cheerful and energetic. In his old age he was often ill.

In 1896 Fyodorov was elected a member of the Bavarian Academy of Sciences and in 1901 an adjunct of the Petersburg Academy of Sciences; but, not having received support for his demands for the creation of a mineralogical institute, he withdrew from the Petersburg academy in 1905. He was elected a member of the Soviet Academy of Sciences in 1919, when an institute in which mineralogy occupied an important place was organized.

Revolutionary activity gave meaning to Fyodorov's life. In 1876 he became a member of the populist Land and Freedom party; the following year he was commissioned to set up connections with revolutionary organizations in France, Belgium, and Germany, a task which he handled well. His apartment in Petersburg contained an underground revolutionary press.

Fyodorov's scientific and literary work is distinguished for its richness and extraordinary variety. Most numerous among his more than 500 scientific published works are those on crystallography, followed by geometry, mineralogy, petrography, geology, history of science, and philosophy.

Fyodorov devoted forty-three publications to mineralogy, but the only one to deal with the field as a whole is *Kritichesky peresmotr form mineralnogo tsarstva* (1903), in which the morphology of minerals is examined relative to crystal structure theory. Fyodorov exerted a very strong influence on the development of mineralogy and opened a new stage in it. He also contributed to the accumulation of significant new factual material and helped to change the methodological approach to the study of minerals. He used the analytical approach and attempted to understand natural processes and phenomena by starting from more general mathematical and physical-chemical principles. Through his work Fyodorov laid the foundations for the analytical period in the development of mineralogy.

The foundation of all of Fyodorov's scientific work was geometry. Among his first works was the monograph *Nachala uchenia o figurakh,* and his last article treated questions of the new geometry. Geometrical research led Fyodorov to the brilliant derivation of the 230 space groups—the symmetry groups governing the periodic distribution within crystalline matter. The derivation is the foundation of contemporary mineralogy and the basis of the atomic structure of minerals. His first work was an exposition of all those parts of the theory of figures which constitute the basis of contemporary crystallography.

The period of the first geometrical investigations and publications was crowned by the classic work *Simmetria pravilnykh sistem figur* (1890), which contained the first deduction of the 230 space groups. The publication in 1891 of Schoenflies' book with his derivation of the 230 space groups prompted Fyodorov to publish several articles in the *Zeitschrift für Kristallographie.* He compared his results with those of Schoenflies and made a series of essential corrections and notations. In these articles he gave a strict mathematical definition of thirty-two point groups for six crystallographic systems, which still retain their significance. At the basis of this classification he placed a number of single and symmetrically equivalent axes in crystals. This classification led to the working out of a new nomenclature of systems and point group symmetries, accepted throughout the world and known as Fyodorov-Groth nomenclature. For these accomplishments, and at the insistence of such eminent crystallographers as Groth and L. Sohncke, Fyodorov was elected a member of the Bavarian Academy of Sciences in 1896. Fyodorov himself considered these works as belonging to the theory of crystallography, specifically to geometric mineralogy. Fyodorov's group classifications are, with the aid of X-ray diffraction, at the base of modern mineralogical determinations of the atomic structure of minerals.

In the category of physical crystallography are Fyodorov's works that explain a universal method of optical research, which played an important role in mineralogy and petrography. In 1889, at a session of the Mineralogical Society, Fyodorov reported on his projected two-circle optical goniometer for the measurement of all angles in crystals with a single setting of the specimen. It differed from previous goniometers, which had only a single axis of rotation. (A two-circle goniometer had been proposed earlier by W. H. Miller.) This produced a revolution in the method of investigating minerals. Following Fyodorov and using his idea, Victor Goldschmidt, S. Czapski, Y. Flint, and others designed two-circle goniometers. Crystallographers and mineralogists throughout the world began to work exclusively with these instruments.

In 1891 Fyodorov proposed to the Geological Committee the construction of a universal stage for the petrographic microscope that would locate the specimen at the center of two glass hemispheres. In essence this method is crystallographic, but its application is to mineralogy and petrography. With what became known as the Fyodorov method the optical constants of minerals could be established and, without resorting to chemical analysis, the composition of the isomorphic lime-soda feldspars (plagioclases) was determined, as were those of other minerals.

Of all the instruments constructed and developed by Fyodorov, the universal stage (also called U-stage or Fyodorov table) has enjoyed the greatest popularity. Special courses in its use are given to students of mineralogy and petrography. Handbooks and special studies on the Fyodorov method have been published by Russian and foreign authors: S. N. Nikitin, M. A. Usov, V. S. Sobolev, L. Duparc, M. Reinhard, M. Berek, and others. The Fyodorov method has allowed researchers to carry out quickly the optical study of plagioclases, pyroxenes, and other minerals, using thin sections of rock. The present Fyodorov table is a refined instrument with five axes of rotation, convenient for the study of minerals in any cross section.

In describing Fyodorov's activity in petrography and mineralogy, it must be noted that he himself never drew a sharp boundary between these sciences. He considered that all the physical, mathematical, and natural sciences were used in them. He also believed that in the cycle of mineralogical and geological sciences one used the totality of knowledge of the earth—which, in his view, is located in infinite, starry space and interacts with it. These ideas are only now being worked out in detail by his followers in the fields of astrogeology and planetology.

Fyodorov gave much attention to the chemical composition of rocks and their graphic representation, and he introduced symbols of chemical composition, petrographic nomenclature, and rock classification. He conducted important research on the northern Urals, the Bogoslovsky (now Sverdlovsk) district, the coast of the White Sea, the Caucasus, and Kazakhstan. He was one of the first to show the great importance of the apatite resources lying in the depths of the Soviet north (1909).

In one of his first scientific works, the tract "Perfektsionizm" (1906), Fyodorov showed that he was a convinced materialist. Starting from the materialistic principle that natural conditions are in essence conditions of eternal change, he attacked authors who teach the theory of stability and equilibrium in nature. The essence of evolution, in his opinion, is not in the tendency toward a higher order, stability, and equilibrium of organisms but in their life movement. Criticizing the outlook of Herbert Spencer and other partisans of equilibrium in nature, Fyodorov showed that the main effect of such points of view when applied to the evolution of natural history was to give attention to the least changeable. But the creators of these systems of philosophy systematically failed to take into account the fact that equilibrium is attained only at the moment of death. As long as life is active, changing forms are developing. For this reason Fyodorov considered deeply erroneous the introduction into natural philosophy of the concept of the constant and the stable as the supreme mission of life. He asserted that life never finally achieves anything but eternally strives to achieve. It was in this that the true philosophy of nature lay for him.

Later, in published statements, Fyodorov defended science against positivism, which, in his view, reduces the significance of mind to simply a mold for the more convenient organization of material gathered by experimentation. Attacking the attempts of positivists and followers of Ernst Mach to disregard the atomic theory, Fyodorov wished to remove all metaphysical errors from contemporary science and to be led by the clear guide of atomic theory, which has produced so many valuable and stunning developments in contemporary theory.

Fyodorov's work harmoniously combined the achievements of varied fields of science. Mathematics was the basis of Fyodorov's theory of structure and symmetry of crystals. He was able to combine the methods drawn from mathematical analysis with the older empirical laws of crystallography and the methods of crystallographic research with descriptive mineralogy; he introduced principles of geometry into petrography; he combined chemistry with crystallography, thus creating crystal chemistry; and he introduced the principles of the new geometry into mine surveying. Fyodorov knew how to make generalizations and find simple solutions in the analysis of natural phenomena. His "simple" theodolite method in crystallography and petrography played a role in the history of these sciences no less than the most profound generalizations and theoretical achievements. Fyodorov presented all his scientific conclusions in mathematical form. He asserted that the crown of man's conscious activity, of man's intelligence, was the solution of the questions facing him by means of mathematical analysis.

The enormous *Tsarstvo kristallov* ("The Crystal Kingdom," 1920) was the fruit of forty years of work by Fyodorov and his colleagues. In it he noted that strongly developed sciences satisfy the spiritual needs of part of mankind and at the same time provide great power to direct the active forces of nature for man's use, thus forcing nature to serve man to a great degree. Lately it has become clear that special sciences can master nature in some respects and in certain areas of natural phenomena, directing them according to the wishes of man.

BIBLIOGRAPHY

I. Original Works. Fyodorov's writings include "Teodolitny metod v mineralogii i petrografii" ("The Theodolitic Method in Mineralogy and Petrography"), in *Trudy Geologicheskogo komiteta,* **10,** no. 2 (1893), 1-191; "Iz itogov tridtsatipyatiletia" ("From the Results of Thirty-five Years"), in *Rech i otchet, chitannye v godichnom sobranii Moskovskogo selskokhozyaistvennago instituta, 26 sentyabrya 1904 g.* ("Speech and Report Given at the Annual Meeting of the Moscow Agricultural Institute, 26 September 1904," Moscow, 1904), pp. 1-15; "Perfektsionizm" ("Perfectionism"), in *Izvestiya S. Peterburgskoi biologicheskoi laboratorii,* **8,** pt. 1 (1906), 25-65; *ibid.,* pt. 2, 9-67; "Beloe more kak istochnik materiala dlya selskokhozyaystvennoy kultury" ("The White Sea as a Source of Material for Agriculture"), in *Izvestiya Moskovskago selskokhozyaistvennago instituta,* **1** (1908), 94-97; "Iz rezultatov poezdki v Bogoslovsky okrug letom 1911 g." ("From the Results of a Trip to the Bogoslov District in the Summer of 1911"), in *Zapiski Gornago instituta Imperatritsy Ekateriny II,* **3** (1912), 340-348; "Tsarstvo kristallov" ("The Crystal Kingdom"), in *Zapiski Rossiiskoi akademii nauk,* **36** (1920); and *Nạchala uchenia o figurakh* ("Principles of the Theory of Figures," Leningrad, 1953).

II. Secondary Literature. On Fyodorov or his work, see O. M. Ansheles, "100-letie so dnya rozhdenia velikogo russkogo uchenogo E. S. Fyodorova" ("Centenary of the Birth of the Great Russian Scientist E. S. Fyodorov"), in *Vestnik Leningradskogo gosudarstvennogo universiteta,* no. 1 (1954), 223-226; N. V. Belov, *Chetyrnadtsat reshetok Brave i 230 prostranstvennykh grupp simmetrii* ("The Fourteen Bravais Lattices and the 230 Three-Dimensional Groups of Symmetries," Moscow-Leningrad, 1962); N. V. Belov and I. I. Shafranovsky, "Rol E. S. Fyodorov v predistorii rentgenostrukturnoy kristallografii . . ." ("E. S. Fyodorov's Role in the Early Development of X-ray Structural Crystallography . . ."), in *Zapiski Vsesoyuznogo mineralogicheskogo obshchestva,* pt. 91, no. 4 (1962),

465–471; G. B. Boky, "O zakone raspolozhenia atomov v kristallakh" ("On the Law of Arrangement of Atoms in Crystals"), no. 5 in the collection *Kristallografiya* (Leningrad, 1956), pp. 25–36; F. Y. Levinson-Lessing, "Neskolko yubileynykh dat v petrografii (v tom chisle 'Sorokopyatiletie tak nazyvaemogo universalnogo, ili fyodorovskogo metoda v petrografii')" ("Several Jubilee Dates in Petrography [Including the 'Fortieth Anniversary of the So-called Universal or Fyodorov Method in Petrography']"), in *Priroda* (1938), no. 6, 137–144; I. I. Shafranovsky, *Evgraf Stepanovich Fyodorov* (Moscow-Leningrad, 1963); and N. M. Sokolov, "O mirovozzrenii E. S. Fyodorov" ("On the World View of E. S. Fyodorov"), in *Kristallografiya,* no. 5 (Leningrad, 1956), pp. 5–23.

A. MENIAILOV

GABB, WILLIAM MORE (*b.* Philadelphia, Pennsylvania, 20 January 1839; *d.* Philadelphia, 30 May 1878), *geology.*

A native of the leading American scientific city of the time, Gabb became acquainted early with the Academy of Natural Sciences of Philadelphia. His father, Joseph Gabb, was a salesman and may have died when the boy was fourteen, at which time his mother, known only as J. H. More Gabb, became a milliner. Gabb did well at Central High School in Philadelphia, where Martin Hans Boyé taught natural science. The boy was already collecting minerals and shells. He became a good friend of George H. Horn, later a paleontologist and entomologist, and George W. Tryon, Jr., later a conchologist.

In 1857 Gabb chose geology as his field and sought aid from the noted James Hall, whose pupil and assistant he became. In 1860 he spent some time at the Philadelphia Academy and then briefly joined the enthusiastic scientific group around Spencer F. Baird at the Smithsonian Institution. Recommended as a foremost authority on Cretaceous fossils, Gabb in 1862 joined the California State Geological Survey under Josiah Dwight Whitney. For six years he traveled throughout much of California and beyond, from Vancouver Island to the tip of Baja California. From 1869 to 1872 he conducted a topographical and geologic survey of Santo Domingo for its government and, from 1873 to 1876, a similar survey in Costa Rica. Tuberculosis ended his career.

Gabb was elected a member and curator of paleontology of the California Academy of Sciences in 1862 and was elected to the National Academy of Sciences in 1876.

A very competent field man, Gabb was a diligent worker and was early recognized as the authority on New World invertebrate Cretaceous fossils, of which he described many. As part of the California survey, he wrote monographs on the state's Upper Mesozoic and Tertiary rocks. Although his later paleontological work was unfinished, he contributed much on the geography of Baja California, Santo Domingo, and Costa Rica. On his extensive journeys he collected many geologic, ethnologic, entomological, and other natural history specimens for the Smithsonian Institution and other museums.

BIBLIOGRAPHY

I. ORIGINAL WORKS. Gabb's publications, listed in Dall's memoir (cited below), include a number of taxonomic papers and several valuable areal reports: "Description of the Triassic Fossils of California and the Adjacent Territories," in *Geological Survey of California, Paleontology,* I (Philadelphia, 1864), 17–35; "Description of the Cretaceous Fossils," *ibid.,* 55–243; "Cretaceous and Tertiary Fossils," *ibid.,* II (1869); and also "On the Topography and Geology of Santo Domingo," in *Transactions of the American Philosophical Society,* **15** (1872), 49–260. Several papers on the geology of Costa Rica appeared in *American Journal of Science* (1874, 1875). "Notes on the Geology of Lower California," in *Geological Survey of California,* II (Philadelphia, 1882), app. 137–148, was published after Gabb's death. George W. Tryon, Jr., completed several of Gabb's taxonomic papers after Gabb died.

II. SECONDARY LITERATURE. Gabb's early life is incompletely known. The available material and a summary of his professional life was presented by William H. Dall, in *Biographical Memoirs. National Academy of Sciences,* **6** (1909), 347–361. E. O. Essig's *History of Entomology* (New York, 1965), p. 638, refers briefly to Gabb's insect collecting.

ELIZABETH NOBLE SHOR

GABRIEL, SIEGMUND (*b.* Berlin, Germany, 7 November 1851; *d.* Berlin, 22 March 1924), *chemistry.*

The son of Aron and Golde Pollnow Gabriel, Siegmund Gabriel is noted for his method of preparing primary amines and his studies of the heterocyclic compounds of nitrogen. During his last year of secondary school he developed an interest in science, having been particularly impressed by *Kurzes Lehrbuch der Chemie,* Adolph F. L. Strecker's translation and revision of Henri Victor Regnault's popular textbook. Deciding on chemistry as a career, Gabriel enrolled at the University of Berlin and attended lectures in organic chemistry by August Wilhelm von Hofmann and in inorganic chemistry by E. A. Schneider for two semesters beginning in 1871.

At Heidelberg in the spring of 1872 Gabriel studied under Robert Wilhelm Bunsen. A year of military service interrupted his studies, but he returned to Heidelberg in the autumn of 1873 and passed his doctoral examinations *summa cum laude* in 1874. Gabriel received the degree without writing a dissertation, since at that time Bunsen did not customarily require it.

Returning to the University of Berlin, where he spent his entire career, Gabriel assisted Hofmann in the inorganic section of the university laboratory. Since his own interests coincided with those of Hofmann, Gabriel spent his years as assistant on problems in organic chemistry and subsequently devoted his life to that branch of chemistry.

In 1883 Gabriel married Anna Fraenkel; they had two sons, both of whom chose medical careers. In 1886 Gabriel was appointed professor of chemistry at Berlin. When Hofmann died in 1892, Emil Fischer, then at Würzburg, was chosen to succeed him. Fischer and Gabriel became great friends, and in the dedication of his book *Aus meinem Leben* Fischer praised Gabriel for his scientific capability, his technical knowledge, and his absolute reliability.

Gabriel's first research at Berlin, begun in 1876, was on the halogenation of aromatic azo compounds, and in the following year he began a collaboration with the American chemist Arthur Michael on the condensation products of phthalic anhydride. As a result of this work Gabriel elucidated the structure of phthalylacetic acid in 1884 and in 1886 first synthesized isoquinoline, which had been discovered in coal tar in 1885 by Sebastian Hoogewerff and W. A. van Dorp, who also established its constitution. From this time on, his research was concerned almost exclusively with the heterocyclic compounds of nitrogen.

One of Gabriel's most significant contributions to organic chemistry was made in 1887, when he announced the important general method for synthesizing pure primary amines, involving the reaction of potassium phthalimide with an alkyl halide, followed by hydrolysis. This reaction, called the Gabriel synthesis, was adapted by Gabriel in 1889 to a procedure for the preparation of amino acids.

In 1891 Gabriel synthesized pyrrolidine from 1-amino-4-chlorobutane, and in 1892, using the same procedure, he prepared piperidine from 1-amino-5-chloropentane. From these heterocyclic rings containing one nitrogen atom, Gabriel turned to a thorough investigation of the diazines; he was the first to prepare phthalazine in 1893 and, with his student James Colman, pyrimidine in 1899. In 1900 he devised a simpler method for obtaining pyrimidine using barbituric acid, and in 1903 he first prepared quinazoline. Gabriel also investigated oxazole, thiazole, and their derivatives. He retired from his professorship of organic chemistry at Berlin in 1921 and died in 1924 after a short illness.

BIBLIOGRAPHY

Some of Gabriel's most important contributions were first reported in the following papers: "Uber die Constitution der Phtalylessigsäure." in *Berichte der Deutschen chemischen Gesellschaft,* **17** (1884), 2521–2527; "Synthese des Isochinolins," *ibid.,* **19** (1886), 1653–1656; "Zur Kenntniss des Isochinolins und seiner Derivate," *ibid.,* 2354–2363; "Ueber eine Darstellungsweise primärer Amine aus den entsprechenden Halogenverbindungen," *ibid.,* **20** (1887), 2224–2236; "Ueber das Phtalazin," *ibid.,* **26** (1893), 2210–2216, written with Georg Pinkus; "Ueber das Pyrimidin," *ibid.,* **32** (1899), 1525–1538, 4083, and **33** (1900), 4189, written with James Colman; "Pyrimidin aus Barbitursäure," *ibid.,* **33** (1900), 3666–3668; and "Synthese des Chinazolin," *ibid.,* **36** (1903), 800–813.

For a short biography and review of Gabriel's research, see James Colman and August Albert, "Siegmund Gabriel," in *Berichte der Deutschen chemischen Gesellschaft,* **59A** (1926), 7–26.

A. ALBERT BAKER, JR.

GADOLIN, JOHAN (*b.* Åbo [now Turku], Finland, 5 June 1760; *d.* Wirmo, Finland, 15 August 1852), *chemistry, mineralogy.*

Gadolin's father, Jacob, was professor of physics and theology at the Finnish University at Åbo and later became bishop of Åbo. His maternal grandfather, Johan Brovallius, was also professor of physics at Åbo and a friend of Linnaeus. Gadolin studied chemistry under Pehr Adrian Gadd, the first professor of chemistry at Åbo. He then spent four years at Uppsala studying with Torbern Bergman, during which time he began his work on mineralogy and specific heats.

Upon Bergman's death in 1784 Gadolin became a candidate for the chair of chemistry at Uppsala, but Johann Afzelius, adjunct at Uppsala, was selected. After having become extraordinary professor at Åbo in 1785, Gadolin had sufficient time to travel in Europe and become well acquainted with Richard Kirwan, Adair Crawford, and Lorenz F. F. von Crell, to whose *Chemische Annalen* he later contributed frequently. When Gadd died in 1797, Gadolin became ordinary professor, a post which he held until his retirement in 1822. The great fire of 1827 destroyed his extensive mineral collection (and much of Åbo) and ended his scientific career. He retired to the country, where he died at the age of ninety-two.

As an educator Gadolin was significant for opening his chemical laboratory to students, preceding by many years Liebig's famous laboratory at Giessen. His *Inleding till chemien* (1798) was the first Swedish-language textbook written in the spirit of the new combustion theory.

Although he accepted the phlogiston theory early

in his career, Gadolin attempted to understand Lavoisier's ideas. In a paper published in 1788 he tried to define phlogiston and admitted that the French explanation of combustion was superior to some phlogiston theories, but for a long time he was not wholly converted. His lectures always made use of the new chemistry, and he eventually became the spokesman in Scandinavia for Lavoisier's nomenclature and combustion theory, often encountering Berzelius' opposition. Despite his willingness to accept these new ideas, he never made use of the work of Dalton, Davy, or Gay-Lussac.

Gadolin's chemical contributions cover a large area. By 1784 he had published two important papers on specific heat, and in 1791 he published one on the latent heat of steam. Having established the composition of Prussian blue, he made a significant contribution to analytical chemistry by suggesting the ferricyanide titration of ferrous iron (precipitating the ferrous ion quantitatively as ferro ferricyanide). This volumetric analysis preceded Gay-Lussac's classic work by forty years.

Best remembered for his studies in mineralogy, Gadolin in 1792–1793 analyzed a new black mineral (later named gadolinite) from Ytterby, Sweden, and discovered in it a new earth, yttria, later shown to contain several elements of the rare-earth series. In 1886 Jean Charles Marignac isolated a new rare-earth element and named it gadolinium, the first element named for a person.

Honored by his contemporaries with memberships in several European scientific societies, Gadolin declined a call to succeed J. F. Gmelin to a full professorship at Göttingen in 1804. Interested in politics, he was influential in bringing about the political separation of Finland from Sweden.

BIBLIOGRAPHY

I. Original Works. Gadolin's most significant publication is his textbook *Inleding till chemien* (Åbo, 1798). A lengthy essay on chemical affinity is *Dissertatio academia historiam doctrinae de affinatibus chemicis exhibens* (Åbo, 1815). His classification of minerals was published as *Systema fossilium analysibus chemicis examinatorum secundum partium constitutivarum rationes ordinatorium* (Berlin, 1825). Reports of many of Gadolin's chemical investigations appeared in German in Crell's *Chemische Annalen für die Freunde der Naturlehre, Arzneygelahrheit, Haushaltungskeit und Manufacturen.* Among the more important publications in the *Chemische Annalen* are his theory of combustion (1788), **1**, 1–17; and his discovery of the new earth, yttria (1796), **1**, 313.

II. Secondary Literature. Numerous short biographical sketches of Gadolin exist in the literature. Among the most useful and accessible are Vieno Ojala and Ernest R. Schierz, "Finnish Chemists," in *Journal of Chemical Education,* **14** (1937), 161–165; and T. E. T. [probably Thomas Edward Thorpe], "Johan Gadolin," in *Nature,* **86** (1911), 48–49. A book-length biography in Finnish is Robert A. A. Tigerstedt, *Johan Gadolin. Ett bidrag till de induktiva vetenskapernas historia in Finland* (Helsinki, 1877). A collection of German and Latin essays in honor of Gadolin is Edvard Hjelt and Robert Tigerstedt, eds., *Johan Gadolin 1760–1852, in memoriam . . .* (Leipzig, 1910).

SHELDON J. KOPPERL

GAERTNER, JOSEPH (*b.* Calw, Germany, 12 March 1732; *d.* Calw, 14 June 1791), *botany.*

While Gaertner is best known for his *De fructibus et seminibus plantarum* (1788–1792), which describes the fruits and seeds of 1,050 genera, Julius von Sachs considered his "valuable reflections" on sexuality in plants to be of great theoretical significance.

Gaertner was the son of a court physician. Orphaned at a young age, he was first destined for the church, then law, and finally medicine. In 1751 he entered the University of Tübingen, where he came under the influence of Haller. He received the M.D. degree from Tübingen in 1753 with his dissertation "De viis urinae ordinariis et extraordinariis," but he did not practice medicine. After visiting several cities in Italy, he arrived in Lyons, then spent six months each in Montpellier and Paris, and tarried in England for nearly a year (1755), pursuing mathematics, optics, and mechanics. During 1759 he attended with enthusiasm Adrian van Royen's botany lectures at Leiden and he soon commenced marine investigations. Peter Pallas published Gaertner's studies on zoophytes, and his "Account of the Urtica marina in a Letter to Mr. Peter Collinson" appeared in the *Philosophical Transactions of the Royal Society,* **52** (1761), 75–85.

Gaertner became in turn professor of anatomy at Tübingen, professor of botany at St. Petersburg, cataloger of the empress' cabinet of curiosities, and botanical traveler with Count Grigory Orlov in the Ukraine, where he discovered many undescribed plants before returning to Calw in 1770. Thenceforth he gave his attention to carpology.

Learning that Sir Joseph Banks, Daniel Solander, and the Forsters had brought back rich collections of plants and seeds from Cook's voyages around the world, Gaertner hastened to England in the spring of 1778, seeking to add these novelties to his survey of fruits and seeds. He found Banks openhanded in granting their study and in gifts of duplicates for use in *De fructibus.* At Rotterdam, Gaertner met Karl Thunberg, who, recently returned from South Africa and Japan, also generously assisted him. From these collections, as well as those found in botanical gardens at Leiden, Amsterdam, and Lyons, and pharmaceutical plots at Stuttgart, Gaertner proposed fifty new genera.

De fructibus was issued in five parts, the first late in 1788 (cf. Frans Stafleu, "Dates of Botanical Publications, 1788–1792" [1963], and *Taxonomic Literature* [1967]). The *Supplementum carpologicae,* issued in three parts (1805–1807), was published in Leipzig by Gaertner's son, Karl Friedrich. Volume I of *De fructibus* was fittingly dedicated to Banks and illustrated from Gaertner's sketches with 180 copperplate drawings by Gaertner and by Hermann Jakob Tyroff. The work, however, went almost unnoticed in Germany where only 200 copies were sold in three years, and this commercial failure even threatened its completion. Yet in France, it met with appreciation, coming as it did at the same time as Jussieu's *Genera plantarum* (Paris, 1789).

Gaertner demonstrated that the spores of Cryptogamia (which he called gemmae), being without an embryo yet capable of germination, were essentially different from seeds of Phanerogamia, which contain an embryo. He recognized that the early stages of an organ presented more significant information on origins and affinities of different forms than did a comparison of their mature condition. He established terminology, heretofore vague, for fruits and seeds. He distinguished between the pericarp, however dry and anomalous it may be in one-seeded fruits, and integuments. Further, he characterized endosperm (calling it albumen) as distinct from cotyledons, which he correctly interpreted as appendages of the embryo. His scheme of classifying fruits and seeds contributed importantly to Jussieu's emerging natural system of plant families.

The Achilles' heel of Gaertner's interpretation was his concept of what he called the vitellus, a term he used to embrace such diverse structures as the scutellum of grasses, cotyledons of *Zamia,* and the spore contents of various Cryptogamia. In the course of examining the reproductive structures of *Spirogyra,* Gaertner witnessed zygospore formation. This observation led Johann Hedwig to suggest, and Jean Vaucher subsequently to assert, that true sexuality occurs in algae.

BIBLIOGRAPHY

I. Original Works. For bibliographic details of *De fructibus* see Frans Stafleu, "Dates of Botanical Publications, 1788-1792," in *Taxon,* **12** (1963), 60–62, and *Taxonomic Literature* (1967), 162–163. Gaertner's minor papers are listed in Jonas Dryander, *Catalogus bibliothecae historico-naturalis Josephi Banks* (London, 1798–1800).

II. Secondary Literature. For interpretative commentary on Gaertner, see Julius von Sachs, *Geschichte der Botanik vom 16. Jahrhundert bis 1860* (Munich, 1875), 132–135, 222, 447; English trans. by H. E. F. Garnsey and Isaac Bayley Balfour (Oxford, 1906), 122–125, 207, 413; French trans. by Henry de Varigny (Paris, 1892), 128–132, 216, 428.

The fundamental biographical account is Joseph P. F. Deleuze, "Notice sur la vie et les ouvrages de Gaertner," in *Annales du muséum national d'histoire naturelle,* **1** (an XI [1802]), 207–233, to which a few details are added by François Chaumeton, in *Biographie universelle,* XV (1856), 342–343; and Paul Ascherson, in *Allgemeine deutsche Biographie,* VIII (1878), 377–380. A calendar of eight letters from Gaertner is given by Warren R. Dawson, *The Banks Letters* (London, 1958), 351–352. Stafleu (cited above) presents different evidence from George K. Brizicky, "Dates of Publication of Gaertner's *De Fructibus et Seminibus Plantarum,*" in *Rhodora,* **62** (1960), 81–84.

Joseph Ewan

GAERTNER, KARL FRIEDRICH VON (*b.* Göppingen, Germany, 1 May 1772; *d.* Calw, Württemberg, Germany, 1 September 1850), *botany.*

Gaertner was born out of wedlock to Joseph Gaertner and Maria Rebekka Mütschelin. His father, who never married, officially recognized him in 1773 and legally adopted him in 1787. Gaertner's paternal ancestors were apothecaries and physicians; his father also acquired a reputation as a botanist. Appointed professor of anatomy at Tübingen in 1761, Joseph Gaertner became professor of botany and natural history at St. Petersburg in 1768; until 1770 he was also in charge of the botanical garden and the natural history museum there. In addition, he undertook several scientific expeditions to various regions of Europe. His masterpiece was *De fructibus et seminibus plantarum* (1788–1792). The studies in comparative plant anatomy presented in this work contributed to the development of carpology and of the natural system of classification.

Gaertner spent his youth in his father's home. He attended the local Latin school and then, from October 1787, the lower convent school in Bebenhausen. In 1791, after a two-year apprenticeship at the royal pharmacy in Stuttgart, he began to study medicine at the Hohe Karlsschule. His interest in chemistry having been awakened by K. F. Kielmeyer, he went in 1794 to Johann Göttling's laboratory in Jena, where he also heard Christoph Hufeland's lectures. The following year he studied at Göttingen. In 1796, after earning his medical degree at Tübingen, he set up practice in Calw. He traveled to Paris, England, and Holland in 1802 and met the leading natural scientists of the period, many of whom had been friends of his father, including Georges Cuvier, A. L. de Jussieu, J. P. F. Deleuze, R. L. Desfontaines, Joseph Banks, and K. P. Thunberg.

In 1803 at Calw, Gaertner married Christine Sybille Wagner, the daughter of a wholesale merchant. His descendants include the political economist Gustav von Schmoller (a grandson) and the chemist Walter Hückel and the physicist Erich Hückel (great-grandsons). Gaertner was granted a title of personal nobility in 1846.

Like his father, Gaertner contracted an eye ailment in the course of his microscopical investigations. He therefore discontinued them and ceased his medical practice as well. Beginning about 1824 he devoted his energies entirely to research on plant hybridization. Gaertner, who conducted his studies as an independent scholar, became a member of the Leopoldina in 1826 and of the Royal Netherlands Academy of Sciences in 1849.

Gaertner's earliest research dealt with medical and physiological questions and with the chemical analysis of organic substances, including bone and urine. After 1800 he concentrated exclusively on botany. He prepared a supplementary fifth volume on the cryptogams to J. G. Gmelin's *Flora Sibirica* as well as a further supplement to that volume containing data on the plants his father had gathered in the Ukraine. Following his trip abroad in 1802, Gaertner worked until 1805 on editing another supplementary volume to the *Flora,* this one dealing with carpology and written by his father. He then began a series of systematic and morphological investigations of the grasses.

The writings of his father's friend J. G. Koelreuter had already drawn Gaertner's attention to the problems of the hybrid fertilization of plants. When F. J. Schelver and his student A. W. Henschel again brought the sexuality of plants into doubt on the basis of principles derived from *Naturphilosophie,* the question became the subject of much debate. In 1825, Gaertner began comprehensive research on this problem after planning and beginning a general treatise on plant physiology. He published his first results in 1826, and he made further contributions almost yearly. In 1837 he won a prize for his solution of a problem presented by the Netherlands Society of Sciences at Haarlem. The first part of his masterpiece, *Versuche und Beobachtungen über die Befruchtungsorgane der vollkommeneren Gewächse . . .,* appeared in 1844; the second and larger part in 1849, under the title *Versuche und Beobachtungen über die Bastarderzeugung im Pflanzenreich.*

The first part of this work treated the relationships and conditions of natural and artificial fertilization, as well as the functions and alterations of the individual parts of the flower during fertilization. The second part reported results of experiments carried on over decades; the experimental methods themselves were described in a supplement. In this treatise Gaertner set forth the different ways in which hybrid fertilization can occur and discussed the capacity for hybridization among the various systematic units (family, genus, species, variety). He also considered the question of the "regularities" in the behavior of several generations of hybrids, although he did not formulate any general rules. He referred to certain dominant characteristics as "decidirte Typen" ("definite types"). He observed alterations of individual characteristics but did not study them systematically. He denied the possibility of "the transformation of one species into another through hybridization" and believed in the stability of species, which he regarded as fixed types. Gaertner classified hybrids "according to their structure and origin" and collected data on the general "characteristics and properties of hybrids," as, for example, those pertaining to their fertility.

Although Gaertner's general theoretical conclusions were deficient in terms of contemporary biological knowledge, his writings were extremely rich in observations, presented new methodology, and, in sum, constituted the first comprehensive treatment of the problem of hybridization. In them the sexuality of plants was definitively established, and at the same time the attention of researchers was drawn to the biological problems connected with sexual reproduction. Charles Darwin read Gaertner closely when he was developing his theory of pangenesis. However, Gaertner's work achieved its greatest impact through its influence on Gregor Mendel, whose investigations were directly inspired by it.

BIBLIOGRAPHY

I. Original Works. Gaertner's major works are "Fortgesetzte Nachrichten über Bastardgewächse," in *Flora* (Regensburg), **10–21** (1827–1838); "Over de voortteling van bastaard-planten," in *Natuurkundige verhandelingen van de Hollandsche maatschappij der wetenschappen te Haarlem,* **24** (1844), 1–202; *Versuche und Beobachtungen über die Befruchtungsorgane der vollkommeneren Gewächse und über die naturliche und künstliche Befruchtung durch den eigenen Pollen* (Stuttgart, 1844); and *Versuche und Beobachtungen über die Bastarderzeugung im Pflanzenreich* (Stuttgart, 1849).

II. Secondary Literature. An obituary is in *Flora,* **34**

(1851), 135–143. See also F. Reinöhl, in *Schwäbische Lebensbilder,* III (Stuttgart, 1942), 190–198, with portrait, bibliography of his works, and list of the literature.

BRIGITTE HOPPE

GAFFKY, GEORG THEODOR AUGUST (*b.* Hannover, Germany, 17 February 1850; *d.* Hannover, 23 September 1918), *bacteriology, public health.*

Gaffky was the son of Georg Friedrich Wilhelm Gaffky, a shipping agent, and Emma Wilhelmine Mathilde Schumacher. After attending a Gymnasium in Hannover, he studied medicine at the University of Berlin. His studies were interrupted by the Franco-Prussian War, however, and he served as a hospital orderly, then returned to the university to take the M.D. in 1873, with a dissertation on the causal relation between chronic lead poisoning and kidney disease. He was an assistant at the Charité, and passed the *Staatsexamen* in 1875. He then spent several years as a military surgeon posted to various garrisons.

Gaffky's career took a new turn in 1880 when he and Friedrich Löffler were ordered to assist Robert Koch at the recently founded imperial health office in Berlin. They were the first two of the brilliant group of assistants that Koch was assembling there. Under Koch's tutelage, Gaffky participated in developing new bacteriological methods and in demonstrating the causes of infectious disease.

From the beginning of his work with Koch, Gaffky was drawn into a variety of researches at the public health laboratory. In 1881 he reported on experimentally produced septicemia in animals. Controverting Naegeli's view that pathogenic bacteria might eventually arise through the accommodation and indefinite variability of common, previously harmless forms, Gaffky maintained that these disease-producing bacteria were specific and derived only from forms like themselves. He took part with Löffler in Koch's work on steam disinfection, and participated in the investigations on anthrax, cholera, and tuberculosis.

Gaffky's most important contribution, however, was in the isolation and culture of the bacillus that is the causative agent of typhoid fever. In 1880 Karl Joseph Eberth had seen and described a bacillus which he believed to be the cause of this disease, while Koch had independently observed the organism and photographed masses of the bacilli. But Eberth and Koch had been able to discern the bacillus in no more than half the cases of typhoid fever in which they had made their examinations. It was Gaffky's hypothesis that this difficulty might be due in part to the culture methods employed, and for the next several years he sought ways to obtain the bacillus with high consistency in pure culture. To do so, it was necessary for him to differentiate between the causative agent of typhoid fever—or *Typhus abdominalis,* as he called it—and similar bacilli that might be present but represent secondary invaders of the diseased tissues.

The bacilli—typically short rods with rounded ends—could be found in the mesenteric glands, spleen, liver, and kidneys of typhoid victims, sometimes in isolation, but more frequently grouped in masses or threadlike arrangements. Using various techniques, Gaffky grew cultures of the bacillus in solid nutrient gelatin, on the surface of boiled potatoes (where a characteristic film formed), in solidified sheep blood serum (according to Koch's procedures), in fluid serum, and in bouillon. He identified the bacillus and believed that he had demonstrated its spores. The organism was clearly visible in stained sections, while in fluid media the living bacillus exhibited a distinctive spontaneous movement and there was a characteristic motion of the bacillar threads. Despite this success in culturing the bacillus in different media, Gaffky was never able to cultivate the bacillus in living animals to produce the disease, although he tried repeatedly to achieve this further proof. In vain he experimentally fed infective material to Java monkeys, mice, guinea pigs, and other animals in an attempt to induce typhoid fever in them.

Still, Gaffky could report that he had with the highest probability isolated the etiologic agent of typhoid fever, for his examinations had disclosed the presence of the bacillus in twenty-six of twenty-eight cases of the disease and he published these results of his investigations in the *Mittheilungen aus dem K. Gesundheitsamte* in 1884.

In 1883–1884 Gaffky was a member of the expedition, sponsored by the German state and led by Koch, that was sent to Egypt and India to investigate the outbreak of cholera there. On the commission's return, Koch reported the identification of the cholera bacillus and described the ways in which the infection was transmitted; Gaffky was responsible for preparing a detailed documentary report on the journey and its scientific results, published in the *Arbeiten aus dem K. Gesundheitsamte* in 1887. Its frontispiece showed a scene on the Hooghly River in which people were bathing, washing clothes, and carrying off drinking water, while boats lay nearby; the text was illustrated with photomicrographs of Koch's cultures of the vibrio and with maps and charts of epidemic statistics.

In 1885 Koch accepted the chair of hygiene at the University of Berlin and Gaffky succeeded him as director of the imperial health office. In 1888 Gaffky was appointed professor of hygiene at the University of Giessen and undertook the direction of the new Hygienic Institute there. While he was at Giessen in 1892 cholera broke out in Hamburg, and Gaffky interrupted his teaching to advise the government in combating the epidemic. He was rector of the university from 1894 to 1895.

Gaffky returned to India—this time as leader of the government commission—in 1897, when bubonic plague was rife in Bombay and other centers. Koch was at this time in South Africa, investigating rinderpest; he later assumed leadership of the plague commission, and Gaffky collaborated in its report.

Gaffky left Giessen in 1904 when Koch suggested that he succeed him as director of the Institut für Infektionskrankheiten. He was an able administrator and under his guidance the institute was enlarged by a division for tropical diseases, a rabies station, and a division for protozoology. He also served as coeditor of the *Zeitschrift für Hygiene und Infektionskrankheiten.*

In 1913 Gaffky left Berlin for the quieter surroundings of Hannover. He had intended to resume his own studies, but when World War I broke out he was again called to serve the government as adviser on hygiene and public health. He died just before the war ended.

In his career Gaffky followed in Koch's footsteps, but his own contributions to bacteriology and public health were significant. A genus of the family Micrococcaceae is named Gaffkya after him.

BIBLIOGRAPHY

I. ORIGINAL WORKS. Gaffky's writings include "Experimentell erzeugte Septicämie mit Rücksicht auf progressive Virulenz und accomodative Züchtung," in *Mittheilungen aus dem K. Gesundheitsamte,* **1** (1881), 80–133; "Ein Beitrag zum Verhalten der Tuberkelbacillen im Sputum," *ibid.,* 126–130; "Zur Aetiologie des Abdominaltyphus," *ibid.,* **2** (1884), 372–420, trans. by J. J. Pringle as "On the Etiology of Enteric Fever," in W. Watson Cheyne, ed., *Recent Essays by Various Authors on Bacteria in Relation to Disease* (London, 1886), pp. 203–257; "Versuche über Desinfection des Kiel- oder Bilgeraums von Schiffen," in *Arbeiten aus dem K. Gesundheitsamte,* **1** (1886), 199–221, written with R. Koch; "Bericht über die Thätigkeit der zur Erforschung der Cholera im Jahre 1883 nach Egypten und Indien entsandten Kommission," *ibid.,* **3** (1887), compiled with Koch; and "Die Verbreitung der orientalischen Beulenpest durch sogenannte 'Dauerausscheider' und 'Bazillenträger,'" in *Klinisches Jahrbuch,* **19** (1908), 491–496. In addition, he edited the *Gesammelte Werke von Robert Koch* (Leipzig, 1912) with E. Pfuhl. Olpp and Pagel (see below) provide further bibliographical data.

II. SECONDARY LITERATURE. See B. Harms, "Georg Gaffky zum Gedächtnis," in *Zentralblatt für Bakteriologie, Parasitenkunde, Infektionskrankheiten und Hygiene,* **156** (1950), 1–2; Wilhelm Katner, "Georg Theodor August Gaffky," in *Neue deutsche Biographie,* VI (Berlin, 1964), 28; Kirchner, "Georg Gaffky," in *Zeitschrift für ärztliche Fortbildung,* **15** (1918), 614–615; H. Kossel, "Georg Gaffky," in *Münchener medizinische Wochenschrift,* **65,** pt. 2 (1918), 1191–1192; E. Neufeld, "Georg Gaffky," in *Berliner klinische Wochenschrift,* **55,** pt. 2 (1918), 1062–1063; G. Olpp, *Hervorragende Tropenärzte in Wort und Bild* (Munich, 1932), pp. 139–141; "Georg Theodor August Gaffky," in J. Pagel, *Biographisches Lexikon hervorragender Ärzte des neunzehnten Jahrhunderts* (Berlin, 1901), pp. 577–578; and R. Pfeiffer, "Georg Gaffky," in *Deutsche medizinische Wochenschrift,* **44,** pt. 2 (1918), 1199.

GLORIA ROBINSON

GAGLIARDI, DOMENICO (*b.* Rome [?], Italy, 1660; *d.* Rome [?], *ca.* 1725), *anatomy.*

There is little or no information on Gagliardi's life. He was probably born in Rome or somewhere in the Papal States. The scanty information provided by biographers indicates that he was a professor of medicine at the University of Rome; but since his name does not appear in the *rotoli,* the lists of professors compiled each year for administrative purposes, such a statement cannot be considered reliably documented.

Gagliardi was also the *protomedico* of the Papal States, and of Rome in particular, a function in some measure similar to that of a chief provincial doctor, and he acquired great fame as a doctor and as an anatomist. His name is especially connected with anatomy, particularly the skeletal system, which he summarized in *Anatome ossium novis inventis illustrata* (1689). Gagliardi carried out morphological and microscopic investigations on human bones, using chemical reagents in order to bring out the fine structure; he also made comparative anatomical studies of the skull and vertebrae of man and calf.

His morphological and microscopic work was accompanied by anatomicopathologic research. His *Anatome ossium novis* contains the first description of a case of what is presumably tuberculosis of the bone. In order to emphasize the structure of bone lamellae, Gagliardi used solutions of various acid substances; on the basis of his results he proposed a theory that the "softening" of bones which he described was caused by the action of an "acid" present in the organism.

In 1720 Gagliardi had an opportunity to do a close study of the pneumonia epidemic raging in Rome;

the interest of this study lies in the fact that, before G. B. Morgagni, it was anatomicopathological in approach and based on carefully conducted autopsies. He was also interested in medical deontology and in what today would be called scientific popularization. He warned patients against the activity of charlatans, who in papal Rome appear to have had a large following. Two volumes, dedicated to moral and deontological topics and written expressly for the layman, make very clear the limits of the art of medicine. Written in a richly erudite and very ponderous style, according to the taste of the times, these works are full of precepts for reaching an advanced age by following certain rules of hygiene and sanitation.

Gagliardi left a third book of a more strictly deontological character, in which he gave young doctors advice on correct professional behavior toward patients and many rules of a more strictly medical-scientific nature.

BIBLIOGRAPHY

Gagliardi's writings are *Anatome ossium novis inventis illustrata* (Rome, 1689); *Idea del vero medico fisico e morale fermata secondo li documenti ed operazioni d'Ippocrate* (Rome, 1718); *L'infermo istruito nella scuola del disinganno* (Rome, 1719); and *De educatione filiorum* (Rome, 1723).

CARLO CASTELLANI

GAGNEBIN, ÉLIE (*b.* Liège, Belgium, 4 February 1891; *d.* Lausanne, Switzerland, 16 July 1949), *geology.*

Gagnebin was the eleventh of the twelve children of Henri Gagnebin, a minister, and the former Adolphine Heshuysen. In 1892 the family moved to Switzerland, where the father was pastor of the Free Church (Église Libre) in Biel and, from 1899, in Lausanne. Gagnebin attended the classical Gymnasium in Lausanne and took the *bachelier ès lettres* when he was eighteen; he then attended the University of Lausanne, where the program in natural sciences did not sufficiently engage his critical spirit and high intelligence. He became a member of the Société des Belles Lettres, a merry group of student revolutionaries.

In 1912 Gagnebin earned the *licence* in natural and physical sciences and became assistant to Maurice Lugeon, a specialist in the tectonics of Switzerland and one of the first advocates of the nappe theory of the Alps. He began geological researches toward his doctorate in 1913; they dealt with the Préalpes Bordières and the region of Châtel St. Denis, famous for its wealth of fossils. (The Préalpes, or fore-Alps, are divided into a northwest front, the Préalpes Bordières; a distinct central zone, the Préalpes Médianes; and a southeast Zone des Cols, or Préalpes Internes.) He received the doctorate at the University of Lausanne on 5 July 1920 with a dissertation (published in 1924) which he modestly entitled *Communication préliminaire.* In this *Communication,* Gagnebin set forth the main features of the stratigraphy and tectonics of the Préalpes Bordières, including the northward movement of the Ultrahelvetian nappes and klippes into the region. He continued to study this region during the next few years while furthering his professional knowledge by working under Wilfrid Kilian at Grenoble (1920) and Émile Haug at Paris (1921).

Gagnebin began his academic career in 1917, when he occasionally replaced Lugeon as lecturer in paleontology; he was officially assigned to this post in 1928. He was promoted to associate professor in 1933 and delivered an inaugural lecture, "La durée des temps géologiques," on 16 May of that year. In 1940 he succeeded Lugeon as full professor.

As a field geologist Gagnebin had made his mark as early as 1922 when he published his *Carte géologique des Préalpes entre Montreux et le Moléson et du Mt.-Pèlerin.* On the basis of this work the Swiss Geological Commission entrusted him with preparing the map of St. Maurice, a project that occupied Gagnebin's summers from 1925 to 1933 and was published in 1934. From 1931 he was also a member of the Service de la Carte Géologique de France.

In 1939 Gagnebin published his observations on the shredding of the Simme nappe in the Chablais Préalpes. In 1941, with Lugeon, he brought out the classic investigation "Observations et vues nouvelles sur la géologie des Préalpes romandes." In this study Gagnebin and Lugeon proposed continental drift as the primary process in the formation of the Alps; gravity then caused the resulting accumulation of faulting and nappes to slide into their present positions. (The gravity sliding hypothesis had earlier been advanced by Lugeon and Hans Schardt and had received new attention through the work of Daniel Schneegans in 1938.) Gagnebin extended this hypothesis to the Helvetic Alps of eastern Switzerland in 1945.

Gagnebin's other publications include a few short communications on chance paleontological finds and two popular works, *Le transformisme et l'origine de l'homme* (1943) and *Histoire de la terre et des êtres vivants* (1946). A study of the Quaternary led him to the concerns of the earlier book; in it he demonstrated man's descent from a branch of the anthropoids and stated the hope that man is still evolving and that "a different and more developed race will succeed ours." The success of this book encouraged him to write the *Histoire,* in the final chapter of which he formulated a finalistic ethics—"Good is that which goes in the direction of life . . ."—and called for a new Aquinas to create "a metaphysics and a religious doctrine capable of integrating the sum of truths of which man has become aware in the last three or four centuries. . . ."

Gagnebin was in addition an ardent champion of modern music. With his friend the Vaudois writer C. F. Ramuz, the composer Igor Stravinsky, and the conductor Ernest Ansermet, he created the drama *L'histoire du soldat* (1918), in which he took the role of the narrator.

BIBLIOGRAPHY

Gagnebin's most important works are *Carte géologique des Préalpes entre Montreux et le Moléson et du Mt.-Pèlerin,* carte spéciale no. 99, Matériaux pour la Carte de la Suisse (Bern, 1922); "Description géologique des Préalpes bordières entre Montreux et Semsales," in *Mémoires de la Société vaudoise des sciences naturelles,* **2,** no. 1 (1924), 1–70, diss.; "La finalité dans les sciences biologiques," in *Revue de théologie et de philosophie,* no. 78 (1931), 1–38; "St.-Maurice," map. no. 8 in *Atlas géologique de la Suisse au 1:25,000* (Bern, 1934), written with F. de Loys, M. Reinhard, M. Lugeon, N. Oulianoff, W. Hotz, and E. Poldini; "La durée des temps géologiques," in *Bulletin de la Société vaudoise des sciences naturelles,* **58** (1934), 125–146; "Notice explicative de la feuille St.-Maurice," in *Atlas géologique de la Suisse au 1:25,000* (1934), pp. 1–6; "Ossements de mammouth trouvés dans la moraine de Renens, près de Lausanne, et recensement des restes de mammouths connus dans la région lémanique," in *Bulletin de la Société vaudoise des sciences naturelles,* **58** (1935), 385–391; "Mécanisme ou vitalisme en biologie?" in *Revue de théologie et de philosophie,* no. 100 (1936), 1–7; "Découverte d'un lambeau de la nappe de la Simme dans les Préalpes du Chablais," in *Comptes rendus hebdomadaires des séances de l'Académie des sciences,* **208** (1939), 822; "Découverte d'une nouvelle défense de mammouth dans la terrasse du Boiron, près de Morges, et précisions sur quelques restes de mammouths de la région lémanique," in *Bulletin de la Société vaudoise des sciences naturelles,* **61** (1940), 291–296; "Observations et vues nouvelles sur la géologie des Préalpes romandes," in *Mémoires de la Société vaudoise des sciences naturelles,* **7,** no. 1 (1941), 1–90, written with M. Lugeon; *Le transformisme et l'origine de l'homme* (Lausanne, 1943; 2nd ed., 1947); "Quelques problèmes de la tectonique d'écoulement en Suisse orientale," in *Bulletin de la Société vaudoise des sciences naturelles,* **62** (1945), 476–494; *Histoire de la terre et des êtres vivants,* no. 10 in the series Gai Savoir (Lausanne, 1946); and "La notion d'espèce en biologie," in *Dialectica,* **1,** no. 3 (1947), 229–242.

An excellent appreciation is Maurice Lugeon, "E. Gagnebin, 1891–1949," in *Verhandlungen der Schweizerischen naturforschenden Gesellschaft* (1949), 382–399, with portrait.

EMIL KUHN-SCHNYDER

GAHN, JOHAN GOTTLIEB (*b.* Ovanåker, Sweden, 19 August 1745; *d.* Falun, Sweden, 8 December 1818), *mineralogy, chemistry.*

Gahn studied physics and chemistry at Uppsala from 1762 to 1770. When Torbern Bergman was appointed professor of chemistry there in 1767, Gahn became his laboratory assistant. After passing in 1770 the examination for mining engineer, he worked at the College of Mining, where he was assigned the task of applying new and more scientific methods to the copper smelting processes at the Falun mine in the Kopparberg district. For four years he worked exclusively with copper smelting, introducing important improvements and solving many technical problems. Above all, he modernized the methods for using the by-products of the smelting process, among them sulfur, iron sulfate, red pigment, copper mastic, and copper precipitate. Gahn performed his chemical research in a well-equipped laboratory that he installed at his own expense in his garden at Falun.

Although he seldom took the time to write down his observations and published almost nothing, rumors of Gahn's extensive chemical and technical abilities spread beyond Sweden; Falun became a mecca for scholars, factory owners, and industrialists seeking advice and guidance in technical problems. "Gahn is building in Sweden a real center for everything that happens in the technical field. The country still lacks a Polytechnic Institute where new ideas can be tried out and from which innovations and projects can emanate. Gahn supplies that" (Johann F. L. Hausman, *Reise durch Skandinavien in den Jahren 1806 und 1807* [Leipzig, 1811–1818]). Such merit did not remain unnoticed. In 1780 the College of Mining awarded Gahn its gold medal and two years later informed King Gustavus III of the improvements and growth that Gahn's work had brought to the refining of copper. On this basis the king conferred on him in 1782 the honorary title of superintendent of mines and in 1784 authorization as associate member at the College of Mining. In the same year he was elected member of the Academy of Science in Stockholm.

It was of great importance to contemporary Swedish chemistry that Scheele, who worked in the pharmacy Uplands Wapen in Uppsala from 1770 to 1775, was introduced by Gahn to Torbern Bergman. Gahn collaborated in the work of both of these men; and Bergman, who in many cases benefited from

Gahn's experimental ability, emphasized this both in his letters and published works. For instance, he mentions, concerning the mineral pyrolusite, that he himself had doubted that it contained any metal but that Gahn was the first to reduce the mineral and to discover, in 1774, the pure metal later named manganese.

Gahn shared a friendship and an exchange of ideas with Scheele that were fruitful for the work of both. Unfortunately, their correspondence provides no information about Gahn's contributions; although Gahn conscientiously preserved Scheele's letters during the 1770's, Scheele was so indifferent toward preserving his correspondence from Gahn that only a few writings saved at random still exist. Scheele's letters reveal that he often solicited and received valuable explanations for his experiments with pyrolusite and barium sulfate. It is interesting that Scheele thanks Gahn especially for the suggestion of an important study concerning what is now called solid-state reactivity.

Gahn was a capable chemical experimenter, but Scheele was his unchallenged superior in everything except blowpipe analysis, in which Gahn was unsurpassed. It is therefore not surprising that the possibility of conceptual cross-fertilization that existed here would materialize. A conversation with Scheele in the spring of 1770 concerning his research with inorganic substances in animal bones, the so-called animal earth, provided the incentive for Gahn to study this material more carefully; he was then able to show, with the aid of the blowpipe, the presence of phosphorus. This observation later led to Scheele's method of obtaining phosphorus from animal bones.

Preserved letters indicate that—at least in the first part of the 1770's—Gahn was the trusted friend for whose opinion Scheele first sent his scientific articles.

Gahn also worked with J. J. Berzelius. Among other things they were both financially and scientifically interested in a sulfuric acid factory near Gripsholm. Berzelius tried unsuccessfully to persuade Gahn to go to Stockholm, but ultimately he traveled to Falun to meet Gahn in the summers of 1813–1816. The two friends explored the area's rich mineral deposits and, as Berzelius wrote, "a number of entirely new minerals were discovered . . . and analysed at the time in Gahn's excellently equipped laboratory" (*Jöns Jacob Berzelius Autobiographical Notes,* trans. by Olof Larsell [Baltimore, 1934], p. 91).

BIBLIOGRAPHY

I. Original Works. Gahn's works include *Några anmärkningar i svenska bergs-lagfarenheten om författningar till befrämjande av god hushållning vid järnhyttor* (Uppsala, 1770), his doctoral diss.; "Yttrande över Kommerskollegii fråga om någon ljusare och gladare färg än rödfärg," in *Kongliga Vetenskaps Academiens nya Handlingar,* **25** (1804), 289–301; and *Underrättelse om upställningen och nyttjandet af herr assessor J. G. Gahns förbättrade appareil för vattens aererande med tabell* (Uppsala, 1804).

The principal part of Gahn's literary remains is kept in the library of the Royal Institute of Technology. Certain parts of his correspondence are preserved in the archives of the Nordic Museum and in the National Record Office. The important letters from Scheele and Bergman as well as Gahn's correspondence with Berzelius are to be found in the library of the Royal Academy of Science. Gahn's correspondence with Berzelius is in *Jac. Berzelius brev,* H. G. Söderbaum, ed., IX (Stockholm, 1922). The 38 surviving letters from Gahn to Bergman (1768–1778) are in the university library of Uppsala.

II. Secondary Literature. On Gahn and his work, see J. A. Almquist, *Bergskollegium och bergslagsstaterna* (Stockholm, 1909); J. G. Anrep, *Svenska slägtboken,* 3 vols. (Stockholm, 1871–1875); J. Berzelius, *Själfbiografiska anteckningar* (Stockholm, 1901), and in the trans. by Olof Larsell, *Jöns Jacob Berzelius Autobiographical Notes* (Baltimore, 1934); B. Boethius, *Grycksbo 1382–1940* (Stockholm, 1942); U. Boklund, "När Gahn upptäckte Scheele på Lokks apotek," in *Lychnos* (1959), 217–222; Hans Järta, *Åminnelse-Tal öfver . . . Herr Joh. Gottl. Gahn . . . hållet inför Kongl. Vetenskaps-Academien den 8 October 1831* (Stockholm, 1832); AB Ferrolegeringar (publisher), *Av meteorernas ätt. En krönika om mangan . . .* (Stockholm, 1962); S. Lindroth, *Gruvbrytning och kopparhantering vid Stora Kopparberget . . .,* II (Stockholm, 1955); and C. Sahlin, "Johan Gottlieb Gahns laboratorium och samlingar," in *Blad för bergshanteringens vänner,* **16** (1919–1921). See also J. E. Jorpes, *Jac. Berzelius, His Life and Work* (Stockholm, 1966).

Uno Boklund

GAILLOT, AIMABLE JEAN-BAPTISTE (*b.* Saint-Jean-sur-Tourbe, Marne, France, 27 April 1834; *d.* Chartres, France, 4 June 1921), *astronomy, celestial mechanics.*

Gaillot spent his entire career at the Bureau of Computation of the Paris observatory, to which he was assigned at the time of his recruitment by Urbain Le Verrier in 1861, and was director of the bureau from 1873. He became astronomer in 1864 and chief astronomer in 1874, and was made assistant director of the Paris observatory in 1897.

In astronomy Gaillot concentrated on the calculations that would make his colleagues' observations most useful. He directed the publication of the *Catalogue de l'Observatoire de Paris,* which classified the 387,474 meridian observations made between 1837 and 1881. Despite poor health Gaillot saw this twenty-year task to completion before retiring in 1903.

He continued his research in celestial mechanics until he was eighty. His important contributions in this field brought him four awards from the Academy of Sciences, of which he became a corresponding member in 1908.

Gaillot was Le Verrier's only collaborator. The latter's widow wrote to him in 1877: "I especially want to express my deep gratitude to the devoted and intelligent collaborator who enabled my beloved husband to complete his colossal project. It pleased him to recognize that without you, this would have been impossible."

To complete Le Verrier's work, Gaillot amended the latter's analytical theories concerning Jupiter, Saturn, Uranus, and Neptune. By using a laborious but effective method of interpolation, he eliminated all discordances: his values for the mass of these planets turned out to be excellent and the positions he calculated were confirmed by observations to an accuracy of one or two seconds. Since their publication Gaillot's tables have served as a basis for the international ephemerides found in *Connaissance des temps.*

BIBLIOGRAPHY

In celestial mechanics three broad *mémoires* covering all of Gaillot's earlier research concern Le Verrier's theories on the motion of the planets; two of them furnish, for Saturn and Jupiter, additions to these theories and also corrected tables—see *Annales de l'Observatoire de Paris,* **24** (1904), 1–512, and **31** (1913), 1–317; the third, concerning Uranus and Neptune, includes Le Verrier's theory, which is considerably elaborated, and new tables: *ibid.,* **28** (1910), 1–649. See also "Contribution à la recherche des planètes ultraneptuniennes," in *Comptes rendus hebdomadaires des séances de l'Académie des sciences,* **148** (1909), 754–758; and "Le Verrier et son oeuvre," in *Bulletin des sciences mathématiques et astronomiques,* **2** (1878), 29–40.

In fundamental astronomy, see "Influence de l'attraction luni-solaire sur la verticale, la pesanteur et la marche des pendules," in *Bulletin astronomique,* **1** (1884), 113–118, 217–220; "Détermination géométrique des positions des circumpolaires," *ibid.,* 375–381, 577–583; "Sur la mesure du temps," *ibid.,* **3** (1886), 221–232; "Changements de la durée de l'année julienne . . .," in *Comptes rendus hebdomadaires des séances de l'Académie des sciences,* **97** (1883), 151–154; "Sur les mesures du temps," *ibid.,* 544–546; "Détermination de la constante de la réfraction . . .," *ibid.,* **102** (1886), 200–204, 247–250; "Sur les variations de la latitude . . .," *ibid.,* **111** (1890), 559–561; **112** (1890), 651–563; and "Sur les formules de l'aberration annuelle," *ibid.,* **116** (1893), 563–565. On the work on star catalogs, see "Discordances in d'Agelet's Observations," in *Astronomical Journal,* **16** (1896), 182–183; and, especially, the "Introduction" in *Catalogue de l'Observatoire de Paris,* I (Paris, 1887), (1)–(22).

For information about Gaillot, see B. Baillaud, "Notice nécrologique, A. Gaillot," in *Comptes rendus hebdomadaires des séances de l'Académie des sciences,* **172** (1921), 1393–1394.

JACQUES R. LÉVY

GAIMARD, JOSEPH PAUL (*b.* St. Zacherie, France, 31 January 1796; *d.* Paris [?], France, 10 December 1858), *natural history, scientific exploration, naval medicine.*

Born and educated in the French Midi, Paul Gaimard became one of the most widely traveled naturalists in the history of scientific exploration. Since his father had died in 1799 during uprisings in the Midi, Gaimard's early training was directed by relatives. He entered the naval medical school at Toulon in 1816 and, through success in academic competition, was named surgeon in the royal navy. His talents and background earned him a place as surgeon and naturalist aboard the *Uranie,* commanded by Louis Claude de Freycinet and charged with investigating the meteorology, oceanography, and natural history of vast areas of the South Pacific Ocean. Assisting him were Jean René Constant Quoy, surgeon and naturalist; Charles Gaudichaud-Beaupré, pharmacologist and botanist; and François Arago's youngest brother, Jacques, draftsman.

All were subject to regular naval discipline, Freycinet hoping to avoid the customary willfulness of scientific explorers. Upon their return from the circumnavigation of the globe (1817–1820) Gaimard and Quoy prepared a detailed account of their zoological discoveries. Gaimard thus early made his mark in one of the great periods of French maritime activity and earnest overseas scientific exploration.

Early in 1826 he toured Europe to inspect natural history collections and to prepare for his departure as first surgeon to the famed expedition of J. S. C. Dumont d'Urville. As captain of the *Astrolabe,* Dumont d'Urville's double task was to conduct a scientific survey of Oceania and to seek traces of the lost La Pérouse expedition. Between 1826 and 1829 Gaimard was again in the South Pacific, and once again he and Quoy prepared an account of their zoological collections and discoveries. While this work was in press, an outbreak of Asiatic cholera was reported from western Russia. The indefatigable and audacious Gaimard immediately set out to assess the epidemic. He spent several months observing the disease in eastern Europe and encountered it again upon his return to Paris in 1832. His report on the cholera, an affliction all the more terrifying for its utter novelty in western Europe, remains a classic account of the disease.

Gaimard soon set off on further exploratory voyages. He led a large scientific team aboard the *Recherche* to Iceland and Greenland (1835–1836), and a few years later, serving as director of the Scientific Commission for the North, he conducted extensive explorations in Lapland and on Spitsbergen and the Faeroes. With the latter journey (1838–1840) Gaimard's frenetic, albeit highly productive, wandering apparently came to an end. His later years remain a supreme mystery, but he evidently settled in Paris and was fully occupied with the preparation and publication of the official reports of the expeditions to Iceland and to northern Europe.

Of Gaimard's personality little is known save for effusive but perhaps accurate references to his uncommon benevolence and a readiness to serve France whatever be the task imposed. Details of his personal life also remain quite unknown. Clearly, Gaimard was devoted as much to the sheer pleasure of travel as to the joy of scientific discovery. His talents as a naturalist were indeed great, and he was assiduous and successful in seeing to completion the official reports of every expedition in which he participated. Those reports, for all—or the little—that we know of him, constitute the man himself.

BIBLIOGRAPHY

I. ORIGINAL WORKS. Gaimard's principal publications are *Voyage autour du monde . . . exécuté sur les corvettes . . . Uranie et la Physicienne, pendant les années 1817, 1818, 1819, et 1820 . . . Zoologie par MM. Quoy et Gaimard,* 1 vol. and atlas (Paris, 1824), an assessment of which is given by Cuvier (see below); *Voyage de découvertes de l'Astrolabe . . . pendant les années 1826, 1827, 1828, 1829 . . . Zoologie par MM. Quoy et Gaimard,* 4 vols., and atlas, 2 vols. (Paris, 1830–1832); *Voyage en Islande et au Groënland exécuté pendant les années 1835 et 1836,* 8 vols., and atlas, 3 vols. (Paris, 1838–1852), of which only vol. I, *Histoire du Voyage,* was written by Gaimard himself, the other volumes being prepared under his editorship; *Voyages de la commission scientifique du Nord . . . pendant les années 1838, 1839 et 1840,* 17 vols., and atlas, 5 vols. (Paris, 1843–1855); and *Du choléra morbus en Russie, en Prusse et en Autriche, pendant les années 1831 et 1832* (Paris, 1832), written with Auguste Gérardin.

During the 1820's and 1830's Gaimard and Quoy published numerous reports on the zoology and ethnography of the Pacific area; these are listed in the Royal Society's *Catalogue of Scientific Papers,* II (London, 1868), 755–756. The Bibliothèque Centrale of the Muséum d'Histoire Naturelle, Paris, possesses a number of MSS by Gaimard; these relate principally to the zoological collections made on the *Astrolabe* (information courtesy of Yves Laissus).

II. SECONDARY LITERATURE. Apparently no account of the full career of Gaimard's life exists. A sentimental and very brief report on his activities until about 1837 was published by the Société Montyon et Franklin: A. Jarry de Mancy, "Notice sur Paul Gaimard," in *Portraits et histoire des hommes utiles* (Paris, 1837), 192–196.

Notices in biographical dictionaries and encyclopedias are uniformly obscure. An exception is "Gaimard, Paul," in August Hirsch *et al.,* eds., *Biographisches Lexikon der hervorragenden Ärzte aller Zeiten und Völker,* 2nd ed., II (Berlin–Vienna, 1930), 656. On the background and motives of the naval expeditions in which Gaimard participated, see the excellent review by John Dunmore, *French Explorers of the Pacific,* II, *The Nineteenth Century* (Oxford, 1969), 63–108, 178–227. See also a review of Gaimard's work by Georges Cuvier, in *Annales des sciences naturelles,* **10** (1827), 239–243.

WILLIAM COLEMAN

GAINES, WALTER LEE (*b.* Crete, Illinois, 17 March 1881; *d.* Urbana, Illinois, 20 November 1950), *dairy science.*

Gaines was raised on a farm near Crete, where he received his preliminary education and the direction for his lifework. The prospect of improving farm production guided his studies at the University of Illinois, from which he received the B.S. degree in 1908 and the M.S. in agriculture in 1910. He was able to focus the direction of his research career by graduate work at the University of Chicago, where he obtained the Ph.D. in 1915 with a contribution to the physiology of lactation.

After a brief interval at his home farm in Crete, Gaines returned to the University of Illinois to assist a federal program for increasing food production during World War I. He was professor of milk production at the University of Illinois from 1919 to 1949, during which time he wrote twenty-nine research reports, was co-author of seventeen others, and contributed frequently to farm journals, primarily on the problems of increasing milk production.

His studies on milk secretion included the production of lactose; the effects on lactation of pituitary hormones, blood transfusions, and pregnancy; the storage capacity of udders; the rates of secretion of milk constituents; and the relationship between milk yield and frequency of conception. By intravenous injections of pituitary extracts, Gaines demonstrated that milk is formed continuously by mammary alveoli. He studied the effect of weight changes on future milk production during early development and showed the efficacy of milk production per live weight as a measure of lactation in genetic studies. He also was able to distinguish between milk nutrients assimilated for maintenance and those transformed into milk. He devised a widely used "fat-corrected milk" (F.C.M.) formula for expressing the energy equivalent of milk by comparison with a base of 4 percent butterfat.

In 1949 the American Dairy Science Association gave Gaines its highest honor, the Borden Award, citing him as "the modest leader in the United States of the scientific approach to the problems of milk secretion."

BIBLIOGRAPHY

Gaines's works include "A Contribution to the Physiology of Lactation, in *American Journal of Physiology,* **38** (1915), 285-312; "Relative Rates of Secretion of Various Milk Constituents," in *Journal of Dairy Science,* **8** (1925), 486-496; "Milk Yield in Relation to the Recurrence of Conception," *ibid.,* **10** (1927), 117-125; "The Energy Basis of Measuring Milk Yield in Dairy Cows," in *Illinois Agricultural Experiment Station Bulletin* (1928), p. 308; "Size of Cow and Efficiency of Milk Production," in *Journal of Dairy Science,* **14** (1931), 14-21; and "Live Weight and Milk-Energy Yield in the Wisconsin Dairy Cow Competition," *ibid.,* **22** (1939), 49-53.

RICHARD P. AULIE

GALEAZZI, DOMENICO GUSMANO (*b.* Bologna, Italy, 4 August 1686; *d.* Bologna, 30 July 1775), *anatomy, biochemistry.*

Galeazzi (sometimes wrongly called Galeati), of whose background little is known, attended the Jesuit College in Bologna and studied medicine with the physician Matteo Bazzani, who is supposed to have discovered the coloring of bones in animals fed with madder root. He learned anatomy in the atmosphere created by Antonio Maria Valsalva, who in 1705 was named professor of anatomy at Bologna.

Galeazzi was graduated Doctor of Philosophy and Medicine in 1709 and took up science under the influence of Giacomo Bartolomeo Beccari, then professor of physics at Bologna. He was immediately appointed substitute lecturer in experimental physics; in 1734, when Beccari transferred to the chair of chemistry, Galeazzi succeeded him as professor of physics. His first published work in physics dealt with the construction of mercury thermometers.

In 1714 Galeazzi visited Paris, where he met Jacques Cassini, Louis Lémery, Malebranche, Réaumur, and other men of science and attended meetings of the Académie Royale des Sciences. During those meetings he became interested in the debate between Claude Geoffroy and Lémery concerning the significance of microscopic iron particles in living organisms: Geoffroy contended that these particles were produced by the organism, while Lémery asserted that they had been assimilated. On his return to Bologna, Galeazzi conducted experiments and demonstrated through chemical analysis that the iron particles were assimilated by the organism. He then made a systematic study to discover the connection between the iron in living organisms and iron salts in the soil. Later, in 1746, Galeazzi first ascertained the presence of iron in the human blood; his pupil Vincenzo Menghini detected whole hematic iron in erythrocytes.

In 1716 Galeazzi was appointed professor of philosophy at Bologna, a post he held for forty years. In 1719 he made geological observations in the Emilian Apennines. Later, in entomology, he discovered the endophagous generation of the fly and the oviparous generation of a cochineal, *Pulvinaria vitis* (L.). Galeazzi also had a successful medical practice and wrote on the use of Peruvian bark (cinchona), on jaundice, and on gallstones and kidney stones. He is remembered today primarily for his anatomical research.

Galeazzi began his anatomical work in 1711, when he observed corpora lutea in different stages of regression in pregnant women; but his most important anatomical discoveries were in the gastrointestinal system. He defined the positions of the three layers of muscle fibers in the stomach and described the peculiar arrangement of the superficial layer of longitudinal muscle fibers. He described two layers of muscle fibers in the small intestine: the interior circular and the external longitudinal; in the colon he considered only the circular layer important, because the external layer of longitudinal fibers forms only three longitudinal bands.

In the mucous coat of the intestines Galeazzi described the glands now called Lieberkühn's glands. Johann Nathanael Lieberkühn described them in 1745; Galeazzi made his observations in 1725 and published them in 1731. The existence of intestinal glands had already been claimed by Malpighi (1688), the villi of the small intestine had been described by Gaspare Aselli, and Thomas Bartholin had studied the villi in connection with the chyliferous vessels. In Galeazzi's time the question was whether the villi were hollow siphons, spongy perforated papillae, or unperforated papillae. Galeazzi clarified the structure of the villus: it can be long and cylindrical or short and squat, but he denied the existence of any free lymphatic opening on its surface.

Galeazzi discovered many minute pores not on the villi but between them, distributed over the entire intestinal surface. He concluded that a special sieve-like membrane exists on the interior surface of the intestines and that each of these numerous pores is an opening of a glandular structure in the intestinal wall. Galeazzi also wrote that these glandular structures discharge a secretion into the intestinal cavity.

In 1756 Galeazzi retired from teaching philosophy; although he was a distinguished anatomist, Galeazzi never held the chair of anatomy. He died at the age of eighty-eight and was buried in the Church of the Confraternity of St. Philip Neri in Bologna.

BIBLIOGRAPHY

I. ORIGINAL WORKS. Galeazzi's writings include "De muliebrium ovariorum vesiculis," in *Commentarii de Bononiensi Scientiarum et Artium Instituto atque Academia,* **1,** pt. 2 (1731), 127–130; "De calculis in cystifellea repertis," *ibid.,* 354–358; "De cribriformi intestinorum tunica," *ibid.,* 359–370; "De ferreis particulis quae in corporibus reperiuntur," *ibid.,* **2,** pt. 2 (1746), 20–38; "De thermometris Amontonianis conficiendis," *ibid.,* 201–209; "De carnea ventriculi et intestinorum tunica," *ibid.,* 238–243; "De insecto quodam in vite reperto," *ibid.,* 279–284; "De moscho," *ibid.,* **3** (1755), 177–193; "De morbis duobus," *ibid.,* **4** (1757), 26–43; "De renum morbis," *ibid.,* **5** (1757), 139–150, 249–260; "De cortice peruviano," *ibid.,* 216; and "De sudore quodam atque urina colore nigerrimo infectis," *ibid.,* **6** (1783), 1–12.

II. SECONDARY LITERATURE. On Galeazzi or his work, see A. Corti, "L'anatomico bolognese Domenico Gusmano Galeazzi e la sua esauriente descrizione delle ghiandole intestinali che molti dicono di Lieberkühn," in *Archivio italiano di anatomia e di embriologia,* **19** (1922), 407–434; and "Note storiche e biografiche su Bologna e il suo Studio," in *Rivista di storia delle scienze mediche e naturali,* **40** (1949), 19–51; J. N. Lieberkühn, *Dissertatio anatomico-physiologica de fabrica et actione villorum intestinorum tenuium hominis* (Leiden, 1745); M. Malpighi, "De structura glandularum conglobatarum," a letter to the Royal Society (1688), in *Marcelli Malpighii opera posthuma* (London, 1697), pp. 152–165; M. Medici, *Compendio storico della scuola anatomica di Bologna dal Rinascimento a tutto il secolo XVIII* (Bologna, 1857), 256–272; and V. Menghini, "De ferrearum particularum sede in sanguine," in *Commentarii de bononiensi scientiarum et artium instituto atque academia,* **2,** pt. 2 (1746), 244–266.

PIETRO FRANCESCHINI

GALEN (*b.* Pergamum, A.D. 129/130; *d.* 199/200), *medicine.*

The frequently cited forename "Claudius" is not documented in the ancient texts and seems to have been added in the Renaissance.[1]

In earlier research four years were accepted as possible birth dates: 128, 129, 130, and 131. After J. Ilberg, one of the foremost experts on Galen's biography, had committed himself to 129,[2] J. Walsh advocated the year 130, and the period around 22 September as the actual day of birth.[3] Ilberg defended his own date,[4] and Walsh again established his case with weighty and well-grounded arguments in a detailed reply to Ilberg,[5] whose sudden death prevented his responding. The writer is inclined, however, to accept Ilberg's chronology. Complete certainty cannot be achieved, but 128 and 131 are out of the question.

Parentage. Galen's father, Nikon, was an architect and geometer in Pergamum.[6,7] Galen's personal relationships with his parents were such that he spoke of his father with the greatest respect but compared his mother to Xanthippe.[8] Galen provided extensive data concerning his own life,[9] following the ancient tradition of autobiography.[10] The most important, composed in his later years, are *On the Arrangement of His Own Writings* and *On His Own Writings.*[11] A wealth of autobiographical statements are contained in many of Galen's other extant writings,[12] and additional details are in the Arabic translations.[13] The evocatively titled *On Slander, in Which Is Also Discussed His Own Life* is unfortunately lost.[14] Good introductions and surveys are Sarton[15] and Diepgen,[16] but Deichgräber[17] has justly remarked that these books are mainly biographies of Galen the writer.

Education. Continuing a family tradition, Galen's father had received an intensive education in mathematics and was generally a very cultivated man; similarly, he began to give his own son private lessons at an early age.[18] At fourteen, Galen received instruction in philosophy that encompassed the teachings of all the various schools.[19] Two years later he had to decide on an occupation; a dream allegedly caused him and his father to decide definitely that he should undertake medical studies.[20] (The medical literature of the time advised those interested in the profession to begin the study of medicine at the earliest possible age, usually at about fifteen.[21] Thus, Galen was not at all exceptional.) As to his motivation, the supposed dream is surely to be understood merely symbolically. It seems that at this time the young Galen was undergoing a kind of intellectual crisis as a result of his very extensive and eclectic philosophical education. According to his own testimony, he was rescued from this troubled state only through the help of mathematics—that is to say, geometry—with its certainty and its indubitable systematic foundation. Evidently, Galen was already seeking in the empirical realm the same certainty that he hoped to find in medicine, above all in a knowledge of the body.[22]

Galen's first medical teacher in Pergamum was Satyrus.[23] The latter, Galen reports, had been in that city for "four years already" along with Rufinus, the founder of the Asclepeum in Pergamum.[24] In all probability this Rufinus is Lucius Cuspius Rufinus, who had been consul in the year 142.[25] (The date Galen gives could refer to the year 146; this would fit with 130 as the year of his birth and at the same time agree with the report that Galen began his medical studies at the age of sixteen.) Hence it appears that even at this early date Galen was in contact with leading personalities of Pergamene society. It is not without interest in this connection that Satyrus treated the famous Sophist Aristides, and thus the young Galen very probably met the latter in Pergamum.[26] In these encounters, therefore, lie the origins of Galen's relation to the so-called Second Sophistic, of which he was later to become one of the leading medical representatives and which was so important in the intellectual life of the early Christian era.[27]

Galen composed several works while still a student in Pergamum. He himself names three of them: *On the Anatomy of the Uterus,* the *Diagnosis of Diseases of the Eye,* and *On Medical Experience.*[28] The second has not been preserved. The treatise on the uterus (written at the request of a midwife) confirms that Galen at first devoted his medical studies primarily to anatomy. The work on medical experience, on the other hand, shows that from the beginning Galen was also interested, both philosophically and practically, in the problem of certainty in the empirical sciences. This work was obviously written at the end of his first period in Pergamum—that is, about 150—since it reflects a two-day debate between the physicians Pelops and Philippus in Smyrna. This contact with Pelops induced Galen to go to Smyrna as his student.[29]

These three works, however, are clearly not the only ones Galen wrote during the first Pergamene period of study. In the treatise *On Medical Experience* he explicitly refers to an earlier work, *On the Best Sect,* which consequently must have been among his very earliest writings.[30] It is at the least very questionable whether it was identical with what has come down to us under Galen's name as *On the Best Sect, for Thrasybulos;* the latter work, as I. von Müller has shown, is very probably not genuine.[31] Here then, perhaps, is one of the not unusual cases in which a forgery has strayed into the gigantic *Corpus Galenicum.* This happened even in Galen's own lifetime, as he himself reports.[32]

Finally, in this group of earliest writings should be included, tentatively, the short treatise *On Pleuritis, for Patrophilus.*[33] If Patrophilus were identical with Calvisius Patrophilus, who held a high position in Egypt in the year 147–148,[34] this would provide further evidence of Galen's having had early links with influential people. Moreover, he later incorporated this short work verbatim into the larger *On the Constitution of the Medical Art* (also dedicated to Patrophilus),[35] a not unusual practice for Galen. The short treatise on pleuritis is constructed almost like a mathematical-geometric demonstration (it uses short, precise statements, and the phrase "from this it necessarily follows" recurs with striking frequency). This manner of construction seems, therefore, to be the first concrete application of the principle that he considered best suited to overcome his skeptical despair—namely, the employment of the form of the geometric proof in demonstrating the real facts of natural science and medicine.[36]

The problem of Galen's earliest writings has been discussed in detail as the best procedure for tracing what may be called the concretization of his original intellectual impulses. In what follows references to Galen's writings and their chronology will be made only occasionally and allusively.[37]

Galen's father died when his son was twenty and still living in Pergamum.[38] Not long afterward Galen went to Smyrna to study medicine with Pelops, whom he called his second medical teacher,[39] and Platonic philosophy with Albinus.[40] In philosophy Galen was most influenced by Platonism, just as later Hippocratism exercised the greatest influence on him in medicine;[41] indeed, he set forth a connection between the two in his great work *On The Doctrines of Hippocrates and Plato.*

From Smyrna, Galen went to Corinth, to continue his medical education with Numisianus,[42] and finally to Alexandria,[43] then the most famous center of research and training in medicine. It is generally assumed that Galen remained there for several years,[44] considerably longer than in Smyrna and Corinth. Yet, he himself says that after a stay in Smyrna, "I was in Corinth . . . in Alexandria and among several other peoples."[45] Doubtless Alexandria was very attractive to him. Moreover, it offered the only opportunity to examine human skeletons thoroughly (although not cadavers).[46] Nevertheless, Galen was highly critical of the research and pedagogical activity then being conducted at Alexandria, as is proved by numerous later sarcastic remarks about "Alexandrian prophets" and Alexandrian "scholasticism."[47]

Thus, Galen pursued his extended study of medicine purposively and intensively on the basis of definite intellectual presuppositions but was not, in fact, fully satisfied with them and at the conclusion of this study still had not completely decided on his own definitive approach. At the age of twenty-eight he returned to his native Pergamum as physician to the gladiators,[48] having studied medicine for about twelve years, much longer than was then customary. This does not mean, however, that he could not perhaps have practiced medicine on some occasions during this long period.[49]

Galen continued to treat the gladiators in Pergamum for several years. His experiences in this capacity brought him some chance discoveries (for example, the behavior of certain nerves and tendons), which were important for his later researches.[50] Yet his most important work was still before him.

Galen and Rome. In the year 161, at the beginning of the reign of the two Antonine emperors, Galen arrived at Rome where he quickly established a medical practice.[51,52] He succeeded in effecting several startling cures of influential patients.[53] Among them was the Peripatetic philosopher Eudemus, who introduced Galen to the high government official Flavius Boethus. The latter prompted Galen to compose his first major anatomical and physiological works. At this point a basic observation regarding Galen's literary activity should be made: as can be seen from the *Anatomical Procedures,* for example, Galen revised many of his works. The first version of the great anatomical work, written for Flavius Boethus during the first stay in Rome, contained only two books;[54] only later did it reach the dimensions in which it has been preserved. For certain reasons Galen later revised other of his works stylistically or substantively. On the whole, he had not at first planned on a "public edition" of some of the works, and such writings or versions of writings are fundamentally different from those destined for publication.[55]

Flavius Boethus also inspired Galen to hold public anatomical lectures and demonstrations. Such public medical lectures had come into fashion in the first century B.C.[56] in the context of an accelerated activity aimed at increasing the level of general knowledge, and they had been enthusiastically taken up again at the end of the first century A.D. by practitioners of the Second Sophistic. Among Galen's auditors were not only high Roman officials, including the consuls Lucius Sergius Paullus and Gnaeus Claudius Severus, but also famous Sophists and rhetoricians, such as Hadrian of Tyre and Demetrius of Alexandria. This closeness among highly placed Romans, Sophist rhetoricians, and scientific experts (particularly physicians) is typical of the Second Sophistic.

Galen himself vigorously insisted that it was not primarily *logoi sophistikoi* but rather medical successes that established his fame in Rome.[57] On the other hand, the Second Sophistic exercised a great influence on him, and he cannot be seen apart from this intellectual movement. His own teacher Satyrus was referred to as a physician and Sophist;[58] and the "iatrosophists" and "iatrophilosophers" were a typical phenomenon of the age. Among them were some extremely dubious individuals, and the whole school of thought, the physicians who subscribed to it in particular, occasionally ran the risk of slipping into nonsense or irrationality.[59] Nevertheless, this specific form of intellectual-social culture also contained some very positive features, which Bowersock has recently described. Galen was among the very best representatives in medicine of this tendency, but he too is not free of its negative traits.

Three such characteristics, which are frequently discussed and which can perhaps be judged most fairly by viewing Galen as a Sophist, are his prolixity, his vainglory, and his taste for dispute and polemic. Undoubtedly many of Galen's writings are fatiguingly diffuse—for which reason the great classical philologist Wilamowitz bestowed upon him the malicious epithet *Seichbeutel* ("windbag").[60] Comparison of these writings with several of his terse, mathematically precise earlier works will reveal a change in style and an increased boastfulness, surely attributable to the Sophistic influence, which became especially intense while he was practicing in Rome. The same is true of his proclivity for debate and polemic—Galen may here have inherited something from his mother. Yet, at least as important are the professional quarrels that, under the influence of Sophism, were completely typical of that period.[61] It is against this background that, for instance, Galen's polemic with his colleague Martialius during the first stay in Rome must be seen,[62] and no doubt his relations with other physicians were in general affected in the same way.[63]

At the time of his dispute with Martialius, Galen was thirty-four.[64] He stayed in Rome for three more years. Looking back on his public lectures and polemics of this period, he felt a certain degree of remorse and declared that he had decided not to act in this manner in public again—one of the good resolutions in which he did not persevere. Although he often repeated assurances that he wished to approach all things *sine ira et studio,*[65] he could free himself from neither his own temperament nor tradition.

Apparently, however, the many quarrels and polemical debates during his first Roman period upset him inwardly, so that after a while he longed to return to Pergamum.[66] He states that his Roman patrons wished to keep him in Rome and that this strengthened his resolve to go back to his native city.[67] In any case, Galen left Rome in the spring, shortly before the return of Lucius Verus to the capital. As he himself records: "When the great plague [an epidemic that accompanied the soldiers Lucius Verus was leading back from the Parthian War] broke out, I left the city and hastened home."[68] This departure has generally been explained as simply an escape in the face of the contagion—not exactly laudable behavior for a physician. On the other hand, Walsh has pointed out that even before this time Galen had become what might be called "Rome-weary." [69] Surely, many factors conjoined to produce his decision.[70]

Galen relates that following his return "he stuck to the customary things." [71] It seems that he also undertook other journeys for scientific purposes.[72] But this period did not last long: he received a letter from the two rulers Marcus Aurelius and Lucius Verus summoning him to Aquileia. He responded to this call and succeeded in escaping a renewed outbreak of the plague. He became personal physician to the young Commodus; he held this position for several years and was thereby able to pursue his medical research and literary activity in various Italian cities—although at first not in Rome. When Commodus became emperor in 180, Galen remained in close contact with him, just as he had been on friendly terms with Marcus Aurelius, and enjoyed his protection. He was likewise friendly with Septimius Severus, who became emperor in 193. Although Galen should not, on this account, automatically be considered "physician in ordinary" or "court physician" in a strict sense, beginning with his return to Italy he remained in contact with the imperial family as both a physician and a socially prominent personality; he was undoubtedly "a lion of society." [73] Moreover, he enjoyed the favor of such highly placed figures as the Sophist Aelius Antipater, secretary to Septimius Severus.[74]

Nor, in his second Roman period (which lasted several decades), was he spared public controversies. The most famous episode, concerning the originality of some of his anatomical conclusions, took place in the Temple of Peace in Rome.[75] A heavy personal blow for Galen was the loss of a large part of his library through a fire in the temple in the year 192. It is not known whether Galen spent the last years of his life in Rome or in his native city.

Standpoint and Position in Ancient Medicine. W. Pagel's general characterization of Galen is most concise: "a genius who is 'modern' and indispensable in so many ways and yet not easy to grasp in view of his limitations, obscurities, and apparent self-contradictions." [76] It is understandable then that there exists as yet no work that comprehensively and exhaustively treats Galen or even limited aspects of his personality and work. The following remarks are thus to be understood merely as hints or suggestions.

As a physician Galen accepted the "fourfold scheme" which brought the humors, the elementary qualities, the elements, the seasons, age, and other factors into common accord.[77] This fundamental theoretical system obviously satisfied Galen's striving for certainty, yet not infrequently he, who so often pleaded for a purely scientific basis and methodology in medicine, was forced to perform complicated intellectual maneuvers. This is especially evident in his making the mysterious black bile into a physiologically important humor, which subject he treated in *On the Black Bile.* Using the fourfold scheme, Galen attempted to restore medicine to its Hippocratic basis. After all the debates with many schools of medical thought, he still considered Hippocratism the most secure foundation and enunciated this belief most clearly in *On the Elements According to Hippocrates, On Mixtures,* and the commentary to the Hippocratic work *On the Nature of Man.* Galen constructed his own Hippocratism, however; Hippocrates himself (to the extent that we can grasp the genuine Hippocrates) was not acquainted with any fourfold system in Galen's sense. Nonetheless, Galen's suggestive construction was dominant for centuries.

Galen's anatomy suffers from a similar conflict. On the one hand, he was an energetic advocate of anatomy as the foundation of medicine, and his own accomplishments in anatomy, both as writer and as researcher and demonstrator, are without doubt considerable.[78] The great work *Anatomical Procedures* is proof of this, as is a series of his more specialized writings. On the other hand, his anatomy necessarily suffered from the lack of opportunity to examine human cadavers (human dissection was no longer possible for cultural reasons). Moreover, in attempting to call into question—in principle, at least—some of the anatomico-physiological achievements of Erasistratus (especially in regard to the role of the spleen) and in trying to place anatomy as well on a kind of Hippocratic basis, he necessarily introduced a speculative element into his anatomy.

The same is true of Galen's physiology. He had a clear conception of the importance of physiological experiment, and his knowledge of the physiology of the nerves was considerable and justly celebrated. Yet here again there is speculation, in substantial part teleological, as in the great physiologico-anatomical treatise *On the Usefulness of the Parts of the Body.*[79] As a teleologist in physiology Galen was a determined Aristotelian.[80] He consequently defended in almost hymnic praises the notion that the Demiurge has created everything for the best.

As a dietitian, Galen continued an illustrious and ancient tradition.[81] In this area conflict is less noticeable. Indeed, it is precisely in this field that Galen the author composed what even the layman would consider his most interesting and exciting works, especially the *Hygieina.*[82]

Among those writings that best illustrate Galen's Hippocratism are his commentaries on his predecessor. From them we learn that what Galen thought was genuinely Hippocratic was often subjectively established, as is obvious from his claims for the genuineness of the treatise *On the Nature of Man.* Many critics held that it was a work of Polybus; Galen, however, allegedly in agreement with most physicians, declared the work to be genuinely Hippocratic, because it provided the testimony he sought for his doctrine of the four humors.[83] He also composed a work now lost, *On Genuine and Ungenuine Hippocratic Writings.* His commentaries were not at all confined to technical medical explanation but also treated purely philological problems (see below). Originally these commentaries did not take into account the explanations of other authors.[84] Later, when he was planning a public edition of his writings, he considered such interpretations and recast his already existing commentary to integrate it with them. Here Galen can be seen at work as a polemicist who not only criticized content but also did not shrink from personal defamation.[85] Thus, for example, he reproached a Jewish colleague for being incapable of understanding the books of the ancients and, consequently, being unable to comment on Hippocrates.[86] In this enterprise he not infrequently abandoned the principle of *sine ira et studio,* for which he argued so strongly elsewhere.

It must be stressed in regard to Galen as a clinician that he was without doubt a brilliant diagnostician. He composed a series of important works on the division of diseases and on their various symptoms.[87] A splendid example of Galen's diagnostic art is his short treatise on malingerers;[88] surely the diagnostic accuracy of a physician is put to the test in this field.

If Galen had very great merits as a diagnostician (and naturally went far beyond his esteemed Hippocrates), the same cannot be said of his views on prognosis. In this field he remained far more of a Hippocratic: first, he developed, as a general principle, a self-reliance in prognosis that was unjustified. The resources he employed were the traditional ones—the famous doctrine of the "critical days," saturated with several prerational elements as it doubtless was, could nonetheless satisfy particularly well Galen's need for certainty and his predilection for mathematical regularity (apparent in his special studies *On Critical Days* and *On Crises*). As a Hippocratic he found in his model something that Lichtenthaeler has termed "logos mathématique."[89] To be sure, the theory of the critical days had an empirical root in the observation of fever (malaria) cycles. On the whole, however, it had been expanded into a speculative system under the influence of a "rationalization of an old arithmological foundation," as Joly has accurately expressed it.[90] As stated above, this speculative system of the critical days, penetrated by prerational elements, satisfied Galen's desire for certainty, just as it suited his taste for theorizing. The same is true of the two other traditional tools of prognosis, which he used willingly and extensively: the doctrines of the pulse and of the urine. The behavior of the pulse, which like all bodily "palpitations" was originally considered a mantic phenomenon, is analyzed in extreme detail in Galen's many works on sphygmology and is employed in both diagnosis and prognosis.[91] Yet in just this subtle division of the "qualities" of the pulse lay the danger of speculation. (Characteristically, Galen had little respect for the quantitative measurement of the pulse, despite the beginnings that Herophilus, among others, had made.)

In his knowledge of the formation of the urine, Galen went far beyond Hippocrates; but, as a clinician, he cherished the same speculative conception as Hippocrates, who had employed the consistency, the sediments, and the color of the urine not only in diagnosis but also in prognosis. The crucial thing is that Galen, like Hippocrates, did not apply the three criteria of consistency, sediments, and color in an exact fashion but rather in a vague, subjective way.[92]

Galen's knowledge of therapeutics is set forth mainly in the voluminous work *Therapeutic Method,* generally known in English as *On the Art of Healing.* Once again much interesting and correct material stands side by side with conjecture, above all for the medical preparations Galen employs and for his notions of their mode of action (on this, see *On the Mixture and Action of Simple Medicines, On the Composition of Medicines According to Locality,* and *On the Composition of Medicines According to Types*). In general, while Galen did in truth place the highest value on the empirical testing of medicines, his speculative conceptions of the way they worked constrained him occasionally to see a positive value in such "medicines" as excrement and amulets, in spite of his rejection of the magico-irrational medicine, which was then very popular.[93]

The impression that Galen possessed all clinical skills is only apparent. On closer examination he seems to have had no experience in operative gynecology[94] and obstetrics or in surgery in general, and it is obviously for this reason that he devoted none of his own writings to these fields.[95] Still more remarkable is his personal attitude toward surgery. On the whole, Galen was an inveterate internist and as such had a deep distaste for surgery, with the exception of surgery to repair injuries or suppurations, undertaken in treating gladiators. In those cases in which he did consider surgical questions, even regressive views can sometimes be detected. This prejudice is consistent with, among other things, his prolonged polemic against Erasistratus (and the so-called Erasistrateans), who had been one of the first to put operative surgery on a new basis. Galen, on the contrary, was, so to speak, a Hippocratic even as a surgeon; that is, he confined operative surgery—when he allowed it at all—to a relatively narrowed concept and area. Here the characteristic inconsistency and limitations of his otherwise universal mind show themselves with particular clarity.

In summary, then, as a physician, Galen was a Hippocratic and, as a scientist (anatomist and physiologist), an Aristotelian; and he adhered to these basic commitments even when he was ostensibly an eclectic. To this extent he was far from being primarily an eclectic, a designation he is not infrequently given. His inclination for philosophy went so far that he attempted to reconcile Hippocrates and Plato, and in a work whose title was chosen with this purpose in mind, too, he claimed "that the best physician is also a philosopher." On the other hand, he recognized and emphasized the boundary between medicine and philosophy.[96] All this, together with the contradictions in his behavior sketched above, should perhaps be viewed in the light of his constant striving for certainty. Thus, in the end, Galen became as much the "savior of a medicine which had become bankrupt" as the "executor of a faulty development."[97]

Philosophy and Philology. Aside from his medicophilosophical efforts, Galen not only interpreted the work of other philosophers (Plato, Aristotle, Theophrastus, Chrysippus, Epicurus) in some of his works[98] but also became known as a philosopher in his own right, above all in the field of logic, in such works as *On Scientific Proof* and *Introduction to Logic.* His many ethical writings have not been preserved, but this is not a significant loss, since as a philosopher Galen was essentially unoriginal.

His most outstanding appearance as a philologist and grammarian is in his commentaries on Hippocrates.[99] He also wrote a series of works dealing with lexicographical and stylistic problems, but they have been lost.[100] The work that has come down under his name as *Hippocrates Glossary* is quite possibly not genuine. Galen's philosophical and philological interests were, moreover, only part of the total activity of a man of truly universal education whose numerous writings contain an abundance of information.

Religion. This is a subject which perhaps merits separate examination. Here, too, a good deal of inconsistency seems to become evident. On the one hand, Galen has been called a typical representative of the "cultivated religion" of his time.[101] This means that as an enlightened man he quite possibly took a certain interest in religious phenomena, but one without genuine religious commitment behind it, and that, for the rest, he "officially" believed in the gods in the traditional manner. This view is supported by the lack of any real understanding in his utterances about Judaism and Christianity.[102] Furthermore, it is certain that he did not yield to his age's widespread passion for mysticism, often encountered even among the educated and particularly among physicians.[103] On the other hand, he has been termed "deeply religious"[104] because of the almost hymnic praise of the "Creator" (*demiourgos*) in his great physiological work *On the Usefulness of the Parts.* But, is teleology—the real subject of this treatise—identical with religiosity? Do we have here a secret religious yearning, or is it simply a question of the stiff, formal language of allegory? We would like to know the answer for several reasons. First, it would be significant to learn whether Galen considered religious commitment to be an unavoidable component of medical ethics. Second, Galen's revered predecessor Hippocrates was surely not "deeply religious" in the ordinary sense of the term.[105] In this connection one would wish to ask how Galen viewed the problem of Hippocratic religiosity. In addition, his relationship to Asclepius and to the "god-sent" dreams would have to be thoroughly analyzed once again.[106] Perhaps Galen's religiosity, too, must be considered in terms of that dichotomy characteristic of so much of his work.

Pseudo-Galenica. Those writings falsely attributed to Galen form a special chapter in the history of his influence. That such spurious writings existed during Galen's own lifetime has already been noted and is proof of the great authority and attractiveness of his name, an obvious incentive to forgers. In many instances the intellectual milieu out of which such falsifications arose is known (although more work should be done in this area). For example, the extant treatise *For Gauros, On the Question of How Embryos Are Ensouled* belongs to the circle of Porphyry, that is, to early Neoplatonism; and the lost work *On Medicine in Homer* appears to have come from the group around Sextus Julius Africanus, that is, from early Christianity and Neoplatonism.[107] In these cases, there was an attempt to legitimate certain views by placing them under a great, authoritative name.

Other spurious writings emerged when something written on a popular subject could more easily be sold under a distinguished name. For example, the forged works on urine, printed in volume XIX of Kühn's edition, must have originated in this way (witness the popularity of urine prognostication in late antiquity and the Middle Ages). Likewise, the treatise *On Sudden Death* was a contribution to the much discussed subject of the forecasting of death.[108]

Still other false Galenic works obviously had their origin in the medical teaching of late antiquity and the Middle Ages. Among these are the so-called *Summaria Alexandrina,* in which Galen's longer writings are presented in the form of a summary or abridged edition—and thereby often simplified and distorted.[109] Such compendia must have begun to be produced soon after Galen's death; an early example is the short tractate on *Galen's Hippocratic Principles.*[110] The great majority of these forgeries were probably written in Greek. The Greek originals of some of the works of this kind are extant, while others are available only in Latin or Arabic translations. The Arabs were well aware that such spurious works existed and to some extent made an effort to discover which ones they were.[111] Yet it is not out of the question that among the mass of Arabic writings in Galen's name one or another was actually composed by an Arab author and smuggled into the Galenic corpus. Works were still being forged in the Renaissance—e.g., the commentaries on the pseudo-Hippocratic *On Nourishment*[112] and *On the Humors.*[113]

The spurious Galenic writings will someday have to be studied as a whole. In view of the mass of Galen's works that are still unedited and in the absence of a critical, philologically sound complete edition of Galen, such a task would be arduous. In considering the extant Greek writings in the course of such an undertaking, one would have to employ, for example, stylistic comparison; but little preparatory work for a study of Galen's style has been done.

Galen's Influence. Far too little attention has been paid to the fact that, although he was very interested in medical pedagogy, Galen had no real students of his own[114] and, unlike many of his colleagues, founded no school. Even in his own lifetime he was a quite exceptional figure. His stature was explicitly acknowledged immediately after his death; it was the enormous range of his literary works, above all, that led to his being called divine.[115] In the medical schools of late antiquity and the Middle Ages, Galen's writings constituted the principal element of the curriculum (the *Summaria Alexandrina* has already been cited), and excerpts from Galen occupy considerable space in the great medical encyclopedias of Oribasius and Aetius of Amida. Byzantine physicians—Alexander of Tralles, for example—did not always accept Galen uncritically by any means; in general, however, they were all crucially dependent on him.

In the non-Greek world Galen's influence was based on innumerable translations of his works. Of those in Latin only a few need be cited: those by Cassius Felix, who in the fifth century translated Greek authors *logicae sectae,* including Galen, in his *De medicina liber;* and, in the medieval period, the important translations of Pietro d'Abano[116] and Nicola da Reggio.[117] In addition, Galen was early translated into Syriac;[118] but the Arabic translations had the greatest impact. In this regard the achievements of Ḥunayn ibn Isḥāq and his school are especially outstanding; moreover, he has also provided a survey of the Syriac and Arabic translations.[119]

The influence of Galen, transmitted equally by his own writings, in both the original Greek texts and translations, and by summaries, compendia, commentaries by other physicians, and even forgeries, created Galenism, which dominated the medicine of the Middle Ages. The real battle between the Galenists and the medical "revolutionaries" took place in the Renaissance. With the introduction of printing there occurred a revival of the genuine Galen in the form of text editions and commentaries.[120] The most important criticisms directed against him were in the fields of anatomy (where he was exposed as an "ape anatomist" and corrected), physiology (in which his dogma of the liver as the starting point of the blood was overthrown), and therapy (from which the bloodletting controversy linked primarily with the name of Brissot emerged). If Galen's authority was not destroyed in the Renaissance, it was seriously called into question.[121] Yet his influence was far from being eliminated thereby. For one thing, the results of the criticism of Galen (for example, Harvey's discovery of the circulation of the blood) occasionally required a long time to be definitively accepted among physicians. For another, the conception of, for example, humoral pathology in the form codified by Galen, encompassing such ideas as bad humors and blood purification, was so deeply rooted outside of the so-called school medicine that even around 1900 one could speak of a "Neogalenism."[122]

FRIDOLF KUDLIEN

GALEN: Anatomy and Physiology.

Galen's physiological system was, from the second century A.D. until the time of William Harvey, the basis for the explanation of the physiology of the body. His physiological theories are of particular interest because they included concepts of digestion, assimilation, blood formation, the maintenance of the tissues, nerve function, respiration, the heart beat, the arterial pulse, and the maintenance of vital warmth throughout the body—concepts which together formed a comprehensive and connected account of the functioning of the living animal body. His physiological system was based in large part on the work of such earlier anatomists as Aristotle, Praxagoras, Herophilus, and Erasistratus, but Galen made fundamental changes and additions to their theories and the resultant system was identifiably his own.

Aristotle had drawn attention to the role of the blood in forming the tissues of the developing embryo and a natural corollary of this role was that the blood should serve also to nourish and maintain the flesh of the adult body. Erasistratus had said that the food digested in the stomach and intestines was absorbed through the intestinal wall into the mesenteric veins as chyle, and the chyle was carried by these veins to the liver where it was transformed into blood. From the liver the blood was poured through the hepatic veins into the vena cava and thence distributed through the venous system to nourish the whole body. Galen adopted the same view. He considered the liver to be the chief organ governing the vegetative functions of the body, those functions which Aristotle said were governed by the vegetative soul. The liver attracted the blood-forming elements of the chyle and transformed them into blood; the gallbladder attracted those elements of the chyle unsuitable to form blood and discharged them as bile into the intestine. The bile was a by-product of blood formation.

Erasistratus had also thought that the blood which entered the right ventricle of the heart from the vena cava was prevented from returning by the tricuspid valve. The blood was then sent on via the pulmonary artery (or artery-like vein) to the lungs, which it served to nourish. Thus, the right ventricle and the pulmonary artery existed, according to Erasistratus, for nourishing the lungs, and Galen adopted the same view.

In order to study the distribution of the blood vessels Aristotle had advised that an animal intended for dissection should be killed by strangulation so as to retain the blood within the body. A result of this method of killing animals was that the left side of the heart and the arteries were left largely empty of blood. The arteries thus appeared as empty tubes running through the flesh, and Praxagoras of Cos had therefore distinguished them from the veins, or blood vessels, and had considered them to be air tubes. Erasistratus, working a generation or more after Praxagoras, in the early third century B.C., seems to have discovered and named the tricuspid and bicuspid valves guarding the entrances to the right and left ventricles of the heart respectively. He also understood that these structures functioned as valves, that is, as mechanical devices to allow the flow of materials in only one direction. Furthermore Erasistratus thought that the heart functioned like a bellows, that it distended itself actively in diastole, and the partial vacuum formed by the enlargement of the ventricles caused blood to flow into the right ventricle from the vena cava, and breath or *pneuma* to flow into the left ventricle from the lung through the pulmonary vein (vein-like artery). The contraction of the ventricles of the heart then forced blood from the right ventricle into the lungs and pneuma from the left ventricle into the arterial system. Thus, according to Erasistratus, the arterial pulse resulted from the filling of the arteries with pneuma by each contraction of the heart, and the arterial system served to convey pneuma to the whole body.

Erasistratus knew that when an artery was opened blood flowed from it, but he thought that the blood flowing from an opened artery was merely flowing through the artery from its principal reservoir in the veins. He considered that when an artery was opened the pneuma escaped from it, thereby creating a vacuum within its cavity and the blood then entered the artery from the veins through the *synanastomoses,* numerous minute, invisible passages connecting the arterial and venous systems throughout the body. He knew of the existence of the synanastomoses from the fact that when an animal was bled to death from an opened artery all of the blood in the veins was also drained away. Since there was no visible connection between the arterial and venous systems there must be a multitude of invisible connections. Erasistratus thought that these connections were normally closed, but that they opened in fevers when the presence of blood in the arteries was indicated by a flushed skin and a throbbing pulse. Similarly the opening of an artery in an animal created an abnormal and pathological condition which permitted blood to flow from the veins into the arteries.

The fundamental change which Galen made in the physiology of the heart, lungs, and vessels was to show that both the left ventricle of the heart and the arteries invariably contain blood and that this is their normal condition, not a sign of disease. By his demonstration of the normal presence of blood in the arteries, Galen destroyed Erasistratus' theory of how the pneuma was conveyed to the whole body.

Galen's proof of the normal presence of blood in the arteries is contained in his short work *Whether Blood Is Contained in the Arteries in Nature.* He observed that if Erasistratus were right that the pneuma escaped when an artery was opened the pneuma should be seen to escape first before the blood poured forth, but in fact the blood pours forth at once. Yet the pneuma, according to Erasistratus, was simply air taken into the body in breathing so that it could not be such a rarefied substance that all of the pneuma in the body could escape instantaneously through a mere pinprick in an artery. Galen also observed the presence of blood in the arteries of the transparent mesentery, and then he showed experimentally that when he isolated a portion of an artery in a living animal—he tied it off with ligatures so that no blood could flow into it from elsewhere and then opened it—he always found it full of blood. By opening the chest of a living animal he demonstrated that blood was present in the left ventricle of the heart.

Galen then had to devise new theories to account for the functions of the heart and arteries. He supposed that the prime function of respiration was to cool the excess heat of the heart. Since the lungs surround the heart in the chest cavity they might by that fact alone exert a cooling influence on the heart. In addition air might pass from the lungs along the pulmonary vein into the left ventricle, and there serve both to nourish and cool the innate heat of the heart and then return to the lungs accompanied by something like smoke. The pulse in the arteries was generated from the heart. In accounting for the arterial pulse Galen adopted an idea suggested originally by Herophilus that when the heart was in diastole a wave of dilatation passed along the walls of the arteries. The arteries thus dilated drew into themselves blood from the veins through the synanastomoses and pneuma from the surrounding air through pores in the skin. Thus the arterial pulse caused the whole body to breathe in and out and and served to nourish the innate heat throughout the body. If the pulse were cut off from a limb by a ligature, the limb became pale and cold, because, according to Galen, its innate heat was no longer nourished by the vital pneuma drawn into the arteries by the pulse.

Galen was obliged by his theory to suppose that the mitral valve, opening into the left ventricle of the heart, did not act as Erasistratus had seen that its structure would require it to act, as a device to allow the flow of materials in one direction only, into the heart. Since the mitral valve had only two flaps Galen argued that it would allow the return of air and smoky vapors from the heart to the lungs. In the right ventricle of the heart, however, Galen considered that the tricuspid valve with its three flaps was a tight valve. Blood entering the right ventricle from the vena cava could not return. Some of it passed through the pulmonary artery (artery-like vein) to the lungs, but since the pulmonary artery was smaller than the vena cava Galen thought that it could not remove all of the blood entering the right ventricle. Therefore, he said, some blood must pass through the interventricular septum into the left ventricle. Since there were synanastomoses between the venous and arterial systems throughout the body Galen thought they should also be present in the septum and in this way he explained how the left ventricle was supplied with blood. However, in his work *On the Usefulness of the Parts of the Body,* Galen considered that both ventricles contained both blood and pneuma, but that the left ventricle contained pneuma in larger proportion.

Although physiology remained for fourteen centuries after Galen's death basically Galenic it did not always coincide exactly with what Galen had taught. Galen had developed his theories in close relation to those of his predecessors, particularly Herophilus and Erasistratus, and he was not able to free them completely from inconsistencies. Furthermore, he frequently contradicted himself in different works. Galen's successors, in attempting to make his physiology simpler and more consistent, tended to revert to Erasistratus' view that the left ventricle of the heart and the arterial system contained pneuma rather than blood.

In his work *On the Doctrines of Hippocrates and Plato* Galen defended Plato's concept of a tripartite soul (that is, a nutritive soul, an animal soul, and a rational soul) against the Stoic doctrine of the soul as single and indivisible. Galen showed that in his physiological system the liver and the veins supplied the body with nutrition, the lungs, the left ventricle of the heart and the arteries maintained the pneuma and the innate heat throughout the body, while the brain and nerves controlled sensation and muscular movement through the medium of a special psychic pneuma. The later systematizers of Galen held that there were three kinds of pneuma or spirits corresponding to these three functional systems: the natural spirits formed in the liver, the vital spirits formed in the heart and arteries, and the animal spirits formed in the brain.

LEONARD G. WILSON

NOTES

1. Cf. W. Crönert, "Klaudios Galenos," in *Mitteilungen zur Geschichte der Medizin und der Naturwissenschaften und der Technik,* **1** (1902), 3 f.; K. Kalbfleisch, "Claudius Galenus," in *Berliner philologische Wochenschrift,* **22** (1902), 413.
2. J. Ilberg, "Aus Galens Praxis," in *Neue Jahrbücher für das klassische Altertum,* **15** (1905), 277, n. 1.
3. J. Walsh, "Date of Galen's Birth," in *Annals of Medical History,* n.s. **1** (1929), 378–382.
4. Ilberg, "Wann ist Galenos geboren?" in *Sudhoffs Archiv,* **23** (1930), 289–292.
5. Walsh, "Refutation of Ilberg as to the Date of Galen's Birth," in *Annals of Medical History,* n.s. **4** (1932), 126–146.
6. Crönert, p. 4.
7. H. Diller, "Nikon 18," in Pauly-Wissowa, *Real-Encyclopädie,* XVII, pt. 1 (1936), col. 507 f.
8. Galen V. 40 f.; here and following, references are, if not otherwise stated, to the Kühn ed.

9. Cf. I. Veith, "Galen, the First Medical Autobiographer," in *Modern Medicine* (Minneapolis), **27** (1959), 232–245.
10. G. Misch, *Geschichte der Autobiographie,* 4 vols., 3rd ed., enl., I, pt. 1 (Bern, 1949).
11. Cf. *ibid.,* p. 344.
12. See the enumeration of these by J. C. G. Ackermann, in Galen I. xxi. n.*A.*
13. See M. Meyerhof, "Autobiographische Bruchstücke Galens aus arabischen Quellen," in *Sudhoffs Archiv,* **22** (1929), 72–86.
14. Cf. Galen XIX. 46.
15. G. Sarton, *Galen of Pergamon* (Lawrence, Kans., 1954).
16. P. Diepgen, *Geschichte der Medizin* (Berlin, 1949), I, 119 ff.
17. K. Deichgräber, *Galen als Erforscher des menschlichen Pulses* (Berlin, 1957), p. 32.
18. Diller, col. 507, l. 20 ff.
19. Galen V. 41 f.; cf. X. 561, 609. A list of his teachers in philosophy is given in E. Groag and A. Stein, *Prosopographia imperii Romani,* 4 vols., 2nd ed., (Berlin, 1952), IV, art. G24
20. Galen X. 609.
21. See F. Kudlien, "Medical Education in Classical Antiquity," in C. D. O'Malley, ed., *History of Medical Education* (Berkeley–Los Angeles–London, 1970), p. 35, n. 83.
22. Cf. Sarton, p. 17; and Misch, p. 346.
23. Galen XIX. 57.
24. *Ibid.,* II. 224.
25. Cf. G. W. Bowersock, *Greek Sophists in the Roman Empire* (Oxford, 1969), pp. 60 f.
26. *Ibid.,* pp. 61 f.
27. *Ibid.,* ch. 5, *passim.*
28. Galen XIX. 16.
29. *Ibid.;* the treatise *On Medical Experience* is edited by R. Walzer (London–New York–Toronto, 1944).
30. Walzer, *Galen on Medical Experience,* p. 87; and p. viii, n. 5.
31. I. von Müller, "Über die dem Galen zugeschriebene Abhandlung Peri tes aristes haireseos," in *Sitzungsberichte der Bayerischen Akademie* (1898), pp. 53–162.
32. Galen XIX. 8 f.
33. See H. Diels, "Die Handschriften der antiken Ärzte," in *Abhandlungen der Preussischen Akademie* (1906), p. 129.
34. See A. Stein, "Calvisius 6," in Pauly-Wissowa, III, pt. 1 (1897), 1410.
35. Galen I. 274.2–279.5.
36. *Ibid.,* XIX. 40.
37. On the chronology of Galen's writings, see Ilberg, "Über die Schriftstellerei des Klaudios Galenos," in *Rheinisches Museum,* **44** (1889), 207–239; **47** (1892), 489–514; **51** (1896), 165–196; and **52** (1897), 591–623. See also K. Bardong, "Beiträge zur Hippokrates- und Galenforschung, Teil 2," in *Nachrichten. Akademie der Wissenschaften in Göttingen,* Phil.-hist. Kl., **7** (1942), pp. 603–640.
38. Galen VI. 756.
39. *Ibid.,* II. 217.
40. *Ibid.,* XIX. 16.
41. Cf. Deichgräber, pp. 33–36: "Zu Galen als Platoniker."
42. Galen II. 217.
43. On Galen's Alexandrian period, see Walsh, "Galen's Studies at the Alexandrian School," in *Annals of Medical History,* **9** (1927), 132–143.
44. Cf., for example, J. Mewaldt, "Galenos 2," in Pauly-Wissowa, VII, pt. 1 (1910), 579, lines 20 f.
45. Galen II. 217 f.
46. For this, cf. Kudlien, "Antike Anatomie und menschlicher Leichnam," in *Hermes,* **97** (1969), 79 f.
47. For this, cf. Kudlien, in O'Malley, pp. 23, 36, notes 97, 98.
48. Galen XIII. 599.
49. The early *Diagnosis of Diseases of the Eye* apparently had its source in practical experience; see Galen XIX. 16.
50. Cf. Galen XIII. 599 ff.
51. *Ibid.,* II. 215.
52. *Ibid.,* XVIIIA. 347.
53. On what follows, cf. Mewaldt, p. 579, lines 30 ff.; and Bowersock, pp. 62 ff., 82–84.
54. See Galen II. 216.
55. For this, cf., for example, Kudlien, *Die handschriftliche Überlieferung des Galenkommentars zu Hippokrates De articulis* (Berlin, 1960), pp. 19 f. In this special case, the earlier as well as the later, "official" version can be reconstructed from the manuscript tradition.
56. Cf. Kudlien, in O'Malley, pp. 20, 35, notes 84 and 85.
57. Galen VIII. 144.
58. Cf. Bowersock, p. 67.
59. Cf. Kudlien, "The Third Century A.D.—A Blank Spot in the History of Medicine?" in L. G. Stevenson and R. Multhauf, eds., *Medicine, Science and Culture: Historical Essays in Honor of Owsei Temkin* (Baltimore, 1968), pp. 32 f.
60. Wilamowitz later revised his judgment; see Deichgräber, p. 33.
61. For them, see Bowersock, ch. 7.
62. See Mewaldt, p. 579, lines 55 ff.
63. See J. Kollesch, "Galen und seine ärztlichen Kollegen," in *Das Altertum,* **11** (1965), 47–53.
64. For this and what follows, see Galen XIX. 15.
65. Cf. Deichgräber, p. 33.
66. Galen XIV. 622, 624.
67. *Ibid.,* pp. 647 f.
68. *Ibid.,* XIX. 15.
69. Walsh, "Refutation of the Charges of Cowardice Made Against Galen," in *Annals of Medical History,* n.s. **3** (1931), 195–208.
70. For a negative interpretation of his flight from Rome, see Ilberg, "Aus Galens Praxis," reprinted in H. Flashar, ed., *Antike Medizin* (Darmstadt, 1971), pp. 388 f.
71. On this and what follows, cf. Mewaldt, p. 580, lines 37 ff.
72. Cf. P. E. M. Berthelot, "Sur les voyages de Galien et de Zosime dans l'Archipel et en Asie et sur la matière médicale dans l'antiquité," in *Journal des savants* (1895), 382–387.
73. Bowersock, p. 66.
74. *Ibid.,* pp. 63 f. Some questions dealing with Galen's accomplishments as court physician are discussed in Kollesch, "Aus Galens Praxis am römischen Kaiserhof," in E. C. Welskopf, ed., *Neue Beiträge zur Geschichte der alten Welt,* II, 57–61.
75. On this and what follows, see Mewaldt, p. 580, lines 55 ff.
76. Cf. W. Pagel's review of May's trans. of *On the Usefulness of the Parts of the Body,* in *Medical History,* **14** (1970), 408.
77. Cf. W. Schöner, *Das Viererschema in der antiken Humoralpathologie* (Wiesbaden, 1964), pp. 86 ff., esp. 92.
78. For an evaluation of Galen's anatomy, see, for example, O. Temkin and W. L. Strauss, "Galen's Dissection of the Liver and of the Muscles Moving the Forearm," in *Bulletin of the History of Medicine,* **19** (1946), 167–176.
79. For an evaluation of Galen's physiology, see, for example, O. Temkin, "On Galen's Pneumatology," in *Gesnerus,* **8** (1961), 180–189; "A Galenic Model for Quantitative Physiological Reasoning?" in *Bulletin of the History of Medicine,* **35** (1961), 470–475; and "The Classical Roots of Glisson's Doctrine of Irritation," *ibid.,* **38** (1964), 297–328.
80. See Sarton, pp. 56 ff.
81. See L. Edelstein, "The Dietetics of Antiquity," in *Ancient Medicine. Selected Papers of Ludwig Edelstein,* O. and C. L. Temkin, eds. (Baltimore, 1967), pp. 303–316.
82. Mewaldt, p. 585, lines 53 ff.
83. Cf. Galen, in *Corpus medicorum Graecorum,* V, pt. 9, 1, 7 f.
84. Cf. Kudlien, *Die handschriftliche Überlieferung,* pp. 19 f.
85. Cf. L. Bröcker, "Die Methoden Galens in der literarischen Kritik," in *Rheinisches Museum,* **40** (1885), 415–438.
86. Cf. Galen, in *Corpus Medicorum Graecorum,* V, pt. 10, 2, 2, p. 413, lines 37 f.
87. Cf. Mewaldt, p. 586, lines 9 ff.
88. See Kudlien, "Wie erkannten die antiken Ärzte einen Simulanten?" in *Das Altertum,* **7** (1961), 226–233.
89. C. Lichtenthaeler, *Quatrième série d'études hippocratiques (VII–X)* (Geneva, 1963), pp. 109–135.
90. R. Joly, *Le niveau de la science hippocratique* (Paris, 1966), p. 234.

91. See Mewaldt, p. 585, lines 23 ff.
92. Cf. H. Koelbing, *Der Urin im medizinischen Denken,* pt. 5: "Die antiken Grundlagen der Harnschau," Documenta Geigy (Basel, 1967), *passim.*
93. Cf. Rothkopf, *Zum Problem des Irrationalen in der Medizin der römischen Kaiserzeit* (Kiel, 1969), 8 f., 16–19.
94. On other achievements of Galen in gynecology, see Ilberg, in Flashar, pp. 383 f., 408.
95. On what follows, see M. Michler, *Das Spezialisierungsproblem und die antike Chirurgie* (Bern–Stuttgart–Vienna, 1969), 50 ff.
96. Cf. O. Temkin, "Greek Medicine as Science and Craft," in *Isis,* **44** (1953), 224 f.
97. Michler, p. 62.
98. Cf. Mewaldt, p. 588, lines 42 ff.
99. See I. von Müller, "Galen als Philologe," in *Verhandlungen der 41. Versammlung deutscher Philologen und Schulmänner* (Munich, 1891), pp. 80–91.
100. See Mewaldt, p. 589, lines 9 ff.
101. G. Strohmaier, "Galen als Vertreter der Gebildetenreligion seiner Zeit," in Welskopf, II, 375–379.
102. Cf. R. Walzer, *Galen on Jews and Christians* (Oxford, 1949).
103. Cf. Deichgräber, p. 35.
104. See Sarton, p. 56; on Galen's religiosity, see pp. 82 ff.
105. See V. Schöllkopf, *Zum Problem der Religiosität älterer griechischer Ärzte* (Kiel, 1968).
106. Cf. Ilberg, in Flashar, p. 365.
107. Cf. Kudlien, "Zum Thema 'Homer und die Medizin,'" in *Rheinisches Museum,* **108** (1965), 299.
108. See M. Issa, *Die "galenische" Schrift "Über den plötzlichen Tod"* (Kiel, 1969).
109. It is to be hoped that O. Temkin will continue his "Studies on Late Alexandrian Medicine" (cf. *Bulletin of the History of Medicine,* **3** [1935], 405–430) and therein deal with the problem of the *Summaria Alexandrina.*
110. Cf. Kudlien, in Stevenson and Multhauf, pp. 29 f.
111. Cf. G. Bergsträsser, *Neue Materialien zu Hunain Ibn Ishaq's Galen-Bibliographie* (Nendeln, Liechtenstein, 1966), 95–98.
112. Cf. H. Diels, "Bericht über das Corpus Medicorum Graecorum," in *Sitzungsberichte der Preussischen Akademie der Wissenschaften zu Berlin* (1914), p. 128.
113. *Ibid.* (1913), p. 115; (1915), pp. 92 f.; and (1916), pp. 138 f.
114. Whether Epigenes—to whom Galen dedicated *On Prognosis*—was a doctor is not certain. Cf. Ilberg, in Flashar, p. 375.
115. On this and what follows, see Kudlien, in Stevenson and Multhauf, pp. 27 f.
116. See L. Thorndike, "Translations of the Works of Galen From the Greek by Peter of Abano," in *Isis,* **33** (1942), 649–653.
117. See Thorndike, "Translations of the Works of Galen by Nicola da Reggio," in *Byzantina Metabyzantina,* **1** (1946), 213–235; cf. I. Wille, "Überlieferung und Übersetzung. Zur Übersetzungstechnik des Nikolaus v. Rhegium in Galens Schrift De temporibus morborum," in *Helikon,* **3** (1963), 259–277.
118. Cf. M. Meyerhof, "Les versions syriaques et arabes des écrits Galeniques," in *Byzantion,* **3** (1926), 33–51.
119. Cf. Bergsträsser, *Hunain Ibn Ishaq: Über die syrischen und arabischen Galenübersetzungen,* repr. (Nendeln, 1966).
120. Cf. R. J. Durling, "A Chronological Census of Renaissance Editions and Translations of Galen," in *Journal of the Warburg and Courtauld Institutes,* **24** (1961), 230–305.
121. Cf. H. Heinrichs, *Die Überwindung der Autorität Galens durch die Denker der Renaissancezeit* (Bonn, 1914).
122. See Bachmann, "Neo-Galenismus," in *Janus,* **7** (1902), 455–459.

BIBLIOGRAPHY

The only complete ed. of Galen (Greek text with Latin trans.) is C. G. Kühn, *Claudii Galeni Opera Omnia,* 20 vols. (repr., Hildesheim, 1964–1965). The Greek text of this ed. is very defective. The *Corpus Medicorum Graecorum,* in its Abt. V and in supplementary vols., is publishing a series of philological-critical eds. of Galenic writings.

The Galenic MSS (for original texts and translations) are listed in H. Diels, "Die Handschriften der antiken Ärzte, Griechische Abteilung," in *Abhandlungen der königlich Preussischen Akademie der Wissenschaften* (Berlin, 1906), pp. 58–158; a supp. is *ibid.* (1907), 29–41. See also R. J. Durling, "Corrigenda et Addenda to Diel's Galenica," in *Traditio,* **23** (1967), 461–476.

There is no complete trans. of the works of Galen in a modern language. Among the English trans. of individual writings are *On Anatomical Procedures,* Charles Singer, trans. (Oxford, 1956), the surviving books; and W. L. H. Duckworth (Cambridge, 1962), the later books; *On the Natural Faculties,* A. J. Brock, trans., Loeb Classics (London–Cambridge, Mass., 1952); *Hygiene,* R. M. Green, trans. (Springfield, Ill., 1951); *On the Passions and Errors of the Soul,* P. W. Harkins and W. Riese, trans. (Columbus, Ohio, 1963); *On the Usefulness of the Parts of the Body,* M. T. May, trans., 2 vols. (Ithaca, N.Y., 1968); and *On Medical Experience,* R. Walzer, trans. (London–New York–Toronto, 1944), based on the 1st ed. of the Arabic version.

The most extensive modern bibliography is K. Schubring, in the Kühn ed., XX, xvii–lxii.

See also Jerome J. Bylebyl, *Cardiovascular Physiology in the Sixteenth and Early Seventeenth Centuries,* unpub. doctoral diss. (Yale University, 1969), pp. 10–137; Donald Fleming, "Galen on the Motions of the Blood in the Heart and Lungs," in *Isis,* **46** (1955), 14–21; and Leonard G. Wilson, "Erasistratus, Galen and the *Pneuma,*" in *Bulletin of the History of Medicine,* **33** (1959), 293–314.

GALERKIN, BORIS GRIGORIEVICH (*b.* Polotsk, Russia, 4 March 1871; *d.* Moscow, U.S.S.R., 12 June 1945), *mechanics, mathematics.*

For a detailed study of his life and work, see Supplement.

GALILEI, GALILEO (*b.* Pisa, Italy, 15 February 1564; *d.* Arcetri, Italy, 8 January 1642), *physics, astronomy.*

The name of Galileo is inextricably linked with the advent, early in the seventeenth century, of a marked change in the balance between speculative philosophy, mathematics, and experimental evidence in the study of natural phenomena. The period covered by his scientific publications began with the announcement of the first telescopic astronomical discoveries in 1610 and closed with the first systematic attempt to extend the mathematical treatment of physics from statics to kinematics and the strength of materials in 1638. The same period witnessed Kepler's mathematical transformation of planetary theory and Harvey's experimental attack on physiological dogma. Historians are divided in their assessment of this widespread scientific revolution with respect to its elements of continuity and innovation, both as to method and as to content. Of central importance to its understanding are the life and works of Galileo, whose personal conflict with religious authority dramatized the extent and profundity of the changing approach to nature.

Early Years. Galileo's father was Vincenzio Galilei, a musician and musical theorist and a descendant of a Florentine patrician family distinguished in medicine and public affairs. He was a member of the Florentine *Camerata,* a cultural group which included musicians whose devotion to the revival of Greek music and monody gave birth to opera. It was headed by Giovanni Bardi, who sponsored Vincenzio's musical studies under Gioseffo Zarlino at Venice around 1561. In 1562 he married Giulia Ammannati of Pescia, with whom he settled at Pisa. Galileo was the eldest of seven children. His brother Michelangelo became a professional musician and spent most of his life abroad. Two of his sisters, Virginia and Livia, married and settled in Florence. Of the other children no record survives beyond that of their births.

Galileo was first tutored at Pisa by one Jacopo Borghini. Early in the 1570's, Vincenzio returned to Florence, where he resettled the family about 1575. Galileo was then sent to school at the celebrated monastery of Santa Maria at Vallombrosa. In 1578 he entered the order as a novice, against the wishes of his father, who removed him again to Florence and applied unsuccessfully for a scholarship on his behalf at the University of Pisa. Galileo resumed his studies with the Vallombrosan monks in Florence until 1581, when he was enrolled at the University of Pisa as a medical student.

The chair of mathematics appears to have been vacant during most of Galileo's years as a student at Pisa. His formal education in astronomy was thus probably confined to lectures on the Aristotelian *De caelo* by the philosopher Francesco Buonamici. Physics was likewise taught by Aristotelian lectures, given by Buonamici and Girolamo Borro. As a medical student, Galileo may have received instruction from Andrea Cesalpino. His interest in medicine was not great; he was instead attracted to mathematics in 1583, receiving instruction from Ostilio Ricci outside the university. Ricci, a friend of Galileo's father and later a member of the Academy of Design at Florence, is said to have been a pupil of Niccolò Tartaglia. Galileo's studies of mathematics, opposed at first by his father, progressed rapidly; in 1585 he left the university without a degree and returned to Florence, where he pursued the study of Euclid and Archimedes privately.

From 1585 to 1589 Galileo gave private lessons in mathematics at Florence and private and public instruction at Siena. In 1586 he composed a short work, *La bilancetta,* in which he reconstructed the reasoning of Archimedes in the detection of the goldsmith's fraud in the matter of the crown of Hieron and described an improved hydrostatic balance. During the same period he became interested in problems of centers of gravity in solid bodies. During a visit to Rome in 1587, he made the acquaintance of the Jesuit mathematician Christoph Klau (Clavius). In 1588 he was invited by the Florentine Academy to lecture on the geography of Dante's *Inferno* treated mathematically. In the same year he applied for the chair of mathematics at the University of Bologna, seeking and obtaining from Guidobaldo del Monte an endorsement based on his theorems on the centers of gravity of paraboloids of revolution. The chair was awarded, however, to Giovanni Antonio Magini, probably on the basis of his superiority in astronomy, a subject in which Galileo appears to have shown little interest up to this time.

While Galileo was residing in Florence, his father was engaged in a controversy with Zarlino over musical theory. To destroy the old numerical theory of harmony, Vincenzio performed a series of experimental investigations of consonance and its relation to the lengths and tensions of musical strings. These he embodied in a published polemic of 1589, the *Discorso intorno all'opere di messer Gioseffo Zarlino da Chioggia,* and two unpublished treatises that survive among Galileo's papers. It is probable that Galileo's interest in the testing of mathematical rules by physical observations began with the musical experiments devised by his father during these years.

Professorship at Pisa. In 1589, on the recommendation of Guidobaldo, Galileo gained the chair of mathematics at the University of Pisa. The philosopher Jacopo Mazzoni, who came to Pisa at the same time, and Girolamo Mercuriale, professor of medicine, were close friends of the young mathematician. Luca Valerio, a Roman mathematician noted particularly for his later treatise on centers of gravity, met Galileo on a visit to Pisa and later corresponded with him. With other professors at Pisa, however, Galileo's relations were not so cordial, chiefly because of his campaign to discredit the prevailing Aristotelian physics to the advantage of his mathematical chair. His alleged demonstration at the Leaning Tower of Pisa that bodies of the same material but different weight fall with equal speed—if actually performed—was clearly not an experiment but a public challenge to the philosophers.

During Galileo's professorship at Pisa, he composed an untitled treatise on motion against the Aristotelian physics, now usually referred to as *De motu.* Its opening sections developed a theory of falling bodies derived from the buoyancy principle of Archimedes, an idea previously published by Giovanni Battista Benedetti in 1553–1554 and again in 1585. In the same treatise, Galileo derived the law governing equilibrium of weights on inclined planes and attempted to relate this law to speeds of descent. The result did not accord with experience—as Galileo noted—which may be the principal reason for his having withheld the treatise from publication. The discrepancy arose from his neglect of acceleration, a phenomenon that he then considered to be evanescent in free fall and that he accounted for by a Hipparchian theory of residual impressed force. In order to reconcile that theory with fall from rest, Galileo introduced a conception of static forces closely allied to Newton's third law of motion. Equality of action and reaction, together with the idea of virtual velocities, pervades much of Galileo's physics. From his earliest demonstrations of equilibrium on inclined planes, Galileo limited the action of tendencies to motion to infinitesimal distances, unlike his ancient and medieval predecessors. In so doing, he was able to relate vertical fall to descent along circular arcs and tangential inclined planes, an achievement that was to provide him with the key to many phenomena after he recognized the essential role of acceleration.

In his *De motu,* Galileo undertook to destroy the Aristotelian dichotomy of all motions into natural and forced motions. He did this by introducing imaginary rotations of massive spheres. Rotations of homogeneous spheres, or of any sphere having its geometric center or its center of gravity at the center of the universe, he declared to be "neutral" motions, neither natural nor forced. Motions on the horizontal plane, or on imaginary spheres concentric with the earth's center, were likewise neutral—a conception that led Galileo to his restricted concept of inertia in terrestrial physics. His discussion of spheres in *De motu* shows further that in 1590 Galileo had not yet abandoned the geocentric astronomy, but suggests that he saw no difficulty in the earth's rotation as assumed in the semi-Tychonic astronomy.

Vincenzio Galilei died in 1591, leaving Galileo, as eldest son, with heavy domestic and financial responsibilities. Galileo's position at Pisa was poorly paid; he was out of favor with the faculty of philosophy and he had offended Giovanni de' Medici by criticizing a scheme for the dredging of the harbor of Leghorn. His disrespectful attitude toward the university administration is reflected in a jocular poem he composed against the wearing of academic robes. Thus, at the end of his three-year contract, Galileo had no hope of strengthening his position at Pisa and little promise even of reappointment. Once more with the aid of Guidobaldo, he moved to the chair of mathematics at Padua. The rival candidate was again Magini, whose hostility toward Galileo after this defeat became extreme.

Professorship at Padua. The atmosphere at Padua was propitious in every way to Galileo's development. He quickly made the acquaintance of free and erudite spirits, in such men as G. V. Pinelli and Paolo Sarpi. Among his students were Gianfrancesco Sagredo and Benedetto Castelli. A conservative professor, Cesare Cremonini, became his personal friend while staunchly opposing his anti-Aristotelian views. Padua was a gathering point of the best scholars in Italy and drew students from all over Europe. Under the Venetian government, the university enjoyed virtually complete freedom from outside interference.

Galileo lectured publicly on the prescribed topics: Euclid, Sacrobosco, Ptolemy, and the pseudo-Aristotelian *Questions of Mechanics.* Privately he gave instruction also on fortification, military engineering, mechanics, and possibly also on astronomy, although we lack concrete evidence of his having become deeply interested in that subject much before 1604. He composed several treatises for the use of his students. One, usually known as *Le meccaniche,* survives in three successive forms, dating probably from 1593, 1594, and about 1600. In this treatise, besides developing further his treatment of inclined planes, he utilized as a bridge between statics and dynamics the remark that an infinitesimal force would serve to disturb equilibrium. This move, although itself not unobjectionable, removed serious existing obstacles (which had been raised on logical grounds by Guidobaldo and Simon Stevin) from the mathematical analysis of dynamic problems. Galileo's treatise, before it was first published in a French translation by Marin Mersenne in 1634, circulated widely in manuscript, and an English manuscript translation was made in 1626. Its authorship was not always known to readers even in Italy, because Galileo's treatises composed for his students were invariably supplied in copies bearing no title or signature.

In May 1597 Galileo wrote to his former colleague at Pisa, Jacopo Mazzoni, defending the Copernican system against a mistaken criticism. In August of the same year he received copies of the *Mysterium cosmographicum,* the first book by Johannes Kepler, to whom he wrote expressing his sympathies with Copernicanism. Kepler replied, urging him to support Copernicus openly, but Galileo allowed this correspondence to languish. His preference for Copernicus at this time seems to have had a mechanical rather than an astronomical basis; he wrote to Kepler that it afforded an explanation of physical effects not given by its rivals. This referred to a tidal theory of Galileo's in which the double motion of the earth was invoked to account for the periodic disturbance of its water. The first notation concerning this theory occurs in the notebooks of Sarpi in 1595. Galileo wrote a treatise on it early in 1616, and wished to make it the central theme of his Copernican *Dialogue* of 1632, considering the tides to offer a compelling argument for the double motion of the earth.

It was also in 1597 that Galileo began the production—for sale—of a mathematical instrument, the sector or proportional compass. The idea for this instrument probably came to him from Guidobaldo, whose knowledge of it may in turn have been derived from Michel Coignet. Galileo transformed it from a simple device of limited use to an elaborate calculating instrument of varied uses and of great practical utility by adding to it a number of supplementary scales. He employed a skilled artisan to produce it (and other mathematical instruments) in his own workshop and wrote a treatise on its use for engineers and military men.

During his residence at Padua, Galileo took a Venetian mistress named Marina Gamba, by whom he had two daughters and a son. The elder daughter, Virginia, who was born in 1600, later became Galileo's chief solace in life. The vivacity of her mind and the sensitivity of her spirit—as well as her many impositions on her father's good nature—are evident in the letters that Galileo received and treasured. Both she and her sister Livia were entered in a nunnery near Florence at an early age, Virginia taking the name Maria Celeste. Livia, who took the name Arcangela, was of a peevish disposition and frail health. The son, Vincenzio, was later legitimized. After periods of estrangement from his father, Vincenzio became reconciled with him in his last years but did not long survive him. Marina Gamba remained at Venice when Galileo returned to Florence, and shortly afterward she married.

Early Work on Free Fall. Toward the end of 1602, Galileo wrote to Guidobaldo concerning the motions of pendulums and the descent of bodies along the arcs and chords of circles. His deep interest in phenomena of acceleration appears to date from this time. The correct law of falling bodies, but with a false assumption behind it, is embodied in a letter to Sarpi in 1604. Associated with the letter is a fragment, separately preserved, containing an attempted proof of the correct law from the false assumption. No clue is given as to the source of Galileo's knowledge of the law that the ratios of spaces traversed from rest in free fall are as those of the squares of the elapsed times. The law is algebraically derivable from the medieval mean-degree theorem known as the Merton rule, but Galileo's false assumption in 1604 contradicts the specific association of speed and time that is always found in medieval derivations of that theorem. Moreover, Galileo's faulty demonstration invoked no single instantaneous velocity as a mean or representative value; instead, it proceeded by comparison of *ratios* between infinite sets of instantaneously varying velocities. It is probable either that he observed a rough 1, 3, 5, . . . progression of spaces traversed along inclined planes in equal times and assumed this to be exact, or that he reasoned (as Christian Huygens later did) that only the odd-number rule of spaces would preserve the ratios unchanged for arbitrary changes of the unit time. From this fact, the times-squared law follows immediately. Galileo's derivation of it from the correct definition of uniform acceleration followed only at a considerably later date.

The appearance of a supernova in 1604 led to disputes about the Aristotelian idea of the incorruptibility of the heavens, in which Galileo took an active part. He delivered three lectures to overflow crowds at Padua and prepared to publish an astronomical work; he did not do so, however, and only a short fragment of the manuscript survives. Lodovico delle Colombe, who published a theory of new stars at Florence, suspected Galileo of having written a pseudonymous attack on him, and it is certain that Galileo's ideas are reflected in still another pseudonymous work, published in rustic dialect at Padua in 1605, which ridiculed the professors of philosophy. In 1606, however, Galileo's attention was diverted from this dispute by the plagiarism of his proportional compass by Simon Mayr (or Marius, in the Latinized form used for publication), a German then at Padua, and Mayr's pupil Baldassar Capra. Galileo had privately printed a small edition of his treatise on the use of the compass in that year; Mayr and Capra produced a Latin book on the construction and use of the same instrument, claiming that Galileo had stolen it from them. Mayr had returned to Germany, so Galileo brought his action against Capra. The book was suppressed and Capra was expelled from the university. In the following year Galileo published a full account of the case in his first publicly circulated printed work, the *Difesa . . . contro alle calunnie & imposture di Baldessar Capra.*

Early in 1609, Galileo began the composition of a systematic treatise on motion in which his studies of inclined planes and of pendulums were to be integrated under the law of acceleration, known to him at least since 1604. In the composition of his treatise, he became aware that there was something wrong with his attempted derivation of 1604, which had assumed proportionality of speed to space traversed. Accordingly, he introduced in its place two propositions drawn from mechanics, which he submitted for criticism to Valerio. Galileo received Valerio's reply in July 1609, just after his attention had again been diverted from mechanics, this time by news of the invention of the telescope.

The Telescope. A Dutch lens-grinder, Hans Lipperhey, had applied in October 1608 to Count Maurice of Nassau for a patent on a device to make distant objects appear closer. Sarpi, whose extensive correspondence (maintained for theological and political reasons) kept him currently informed, learned of this device within a month. Somewhat skeptical, he applied for further information to Jacques Badovere (Giacomo Badoer), a former pupil of Galileo's then at Paris. In due course the report was confirmed. Galileo heard discussions of the news during a visit to Venice in July 1609, learned from Sarpi that the device was real, and probably heard of the simultaneous arrival at Padua of a foreigner who had brought one to Italy. He hastened back to Padua, found that the foreigner had left for Venice, and at once attempted to construct such a device himself. In this he quickly succeeded, sent word of it to Sarpi, and applied himself to the improvement of the instrument. Sarpi, who had meanwhile been selected by the Venetian government to assess the value of the device offered for sale to them by the stranger, discouraged its purchase. Late in August, Galileo arrived at Venice with a nine-power telescope, three times as effective as the other. The practical value of this instrument to a maritime power obtained for him a lifetime appointment to the university, with an unprecedented salary for the chair of mathematics. The official document he received, however, did not conform to his understanding of the terms he had accepted. As a result, he pressed his application for a post at the Tuscan court, begun a year or two earlier.

Galileo's swift improvement of the telescope continued until, at the end of 1609, he had one of about thirty power. This was the practicable limit for a telescope of the Galilean type, with plano-convex objective and plano-concave eyepiece. He turned this new instrument to the skies early in January 1610, with startling results. Not only was the moon revealed to be mountainous and the Milky Way to be a congeries of separate stars, contrary to Aristotelian principles, but a host of new fixed stars and four satellites of Jupiter were promptly discovered. Working with great haste but impressive accuracy, Galileo recited these discoveries in the *Sidereus nuncius,* published at Venice early in March 1610.

His sudden fame assisted Galileo in his negotiations at Florence. Moreover, the new discoveries made him reluctant to continue teaching the old astronomy. In the summer of 1610, he resigned the chair at Padua and returned to Florence as mathematician and philosopher to the grand duke of Tuscany, and chief mathematician of the University of Pisa, without obligation to teach.

Galileo's book created excitement throughout Europe and a second edition was published in the same year at Frankfurt. Kepler endorsed it in two small books, the *Dissertatio cum Nuncio Sidereo,* published before he had personally observed the new phenomena, and the *Narratio de observatis a se quatuor Jovis satellitibus,* published a few months later. Other writers attacked the claimed discoveries as a fraud. Galileo did not enter the controversy but applied himself to further observations. He discovered, later in 1610, the oval appearance of Saturn and the phases of Venus. His telescope was inadequate to resolve Saturn's rings, which he took to be satellites very close to the planet. The phases of Venus removed a serious objection to the Copernican system, and he saw in the satellites of Jupiter a miniature planetary system in which, as in the Copernican astronomy, it could no longer be held that all moving heavenly bodies revolved exclusively about the earth.

Early in 1611 Galileo journeyed to Rome to exhibit his telescopic discoveries. The Jesuits of the Roman College, who had at first been dubious, confirmed them and honored Galileo. Federico Cesi feted Galileo and made him a member of the Lincean Academy, the first truly scientific academy, founded in 1603. The pope and several cardinals also showed their esteem for Galileo.

Controversies at Florence. Shortly after his return to Florence, Galileo became involved in a controversy over floating bodies. In that controversy an important role was played by Colombe, who became the leader of a group of dissident professors and intriguing courtiers that resented Galileo's position at court. Maffeo Barberini—then a cardinal but later to become pope—took Galileo's side in the dispute. Turning again to physics, Galileo composed and published a book on the behavior of bodies placed in water (*Discurso . . . intorno alle cose che stanno in su l'acqua, o in quella si muovono*), in support of Archimedes and against Aristotle, of which two editions appeared in 1612. Using the concept of moment and the principle of virtual velocities, Galileo extended the scope of the Archimedean work beyond purely hydrostatic considerations.

While this work was in progress, Galileo received from Marcus Welser of Augsburg a short treatise on sunspots that Welser had published pseudonymously for the Jesuit Christoph Scheiner, asking Galileo's opinion of it. Galileo replied in three long letters during 1612, demolishing Scheiner's conjecture that the spots were tiny planets. He asserted also that he had observed sunspots much earlier and had shown them to others at Rome early in 1611. This set the stage for a deep enmity of Scheiner toward Galileo, which, however, did not take active form at once.

Galileo's *Letters on Sunspots* was published at Rome in 1613 under the auspices of the Lincean Academy. In this book Galileo spoke out decisively for the Copernican system for the first time in print. In the same book he found a place for his first published mention of the concept of conservation of angular momentum and an associated inertial concept. During its composition he had taken pains to determine the theological status of the idea of incorruptibility of the heavens, finding that this was regarded by churchmen as an Aristotelian rather than a Catholic dogma. But attacks against Galileo and his followers soon appeared in ecclesiastical quarters. These came to a head with a denunciation from the pulpit in Florence late in 1614.

In December 1613 it had happened that theological objections to Copernicanism were raised, in Galileo's absence, at a court dinner, where Galileo's part was upheld by Benedetto Castelli. Learning of this, Galileo wrote a long letter to Castelli concerning the inadmissibility of theological interference in purely scientific questions. After the public denunciation in 1614, Castelli showed this letter to an influential Dominican priest, who made a copy of it and sent it to the Roman Inquisition for investigation. Galileo then promptly sent an authoritative text of the letter to Rome and began its expansion into the *Letter to Christina,* composed in 1615 and eventually published in 1636. Galileo argued that neither the Bible nor nature could speak falsely and that the investigation of nature was the province of the scientist, while the reconciliation of scientific facts with the language of the Bible was that of the theologian.

The book on bodies in water drew attacks from four Aristotelian professors at Florence and Pisa, while a book strongly supporting Galileo's position appeared at Rome. Galileo prepared answers to his critics, which he turned over to Castelli for publication in order to avoid personal involvement. Detailed replies to two of them (Colombe and Grazia), written principally by Galileo himself, appeared anonymously in 1615, with a prefatory note by Castelli implying that he was the author and that Galileo would have been more severe.

Late in 1615 Galileo went to Rome (against the advice of his friends and the Tuscan ambassador) to clear his own name and to prevent, if possible, the official suppression of the teaching of Copernicanism. In the first, he succeeded; no disciplinary action against him was taken on the basis of his letter to Castelli or his Copernican declaration in the book on sunspots. In the second objective, however, he failed. Pope Paul V, irritated by the agitation of questions of biblical interpretation—then a bone of contention with the Protestants—appointed a commission to determine the theological status of the earth's motion. The determination was adverse, and Galileo was instructed on 26 February 1616 to abandon the holding or defending of that view. No action was taken against him, nor were any of his books suspended. A book by the theologian Paolo Antonio Foscarini reconciling the earth's motion with the Bible was condemned, and the work of Copernicus and a commentary on Job by Diego de Zuñiga were suspended pending the correction of a few passages. One contemporary document, bound into the proceedings but of uncertain reliability, states that Galileo was also ordered never to discuss the forbidden doctrine again. If such an order was given, it was in contravention of certain specific instructions of the pope and had no legal force.

Returning to Florence, Galileo took up a practical and noncontroversial problem, the determination of longitudes at sea. He believed that this could be solved by the preparation of accurate tables of the eclipses of the satellites of Jupiter, which were of frequent occurrence and could be observed telescopically from any point on the earth. As a practical matter, the eclipses could neither be predicted with sufficient accuracy nor observed at sea with sufficient convenience to make the method useful.

It is probable that Galileo also returned during this period to his mechanical investigations, interrupted in 1609 by the advent of the telescope. A Latin treatise by Galileo, *De motu accelerato,* which correctly defines uniform acceleration and much resembles the definitive text reproduced in his final book, seems to date from this intermediate period, and copies of many of his propositions in kinematics exist in the handwriting of Mario Guiducci, who studied under Galileo at this time.

In 1618 three comets attracted the attention of Europe and became the subject of many pamphlets and books. One such book was printed anonymously by Orazio Grassi, the mathematician of the Jesuit Roman College. Galileo was bedridden at the time, but he discussed his views on comets with Guiducci, who then delivered lectures on them to the Florentine Academy and published them over his own name. In these lectures, which were largely dictated or corrected by Galileo, the anonymous Jesuit was subjected to criticism. The result was a direct attack on Galileo by Grassi, under the pseudonym of Lotario Sarsi, published in 1619.

Galileo replied, after much delay, with one of the most celebrated polemics in science, *Il saggiatore* (*The Assayer*). It was addressed to Virginio Cesarini, a young man who had heard Galileo debate at Rome in 1615–1616 and had written to him in 1619 to extol the method by which Galileo had opened to him a new road to truth. Since he could no longer defend Copernicus, Galileo avoided the question of the earth's motion; instead, he set forth a general scientific approach to the investigation of celestial phenomena. He gave no positive theory of comets, but developed the thesis that arguments from parallax could not be decisive concerning their location until it was first demonstrated that they were concrete moving objects rather than mere optical effects of solar reflection in seas of vapor. No such proof appeared to him to be available. In the course of his argument, Galileo distinguished physical properties of objects from their sensory effects, repudiated authority in any matter that was subject to direct investigation, and remarked that the book of nature, being written in mathematical characters, could be deciphered only by those who knew mathematics.

The *Saggiatore* was printed in 1623 under the auspices of the Lincean Academy. Just before it emerged from the press, Maffeo Barberini became pope as Urban VIII. The academicians dedicated the book to him at the last minute. Cesarini was appointed chamberlain by the new pope, who had long been Galileo's friend and was a patron of science and letters. Galileo journeyed to Rome in 1624 to pay his respects to Urban, and secured from him permission to discuss the Copernican system in a book, provided that the arguments for the Ptolemaic view were given an equal and impartial discussion. Urban refused to rescind the edict of 1616, although he remarked that had it been up to him, the edict would not have been adopted.

Dialogue on the World Systems. The *Dialogue Concerning the Two Chief World Systems* occupied Galileo for the next six years. It has the literary form of a discussion between a spokesman for Copernicus, one for Ptolemy and Aristotle, and an educated layman for whose support the other two strive. Galileo thus remains technically uncommitted except in a preface which ostensibly supports the anti-Copernican edict of 1616. The book will prove, he says, that the edict did not reflect any ignorance in Italy of the strength of pro-Copernican arguments. The contrary is the case; Galileo will add Copernican arguments of his own invention, and thus he will show that not ignorance of or antagonism to science, but concern for spiritual welfare alone, guided the Church in its decision.

The opening section of the *Dialogue* critically examines the Aristotelian cosmology. Only those things in it are rejected that would conflict with the motion of the earth and stability of the sun or that would sharply distinguish celestial from terrestrial material and motions. Thus the idea that the universe has a center, or that the earth is located in such a center, is rejected, as is the idea that the motion of heavy bodies is directed to the center of the universe rather than to that of the earth. On the other hand, the Aristotelian concept of celestial motions as naturally circular is not rejected; instead, Galileo argues that natural circular motions apply equally to terrestrial and celestial objects. This position appears to conflict with statements in later sections of the book concerning terrestrial physics. But uniform motion in precise circular orbits also conflicts with actual observations of planetary motions, whatever center is chosen for all orbits. Actual planetary motions had not been made literally homocentric by any influential astronomer since the time of Aristotle. Galileo is no exception; in a later section he remarked on the irregularities that still remained to be explained. Opinion today is divided; some hold that the opening arguments of the *Dialogue* should be taken as representative of Galileo's deepest physical and philosophical convictions, while others view them as mere stratagems to reduce orthodox Aristotelian opposition to the earth's motion.

Important in the *Dialogue* are the concepts of relativity of motion and conservation of motion, both angular and inertial, introduced to reconcile terrestrial physics with large motions of the earth, in answer to the standard arguments of Ptolemy and those added by Tycho Brahe. The law of falling bodies and the composition of motions are likewise utilized. Corrections concerning the visual sizes and the probable distances and positions of fixed stars are discussed. A program for the detection of parallactic displacements among fixed stars is outlined, and the phases of Venus are adduced to account for the failure of that planet to exhibit great differences in size to the naked eye at perigee and apogee. Kepler's modification of the circular Copernican orbits is not mentioned; indeed, the Copernican system is presented as more regular and simpler than Copernicus himself had made it. Technical astronomy is discussed with respect only to observational problems, not to planetary theory.

To the refutation of conventional physical objections against terrestrial motion, Galileo added two arguments in its favor. One concerned the annual variations in the paths of sunspots, which could not be dynamically reconciled with an absolutely stationary earth. Geometrically, all rotations and revolutions could be assigned to the sun, but their conservation would require very complicated forces. The Copernican distribution of one rotation to the sun and one rotation and one revolution to the earth fitted a very simple dynamics. The second new argument concerned the existence of ocean tides, which Galileo declared, quite correctly, to be incapable of any physical explanation without a motion of the earth. His own explanation happened to be incorrect; he argued that the earth's double motion of rotation and revolution caused a daily maximum and minimum velocity, and a continual change of speed, at every point on the earth. The continual variation of speed of sea basins imparted different speeds to their contained waters. The water, free to move within the basins, underwent periodic disturbances of level, greatest at their coasts; the period depended on sizes of basins, their east-west orientations, depths, and extraneous factors such as prevailing winds. In order to account for monthly and annual variations in the tides, Galileo invoked an uneven speed of the earth-moon system through the ecliptic during each month, caused by the moon's motion with respect to the earth-sun vector; for annual seasonal effects, he noted changes of the composition of rotational and revolutional components in the basic disturbing cause.

The *Dialogue* was completed early in 1630. Galileo took it to Rome, where it was intended to be published by the Lincean Academy. There he sought to secure a license for its printing. This was not immediately granted, and he returned to Florence without it. While the matter was still pending, Federico Cesi died, depriving the Academy of both effective leadership and funds. Castelli wrote to Galileo, intimating that for other reasons he would never get the Roman imprimatur and advising him to print the book at Florence without delay. Negotiations ensued for permission to print the book at Florence. Ultimately these were successful, and the *Dialogue* appeared at Florence in March 1632. A few copies were sent to Rome, and for a time no disturbance ensued. Then, quite suddenly, the printer was ordered to halt further sales, and Galileo was instructed to come to Rome and present himself to the Inquisition during the month of October.

The Trial of Galileo. The background of the action is fairly clear. Several ecclesiastical factions were hostile to the book but at first produced only shallow pretexts to suppress it. More serious charges were lodged against Galileo when Urban was persuaded that his own decisive argument against the literal truth of the earth's motion—that God could produce any effect desired by any means—had been put in the mouth of the simpleminded Aristotelian in the dialogue as a deliberate personal taunt by Galileo. Next, a search of the Inquisition files of 1616 disclosed the questionable document previously mentioned, which contained a specific threat of imprisonment for Galileo if he ever again discussed the Copernican doctrine in any way. Urban, having known nothing of any personal injunction at the time Galileo sought his permission to write the book, assumed that Galileo had deceitfully concealed it from him. The case was thereafter prosecuted with vindictive hostility. Galileo, who had either never received a personal injunction or had been told that it was without force, was unaware of any wrongdoing in this respect.

Confined to bed by serious illness, he at first refused to go to Rome. The grand duke and his Roman ambassador intervened stoutly in his behalf, but the pope was adamant. Despite medical certificates that travel in the winter might be fatal, Galileo was threatened with forcible removal in chains unless he capitulated. The grand duke, feeling that no more could be done, provided a litter for the journey, and Galileo was taken to Rome in February 1633.

The outcome of the trial, which began in April, was inevitable. Although Galileo was able to produce an affidavit of Cardinal Bellarmine to the effect that he had been instructed only according to the general edict that governed all Catholics, he was persuaded in an extrajudicial procedure to acknowledge that in the *Dialogue* he had gone too far in his arguments for Copernicus. On the basis of that admission, his *Dialogue* was put on the Index, and Galileo was sentenced to life imprisonment after abjuring the Copernican "heresy." The terms of imprisonment were immediately commuted to permanent house arrest under surveillance. He was at first sent to Siena, under the charge of its archbishop, Ascanio Piccolomini. Piccolomini, who is said to have been Galileo's former pupil, was very friendly to him. Within a few weeks he had revived Galileo's spirits—so crushed by the sentence that his life had been feared for—and induced him to take up once more his old work in mechanics and bring it to a conclusion. While at Siena, Galileo began the task of putting his lifelong achievements in physics into dialogue form, using the same interlocutors as in the *Dialogue.*

Piccolomini's treatment of Galileo as an honored guest, rather than as a prisoner of the Inquisition, was duly reported to Rome. To avoid further scandal, Galileo was transferred early in 1634 to his villa at

Arcetri, in the hills above Florence. It was probably on the occasion of his departure from Siena that he uttered the celebrated phrase "Eppur si muove," apocryphally said to have been muttered as he rose to his feet after abjuring on his knees before the Cardinals Inquisitors in Rome. The celebrated phrase, long considered legendary, was ultimately discovered on a fanciful portrait of Galileo in prison, executed about 1640 by Murillo or one of his pupils at Madrid, where the archbishop's brother was stationed as a military officer.

Galileo was particularly anxious to return to Florence to be near his elder daughter. But she died shortly after his return, in April 1634, following a brief illness. For a time, Galileo lost all interest in his work and in life itself. But the unfinished work on motion again absorbed his attention, and within a year it was virtually finished. Now another problem faced him: the printing of any of his books, old or new, had been forbidden by the Congregation of the Index. A manuscript copy was nevertheless smuggled out to France, and the Elzevirs at Leiden undertook to print it. By the time it was issued, in 1638, Galileo had become completely blind.

Two New Sciences. The title of his final work, *Discourses and Mathematical Demonstrations Concerning Two New Sciences* (generally known in English by the last three words), hardly conveys a clear idea of its organization and contents. The two sciences with which the book principally deals are the engineering science of strength of materials and the mathematical science of kinematics. The first, as Galileo presents it, is founded on the law of the lever; breaking strength is treated as a branch of statics. The second has its basis in the assumption of uniformity and simplicity in nature, complemented by certain dynamic assumptions. Galileo is clearly uncomfortable about the necessity of borrowing anything from mechanics in his mathematical treatment of motion. A supplementary justification for that procedure was dictated later by the blind Galileo for inclusion in future editions.

Of the four dialogues contained in the book, the last two are devoted to the treatment of uniform and accelerated motion and the discussion of parabolic trajectories. The first two deal with problems related to the constitution of matter; the nature of mathematics; the place of experiment and reason in science; the weight of air; the nature of sound; the speed of light; and other fragmentary comments on physics as a whole. Thus Galileo's *Two New Sciences* underlies modern physics not only because it contains the elements of the mathematical treatment of motion, but also because most of the problems that came rather quickly to be seen as problems amenable to physical experiment and mathematical analysis were gathered together in this book with suggestive discussions of their possible solution. Philosophical considerations as such were minimized.

The book opens with the observation that practical mechanics affords a vast field for investigation. Shipbuilders know that large frameworks must be strongly supported lest they break of their own weight, while small frameworks are in no such danger. But if mathematics underlies physics, why should geometrically similar figures behave differently by reason of size alone? In this way the subject of strength of materials is introduced. The virtual lever is made the basis of a theory of fracture, without consideration of compression or stress; we can see at once the inadequacy of the theory and its value as a starting point for correct analysis. Galileo's attention turns next to the problem of cohesion. It seems to him that matter consists of finite indivisible parts, *parti quante,* while at the same time the analysis of matter must, by its mathematical nature, involve infinitesimals, *parti non quante.* He does not conceal—but rather stresses—the resulting paradoxes. An inability to solve them (as he saw it) must not cause us to despair of understanding what we can. Galileo regards the concepts of "greater than," "less than," and "equal to" as simply not applicable to infinite multitudes; he illustrates this by putting the natural numbers and their squares in one-to-one correspondence.

Galileo had composed a treatise on continuous quantity (now lost) as early as 1609 and had devoted much further study to the subject. Bonaventura Cavalieri, who took his start from Galileo's analysis, importuned him to publish that work in order that Cavalieri might proceed with the publication of his own *Geometry by Indivisibles.* But Galileo's interest in pure mathematics was always overshadowed by his concern with physics, and all that is known of his analysis of the continuum is to be found among his digressions when discussing physical problems.

Galileo's *parti non quante* seem to account for his curious physical treatment of vacua. His attention had been directed to failure of suction pumps and siphons for columns of water beyond a fixed height. He accounted for this by treating water as a material having its own limited tensile strength, on the analogy of rope or copper wire, which will break of its own weight if sufficiently long. The cohesion of matter seemed to him best explained by the existence of minute vacua. Not only did he fail to suggest the weight of air as an explanation of the siphon phenomena, but he rejected that explanation when it was clearly offered to him in a letter by G. B. Baliani.

Yet Galileo was not only familiar with the weight of air; he had himself devised practicable methods for its determination, set forth in this same book, giving even the correction for the buoyancy of the air in which the weighing was conducted.

Phenomena of the pendulum occupy a considerable place in the *Two New Sciences.* The relation of period to length of pendulum was first given here, although it probably represents one of Galileo's earliest precise physical observations. Precise isochronism of the pendulum appears to have been the one result he most wished to derive deductively. In discussing resistance of the air to projectile motion, he invoked observations (grossly exaggerated) of the identity of period between two pendulums of equal length weighted by bobs of widely different specific gravity. He deduced the existence of terminal constant velocity for any body falling through air, or any other medium, but mistakenly believed increase of resistance to be proportional to velocity.

Like the pendulum, the inclined plane plays a large role in Galileo's ultimate discussion of motion. The logical structure of his kinematics, as presented in the *Two New Sciences,* is this: He first defines uniform motion as that in which proportional spaces are covered in proportional times, and he then develops its laws. Next he defines uniform acceleration as that in which equal increments of velocity are acquired in equal times and shows that the resulting relations conform to those found in free fall. Postulating that the path of descent from a given height does not affect the velocity acquired at the end of a given vertical drop, he describes an experimental apparatus capable of disclosing time and distance ratios along planes of differing tilts and lengths; finally, he asserts the agreement of experiment with his theory. The experiments have been repeated in modern times, precisely as described in the *Two New Sciences,* and they give the results asserted. Following these definitions, assumptions, and confirmation by experiment, Galileo proceeds to derive a great many theorems related to accelerated motion.

In the last section Galileo deduces the parabolic trajectory of projectiles from a composition of uniform horizontal motion and accelerated vertical motion. Here the concept of rectilinear inertia, previously illustrated in the *Dialogue* ("Second Day"), is mathematically applied but not expressly formulated. This is followed by additional theorems relating to trajectories and by tables of altitude and distance calculated for oblique initial paths. Because of air resistance at high velocities, the tables assumed low speeds and hence were of no practical importance in gunnery. But like Galileo's theory of fracture, they opened the way for rapid successive refinements at the hands of others.

Last Years. Galileo lived four years, totally blind, beyond the publication of his final book. During this time, he had the companionship of Vincenzio Viviani, who succeeded him (after Evangelista Torricelli) as mathematician to the grand duke and who inherited his papers. Viviani wrote a brief account of Galileo's life in 1654 at the request of Leopold de' Medici, which, despite some demonstrable errors, is still a principal source of biographical information, in conjunction with the voluminous correspondence of Galileo that has survived and with the autobiographical passages in his works. Near the end of his life, Galileo was also visited by Torricelli, a pupil of Castelli and the ablest physicist among Galileo's immediate disciples. Galileo's son, Vincenzio, also assisted in taking notes of his father's later reflections, in particular the design of a timekeeping device controlled by a pendulum.

Galileo died at Arcetri early in 1642, five weeks before his seventy-eighth birthday. The vindictiveness of Urban VIII, who had denied even Galileo's requests to attend mass on Easter and to consult doctors in nearby Florence when his sight was failing, continued after Galileo's death: The grand duke wished to erect a suitable tomb for Galileo but was warned to do nothing that might reflect unfavorably on the Holy Office. Galileo was buried at Santa Croce in Florence, but nearly a century elapsed before his remains were transferred, with a suitable monument and inscription, to their present place in the same church.

Sources of Galileo's Physics. The habitual association of Galileo's name with the rapid rise of scientific activity after 1600 makes the investigation of his sources a matter of particular interest to historians of science.

All agree that Archimedes was a prime source and model for Galileo, who himself avowed the fact. The work of Aristotle and the pseudo-Aristotelian *Questions of Mechanics* were likewise admitted inspirations to Galileo, although often only as targets of criticism and attack. The astronomy of Copernicus and the magnetic researches of William Gilbert were obvious and acknowledged sources of his work. Beyond these, there is little agreement.

Among sixteenth-century writers, Galileo probably drew chiefly on Niccolò Tartaglia, Girolamo Cardano, and Guidobaldo del Monte. Parallels between his early unpublished work and that of Benedetti are very striking, but the establishment of a direct connection is difficult. As with the case of Stevin, the parallels in thought may result from the Archimedean revival and a common outlook rather than from early and direct knowledge of Benedetti's work.

Similarly, a direct influence of medieval writers on Galileo, although widely accepted by most historians, is still largely conjectured on the basis of specific parallels. The statics of Jordanus de Nemore was widely known in Italy after 1546, when Tartaglia published in Italian and endorsed the "science of weights" as necessary to an understanding of the balance; yet all subsequent writers (at least in Italy) condemned it in favor of the Archimedean approach. Writings of the Merton school, published repeatedly in Italy up to about 1520, continued to be discussed thereafter at Paris and in Spain. Galileo's reasoning about acceleration, after his recognition of its importance around 1602, invariably proceeded by comparison of ratios, whereas medieval writers adopted a mean speed as representative of uniformly changing velocities. Medieval impetus theory, which Galileo adopted at first for the explanation of projectile motion, had no place in the concept of neutral motions that led him eventually to an inertial terrestrial physics. A connection of Galileo's own physical thought with medieval sources may yet be convincingly established, but at present this has not been done.

Experiment and Mathematics. The role of experiment in Galileo's physics was limited to the testing of preconceived mathematical rules and did not extend to the systematic search for such rules. It is probable that his use of experiment had its roots in the musical controversy conducted by his father rather than in philosophical considerations of method. Appeal to experiment in his published works was resorted to by Galileo chiefly as a means of confuting rival theories, as in the dispute over bodies in water and in his rejection of proportionality of speed to space traversed in free fall.

It is difficult to find older sources for Galileo's attitude toward mathematics, which was strikingly modern. He considered mathematics to enjoy a superior certainty over logic. Where a mathematical relation could be found in nature, Galileo accepted it as a valid description and discouraged further search for ulterior causes. He attributed discrepancies between mathematics and physical events to the investigator who did not yet know how to balance his books. Galileo did not adopt the traditional Platonist view that our world is a defective copy of the "real" world, and he derided philosophical speculation about a world on paper.

The Influence of Galileo. Except with respect to the acceptance of Copernican astronomy, Galileo's direct influence on science outside Italy was probably not very great. After 1610 he published his books in Italian and made little effort to persuade professional scholars either at home or abroad. His influence on educated laymen both in Italy and abroad was considerable; on university professors, except for a few who were his own pupils, it was negligible. Latin translations of his *Dialogue* appeared in Holland in 1635, in France in 1641, and in England in 1663; but the only Latin translation of the *Two New Sciences* was published in 1700, long after Newton's *Principia* had superseded it.

Between Galileo and Newton, science was Cartesian rather than Galilean. Indirectly, Galileo's science exerted some influence in France through Marin Mersenne, Pierre Gassendi, and Nicholas Fabri de Peiresc; in Germany through Kepler; and in England through John Wilkins and John Wallis. Descartes, who repudiated Galileo's approach to physics because of its neglect of the essence of motion and physical causation, did not mention him in any published work. Newton seems not to have read Galileo's *Two New Sciences,* at least not before 1700, but knew his *Dialogue* as early as 1666. Aware of his achievements in physics only indirectly, Newton, in the *Principia,* mistakenly credited Galileo with a derivation of the laws of falling bodies from the law of inertia and the force-acceleration relationship.

Within Italy, Galileo had a strong following both in scientific and nonscientific circles. His ablest pupil, Castelli, was the teacher of Torricelli and Cavalieri, both of whom also had personal acquaintance with Galileo. His last pupil, Viviani, did much to extend Galileo's influence in the succeeding generation, editing the first collection of his works in 1655–1656. But by that time physics and astronomy had both progressed well beyond the point where Galileo had left them.

Outside scientific circles, Galileo's influence was strongly felt in the battle for freedom of inquiry and against authority. English translations of his *Dialogue* and *Letter to Christina,* published in 1661, carried this influence outside academic circles. John Milton cited the fate of Galileo in his *Areopagitica.* French writers during the Enlightenment also made Galileo a symbol of religious persecution.

Personal Traits. Galileo was of average stature, squarely built, and of lively appearance and disposition. Viviani remarks that he was quick to anger and as quickly mollified. His unusual talents as a speaker and as a teacher are beyond question. Among those who knew him personally, even including adversaries, few seem to have disliked him. Many distinguished men became his devoted friends, and some sacrificed their own interests in his support at crucial periods. On the other hand, there were many contemporary rumors discreditable to Galileo, and demonstrable slanders occur in letters of Georg Fugger, Martin Horky, and others. Pugnacious rather than belligerent, he refrained from starting polemic battles but was ruthless in their prosecution when he answered an attack at all. His friends included artists and men of letters as well as mathematicians and scientists; cardinals as well as rulers; craftsmen as well as learned men. His enemies included conservative professors, several priests, most philosophers, and those scientists who had publicly challenged him and felt the bite of his sarcasm in return.

Caution and daring both had a place in Galileo's personality. His reluctance to speak out for the Copernican system until he had optical evidence against the rival theories is evidence of scientific prudence rather than of professorial timidity. Once convinced by his own eyes and mind, he would not be swayed even by the advice of well-informed friends who urged him to proceed with caution. In the writings he withheld from publication, as in his surviving notes, many errors and wrong conjectures are to be found; in his published works, very few. He was as respectful of authority in religion and politics as he was contemptuous of it in matters he could investigate for himself. It is noteworthy that before his Copernican stand was challenged by an official Church edict, he had composed and submitted to the authorities a carefully documented program, based on positions of Church fathers, that would have obviated official intervention against his science—a program that was in fact adopted by a pope nearly three centuries later as theologically sound.

BIBLIOGRAPHY

I. Original Works. All works by Galileo and virtually all known Galilean correspondence and manuscripts are contained in *Le opere di Galileo Galilei,* Antonio Favaro, ed., 20 vols. (Florence, 1890–1909); repr. with some additions (Florence, 1929–1939; 1965). English translations of Galileo's principal works are listed below. Following the translator's name are the English book title, the abbreviated original title of each work included, and date of first ed. or approximate date of composition.

T. Salusbury, *Mathematical Collections and Translations,* I (London, 1661; repr. 1967), *Lettera a Madama Cristina* (*ca.* 1615) and *Dialogo* (Florence, 1632); II (London, 1665; repr. 1967), *La bilancetta* (*ca.* 1586); *Le meccaniche* (*ca.* 1600); *Discorso . . . intorno alle cose che stanno in su l'acqua* (Florence, 1612); and *Discorsi* (Leiden, 1638).

T. Weston, *Mathematical Discourses Concerning Two New Sciences* (London, 1730; 2nd ed. 1734): *Discorsi* (Leiden, 1638).

E. Carlos, *The Sidereal Messenger* (London, 1880; repr. 1959): *Sidereus nuncius* (Venice, 1610).

H. Crew and A. De Salvio, *Dialogues Concerning Two New Sciences* (New York, 1914; repr. n.d.): *Discorsi* (Leiden, 1638).

G. de Santillana, ed., *Dialogue on the Great World Systems* (Chicago, 1953), the Salusbury trans.: *Dialogo* (Florence, 1632).

S. Drake, *Dialogue Concerning the Two Chief World Systems* (Berkeley, Cal., 1953; rev. 1967): *Dialogo* (Florence, 1632).

S. Drake, *Discoveries and Opinions of Galileo* (New York, 1957): *Sidereus nuncius* (Venice, 1610); *Lettere sulle macchie solari* (Rome, 1613); *Lettera a Madama Cristina* (*ca.* 1615); and *Il saggiatore* (Rome, 1623).

I. Drabkin and S. Drake, *Galileo on Motion and on Mechanics* (Madison, Wis., 1960): *De motu* (*ca.* 1590), and *Le meccaniche* (*ca.* 1600).

S. Drake and C. D. O'Malley, *The Controversy on the Comets of 1618* (Philadelphia, 1960): *Discorso sulle comete* (Florence, 1619), and *Il saggiatore* (Rome, 1623).

S. Drake, ed., *Galileo on Bodies in Water,* (Urbana, Ill., 1960), the Salusbury trans.: *Discorso* (Florence, 1612).

L. Fermi and G. Bernadini, *Galileo and the Scientific Revolution* (New York, 1961): C. S. Smith, trans., *La bilancetta* (*ca.* 1586).

S. Drake and I. Drabkin, *Mechanics in Sixteenth-Century Italy* (Madison, Wis., 1969): *Dialogus de motu* (*ca.* 1589).

II. Secondary Literature. Nearly 6,000 titles relating to Galileo are listed in the following bibliographies: *Bibliografia Galileiana, 1568–1895,* A. Carli and A. Favaro, eds. (Rome, 1896); *Bibliografia Galileiana, Primo Supplemento, 1896–1940,* G. Boffito, ed. (Rome, 1943); "Bibliografia Galileiana, 1940–1964," in *Galileo, Man of Science,* E. McMullin, ed. (New York, 1967); E. Gentili, *Bibliografia Galileiana fra i due centenari* (*1942–1964*) (Varese, 1966).

Selected biographies are A. Banfi, *Galileo Galilei* (Milan, 1948); J. Fahie, *Galileo: His Life and Works* (London, 1903); A. Favaro, *Galileo e lo studio di Padova* (Florence, 1883), and *Galileo Galilei e Suor Maria Celeste* (Florence, 1891); K. von Gebler, *Galileo Galilei and the Roman Curia* (London, 1879), English trans., Mrs. G. Sturge; L. Geymonat, *Galileo Galilei* (Milan, 1957), English trans., S. Drake (New York, 1965); T. Martin, *Galilée* (Paris, 1868); L. Olschki, *Galilei und seine Zeit* (Halle, 1927; repr., Vaduz, 1965); M. Allen-Olney, *The Private Life of Galileo* (London, 1870); P. Paschini, *Vita e opere di Galileo Galilei* (Rome, 1965); F. Reusch, *Der Process Galilei's und die Jesuiten* (Bonn, 1879); G. de Santillana, *The Crime of Galileo* (Chicago, 1955); F. Taylor, *Galileo and the Freedom of Thought* (London, 1938); E. Wohlwill, *Galilei und sein Kampf* (Hamburg–Leipzig, 1909, 1926).

Fundamental to the study of Galileo's scientific work are the publications of A. Favaro listed in G. Favaro, *Bibliografia Galileiana di A. Favaro* (Venice, 1942); A. Koyré, *Études Galiléennes* (Paris, 1939; repr., Paris, 1966); and M. Clavelin, *La philosophie naturelle de Galilée* (Paris, 1968).

Collections of modern Galilean studies include *Nel terzo*

centenario della morte di Galileo Galilei (Milan, 1942); M. Kaplon, ed., *Homage to Galileo* (Cambridge, Mass., 1965); *Nel quarto centenario della nascita di Galileo Galilei* (Milan, 1966); C. Golino, ed., *Galileo Reappraised* (Berkeley, Cal., 1966); *Atti del Symposium Internazionale . . . "Galileo nella storia e nella filosofia della scienza"* (Vinci, 1967); C. Maccagni, ed., *Saggi su Galileo Galilei* (Florence, 1967–); E. McMullin, ed., *Galileo: Man of Science* (New York, 1967); *Galilée, Aspects de sa vie et de son oeuvre,* preface by Suzanne Delorme (Paris, 1968); and S. Drake, *Galileo Studies* (Ann Arbor, Mich., 1970).

Separate articles and monographs are listed in the bibliographies cited above.

STILLMAN DRAKE

GALILEI, VINCENZIO (*b.* Santa Maria a Monte, Italy, *ca.* 1520; *d.* Florence, Italy, July [?] 1591), *music theory, acoustics.*

Vincenzio, father of Galileo Galilei, was of a Florentine patrician family originally surnamed Bonajuti, renamed in the fourteenth century. The son of Michelangelo Galilei and Maddalena di Bergo, he began the study of music at Florence about 1540. After establishing his reputation as a lutenist, he studied at Venice under Gioseffo Zarlino, the foremost music theorist of the time, probably about 1561–1562. On 5 July 1562 Galilei married Giulia Ammannati of Pescia and settled near Pisa. Galileo was the eldest of their seven children.

Through correspondence with Girolamo Mei at Rome during the 1570's, Galilei became interested in ancient Greek music and was encouraged to put to direct experimental test the teachings of Zarlino concerning intonation and tuning. The result was a bitter polemic with Zarlino, who in 1580–1581 appears to have used his influence to oppose the publication of Galilei's principal theoretical work at Venice and its sale there after it was printed at Florence.

Galilei's *Dialogo della musica antica e della moderna* (1581) attacked the prevailing basis of musical theory. This was rooted in the Pythagorean doctrine that the cause of consonance lay in the existence of the "sonorous numbers," two, three, and four, which in their ratios with one another and with unity were considered to produce the only true consonances. A modified tuning given by Ptolemy (the syntonic diatonic) was favored by Zarlino, who rationalized this tuning by extending the sonorous numbers to six. Galilei observed that musical practice did not conform to this (or any other) numerical system based on superparticular ratios (which, expressed as fractions, have numerators exceeding their denominators by unity). He declared that neither the authority of ancient writers nor speculative number theories could be valid against the evidence of the musician's ear. Although he recommended placing frets on lute and viol in the ratio 18:17, he recognized this as merely approximate in obtaining an equally tempered scale suitable for unrestricted modulation, in the direction of which musical practice was rapidly moving.

Renaissance physicists had already recognized the inadequacy of speculative mathematical acoustics. Giovanni Battista Benedetti had questioned the older tunings in letters to Cipriano da Rore, whom Zarlino succeeded as choirmaster at St. Mark's in Venice in 1565. Simon Stevin, in an unpublished treatise on music, advocated the outright abandonment of rational numbers and the division of the scale in true equal temperament based on the twelfth root of two. As mathematics matured, modern harmony replaced polyphony.

Zarlino defended his system based on the number six (the *senario*) in his *Sopplementi musicali,* published at Venice in 1588. His former pupil Galilei was a principal target of attack in this book, although Zarlino did not name him and although Bernardino Baldi, in a short biography of Zarlino, wrongly identified the adversary as Francisco de Salinas. Galilei replied with a spirited polemic, the *Discorso,* published in 1589. In this work he stated the law that a given musical interval between similar strings is produced either by different lengths, or by tensions inversely as the squares of those lengths. Thus the perfect fifth, which is produced by lengths related as 3:2, is also given when weights in the ratio of 4:9 are hung from strings of equal length. This is probably the first mathematical law of physics to have been derived by systematic experimentation, or at any rate the first to replace a universally accepted rival law, for a standard illustration in music books showed the Pythagorean sonorous numbers applying to weights on equal strings as well as to lengths of unequal strings (or air columns).

Galilei employed this experimental result to show that the traditional association of numbers with particular musical intervals was capricious. The musical qualities of intervals had to be determined by the ear, he argued, and mathematics had no authority where the senses were concerned.

Galilei's empirical attitude toward musical theory had an ancient counterpart in Aristoxenus, a prominent pupil of Aristotle's who shared his distrust of Pythagorean numerology. But in the sixteenth century music was again regarded as a branch of mathematics. Galilei's *Discorso* foreshadowed the subordination of mathematics to experience and the discovery of unexpected laws through close observation that was to distinguish science in the seventeenth century from its predecessors. Galilei was driven to experiment in order to refute erroneous entrenched musical theory, as his son Galileo later attacked ancient physical theory. Among the manuscripts inherited by Galileo is Vincenzio Galilei's untitled treatise beginning with the words "L'arte et la pratica del moderno contrapunto . . .," of which Claude Palisca has said: "For prophetic vision, originality, and integrity, it has few equals in the history of music theory."

Galileo gave two separate accounts of his introduction to mathematics, both indicating that his father opposed this introduction. Vincenzio's mathematical skills seem inconsistent with this attitude. His writings, however, reveal a deep hostility toward specious reasoning in practical matters induced by fascination with numerical relations and geometrical designs. It is understandable if he did not want his eldest son to be so beguiled.

BIBLIOGRAPHY

I. Original Works. Galilei's writings, excluding musical compositions, are *Fronimo, Dialogo . . . del intavolare la musica nel liuto* (Venice, 1568; 2nd ed., 1584; facs. ed., Bologna, 1969); *Dialogo della musica antica e della moderna* (Florence, 1581; 2nd ed., 1602; facs. of 1st ed., Rome, 1934; abr. ed. of 1st ed., Milan, 1947); and *Discorso intorno all'opere di messer Gioseffo Zarlino da Chioggia* (Florence, 1589; facs. ed., Milan, 1933). MSS of unpublished works are preserved in the Biblioteca Nazionale, Florence, MSS Galileiani.

An excerpt from Galilei's *Dialogo* of 1581 is translated in O. Strunk, ed., *Source Readings in Music History* (New York, 1950; repr. New York, 1965), vol. II, *The Renaissance Era,* 112–134. The same vol. contains part of a "Discourse on Ancient Music and Good Singing" (pp. 100–111), published as the work of Giovanni Bardi but perhaps written for him by Galilei about 1578.

II. Secondary Literature. The principal biography is Claude Palisca, "V. Galilei," in F. Blume, ed., *Die Musik in Geschichte und Gegenwart,* IV (Kassel–Basel, 1955), cols. 1903–1905, with bibliography to 1950. See also C. Palisca, "Vincenzio Galilei's Counterpoint Treatise: A Code for the *Seconda Pratica,*" in *Journal of the American Musicological Society,* **9** (1956), 81–96; "Scientific Empiricism in Musical Thought," in S. Toulmin and D. Bush, eds., *Seventeenth Century Science and the Arts* (Princeton, 1961), 91–137; "Vincenzio Galilei's Arrangements for Voice and Lute," in G. Reese and R. J. Snow, eds., *Essays in Musicology in Honor of Dragan Plamenac* (Pittsburgh, Pa., 1969), 207–232; and "Ideas of Music and Science," in P. P. Wiener and C. E. Pettie, eds., *Dictionary of the History of Ideas* (New York, in press); and S. Drake, "Renaissance Music and Experimental Science," in *Journal of the History of Ideas,* **31** (1970), 483–500; and "Vincenzio Galilei and Galileo," in *Galileo Studies* (Ann Arbor, Mich., 1970), 43–62.

Stillman Drake

GALITZIN, B. B. See **Golitsyn, B. B.**

GALL, FRANZ JOSEPH (*b.* Tiefenbronn, near Pforzheim, Germany, 9 March 1758; *d.* Paris, France, 22 August 1828), *neuroanatomy, psychology.*

Gall's father, Joseph Anthony Gall, was a modest merchant and sometime mayor of the village of Tiefenbronn. He was of Italian extraction (the original name was Gallo); and both he and his wife, Anna Maria Billingerin, were devout Roman Catholics. They intended Franz for the church; but although he remained nominally religious and even included an organ for religion in his theory of cerebral structure, it cannot be said that he was devout, that he led a morally conventional life, or that his work was well received by the church. His passions for science and gardening were complemented by strong appetites for money and women. He had many mistresses and once mentioned an illegitimate son. Gall's books were placed on the Index; and he was denied a religious burial, even though he claimed that the existence of the "organ of religion" was a new proof for the existence of God.

Gall married a young Alsatian girl surnamed Lieser, who had cared for him when he had typhus; the marriage was an unhappy one. They had no children, but his wife's niece and nephews lived with them at various times. After his wife died at Vienna in 1825, Gall married Marie Anne Barbe, with whom he had had a long-standing relationship. In 1826 signs of cerebral and coronary sclerosis appeared, and he died of an apoplectic stroke two years later.

Gall received his early education from his uncle, who was a priest, and in schools at Baden and Bruchsal. He began to study medicine at Strasbourg in 1777 and married while he was there. In 1781 he moved to Vienna, where he received the M.D. in 1785. In Vienna he carried on an active and successful medical practice which included many eminent patients. When he moved to Paris he was equally successful and numbered Stendhal, Saint-Simon, and Metternich, along with the staffs of twelve embassies, among his patients. On the other hand, he never held an academic post; and his relations with authority and orthodoxy were almost uniformly bad. His lectures at Vienna were proscribed by Emperor Francis I, and Napoleon took steps to restrict his influence in Paris. His doctrines were rejected by the Institut de France in 1808; and in 1821 he failed to gain admission to the Academy, although his candidacy was supported by Étienne Geoffroy Saint-Hilaire.

Gall had a flamboyant personality and was something of a showman. He gave numerous courses of public lectures in Vienna, Paris, and other cities throughout Europe. He was heavily criticized for charging admission to his scientific demonstrations; but he was generous in spending his considerable earnings from this source and from his practice on the pursuit and publication of his research, as well as on his full social life. Gall was as vehement and effective a controversialist as he was a devoted bon vivant. Indeed, his life-style was consistent with his major intellectual preoccupation: the integration of the scientific problems of mind and brain with those of life and society.

The first publication of the principles of his lifework was a treatise on the philosophy of medicine in 1791. Gall developed his views in public lectures and demonstrations in Vienna between 1796 and 1801, when the emperor, in a personal letter, forbade these activities, on the ground that his doctrines were conducive to materialism, immorality, and atheism. Repeated appeals and a long petition and remonstrance to the emperor failed to alter the position. In 1800 Gall had been joined by Johann C. Spurzheim, who served as research assistant and collaborator; and in 1805 they went on an extended and highly successful tour of the intellectual centers of Germany, Switzerland, Holland, and Denmark, visiting schools, hospitals, prisons, and insane asylums to gather evidence and demonstrate their doctrines. Gall also visited his parents during this period; and he and Spurzheim eventually found their way to Paris in November 1807. Gall remained there until his death, except for a brief trip to England in 1823. He became a French citizen in 1819.

Beginning in 1800, with the assistance of Spurzheim, Gall made a number of important neuroanatomical discoveries. Their full significance was not appreciated until the development of histological and neurophysiological findings was integrated with the influence of his theoretical and speculative conceptions many decades after his death. The unifying theme in his neuroanatomical work was the conception of the nervous system as a hierarchically ordered series of separate but interrelated ganglia designed on a unified plan. Higher structures developed from lower ones, receiving reinforcement from other nerve pathways along the way. The gray matter was the matrix of the nerves, and the fibrous white matter served a conducting function. The inclusion of the cerebral cortex in this scheme was an important development away from lingering glandular and humoral conceptions. The spinal cord was, Gall argued, arranged in the same way; and he noticed its segmental structure and successive swellings. He also discovered the origins of the first eight cranial nerves and traced the fibers of the medulla oblongata to the basal ganglia. In the cerebellum he described the systems of fibers now known as projection and commissural. In the cerebral cortex he finally established the contralateral decussation of the pyramids and drew attention to the detailed anatomy of the convolutions.

Gall and Spurzheim's investigations gave considerable impetus to the study of neuroanatomy, and both their findings and their general conceptions proved very important when they were later integrated with an evolutionary view of the nervous system and with the neuron theory. Gall vehemently opposed the contemporary practice of brain dissection by successive slicing and insisted on following the brain's own structural organization. In 1863, when his best-known theories were almost totally discredited, his most effective critic, Pierre Flourens, recalled that when he had first seen Gall dissect a brain, he felt as though he had never seen the organ before; and he called Gall "the author of the true anatomy of the brain."

Gall's conceptions were importantly influenced by the theories of J. G. von Herder and involved strong emphasis on comparative and developmental studies, along with more general themes from *Naturphilosophie,* such as the unity of plan and analogies drawn from botany. In addition to his specific discoveries, Gall's neuroanatomical work helped to alter the context of the study of the brain from the prevailing mechanical and humoral theories to an organic, biological perspective.

Yet it would be almost totally misleading to suggest that Gall's best-known and most influential theories grew inductively out of his neuroanatomical research. On the contrary, he had published the basic principles of his theory of the functions of the brain in 1791: the plurality and independence of the cerebral organs. His public lectures contained sufficiently detailed and provocative findings to lead to their suppression. In 1798 he spelled out the main argument of his major work in a letter to Baron von Retzer. This was two years before he undertook detailed dissections of the central nervous system, work which he did as a consequence of his general doctrines.

Nor can it be argued that Gall's neuroanatomical findings led to important elaborations or modifications of his general doctrines. It was pointed out by a commission of the Institut de France, including such eminent scientists as J. R. Tenon, Antoine Portal, R. B. Sabatier, Philippe Pinel, and Georges Cuvier, that the two aspects of his work were not inconsistent—but neither were they closely integrated. The commission sought to separate the two aspects of Gall's work for philosophical reasons; but it was, nevertheless, correct in its evaluation of the relationship between them. The conception of the nervous system as a series of relatively independent ganglia was common to both, but neither aspect was based on the other. Gall granted that any doctrine of the functions of the brain which was incompatible with its structure must necessarily be false. Nevertheless, the fundamental principle of his lifework was that it was essential that the issue be approached from the other side. He said that the knowledge of the functions had always preceded that of the parts and that all his physiological discoveries had been made without the anatomy of the brain; these discoveries might have existed for ages without their agreement with the organization of the brain having been detected. The commission was striking at the heart of Gall's doctrine by refusing, in principle, to consider the relationship between structure and function; but he and Spurzheim had presented no compelling evidence of that relationship.

Gall's theory of the functions of the brain and each of its parts calls for careful historical treatment, since the important features of his work and his influence are bounded on all sides by what are now seen as undoubted absurdities, although this was not at all clear in the context of contemporary science. With one notable exception, none of his localizations of cortical functions has been substantiated by subsequent research. The detailed methodology on which he based his physiological conclusions provides an excellent case study of the dangers of anecdotal and correlative methods, uncontrolled by statistical tests and attempts to seek out potentially falsifying evidence. Finally, the popular application of his theories in the form of phrenology soon came to be seen as a classic example of pseudoscience and its practice a form of quackery.

Yet those who would attempt sharply to demarcate science from pseudoscience and the internal history of science from external factors would stumble as badly over Gall's work as they have over Robert Chambers' and Herbert Spencer's. Embedded in his crude methodology and his detailed, although wholly incorrect, findings were a set of principles and a biological, adaptive, and functional approach to the study of mind and brain which have led to the recognition of his work as seminal in three spheres: (1) the origination of the modern doctrine of cerebral localization of functions, (2) the establishment of psychology as biological science, and (3), at a more general level, the use of his work and its popularizations as the vehicle for a naturalistic approach to the study of man which was very influential in the development of evolutionary theory, physical anthropology, and sociology. These points should be borne in mind when considering the curious amalgam which makes up Gall's systematic writings.

His psychophysiology had its origins in childhood experiences. As a schoolboy he noticed that those who were better than he at memorizing had "large flaring eyes." It was a popular contemporary doctrine that all aspects of character had external signs, and the initial theoretical context for his ideas was therefore a straightforward physiognomical correlation of the kind which J. C. Lavater had made popular—it had no detailed causal basis. When Gall later noticed the same correlation among his fellow medical students, he reflected on a possible physiological basis for it. Every physiological function had its own organ, as did each of the five external senses. Why should it not be the same with the talents and propensities of men? If this could be established, a doctrine of the nature of man could be founded on a doctrine of the functional organization of the brain. Localization of cerebral functions was also a long-held idea with contemporary exponents, but neither the functions nor their localizations were being actively studied in detail; Gall set out to till an existing, although fallow, field.

He immediately found himself faced with a number of conceptual boundary disputes; and in attempting to work out a consistent theory he had to address himself to fundamental problems in the borderlands of ontology, epistemology, psychology, physiology, and general biology. These issues lie unresolved at the heart of the assumptions of modern science and its philosophy of nature: mind and body, primary and secondary qualities. Gall pioneered the hope that the problems of a dualistic ontology and epistemology could be resolved by taking a biological point of view. The most fundamental result of his work stems, therefore, from the way he asked the question. He treated the problem of brain and mind analogously to that of any other organ and its function, thereby bringing the mind-body problem into the domain of dynamic physiology and biology. If one traces the concept of "function" as applied to psychological and social phenomena back from its late-nineteenth and twentieth-century uses, one finds its source in the writings of Gall and his followers.

This is not to say that Gall was original in arguing that the brain is the organ of the mind or that mental phenomena should be treated as analogous to physiological function. As he pointed out in his petition to Francis I, the conception of the brain as the organ of mind had been reiterated since the beginnings of anatomy and physiology. In Gall's own period the *idéologues* had treated mental phenomena in physiological terms, but it was Gall who united these conceptions and treated them in consistently biological terms. He argued that the sensationalism of Étienne Condillac and the *idéologues,* especially P. J. G. Cabanis and A. L. C. Destutt de Tracy, could not account for the observed differences between the talents and propensities of individuals and those between species. The origins of character and personality could not be adequately explained by experience alone. Gall claimed that the causes of the behavior of men and animals were innate, although modifiable by experience. Sensationalist psychology had been elaborated in opposition to idealist belief in innate ideas, but Gall was not treating the problem from a primarily epistemological point of view. He saw the talents and propensities as inherited instincts based on cerebral endowment.

Gall's organic conception was also opposed to the related doctrine of Charles Bonnet, that sensationalism could be related in mechanical terms to the fibrous connections in the nervous system. Thus, Gall rejected both sensationalism and its putative cerebral basis. Instead of synthesizing complex mental phenomena from simple ones by the mechanism of the association of ideas connected in the fibers of the nervous system, Gall argued for unitary faculties based on cerebral ganglia which served as centers for each determinate talent or propensity. Of course, his faculty psychology raised at least as many problems as it solved, but there seemed to be more hope of solving them in a biological context which was relatively free from attempts to interpret mental phenomena by analogy to the concepts of corpuscular physics.

Gall was interested not only in the intellectual functions but also in the passions, and it was not generally conceded that the latter had their seat in the brain. For example, the eminent physiologists Cabanis and Xavier Bichat still claimed that the passions had their seat in the thorax and abdomen. Gall claimed that the brain was the organ of all mental functions. As a result of his systematic investigations and his consistent reiteration of this claim, he succeeded in gaining final acceptance for the principle. Once again, it was Flourens who granted that although the proposition that the brain was the exclusive organ of the mind existed in science before Gall appeared, it was as a result of his work that it reigned in science by the middle of the nineteenth century.

Even more important was Gall's insistence that neither the faculties nor their localizations in the brain were known and that they had to be determined by empirical, naturalistic studies of men in society and of other species in nature. The prevailing categories of psychological analysis were derived from philosophical—especially epistemological—preoccupations: reason, memory, imagination, perception, and so on. These were concerned with the attributes of mind in general, not with a differential psychology which could account for individual and species differences. Gall called for faculties, the different distributions of which determine the behavior of different species of animals, and the different proportions of which explain individual human differences. The result of the application of this principle was the origination of the systematic empirical search for a natural classification of fundamental variables in animal and human nature and personality. When Alexander Bain turned to this issue again in 1861, he described phrenology as the only system of character hitherto elaborated; and subsequent research in personality theory, as well as comparative psychology, can be traced, in large part, to Gall's direct or indirect influence. Although the issues remain unresolved—and can be argued to have no unique scientific resolution—it was Gall who raised them in their modern form.

In his attempt to arrive at a list of determinate faculties, Gall sought out people who showed extremes of talents or other striking propensities, including manias. He related these to the behavior of animals; and although his analogies are often extremely far-fetched, his approach extended the comparative method to psychology in a systematic way. His extensive case records from insane asylums, prisons, schools, and public life were supplemented by large collections of craniums and plaster casts, the last of which was bought by the French government and deposited in the Musée de l'Homme. Gall concluded that men and animals shared nineteen of the twenty-seven fundamental faculties.

The results of his work were published at his own expense in four quarto volumes and an atlas of 1,000 plates as *Anatomie et physiologie du système nerveux en général, et du cerveau en particulier, avec des observations sur la possibilité de reconnoitre plusieurs dispositions intellectuelles et morales de l'homme et des animaux, par la configuration de leurs têtes* between 1810 and 1819. (Spurzheim was coauthor of the first two volumes, but they parted company after that.) An inexpensive edition appeared between 1822 and 1825 as *Sur les fonctions du cerveau et sur celle de chacune de ses parties;* the atlas was omitted and a volume of replies to his critics was added. Gall summarized his theory in four fundamental suppositions: (1) that the moral and intellectual faculties are innate; (2) that their exercise or manifestation depends on organization; (3) that the brain is the organ of all the propensities, sentiments, and faculties; (4) that the brain is composed of as many particular organs as there are propensities, sentiments, and faculties which differ essentially from each other. The Achilles heel of the elaboration of these suppositions—the "special organology"—was a set of related beliefs: that the activity of a given organ varies with its size, that all of the cerebral organs impinge on bony structures of the cranium, and that in most cases the cranium faithfully reflects the conformation of the underlying cerebrum. The result of these subsidiary beliefs was the pseudoscience of cranioscopy, later popularized as phrenology—the reading of character from the conformation of the skull. During the nineteenth century this progressively became an object of ridicule; and although there are still practitioners of phrenological delineation, its critics have obscured Gall's more important contributions.

Gall was cautious—but not cautious enough—about making inferences to the brain from the study of the skull. In practice, most of his faculties were discovered by correlating a striking talent, propensity, or passion with prominences on the skulls of men and animals. From this evidence he went on to infer the existence of an innate faculty and a cortical organ. Having formulated a hypothesis about a given faculty, he collected a great deal of evidence to confirm his correlations. This was done uncritically; and although the theoretical aspects of his systematic edifice have passed into the foundations of the assumptions of modern psychology, neurophysiology, biology, and social theory, the structure itself has not stood. Gall made no claim to finality for his list of faculties or for precision in his cerebral localizations. He considered the detailed working out of the system to be a problem for the future. In any case, he was more interested in the nature of the functions than in their localizations. His opponents rejected the entire basis of his work, while his followers prematurely codified his system.

Neither Gall's detailed classification nor his faculty psychology have appealed to subsequent investigators. However, the questions which he asked have remained leading topics in neurology, psychology, and ethology. Thus, for example, his localization of sexual passion in the cerebellum has been totally discredited by experimental findings; but the study of the neurophysiological basis of sexual and other emotional functions plays a leading part in current research in physiological psychology. Similarly, although it was set aside for over a century, his insistence that the study of the organization of the brain should march side by side with that of its functions is once again the basic principle of biological psychology. Whatever the judgment of Gall's contemporaries, the organ-function paradigm which he elaborated for the study of man in society has become the predominant approach.

The reception of Gall's doctrines and his influence are as confusing and complex as would be expected from the intimate mixture of important principles, methodological crudity, and detailed nonsense which made up his work. There was vehement and sustained opposition from those who saw his theories leading to materialism, immorality, fatalism, and atheism. His division of the mind and its organ into separate compartments was anathema to those who followed Descartes in claiming that the mind is indivisible. At the other extreme, sensationalists opposed his faculty psychology and his belief in innate instincts. Physiologists who were beginning to find experimental support for the interpretation of the nervous system in sensory-motor terms could not, in principle, find any basis for Gall's conception of the fundamental faculties. These promising findings began to be made only in 1822; and Gall criticized both the methods and the generalizations of experimental neurophysiology, arguing that they would lead to the reduction of life and character to sensibility, motion, and association. He was quite prescient in arguing that those who took this approach would fail to address themselves to fundamental human problems.

Gall was preoccupied with the psychological question "What are the functions of the brain?" while the experimentalists were concerned with the narrower—but scientifically more fruitful—question of how the brain functions. Since 1822, the approaches of experimental neurophysiology and of personality psychology have diverged, and efforts to relate them have not been notably successful. As the experimental tradition developed, it lost sight of the significance of Gall's questions and concentrated on the localization of sensory, motor, and associative functions, with little thought about how they were to be related to the concepts of the layman, thereby reverting to the analytic categories which Gall had set aside at the beginning of his inquiries. The model of the elements of mind as analogous to corpuscular physics prevailed over the holistic characterological approach.

There were many devotees of Gall's special organology and his cranioscopic method, especially in France, Britain, and America. Societies with eminent medical and scientific members sprang up and were immensely popular in France and Britain until the 1840's and even later in America. Although their influence is not significant for the history of science in the narrow sense, failure to appreciate the importance of popular phrenology would blind one to the most important vehicle of scientific naturalism in the decades before evolutionary theory assumed this role. The list of eminent political, philosophical, and literary figures who took it seriously is astonishing and includes G. W. F. Hegel, Otto von Bismarck, Marx,

Balzac, the Brontës, George Eliot, President James Garfield, Walt Whitman, and Queen Victoria. Its leading popularizers were Spurzheim and George Combe; and it has been said that homes in Britain which contained only three books would have the Bible, Bunyan's *Pilgrim's Progress,* and Combe's *System of Phrenology.* The particular influence of phrenology can be traced in the writings of educationalists, advocates of public health, penal reform, and improvements in the care of the insane, as well as in the scientific writings of Auguste Comte, G. H. Lewes, Spencer, Chambers, and A. R. Wallace. The adaptive, biological view of man and mind was carried by phrenology into the formulation of theories of evolution and into the use of biological analogies in theories of society. This is most striking in psychology, where Gall was the main figure in altering the context of the study of mind from that of epistemology to that of general biology.

More straightforward scientific influences can be traced in physical anthropology—especially its preoccupation with skulls throughout the nineteenth century—and in somatist psychiatry's fundamental belief that all mental disease is brain disease. Of course, the most obvious influence of Gall's work lay in neurology and neurophysiology. Beginning in 1861 with Paul Broca's clinicopathologic localization of the lesion causing aphasia in the place where Gall had localized the faculty of "memory for words," localization of function has been the central conception in neurology, as it later became in neurosurgery. Once again, Gall's specific concepts were set aside, while his general principles were adopted. The same can be said of the localization of functions in experimental neurophysiology, which began in 1870 with the work of Gustav Fritsch and Eduard Hitzig and was carried on by workers in France, Germany, Italy, Britain, and America. This tradition was called, only half jokingly, "the new phrenology" by C. S. Sherrington, who claimed that all students of the correlations of brain, mind, and behavior are phrenologists of sorts.

In 1857, as Gall's reputation was waning, G. H. Lewes wrote a history of the development of thought on positivist lines. Although he was critical of Gall's detailed findings, he said that by placing man firmly in nature, Gall had rescued the problem of mental functions from metaphysics and made it one of biology. Gall's vision of psychology as a biological science may be said, he concluded, to have given the science its basis. Auguste Comte and Herbert Spencer, the founders of modern sociology, also acknowledged Gall's fundamental contribution to their views on man and society. His theory played an important role in the evolutionary theories of Robert Chambers, Spencer, and A. R. Wallace, the last of whom considered the neglect of phrenology as one of the greatest failures of nineteenth-century thought. But in rejecting the details of his work, modern science, and its twin brother scientism, embraced Gall's principles and his point of view, as a result of which he can be said to have made a central contribution to scientific naturalism in the biological and human sciences. Along with astrology, alchemy, Hermetism, mesmerism, and spiritualism, Gall's science and its manifold influence challenge any attempt to establish neat demarcations between the origins, the substance, the applications, and the validity of scientific ideas in their philosophical, theological, and social contexts.

BIBLIOGRAPHY

I. Original Works. Gall's writings include *Philosophisch-medicinische Untersuchungen über Natur und Kunst im kranken und gesunden Zustande des Menschen* (Vienna, 1791); *Recherches sur le système nerveux en général, et sur celui du cerveau en particulier; mémoire présenté à l'Institut de France, le 14 mars 1808; suivi d'observations sur le rapport qui en a été fait à cette compagnie par les commissaires* (Paris, 1809), written with Spurzheim; *Anatomie et physiologie du système nerveux* (see text for full title), 4 vols. and atlas (Paris, 1810–1819); *Sur les fonctions du cerveau et sur celles de chacune de ses parties,* 6 vols. (Paris, 1822–1825), English trans. by W. Lewis, Jr., with a biography including the letter to Baron von Retzer, 6 vols. (Boston, 1835); and Gall *et al., On the Functions of the Cerebellum by Drs Gall, Vimont and Broussais,* English trans. by G. Combe, including Gall's petition and remonstrance to Emperor Francis I (Edinburgh, 1838). Gall's letters have been published in M. Neuburger, "Briefe Galls an Andreas und Nanette Streicher," in *Archiv für Geschichte der Medizin,* **10** (1917), 3–70; and E. Ebstein, "Franz Joseph Gall im Kampf um seine Lehre," in C. Singer and H. E. Sigerist, eds., *Essays on the History of Medicine Presented to Karl Sudhoff* (London–Zurich, 1924), pp. 269–322.

II. Secondary Literature. The best single source is O. Temkin, "Gall and the Phrenological Movement," in *Bulletin of the History of Medicine,* **21** (1947), 275–321. See also the unsigned "Researches of Malcarne and Reil—Present State of Cerebral Anatomy," in *Edinburgh Medical and Surgical Journal,* **21** (1824), 98–141; and "Recent Discoveries on the Physiology of the Nervous System," *ibid.,* 141–159; A. Bain, *On the Study of Character, Including an Estimate of Phrenology* (London, 1861); M. Bentley, "The Psychological Antecedents of Phrenology," in *Psychological Monographs,* **21,** 4, no. 92 (1916), 102–115; C. Blondel, *La psycho-physiologie de Gall* (Paris, 1914); [R. Chevenix], "Gall and Spurzheim—Phrenology," in *Foreign Quarterly Review,* **2** (1828), 1–59; G. von Bonin, *Some Papers on the Cerebral Cortex* (Springfield,

Ill., 1960), which includes the papers of Broca and of Fritsch and Hitzig on cerebral localization; K. M. Dallenbach, "The History and Derivation of the Word 'Function' as a Systematic Term in Psychology," in *American Journal of Psychology,* **26** (1915), 473–484; P. Flourens, *Examen de la phrénologie* (Paris, 1842), English trans. by C. de L. Meigs (Philadelphia, 1846); and *De la phrénologie et des études vraies sur le cerveau* (Paris, 1863); [J. Gordon], "Functions of the Nervous System," in *Edinburgh Review,* **24** (1815), 439–452; H. Head, *Aphasia and Kindred Disorders of Speech,* 2 vols. (Cambridge, 1926); C. W. Hufeland, *Dr. Gall's New Theory of Physiognomy* (London, 1807); J. Hunt, "On the Localisation of Functions in the Brain, With Special Reference to the Faculty of Language," in *Anthropological Review,* **6** (1868), 329–345, and **7** (1869), 100–116, 201–214; T. Laycock, "Phrenology," in *Encyclopaedia Britannica,* 8th ed. (1859), XVII, 556–567; G. H. Lewes, "Phrenology in France," in *Blackwood's Edinburgh Magazine,* **82** (1857), 665–674; and *The History of Philosophy From Thales to Comte,* 3rd ed., 2 vols. (London, 1867–1871); A. Macalister, "Phrenology," in *Encyclopaedia Britannica,* 9th ed. (1885), XVIII, 842–849; C. S. Sherrington, "Sir David Ferrier, 1843–1928," in *Proceedings of the Royal Society,* **103B** (1928), viii–xvi; J. Soury, *Le système nerveux central* (Paris, 1899); H. Spencer, *Principles of Psychology* (London, 1855); J. R. Tenon *et al.,* "Report on a Memoir of Drs Gall and Spurzheim, Relative to the Anatomy of the Brain, Presented to and Adopted by the Class of Mathematical and Physical Sciences of the National Institute," in *Edinburgh Medical and Surgical Journal,* **5** (1809), 36–66; A. R. Wallace, *The Wonderful Century, Its Successes and Failures* (London, 1898); and S. Wilks, "Notes on the History of the Physiology of the Nervous System, Taken More Especially From Writers on Phrenology," in *Guy's Hospital Reports,* 3rd ser., **24** (1879), 57–94.

On the context of sensationalism and sensory-motor physiology, see O. Temkin, "The Philosophical Background of Magendie's Physiology," in *Bulletin of the History of Medicine,* **20** (1946), 10–35; on Gall's neuroanatomy, see Temkin's "Remarks on the Neurology of Gall and Spurzheim," in E. A. Underwood, ed., *Science, Medicine and History, Essays in Honor of Charles Singer,* 2 vols. (London, 1953), II, 282–289. See also E. H. Ackerknecht and H. V. Vallois, *Franz Joseph Gall, Inventor of Phrenology, and His Collection* (Madison, Wis., 1956); J. C. Greene, "Biology and Social Theory in the Nineteenth Century: Auguste Comte and Herbert Spencer," in M. Clagett, ed., *Critical Problems in the History of Science* (Madison, Wis., 1959); G. Jefferson, *Selected Papers* (London, 1960); E. Lesky, "Structure and Function in Gall," in *Bulletin of the History of Medicine,* **44** (1970), 297–314; W. Reise and E. C. Hoff, "A History of the Doctrine of Cerebral Localization," in *Journal of the History of Medicine,* **5** (1950), 51–71, and **6** (1951), 439–470; R. M. Young, "The Functions of the Brain: Gall to Ferrier (1808–1886)," in *Isis,* **59** (1968), 251–268; and *Mind, Brain and Adaptation in the Nineteenth Century: Cerebral Localization and Its Biological Context From Gall to Ferrier* (Oxford, 1970); and O. L. Zangwill, "The Cerebral Localization of Psychological Functions," in *Advancement of Science,* **20** (1963–1964), 335–344.

ROBERT M. YOUNG

GALLE, JOHANN GOTTFRIED (*b.* Pabsthaus, near Gräfenhainichen, Germany, 9 June 1812; *d.* Potsdam, Germany, 10 July 1910), *astronomy.*

Galle was the son of J. Gottfried Galle and Henriette Pannier. He was born in an isolated house on the Dübener Heide, a wooded heath between the Elbe and the Mulde, where his father was manager of a tar distillery. He attended school at Radis, his mother's birthplace. There the local clergyman prepared both one of his own sons and Galle for the secondary school at Wittenberg.

Galle was at Wittenberg from April 1825 until April 1830, when he went to study in Berlin. His teachers there included Hegel, Dirichlet, Dirksen, Dove, Ideler, and—most important—Encke, who was to be highly influential in his later career. In 1833 Galle was granted the *facultas docendi* to teach mathematics and physics at the Gymnasium level. He spent the required probationary year teaching at Guben and Berlin, where he was made assistant teacher at the Friedrich-Werder Gymnasium in March 1834. While he was teaching in secondary school, Galle kept in touch with Encke; and in 1835 Encke, who had become director of the Berlin Observatory (and had had it newly rebuilt to his own specifications), had Galle appointed to an assistantship that had been created especially for him.

Galle spent the next sixteen years at the observatory, where his duties concerned him largely with astrometry. He became in addition an avid observer of comets, including Halley's comet in its appearance of 1835 (he was to live to see it again in 1910); the comet newly discovered by Boguslavsky; and Encke's comet. In 1839 and 1840 Galle himself discovered, in quick succession, three new comets, and thus attracted the attention of experts in the field as well as royal recognition.

In 1836 Alexander von Humboldt invited Galle to participate in the computation of the astronomical material that he had collected during his journeys and thereby initiated a professional association that was to last fifteen years. During this same period, Galle again attended Encke's lectures in order to further his theoretical knowledge, and Encke entrusted him with further computational work involving the minor planets, especially Pallas, which he had previously observed. In about 1839 Galle began to compute the ephemerides of this planet for the *Berliner astronomisches Jahrbuch;* he continued these calculations for thirty years. He made other computations of the elements and ephemerides of comets, including two of those that he had discovered. In 1838 he observed the crepe ring of Saturn, although he did not publish this discovery.

Having continued his theoretical studies, Galle wished to obtain the doctorate. The government gave him financial aid and he received the degree on 1 March 1845. His thesis, *Olai Roemeri triduum observationum astronomicarum,* was based upon unanalyzed data from three days of exceptionally good meridian observations made by the Danish astronomer in 1706. (Except for these three days, the contents of Roemer's other valuable observations had been destroyed by fire.) Galle sent a copy of this thesis to Le Verrier, to whom he thought Roemer's observations would be of value.

Le Verrier did not immediately acknowledge the receipt of Galle's work, but when he did he also informed Galle of the presumed position of a planet beyond Uranus whose orbit he had computed from the perturbations of Uranus' motion. He encouraged Galle to look for this planet, since he thought the telescopes available to him at the Paris observatory inadequate to this purpose. Galle began to look for the planet the same evening that he received Le Verrier's letter; on 23 September 1846 he and d'Arrest, who was at that time studying in Berlin, searched the region cited, but without success. Galle had made no special preparations for his search, since the diameter given by Le Verrier seemed to be sufficient for recognizing the planet as such. Additional data were necessary, however; fortunately the *Berliner akademische Sternkarten* were being readied for publication and the chart covering the area of observation had just been printed. The chart was not yet available commercially, but Encke had a copy. Galle borrowed it, and described what happened next:

> Returning with the chart to the telescope I discovered a star of the eighth magnitude—not at first glance, to tell the truth, but after several comparisons. Its absence from the chart was so obvious that we had to try to observe it. Encke, who had been informed of all the details, took part in the observation on the same night. We observed the star until early morning; but, despite all duplications of effort, we did not succeed in discerning a definite motion, although a trace of change in the required sense seemed to occur. Full of excitement, we had to wait for the evening of 24 September, when our research was also favored by the weather and when the existence of the planet was proved [*Astronomische Nachrichten,* **89** (1877), 349–352].

The planet was at first called "Le Verrier's planet," but its name was shortly thereafter changed to Neptune. The location of the hypothetical planet had been computed simultaneously by Le Verrier and by John Couch Adams, working at Cambridge. The Cambridge astronomers were not able to find the planet and a long controversy arose concerning the priority of its computation. The possession of the new *Sternkarten* was of great advantage to the observers in Berlin; it was in all probability Arago, a close friend of Humboldt's, who knew of the chart and suggested to Le Verrier that help might be available. Both Le Verrier and Adams were aware that the time to search for the planet was ripe, despite the uncertainties inherent in their computations; possible errors in calculating both the mass and the distance of the undiscovered body disturbing Uranus would only be magnified at a later date. (It is interesting to note that Galle found Neptune less than one degree from where Le Verrier predicted it would be.)

Following the discovery of Neptune, Galle contributed observations and computations of a provisional circular orbit toward the further tracking of the planet. His modesty prevented him from capitalizing on his discovery, and it was Encke who reported in detail on it to the Berlin Academy and in the *Astronomische Nachrichten* (of which volume **23** contains several articles on Neptune, including some account of the theoretical work that preceded its discovery). Galle's achievement was nevertheless widely hailed.

Galle continued to work in Berlin as Encke's assistant—he was even referred to as his teacher's mirror image. (Encke's influence, indeed, is to be seen throughout Galle's lifework.) Among other projects, Galle made numerous distance measurements of double stars and, in 1847, published a supplement to the new edition of Olbers' *Abhandlungen . . . die Bahn eines Kometen zu berechnen,* a list of all comet orbits computed up to that time, with important emendations and references to the literature.

In June 1851 Boguslavsky died at Breslau and Galle was offered the post of director of the observatory and professor of the university there. It was not easy for him to decide to leave the well-equipped Berlin Observatory for a small, almost obsolete observatory situated in the very center of the provincial town, but he accepted the opportunity to do independent work. Galle stayed at Breslau for forty-six years; in 1874–1875 he performed the duties of rector of the university. He taught all aspects of astronometry and meteorology, but devoted much of his classroom activity (as well as his research) to studies of comets and planetoids. He was a vivid lecturer and attracted large audiences—as many as sixty auditors are recorded at one time.

The primitive equipment available at the Breslau

observatory did not permit Galle to do any pioneer work. He did, however, often participate in astronomical-geodetical tasks for the Europäische Gradmessung; as late as 1885 and 1888, he took part in the determinations of longitude between Berlin and Breslau. He also continued to observe comets, although he was mainly concerned with meteors, a continuation of his work in Berlin. He had already found that there is a relationship between the meteor showers recorded over the centuries and the appearance of comets.

Galle therefore tried to compute the orbit of the Lyrid meteor shower around the sun and to demonstrate its connection with comet 1861 I, discovered by Biela. He proved that meteors were to be expected to attend the descending node of the comet's orbit; his theoretical assumptions were confirmed by a great number of shooting stars as predicted on the night of 28 November 1872, establishing the relation between meteor showers and the decomposition of a parent comet. Galle continued these investigations, examining a variety of significant meteor appearances and computing the cosmic orbits of such meteors, which he classified as often hyperbolic.

It is known from a notice in a newspaper that at this time Galle was also considering the possible existence of a planet between Mercury and the sun, a hypothesis repeatedly put forth by Le Verrier. He seems to have dismissed its likelihood, however, reasoning that such a planet of any notable magnitude would be visible during total solar eclipses or on other occasions. He also, in 1864, issued a new edition of Olbers' *Abhandlungen,* this time including the orbits of 231 comets (in a supplement of 1885, he increased the number to 286).

Galle's interest in the minor planets led him to propose in 1872 that corresponding data on these bodies, observed at a close approach to the earth, be used to determine the solar parallax. The oppositions of Mars and lower conjunctions of Venus, particularly its passages in front of the sun's disk, had already been observed with this objective; but Galle, who was widely experienced in the observation of the larger planets, correctly stressed that observations of the planetoids should be free from systematic errors. Galle corresponded extensively with astronomers of leading observatories (particularly those in the southern hemisphere) on this proposal; his suggestions were adopted and a series of simultaneous observations of Flora were made. These showed close agreement with the values derived by Simon Newcomb from other measurements. Galle took active part in these observations; he also witnessed the great advance in the method he had designed that resulted from the discovery of the planetoid Eros, although he did not participate in the discovery itself.

As did many of his fellow astronomers, Galle made regular meteorological observations or had them made for him. As conditions for astronomical observations became worse at the Breslau observatory, he placed increasing emphasis on meteorological and even geomagnetic measurements. He conducted the latter from 1869 to 1897; these were considerably impaired, however, by the construction of a streetcar line near the university, started in 1893. Through these abortive observations Galle wished to examine the magnetism of the earth in relation to "northern lights and other terrestrial and even cosmic conditions." He also published a series of papers on climatology and weather forecasting; he was convinced that accurate scientific forecasting had not yet become feasible. Further works that he published late in his life touched upon several minor matters in a variety of fields.

In 1857 Galle married C. E. M. Regenbrecht, the daughter of a professor from Breslau. She died in 1887. They had two sons, one of whom, Andreas, was for many years an astronomer and geodesist at Potsdam. Throughout his long life Galle received numerous honors, especially memberships in scientific societies all over the world. He attained the age of ninety-eight in good physical and mental health and exerted a great influence on several generations of German astronomers. In his eulogy of Galle, W. Foerster accurately summarized his pedagogical career: "Without the men trained in theory and computation at the Breslau school . . ., it would not have been possible to cope with the enormous amount of computational work that resulted in the last fifty years from the discovery of more than half a thousand small planets between the orbits of Mars and Jupiter."

BIBLIOGRAPHY

I. ORIGINAL WORKS. Poggendorff lists Galle's major works. Many of his most important papers were published in *Astronomische Nachrichten;* these include "Einige Messungen des Durchmessers des Saturns," in *Astronomische Nachrichten,* **32** (1851), 187–190; "Über den mutmasslichen Zusammenhang der periodischen Sternschnuppen des 24 April mit dem 1. Kometen des Jahres 1861," *ibid.,* **69** (1867), 33–36; "Sternschnuppenbeobachtungen in Breslau 27 Nov. 1872," *ibid.,* **80** (1873), 279–282; "Über die Berechnung der Bahnen heller und an vielen Orten beobachteter Meteore," *ibid.,* **83** (1874), 21–50; and "Nachtrag zu den in Band 23 der Astronomischen Nachrichten gegebenen Berichten über die erste Auffindung des Planeten Neptun," *ibid.,* **89** (1877), 349–352.

Individual works include *Grundzüge der schlesischen Klimatologie* (Breslau, 1857); *Über die Verbesserung der Planetenelemente* (Breslau, 1858); *Über eine Bestimmung der Sonnenparallaxe aus korrespondierenden Beobachtungen des Planeten Flora* (Breslau, 1875); and *Mitteilungen der Königlichen Universitäts-Sternwarte Breslau über hier bisher gewonnene Resultate für die geographischen und klimatologischen Ortsverhältnisse* (Breslau, 1879).

II. SECONDARY LITERATURE. Works on Galle and his work are W. Foerster, "J. G. Galle," in *Vierteljahrsschrift der Astronomischen Gesellschaft,* **46** (1911), 17–22; and D. Wattenberg, *J. G. Galle* (Leipzig, 1963).

H. C. FREIESLEBEN

GALLOIS, JEAN (*b.* Paris, France, 11 June 1632; *d.* Paris, 19 April 1707), *history of science.*

The son of a counsel to the Parlement of Paris, Gallois seems to have distinguished himself in that city around 1664 by the breadth of his learning, by his knowledge of Hebrew and of both living and classical languages, by his interest in the sciences, and by a genuine literary talent. Today his name is associated with the famous *Journal des sçavans.* He collaborated with its founder, Denys de Sallo, from January to April 1665, during the brief period in which the new publication provoked the violent polemics that led to its suspension; and it was to him that Colbert assigned its resumption. Gallois made the periodical a success, publishing forty-two issues as sole editor, beginning in 1666. The Académie Royale des Sciences, established that year, found a vehicle of expression in the *Journal;* yet, despite its support, the number of issues published decreased to sixteen in 1667 and to thirteen in 1668. Named a member of the Academy in 1667, Gallois temporarily assumed the duties of the perpetual secretary, Jean Baptiste Duhamel, who was on a diplomatic mission to England. The *Journal des sçavans* continued to appear under Gallois's editorship, but with steadily decreasing frequency.

Gallois entered the Académie Française in 1673 and in 1675 turned over the editorship of the *Journal* to the Abbé Jean-Paul de La Roque, although he became involved with the *Journal* again in 1684. Meanwhile, the death of his patron Colbert had led him to seek the position of custodian of the Royal Library. A few years later he was appointed professor of Greek at the Collège Royal. His name is mentioned in conjunction with various publications planned by the Académie Royale des Sciences, especially in 1692–1693. Starting in this period Gallois became an opponent of the introduction of infinitesimal methods in mathematics.

With the reorganization of the Académie Royale des Sciences in 1699 Gallois was made pensionary geometer with Michel Rolle and Pierre Varignon. He stated his intention of publishing a critical translation of Pappus, but nothing came of this project. Instead, he stimulated the quarrel between his two colleagues concerning differential calculus and impeded its settlement until 1706.

Despite this negative attitude, the consequences of which might have been disastrous, Gallois deserves recognition by historians of science for his activities as a publicist. Although he wrote somewhat fancifully and with little concern for coherence, he was of service in his time as a disseminator of ideas and his work is still valuable as an historical source.

BIBLIOGRAPHY

I. ORIGINAL WORKS. Gallois's translations and other works include *Traduction latine du traité de paix des Pyrénées* (Paris, 1659); *Breviarum Colbertinum* (Paris, 1679); "Extrait du livre intitulé: Observations physiques et mathématiques envoyées des Indes et de la Chine . . . par les P. P. Jésuites . . . à Paris . . . par l'abbé Galloys," in *Mémoires de mathématiques et de physique tirés des registres de l'Académie royale des sciences* (31 July 1692), pp. 113–120; "Extrait d'un écrit composé par Dom François Quesnet, religieux bénédictin, et envoyé à l'Académie royale des sciences, touchant les effets extraordinaires d'un écho," *ibid.* (30 Nov. 1692), pp. 158–160; "Extrait du livre intitulé: Divers ouvrages de mathématiques et de physique par messieurs de l'Académie royale des sciences," *ibid.* (30 Apr. 1693), pp. 49–64; and "Réponse à l'écrit de David Gregory touchant les lignes appelées Robervalliennes qui servent à transformer les figures," in *Mémoires de l'Académie royale des sciences pour l'année 1703* (Paris, 1705), pp. 70–77.

Many accounts of sessions are in the MS registers of *Procès-verbaux des séances de l'Académie royale des sciences* (1668–1699), *passim.* Correspondence with Leibniz is Hannover, LBr 295, 35 fol.

II. SECONDARY LITERATURE. See Denis-François Camusat, *Histoire critique des journaux* (Amsterdam, 1734), pp. 214–310; Bernard de Fontenelle, "Éloge de M^r^ l'abbé Gallois," in *Histoire et mémoires de l'Académie royale des sciences pour l'année 1707;* and "Bibliographie de Jean Galloys," in *Histoire de l'Académie royale des sciences depuis 1666 jusqu'à son renouvellement en 1699,* II (Paris, 1733), p. 360.

PIERRE COSTABEL

GALOIS, EVARISTE (*b.* Bourg-la-Reine, near Paris, France, 25 October 1811; *d.* Paris, 31 May 1832), *mathematics.*

There have been few mathematicians with personalities as engaging as that of Galois, who died at the age of twenty years and seven months from wounds received in a mysterious duel. He left a body of work—for the most part published posthumously—of less than 100 pages, the astonishing richness of which was revealed in the second half of the nineteenth century. Far from being a cloistered scholar, this extraordinarily precocious and exceptionally profound genius had an extremely tormented life. A militant republican, driven to revolt by the adversity that overwhelmed him and by the incomprehension and disdain with which the scientific world received his works, to most of his contemporaries he was only a political agitator. Yet in fact, continuing the work of Abel, he produced with the aid of group theory a definitive answer to the problem of the solvability of algebraic equations, a problem that had absorbed the attention of mathematicians since the eighteenth century; he thereby laid one of the foundations of modern algebra. The few sketches remaining of other works that he devoted to the theory of elliptic functions and that of Abelian integrals and his reflections on the philosophy and methodology of mathematics display an uncanny foreknowledge of modern mathematics.

Galois's father, Nicolas-Gabriel Galois, an amiable and witty liberal thinker, directed a school accommodating about sixty boarders. Elected mayor of Bourg-la-Reine during the Hundred Days, he retained this position under the second Restoration. Galois's mother, Adelaïde-Marie Demante, was from a family of jurists and had received a more traditional education. She had a headstrong personality and was eccentric, even somewhat odd. Having taken charge of her son's early education, she sought to inculcate in him, along with the elements of classical culture, the principles of an austere religion and respect for a Stoic morality. Affected by his father's imagination and liberalism, the varying severity of his mother's eccentricity, and the affection of his elder sister Nathalie-Théodore, Galois seems to have had an early youth that was both happy and studious.

Galois continued his studies at the Collège Louis-le-Grand in Paris, entering as a fourth-form boarder in October 1823. He found it difficult to submit to the harsh discipline imposed by the school during the Restoration at the orders of the political authorities and the Church, and although a brilliant student, he presented problems. In the early months of 1827 he attended the first-year preparatory mathematics courses given by H. J. Vernier, and this first contact with mathematics was a revelation for him. But he rapidly tired of the elementary character of this instruction and of the inadequacies of certain of the textbooks and soon turned to reading the original works themselves. After appreciating the rigor of Legendre's *Géométrie,* Galois acquired a solid grounding from the major works of Lagrange. During the next two years he followed the second-year preparatory mathematics courses taught by Vernier, then the more advanced ones of L.-P.-E. Richard, who was the first to recognize his indisputable superiority in mathematics. With this perceptive teacher Galois was an excellent student, even though he was already devoting much more of his time to his personal work than to his classwork. In 1828 he began to study certain recent works on the theory of equations, number theory, and the theory of elliptic functions. This was the period of his first memorandum, published in March 1829 in Gergonne's *Annales de mathématiques pures et appliquées;* making more explicit and demonstrating a result of Lagrange's concerning continuous fractions, it reveals a certain ingenuity but does not herald an exceptional talent.

By his own account, in the course of 1828 Galois wrongly believed—as Abel had eight years earlier—that he had solved the general fifth-degree equation. Rapidly undeceived, he resumed on a new basis the study of the theory of equations, which he pursued until he achieved the elucidation of the general problem with the help of group theory. The results he obtained in May 1829 were communicated to the Académie des Sciences by a particularly competent judge, Cauchy. But events were to frustrate these brilliant beginnings and to leave a deep mark on the personality of the young mathematician. First, at the beginning of July came the suicide of his father, who had been persecuted for his liberal opinions. Second, a month later he failed the entrance examination for the École Polytechnique, owing to his refusal to follow the method of exposition suggested by the examiner. Seeing his hopes vanish for entering the school which attracted him because of its scientific prestige and liberal tradition, he took the entrance examination for the École Normale Supérieure (then called the École Préparatoire), which trained future secondary school teachers. Admitted as the result of an excellent grade in mathematics, he entered this institution in November 1829; it was then housed in an annex of the Collège Louis-le-Grand, where he had spent the previous six years. At this time, through reading Férussac's *Bulletin des sciences mathématiques,* he learned of Abel's recent death and, at the same time, that Abel's last published memoir contained a good number of the results he himself had presented as original in his memoir to the Academy.

Cauchy, assigned to report on Galois's work, had to counsel him to revise his memoir, taking into account Abel's researches and the new results he had obtained. (It was for this reason that Cauchy did not present a report on his memoir.) Galois actually composed a new text that he submitted to the Academy at the end of February 1830, hoping to win the *grand prix* in mathematics. Unfortunately this memoir was lost upon the death of Fourier, who had been appointed to examine it. Brusquely eliminated from the competition, Galois believed himself to be the object of a new persecution by the representatives of official science and of society in general. His manuscripts have preserved a partial record of the elaboration of this memoir of February 1830, a brief analysis of which was published in Férussac's *Bulletin des sciences mathématiques* of April 1830. In June 1830 Galois published in the same journal a short note on the resolution of numerical equations and a much more important article, "Sur la théorie des nombres," in which he introduced the remarkable theory of "Galois imaginaries." That this same issue contains original works by Cauchy and Poisson is sufficient testimony to the reputation Galois had already acquired, despite the misfortune that plagued him. The July Revolution of 1830, however, was to mark a severe change in his career.

After several weeks of apparent calm the revolution provoked a renewal of political agitation in France and an intensification in republican propaganda, especially among intellectuals and students. It was then Galois became politicized. Before returning for a second year to the École Normale Supérieure in November 1830, he already had formed friendships with several republican leaders, particularly Blanqui and Raspail. He became less and less able to bear the strict discipline in his school, and he published a violent article against its director in an opposition journal, the *Gazette des écoles.* For this he was expelled on 8 December 1830, a measure approved by the Royal Council on 4 January 1831.

Left to himself, Galois devoted most of his time to political propaganda and participated in the demonstrations and riots then agitating Paris. He was arrested for the first time following a regicide toast that he had given at a republican banquet on 9 May 1831, but he was acquitted on 15 June by the assize court of the Seine. Meanwhile, to a certain extent he continued his mathematical research. His last two publications were a short note on analysis in Férussac's *Bulletin des sciences mathématiques* of December 1830 and "Lettre sur l'enseignement des sciences," which appeared on 2 January 1831 in the *Gazette des écoles.* On 13 January he began a public course on advanced algebra in which he planned to present his own discoveries; but this project seems not to have had much success. On 17 January 1831 Galois presented to the Academy a new version of his "Mémoire sur la résolution des équations algébriques," hastily written up at the request of Poisson. Unfortunately, in his report of 4 July 1831 on this, Galois's most important piece of work, Poisson hinted that a portion of the results could be found in several posthumous writings of Abel recently published and that the remainder was incomprehensible. Such a judgment, the profound injustice of which would become apparent in the future, could only stiffen Galois's rebellion.

Galois was arrested again during a republican demonstration on 14 July 1831 and placed in detention at the prison of Sainte-Pélagie, where in a troubled and often painful situation he pursued his mathematical investigations, revised his memoir on equations, and worked on the applications of his theory and on elliptic functions. On 16 March 1832, upon the announcement of a cholera epidemic, he was transferred to a nursing home, where he resumed his research, wrote several essays on the philosophy of science, and became involved in a love affair, of which the unhappy ending grieved him deeply.

Provoked to a duel in unclear circumstances following this breakup, Galois felt his death was near. On 29 May he wrote desperate letters to his republican friends, hastily sorted his papers, and addressed to his friend Auguste Chevalier—but really intended for Gauss and Jacobi—a testamentary letter, a tragic document in which he attempted to sketch the principal results he had achieved. On 30 May, mortally wounded by an unknown adversary, he was hospitalized; he died the following day. His funeral, on 2 June, was the occasion for a republican demonstration heralding the tragic riots that bloodied Paris in the days that followed.

Galois's work seems not to have been fully appreciated by any of his contemporaries. Cauchy, who would have been capable of grasping its importance, had left France in September 1830, having seen only its first outlines. Moreover, the few fragments published during Galois's lifetime did not give an overall view of his achievement and, in particular, did not afford a means of judging the exceptional interest of the results obtained in the theory of equations and rejected by Poisson. The publication in September 1832 of the famous testamentary letter does not appear to have attracted the attention it deserved. It was not until September 1843 that Liouville, who prepared Galois's manuscripts for publication, announced officially to the Academy that the young mathematician had effectively solved the problem, already considered by Abel, of deciding whether an irreducible first-degree equation is or is not "solvable with the aid of radicals." Although announced and prepared for the end of 1843, the publication of the celebrated 1831 memoir and of a fragment on the "primitive equations solvable by radicals" did not occur until the October–November 1846 issue of the *Journal de mathématiques pures et appliquées.*

It was, therefore, not until over fourteen years after Galois's death that the essential elements of his work became available to mathematicians. By this time the evolution of mathematical research had created a climate much more favorable to its reception: the dominance of mathematical physics in the French school had lessened, and pure research was receiving a new impetus. Furthermore, the recent publication of the two-volume *Oeuvres complètes de Niels-Henrik Abel* (1839), which contained fundamental work on the algebraic theory of elliptic functions and an important, unfinished memoir, "Sur la résolution algébrique des équations," had awakened interest in certain of the fields in which Galois has become famous. Lastly, in a series of publications appearing in 1844–1846, Cauchy, pursuing studies begun in 1815 but soon abandoned, had—implicitly—given group theory a new scope by the systematic construction of his famous theory of permutations.

Beginning with Liouville's edition, which was reproduced in book form in 1897 by J. Picard, Galois's work became progressively known to mathematicians and exerted a profound influence on the development of modern mathematics. Also important, although they came to light too late to contribute to the advance of mathematics, are the previously unpublished texts that appeared later. In 1906–1907 various manuscript fragments edited by J. Tannery revealed the great originality of the young mathematician's epistemological writings and provided new information about his research. Finally, in 1961 the exemplary critical edition of R. Bourgne and J. P. Azra united all of Galois's previously published writings and most of the remaining mathematical outlines and rough drafts. While this new documentary material provides no assistance to present-day mathematicians with their own problems, it does permit us to understand better certain aspects of Galois's research, and it will perhaps help in resolving a few remaining enigmas concerning the basic sources of his thought.

To comprehend Galois's work, it is important to consider the earlier writings that influenced its initial orientation and the contemporary investigations that contributed to guiding and diversifying it. It is equally necessary to insist on Galois's great originality: while assimilating the most vital currents of contemporary mathematical thought, he was able to transcend them thanks to a kind of prescience about the conceptual character of modern mathematics. The epistemological texts extracted from his rough drafts sketch, in a few sentences, the principal directions of present-day research; and the clarity, conciseness, and precision of the style add to the novelty and impact of the ideas. Galois was undoubtedly the beneficiary of his predecessors and of his rivals, but his multifaceted personality and his brilliant sense of the indispensable renewal of mathematical thinking made him an exceptional innovator whose influence was long felt in vast areas of mathematics.

Galois's first investigations, like Abel's, were inspired by the works of Lagrange and of Gauss on the conditions of solvability of certain types of algebraic equations and by Cauchy's memoirs on the theory of substitutions. Consequently their similarity is not surprising, nor is the particular fact that the principal results announced by Galois in May–June 1829 had previously been obtained by Abel. In the second half of 1829 Galois learned that Abel had published his findings in Crelle's *Journal für die reine und angewandte Mathematik* a few days before he himself died young. The interest that Galois took from that time in the work of Abel and of his other youthful rival, Jacobi, is evident from numerous reading notes. If, as a result of the progressive elaboration of group theory, Galois pursued the elucidation of the theory of algebraic equations far beyond the results published by Abel, beginning with the first months of 1830 he directed a large proportion of his research toward other new directions opened by both Abel and Jacobi, notably toward the theory of elliptic functions and of certain types of integrals.

The advances that Galois made in his first area of research, that of the theory of algebraic equations, are marked by two great synthetic studies. The first was written in February 1830 for the Academy's grand prize; the summary of it that Galois published in April 1830 in Férussac's *Bulletin des sciences mathématiques* establishes that he had made significant progress beyond Abel's recent memoir but that certain obstacles still stood in the way of an overall solution. The publication in Crelle's *Journal für die reine und angewandte Mathematik* of some posthumous fragments of Abel's work containing more advanced results (the unfinished posthumous memoir on this subject was not published until 1839) encouraged Galois to persevere in his efforts to overcome the remaining difficulties and to write a restatement of his studies. This was the purpose of the new version of the "Mémoire sur la résolution des équations algébriques" that he presented before the Academy.

Despite Poisson's criticisms Galois rightly persisted in thinking that he had furnished a definitive solution to the problem of the solvability of algebraic equations and, after having made a few corrections in it, he gave this memoir the first place in the list of his writings in his testamentary letter of 29 May 1837. This was the "definitive" version of his fundamental memoir, and in it Galois continued the studies of his predecessors but at the same time produced a thoroughly original work. True, he formulated in a more precise manner essential ideas that were already in the air, but he also introduced others that, once stated, played an important role in the genesis of modern algebra. Moreover, he daringly generalized certain classic methods in other fields and succeeded in providing a complete solution—and indeed a generalization—of the problem in question by systematically drawing upon group theory, a subject he had founded concurrently with his work on equations.

Lagrange had shown that the solvability of an algebraic equation depends on the possibility of finding a chain of intermediate equations of binomial type, known as resolvent equations. He had thus succeeded in finding the classic resolution formulas of the "general" equations of second, third, and fourth degree but had not been able to reach any definitive conclusion regarding the general fifth-degree equation. The impossibility of solving this last type of equation through the use of radicals was demonstrated by Paolo Ruffini and in a more satisfactory manner by Abel in 1824. Meanwhile, in 1801, Gauss had published an important study of binomial equations and the primitive roots of unity; and Cauchy in 1815 had made important contributions to the theory of permutations, a particular form of the future group theory.

In his study of the solvability of algebraic equations, Galois, developing an idea of Abel's, considered that with each intermediate resolvent equation there is associated a field of algebraic numbers that is intermediate between the field generated by the roots of the equation under study and the field determined by the coefficients of this equation. His leading idea, however, was to have successfully associated with the given equation, and with the different intermediate fields involved, a sequence of groups such that the group corresponding to a certain field of the sequence associated with the equation is a subgroup distinct from the one associated with the antecedent field. Such a method obviously presupposes the clarification of the concept of field already suspected (without use of the term) by Gauss and Abel, as well as a searching study of group theory, of which Galois can be considered the creator.

Galois thus showed that for an irreducible algebraic equation to be solvable by radicals, it is necessary and sufficient that its group be solvable, i.e., possess a series of composition formed of proper subgroups having certain precisely defined properties. Although this general rule did not in fact make the actual resolution of a determinate equation any simpler, it did provide the means for finding, as particular cases, all the known results concerning the solvability of the general equations of less than fifth degree as well as binomial equations and certain other particular types of equations; it also permitted almost immediate demonstration that the general equation of higher than fourth degree is not solvable by radicals, the associated group (permutation group of n objects) not being solvable. Galois was aware that his study went beyond the limited problem of the solvability of algebraic equations by means of radicals and that it allowed one to take up the much more general problem of the classification of the irrationals.

In his testamentary letter, Galois summarized a second memoir (of which several fragments are extant) that dealt with certain developments and applications of the theory of equations and of group theory. The article "Sur la théorie des nombres" is linked with it; it contained, notably, a daring generalization of the theory of congruences by means of new numbers that are today called Galois imaginaries and its application to research in those cases where a primitive equation is solvable by radicals. Beyond the precise definition of the decomposition of a group, this second memoir included applications of Galois's theory to elliptic functions; in treating the algebraic equations obtained through the division and transformation of these functions, it presents, without demonstration, the results concerning the modular equations upon which the division of the periods depends.

The third memoir that Galois mentions in his testamentary letter is known only through the information contained in this poignant document. This information very clearly demonstrates that, like Abel and Jacobi, Galois passed from the study of elliptic functions to consideration of the integrals of the most general algebraic differentials, today called Abelian integrals. It seems that his research in this area was already quite advanced, since the letter summarizes the results he had achieved, particularly the classification of these integrals into three categories, a result obtained by Riemann in 1857. This same letter alludes to recent meditations entitled "Sur l'application à l'analyse transcendante de la théorie de l'ambiguïté," but the allusion is too vague to be interpreted conclusively.

Galois often expressed prophetic reflections on the spirit of modern mathematics: "Jump with both feet on the calculus and group the operations, classifying them according to their difficulties and not according to their forms; such, in my view, is the task of future mathematicians" (*Écrits et mémoires,* p. 9).

He also reflected on the conditions of scientific creativity: "A mind that had the power to perceive at once the totality of mathematical truths—not just those known to us, but all the truths possible—would be able to deduce them regularly and, as it were, mechanically . . . but it does not happen like that" (*ibid.,* pp. 13–14). Or, again, "Science progresses by a series of combinations in which chance does not play the smallest role; its life is unreasoning and planless [*brute*] and resembles that of minerals that grow by juxtaposition" (*ibid.,* p. 15).

Yet we must also recall the ironic, mordant, and provocative tone of Galois's allusions to established scientists: "I do not say to anyone that I owe to his counsel or to his encouragement everything that is good in this work. I do not say it, for that would be to lie" (*ibid.,* p. 3). The contempt that he felt for these scientists was such that he hoped the extreme conciseness of his arguments would make them accessible only to the best among them.

Galois's terse style, combined with the great originality of his thought and the modernity of his conceptions, contributed as much as the delay in publication to the length of time that passed before Galois's work was understood, recognized at its true worth, and fully developed. Indeed, very few mathematicians of the mid-nineteenth century were ready to assimilate such a revolutionary work directly. Consequently the first publications that dealt with it, those of Enrico Betti (beginning in 1851), T. Schönemann, Leopold Kronecker, and Charles Hermite, are simply commentaries, explanations, or immediate and limited applications. It was only with the publication in 1866 of the third edition of Alfred Serret's *Cours d'algèbre supérieure* and, in 1870, of Camille Jordan's *Traité des substitutions* that group theory and the whole of Galois's *oeuvre* were truly integrated into the body of mathematics. From that time on, its development was very rapid and the field of application was extended to the most varied branches of the science; in fact, group theory and other more subtle elements included in Galois's writings played an important role in the birth of modern algebra.

BIBLIOGRAPHY

I. Original Works. Galois's scientific writings have appeared in the following versions: "Oeuvres mathématiques d'Evariste Galois," J. Liouville, ed., in *Journal de mathématiques pures et appliquées,* **11** (Oct.–Nov. 1846), 381–448; *Oeuvres mathématiques d'Evariste Galois,* J. Picard, ed. (Paris, 1897), also in facs. repro. (Paris, 1951) with a study by G. Verriest; "Manuscrits et papiers inédits de Galois," J. Tannery, ed., in *Bulletin des sciences mathématiques,* 2nd ser., **30** (Aug.–Sept. 1906), 246–248, 255–263; **31** (Nov. 1907), 275–308; *Manuscrits d'Evariste Galois,* J. Tannery, ed. (Paris, 1908); and *Écrits et mémoires mathématiques d'Evariste Galois,* R. Bourgne and J.-P. Azra, eds. (Paris, 1962), with pref. by J. Dieudonné. These eds. will be designated, respectively, as "Oeuvres," *Oeuvres,* "Manuscrits," *Manuscrits,* and *Écrits et mémoires.* Since the *Oeuvres* and *Manuscrits* are simply reeditions in book form of the "Oeuvres" and of the "Manuscrits," they are not analyzed below; the contents of the other three are specified according to date in the following list.

1. Scientific texts published during his lifetime.

Apr. 1829: "Démonstration d'un théorème sur les fractions continues périodiques," in Gergonne's *Annales de mathématiques pures et appliquées,* **19,** 294–301.

Apr. 1830: "Analyse d'un mémoire sur la résolution algébrique des équations," in Férussac's *Bulletin des sciences mathématiques,* **13,** 271–272.

June 1830: "Note sur la résolution des équations numériques," *ibid.,* 413–414.

June 1830: "Sur la théorie des nombres," *ibid.,* 428–436.

Dec. 1830: "Notes sur quelques points d'analyse," in Gergonne's *Annales de mathématiques pures et appliquées,* **21,** 182–184.

Jan. 1831: "Lettre sur l'enseignement des sciences," in *Gazette des écoles,* no. 110 (2 Jan. 1831).

2. Posthumous publications.

Sept. 1832: "Lettre à Auguste Chevalier," in *Revue encyclopédique,* **55,** 568–576.

Oct.–Nov. 1846: "Oeuvres," considered definitive until 1906; in addition to the memoirs published in Galois's lifetime (except for the last) and the letter to Auguste Chevalier, this ed. contains the following previously unpublished memoirs: "Mémoire sur les conditions de résolubilité des équations par radicaux," pp. 417–433; and "Des équations primitives qui sont solubles par radicaux," pp. 434–444.

Aug.–Sept. 1906: "Manuscrits," pt. 1, which contains, besides a description of Galois's MSS, the text of the following previously unpublished fragments (titles given are those in *Écrits et mémoires*): "Discours préliminaire"; "Projet de publication"; "Note sur Abel"; "Préface" (partial); "Discussions sur les progrès de l'analyse pure"; "Fragments"; "Science, hiérarchie, écoles"; and "Catalogue, note sur la théorie des équations."

Nov. 1907: "Manuscrits," pt. 2, containing "Recherches sur la théorie des permutations et des équations algébriques"; "Comment la théorie des équations dépend de celle des permutations"; "Note manuscrite"; "Addition au second mémoire"; "Mémoire sur la division des fonctions elliptiques de première espèce"; "Note sur l'intégration des équations linéaires"; "Recherches sur les équations du second degré."

Jan.–Mar. 1948; entire text of the "Préface" and of the "Projet de publication," R. Taton, ed., in *Revue d'histoire des sciences,* **1,** 123–128.

1956: "Lettre sur l'enseignement des sciences," repr. in

A. Dalmas, *Evariste Galois . . .* (Paris, 1956), pp. 105–108.

1962: *Écrits et mémoires mathématiques d'Evariste Galois,* R. Bourgne and J.-P. Azra, eds. (Paris, 1962). This remarkable ed. contains all of Galois's *oeuvre:* the articles published in his lifetime and a critical ed., with corrections and variants, of all his MSS, including his rough drafts. The majority of the many previously unpublished texts presented here are grouped in two categories: the "Essais," dating from the period when Galois was a student (pp. 403–453, 519–521) and the "Calculs et brouillons inédits" (pp. 187–361, 526–538), classed under five headings—"Intégrales eulériennes," "Calcul intégral," "Fonctions elliptiques," "Groupes de substitutions," and "Annexe." Galois's nine known letters are reproduced and described (pp. 459–471, 523–525). Galois's MSS, preserved at the Bibliothèque de l'Institut de France (MS 2108), are the subject of a detailed description that provides many complementary details (App. I, 478–521; App. II, 526–538).

II. SECONDARY LITERATURE. At the present time there is no major synthetic study of Galois's life and work. The principal biographical source remains P. Dupuy, "La vie d'Evariste Galois," in *Annales scientifiques de l'École normale supérieure,* 3rd ser., **13** (1896), 197–266, with documents and two portraits; reiss. as *Cahiers de la quinzaine,* 5th ser., no. 2 (Paris, 1903).

Among the few earlier articles the only ones of any documentary value are the two brief obituaries in *Revue encyclopédique,* **55** (Sept. 1832): the first (pp. 566–568), unsigned, is very general; the second ("Nécrologie," pp. 744–754), by Auguste Chevalier, Galois's best friend, is a source of valuable information. See also an anonymous notice, inspired by Evariste's younger brother, Alfred Galois, and by one of his former classmates, P.-P. Flaugergues, in *Magasin pittoresque,* **16** (1848), 227–228; and a note by O. Terquem in *Nouvelles annales de mathématiques,* **8** (1849), 452.

Of the later biographical studies a few present new information: J. Bertrand, "La vie d'Evariste Galois par P. Dupuy," in *Journal des savants* (July 1899), pp. 389–400, reiss. in *Éloges académiques,* n.s. (Paris, 1902), pp. 331–345; R. Taton, "Les relations scientifiques d'Evariste Galois avec les mathématiciens de son temps," in *Revue d'histoire des sciences,* **1** (1947), 114–130; A. Dalmas, *Evariste Galois, révolutionnaire et géomètre* (Paris, 1956); the ed. of *Écrits et mémoires mathématiques* by R. Bourgne and J.-P. Azra cited above; C. A. Infantozzi, "Sur la mort d'Evariste Galois," in *Revue d'histoire des sciences,* **21** (1968), 157–160; art. by J.-P. Azra and R. Bourgne in *Encyclopaedia universalis,* VII (Paris, 1970), 450–451; and R. Taton, "Sur les relations mathématiques d'Augustin Cauchy et d'Evariste Galois," in *Revue d'histoire des sciences,* **24** (1971), 123–148.

G. Sarton, "Evariste Galois," in *Scientific Monthly,* **13** (Oct. 1921), 363–375, repr. in *Osiris,* **3** (1937), 241–254; and E. T. Bell, *Men of Mathematics* (New York, 1937), pp. 362–377, were directly inspired by Dupuy. L. Infeld, *Whom the Gods Love. The Story of Evariste Galois* (New York, 1948); and A. Arnoux, *Algorithme* (Paris, 1948), mix facts with romantic elements.

Galois's scientific work has not yet received the thorough study it merits, although numerous articles attempt to bring out its main features. Among the older ones, beyond the "commentaries" of the first disciples, particularly Betti and Jordan, are the following: J. Liouville, "Avertissement" to the "Oeuvres," in *Journal de mathématiques pures et appliquées,* **11** (1846), 381–384; S. Lie, "Influence de Galois sur le développement des mathématiques," in *Le centenaire de l'École normale* (Paris, 1895), pp. 481–489; E. Picard, "Introduction" to *Oeuvres* (Paris, 1897), pp. v–x; J. Pierpont, "Early History of Galois's Theory of Equations," in *Bulletin of the American Mathematical Society,* **4** (Apr. 1898), 332–340; J. Tannery, "Introduction" to "Manuscrits" in *Bulletin des sciences mathématiques,* **30** (1906), 1–19, repr. in *Manuscrits,* pp. 1–19.

The most important recent studies are G. Verriest, *Evariste Galois et la théorie des équations algébriques* (Louvain-Paris, 1934; reiss. Paris, 1951); L. Kollros, *Evariste Galois* (Basel, 1949); J. Dieudonné, "Préface" (pp. v–vii), R. Bourgne, "Avertissement" (pp. ix–xvi), and J.-P. Azra, "Appendice" (pp. 475–538), in *Écrits et mémoires mathématiques* (cited above); N. Bourbaki, *Éléments d'histoire des mathématiques,* 2nd ed. (Paris, 1969), pp. 73-74, 104-109; and K. Wussing, *Die Genesis des abstrakten Gruppenbegriffes* (Berlin, 1969), esp. pp. 73-87, 206-211.

RENÉ TATON

GALTON, FRANCIS (*b.* Birmingham, England, 16 February 1822; *d.* Haslemere, Surrey, England, 17 January 1911), *statistics, anthropometry, experimental psychology, heredity.*

Galton's paternal ancestors were bankers and gunsmiths, of the Quaker faith, and long-lived. His mother was Erasmus Darwin's daughter, and thus he was Charles Darwin's cousin. Galton's intellectual precocity has become a textbook item, and Lewis Terman estimated his IQ to have been of the order of 200. His education, though, was desultory, its formal peaks being a few mathematics courses at Cambridge (he took a pass degree) and some unfinished medical studies in London. He quit the latter at the age of twenty-two when his father died, leaving him a fortune. He then traveled. Journeying through virtually unknown parts of southwestern Africa in 1850–1852, Galton acquired fame as an intrepid explorer. His immediate reward was a gold medal from the Geographical Society, and his later reports led to election as a fellow of the Royal Society in 1860. In 1853 he married, and in 1857 he settled into a quiet London home, where he remained, except for occasional European vacations, until his death over half a century later. Galton was knighted in 1909. He died childless.

Galton was perhaps the last of a now extinct breed—the gentleman scientist. He never held any academic or professional post, and most of his experiments were done at home or while traveling, or were farmed out to friends. He was not a great reader, and his small personal library was said to consist mainly of autographed copies of fellow scientists' books. He composed no *magnum opus,* but he kept up a rich flow of original ideas. An endless curiosity about the phenomena of nature and mankind was nicely coupled with mechanical ingenuity and inventiveness. Secure and contented in the employment of his wide-ranging talents, Galton was an unusually equable person. Anger and polemic were alien to him. In his later years he was fortunate in having the ebullient Karl Pearson as champion and extender of his ideas. Pearson subsequently became the first holder of the chair of eugenics at University College, London, that Galton had endowed in his will.

Galton's earliest notable researches were meteorologic, and it was he who first recognized and named the anticyclone.

Foremost in Galton's life was a belief that virtually anything is quantifiable. Some of his exercises in this direction are now merely amusing—a solemn assessment of womanly beauty on a pocket scale, a study of the body weights of three generations of British peers, and a statistical inquiry into the efficacy of prayer are examples—but there can be little doubt that his general attitude was salutary in its day. Moreover, against the trivia have to be set such good things as his developing Quetelet's observation that certain measurable human characteristics are distributed like the error function. Galton initiated an important reversal of outlook on biological and psychological variation, previously regarded as an uninteresting nuisance. In his own words: "The primary objects of the Gaussian Law of Errors were exactly opposed, in one sense, to those to which I applied them. They were to get rid of, or to provide a just allowance for, errors. But these errors or deviations were the very things I wanted to preserve and know about." In psychology Galton sowed the seeds of mental testing, of measuring sensory acuity, and of scaling and typing. In statistics he originated the concepts of regression and correlation.

Galton's best-known work was on the inheritance of talent—scholarly, artistic, and athletic—the raw data being the records of notable families. He found strong evidence of inheritance. Upholders of the rival nurture-not-nature theory attacked the work, on the ground that the children of gifted and successful parents are environmentally favored; but even when allowance was made for this truth, Galton's contention could not be wholly denied. One outcome of the investigation was a conviction in many people's minds—and particularly deeply in Galton's own mind—that a eugenic program to foster talent and healthiness and to suppress stupidity and sickliness was a *sine qua non* in any society that wished to maintain, let alone promote, its quality and status. (Galton coined the word "eugenics" in 1883.)

Galton's views on genetics are historically curious. Influenced by Darwin's belief that inheritance is conditioned by a blending mechanism, Galton propounded his law of ancestral heredity, which set the average contribution of each parent at 1/4, of each grandparent at 1/16, and so forth (the sum, over all ancestors of both parents, being asymptotic to unity). Karl Pearson and his colleagues pursued the notion in a series of sophisticated researches, but Galton's law received withering criticisms after the rediscovery, in 1900, of Mendel's work on particulate inheritance. Yet Galton had himself toyed with the notion of particulate inheritance, and in a remarkable correspondence with Darwin in 1875 he sketched the essence of the theory and even discussed something very like what we now know as genotypes and phenotypes under the names "latent" and "patent" characteristics. He did not press these views, perhaps because of the strong climate of opinion in favor of blending inheritance at that time.

Galton's establishment of fingerprinting as an easy and almost infallible means of human identification transformed a difficult subject, and his taxonomy of prints is basically that used today. He was disappointed, however, to find no familial, racial, moral, or intellectual subgroupings in the collections he examined.

BIBLIOGRAPHY

I. Original Works. Galton wrote sixteen books and more than 200 papers. Of the books, recent printings are *Hereditary Genius* (London, 1869; 3rd ed., 1950); *Art of Travel* (5th ed., London, 1872; repr. Harrisburg, Pa., 1971); and *Finger Prints* (London, 1893; facs., New York, 1965). An unpublished utopian book, "The Eugenic College of Kantsaywhere," written toward the end of his life, is excerpted in Karl Pearson's biography (see below). His autobiography, *Memories of My Life* (London, 1908), is worth reading. The best listing of Galton's publications is appended to Blacker's book (see below).

II. Secondary Literature. Immediately after Galton's death his friend Karl Pearson started a biography that was to become one of the most elaborate and comprehensive works of its kind in this century: *The Life, Letters and Labours of Francis Galton,* 4 vols. (London, 1914–1930). A treatment emphasizing the interests of his later years is C. P. Blacker, *Eugenics, Galton and After* (London, 1952). A good survey of his psychologic contributions is H. E. Garratt, *Great Experiments in Psychology* (New York, 1951), ch. 13. The 1965 repr. of *Finger Prints* (see above) contains a biographical intro. by Harold Cummins that places Galton's fingerprint work in historic context.

NORMAN T. GRIDGEMAN

GALVANI, LUIGI (*b.* Bologna, Italy, 9 September 1737; *d.* Bologna, 4 December 1798), *anatomy, physiology, physics.*

Galvani, who is most famous for his work relating to the discovery of current electricity, received his professional training in medicine. He studied at Bologna with several leading medical teachers of his time, including Jacopo Bartolomeo Beccari and Domenico Galeazzi. After receiving his degree in medicine and philosophy on 15 July 1759, Galvani divided the first years of his professional career between medical and surgical practice, anatomical research, and lecturing on medicine. After spending several years as an honorary lecturer, on 22 June 1768 he became a paid lecturer at the college he had attended, and on 12 December 1775 he became Galeazzi's adjunct in anatomy at the University of Bologna. The Senate of Bologna had installed Galvani as curator and demonstrator of the anatomical museum in March 1766, and on 26 February 1782 it elected him professor of obstetric arts at the Istituto delle Scienze. During the last years of his life Galvani suffered several personal misfortunes. In 1790 his beloved wife, Lucia Galeazzi, daughter of his anatomical preceptor, died; and a few years later he was deprived of his offices at the university and the Istituto delle Scienze because of his refusal to swear allegiance to Napoleon's Cisalpine Republic. He died in poverty and sorrow.

Galvani devoted most of his early scientific efforts to important but rather straightforward anatomical topics. His first publication, in 1762, was a dissertation on the structure, function, and pathology of bones. He described the chemical and anatomical elements from which bones are constructed, their pattern of growth, and various diseases to which they are subject. In 1767 he published an essay on the kidneys of birds, in which he described, among other things, the three-layered ureteral wall and its peristaltic and antiperistaltic movement upon irritation. Galvani also devoted several papers to the anatomy of the ear in birds, just before Antonio Scarpa published on this subject. He recounted with particular precision the comparative anatomy of the auditory canal in several species of birds, devoting some attention to the distribution of blood vessels, muscles, and nerves in the middle and inner ear.

Galvani addressed his most important and best-remembered investigations to problems of animal electricity. During the 1770's his research interests shifted to a considerable extent from largely anatomical to more strictly physiological studies, specifically on nerves and muscles. In 1772 Galvani read a paper on Hallerian irritability to the Istituto delle Scienze, and in 1773 he discussed the muscle movement of frogs before the same body. In 1774 he read a paper on the effect of opiates on frog nerves. These researches fused in his mind with slightly earlier eighteenth-century studies, several of them by Italians, on the electrical stimulation of nerves and muscles. Picking up where Beccaria, Leopoldo Caldani, Felice Fontana, and Tommaso Laghi had recently left off, Galvani began in late 1780 an extensive and meticulous series of investigations into the irritable responses elicited by static electricity in properly prepared frogs.

Galvani's frog preparations consisted of the spinal cords, crural nerves, and lower limbs dissected as a unit. Using these preparations, he at first touched the conductor of a static electrical machine directly to the spinal cord (kept on a pane of glass) and watched the convulsive contractions of the muscles in the lower limbs, which rested on a so-called "magic square," a flat plate condenser made by attaching a sheet of metal foil to both sides of a single pane of glass. Galvani was apparently trying to arrive at general laws relating the forcefulness of muscle contraction directly to the quantity of electric fluid applied and inversely to the distance of the nerve and muscle from the conductor. After much repetition and sometimes complex variation of this basic procedure, Galvani was faced with one quite unanticipated result: the lower limbs contracted even when the frog was completely insulated from the machine and removed some distance from it. As long as the crural nerves were touched by a grounded conductor, the muscles contracted whenever a spark was drawn from an electrical machine, even though the spark did not directly strike the frog preparation.

In the course of investigating this strange result, Galvani in the mid-1780's uncovered an even stranger one. He and his research associates had begun to explore the effects of atmospheric electricity on frog preparations, on the assumption that some analogy existed between convulsions induced by distant electrical machines and those sometimes induced by static discharge in the atmosphere. The expected analogous results were obtained. But then Galvani made the unanticipated observation that muscle contractions occurred even without discharge of atmospheric electricity. As he explained later in his *De viribus electricitatis in motu musculari commentarius* (1791), Galvani at one point fastened some prepared frogs by "brass hooks in their spinal cord to an iron railing which surrounded a certain hanging garden of my house." He noticed that these frogs went into contractions "not only when lightning flashed but even at times when the sky was quiet and serene," and he was able to intensify these effects by deliberately pressing the brass hooks in the spinal cord to the iron railing. He obtained similar results indoors by placing the frog on an iron plate and pushing the brass hook against it. Contractions resulted indoors only when metals, rather than glass or resin, were used; and these contractions seemed stronger with certain metals than with others. In a follow-up series of investigations, Galvani experimented with metallic arcs. He tried various bent metal conductors, touching one end to the hook in the spinal cord and the other to the muscles in the frog's leg. Contractions resulted, their strength depending on the metals used for the hook and the arc. Contractions did not result when a nonconductor replaced the metal in the arc.

Galvani had here hit upon the central phenomenon of galvanism: the production of electric current from the contact of two different metals in a moist environment. He did not, however, interpret his own discovery this way. Instead, Galvani thought that he had finally obtained confirmation for the suspicion, entertained from time to time during the eighteenth century, that animals possess in their nerves and muscles a subtle fluid quite analogous to ordinary electricity. He himself had occasionally flirted with this idea but had never previously made much of it. But his experiments with the metallic arcs seemed to provide clear and unmistakable proof of a special "animal electricity," and he spent considerable effort in specifying and elaborating his theory.

Galvani's fullest statement is in part IV of his *Commentarius.* He explains that the muscle can be compared to a small Leyden jar charged with a dual electrical charge, and the nerve to the jar's conductor. Animal electrical fluid is generated from the blood in the brain and passes via the nerves into the core of the muscles, which thus become positively charged while the outside becomes negative. Electrical equilibrium in the muscle, as in a Leyden jar, can be disrupted by applying an arc between conductor and core or by drawing a spark from an electrical machine. When the muscle discharges in either of these ways, its fibers are stimulated to violent, irritable contraction. Both the original anomaly of convulsive contraction upon distant sparking and the subsequent observation of contractions provoked by the metallic arc were thus explained in terms of "animal electricity" and its special discharge pathways.

Reaction to Galvani's published reflections was vigorous although somewhat confused. Alessandro Volta, the noted Italian electrician, was among the first to take up the new theory of animal electricity, but by 1792/1793 his original support turned to skeptical reserve. In papers published in the *Philosophical Transactions of the Royal Society,* Volta professed belief in Galvani's theory but simultaneously advanced the thesis that the "metals used in the experiments, being applied to the moist bodies of animals, can by themselves . . . excite and dislodge the electric fluid from its state of rest; so that the organs of the animal act only passively." By the end of 1793 Volta had discarded Galvani's animal electricity for his own theory of "contact," according to which conducting bodies of certain kinds, especially metals, can by their mere contact excite electrical fluid, which can in turn stimulate various irritable responses. Galvani was not prepared to concede defeat, and he and his nephew Giovanni Aldini mounted a campaign in the mid-1790's to establish beyond doubt the existence of a special animal electricity. In 1794 and 1797 he announced experiments employing only frog nerve-muscle preparations (without metals) and showed that convulsive contractions could be produced merely by touching nerves to muscles.

At the same time, Galvani extensively examined the electrical properties of marine torpedoes. He found that the strong electrical discharge is generated in these animals in structures analogous to ordinary nerves and muscles, and this seemed to supply additional support for the theory of animal electricity. Volta's counterattack led in 1799 to his invention of the pile, a stack of metal-metal-moist-conductor elements which was, in fact, the first primitive wet-cell battery. When Galvani died, prospects for the survival of his theory were very uncertain. Nevertheless, support for the concept of animal electricity survived into the nineteenth century and ultimately led in the 1840's to the basic work of Emil du Bois-Reymond.

BIBLIOGRAPHY

I. Original Works. Galvani's most famous work is *De viribus electricitatis in motu musculari commentarius* (Bologna, 1791). It has been published several times since, reproduced in facsimile, and issued in several translations. A facsimile of the original Latin ed., together with an English trans., was issued by the Burndy Library (Norwalk, Conn., 1953). Fuller eds. of Galvani's writings include *Opere edite ed inedite* (Bologna, 1841), which contains several of his early anatomical papers and a report on then known MSS; *Memorie ed esperimenti inediti* (Bologna, 1937), which includes a transcription of Galvani's notes for his experiments in the early 1780's and a few draft papers on animal electricity from the same period; and a facsimile of *Taccuino* (Bologna, 1937), a notebook of Galvani's investigations into torpedoes in the mid-1790's.

II. SECONDARY LITERATURE. There is no full-length modern biography of Galvani, but several older *éloges,* e.g., by J. L. Alibert (Paris, 1806), are still useful and are supplemented by some extremely useful monographic work. Hebbel E. Hoff, "Galvani and the Pre-Galvanian Electrophysiologists," in *Annals of Science,* **1** (1936), 157–172, is a basic source, as is I. B. Cohen's "Introduction" to the Burndy Library ed. of the *Commentarius.* Also of fundamental importance are Giulio C. Pupilli's "Introduction" to the ed. of the *Commentarius* published by Richard Montraville Green (Cambridge, Mass., 1953); and John F. Fulton and Harvey Cushing, "A Bibliographic Study of the Galvani and Aldini Writings on Animal Electricity," in *Annals of Science,* **1** (1936), 239–268. Also worth consulting is Marc Sirol, *Galvani et le galvanisme* (Paris, 1939).

THEODORE M. BROWN

GAMALEYA, NIKOLAY FYODOROVICH (*b.* Odessa, Russia, 17 February 1859; *d.* Moscow, U.S.S.R., 29 March 1949), *microbiology.*

Gamaleya came from a Ukrainian family that had risen through service to the country since the seventeenth century. His father, Fyodor Mikhailovich Gamaleya, was a soldier; his mother, Karolina Vikentievna Gamaleya, was of Polish extraction.

Having graduated from the Gymnasium in 1876, Gamaleya enrolled in the Physics and Mathematics Faculty at Novorossysky University. While a student there he became fascinated with biology. One of his teachers was E. I. Mechnikov, and in Strasbourg, where Gamaleya went for vacations, he studied biochemistry under Hoppe-Seyler.

After graduation from the university in 1881, Gamaleya enrolled in the Military Medical Academy at St. Petersburg, then the center of medical education in Russia. His teachers included such prominent figures as S. P. Botkin, V. V. Pashutin, and V. A. Manassein. After graduation in 1883 with the title of physician, Gamaleya returned to Odessa. The young doctor became actively interested in bacteriology, a science then in its infancy, and conducted research in a bacteriological laboratory that he had set up in his apartment.

Pasteur's successful inoculation against rabies in 1885 definitively determined Gamaleya's scientific interests. In 1886 the Odessa Society of Physicians commissioned him to familiarize himself at Pasteur's laboratory with the technique of performing antirabies inoculations. His persistence and curiosity, medical knowledge, and microbiological training enabled him to master the method. The acquaintance with Pasteur was the beginning of creative collaboration and of a personal friendship that was strengthened by the struggle with opponents of Pasteur's method. At the time of especially sharp criticism of his method in England, Pasteur asked Gamaleya to defend it. Gamaleya was the first to inoculate himself with the antirabies vaccine, thereby proving its harmlessness to a healthy organism.

In 1886 the world's second bacteriological station—there was already one in Paris—was established in Odessa, with the participation of Mechnikov and Gamaleya. Here antirabies inoculations were successfully administered according to Pasteur's method, which undoubtedly was its best propaganda and defense. An ardent supporter of this method, Gamaleya used it widely and introduced important additions to its theoretical basis and valuable practical refinements.

In preparations containing the living virus, Gamaleya established that the effectiveness of antirabies vaccination depends on its quantitative content. On the basis of this principle he developed an intensive method of vaccination through the utilization of brain tissue less subject to drying. In addition, he discovered that inoculative antirabies immunity is physiologically limited and that vaccination is ineffective against manifest rabies as well as during the latent period of infection (about fourteen days).

In the 1880's, Gamaleya studied questions relating to the preparation of a vaccine against Siberian plague (anthrax). In 1887 he discovered a vibrio similar to that of cholera in the intestines of sick birds, which he named the Mechnikov bacillus. The study of this bacillus marked the beginning of many years of research in cholera.

In Pasteur's laboratory, as well as in those of Charles Bouchard and Joseph Strauss, Gamaleya studied the phenomena of inflammation and the processes whereby microbes are destroyed in an organism. He believed that microbes invading a living organism are subjected to the action of two closely related factors—humoral and cellular, that is, the action of soluble antibodies produced by the cells of the reticuloendothelial system. This research produced new data and concepts concerning these phenomena.

Returning to Russia in 1892 from France, where he had worked for a total of six years, Gamaleya initiated his study of cholera. In 1893 he defended his doctoral dissertation, *Etiologia kholery s tochki zrenia eksperimentalnoy patologii* ("The Etiology of Cholera From the Point of View of Experimental Pathology"). The study of cholera and the struggle against this disease occupied a conspicuous position in Gamaleya's scientific work and in his activities as a physician.

In 1899 Gamaleya published the textbook *Osnovy obshchey bakteriologii* ("Foundations of General Bacteriology"); its fruitful generalizations and original views on fundamental questions in bacteriology had great significance for the development of the new science. The hypothesis of a viral origin for cancer was first stated in this book, and in 1910 Mechnikov supported this hypothesis.

Until 1910 Gamaleya worked in Odessa at the Bacteriological-Physiological Institute, which he had founded, lectured on general bacteriology at the stomatology school, and published many works.

Gamaleya's importance in the history of bacteriology is as an outstanding researcher and fighter against bubonic plague. In 1902, in connection with a plague epidemic that had broken out in Odessa, Gamaleya began a theoretical investigation of its epidemiology. The system of practical measures he developed had a decisive significance in the liquidation and prevention of this dreaded disease.

In the period preceding the 1917 Revolution, Gamaleya actively concerned himself with prevention of epidemics. In 1908–1909 he conducted investigations of typhus; he was the initiator of a program of fumigation in Russia. From 1912 through 1928 he studied smallpox, which was endemic in Russia. As director of the Smallpox Inoculation Institute, he developed a new, refined means for obtaining smallpox detritus.

Exhaustive study of the theory and practical use of inoculations against rabies enabled Gamaleya to explain the causes of failures that had been observed in the application of the method and to propose the so-called intensive method, which was immediately accepted by Pasteur and introduced into wide use in critical cases of rabies. Gamaleya's work in paralytic rabies, then unstudied, was important. His research gained the high appreciation of Pasteur, who in 1887 conveyed his "keen appreciation for your rare services."

Gamaleya's proposals regarding the fight against cholera were exceptionally valuable in pre-Revolutionary Russia, where the low level of sanitation led to wide propagation of epidemic diseases. In contradistinction to the then accepted idea that cholera was spread exclusively by personal contact, Gamaleya contended that epidemics resulted from colossal multiplication of cholera bacilli in stagnant water. In this connection, he insisted on maximal observance of sanitation measures in densely populated areas. Moreover, Gamaleya proposed that cholera vaccinations be administered as prophylaxis. The success of this arrangement led to the complete elimination in the 1920's of cholera in the Soviet Union.

In 1883 Mechnikov had voiced his phagocyte theory of immunity. Gamaleya turned to a study of the mechanism of immunity against anthrax. Extensive and careful experiments in the preparation of vaccines and microscopic study of their action on anthrax bacilli in an organism enabled Gamaleya to establish the important regularity of the relationship between fever in the vaccinated organism and the manufacture of antibodies.

Study of the epidemiology of bubonic plague confirmed that it was transferred by the fleas on rodents. Having explained, in particular, the role of gray rats as carriers of the plague, Gamaleya launched a campaign during a plague epidemic for their complete extermination in cities. He also demonstrated that epidemic jaundice, mange, and typhus are also spread by rats. Following Gamaleya's suggestion, rats were annihilated not only by poison but also with the aid of microbes belonging to the paratyphoid group.

Gamaleya's many investigations of typhus were the result of much work on the surveillance of public sanitation. As early as 1874 the physician G. N. Minkh, having inoculated himself with the blood of a person suffering from relapsing fever, proved the contagiousness of this disease and put forth the hypothesis that it was carried by lice. In 1908 Gamaleya confirmed this hypothesis by epidemiological investigations. Studying methods for the annihilation of lice, he found that the only effective method was dry heat treatment (100°C.) of the infected insects, since their behavior is determined not by chemotaxis, as had been supposed, but solely by thermotaxis.

In studying tuberculosis, Gamaleya discovered various types of microbes that cause the disease. In 1910 he discovered a method for the cultivation of the tubercle bacillus in an artificial medium. He persistently worked on the creation of tuberculosis immunity and specific methods for treating the disease.

Gamaleya contributed greatly to the history of virology. He was the first to state, as early as 1886, that filterable viruses are pathogens of various illnesses. The subsequent development of virology has confirmed this brilliant vision.

Study of inflammation and the processes for destroying microbes led Gamaleya to the discovery in 1898 of certain bacteriolytic substances that destroy microbes. These previously unknown agents turned out to be bacteriophages, whose presence in nature was confirmed by d'Hérelle.

After 1917 Gamaleya successfully worked on problems of immunology, virology, and tuberculosis. Questions of sanitation, hygiene, and prophylactic medicine continued to remain the center of his attention. He was the scientific director of the Central

Institute of Microbiology and Epidemiology (1929–1931), which now bears his name. In 1931 he headed the organization of the Institute of Epidemiology and Microbiology in Yerevan. From 1938 Gamaleya headed the department of microbiology at the Second Moscow Institute of Medicine. He served as the organizer and permanent chairman of the All-Union Society of Microbiologists, Epidemiologists, and Infectionists.

Of Gamaleya's more than 350 works, over 100—primarily fundamental works and monographs—were written after 1917. Many have been published in translation.

BIBLIOGRAPHY

I. Original Works. Gamaleya's collected works were published as *Sobranie sochineny* (Moscow, 1956). Among them are *Etiologia kholery s tochki zrenia eksperimentalnoy patologii* ("The Etiology of Cholera From the Point of View of Experimental Pathology," St. Petersburg, 1893), his diss.; *Bakterynye yady* ("Bacterial Poisons," Moscow, 1893); *Osnovy obshchey bakteriologii* ("Foundations of General Biology," Odessa, 1899); *Osnovy immunologii* ("Foundations of Immunology," Moscow-Leningrad, 1928); *Filtruyushchiesya virusy* ("Filterable Viruses," Moscow-Leningrad, 1930); *Ospoprivivanie* ("Smallpox Inoculation," Moscow-Leningrad, 1934); and *Uchebnik meditsinskoy mikrobiologii* ("Textbook of Medical Microbiology," Moscow, 1943).

II. Secondary Literature. On Gamaleya or his work, see E. Finn, *Akademik Gamaleya. Ocherk zhizni i deyatelnosti* ("Academician Gamaleya. An Essay on His Life and Career," Moscow, 1963); N. P. Gracheva, *Bolshaya zhizn* ("A Great Life," Moscow, 1959); I. Gryaznov, *Nikolay Fyodorovich Gamaleya* (Moscow, 1949); Y. I. Milenushkin, *N. F. Gamaleya. Ocherk zhizni i deyatelnosti* ("N. F. Gamaleya. An Essay on His Life and Career," Moscow, 1954); and N. A. Semashko, "Pochetny akademik N. F. Gamaleya" ("Honorary Academician N. F. Gamaleya"), in *Nauka i zhizn,* no. 2 (1949), pp. 39–40.

V. Gutina

GAMBEY, HENRI-PRUDENCE (*b.* Troyes, France, 8 October 1787; *d.* Paris, France, 28 January 1847), *precision instrumentation.*

Gambey was a workman and then supervisor at the École des Arts et Métiers in Compiègne. He then worked for a time in Châlons-sur-Marne; on the death of his father he returned to Paris, where he started a small shop in St. Denis. There he manufactured precision instruments for physicists and astronomers.

The high quality of Gambey's instruments soon brought him to the attention of French scientific circles. In 1819 he was asked by the director of the Paris Exhibition to display some of his work there (perhaps as an attempt to regain the international prestige of French instrumentation, lost to Ramsden in England and Fraunhofer and Georg von Reichenbach in Germany). Gambey had only two months in which to prepare his work for the exposition; nevertheless, his instruments were awarded the gold medal and the Royal Society of London characterized them as being unsurpassed in Europe for elegance and precision.

Shortly thereafter Gambey built a portable theodolite for the Bureau des Longitudes. He also made the first cathetometer, for Dulong and Petit; a heliostat for Fresnel; and a vastly improved compass for Coulomb. Most important, however, he constructed a number of major instruments for the Paris observatory, of which the mural circle that he finished just before he died is his masterpiece. (A gigantic new equatorial was built from his plans after his death.)

Gambey won further gold medals at the Paris exhibitions of 1824 and 1829. He was a member of the Bureau des Longitudes and was elected to the Académie des Sciences in 1837 to replace Mollart.

At one time Gambey planned to emigrate to America, but was persuaded to stay in France by François Arago. Arago later said that whenever French scientists needed new and delicate instruments they turned to Gambey, who invariably solved the problem to their satisfaction.

Asit K. Biswas
Margaret R. Biswas

GAMOW, GEORGE (*b.* Odessa, Russia, 4 March 1904; *d.* Boulder, Colorado, 20 August 1968), *physics.*

Gamow's father, Anton Gamow, taught Russian language and literature. Gamow was an outstanding student at the Odessa Normal School (1914–1920) but, owing to the turbulent political conditions of the time, his early education in general was rather sporadic. In 1922 he enrolled in the Physico-Mathematical Faculty of Novorossysky University, but within a year he transferred to the University of Petrograd (Leningrad). There, in 1925, he carried out experimental researches on optical glasses and briefly studied relativistic cosmology under A. A. Friedmann before his attention was drawn to the exciting and profound discoveries being made in quantum theory in Europe: his first publication (1926) involved an attempt to consider Erwin Schrödinger's wave function as the fifth dimension (the other four being the usual spatial and temporal dimensions).

In the summer of 1928, the year he received his Ph.D., Gamow traveled to Göttingen, where he made his first major contribution to physics: his theory of nuclear α decay. Ernest Rutherford had found (1927) that RaC α particles incident on uranium cannot penetrate the nucleus, although their energy is roughly double that of α particles emitted by uranium. Gamow immediately recognized that the apparent paradox vanished if the emitted α particles were "tunneling through" the nuclear potential barrier—a characteristic wave mechanical effect. Quantitative calculations proved that the empirically established relationship between the nuclear decay constant and the energy of the emitted α particles (the Geiger-Nuttall law) could be completely understood. This same conclusion was reached virtually simultaneously (see *Nature,* **122** [22 Sept. 1928]) by R. W. Gurney and E. U. Condon at Princeton University.

Niels Bohr, impressed by Gamow's achievement, offered him a Carlsberg fellowship to enable him to spend 1928–1929 at his Copenhagen Institute of Theoretical Physics, where Gamow continued to study problems in theoretical nuclear physics—for example, the parameters governing the yield of protons in α-bombardment reactions. In addition, through correspondence and personal contact with F. A. Houtermans and Robert Atkinson, he helped make pioneering contributions to the theory of thermonuclear reaction rates in stellar interiors. In the fall of 1929, after a visit to the Soviet Union, Gamow went to the Cavendish Laboratory at Cambridge on a Rockefeller fellowship. There he recognized that Heinz Pose's recent results on the α bombardment of aluminum indicated that the α particles were undergoing nuclear resonance. Later in the year Rutherford asked Gamow to estimate the energy required to split the nucleus by means of artificially accelerated protons and, encouraged by the result, set J. D. Cockcroft and Ernest Walton to work on the construction of the accelerator, with well-known results.

In 1930–1931 Gamow received further fellowship aid to return to Bohr's institute in Copenhagen, where a major part of his time was devoted to preparing a paper on the quantum theory of nuclear structure, which he had been invited to deliver at Rome in October 1931, to the first International Congress on Nuclear Physics. After returning to the Soviet Union to renew his visa in the spring of 1931 he was denied permission to attend the Rome conference. Gamow spent the next two years as professor of physics at the University of Leningrad; then he and his wife, Lyubov Vokhminzeva, whom he had married in 1931, were permitted to attend the Solvay Conference at Brussels—an opportunity they took to leave the Soviet Union for good. After the conference was over, they spent successive two-month periods in Paris at the Pierre Curie Institute, in Cambridge at the Cavendish Laboratory, and in Copenhagen at Bohr's institute, before going to the University of Michigan. In the fall of 1934 Gamow was appointed professor of physics at George Washington University in Washington, D.C. He remained at George Washington University until 1956, when he transferred to the University of Colorado. At the same time, after twenty-five years of marriage, he and his wife were divorced; two years later he married Barbara Perkins.

Soon after accepting his position at George Washington University, Gamow persuaded Edward Teller to join him. By mid-1936 they had jointly discovered what is now known as the Gamow-Teller selection rule for β decay—Gamow's last major contribution to "pure" nuclear theory. Subsequently he concerned himself largely with applying nuclear physics to astronomical phenomena. Early in 1938, for example, he used his knowledge of nuclear reactions to interpret stellar evolution, that is, the Hertzsprung-Russell diagram and the mass-luminosity relation. At about the same time he organized a conference on thermonuclear reactions, the discussions at which contributed significantly to Hans Bethe's discovery of the carbon cycle. In 1939 Gamow and Teller, both of whom were strong advocates of the expanding-universe theory, traced the origin of the great nebulae to the formation of ancient stellar condensations which subsequently began separating from each other; in addition, they investigated the energy production in red giants. In 1940–1941 Gamow and M. Schoenberg explicated the role of neutrino emission in the production of the rapid and tremendously large increase in luminosity associated with novae and supernovae (exploding stars).

Concurrently, Gamow was establishing his reputation among nonscientists as one of the most talented and creative popularizers of science of all time. His first book-length venture, the well-known *Mr. Tompkins in Wonderland,* grew out of a popular article on relativity entitled "A Toy Universe" which he wrote in 1937 but which was rejected by *Harper's Magazine* and several other magazines. Not until C. P. Snow, then editor of *Discovery,* read it, published it, and solicited more was Gamow's career launched. In all, Gamow wrote almost thirty books, most of which were of a popular nature and most of which he illustrated himself. In 1956 his popular writings brought him the UNESCO Kalinga Prize and a lecture tour to India and Japan.

During World War II, Gamow served as a consultant to the Division of High Explosives in the Bureau of Ordnance of the U.S. Navy Department, studying, for example, the propagation of shock and detonation waves in various conventional explosives. Immediately after the war he went as an observer to the Bikini atomic bomb test, contributed to the theory of war games for the U.S. Army, and (after gaining top security clearance in 1948) worked with Teller and Stanislaw Ulam on the hydrogen bomb project at Los Alamos.

Yet Gamow's thoughts were never far from relativity and cosmology. In 1948 he predicted that all matter in the universe is in a state of general rotation about some distant center; at the same time he began developing his ideas on the origin and frequency distribution of the chemical elements, postulating that before the "big bang" there existed a primordial state of matter ("ylem") consisting of neutrons and their decay products, protons and electrons, mixed together in a sea of high-energy radiation—the basic ingredients necessary for the formation of deuterons and heavier and heavier nuclei as the universe subsequently expanded. Most of the detailed theoretical calculations were carried out by R. Alpher (assisted by R. Herman), which resulted in the well-known Alpher-Bethe-Gamow letter in *Physical Review* of 1 April 1948—Bethe's name, in one of Gamow's more famous jokes, being added gratuitously to conform to the Greek alphabet. This work also led to the prediction of a residual blackbody radiation spectrum, the remnant from the primordial "big bang," corresponding to a few degrees Kelvin. This radiation was first detected in early 1965 by A. A. Penzias and R. W. Wilson; much more definite evidence was found the following year by P. G. Roll and D. T. Wilkinson (in experiments initiated by R. H. Dicke and P. J. E. Peebles) at Princeton University. Cosmological questions concerned Gamow to the end, one of his last investigations being on the possible inconstancy of the gravitational constant and the charge of the electron.

In early 1954, less than a year after J. D. Watson and Francis Crick discovered the double helical structure of DNA, Gamow recognized that the information contained in the four different kinds of nucleotides (adenine, thymine, guanine, cytosine) constituting the DNA chains could be translated into the sequence of twenty amino acids which form protein molecules by counting all possible triplets one can form from four different quantities. This remarkable way in which Gamow could rapidly enter a more or less unfamiliar field at the forefront of its activity and make a highly creative contribution to it, often far more by intuition than by calculation, led Ulam to characterize his work as "perhaps the last example of amateurism in scientific work on a grand scale."

It earned him membership in a number of professional societies—American Physical Society, Washington Philosophical Society, International Astronomical Union, American Astronomical Society, U.S. National Academy of Sciences, Royal Danish Academy of Sciences and Letters—as well as an overseas fellowship in Churchill College, Cambridge.

Gamow was a tremendously prolific writer, having roughly 140 technical and popular articles, in addition to his many books, to his credit. (On the negative side, his historical writings, which like most of his books are of a basically "popular" character, are of marginal value.) He was tall, fair-haired, blue-eyed, and possessed a legendary sense of humor. He was very widely traveled, greatly enjoyed reading and memorizing poetry, spoke six languages (all dialects of "Gamowian"), and loved collecting photographs and other memorabilia.

BIBLIOGRAPHY

I. Original Works. A bibliography of Gamow's scientific and popular writings is included in his autobiography, *My World Line* (New York, 1970). The most important scientific papers consulted and referred to in text are the following: "Zur Wellentheorie der Materie," in *Zeitschrift für Physik,* **39** (1926), 865–868, written with D. D. Ivanenko; "Zur Quantentheorie des Atomkernes," *ibid.,* **51** (1928), 204–212; "Selection Rules for the β-Disintegration," in *Physical Review,* **49** (1936), 895–899, written with E. Teller; "Nuclear Energy Sources and Stellar Evolution," *ibid.,* **53** (1938), 595–604; "The Expanding Universe and the Origin of the Great Nebulae," in *Nature,* **143** (1939), 116–117, 375, written with E. Teller; "On the Origin of Great Nebulae," in *Physical Review,* **53** (1939), 654–657, written with E. Teller; "Energy Production in Red Giants," *ibid.,* 719, written with E. Teller; "The Possible Role of Neutrinos in Stellar Evolution," *ibid.,* **58** (1940), 117, written with M. Schoenberg; "Neutrino Theory of Stellar Collapse," *ibid.,* **59** (1941), 539–547, written with M. Schoenberg; "Rotating Universe?" in *Nature,* **158** (1946), 549; "The Origin of Chemical Elements," in *Physical Review,* **73** (1948), 803–804, written with R. A. Alpher and H. Bethe; "Possible Relation Between Deoxyribonucleic Acid and Protein Structures," in *Nature,* **173** (1954), 318; "Statistical Correlation of Protein and Ribonucleic Acid Composition," in *Proceedings of the National Academy of Sciences of the United States of America,* **41** (1955), 1011–1019, written with M. Yčas; and "History of the Universe," in *Science,* **158** (1967), 766–769.

II. Secondary Literature. See *American Men of Science; Current Biography, 1951; Physics To-day,* **21** (1968), 101–102; and *Nature,* **220** (1968), 723. See also P. G. Roll and D. T. Wilkinson, "Measurement of Cosmic Background Radiation at 3.2-cm. Wavelength," in *Annals of Physics,* **44** (1967), 289–321.

Roger H. Stuewer

GAṆEŚA (*b.* Nandod, Gujarat, India, 1507), *astronomy.*

Gaṇeśa was born into a Brâhmaṇa family of astronomers and astrologers. He was the son of Keśava of the Kauśikagotra and his wife Lakṣmî, and studied under his famous father, on many of whose works he eventually wrote commentaries. In his turn Gaṇeśa trained Nṛsiṃha (*b.* 1548), the son of his brother Râma, and Nṛsiṃha both commented on Gaṇeśa's *Grahalâghava* and wrote, in 1603, a set of astronomical tables entitled *Grahakaumudî* based on that work. Gaṇeśa also taught Divâkara of Golagrâma, many of whose descendants commented on various of his master's books. Gaṇeśa's last dated work, the *Vivâhadîpikâ,* was written in 1554; he must, however, have lived at least a decade longer in order to have been his nephew's teacher. So far as is known, he never left his native village.

Gaṇeśa wrote a number of works on *jyotiḥśâstra* (astronomy and astrology) and *dharmaśâstra* (Hindu law). These are listed by his nephew, Nṛsiṃha, in his commentary, *Harṣakaumudî,* on the *Grahalâghava:*

1. *Grahalâghava* (see essay in Supplement).
2. *Laghutithicintâmaṇi* (see essays in Supplement).
3. *Bṛhattithicintâmaṇi* (see essays in Supplement).
4. *Siddhântaśiromaṇivivṛti* (see essay in Supplement).
5. *Lîlâvatîvyâkṛti* (see essay in Supplement).
6. *Vṛndâvanaṭîkikâ.*
7. *Muhûrtatattvavivṛti.*
8. *Śrâddhâdivinirṇaya.*
9. *Chandorṇavavivṛti.*
10. *Sudhîrañjana.*
11. *Tarjanîyantraka.*
12. *Kṛṣṇâṣṭamînirṇaya.*
13. *Holikânirṇaya.*

To these the following can be added:

14. *Pâtasâraṇî.*
15. *Câbukayantra.*
16. *Pratodayantra.*
17. *Dhruvabhramaṇayantravyâkhyâ.*

The *Grahalâghava* or *Siddhântarahasya,* Gaṇeśa's main work on astronomy, was composed in 1520, when he was thirteen. It contains sixteen chapters:

1. On the mean longitudes of the planets.
2. On the true longitudes of the sun and moon.
3. On the true longitudes of the five "star-planets."
4. On the three problems involving diurnal motion.
5. On lunar eclipses.
6. On solar eclipses.
7. On calendrical problems.
8. On eclipses.
9. On heliacal risings and settings.
10. On the planets' altitudes.
11. On the altitudes of the fixed stars.
12. On the lunar crescent.
13. On planetary conjunctions.
14. On the *pâtas* of the sun and moon.
15. On calculating lunar eclipses with a calendar.
16. Conclusion.

The *Grahalâghava* has been the most popular Sanskrit astronomical treatise in northern and western India since the sixteenth century. Its popularity is reflected in the hundreds of manuscripts of it that are extant, in the several commentaries on it, and in the numerous sets of astronomical tables based on its parameters. The known commentaries are the following (for editions, see the list of editions of the *Grahalâghava* itself given below):

1. *Ṭîkâ* of Mallâri (*fl. ca.* 1600), the son of Divâkara of Golagrâma (published).
2. *Harṣakaumudî* of Nṛsiṃha (*b.* 1548), Gaṇeśa's nephew.
3. *Manoramâ* of Gaṅgâdhara (1586).
4. *Siddhântarahasyodâharaṇa* of Viśvanâtha (1612), the son of Divâkara of Golagrâma (published).
5. *Manoramâ* of Kamalâkara, the great-grandson of Divâkara of Golagrâma.
6. *Udâhṛti* of Nârâyaṇa (1635[?]).
7. *Sadvâsanâ* of Sudhâkara Dvivedin (1904, published).
8. *Sudhâmañjarîvâsanâ* of Sîtârâma Jhâ (1932, published).
9. *Mâdhurî* of Yugeśvara Jhâ (1946, published).
10. *Ṭîkâ* of Bâlagovinda.

The following astronomical tables are based on the *Grahalâghava*:

1. *Grahalâghavasâriṇî I* (the initial epoch is 1520).
2. *Grahakaumudî* of Nṛsiṃha (1603).
3. *Grahasâraṇî* of Gaṅgâdhara (1630).
4. *Grahalâghavasâriṇî* of Premamiśra (1656).
5. *Grahaprabodhasâriṇî* of Yâdava (1663).
6. *Grahalâghavasâriṇî II* (1754).
7. *Grahalâghavîyasâriṇî* of Gaṅgâdhara Varman (Bombay, 1907; 2nd ed., 1923).

Most of these sets of tables are described in D. Pingree, "Sanskrit Astronomical Tables in the United States," in *Transactions of the American Philosophical Society,* n.s. **58,** no. 3 (1968), *passim;* "On the Classification of Indian Planetary Tables," in *Journal of the History of Astronomy,* **1** (1970), 95–108; and "Sanskrit Astronomical Tables in England," in *Journal of Oriental Research* (to be published).

The *Grahalâghava* has often been published in India:

1. Edited with the *Ṭîkâ* of Mallâri by L. Wilkinson (Calcutta, 1848).
2. Edited with the *Tîkâ* of Mallâri and the

Udâharaṇa of Viśvanâtha by Bhâlacandra (Benares, 1864).

3. Edited with the *Udâharaṇa* of Viśvanâtha and a Marâṭhî translation by Kṛṣṇa Śâstrî Goḍabole and Vâmana Kṛṣṇa Jośî Gadre (2nd ed., Bombay, 1873; 5th ed., Poona, 1914; 6th ed., Poona, 1926).

4–7. Edited with the *Ṭîkâ* of Mallâri (Bombay, 1875; Benares, 1877; Delhi, 1877; Bombay, 1883).

8. Edited with the *Udâharaṇa* of Viśvanâtha and a Bengâlî translation by Rasikamohana Cattopâdhyâya (Calcutta, 1887).

9. Edited with the Hindî translation of Jiyârâma Śâstrî by Râmeśvara Bhaṭṭa (Kalyâna–Bombay, 1899).

10. Edited with the *Ṭîkâ* of Mallâri by Hariprasâda Śarman (Bombay, 1901).

11. Edited with the *Ṭîkâ* of Mallâri, the *Udâharaṇa* of Viśvanâtha, and his own *Sadvâsanâ* by Sudhâkara Dvivedin (Benares, 1904; repr. Bombay, 1925).

12. Edited with the *Ṭîkâ* of Mallâri and the *Ândhraṭîkâ* of Mañgipûḍi Vîrayya Siddhântigâr (Masulipatam, 1915).

13. Edited with his own *Sudhâmañjarîvâsanâ* and a Hindî *bhâṣâ* by Sîtârâma Jhâ (Benares, 1932; repr. Benares, 1941).

14. Edited with the *Udâharaṇa* of Viśvanâtha, the *Mâdhurî* of Yugeśvara Jhâ, and a Hindî *ṭîkâ* by Kapileśvara Śâstrî, Kâśî Sanskrit Series 142 (Benares, 1946).

The *Laghutithicintâmaṇi* consists of tables for determining *tithis, nakṣatras,* and *yogas* accompanied by a short introductory text; Gaṇeśa composed it in 1525. Of this work also there are hundreds of manuscripts as well as several commentaries:

1. *Ṭîkâ* of Nṛsiṃha (*b.* 1586), the grandson of Divâkara of Golagrâma and the nephew of Mallâri, the commentator on the *Grahalâghava.*

2. *Udâharaṇa* of Viśvanâtha (1634), the commentator on the *Grahalâghava.* Published.

3. *Ṭippaṇa* of Vyeñkaṭa, alias Bâpû.

4. *Ṭîkâ* of Yajñeśvara.

The *Laghutithicintâmaṇi* has been published twice:

1. Edited with his own Hindî commentary, *Vijayalakṣmî* (1924), by Mâtṛprasâda Pâṇḍeya, Haridas Sanskrit Series 76 (Benares, 1938).

2. Edited with the *Udâharaṇa* of Viśvanâtha by V. G. Âpṭe, Ânandâśrama Sanskrit Series 120 (Poona 1942), part 1.

The tables of the *Laghutithicintâmaṇi* are discussed in D. Pingree, "Sanskrit Astronomical Tables in the United States," pp. 47b–50b; and "Sanskrit Astronomical Tables in England."

The *Bṛhattithicintâmaṇi,* also consisting of tables for computing *tithis, nakṣatras,* and *yogas* and an introductory text, was written in 1552. It was much less popular than the *Laghutithicintâmaṇi;* there are only a dozen manuscripts, and the unique commentary is the *Sùbodhinî* composed by Viṣṇu, the son of Divâkara of Golagrâma and the brother of Mallâri. The text alone with Viṣṇu's *Subodhinî* is published by V. G. Âpṭe, Ânandâśrama Sanskrit Series 120 (Poona, 1942), part 2. The tables are described in D. Pingree, "Sanskrit Astronomical Tables in the United States," pp. 50b–51a; and "Sanskrit Astronomical Tables in England."

The *Lîlâvatîvyâkṛti* or *Buddhivilâsinî,* a commentary on the *Lîlâvatî* of Bhâskara II, was composed by Gaṇeśa in 1545. It was published in the edition of the *Lîlâvatî* produced by Dattâtreya Âpṭe, Ânandâśrama Sanskrit Series 107, 2 vols. (Poona, 1937).

The *Vṛndâvanaṭîkikâ* or *Vivâhadîpikâ,* a commentary on the *Vivâhavṛndâvana* of Keśavârka (a work on astrology applied to marriage), was written by Gaṇeśa in 1554. It was published at Benares in 1868.

The *Muhûrtatattvavivṛti* or *Muhûrtadîpikâ,* a commentary on the *Muhûrtatattva* of his father, Keśava (a work on catarchic astrology), was written by Gaṇeśa before the *Vivâhadîpikâ,* which refers to it. The *Muhûrtadîpikâ* has not yet been published.

The *Śrâddhâdivinirṇaya* is evidently a work on offerings to one's ancestors. No manuscripts are known.

The *Chandorṇavavivṛti* is a commentary on an unidentified work on metrics entitled *Chandorṇava.* No manuscripts are known.

The *Sudhîrañjana* is a work on the astronomical instrument of the same name. It has not yet been published.

The *Tarjanîyantraka* is presumably a work on another astronomical instrument called the *tarjanî.* No manuscripts are known.

The *Kṛṣṇâṣṭamînirṇaya* is a work on the festival of Kṛṣṇa's birthday, which falls on the eighth *tithi* of the *kṛṣṇapakṣa* of the month Śrâvaṇa. No manuscripts are known.

The *Holikânirṇaya* is a work on the festival called Holikâ which falls on the full moon of the month Phâlguna. No manuscripts are known.

The *Pâtasâriṇî* or *Pâtasâdhana* is a set of tables for computing the dates of *pâtas* of the sun and moon, accompanied by a brief explanatory text; Gaṇeśa wrote it in 1522. There are three commentaries:

1. *Vivṛti* of Divâkara (*b.* 1606), a great-grandson of Divâkara of Golagrâma.

2. *Vivṛti* of Viśvanâtha (1631), the son of Divâkara of Golagrâma.

3. *Vivṛti* of Dinakara (1839).

Neither the *Pâtasâriṇî* itself nor any of its commentaries has yet been published.

The *Câbukayantra* and *Pratodayantra* are works on the astronomical instruments called by these names. A manuscript of the latter is said to be dated 1516, when Gaṇeśa was only nine years old. Neither work has been published.

The *Dhruvabhramaṇayantravyâkhyâ* is a commentary on the second *adhikâra* of Padmanâbha's *Yantraratnâvalî* (*ca.* 1360). This *adhikâra* describes the *dhruvabhramaṇayantra,* which is an instrument for observing the north pole star. Its ascription to Gaṇeśa is uncertain. It has not yet been published.

BIBLIOGRAPHY

The editions of Gaṇeśa's works have already been mentioned. Very little else has been written of him or his astronomical system save my articles and books on astronomical tables, to which reference has been made. There are articles on him by Sudhâkara Dvivedin in his *Gaṇakataraṅgiṇî* (Benares, 1933; repr. from *Pandit,* n.s. **14** [1892], 58–63); by Ś. B. Dîkṣita, in *Bhâratîya Jyotiḥśâstra* (Poona, 1931; repr. of 1896 ed.), pp. 259–267; and by G. Thibaut, in *Astronomie, Astrologie und Mathematik* (Strasbourg, 1899), pp. 61–62. M. G. Inamdar, "An Interesting Proof of the Formula for the Area of a (Cyclic) Quadrilateral and a Triangle Given by the Sanskrit Commentator Ganesh in About 1545 A.D.," in *Nagpur University Journal,* **11** (1945), 36–42, deals with a passage in the *Buddhivilâsinî.*

DAVID PINGREE

GARNETT, THOMAS (*b.* Casterton, Westmorland, England, 21 April 1766; *d.* London, England, 28 June 1802), *medicine, natural philosophy.*

Garnett's importance derives from his influence on the aims, style, and method of operation of the Royal Institution in London, where he was the first professor of natural philosophy and chemistry. He was a famed lecture demonstrator who pleased intelligent public audiences. After indifferent schooling, he was voluntarily articled in 1781 to the mathematician and surgeon John Dawson.

In 1785 he matriculated at Edinburgh, where he was profoundly influenced by the chemical lectures of Joseph Black and the medical lectures of John Brown. He took the M.D. in 1788 and finished his medical education in London in 1789. Later that year he wrote the article "Optics" for the *Encyclopaedia Britannica.* He supplemented his medical practice, conducted in the north of England, with chemical analyses and lecture demonstrations, using equipment that he himself had designed and built. In 1795 he married Grace Cleveland. While waiting for passage to America, where he hoped to teach chemistry, he accepted the professorship of natural philosophy at Anderson's Institution in Glasgow. He resigned in 1799 to join the Royal Institution, then being organized. Count Rumford, who knew Garnett by reputation only, accepted his suggestions about necessary facilities and the design of the lectures. On 4 March 1800 Garnett opened the lectures; his first season was highly successful. Unfortunately, he became the victim of bouts of melancholy induced by the death of his wife in childbirth on 25 December 1798, and his second lecture season was not well received. Rumford's high-handed treatment of him only increased the tension growing between Garnett and the managers of the Royal Institution, leading to his resignation on 15 June 1801. Garnett subsequently set himself up in Great Marlborough Street as a lecturer, and he also edited the first volume of the *Annals of Philosophy, Natural History, Chemistry, Literature, Agriculture, and the Mechanical and Fine Arts.*

BIBLIOGRAPHY

I. ORIGINAL WORKS. The library of the Royal Institution owns some Garnett letters; the minute books of the Institution for this early period are regrettably brief, but the information is helpful. J. R. Partington, *History of Chemistry,* IV (London, 1964), 32, lists Garnett's chief publications. Garnett's *Observations on a Tour Through the Highlands and Part of the Western Isles of Scotland, Particularly Staffa and Icolmkill,* 2 vols. (London, 1800), II, 193–205, contains a description of the aims, plans, and *modus operandi* for Anderson's Institution in Glasgow.

II. SECONDARY LITERATURE. All accounts of Garnett derive from an anonymous introduction to his posthumously published *Popular Lectures on Zoonomia, or the Laws of Animal Life, in Health and Disease* (London, 1804), pp. [v]–xii. Garnett's portrait is the frontispiece. H. Bence-Jones, in *The Royal Institution: Its Founder and Its First Professors* (London, 1871), pp. 162–172, supplements this material with excerpts from Garnett's letters, including one of 23 December 1799, which outlines a plan for the operation of the Royal Institution. Richard Garnett wrote the biographical entry in *Dictionary of National Biography,* VII, 886–887. K. D. C. Vernon, "The Foundation and Early Years of the Royal Institution," in *Proceedings of the Royal Institution,* **39,** no. 179 (1963), 364–402, expands Jones's account.

JUNE Z. FULLMER

GARNOT, PROSPER (*b.* Brest, France, 13 January 1794; *d.* Paris, France, 8 August 1838), *medicine, zoology, anthropology, ethnology.*

Garnot became an assistant surgeon in the French navy in 1811. After several voyages to Cayenne and Martinique (1817–1818) as a naturalist, he worked in the Antilles from 1819 to 1820. He received the M.D. in 1822 with the thesis "Essais sur le choléra morbus." In August of that year he joined Duperrey's world voyage on the French corvette *Coquille.* Garnot and the pharmacist R. P. Lesson were to serve as naturalists for the expedition.

After visiting the Falkland Islands and adding much to geographical knowledge of them, the expedition rounded Cape Horn and crossed the Pacific. In the autumn of 1823 Garnot visited the southern Moluccas, New Zealand, and the island of New Guinea, and in January 1824 the *Coquille* went to Port Jackson for repairs. Garnot fell ill and returned to Europe on a merchantman, taking a great part of the expedition's collected material with him. Nearly all of this material was lost by shipwreck in July 1824.

During the *Coquille*'s voyage, Garnot paid special attention to the vertebrate animals and to several human tribes in the South Pacific. He collected and measured a number of skulls from these tribes and described the Alfurs, a little-known people who inhabit the interior of New Guinea. In addition, he found a plant, which was named garnotia.

The results of the voyage were published by Duperrey as *Voyage autour du monde exécuté par ordre du roi sur la corvette La Coquille pendant les années 1822–1825* (Paris, 1828–1832). The first section of this work, dealing with zoology, was written by Garnot and Lesson.

Garnot became surgeon first-class in 1825, and from 1827 to 1828 he worked at hospitals in Brest. He then became second surgeon in Martinique, where he worked as an obstetrician after his retirement in 1833. He was a corresponding member of the Académie Royale des Médecins and a member of several scientific institutions.

BIBLIOGRAPHY

I. ORIGINAL WORKS. Garnot's works include *Remarques sur la zoologie des îles Malonines, faites pendant le voyage autour du monde de la corvette La Coquille exécuté en 1822–1825* (Paris, 1826); "Lettre sur les préparations anatomiques artificielles du docteur Auzoux," in *Annales maritimes et coloniales* (1827); *Leçons élémentaires sur l'art des accouchements destinées aux élèves sages-femmes dans les colonies françaises,* 2nd ed. (Paris, 1834); and *De l'homme considéré sous le rapport de ses caractères physiques* (Paris, 1836). Articles by Garnot are in *Bulletin de l'Académie ébroicienne d'Évreux, France maritime, Journal des voyages, découvertes et navigations modernes,* and *Bulletin des sciences médicales,* **8** (1826), 273–275.

II. SECONDARY LITERATURE. For information on Garnot, see *Almanac général de médecine* (1839), p. 370; Charles Berger and Henry Ray, "Répertoire bibliographique des travaux des médecins et des pharmaciens de la marine française, 1698–1873," app. to *Archives de médecine navale* (Paris, 1874); A. C. P. Callisen, *Medicinisches Schriftsteller Lexicon* (Copenhagen, 1831; repr. Nieukoop, 1963), VII, 57; XXVIII, 155–156; and A. Hirsch, *Biographisches Lexikon der hervorragenden Aerzte,* II (Munich–Berlin, 1962), 689.

A. P. M. SANDERS

GARREAU, LAZARE (*b.* Autun, France, 16 March 1812; *d.* Lille, France, 1892), *botany.*

After military service as assistant surgeon in Maubeuge and Strasbourg (1836–1838) and as surgeon and pharmacist in Algeria (1839–1844), Garreau became professor of natural history at the University of Lille in 1844. His earliest researches dealt with the relative values of both surfaces of a leaf as sites of gaseous exchange, especially the exhalation of water vapor. He measured the amount of water excreted by placing small glass domes, containing a water-absorbing substance, on opposite sides of a leaf and found no direct correlation between the amount of evaporation and the number of stomata. He concluded that the epidermis determines transpiration, the cuticular layer being very important. On the veins, where transpiration was the most intensive, he found almost no cuticle.

Garreau also confirmed that leaves are able to absorb water, as Bonnet had proposed in 1754, and determined the osmotic properties of the epidermis and cuticle. Here he observed a more direct correlation between the exhalation of carbon dioxide and the number of stomata. Garreau discovered that there was no relation between the cuticle and the cells of the epidermis (1850). The cuticle already exists before differentiation of the epidermal cells occurs. He thought that the cuticle was a living tissue and that the younger the organ producing the cuticle, the stronger its osmotic activity.

Garreau also worked on the theory of respiration and nutrition of green plants, proposed by Ingen-Housz in 1779. In 1851 he confirmed the results of the work of H. B. de Saussure, who had shown that the great mass of the vegetable body is derived from the carbon dioxide of the atmosphere and the constituents of water. Garreau observed that reduction of carbon dioxide, which he called the nutritive function, was dependent on light and was independent of respiration. Although not strictly separating the effects of assimilation and respiration, Garreau protested against distinguishing a "diurnal" and a "nocturnal" respiration in green plants.

Further, Garreau showed that there was a direct

relation between respiration and heat production. The idea of a vital force within the plant body was deprived of one of its chief supports when it was recognized that the natural heat of organisms is the result of chemical processes induced by respiration. Garreau explained the high intensity of this phenomenon in *Arum* inflorescences by showing that the surface area is large in relation to volume.

Garreau married in 1846; he had four children. He was an officer of the Académie des Sciences and the Legion of Honor. In 1862 he became a member of the Institut Impérial des Sciences.

BIBLIOGRAPHY

I. Original Works. Garreau's works include "Sur la nature de la cuticule, ses relations avec l'ovule," in *Annales des sciences naturelles (Botanique)*, 3rd ser., **13** (1850), 304–315; "Recherches sur l'absorption et l'exhalation des surfaces aériennes des plantes," *ibid.,* 321–346; "De la respiration chez les plantes," *ibid.,* **15** (1851), 5–36; "Mémoire sur les relations qui existent entre l'oxygène consommé par le spadice de l'Arum Italicum en état de paroxysme, et la chaleur qui se produit," *ibid.,* 250–256; "Nouvelles recherches sur la respiration des plantes," *ibid.,* **16** (1852), 271–292; "Mémoire sur la formation des stomates dans l'épiderme des feuilles de l'éphémère des jardins, et sur l'évolution des cellules qui les avoisinent," *ibid.,* 4th ser., **1** (1854), 213–219; "Recherches sur les formations cellulaires, l'accroissement et l'exfoliation des extrémités radiculaires et fibrillaires des plantes," *ibid.,* **10** (1858), 181–192, written with Brauwers; *Recherches expérimentales: 1° sur les causes qui concourrent à la distribution des matières minérales fixes dans les divers organes des plantes; 2° sur la matière vivante des plantes et la circulation intracellulaire* (Lille, 1859), a diss. presented to the Faculty of Sciences of Strasbourg; "Recherches sur la distribution des matières minérales fixes dans les divers organes des plantes," in *Annales des sciences naturelles,* **13** (1860), 145–218; and "Mémoire sur la composition élémentaire des faisceaux fibro-vasculaires des fougères," in *Comptes rendus hebdomadaires des séances de l'Académie des sciences,* **50** (1860), 854–855.

II. Secondary Literature. Short descriptions of Garreau's work are to be found in M. Duchartre, *Rapport sur le progrès de la botanique physiologique* (Paris, 1868). An obituary notice appeared in *Journal de pharmacie et de chimie,* 5th ser., **28** (1893), 109.

A. P. M. Sanders

GASCOIGNE, WILLIAM (*b.* Middleton, Yorkshire, England, *ca.* 1612;[1] *d.* Marston Moor, Yorkshire, 2 July 1644), *optics, astronomy.*

The eldest son of Henry Gascoigne by his first wife, Margaret Cartwright, Gascoigne appears to have spent most of his short life at the family home in Middleton, between Wakefield and Leeds. By his own testimony his formal education was slight, and there is no hint whatever as to the origin of his interest or competence in scientific matters.[2] One can only say that both were fully developed by 1640, when he entered into scholarly correspondence, and that his work was cut off not long thereafter by his participation in the English Civil War. He died in the royalist disaster at Marston Moor.

From the time of the appearance of the telescope on the scientific scene in 1610, its utility for purely descriptive purposes was taken for granted. Nearly two generations were to pass, however, before its use was extended into the traditional business of positional astronomy. This great advance depended on three quite distinct developments: the conversion of Galileo's terrestrial (concave eyepiece) telescope to obtain a real image, the introduction of cross hairs into the image (focal) plane to enable accurate pointing of the telescope (and the instrument to which it was attached), and the invention of a micrometer to measure small angular distances within the field of view. The first of these was suggested by Johannes Kepler in 1611 and implemented by Christoph Scheiner shortly thereafter. For practical purposes, the remaining two steps had to await the work of Adrien Auzout and Jean Picard in the late 1660's: in fact, however, they were both taken by Gascoigne in the late 1630's. By the beginning of 1641 he had not only a fully developed account of the optical ideas involved but also a working model of the instrument and a limited number of satisfactory observational results.[3] Unfortunately, Gascoigne's work essentially died with him. His micrometer survived in the hands of Richard Towneley but was used by him primarily to dispute the priority claims of the French.[4] A manuscript treatise on optics that Gascoigne is supposed to have left ready for the press had already become untraceable by 1667.[5]

NOTES

1. Until the mid-nineteenth century Gascoigne was believed to have been born sometime around 1620. In 1863 W. Wheater (*Gentlemen's Magazine,* **215,** 760–762) provided evidence suggesting that he was born no later than 1612. John Aubrey, who appears to have been responsible for the original tradition, also indirectly corroborates the newer one with his assertion (*Brief Lives*) that Gascoigne "gave [Sir Jonas Moore, *b.* 1617] good information in mathematicall knowledge."
2. Aubrey credits the Jesuits with Gascoigne's education. Gascoigne himself says only that he "entered upon these studies accidentally" after leaving "both Oxford and London [without knowing] what any proposition in geometry meant."
3. The primary information on Gascoigne's results is found in his letter of February 1641 to William Oughtred, printed by Stephen P. Rigaud in *Correspondence of Scientific Men of the 17th Cen-*

tury, I (Oxford, 1841), 33–59. Extracts from other letters of Gascoigne (to William Crabtree) in the Macclesfield Collection were given by William Derham (*Philosophical Transactions of the Royal Society,* **30** [1717], 603–610), but the letters have never been printed in full.

4. On behalf of the Royal Society, Robert Hooke provided a description, complete with plates, of Gascoigne's instruments (*Philosophical Transactions of the Royal Society,* **2** [1667], 541–544).
5. See Towneley's report in *Philosophical Transactions of the Royal Society,* **2,** 457–458. Various papers including Gascoigne's passed from the Towneley family to William Derham at the beginning of the eighteenth century. See *Philosophical Transactions,* **27** (1711), 270–290. A. Shapiro has kindly called my attention to (1) a statement by John Flamsteed (Francis Baily, *An Account of the Revd. John Flamsteed* [London, 1835], p. 31) attributing to Gascoigne some advanced ideas on geometrical optics and (2) an acknowledgment by William Molyneux ("Admonition to the Reader," *Dioptrica nova* [1692]) of his indebtedness to Gascoigne through Flamsteed. Flamsteed obtained his information from letters written by Gascoigne to Crabtree, which were in the possession of Derham (*op. cit.*) in 1717 but may already have been lost by 1753; at any rate, John Bevis, writing in that year (*Philosophical Transactions of the Royal Society,* **48,** 190–192), cited only the letter to Oughtred contained in the Macclesfield Collection.

VICTOR E. THOREN

GASKELL, WALTER HOLBROOK (*b.* Naples, Italy, 1 November 1847; *d.* Great Shelford, near Cambridge, England, 7 September 1914), *physiology, morphology.*

Gaskell was descended from a prominent Unitarian family in the north of England. He was the third child and younger twin son of John Dakin Gaskell, barrister of the Middle Temple, who practiced his profession only briefly before retiring to private life. His mother, Anne Gaskell, was his father's second cousin.

Gaskell attended the Highgate School, London, and in October 1865 matriculated at Trinity College, Cambridge, where he was elected to a scholarship in 1868. He graduated B.A. in 1869 as twenty-sixth wrangler in the Cambridge mathematical tripos. With the intention of making a career in medicine, he remained at Cambridge to study science and quickly fell under the influence of Michael Foster, who came to Cambridge in 1870 as Trinity College praelector in physiology. Although Gaskell completed clinical training at University College Hospital, London (1872–1874), and received an M.D. from Cambridge in 1878, he never practiced medicine. At Foster's urging, he devoted himself instead to physiological research, beginning in 1874, when he went to Leipzig to work under Carl Ludwig in the famous physiological institute there.

Soon after returning to England in the summer of 1875, Gaskell married Catherine Sharpe Parker, daughter of R. A. Parker, a solicitor, and settled near Cambridge, where he continued his research. His income apparently came chiefly from private sources. From 1883 until his death he was university lecturer in physiology. In 1889 he was elected to fellowship of Trinity Hall, Cambridge, where he also served as praelector in natural science. The Royal Society named Gaskell as Croonian lecturer in 1881, a fellow in 1882, gold medalist in 1889, and Baly medalist in 1895. He received honorary doctorates from the universities of Edinburgh and McGill and served on the Royal Commission on Vivisection (1906–1912). He was survived by two of his four daughters and by his son, John Foster Gaskell.

Gaskell's career in research can be conveniently divided into four periods, corresponding approximately to the following dates and dominant interests: (1) 1874–1879, vasomotor action; (2) 1879–1883, the problem of the heartbeat; (3) 1883–1887, the involuntary nervous system; and (4) 1888–1914, the origin of the vertebrates. Despite the apparent diversity of these interests, there is a remarkable internal unity to Gaskell's work, one investigation leading logically into the next. Much of his work and approach demonstrate clearly the powerful influence exerted upon him by Michael Foster.

In 1874, at the suggestion and with the help of Carl Ludwig, Gaskell followed up work done earlier in the Leipzig laboratory on circulation in skeletal muscle. He focused on the quadriceps extensor muscles of the dog and recorded with a kymograph the effects of nerve action on the rate of blood flow from a severed vein. Upon returning to Cambridge in 1875, Gaskell continued to work on the same general problem but chose to work on the mylohyoid muscle of the frog. In the simpler tissues of the frog, where the arterial diameters could be measured directly with a micrometer eyepiece, Gaskell was able to clarify greatly a number of issues left doubtful in his work on the dog. His most striking result was that stimulation of the mylohyoid nerve in the frog invariably produced a steady dilatation of the arteries in the mylohyoid muscle. According to John Langley, "this was the most decisive instance known at the time of [vasodilator] action in a purely muscular structure." [1]

In 1878, after Rudolf Heidenhain had disputed several of his results and conclusions,[2] Gaskell reinvestigated the effects of nerve action on circulation in the muscle arteries of the dog. He claimed that his new work supported the results he had reached with the frog. "In the dog as in the frog," he wrote, "the vasomotor system for the muscles consists essentially of vaso-dilator fibres. . . ." [3]

By about 1880 Gaskell had turned from vasomotor action to the problem of the heartbeat. The shift was not abrupt, however, and emerged fully only after a transitional study on the tonicity of the heart and arteries. Gaskell found that acidic and alkaline solutions produced the same effects on cardiac muscle as on the smooth muscle of arterial walls. Both in the heart and in the arteries, acidic solutions induced muscular relaxation, while alkaline solutions induced muscular contraction. Gaskell used this result to propose a new mechanism for vasodilatation. He wished to replace the then standard view that dilatation depended on the action of ganglionic nerve centers. He suggested instead that the determining factor was the chemical condition of the lymph fluid which surrounded the muscle walls of the arteries. When a muscle was inactive, this fluid was alkaline and would therefore contribute to vasoconstriction. But during muscular contraction, the surrounding lymph fluid became acidic, so that the muscle walls of the arteries would then relax and the end result would be vasodilatation. This hypothesis was supported by Gaskell's observation that dilatation occurred in a muscle artery whenever that muscle contracted.

But Gaskell was already concerned with a problem of much wider scope than vasodilatation alone. He presented his work on tonicity as a contribution to the general problem of rhythmical motion, two important examples of which were vasomotor action and the heartbeat. He was obviously skeptical toward the prevailing idea that all forms of physiological rhythmicity depended on the action of nerve cells or ganglia. In this he followed the example of his mentor Foster, who was convinced that vasomotor action and the heartbeat were analogous and that both depended not on ganglia but on the inherent properties of relatively undifferentiated muscle tissue. It was directly to the problem of the heartbeat that Gaskell next turned, and it was Foster who most decisively influenced his approach.

In the Croonian lecture for 1881, dealing with the frog heart, Gaskell presented an important new method for studying heart action (later named the "suspension method") and insisted that cardiac inhibition depended less on nerve or ganglionic mechanisms than on the inherent properties of the cardiac musculature. The role of the vagus nerve in inhibition was reduced to that of being the "trophic" (anabolic) nerve of the cardiac muscle. Yet in the same lecture Gaskell produced impressive evidence against Foster's myogenic theory of rhythmicity and advocated instead the neurogenic view that discontinuous ganglionic discharges are responsible for the rhythmicity of the normal heartbeat. The background to this defection was exceedingly complex, but it derived from an initial assumption (which Foster himself accepted) that ganglionic impulses—whatever their role in rhythmicity—are somehow involved in coordinating the normal sequence of the vertebrate heartbeat.

Within three years Gaskell had resolved the problem of the heartbeat in favor of the myogenic theory far more persuasively than Foster had ever thought possible. Experiments on the tortoise heart were the source of Gaskell's new conception of the heartbeat, presented at length in a classic monograph of 1883. He explained that he had turned from the frog heart to the tortoise out of conviction that "the study of the evolution of function . . . . is the true method by which the complex problems of the mammalian heart will receive their final solution."[4] What he had found was physiological and histologico-evolutionary evidence that both the rhythmicity and the sequential character of the heartbeat could be explained without reference to ganglionic action.

Gaskell insisted first that a small strip of muscle cut from the tortoise's ventricle—and therefore clearly isolated from nerve structures—could nonetheless develop rhythmic pulsations at a rate equal to that of the normal heartbeat. Since, moreover, such a strip could continue to beat rhythmically for at least thirty hours after all stimulation had been discontinued, Gaskell argued that rhythmicity could arise automatically in cardiac muscle, that it was in fact "due to some quality inherent in the muscle itself."[5] This conclusion was in keeping with the somewhat similar and earlier work of Foster and Wilhelm Theodor Engelmann.

Far more novel and important was Gaskell's evidence that the sequence, as well as the rhythm, of the heartbeat could be referred solely to the properties of cardiac muscle. As the heartbeat is followed in its course through all the cavities of the heart, distinct pauses are observed at the junctions between the separate cavities. And since it is precisely here, in these junctions, that ganglia are most abundant, it had been assumed even by Foster that ganglia must play some important role in producing the pauses and thus in regulating the sequences. Gaskell was now able to offer an alternative explanation. That he was able to do so depended crucially on his decision to study the tortoise heart instead of the frog heart.

In the tortoise the cardiac nerves and their accompanying ganglia lie outside the heart itself and are relatively easy to remove. Gaskell found that their removal in no way affected the sequence of the heartbeat. He then focused on the cardiac tissue itself and sliced through the auricle until it consisted of two parts (A_s and A_v) joined at an upper ligature by a narrow bridge of auricular tissue. When this bridge was made quite thin, Gaskell could see a wave of contraction pass up A_s and then, after a pause, down A_v to the junction between auricle and ventricle, where another brief pause preceded ventricular contraction. Gaskell concluded that "the ventricle contracts in due sequence with the auricle because a wave of contraction passes along the auricular muscle and induces a ventricular contraction when it reaches the auriculo-ventricular groove."[6] This conclusion was confirmed by continuing to narrow the tissue bridge until it seemed that another section would sever it completely. At that point, the waves of contraction passing up A_s were "blocked" at the bridge and were unable to pass down A_v. The sequence between auricular and ventricular beats was thereby destroyed.

Gaskell then showed that the three muscular cavities of the heart (sinus, auricle, and ventricle) were connected by two narrow rings of relatively undifferentiated muscle tissue through which the waves of contraction could be transmitted from one cavity to the next. To explain why there are normally pauses at the junctions between successive cavities, Gaskell began by positing an antagonism between the capacities for rhythmicity and for rapid conduction of contractile waves. He suggested that the capacity for rhythmicity was greatest in undeveloped muscle tissue, while the capacity for rapid conduction increased as muscle tissue underwent development and specialization. Since the least developed (least striated) muscle fibers are found in the sinus, it must possess the greatest capacity for rhythmicity, and so the heartbeat naturally begins there. The more highly developed auricular and ventricular fibers, on the other hand, are especially adapted to conduct the wave of contraction rapidly; but the muscle rings connecting the heart cavities consist of relatively embryonic tissue, and the contractile wave therefore passes more slowly through them. This, rather than ganglionic action, explained the pauses observed at the sinoauricular and auriculoventricular junctions.

Before the discovery of cardiac ganglia and vagus inhibition in the 1840's, the heartbeat had generally been viewed as a simple peristaltic wave of contraction passing from one end of the heart to the other. In a distinctly evolutionary context, Gaskell now advocated a return to this view and repeatedly insisted that in every really important respect—in its rhythmicity and in its sequence—the vertebrate heartbeat depends in the first place not on nerve influences but on the properties of the cardiac musculature.

Gaskell's work of 1883 did not immediately convince everyone, and the myogenic-neurogenic debate continued for some time, especially in Germany.[7] The task of extending the myogenic theory to the mammalian heart proved more difficult than Gaskell had perhaps expected it to be, and he did not himself contribute to this extension. By about 1910 the extension had been accomplished—chiefly through the work of A. F. S. Kent and Wilhelm His, Jr., on the atrioventricular bundle in mammalian hearts, and through the work of Arthur Keith and Martin Flack on the mammalian cardiac pacemaker. With the possible exception of His, all of these workers depended fundamentally on Gaskell's work. Before long, and especially through the British clinical cardiologists James Mackenzie, Thomas Lewis, and Arthur Cushny, Gaskell's myogenic theory and his concept of heart block became incorporated into the pathology, pharmacology, and therapeutics of the heart. His conclusions have formed the basis of concepts of heart action ever since.

Although Gaskell's interest in the heart did not end abruptly in 1883, it soon became bound up with and eventually submerged in a general study of the involuntary nervous system. The starting point for this work was Gaskell's discovery that cold-blooded animals possess augmentor, as well as inhibitory, cardiac nerves. That mammals possess augmentor or accelerator cardiac nerves had been known for some time, and their existence in cold-blooded animals had been supposed by some. Particularly to explain the bewildering range and variety of the effects produced by vagus stimulation in the frog, the hypothesis had been advanced that the vertebrate vagus was not a simple nerve, composed solely of inhibitory fibers, but a compound nerve containing augmentor fibers as well. Decisive evidence for this hypothesis was lacking, however, and Gaskell himself specifically rejected it both in his Croonian lecture of 1881 on the frog heart and in his monograph of 1883 on the tortoise heart.

But after the summer of 1884, when Gaskell succeeded in distinguishing both inhibitory and augmentor cardiac fibers in the crocodile, he considered it probable that both sets of fibers were also present in other cold-blooded animals. In an elegant paper of 1884 he confirmed this view in the all-important case of the frog. Tracing the frog's vagus from its origin in the medulla oblongata, he found it to consist of two branches which then joined in a large ganglion outside the cranial cavity to form a single nerve trunk which continued toward the heart. It was this trunk that was ordinarily used to examine the effects of vagus stimulation. Gaskell focused instead on the two preganglionic branches and found that stimulation of one branch resulted always in purely augmentor effects, while stimulation of the other resulted always in purely inhibitory effects. The so-called vagus, Gaskell concluded, was in fact the "vago-sympathetic," consisting of a mixture of purely inhibitory and purely augmentor fibers which could be clearly distinguished from one another prior to their merger in the large extracranial ganglion.

Gaskell seems to have been greatly impressed by this discovery. With the help of a Cambridge colleague, the morphologist Hans Gadow, he extended his investigation of the cardiac nerves to as many different species of cold-blooded animals as possible. They found that these nerves were distributed in basically similar ways in all the species they examined. In all cold-blooded vertebrates, as in mammals, there existed two sets of cardiac nerves performing separate, indeed opposing, functions. A flood of ideas now burst forth almost simultaneously from Gaskell, as functional and morphological considerations became intertwined and mutually reinforcing.

For one thing, Gaskell noticed while studying the cardiac nerves in a tortoise that the functional distinction between vagus and augmentor fibers was correlated with a striking morphological distinction: although both kinds of cardiac fibers originated from the spinal cord as medullated fibers, the accelerator fibers emerged from the sympathetic chain without medullas, while the vagus fibers retained their medullas throughout their course. By early 1885 Gaskell had confirmed this rule in a wide variety of vertebrate and mammalian species. Then, in 1886, he showed that vagus stimulation produced in the tortoise's heart an electrical variation opposite in sign to that produced by stimulating the accelerator nerves. In thus providing demonstrable evidence that the two kinds of cardiac nerves did indeed perform opposing functions, Gaskell contributed to the rapidly developing field of cardiac electrophysiology, a field from which the electrocardiogram was soon to emerge.

Already, though, Gaskell was occupied with ideas of far broader significance. For him, as for Foster, the heart was just one example of an involuntary muscle; and he was confident that his results on cardiac innervation could be extended to the smooth muscles of the arterial, alimentary, and glandular systems. Gaskell had long believed (again with Foster) that the inhibitory action of vagus fibers was a constructive, beneficial, or anabolic action. He therefore supposed that the action of the opposing augmentor fibers was destructive or catabolic, like that of a motor nerve, leading to exhaustion of muscle activity. When generalized to the involuntary system as a whole, this concept led to the notion that every involuntary muscle was innervated by two nerves of opposite action, one anabolic and the other catabolic. By further analogy with the cardiac nerves, Gaskell expected these anabolic and catabolic nerves to be histologically distinguishable from one another, particularly on the basis of their medullation after passing the sympathetic chain. It was under the inspiration of these leading themes that Gaskell undertook a full-scale, systematic investigation of the involuntary nervous system.

A classic paper of 1886 contains the major results of Gaskell's work on the involuntary system. He found that the visceral or involuntary nerves arise from the central nervous system in three distinct groups. There is a cervicocranial outflow, a thoracic outflow, and a sacral outflow. In all three groups the visceral fibers leave the central nervous system as peculiarly fine, white, medullated fibers. But the fibers issuing from the thoracic region lose their medullas in the sympathetic ganglia and pass to the viscera as nonmedullated fibers. The fibers issuing from the cervicocranial and from the sacral regions retain their medullas as they pass to the periphery. In action the fibers issuing from the thoracic region appeared to be antagonistic to both the cervicocranial and the sacral outflows. In broad outline, this plan is still accepted, although significant modifications in detail and in terminology were soon made, especially through the work of another of Gaskell's Cambridge colleagues, John Langley, and especially in light of the neuron theory.

From the point of view of basic physiological thought, perhaps the most important result of Gaskell's work on the involuntary system was his discovery that the connection between the central nervous system and the chain of sympathetic ganglia is unidirectional, with the peculiarly small white fibers (the "white rami") supplying the sole connection. Earlier in the century it had been thought that a system of gray rami returned from the sympathetic chain to the central nervous system, creating an interplay between two essentially independent nervous systems. Bichat had christened these two systems the "organic" (central) and the "vegetative" (sympathetic). Although this mode of thinking about the nervous system had since come under criticism, no broad generalization had taken its place until Gaskell clarified the relationship between the sympathetic chain and the central nervous system. He showed that the gray rami are in fact peripheral nerve fibers which supply the blood vessels of the spinal cord and its membranes and which issue not from the sympathetic chain but from the central nervous system, as do the white rami. There is, then, no real separation into "organic" and "vegetative" nervous systems,[8] and, wrote Gaskell in 1908, "no give and take between two independent nervous systems . . . as had been taught formerly, but only one nervous system, the cerebro-spinal."[9] So fundamentally did Gaskell alter the prevailing conceptions of the involuntary system that Walter Langdon-Brown could insist that "to read an account of this system before Gaskell is like reading an account of the circulation before Harvey."[10] After their elaboration and modification by Langley and others, Gaskell's conclusions found clinical application, not only in the interpretation of referred pain by James Mackenzie and Henry Head but, more generally, in the work of Walter B. Cannon.

After 1888 Gaskell devoted all of his research to the problem of the origin of the vertebrates. This interest may at first seem remote from his earlier work, but it evolved logically out of his work on the involuntary nervous system. For what had especially struck Gaskell then was that the involuntary nerves arise not only from three distinct regions of the spinal cord but also from clearly defined segments within these regions. Deeply impressed by the similarity between this vertebrate arrangement and the central nervous system of the segmented invertebrates, he gradually elaborated the extraordinary theory that the vertebrates are descended from an extinct arthropod stock of which the king crab is the nearest living representative. He agreed that earlier attempts to trace the vertebrates to the segmented invertebrates had failed, but only because they all began with the assumption that the transition required a reversal of dorsal and ventral surfaces. This supposition was thought necessary in order to explain how it happens that in vertebrates the nervous system is dorsal to the alimentary canal, while in invertebrates the arrangement is reversed.

To explain this fact, Gaskell proposed the revolutionary hypothesis that the vertebrates arose by the enclosure of the ancestral arthropod gut by the growing central nervous system, and the formation of a new alimentary canal ventral to the nervous system. According to this conception, the vertebrate infundibulum corresponds to the arthropod esophagus, the ventricles in the vertebrate brain to the arthropod stomach, and the vertebrate spinal canal to the arthropod alimentary canal. Perhaps the most controversial element in the theory was Gaskell's notion that in the transition from invertebrate to vertebrate, a new alimentary canal was formed by epidermal invagination. This notion was in direct violation of two settled morphological tenets: (1) that the alimentary canal is the one system which endures throughout evolutionary change, and (2) that in all cases the alimentary canal arises from the hypoblastic germ layer, and never from the epiblastic layer, as Gaskell proposed. Against the first of these tenets Gaskell argued that it was folly to insist upon the importance and durability of the alimentary canal in evolution when the central nervous system, especially the brain, was so obviously the engine of upward progress. In making this point, he coined the aphorism "The race is not to the swift, nor to the strong, but to the wise."[11] Against the second tenet Gaskell argued that morphologists applied the germ-layer theory in a circular manner, deducing the layer from which a structure arose merely from its ultimate morphological destination.

Gaskell developed his remarkable theory in a series of papers from 1888 to 1906, and then—convinced that his ideas were not being seriously considered—gathered the evidence together in a full-length book, *The Origin of Vertebrates* (1908). Despite some minor support and a few pleas for open-mindedness, it too met a chilly reception from most morphologists, with one opponent accusing Gaskell of "diabolical ingenuity."[12] The direction of research since has gone against Gaskell's brave attempt to trace the vertebrates to an arthropod ancestor. While they would probably acknowledge that Gaskell's work contains interesting and suggestive material—on the endocrine system, for example—most morphologists today consider the vertebrates of common origin with the echinoderms.

A large, generous man of open and genial disposition, Gaskell was both criticized and admired for his inclination to bold generalization. His final years were clouded by his wife's debilitating illness and by a feeling that his deeply loved theory of the origin of vertebrates was not receiving a fair hearing. Even at Cambridge, where Gaskell lectured on the topic until his death, his audience decreased over the years until, near the end, the poignant scene is drawn of Gaskell closing his course by shaking hands with a lone remaining auditor.[13]

NOTES

1. J. N. Langley, "Walter Holbrook Gaskell, 1847–1914," in *Proceedings of the Royal Society,* **88B** (1915), xxvii–xxxvi, see xxviii.
2. R. Heidenhain *et al.,* "Beiträge zur Kenntnisse der Gefässinnervation, I, II. Ueber die Innervation der Muskelgefässe," in *Pflügers Archiv für die gesammte Physiologie des Menschen und der Thiere,* **16** (1878), 1–46.
3. "Further Researches on Vasomotor Nerves," p. 281.
4. "On the Innervation of the Heart," p. 48.
5. *Ibid.,* p. 53.
6. *Ibid.,* p. 64.
7. See, e.g., E. Cyon, "Myogen oder Neurogen?," in *Pflügers*

Archiv für die gesammte Physiologie des Menschen und der Thiere, **88** (1902), 222–295.

8. See Donal Sheehan, "Discovery of the Autonomic Nervous System," in *Archives of Neurology and Psychiatry,* **35** (1936), 1081–1115.
9. *Origin of Vertebrates,* p. 2.
10. Walter Langdon-Brown, "W. H. Gaskell and the Cambridge Medical School," in *Proceedings of the Royal Society of Medicine,* **33** (1939), section of the history of medicine, 1–12, see 6.
11. *Origin of Vertebrates,* p. 19.
12. See the lively discussion following Gaskell's paper, "Origin of Vertebrates," in *Proceedings of the Linnean Society of London,* sess. 122 (1910), 9–15. The discussion (pp. 15–50) includes both supporters and opponents of Gaskell's approach and ideas. For an anonymous and largely unfavorable review of Gaskell's book, see *Nature,* **80** (1909), 301–303. Gaskell's response is *ibid.,* pp. 428–429. Even more critical of Gaskell's work was Bashford Dean, in *Science,* n.s. **29** (1909), 816–818.
13. This paragraph is based in part upon a private communication from Lord Edgar Douglas Adrian, O.M., Nobel laureate in physiology or medicine, who was working at Cambridge during Gaskell's final years.

BIBLIOGRAPHY

I. ORIGINAL WORKS. The Royal Society *Catalogue of Scientific Papers,* IX, 967; XII, 262; XV, 220–221, lists thirty-four papers by Gaskell up to 1900. The most important of these are "On the Innervation of the Heart, With Especial Reference to the Heart of the Tortoise," in *Journal of Physiology,* **4** (1883), 43–127; and "On the Structure, Distribution and Function of the Nerves Which Innervate the Visceral and Vascular Systems," *ibid.,* **7** (1886), 1–80.

Other papers discussed in the text are "On the Changes of the Blood-Stream in Muscles Through Stimulation of Their Nerves," in *Journal of Anatomy and Physiology,* **11** (1877), 360–402; "On the Vasomotor Nerves of Striated Muscles," *ibid.,* 720–753; "Further Researches on the Vaso-Motor Nerves of Ordinary Muscles," in *Journal of Physiology,* **1** (1878), 262–302; "On the Tonicity of the Heart and Arteries," in *Proceedings of the Royal Society,* **30** (1880), 225–227, and in *Journal of Physiology,* **3** (1882), 48–75; "The Croonian Lecture: On the Rhythm of the Heart of the Frog, and on the Nature of the Action of the Vagus Nerve [1881]," in *Philosophical Transactions of the Royal Society,* **173** (1882), 993–1033; "On the Action of the Sympathetic Nerves Upon the Heart of the Frog," in *Journal of Physiology,* **5** (1884), xiii–xv; "On the Augmentor (Accelerator) Nerves of the Heart of Cold-Blooded Animals," *ibid.,* 46–48; "On the Anatomy of the Cardiac Nerves in Certain Cold-Blooded Invertebrates," *ibid.,* 362–372, written with Hans Gadow; "On the Relationship Between the Structure and Function of the Nerves Which Innervate the Visceral and Vascular Systems," *ibid.,* **6** (1885), iv–x; and "On the Action of Muscarin Upon the Heart, and on the Electrical Changes in the Non-Beating Cardiac Muscle Brought About by Stimulation of the Inhibitory and Augmentory Nerves," *ibid.,* **8** (1887), 404–415. See also "On the Relations Between the Function, Structure, Origin, and Distribution of the Nerve-Fibres Which Compose the Spinal and Cranial Nerves," in *Transactions of the Medico-Chirurgical Society,* **71** (1888), 363–376.

Gaskell provides some historical background and an excellent account of his mature views on the heartbeat in "The Contraction of Cardiac Muscle," in E. A. Schafer, ed., *Textbook of Physiology,* II (Edinburgh [1900]), 169–227. Of uneven quality is his posthumous monograph, *The Involuntary Nervous System,* J. F. Gaskell, ed. (London, 1916).

The Origin of Vertebrates (London–New York, 1908), pp. 6–7, gives a complete bibliography of Gaskell's papers on that topic up to 1906. The only other paper known to the author, cited in n. 12 above, provides a clear and succinct account of Gaskell's theory.

There is apparently no central repository for Gaskell's letters and MSS, and few seem to have survived. The library of the Cambridge Physiological Laboratory posseses Gaskell's reprint collection, deposited in about 100 file boxes and fully indexed. A very few letters can be found in the Sharpey-Schafer Papers at the Wellcome Institute of the History of Medicine, London.

II. SECONDARY LITERATURE. This article is based chiefly on Gerald L. Geison, "Michael Foster and the Rise of the Cambridge School of Physiology, 1870–1900," unpub. Ph.D. diss. (Yale, 1970), pp. 382–475, 493–513, *passim.* For a clear analysis of Gaskell's major work on the heart, see also Richard D. French, "Darwin and the Physiologists, or the Medusa and Modern Cardiology," in *Journal of the History of Biology,* **3** (1970), 253–274, see 267–273.

Of the available accounts of Gaskell's life and work, the most valuable is that by John Langley (see n. 1 above). Also useful are Walter Langdon-Brown (see n. 10 above) and Henry Head, in *Dictionary of National Biography, 1912–1921,* pp. 207–209. A critical reading should be given to F. H. Garrison and F. H. Pike, in *Science,* n.s. **40** (1914), 802–807.

GERALD L. GEISON

GASSENDI (GASSEND), PIERRE (*b.* Champtercier, France, 22 January 1592; *d.* Paris, France, 24 October 1655), *philosophy, astronomy, scholarship.*

The Gassend family used the form Gassendi, according to the Italianism then in style, but Pierre always signed himself Gassend. When a very young man, he was already a principal professor at Digne. His family had him continue his studies, which he pursued at Aix.

In 1614 he was accepted into minor orders and obtained a doctorate at Avignon. Two years later he took holy orders at Aix, where, from 1617 to 1623, he was charged with the teaching of philosophy. He was then initiated into astronomy by Gaultier de la Valette and into humanism by Peiresc, who became his patron.

A partisan of new ideas, Gassendi had printed in Grenoble a first volume of *Exercitationes paradoxicae*

(1624) aimed against the Scholastics; he prudently withheld a second volume. His reputation—and the size of his correspondence—increased, and a canonry at Digne assured his independence (he became provost in 1634).

In Paris in 1624 and again in 1628, he met Mersenne, Mydorge, the du Puy brothers, and Luillier. In 1629–1630 he traveled with the latter in the Low Countries, where he met Isaac Beeckman.

On 7 November 1631 he observed the transit of Mercury, and in his *Mercurius in sole visus* (1632) he treated the event as a confirmation of Kepler's ideas. He returned to Digne at the end of 1632 and undertook an extensive study of Epicurus' thought, in the course of which he expressed his own. At some junctures he clearly departed from the ancient philosopher, but at others he placed statements inspired by materialism next to affirmations of orthodoxy with which they were difficult to reconcile. He was, however, in no hurry to publish and seems even to have interrupted his researches in 1637 when Peiresc died. He resumed them again under the protection of the new governor of Aix-en-Provence, Louis de Valois, at whose behest he returned to Paris after election to the Assembly of the Clergy, a position he was obliged to renounce in 1641. At the request of Mersenne, he immediately thereafter composed the *Cinquièmes objections* to the *Meditations* of Descartes. The *Instantiae* was published in 1644.

Gassendi's growing influence led Louis de Valois and Cardinal Alphonse de Richelieu, archbishop of Lyons, to appoint him professor of mathematics (i.e., astronomy) at the Collège Royal in Paris in 1645. He published a *Leçon inaugurale* and a *Cours*, in which he set forth the system of Copernicus, while prudently falling back on that of Tycho. He taught for only a short time, however. His health was uncertain, and in 1648 Louis de Valois called him back to Provence, where he spent several years. His *Animadversiones* of 1649 contains a portion of his works on Epicurus together with the Greek text and translation of book 10 of Diogenes Laertius.

In Paris once again in 1653, Gassendi produced a third version of his great work entitled *Syntagma philosophicum,* but he did not resume teaching. He died at the home of his host, Habert de Montmort, and was buried at St. Nicolas des Champs on 26 October 1655.

Gassendi's *Opera omnia* was published in six volumes by his friends in Lyons (1658), according to a plan he had established himself. The first two volumes contain the *Syntagma;* the third, a series of scientific works; the fourth, the astronomical lectures and observations; the fifth, the *Lives of Astronomers* and Epicurean works, as well as the *Life of Peiresc;* and the sixth, the Latin correspondence he had selected to preserve. The *Animadversiones* was not reprinted in its original form until 1675.

Although he excited the curiosity and attention of others, Gassendi did not seek to do so. He was not the leader of the "libertines" and the future "philosophes." Olivier Bloch, in his authoritative thesis, sees in Gassendi a belated humanist rather than an avant-garde thinker.[1] There is no reason to question the sincerity of his testimonies of allegiance to a church of which he was a respected dignitary, as were his best friends, Peiresc and Mersenne. His true intellectual master was Galileo. In the *Exercitationes* of 1624 Gassendi had demonstrated his philosophic independence, and as early as 12 July 1625 he wrote to Galileo that he shared his Copernican ideas. But he never had to suffer the anxieties of the great Florentine. His choice of Epicurean atomism as a framework for the exposition of his ideas appears to have been more a revolt against Scholasticism than the expression of any profound conviction. Moreover, his erudition embraced all doctrines, including those of the church fathers, whereas he rejected such important elements of Epicureanism as the vertical fall and swerving of atoms.

Gassendi's eclecticism was that of a skeptic assured that no one doctrine penetrates to the essence of things—indeed, this is a constant aspect of his thought. Yet he proceeded as would a historian for whom the human mind had exhausted all possibilities, in contrast to Descartes, who wrote as if unaware that anyone had ever done philosophy before him. Gassendi's first published letter (to Pibrac, 8 April 1621) reveals an extreme diversity in what he chose to adopt and a great deal of personal assurance; he rejected only dogmatism, even when Epicurean. Bound by no fixed viewpoint, he could more easily go along with the traditions of his peasant milieu. If his morality preached happiness, his method for attaining it was conformist. A worldly type like Saint-Évremond thought him timid. A fanatic like J.-B. Morin consigned him to the flames. Descartes accused him of nothing less than materialism—thereby contributing more than slightly to the suspicion in which he was held. Gassendi, in turn, treated Descartes as a dogmatist. Moreover, he disappointed the materialists. Gassendi wished, Karl Marx declared, to put a nun's habit on the body of Lais.[2] In reality, Gassendi, believing Aristotle's metaphysics to be pagan, attempted to establish a metaphysics that would be Christian, but in harmony with the fundamentally anti-Aristotelian contemporary science.

In this undertaking Gassendi may simply have become aware of his own ambiguities.[3] A thorough study of the philosophical manuscripts preserved at Carpentras, Tours, and the Laurentian Library, and also of the published works, which repeat and correct each other (*Disquisitio,* 1644; *Animadversiones,* 1649; and the posthumous *Syntagma,* 1658), reveals neither the duplicity nor the denial suspected by Pintard[4] but rather an effort to bring the Epicurean elements, accompanied by their materialist tendency, together with the traditional Christian elements. The two had previously been juxtaposed in Gassendi's writings without being mingled—but not without contradiction. This became evident after the beginning of the dispute with Descartes in 1641 and in the new drafts of the Epicurean works first undertaken in 1642. The factors that Gassendi emphasized to achieve a synthesis between Epicureanism and Christianity were nominalism, finality, and vitalistic or chemical analogies. A discussion of these factors is required before asking whether Gassendi felt that Descartes's reproaches really hit their target.

Nominalism had been born in a Christian atmosphere, where it remained a minority position, inspired by awareness of the limits of human understanding (*modulus intellectionis*). Feeble beings that they are, men (*homonciones*) cannot reach essential truth but only appearances, or phenomena, conditioned by laws that they did not make and cannot understand. God established these laws in order that things might endure and satisfy the needs of living creatures. Man establishes a system of signs, of names, which permits him to identify things perceived and to communicate with other men. But the concepts thus formed are conventions, not universal propositions. The universal does not exist ontologically. God has given man a mind capable only of conceiving the universal as the result of repeated contacts between the senses and well-ordered material realities. In animals imagination and memory record the facts to be retained. In man the rational spirit enables him to combine these representations with a view to action, guided by coherent predictions and based on reflections that take time and that are true inferences and not intuitions of some reality beyond the reach of sensation. But there is an evident providential finality in the Creation thus interpreted, and it is further illustrated by the wonders of the universe, of which man is the consummation and the goal. Hence, final causes are the "Royal Way." They demonstrate the existence of God. The view was opposed to that of Descartes; and Gassendi, incidentally, refuted the ontological argument on which Descartes relied in much the same way that Kant later did.

Gassendi held that the atoms were the first things created, not in infinite number, as Democritus had said, but in a number sufficient to create the finite universe we know. They are endowed with an unalterable (in French *inamissible*) movement propelling them without interference in all directions through the void. There is no swerving (no *clinamen*). The collisions that necessarily take place annul motion and result in the appearance of immobility. Collisions form molecules which are particles identifiable by several attributes. The homogeneous atomic particles for their part are endowed only with shape, resistance, minimum size, and a "weight" that is the effect of their elementary movement. Molecules combine in fewer ways than atoms to form sensible objects, possessing not powers, or internal qualities capable of activity, but mechanical forces. Various circumstances may liberate these forces in such a manner that impressions are made on other objects, notably the senses of living beings. At this level, other forces become effective—for example, chemical forces.[5]

The dynamism that is sometimes noticed in Gassendian physics, and that justifies the expression *semina rerum* (borrowed from Lucretius) to designate the atoms, was merely this accumulation of an energy potential, conceivable even in biology. For living bodies are subjected to the same laws as others. Life is composed of movements of the "flower of matter," the animal soul, which in a way resembles Descartes's animal spirits and subtle matter. Science is thus relative to our needs, a view in which there was both sensationalism and pragmatism. Thus, Gassendi was not only a belated humanist but also a precursor of Locke, Condillac, and the positivists and empiricists of the eighteenth and nineteenth centuries.

These ideas contained the entire arsenal upon which future materialists could draw. Yet Gassendi had no thought of being a materialist in the later sense of d'Holbach or Marx. The clash with Descartes had revealed to him the way in which his works, still unpublished, could scandalize certain readers; his role as a priest led him to take this danger into account. But until then he had been able to conjoin faith with Epicureanism with as little fear as Galileo had earlier felt in juxtaposing Copernicus and the Bible.

Galileo had pointed out in his letter to the grand duchess of Florence (see below) that the Bible had originally been addressed to the early Jews in terms that they could understand, while Copernicus, for his part, had offered his work to the pope, and it was not at first thought heretical. By the same token, in Gassendi's view, God had the power to make the world from atoms, as the Epicureans held, and was equally able to illuminate it by making the earth revolve around the sun on the Copernican hypothesis.

Galileo explained his theological position in relation to science in 1615 in his letter to the grand duchess of Florence, Christine of Lorraine. The argument was immediately and widely disseminated, and Gassendi undoubtedly saw it at Aix. It was published in Latin in Strasbourg as early as 1635,[6] although in response to the condemnation of 1633. Descartes's opposition also obliged Gassendi to take "precautions." The word is Mersenne's, who, by publishing the *Cinquièmes objections* had provoked the dispute with Descartes. He spoke of precautions in praising Gassendi's works in a letter to Rivet (8 February 1642).[7] That was precisely the date on which Gassendi undertook a new draft of his Epicurean works. Gassendi may probably have made these modifications in order to persevere in the same project, not to remove ambiguities or to modify it in some unexpected way. Mersenne gave his approbation to the earlier version, while expressing satisfaction with improvements in the new edition. Freethinkers were the only ones who judged differently and for their own reasons: they hoped that this physics would teach man to dispense with metaphysics.[8]

Was such a result what Gassendi wished? Not at all. In the seventeenth century it was possible to conceive of God's having created the universe in a single stroke, but after a model that permits the most convenient analysis. The "fable du monde," which Descartes imagined to be separate from dogma without contradicting it, played a finalist role despite its author's intentions. The atomic model could be employed in the same fashion. An admirer of Gassendi, the physician Deschamps, asked whether, without impiety, one could say that.[9]

Gassendi's influence on epistemology may now be stated more precisely. Koyré summarized it by saying that Gassendi contributed to the new science "the ontology that it needed."[10] In order to eliminate "powers" and "acts," "accidents" and "qualities," whether occult or not, it was necessary to suppose fixed and measurable data in a medium that in no way influences what is observed. Such are the atoms, endowed with shape, solidity, impenetrability, and a natural tendency to motion, which is weight. Such is the void in which bodies move without interference and without any change occurring in their nature through mere endurance. Time does not "eat away" at things; rather their mechanical and spatial relations change in the course of time. Contrary to the Scholastic view, space and time are neither substance nor accident. They exist when their content disappears and when nothing is happening. They establish the general frame of any knowledge of reality—with atoms redividing in a homogeneous void and moving in the unalterable course of time. Gassendi was one of the first to state this universal, categorial law of space and time.

Despite his influence on the ontology of classical physics, Gassendi's scientific successes were not of the first rank. He owed what he achieved to his fidelity to the Democritean schema. Thus his study of *Parhélies* (1630) suggests a corpuscular explanation of light. His patient and thorough method made him a pioneer of observational astronomy, in which field Galileo had already set the example in 1610.[11] But the observations, which almost fill the fourth volume of his *Oeuvres,* could serve only as a model for his contemporaries without leading him to any major discovery. For example, he corrected the geographical coordinates acknowledged for use in navigation in the Mediterranean, and he rejected the discovery of Jupiter's new satellites announced by de Rheita in 1643.

The observation of the transit of Mercury, in which he alone was successful and which confirmed Kepler and, indirectly, Copernicus, caused widespread discussion. Koyré, however, reproaches him for having disregarded the mathematical form that enabled Kepler to determine the elliptical orbits of the planets.[12] Numerous sketches of various aspects of Saturn did not suggest to him the ring hypothesis, which Huygens proposed in 1659 without access to information that was much superior. Gassendi remained a prisoner of what the senses, even when fortified, are able to show. The *Cours* of 1644 at the Collège Royal (published in 1647) prudently presented Tycho Brahe together with Copernicus, while leaning sufficiently toward the latter to shock J.-B. Morin. In the *De proportione qua gravia decidentia accelerantur* of 1645, as in the *De motu impresso,* Gassendi defended—against the criticism of Le Cazre—the law of freely falling bodies, in which velocity is proportional to the square of the time elapsed and not to the distance traversed. But he never understood the importance of its having been deduced either from simple observations of motion on an inclined plane or in any other way.

In 1654 Gassendi joined to his other lives of astronomers the *Life of Copernicus,* in which the trial of Galileo, although not omitted, is barely mentioned. He thus insisted on the hypothetical and mathematical character of Copernicus' work, whereas in 1647 the *Institutio astronomica* had explained the condemnation of Galileo by considerations relating to Galileo himself, but presenting no objections to Copernicus' theories.[13] It is further worth noting that Gassendi followed Galileo in the error of regarding the phenomenon of the tides as a proof of the motion of the earth. As was well known, the periodicity of the tides does not correspond to that of the diurnal movement, and Descartes did not make this mistake.[14]

On one point—and it is an important one—Gassendi was more successful than Galileo: he correctly stated the principle of inertia. The experiment of the *De motu impresso a motore translato,* performed in 1640 in Marseilles, overthrew the argument of Copernicus' opponents against the movement of the earth. Gassendi arranged to have a weight dropped from the top of a vertical mast on a moving ship in order to demonstrate that it fell at the foot of the mast and not behind it, thus sharing in its fall the forward motion of the ship. Galileo considered the experiment unnecessary; he foresaw the result by reasoning.[15] Others, notably Bruno, had already spoken of it. But Gassendi understood that the composition of motions is a universal phenomenon: Every movement impressed on a body in motion in any direction whatsoever persists in Democritean space, which has neither up nor down. Motion is, in itself, a physical state, a measurable quantity, not—as the Scholastics maintained—the change from one state to another. It changes only through the interposition of another movement or of an obstacle.

Furthermore, Gassendi also corrected the formulation given by Kepler, for whom inertia was a tendency to rest: in classical physics, inertia is indifference to both motion and rest. On this point, Gassendi was guided by Galileo's experiments on the pendulum, in which motion is maintained without any supplementary impetus. In addition, Kepler's idea of magnetic effluents or forces gave him an intimation of the existence of universal attraction or, rather, universal interaction—although he was no more successful than Descartes in conceiving its transmission otherwise than by contact.[16]

Gassendian atoms and Cartesian subtle matter belong, as has been seen, to a single period of thought. Moreover, the idea of inertia was common to Beeckman, Gassendi, and Descartes, who all knew each other, and we know that Newton read Gassendi, as did Boyle and Barrow.

In 1650, on a mountain near Toulon, another experiment repeated the famous one of the Puy-de-Dôme.[17] Gassendi fully appreciated the value of Pascal's work. But the latter, in the *Équilibre des liqueurs,*[18] speaks indiscriminately of "weight and pressure of the air," whereas, guided by the corpuscular picture and not by the hydrostatic scheme referred to in Pascal's title, Gassendi could differentiate weight (which is constant for a given mass of air) from pressure (which varies according to the state of agitation, dilation, or contraction of this same mass). It is variations in pressure that affect the barometer and that measure not only the approximate height of the "column of air" but also the changes of state of the atmosphere, which are capable of influencing subsequent weather conditions. Of course, the barometric vacuum proves that the natural vacuum is not impossible; but what happens in the tube depends only on what happens outside. Koyré rightly points out that in this regard Gassendi anticipated Boyle, who read him closely and regretted not having done so earlier.[19]

Gassendi applied his empirical and experimental sagacity to other fields, often in collaboration with Mersenne. Together they estimated the speed of sound as 1,038 feet per second, a passable approximation for the time.[20] Physiology and dissection also interested Gassendi, as did all of natural history. However, he never completely renounced a false observation made at Aix in his youth when Payen made him "see" a communication between the two parts of the heart; but at least he esteemed Harvey and Pecquet. Numismatics and music also occupied him on occasion.

It is evident that Gassendi's influence on science was more philosophical than technical and more critical than systematic. He rationalized physics by introducing quantity into it through the measurements he undertook but above all by introducing atoms, those mutually combinable units that are capable of joining together in molecules and of producing measurable bodies. It is regrettable that with excessive modesty he refrained from propounding general views of the sort that can direct and enrich experiment a priori and that he did not envisage the possibility of applying mathematics to concrete, physical cases.[21]

NOTES

1. In Gassendi one sees primarily a precursor of Locke and Condillac, mentioned later in this article, as well as Hume. See *Tricentenaire de Gassendi,* pp. 69, 227.
2. "Avant-propos" to "Mémoire sur Démocrite et Épicure," in *Oeuvres,* J. Molitor, trans., I (Paris, 1946), xxii.
3. This and the following three paragraphs have been freely inspired by the excellent thesis of M. Bloch (see below), who generously lent it to the author.
4. Cf. *Libertinage érudit* (Paris, 1943), p. 301, *passim.*
5. On this point, Bloch rehabilitates Étienne de Clave, a chemist condemned in 1624 by the Parlement of Paris.
6. Letter, in *Le opere di Galileo Galilei,* Favaro, ed. (Florence, 1890–1909), V, 309 ff. Gassendi does not approach the position of "double truth" to the extent that Bloch (see especially his ch. 11) thinks he does in his desire to reconcile Epicureanism and literal dogma. He thought he could juxtapose not two truths but facts equally real although differently expressed. Misunderstandings taught him what "precautions" (see fol-

lowing note) to take, precautions that Bloch sets forth with extreme precision; but these do not go as far as fideism.

7. *Correspondance du P. Mersenne,* XI, 38: "M. Gassendi réfute puissament, dans sa Philosophie Épicurienne, tout ce qui est contre le christianisme, et, comme vous avez fort bien remarqué, il y prend des précautions." Rivet did not necessarily see what Mersenne was talking about. Mersenne, however, knew the drafts that preceded the one begun on this date as well as the draft of the *Instantiae,* which was later joined to the *Cinquièmes objections* and Descartes's *Responsa* to form the *Disquisitio metaphysica* (1644).
8. The author's conclusions in this and the preceding paragraph are inspired by new material introduced by Gassendi in later editions that has been studied in depth by Bloch; the author's opinions differ, in accordance with his knowledge of the respective positions of Descartes, Galileo, Gassendi, and Mersenne in regard to each other.
9. Letter of 14 Aug. 1642, in *Correspondance du P. Mersenne,* XI, 229–231.
10. *Tricentenaire,* pp. 176, 186.
11. Galileo sent Gassendi a telescope through Diodati; see letter of 25 July 1634 from Galileo to Diodati.
12. *Tricentenaire,* p. 188, n. 9. However, the *Syntagma,* I, 639a–b, mentions the elliptical trajectories of Kepler.
13. *Opera omnia* (Lyons, 1658), V, 60b, end of book III, ch. 10.
14. *Principes,* IV, 49–52.
15. *Dialogo,* in *Le opere di Galileo Galilei,* VII, 171; and Koyré, *Études galiléennes,* pp. 215, 229, 249, 252; and in *Tricentenaire,* pp. 189 ff.
16. Despite everything that set them apart, Descartes and Gassendi were often bracketed by authors of the end of the seventeenth century. See also n. 5 and the corresponding text.
17. Gassendi had spoken of the Puy-de-Dôme experiment in a supp. to the *Animadversiones* (1649) and of his own in a letter (6 Aug. 1652) to Bernier, who had assisted him in that experiment. (Dating the letter "anno superiore," he called Bernier's memory into question: his own "diaire" testified that the experiment took place on 5 Feb. 1650.) All this is taken up again in the *Syntagma* (*Opera omnia,* I, 203–216). See Rochot's articles in *Aventure de l'esprit* (Mélanges Koyré) and in Koyré, *Tricentenaire,* pp. 184 ff.
18. Pléiade ed., pp. 383 ff.
19. *Tricentenaire,* pp. 184 ff.; see also Bloch, ch. 8, especially n. 190, opposing Koyré.
20. *Tricentenaire,* p. 180.
21. Did Gassendi read the *Saggiatore*? See *Le opere di Galileo Galilei,* VI, 232, as well as the letter to Liceti (Jan. 1641), *ibid.,* XVIII, 295: "The book of nature is written in mathematical language."

BIBLIOGRAPHY

I. Original Works. The contents of the six vols. of the *Opera omnia* (Lyons, 1658), with a preface by Sorbière, are summarily described in the text. The work has been reprinted twice: N. Averrani, ed. (Florence, 1727); and in facs. (Stuttgart, 1964), with a pref. by T. Gregory.

Following is a list of Gassendi's principal individual works.

Scientific Works. Into this class fall *Mercurius in sole visus et Venus invisa* (Paris, 1632; 1658 ed., vol. IV); *De apparente magnitudine solis humilis et sublimis epistolae quatuor* (Paris, 1642; 1658 ed., vol. III); *De motu impresso a motore translato epistolae duae* (Paris, 1642; 1658 ed., vol. III), two letters to Dupuy, to which a third, to Gautier *contra* Morin and dated 1643, was added in the 1658 ed. (Gassendi's friends had published the Gautier letter earlier [Lyons, 1649] without his knowledge); *Oratio inauguralis habita in Regio Collegio, anno 1645, die Novembris XXIII, a P. Gassendo* (Paris, 1645; 1658 ed., vol. IV); *De proportione qua gravia decidentia accelerantur* (Paris, 1646; 1658 ed., vol. III); *Institutio astronomica juxta hypotheseis tam veterum quam Copernici et Tychonis. Dictata a Petro Gassendo. Ejusdem oratio inauguralis iterato edita* (Paris, 1647; 1658 ed., vol. IV); and *Tychonis Brahei . . . N. Copernici, G. Peurbachi et J. Regiomontani . . . vitae* (Paris, 1654; 1658 ed., vol. V).

Philosophical Works. This second class includes *Exercitationum paradoxicarum adversus Aristoteleos libri septem, in quibus praecipua totius Peripateticae doctrinae atque dialecticae excutiuntur; opiniones vero aut novae, aut ex vetustioribus obsoletae stabiliuntur, liber primus: In doctrinam Aristoteleorum universe,* issued independently (Grenoble, 1624); bk. 2, *In dialecticam Aristoteleorum,* did not appear until the 1658 ed. (vol. III) with the shortened title *Exercitationes paradoxicae adversus Aristoteleos, in quibus. . . .* It was separately published shortly afterward as *Exercitationum paradoxicarum liber alter in quo dialecticae Aristoteleae fundamenta excutiuntur* (The Hague, 1659); a text and French trans. appeared as *Dissertations en forme de paradoxes contre les aristotéliciens,* B. Rochot, ed. and trans. (Paris, 1959), in which bk. 2 is corrected according to the MS at the Laurentian Library (this MS was formerly at Tours but was stolen from there by Libri).

Epistolica exercitatio, in qua praecipua principia philosophiae R. Fluddi, medici, reteguntur, et ad recentes illius libros adversus R. P. F. Marinum Mersennum scriptos respondetur (Paris, 1630; 1658 ed., vol. III).

The *Disquisitio metaphysica seu dubitationes et instantiae adversus R. Cartesii metaphysicam, et responsa* (Amsterdam, 1644; 1658 ed., vol. III) consists of the *Objectiones quintae* of 1641 with the publisher Sorbière's addition of the *Instantiae* of 1642, after Descartes's *Responsa.* A text and French trans. of the *Disquisitio* was published as *Recherche de la métaphysique,* B. Rochot, ed. and trans. (Paris, 1962).

De vita et moribus Epicuri libri octo (Lyons, 1647; 1658 ed., vol. V).

Animadversiones in decimum librum Diogenis Laërtii, qui est de vita, moribus placitisque Epicuri, 3 vols. (Lyons, 1649; 2nd ed., 2 vols., 1675), was reproduced only in part in the 1658 ed. The Greek-Latin text of Diogenes, with philological notes, does appear in vol. V. The reworked doctrinal commentary was incorporated into the *Syntagma philosophicum* (see below). The *Philosophiae Epicuri syntagma, cum refutationibus dogmatum quae contra fidem christianam ab eo asserta sunt, oppositis per Petrum Gassendum* (1658 ed., vol. III), a sort of Epicurean breviary added as an appendix to vol. II of the *Animadversiones,* appeared separately (The Hague, 1659) with the preface that Sorbière had placed at the head of the 1658 ed.

His masterpiece, *Syntagma philosophicum* (*logica, physica, ethica*), was published posthumously (1658 ed., vols. I–II).

Correspondence. The *Lettres familières à Fr. Luillier* (*hiver 1632–33*), B. Rochot, ed. (Paris, 1944), is based on a MS that belonged to the heirs of the provost of Digne, now in the Bibliothèque Nationale (fonds latin 2643). The MS contains Gassendi's drafts of the Latin letters in vol. VI of the 1658 ed. Most of the letters addressed to him in the same vol. are in the Bibliothèque Nationale. The French correspondence with Peiresc is in *Lettres de Peiresc,* Tamizey de Larroque, ed., IV (Paris, 1893). Gassendi is frequently mentioned in correspondence of the period; see especially *Correspondance du P. Mersenne,* C. de Waard, Marie Tannery, and B. Rochot, eds. (Paris, 1932–). The bulk of his extensive correspondence in French and Latin is far from entirely known.

Miscellaneous Works. The biography *De Nicolai Claudii Fabricii de Peiresc, senatoris aquisextiensis, vita* (Paris, 1641; 1658 ed., vol. V) appeared in English as *The Mirrour of True Nobility and Gentility, Being the Life of . . . N. C. Fabricius, Lord of Peiresk,* W. Rand, trans. (London, 1657). It is especially useful as a source for the historian of early seventeenth-century science.

A curious, and anonymous, pamphlet of 1654 designed to calm widespread fears occasioned by an eclipse of the sun is reasonably attributed to Gassendi. It was reprinted by B. Rochot, ed., in *Bulletin de la Société d'étude du XVIIe siècle,* no. 27 (Apr. 1955), 161–177.

II. Secondary Literature. The following items have been selected from the bibliography (343 items, including MSS, printed texts, biographical and doctrinal studies, and various articles) in the thesis of Olivier René Bloch, *La philosophie de Gassendi: Nominalisme, matérialisme et métaphysique* (Paris, 1971); F. Bernier, *Abrégé de la philosophie de Gassendi,* 2nd ed., 7 vols. (Lyons, 1684); Henri Berr, *Du scepticisme de Gassendi,* B. Rochot, trans. (Paris, 1960), a trans. of the 1898 thesis *An jure inter scepticos Gassendus numeratus fuerit;* [J. Bougerel], *Vie de Pierre Gassendi* (Paris, 1737), which should be examined carefully because the author had access to documents that are now lost; G. S. Brett, *Philosophy of Gassendi* (London, 1908); G. Cogniot, "Pierre Gassendi, restaurateur de l'épicurisme," in *La pensée,* no. 63 (Sept.–Oct. 1955); P. Damiron, *Histoire de la philosophie au XVIIe siècle* (Paris, 1846), I, 378–503; René Dugas, *La mécanique au XVIIe siècle* (Paris–Neuchâtel, 1954), ch. VI, pp. 103–116; Tullio Gregory, *Scetticismo ed empirismo. Studio su Gassendi* (Bari, 1961); Pierre Humbert, *L'oeuvre astronomique de Gassendi* (Paris, 1936), completed by *Philosophes et savants* (Paris, 1953), pp. 79–107; A. Koyré, *Études galiléennes* (Paris, 1939), pp. 237 ff., repr. (Paris, 1966), pp. 304 ff.; F. A. Lange, *Geschichte der Materialismus und Kritik seiner Bedeutung in der Gegenwart,* 2nd ed., 2 vols. (Iserlohn, 1873–1875), which appeared in French as *Histoire du matérialisme,* B. Pommerol, trans., 2 vols. (Paris, 1921), and in English as *The History of Materialism . . .,* E. C. Thomas, trans., 3rd ed. (London, 1957), contains a section on Gassendi; Kurd Lasswitz, *Geschichte der Atomistik vom Mittelalter bis Newton,* 2 vols. (Hamburg–Leipzig, 1890; 2nd ed., 1928), II, 126–188; L. Mabilleau, *Histoire de la philosophie atomistique* (Paris, 1895), pp. 400–422; P. Pendzig, *Pierre Gassendis Metaphysik . . .* (Bonn, 1908); René Pintard, *Libertinage érudit,* 2 vols. (Paris, 1943), which contains, in vol. I, numerous analyses in which Gassendi is portrayed as the leader of a libertine *tétrade* and, in vol. II, an important bibliography (see also the MSS examined in his *La Mothe Le Vayer, Gassendi, Guy Patin* [Paris, 1943]); B. Rochot, *Les travaux de Gassendi sur Épicure et l'atomisme* (Paris, 1944); G. Sortais, *La philosophie moderne depuis Bacon jusqu'à Leibniz,* II (Paris, 1922); J. S. Spink, *Free Thought From Gassendi to Voltaire* (London, 1960); and P. F. Thomas, *La philosophie de Gassendi* (Paris, 1889). More a summary than an interpretation, it does not take into account the evolution of Gassendi's thought as represented by the *Syntagma.* Two collections of studies are *Pierre Gassendi, sa vie et son oeuvre,* Centre International de Synthèse (Paris, 1955); and *Tricentenaire de Gassendi,* Actes du Congrès de Digne, 1955 (Paris–Digne, 1957).

The MSS enumerated by Bloch are in the Bibliothèque Nationale and in the libraries of Tours (706–710), Carpentras, and Florence (Laurentian). Biographical documents are at Aix-en-Provence, Digne, Grenoble, Marseilles, Munich, Oxford, Stuttgart, and Vienna; in the Archives du Ministère de la Guerre, Paris; and in the Bibliothèque Nationale (fonds français 12270 and fonds Dupuy).

Some texts have been translated into Polish by H. L. Kolakowski (Cracow, 1964) and into Russian by Sitkovsky (Moscow, 1966), with studies.

It should be noted that the important study by G. Gusdorf, *Révolution galiléenne,* vol. III of Les Sciences Humaines et la Pensée Occidentale, 2 vols. (Paris, 1969), was used in the preparation of this article.

Bernard Rochot

GASSER, HERBERT SPENCER (*b.* Platteville, Wisconsin, 5 July 1888; *d.* New York, N.Y., 11 May 1963), *physiology.*

Gasser's father, Herman, was born in the Tyrol and emigrated as a boy to the United States, where he became a country doctor. His mother, Jane Elizabeth Griswold, came from an old Connecticut family. She trained as a teacher in the state Normal School of Platteville, which Gasser himself later attended. The controversies of the time concerning evolution, vitalism, and mechanism had led his father to acquire the works of Darwin, Huxley, and Herbert Spencer, which the younger Gasser read avidly. He entered the University of Wisconsin to major in zoology. Having completed quickly the requirements for a B.A. degree, he took courses in the newly organized medical school, where he first met Joseph Erlanger, with whom he was later to share the Nobel Prize. As the university was then only a half-school (two years) Gasser transferred to Johns Hopkins University, where the approach to medicine exactly suited his aims. Gasser's professional career was, in time, to involve him in teaching and administration as well as research. His other major interests were music, history, literature, and travel. His positions included instructor at the University of Wisconsin (1911–1916); physiologist at Washington University, St. Louis (1916–

1921); pharmacologist in the Chemical Warfare Service (1918); professor of pharmacology at Washington University, St. Louis (1921–1931); professor of physiology at Cornell University Medical College (1931–1935); and director of the Rockefeller Institute for Medical Research (1935–1953). On retirement he continued active research for nearly ten years. From 1923 to 1925 Gasser was in Europe working with A. V. Hill at University College, London; Sir Henry Dale at the National Institute for Medical Research; Walter Straub at Munich; and Louis Lapicque at the Sorbonne.

Gasser received academic honors from many universities both in the United States and Europe. He was a member of the National Academy of Sciences, the American Philosophical Society, and a number of professional societies. In 1944, Gasser and Erlanger were awarded the Nobel Prize for discoveries relating to nerve fibers, and in 1945 the Association of American Physicians awarded Gasser its Kober Medal.

Gasser's early work, dictated by the exigencies of World War I, was concerned largely with problems of traumatic shock and blood volume. Only after the war did his first work on nerves, written with H. S. Newcomer, appear. It concerned application of thermionic vacuum tubes to the study of nerve action currents. Then came the pioneering study, in association with Erlanger, on use of the cathode-ray oscilloscope as an inertialess instrument for recording action potentials of nerve and the initial analysis of their compound nature. Some problems arising at that time stayed with Gasser only to be resolved finally in his last paper, published in 1960. It is difficult in the days of near-universal television to imagine the early difficulties of oscillographic recording. Light intensity was so low that many repetitions of the nerve response were required to produce a photographic image, and tubes lasted but a few hours. Some consequences of these necessities were from one point of view essentially artifactual in nature. Typically, Gasser always was aware of, and concerned with, the possibilities of artifact. When it became possible to record single responses, it was apparent that they differed from those recorded during repetitive activity. A clue to the difference was found in subsequent study of the subnormal state of nerve, which, by responding repetitively, had influenced the early recordings.

Major problems that commanded Gasser's attention were the compound nature of the nerve action potential; the relation between nerve-fiber size and inpulse-conduction velocity; the excitability of nerve fibers in relation to after-potentials; potentials recordable from the spinal cord; the afferent fibers concerned with pain-producing impulses; and the morphology of unmyelinated fibers, with respect to their compound action potential and diameter-velocity relations.

Some of these studies were direct offshoots from prior work, while others represented an abrupt change in direction or a return to old problems still unsolved, for Gasser espoused the principle that there are two times for working on a problem—before anyone has thought of it and after everyone else has left it. As a result, Gasser was always the innovator or the finalist.

At the height of the controversy over which types of nerve fibers yield various compound action potentials, Gasser turned to the question of after-potentials and associated excitability changes. His studies showed the after-potentials and the excitability states associated with them to be closely correlated, but different in the several groups of nerve fibers. This proved crucial to the characterization of fiber groups, for by this means some somatic fibers and sympathetic preganglionic fibers overlapping in diameter and conduction velocity could be distinguished, as could be the somatic and sympathetic unmyelinated fibers.

Whenever possible, Gasser required that the results of two approaches to the same problem be congruent. A prime example is the convergent information from electron microscopy and oscilloscopic recording that he achieved virtually single-handedly with respect to unmyelinated nerve fibers. He, however, found minor incongruity between the division of somatic afferent myelinated fibers (A fibers) into the subgroups α, β, γ, δ recorded as elevations in the electrical response and the action potential reconstructed from anatomical fiber-size maps of the nerve made on the assumption that velocity varied in direct proportion to the diameter of the fiber. Unsatisfied, he finally identified the incongruity as a product of the method of leading from active nerve. Correcting this, he found that the potential of the skin nerve manifested but two elevations, α and δ. He wrote in his last published work, "Thus the action potential was brought into closer accord with the indications in the maps of fiber diameters." Characteristically, this remark was an understatement.

BIBLIOGRAPHY

A complete bibliography is included in Gasser's "An Autobiographical Memoir," with a preface by J. C. Hinsey, in *Experimental Neurology,* supp. 1 (1964), and in *Electrical Signs of Nervous Activity,* 2nd ed. (Philadelphia, 1969), written with J. Erlanger.

DAVID P. C. LLOYD

GASSICOURT. See **Cadet de Gassicourt.**

GASSIOT, JOHN PETER (*b.* London, England, 2 April 1797; *d.* Isle of Wight, 15 August 1877), *electricity.*

Gassiot, a wealthy wine merchant, was elected a fellow of the Royal Society in 1840 and was one of the founders of the Chemical Society in 1841. He also helped to endow the Kew observatory and for many years was the chairman of the Royal Society's Kew Observatory Committee. In 1863 Gassiot was awarded the Royal Society's Royal Medal in recognition of his work on voltaic electricity and on the discharge of electricity through gases at low pressure.[1]

In the late 1830's, when Gassiot began his investigations, the identity of static and voltaic electricity seemed likely. But if this were so, voltaic, like static, electricity ought to produce sparks before the circuit was completed. In 1839 Gassiot showed that even with a battery of 1,024 Daniell cells no sparks occurred. But if he used these cells either to charge a bank of nine Leyden jars or in conjunction with a circuit interrupter and transformer, he could produce sparks before contact. He also obtained sparks with a Zamboni dry pile of 10,000 cells and, later, of 1,000 cells.[2] But in 1843, using a massive battery of 3,520 zinc-copper rainwater cells, he produced sparks through 0.020 inch of air. Gassiot attributed his success to his great care in insulating the individual cells to prevent the loss of their electrical tension.[3]

At that time it had not been decided whether voltaic electricity is produced by contact between metals or by chemical reaction. In an attempt to decide this question Gassiot showed in the same paper that "the elements constituting the voltaic battery, when arranged in a series, assume polar tension before the circuit is completed. . . ." Yet a few months later he concluded that "to produce *static* effects in a voltaic battery, it is indispensible that the elements should be such as can combine by their chemical affinities. . . ." Furthermore, "in all the experiments I made, the higher the chemical affinities of the elements used, the greater was the evidence of tension." These discoveries gave further evidence to support the decision in favor of the chemical theory that had already been reached in 1839 by Gassiot's friend Michael Faraday.[4]

Faraday's discovery in 1838 of the negative dark space had revived interest in the glow discharge caused by conduction of electricity through gases at low pressure,[5] but Gassiot's interest in this discharge was directly stimulated by W. R. Grove's almost incidental report in 1852 that the discharge was "striated by transverse non-luminous bands. . . ."[6] In his initial investigations Gassiot showed that if enough care were exercised to achieve a sufficiently low pressure, striations could be produced in the Torricellian vacuum. Next he demonstrated that both a static electric machine and a Ruhmkorff coil with a Grove cell produced a striated discharge. This once again confirmed the identity of these two electricities.[7] He also noticed that a powerful electromagnet divided the striations into what appeared to be two distinct columns.[8] The paper in which Gassiot announced these discoveries was honored as the Royal Society's Bakerian lecture for 1858.

During the next two years Gassiot continued his efforts to obtain the striations, which he thought were caused by "pulsations or impulses of a force acting on highly attenuated but a resisting medium. . . ."[9] Although his theory here was not correct, his investigations produced much new information. First, because his 3,520-cell battery or a 400-cell Grove battery unassisted did produce striations, it was clear that the "induction coil is not necessary for the production of the striae. . . ."[10] Next Gassiot demonstrated experimentally that the striae exist only within a narrower range of pressure and temperature than the luminous discharge itself; that a sufficiently low pressure not only ends the discharge but also that this relative vacuum does not conduct electricity; that changes in the electrical resistance of the external circuit change the discharge; and that at least sometimes the luminous discharge is actually intermittent even though it appears to be continuous.[11]

In Gassiot's final group of experiments on the gaseous discharge he showed that in a series circuit containing two discharge tubes, if a magnet is used to interrupt one discharge, the electrical current in both is completely disrupted;[12] that excitation of a spiral "carbonic acid vacuum tube . . ." gives a brilliant white light;[13] that there is a mechanical disruption of the metal in the negative electrode;[14] and that changes in the external resistance in the electrical circuit also change the striae in the discharge.[15] Gassiot also perfected a rotating and vibrating mirror technique that he used to reconfirm his discovery that the discharge, under certain conditions, is intermittent. His last papers generally concerned improvements in spectroscopes. In particular he designed and had constructed a spectroscope with nine glass prisms and another with eleven prisms filled with carbon disulfide, which he presented to Kew observatory.[16]

NOTES

1. "Anniversary Meeting—President's Address," in *Proceedings of the Royal Society,* **13** (1864), 183–185.
2. "An Account of Experiments Made With the View of Ascer-

taining the Possibility of Obtaining a Spark Before the Circuit of the Voltaic Battery Is Completed," in *Philosophical Transactions of the Royal Society,* **130** (1840), 183-192.
3. "A Description of an Extensive Series of the Water Battery," *ibid.,* **134** (1844), 39-42.
4. *Ibid.;* see also Michael Faraday, *Experimental Researches in Electricity,* par. 2053.
5. *Ibid.,* pars. 1544-1560.
6. "On the Electro-Chemical Polarity of Gases," in *Philosophical Transactions of the Royal Society,* **142** (1852), 100.
7. "On the Stratification and Dark Band in Electrical Discharges as Observed in the Torricellian Vacua," *ibid.,* **148** (1858), 6.
8. *Ibid.,* p. 15.
9. *Ibid.,* p. 14.
10. "On the Electrical Discharge *in vacuo* With an Extended Series of the Voltaic Battery," in *Proceedings of the Royal Society,* **10** (1860), 36-37.
11. "On the Stratification in Electrical Discharges Observed in Torricellian and Other Vacua—Second Communication," in *Philosophical Transactions of the Royal Society,* **149** (1859), 137-160.
12. "On the Interruption of the Voltaic Discharge *in vacuo* by Magnetic Force," in *Proceedings of the Royal Society,* **10** (1860), 269-274.
13. *Ibid.,* p. 432.
14. *British Association Report* (London, 1861), section 2, 38-39.
15. "Experimental Investigations on the Stratified Appearance in Electrical Discharges," in *Proceedings of the Royal Society,* **12** (1863), 329-340.
16. *Philosophical Magazine,* **27** (1864), 143-144.

BIBLIOGRAPHY

I. Original Works. Gassiot's papers are listed in Poggendorff, I, 849-850, and III, 495; and in Royal Society, *Catalogue of Scientific Papers,* II, 779-780; VII, 741-742. Michael Faraday assisted Gassiot with some of his experiments on gas discharge. Faraday's notes on these experiments are reprinted in *Faraday's Diary,* VII (London, 1936), 412-461. There is no collected edition of his works.

II. Secondary Literature. There is no biography of Gassiot. Biographical information is based on the article on him in the *Dictionary of National Biography,* VII, 935-936, and on the references given there. The most useful survey of his scientific work is contained in the speech made by Edward Sabine, president of the Royal Society, in presenting Gassiot's Royal Medal. It is reprinted in *Proceedings of the Royal Society,* **13** (1864), 36-39. The debate about the "contact" and "chemical" theories of the voltaic battery is discussed in Edmund Whittaker, *History of the Theories of Aether and Electricity,* I (New York, 1960), 180-184. Whittaker's brief account of the work on conduction of electricity through rarefied gases, pp. 348-366, can be supplemented by J. J. Thomson, *Conduction of Electricity Through Gases,* 2 vols. (3rd ed., Cambridge, 1933).

Edgar W. Morse

GATES, REGINALD RUGGLES (*b.* Middleton, Nova Scotia, 1 May 1882; *d.* London, England, 12 August 1962), *genetics.*

Gates was one of several early geneticists who tried, unsuccessfully, to unravel the genetics of *Oenothera,* a particularly important botanical genus. The son of a farmer and fruit grower, he was educated in Canadian schools: B.A. (1903) and M.A. (1904) from Mount Allison University, Sackville, New Brunswick, and B.Sc. (1906) from McGill. During the summer of 1905 Gates was introduced to the complicated genetics of *Oenothera* (evening primrose) while studying at the Woods Hole Biological Laboratory; he pursued this problem in the research which later (1908) earned him the doctorate at the University of Chicago.

Oenothera had first come to the attention of biologists several years earlier, when Hugo de Vries discussed the genus in announcing the discovery of genetic mutations. De Vries had noticed several strikingly variant individuals in a field of wild evening primroses; these bred true when cultivated experimentally. In answer to a question which had long plagued biologists, de Vries had thus demonstrated the occurrence of new genetic types, appearing spontaneously and following the same inheritance patterns as older varieties.

De Vries' mutation theory was eventually validated on other species—particularly *Drosophila melanogaster*—but his original example did not stand the test of time; the mutant forms of *Oenothera* did not follow classic Mendelian patterns of inheritance. They were not, as biologists later learned, mutant forms in de Vries' original meaning of the phrase. At the time that Gates began his work, the genetics of *Oenothera* was regarded as extremely puzzling.

Gates studied the mutant forms of *Oenothera* cytologically rather than genetically. He discovered that one mutant species, *rubrinervis,* has chromosomes which form rings instead of aligning in pairs during meiosis; sometimes, as Gates demonstrated, this phenomenon can lead to an unequal division of chromosomes. Another species that Gates studied, *Oenothera lata,* had fifteen chromosomes instead of fourteen, the chromosome number of the parent species, *lamarckiana.* A third species, *gigas,* was tetraploid; it had twenty-eight chromosomes.

These cytological studies were widely applauded—Gates was awarded the Huxley Medal and Prize of Imperial College, London (1914), and the Mendel Medal (1911)—but they did little to explain the irregular breeding behavior of the primroses. Several decades passed before biologists were able to understand the genetics of *Oenothera.* Without a full understanding of the gene theory in general, as well as such particular phenomena as translocation, disjunction, and the balanced lethal system, the cytological facts that Gates discovered are difficult to interpret. He tried to interpret them in *The Mutation Factor in Evolution* (1915), but his analysis apparently did not win favor with the biological community.

After leaving Chicago, Gates spent two years at the Missouri Botanical Garden in St. Louis as an experimenter. In 1912 he crossed the Atlantic and began to teach, first as lecturer at St. Thomas Hospital, London, and then as reader (1919) and subsequently head (1921) of the botany department of King's College, University of London. As his administrative duties increased, his research activities decreased. He participated in the work of his graduate students; but until the early 1950's, by which time his interests had shifted from genetics to eugenics, Gates did not publish any additional significant work.

Gates had developed an interest in eugenics during the 1920's and published a textbook on the subject at that time, *Heredity and Eugenics* (1923). His subsequent researches, particularly into the pedigrees of Negro families, convinced him that mankind had had polyphyletic origins and that only a small number of chromosomes were needed to produce racial differences; he was also convinced that racial crossing was genetically harmful. Most anthropologists and geneticists did not agree with Gates on these points; this led him to found a new journal, *Mankind Quarterly,* in which he would be free to voice his opinions. His most significant eugenic discovery dealt with the gene for hairy ear rims, a characteristic of the Ainu of Japan; Gates located it on the Y chromosome.

Gates traveled widely, and late in life he often combined his travels with his eugenic investigations. From 1940 to 1950 he was in the United States, first on a lecture tour and then as honorary research fellow at Harvard. He was a fellow of the Royal Society and an officer of several other British scientific societies.

BIBLIOGRAPHY

A more complete biography of Gates and a complete list of his publications can be found in J. A. Fraser Roberts, "Reginald Ruggles Gates," in *Biographical Memoirs of Fellows of the Royal Society,* **10** (1964), 83–105.

Gates's studies of *Oenothera* mutants were published over several years: "Pollen Development in Hybrids of *Oenothera lata* x *O. lamarckiana,* and Its Relation to Mutation," in *Botanical Gazette,* **43** (1905), 81–115; "Hybridization and Germ Cells of *Oenothera* Mutants," *ibid.,* **44** (1907), 1-21; "A Study of Reduction in *Oenothera rubrinervis,*" *ibid.,* **46** (1908), 1-36; "Chromosomes of *Oenothera,*" in *Science,* n.s. **27** (1908), 193–195; and "Further Studies on the Chromosomes of *Oenothera,*" *ibid.,* 335. This work was summarized, and his theories of mutation advanced, in *The Mutation Factor in Evolution* (London, 1915); see also "The Cytology of *Oenothera,*" in *Bibliographia genetica,* **4** (1928), 401–492.

His eugenic studies and outlook can be sampled in *Heredity and Eugenics* (London, 1923); *Pedigrees of Negro Families* (Philadelphia, 1949); "The Inheritance of Hairy Ear Rims," in *Mankind Quarterly,* **1** (1962), written with P. N. Bhaduri; and his monumental textbook, *Human Genetics,* 2 vols. (London, 1946).

RUTH SCHWARTZ COWAN

GAUDIN, MARC ANTOINE AUGUSTIN (*b.* Saintes, France, 5 April 1804; *d.* Paris, France, 2 April 1880), *chemistry.*

Despite an unacademic family background (his father was a shopkeeper), Gaudin was active in science at an early age. In 1826, from Rochefort, he submitted his first paper to the Académie des Sciences in Paris, and in 1827 he gained the inspiration for much of his later work when he attended Ampère's lectures at the Collège de France. From 1835 to 1864 Gaudin was a calculator at the Bureau des Longitudes in Paris but, never holding a teaching or research post, he remained outside the Parisian scientific establishment. His one application for membership in the Académie des Sciences (1851) was unsuccessful, and the only formal recognition of his work by the Academy came in 1867, when he was awarded the Prix Trémont.

Gaudin's most important work was concerned with the arrangement of atoms within molecules and of molecules within crystals. The earliest statement of his views was contained in two short notes that he submitted to the Académie des Sciences in 1831 and 1832. The first of these notes, published in 1833, is remarkable since it contains a clear exposition of the gas hypothesis of Avogadro written some twenty-five years before the work of Cannizzaro and the Karlsruhe Congress made the hypothesis widely acceptable. Gaudin supported the hypothesis not in the form given it by Ampère but in its modern form. He correctly reconciled it with Gay-Lussac's law of combining volumes by supposing that the common elementary gases, such as hydrogen and oxygen, were diatomic, but that other gaseous substances, mercury vapor, for example, were monatomic, while others, notably many compound gases, were triatomic, and others again were of still greater complexity.

Of the other issues arising in the papers of 1831–1833 the one that was to prove most absorbing for Gaudin concerned the possible relationship between the physical and chemical properties of substances and the spatial arrangement of the atoms that composed them. It was not until 1847 that he returned to the problem, but from that year he wrote extensively on the subject until 1873, when he published his views in a definitive form in his *L'architecture du monde des atomes.* In the forty years that had elapsed since they were first expounded, his ideas had changed little, and they were largely obsolete by 1873. Not surprisingly, the book received little attention and stimulated no further work.

Despite his obvious debt to Ampère and to Haüy, Gaudin's treatment of molecular and crystalline structure showed a good deal of originality. He rejected Ampère's assumption that even the simplest molecules were polyhedral; and although he adopted a polyhedral form for the more complex molecules, he also abandoned Ampère's set of basic molecular shapes. Instead he chose his structures in accordance with a rigorously held belief that the atoms within a molecule were always arranged symmetrically. Hence any structure Gaudin proposed had not only to be consistent with the usual crystallographic data and the evidence of chemical composition but also to show symmetry, and this restriction caused his views on crystal structure to deviate considerably from those of Ampère and Haüy. His preoccupation with symmetry also affected his views on chemical combination. In particular it led him to reject the theory of radicals and the type theory, since he believed that symmetry would be destroyed by the simple replacement of certain atoms by others. According to Gaudin, it was only by a complete rearrangement of the atoms of the combining molecules that symmetry could be restored after a reaction.

In his long scientific career Gaudin was active in several other lines of research. He worked in microscopy, invented an ingenious pneumatic pump (1827), and showed a special interest in experimental work at high temperatures. It was Gaudin who prepared the fused quartz for Biot's work on optical activity in 1839, and he is noted for his method of preparing artificial rubies using an oxyhydrogen blowpipe. An important pioneer of photography, he wrote a comprehensive textbook on this subject in 1844. In his photographic work he was closely associated with his brother Alexis.

BIBLIOGRAPHY

I. ORIGINAL WORKS. *L'architecture du monde des atomes dévoilant la structure des composés chimiques et leur cristallogénie* (Paris, 1873) is Gaudin's most important book, but he published much else. His *Traité pratique de photographie* (Paris, 1844) is an admirable practical handbook of photography, and "Recherches sur la structure intime des corps inorganiques définis," in *Annales de chimie et de physique,* 2nd ser., **52** (1833), 113–133, is of great historical interest. Most of his numerous communications to the Académie des Sciences are noted in *Comptes rendus hebdomadaires des séances de l'Académie des sciences.*

II. SECONDARY LITERATURE. The best studies are M. Delépine, "Une étape de la notion d'atomes et de molécules," in *Bulletin de la Société chimique de France,* 5th ser., **2** (1935), 1–15, with supp. note by G. Urbain, 16–17; and S. H. Mauskopf, "The Atomic Structural Theories of Ampère and Gaudin: Molecular Speculation and Avogadro's Hypothesis," in *Isis,* **60** (1969), 61–74. Biographical information is scarce, but a useful supp. to the standard biographical dictionaries, such as the *Nouvelle biographie générale,* is in *Bulletin de la Société des archives historiques de la Saintonge et de l'Aunis,* **2** (1880), 163.

ROBERT FOX

GAUDRY, ALBERT JEAN (*b.* St.-Germain-en-Laye, France, 15 September 1827; *d.* Paris, France, 27 November 1908), *paleontology.*

Two events of Gaudry's youth strongly influenced his work. First, his mother died when he was quite young and, at the age of seventy, he still cried over her death; this emotional shock, from which he never recovered, may account for the tenderness mixed with mysticism that characterized both the man and his work. Second, his father, a renowned lawyer and historian, collected minerals and associated with geologists; one of these geologists, Alcide d'Orbigny, explorer of South America and founder of modern stratigraphic paleontology, married Gaudry's sister around 1845 and guided Gaudry's career.

Having completed his advanced studies, Gaudry entered the Muséum d'Histoire Naturelle at Paris in 1851, in the laboratory of the mineralogist P. L. A. Cordier. There he prepared a doctoral dissertation on the occurrence of flint in chalk strata, which he defended in 1852. He was then a timid young man, short and frail, with a shrill voice, a refined and gentle face, and blond hair. This fragile appearance concealed much courage, tenacity, and physical strength—qualities demonstrated in 1853, during a fatiguing but profitable geological mission in the countries of the eastern Mediterranean, including Cyprus.

While Gaudry was on this mission, the government, convinced of the scientific importance of fossil study, created a chair of paleontology at the museum for Alcide d'Orbigny, despite the opposition of that institution's professors, who believed that each of them should be entrusted with preserving the fossils relating to his own discipline: the professor of malacology, for example, would be curator of mollusks; the botany professor, of fossil plants; and so on. D'Orbigny made his young brother-in-law his assistant, and Gaudry henceforth devoted the major portion of his time to paleontology. In 1855 and 1860 he carried out two excavations in Attica, in the Tertiary mammal deposit at Pikermi. The fossil remains that he brought back enabled him to reconstruct several skeletons of new species. Some of them displayed characteristics intermediate to those of species already known; and in an article of February 1859 on the life and work of d'Orbigny, who had died in 1857, Gaudry explained that these intermediate species "restore the links which were missing in the great chain of beings." He repeated here almost verbatim the expression used in 1833 by the founder of evolutionary paleontology, Étienne Geoffroy Saint-Hilaire, regarding the fossil remains of Auvergne.

Published nine months before Darwin's *On the Origin of Species,* Gaudry's article drew no inspiration whatever from the ideas of the English naturalist, as Gaudry subsequently indicated. For him, biological evolution resulted from a continuous creation by God. He did not destroy His previous creations (as d'Orbigny believed); rather, He maintained the species through time, perfecting and transforming them until the sublime masterpiece—man—was finally attained. Each transformation reflected the infinite beauty of God, as Gaudry wrote (1862) in his great monograph on Attica, in which he established, following extensive research, remarkable genealogical trees of five large groups of mammals. Several years later he proposed dating stratigraphic terrains according to the degree of evolution of the fossils they contained, and he applied this new method successfully to the mammals of the Tertiary in *Animaux fossiles du Mont-Léberon* (1873).

From 1866 to 1892 Gaudry studied very small reptiles and batrachians, remarkable for their archaic anatomical type and great age, since they originated in the schists of Autun (Sâone-et-Loire), which date from the Lower Permian. He also had a marked predilection for the Quaternary. His thorough excavations at St.-Acheul, near Amiens, in September 1859 removed the last doubts concerning the contemporaneity of man and the large extinct mammals. In 1894 Gaudry confirmed that the archaic chipped flints of Abbeville (Somme) were associated with the teeth of the advanced *Elephas meridionalis,* a finding which placed the appearance of man very far back in time. But the majority of geologists, even his favorite student, Marcellin Boule, refused—wrongly—to believe him, despite his great reputation.

Gaudry's friend and biographer, Gustave-Frédéric Dollfus, remarked: "There are some ideas so advanced that they triumph only after the disappearance of the generation which fought them; Gaudry lived long enough to witness the progressive spread of his doctrine." Nevertheless, during the major portion of his scientific career Gaudry encountered the animosity of the older naturalists, who reproached him for wanting to make paleontology an independent science capable of providing support for the theory of evolution. Fortunately, Gaudry's family and that of his wife were wealthy and had important connections. In 1868 Victor Duruy, the eminent minister of education under Napoleon III, placed Gaudry in charge of a course in paleontology at the Sorbonne and attended the inaugural lecture. In 1871, when Duruy was no longer minister, the course was canceled. In 1872 Gaudry was finally appointed professor of paleontology at the Muséum d'Histoire Naturelle. His colleagues removed from his laboratory the bulk of the paleontology collections, even those that he himself had assembled, and gave them to the professor of comparative anatomy; they were not returned to Gaudry until 1878. In 1885 he began to carry out, in a wooden shed, the project he had conceived in 1859: a museum of evolution where the public would follow, from room to room, the perfecting of the species.

For Gaudry the theory of evolution bore a spiritual message: Living beings form one family, one great unity, which has become more perfect through time; intelligence, created last, has not completed its development; God is the sole fixed point of this universe where everything is changing; if life is an immense progression, then "he who says progression says union, [and] he who says union says love. The great law which rules life is a law of love." Wishing to spread this message, so different from Darwin's, Gaudry devoted time to writing works of high-level popularization. They were presented in a limpid style that revealed his artistic sensibility and were illustrated by beautiful wood engravings. His most important book, published in three volumes under the title *Les enchaînements du monde animal* (1878–1890), was concluded by *Essai de paléontologie philosophique* (1896).

In 1902 paleontologists throughout the world celebrated Gaudry's jubilee. He was the first who ventured to reestablish the respectability of the evolutionary paleontology founded by Étienne Geoffroy Saint-Hilaire, and only paleontology could prove that biological evolution was a tangible reality.

BIBLIOGRAPHY

I. Original Works. A list of Gaudry's scientific writings, in the notice by Thévenin (see below), consists of 191 titles. The Royal Society's *Catalogue of Scientific Papers* (II, 784–785; VII, 744–745; IX, 972–973; XV, 228–229) lists 135 titles published in periodicals (excluding nonscientific journals) to 1900. Gaudry also published two *Notices sur les travaux scientifiques d'A. Gaudry* (Paris, 1878, 1881), in which he commented on his works.

His principal writings are "Alcide d'Orbigny, ses voyages,

et ses travaux," in *Revue des deux mondes,* **19** (1859), 816–847; "Contemporanéité de l'espèce humaine et des diverses espèces animales aujourd'hui éteintes," read to the Academy of Sciences on 3 Oct. 1859, in *L'Institut,* sec. 1, no. 1344 (5 Oct. 1859), pp. 317–318—despite its title this journal had no connection with the Académie des Sciences, which did not publish the note; *Animaux fossiles et géologie de l'Attique,* 2 vols. (Paris, 1862–1867); "La théorie de l'évolution et la détermination des terrains," in *Revue des cours scientifiques* (18 Dec. 1869); *Animaux fossiles du Mont-Léberon* (Paris, 1873), written with P. Fisher and R. Tournouër; "Les reptiles de l'époque permienne aux environs d'Autun," in *Bulletin de la Société géologique de France,* 3rd ser., **7** (1878), 62–77; *Les enchaînements du monde animal dans les temps géologiques,* 3 vols. (Paris, 1878–1890); *Mammifères tertiaires* (1878): *Fossiles primaires* (1883); *Fossiles secondaires* (1890)—the first vol. was translated into German as *Die Vorfahren der Säugetiere in Europa* (Leipzig, 1892); and *Matériaux pour l'histoire des temps quaternaires,* 4 fascs. (Paris, 1876–1892), the last fascicle in collaboration with Marcellin Boule.

II. SECONDARY LITERATURE. Armand Thévenin, "Albert Gaudry, notice nécrologique," in *Bulletin de la Société géologique de France,* 3rd ser., **10** (1910), 351–374, includes a portrait, a bibliography of his works, and a list of fourteen biographical notices. A notice by P. Glangeaud appears in English in *Report of the Board of Regents of the Smithsonian Institution* for 1919, publication no. 1969, pp. 417–429. See also the biography by Gustave-Frédéric Dollfus, *Albert Gaudry 1827–1908* (Paris, 1909), repr. from *Journal de conchyliologie,* **57** (1909), 274–278.

FRANCK BOURDIER

GAULTIER DE CLAUBRY, HENRI-FRANÇOIS (*b.* Paris, France, 21 July 1792; *d.* Paris, 4 July 1878), *chemistry, toxicology, public health.*

Gaultier de Claubry's father, Charles-Daniel, and his older brother, Charles-Emmanuel-Simon, were prominent surgeons and physicians. Following their example, Henri-François first embarked on a medical career but subsequently decided to devote his efforts to scientific pursuits. He served as a *répétiteur* at the École Polytechnique and in 1835 was named assistant professor of chemistry at the École de Pharmacie, a post he held until 1859, when he succeeded J.-B. Caventou as professor of toxicology. In 1825 he was appointed to the Council of Health of the Department of the Seine, and in 1848 he was elected to the Academy of Medicine (Paris).

A prolific author, Gaultier de Claubry is remembered largely for his discovery with J.-J. Colin of the blue color imparted to starch by free iodine (1814). In 1812 he translated into French William Henry's popular textbook, *Elements of Experimental Chemistry.* His investigation of the presence of iodine in seawater and in seaweed was published in 1815, as was his description of the properties of inulin. In succeeding years Gaultier de Claubry dealt with a great variety of subjects and worked in such fields as chemistry, toxicology, public health, medicine, and meteorology. This versatility, which extended to a multiplicity of largely unrelated projects, tended to make his work diffuse.

Nevertheless, Gaultier de Claubry was considered an able scientist by his contemporaries. Particularly noteworthy were his researches on the coloring matter in madder, carried out with J.-F. Persoz and published in 1831. A significant contribution to toxicology was his treatise on legal chemistry, which was incorporated in several editions of J. Briand and E. Chaudé's *Manuel complet de médecine légale,* one of the most authoritative textbooks on legal medicine in nineteenth-century France. The bulk of Gaultier de Claubry's writings on public health—dealing with food adulteration, environmental health, disinfection, industrial hygiene, and related topics—appeared in the *Annales d'hygiène publique et de médecine légale.*

BIBLIOGRAPHY

I. ORIGINAL WORKS. Some of Gaultier de Claubry's most important work is embodied in the following publications: "Mémoire sur les combinaisons de l'iode avec les substances végétales et animales . . .," in *Annales de chimie,* **90** (1814), 87–100; "Des recherches sur l'existence de l'iode dans l'eau de la mer et dans les plantes qui produisent la soude de varecks, et analyse de plusieurs plantes de la famille des algues," *ibid.,* **93** (1815), 75–110, 113–137; "Note sur une substance à laquelle on a donné le nom d'inuline," *ibid.,* **94** (1815), 200–208; and "Mémoire sur les matières colorantes de la garance," *ibid.,* 2nd ser., **48** (1831), 69–79.

A partial listing of Gaultier de Claubry's articles is in the Royal Society of London, *Catalogue of Scientific Papers (1800–1863),* II (London, 1867), 787–788; VII (London, 1877), 746; IX (London, 1891), 974. Most of his articles dealing with various aspects of public health that were published in the *Annales d'hygiène publique et de médecine légale* can be located in two separate index vols., covering the periods 1829–1855 and 1854–1878, respectively. His *Traité élémentaire de chimie légale* was included in J. Briand and E. Chaudé, *Manuel complet de médecine légale,* 4th ed. (Paris, 1846), and several later eds. For additional works, see *Catalogue général des livres imprimés de la Bibliothèque nationale,* LVIII (Paris, 1914), 42–46.

II. SECONDARY LITERATURE. See *Centenaire de l'École supérieure de Pharmacie de l'Université de Paris, 1803–1903* (Paris, 1904), pp. 330–331; Fritz Ferchl, *Chemisch-Pharmazeutisches Bio- und Bibliographikon* (Mittenwald, 1937), p. 173; and G. Vapereau, *Dictionnaire universel des contemporains,* 5th ed. (Paris, 1880), 785. See also J. C. F. Hoefer, ed., *Nouvelle biographie générale* (Paris, 1867),

679; and Pierre Larousse, ed., *Grand dictionnaire universel,* 15 vols. (Paris, 1866–1876), VIII, 1086.

ALEX BERMAN

GAUSS, CARL FRIEDRICH (*b.* Brunswick, Germany, 30 April 1777; *d.* Göttingen, Germany, 23 February 1855), *mathematical sciences.*

The life of Gauss was very simple in external form. During an austere childhood in a poor and unlettered family he showed extraordinary precocity. Beginning when he was fourteen, a stipend from the duke of Brunswick permitted him to concentrate on intellectual interests for sixteen years. Before the age of twenty-five he was famous as a mathematician and astronomer. At thirty he went to Göttingen as director of the observatory. There he worked for forty-seven years, seldom leaving the city except on scientific business, until his death at almost seventy-eight.

In marked contrast to this external simplicity, Gauss's personal life was complicated and tragic. He suffered from the political turmoil and financial insecurity associated with the French Revolution, the Napoleonic period, and the democratic revolutions in Germany. He found no mathematical collaborators and worked alone most of his life. An unsympathetic father, the early death of his first wife, the poor health of his second wife, and unsatisfactory relations with his sons denied him a family sanctuary until late in life.

In this difficult context Gauss maintained an amazingly rich scientific activity. An early passion for numbers and calculations extended first to the theory of numbers and then to algebra, analysis, geometry, probability, and the theory of errors. Concurrently he carried on intensive empirical and theoretical research in many branches of science, including observational astronomy, celestial mechanics, surveying, geodesy, capillarity, geomagnetism, electromagnetism, mechanics, optics, the design of scientific equipment, and actuarial science. His publications, voluminous correspondence, notes, and manuscripts show him to have been one of the greatest scientific virtuosos of all time.

Early Years. Gauss was born into a family of town workers striving on the hard road from peasant to lower middle-class status. His mother, a highly intelligent but only semiliterate daughter of a peasant stonemason, worked as a maid before becoming the second wife of Gauss's father, a gardener, laborer at various trades, foreman ("master of waterworks"), assistant to a merchant, and treasurer of a small insurance fund. The only relative known to have even modest intellectual gifts was the mother's brother, a master weaver. Gauss described his father as "worthy of esteem" but "domineering, uncouth, and unrefined." His mother kept her cheerful disposition in spite of an unhappy marriage, was always her only son's devoted support, and died at ninety-seven, after living in his house for twenty-two years.

Without the help or knowledge of others, Gauss learned to calculate before he could talk. At the age of three, according to a well-authenticated story, he corrected an error in his father's wage calculations. He taught himself to read and must have continued arithmetical experimentation intensively, because in his first arithmetic class at the age of eight he astonished his teacher by instantly solving a busy-work problem: to find the sum of the first hundred integers. Fortunately, his father did not see the possibility of commercially exploiting the calculating prodigy, and his teacher had the insight to supply the boy with books and to encourage his continued intellectual development.

During his eleventh year, Gauss studied with Martin Bartels, then an assistant in the school and later a teacher of Lobachevsky at Kazan. The father was persuaded to allow Carl Friedrich to enter the Gymnasium in 1788 and to study after school instead of spinning to help support the family. At the Gymnasium, Gauss made very rapid progress in all subjects, especially classics and mathematics, largely on his own. E. A. W. Zimmermann, then professor at the local Collegium Carolinum and later privy councillor to the duke of Brunswick, offered friendship, encouragement, and good offices at court. In 1792 Duke Carl Wilhelm Ferdinand began the stipend that made Gauss independent.

When Gauss entered the Brunswick Collegium Carolinum in 1792, he possessed a scientific and classical education far beyond that usual for his age at the time. He was familiar with elementary geometry, algebra, and analysis (often having discovered important theorems before reaching them in his studies), but in addition he possessed a wealth of arithmetical information and many number-theoretic insights. Extensive calculations and observation of the results, often recorded in tables, had led him to an intimate acquaintance with individual numbers and to generalizations that he used to extend his calculating ability. Already his lifelong heuristic pattern had been set: extensive empirical investigation leading to conjectures and new insights that guided further experiment and observation. By such means he had already independently discovered Bode's law of planetary distances, the binomial theorem for rational exponents, and the arithmetic-geometric mean.

During his three years at the Collegium, Gauss continued his empirical arithmetic, on one occasion finding a square root in two different ways to fifty decimal places by ingenious expansions and interpolations. He formulated the principle of least squares, apparently while adjusting unequal approximations and searching for regularity in the distribution of prime numbers. Before entering the University of Göttingen in 1795 he had rediscovered the law of quadratic reciprocity (conjectured by Lagrange in 1785), related the arithmetic-geometric mean to infinite series expansions, conjectured the prime number theorem (first proved by J. Hadamard in 1896), and found some results that would hold if "Euclidean geometry were not the true one."

In Brunswick, Gauss had read Newton's *Principia* and Bernoulli's *Ars conjectandi,* but most mathematical classics were unavailable. At Göttingen, he devoured masterworks and back files of journals, often finding that his own discoveries were not new. Attracted more by the brilliant classicist G. Heyne than by the mediocre mathematician A. G. Kästner, Gauss planned to be a philologist. But in 1796 came a dramatic discovery that marked him as a mathematician. As a by-product of a systematic investigation of the cyclotomic equation (whose solution has the geometric counterpart of dividing a circle into equal arcs), Gauss obtained conditions for the constructibility by ruler and compass of regular polygons and was able to announce that the regular 17-gon was constructible by ruler and compasses, the first advance in this matter in two millennia.

The logical component of Gauss's method matured at Göttingen. His heroes were Archimedes and Newton. But Gauss adopted the spirit of Greek rigor (insistence on precise definition, explicit assumption, and complete proof) without the classical geometric form. He thought numerically and algebraically, after the manner of Euler, and personified the extension of Euclidean rigor to analysis. By his twentieth year, Gauss was driving ahead with incredible speed according to the pattern he was to continue in many contexts—massive empirical investigations in close interaction with intensive meditation and rigorous theory construction.

During the five years from 1796 to 1800, mathematical ideas came so fast that Gauss could hardly write them down. In reviewing one of his seven proofs of the law of quadratic reciprocity in the *Göttingische gelehrte Anzeigen* for March 1817, he wrote autobiographically:

> It is characteristic of higher arithmetic that many of its most beautiful theorems can be discovered by induction with the greatest of ease but have proofs that lie anywhere but near at hand and are often found only after many fruitless investigations with the aid of deep analysis and lucky combinations. This significant phenomenon arises from the wonderful concatenation of different teachings of this branch of mathematics, and from this it often happens that many theorems, whose proof for years was sought in vain, are later proved in many different ways. As soon as a new result is discovered by induction, one must consider as the first requirement the finding of a proof by *any possible* means. But after such good fortune, one must not in higher arithmetic consider the investigation closed or view the search for other proofs as a superfluous luxury. For sometimes one does not at first come upon the most beautiful and simplest proof, and then it is just the insight into the wonderful concatenation of truth in higher arithmetic that is the chief attraction for study and often leads to the discovery of new truths. For these reasons the finding of new proofs for known truths is often at least as important as the discovery itself [*Werke,* II, 159–160].

The Triumphal Decade. In 1798 Gauss returned to Brunswick, where he lived alone and continued his intensive work. The next year, with the first of his four proofs of the fundamental theorem of algebra, he earned the doctorate from the University of Helmstedt under the rather nominal supervision of J. F. Pfaff. In 1801 the creativity of the previous years was reflected in two extraordinary achievements, the *Disquisitiones arithmeticae* and the calculation of the orbit of the newly discovered planet Ceres.

Number theory ("higher arithmetic") is a branch of mathematics that seems least amenable to generalities, although it was cultivated from the earliest times. In the late eighteenth century it consisted of a large collection of isolated results. In his *Disquisitiones* Gauss summarized previous work in a systematic way, solved some of the most difficult outstanding questions, and formulated concepts and questions that set the pattern of research for a century and still have significance today. He introduced congruence of integers with respect to a modulus ($a \equiv b \pmod{c}$ if c divides a-b), the first significant algebraic example of the now ubiquitous concept of equivalence relation. He proved the law of quadratic reciprocity, developed the theory of composition of quadratic forms, and completely analyzed the cyclotomic equation. The *Disquisitiones* almost instantly won Gauss recognition by mathematicians as their prince, but readership was small and the full understanding required for further development came only through the less austere exposition in Dirichlet's *Vorlesungen über Zahlentheorie* of 1863.

In January 1801 G. Piazzi had briefly observed and lost a new planet. During the rest of that year the astronomers vainly tried to relocate it. In September, as his *Disquisitiones* was coming off the press, Gauss decided to take up the challenge. To it he applied both a more accurate orbit theory (based on the ellipse rather than the usual circular approximation) and improved numerical methods (based on least squares). By December the task was done, and Ceres was soon found in the predicted position. This extraordinary feat of locating a tiny, distant heavenly body from seemingly insufficient information appeared to be almost superhuman, especially since Gauss did not reveal his methods. With the *Disquisitiones* it established his reputation as a mathematical and scientific genius of the first order.

The decade that began so auspiciously with the *Disquisitiones* and Ceres was decisive for Gauss. Scientifically it was mainly a period of exploiting the ideas piled up from the previous decade (see Figure 1). It ended with *Theoria motus corporum coelestium in sectionibus conicis solem ambientium* (1809), in which Gauss systematically developed his methods of orbit calculation, including the theory and use of least squares.

Professionally this was a decade of transition from mathematician to astronomer and physical scientist. Although Gauss continued to enjoy the patronage of the duke, who increased his stipend from time to time (especially when Gauss began to receive attractive offers from elsewhere), subsidized publication of the *Disquisitiones,* promised to build an observatory, and treated him like a tenured and highly valued civil servant, Gauss felt insecure and wanted to settle in a more established post. The most obvious course, to become a teacher of mathematics, repelled him because at this time it meant drilling ill-prepared and unmotivated students in the most elementary manipulations. Moreover, he felt that mathematics itself might not be sufficiently useful. When the duke raised

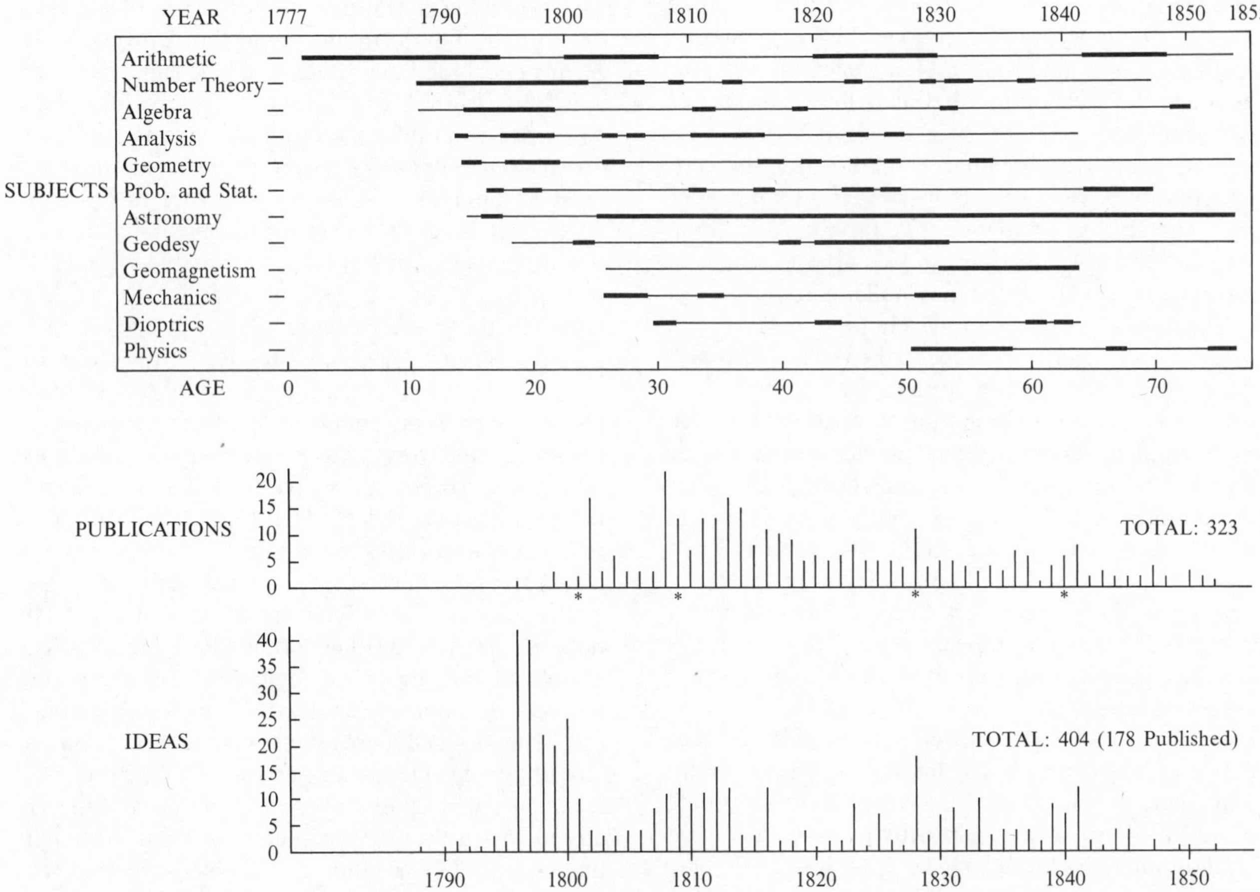

FIGURE 1. Interests, ideas, and publications. The horizontal lines show time spans of Gauss's interests in different subjects. Heavy lines indicate periods of intensive activity. The annual counts of recorded ideas include published and unpublished "results" (conjectures, theorems, proofs, concepts, hypotheses, theories), significant observations, experimental findings, and inventions. They are based on an examination of published materials, including correspondence and notebooks published after his death. Because of intrinsic ambiguities in dating, identification, and evaluation, this chart gives only an approximate picture of creative flux. The graph of publications shows the number of titles published in each year, including reviews. A count of pages would be similar except for surges (marked by *): 1801 (*Disquisitiones*), 1809 (*Theoria motus*), 1828 (least squares, surfaces, astronomy, biquadratic residues), and 1840 (geomagnetism).

his stipend in 1801, Gauss told Zimmermann: "But I have not earned it. I haven't yet done anything for the nation."

Astronomy offered an attractive alternative. A strong interest in celestial mechanics dated from reading Newton, and Gauss had begun observing while a student at Göttingen. The tour de force on Ceres demonstrated both his ability and the public interest, the latter being far greater than he could expect in mathematical achievements. Moreover, the professional astronomer had light teaching duties and, he hoped, more time for research. Gauss decided on a career in astronomy and began to groom himself for the directorship of the Göttingen observatory. A systematic program of theoretical and observational work, including calculation of the orbits of new planets as they were discovered, soon made him the most obvious candidate. When he accepted the position in 1807, he was already well established professionally, as evidenced by a job offer from St. Petersburg (1802) and by affiliations with the London Royal Society and the Russian and French academies.

During this decisive decade Gauss also established personal and professional ties that were to last his lifetime. As a student at Göttingen he had enjoyed a romantic friendship with Wolfgang Bolyai, and the two discussed the foundations of geometry. But Bolyai returned to Hungary to spend his life vainly trying to prove Euclid's parallel postulate. Their correspondence soon practically ceased, to be revived again briefly only when Bolyai sent Gauss his son's work on non-Euclidean geometry. Pfaff was the only German mathematician with whom Gauss could converse, and even then hardly on an equal basis. From 1804 to 1807 Gauss exchanged a few letters on a high mathematical level with Sophie Germain in Paris, and a handful of letters passed between him and the mathematical giants in Paris, but he never visited France or collaborated with them. Gauss remained as isolated in mathematics as he had been since boyhood. By the time mathematicians of stature appeared in Germany (e.g., Jacobi, Plücker, Dirichlet), the uncommunicative habit was too ingrained to change. Gauss inspired Dirichlet, Riemann, and others, but he never had a collaborator, correspondent, or student working closely with him in mathematics.

In other scientific and technical fields things were quite different. There he had students, collaborators, and friends. Over 7,000 letters to and from Gauss are known to be extant, and they undoubtedly represent only a fraction of the total. His most important astronomical collaborators, friends, and correspondents were F. W. Bessel, C. L. Gerling, M. Olbers, J. G. Repsold, H. C. Schumacher. His friendship and correspondence with A. von Humboldt and B. von Lindenau played an important part in his professional life and in the development of science in Germany. These relations were established during the period 1801–1810 and lasted until death. Always Gauss wrote fewer letters, gave more information, and was less cordial than his colleagues, although he often gave practical assistance to his friends and to deserving young scientists.

Also in this decade was established the pattern of working simultaneously on many problems in different fields. Although he never had a second burst of ideas equal to his first, Gauss always had more ideas than he had time to develop. His hopes for leisure were soon dashed by his responsibilities, and he acquired the habit of doing mathematics and other theoretical investigations in the odd hours (sometimes, happily, days) that could be spared. Hence his ideas matured rather slowly, in some cases merely later than they might have with increased leisure, in others more felicitously with increased knowledge and meditation.

This period also saw the fixation of his political and philosophical views. Napoleon seemed to Gauss the personification of the dangers of revolution. The duke of Brunswick, to whom Gauss owed his golden years of freedom, personified the merits of enlightened monarchy. When the duke was humiliated and killed while leading the Prussian armies against Napoleon in 1806, Gauss's conservative tendencies were reinforced. In the struggles for democracy and national unity in Germany, which continued throughout his lifetime, Gauss remained a staunch nationalist and royalist. (He published in Latin not from internationalist sentiments but at the demands of his publishers. He knew French but refused to publish in it and pretended ignorance when speaking to Frenchmen he did not know.) In seeming contradiction, his religious and philosophical views leaned toward those of his political opponents. He was an uncompromising believer in the priority of empiricism in science. He did not adhere to the views of Kant, Hegel, and other idealist philosophers of the day. He was not a churchman and kept his religious views to himself. Moral rectitude and the advancement of scientific knowledge were his avowed principles.

Finally, this decade provided Gauss his one period of personal happiness. In 1805 he married a young woman of similar family background, Johanna Osthoff, who bore him a son and daughter and created around him a cheerful family life. But in 1809 she died soon after bearing a third child, which did not long survive her. Gauss "closed the angel eyes in which for five years I have found a heaven" and was plunged into a loneliness from which he never fully recovered. Less than a year later he married Minna Waldeck, his deceased wife's best friend. She bore him two sons and a daughter, but she was seldom well or happy. Gauss dominated his daughters and quarreled with his younger sons, who immigrated to the United States. He did not achieve a peaceful home life until the younger daughter, Therese, took over the household after her mother's death (1831) and became the intimate companion of his last twenty-four years.

Early Göttingen Years. In his first years at Göttingen, Gauss experienced a second upsurge of ideas and publications in various fields of mathematics. Among the latter were several notable papers inspired by his work on the tiny planet Pallas, perturbed by Jupiter: *Disquisitiones generales circa seriem infinitam* (1813), an early rigorous treatment of series and the introduction of the hypergeometric functions, ancestors of the "special functions" of physics; *Methodus nova integralium valores per approximationem inveniendi* (1816), an important contribution to approximate integration; *Bestimmung der Genauigkeit der Beobachtungen* (1816), an early analysis of the efficiency of statistical estimators; and *Determinatio attractionis quam in punctum quodvis positionis datae exerceret planeta si eius massa per totam orbitam ratione temporis quo singulae partes describuntur uniformiter esset dispertita* (1818), which showed that the perturbation caused by a planet is the same as that of an equal mass distributed along its orbit in proportion to the time spent on an arc. At the same time Gauss continued thinking about unsolved mathematical problems. In 1813 on a single sheet appear notes relating to parallel lines, declinations of stars, number theory, imaginaries, the theory of colors, and prisms (*Werke,* VIII, 166).

Astronomical chores soon dominated Gauss's life. He began with the makeshift observatory in an abandoned tower of the old city walls. A vast amount of time and energy went into equipping the new observatory, which was completed in 1816 and not properly furnished until 1821. In 1816 Gauss, accompanied by his ten-year-old son and one of his students, took a five-week trip to Bavaria, where he met the optical instrument makers G. von Reichenbach, T. L. Ertel (owner of Reichenbach's firm), J. von Fraunhofer, and J. von Utzschneider (Fraunhofer's partner), from whom his best instruments were purchased. As Figure 1 shows, astronomy was the only field in which Gauss worked steadily for the rest of his life. He ended his theoretical astronomical work in 1817 but continued positional observing, calculating, and reporting his results until his final illness. Although assisted by students and colleagues, he observed regularly and was involved in every detail of instrumentation.

It was during these early Göttingen years that Gauss matured his conception of non-Euclidean geometry. He had experimented with the consequences of denying the parallel postulate more than twenty years before, and during his student days he saw the fallaciousness of the proofs of the parallel postulate that were the rage at Göttingen; but he came only very slowly and reluctantly to the idea of a different geometric theory that might be "true." He seems to have been pushed forward by his clear understanding of the weaknesses of previous efforts to prove the parallel postulate and by his successes in finding non-Euclidean results. He was slowed by his deep conservatism, the identification of Euclidean geometry with his beloved old order, and by his fully justified fear of the ridicule of the philistines. Over the years in his correspondence we find him cautiously, but more and more clearly, stating his growing belief that the fifth postulate was unprovable. He privately encouraged others thinking along similar lines but advised secrecy. Only once, in a book review of 1816 (*Werke,* IV, 364–368; VIII, 170–174), did he hint at his views publicly. His ideas were "besmirched with mud" by critics (as he wrote to Schumacher on 15 January 1827), and his caution was confirmed.

But Gauss continued to find results in the new geometry and was again considering writing them up, possibly to be published after his death, when in 1831 came news of the work of János Bolyai. Gauss wrote to Wolfgang Bolyai endorsing the discovery, but he also asserted his own priority, thereby causing the volatile János to suspect a conspiracy to steal his ideas. When Gauss became familiar with Lobachevsky's work a decade later, he acted more positively with a letter of praise and by arranging a corresponding membership in the Göttingen Academy. But he stubbornly refused the public support that would have made the new ideas mathematically respectable. Although the friendships of Gauss with Bartels and W. Bolyai suggest the contrary, careful study of the plentiful documentary evidence has established that Gauss did not inspire the two founders of non-Euclidean geometry. Indeed, he played at best a neutral, and on balance a negative, role, since his silence was considered as agreement with the public ridicule and neglect that continued for several decades and were only gradually overcome, partly by the revelation, beginning in the 1860's, that the prince of mathematicians had been an underground non-Euclidean.

Geodesist. By 1817 Gauss was ready to move toward geodesy, which was to be his preoccupation for the next eight years and a burden for the next thirty.

His interest was of long standing. As early as 1796 he worked on a surveying problem, and in 1799–1800 he advised Lt. K. L. E. von Lecoq, who was engaged in military mapping in Westphalia. Gauss's first publication was a letter on surveying in the *Allgemeine geographische Ephemeriden* of October 1799. In 1802 he participated in surveying with F. X. G. von Zach. From his arrival in Göttingen he was concerned with accurately locating the observatory, and in 1812 his interest in more general problems was stimulated by a discussion of sea levels during a visit to the Seeberg observatory. He began discussing with Schumacher the possibility of extending into Hannover the latter's survey of Denmark. Gauss had many motives for this project. It involved interesting mathematical problems, gave a new field for his calculating abilities, complemented his positional astronomy, competed with the French efforts to calculate the arc length of one degree on the meridian, offered an opportunity to do something useful for the kingdom, provided escape from petty annoyances of his job and family problems, and promised additional income. The last was a nontrivial matter, since Gauss had increasing family responsibilities to meet on a salary that remained fixed from 1807 to 1824.

The triangulation of Hannover was not officially approved until 1820, but already in 1818 Gauss began an arduous program of summer surveying in the field followed by data reduction during the winter. Plagued by poor transportation, uncomfortable living conditions, bad weather, uncooperative officials, accidents, poor health, and inadequate assistance and financial support, Gauss did the fieldwork himself with only minimal help for eight years. After 1825 he confined himself to supervision and calculation, which continued to completion of the triangulation of Hannover in 1847. By then he had handled more than a million numbers without assistance.

An early by-product of fieldwork was the invention of the heliotrope, an instrument for reflecting the sun's rays in a measured direction. It was motivated by dissatisfaction with the existing unsatisfactory methods of observing distant points by using lamps or powder flares at night. Meditating on the need for a beacon bright enough to be observed by day, Gauss hit on the idea of using reflected sunlight. After working out the optical theory, he designed the instrument and had the first model built in 1821. It proved to be very successful in practical work, having the brightness of a first-magnitude star at a distance of fifteen miles. Although heliostats had been described in the literature as early as 1742 (apparently unknown to Gauss), the heliotrope added greater precision by coupling mirrors with a small telescope. It became standard equipment for large-scale triangulation until superseded by improved models from 1840 and by aerial surveying in the twentieth century. Gauss remarked that for the first time there existed a practical method of communicating with the moon.

Almost from the beginning of his surveying work Gauss had misgivings, which proved to be well founded. A variety of practical difficulties made it impossible to achieve the accuracy he had expected, even with his improvements in instrumentation and the skillful use of least squares in data reduction. The hoped-for measurement of an arc of the meridian required linking his work with other surveys that were never made. Too hasty planning resulted in badly laid out base lines and an unsatisfactory network of triangles. He never ceased trying to overcome these faults, but his virtuosity as a mathematician and surveyor could not balance the factors beyond his control. His results were used in making rough geographic and military maps, but they were unsuitable for precise land surveys and for measurement of the earth. Within a generation, the markers were difficult to locate precisely or had disappeared altogether. As he was finishing his fieldwork in July 1825, Gauss wrote to Olbers that he wondered whether other activities might have been more fruitful. Not only did the results seem questionable but he felt during these years, even more than usual, that he was prevented from working out many ideas that still crowded his mind. As he wrote to Bessel on 28 June 1820, "I feel the difficulty of the life of a practical astronomer, without help; and the worst of it is that I can hardly do any connected significant theoretical work."

In spite of these failures and dissatisfactions, the period of preoccupation with geodesy was in fact one of the most scientifically creative of Gauss's long career. Already in 1813 geodesic problems had inspired his *Theoria attractionis corporum sphaeroidicorum ellipticorum homogeneorum methodus nova tractata,* a significant early work on potential theory. The difficulties of mapping the terrestrial ellipsoid on a sphere and plane led him in 1816 to formulate and solve in outline the general problem of mapping one surface on another so that the two are "similar in their smallest parts." In 1822 a prize offered by the Copenhagen Academy stimulated him to write up these ideas in a paper that won first place and was published in 1825 as the *Allgemeine Auflösung der Aufgabe die Theile einer gegebenen Fläche auf einer anderen gegebenen Fläche so auszubilden dass die Abbildung dem Abgebildeten in den kleinsten Theilen ähnlich wird.* This paper, his more detailed *Untersuchungen über Gegenstände der höhern Geodäsie* (1844–1847), and geodesic manuscripts later published in the *Werke* were further developed by

German geodesists and led to the Gauss-Krueger projection (1912), a generalization of the transverse Mercator projection, which attained a secure position as a basis for topographic grids taking into account the spheroidal shape of the earth.

Surveying problems also motivated Gauss to develop his ideas on least squares and more general problems of what is now called mathematical statistics. The result was the definitive exposition of his mature ideas in the *Theoria combinationis observationum erroribus minimis obnoxiae* (1823, with supplement in 1828). In the *Bestimmung des Breitenunterschiedes zwischen den Sternwarten von Göttingen und Altona durch Beobachtungen am Ramsdenschen Zenithsector* of 1828 he summed up his ideas on the figure of the earth, instrumental errors, and the calculus of observations. However, the crowning contribution of the period, and his last breakthrough in a major new direction of mathematical research, was *Disquisitiones generales circa superficies curvas* (1828), which grew out of his geodesic meditations of three decades and was the seed of more than a century of work on differential geometry. Of course, in these years as always, Gauss produced a stream of reviews, reports on observations, and solutions of old and new mathematical problems of varying importance that brought the number of his publications during the decade 1818–1828 to sixty-nine. (See Figure 1.)

Physicist. After the mid-1820's, there were increasing signs that Gauss wished to strike out in a new direction. Financial pressures had been eased by a substantial salary increase in 1824 and by a bonus for the surveying work in 1825. His other motivations for geodesic work were also weakened, and a new negative factor emerged—heart trouble. A fundamentally strong constitution and unbounded energy were essential to the unrelenting pace of work that Gauss maintained in his early years, but in the 1820's the strain began to show. In 1821, family letters show Gauss constantly worried, often very tired, and seriously considering a move to the leisure and financial security promised by Berlin. The hard physical work of surveying in the humid summers brought on symptoms that would now be diagnosed as asthma and heart disease. In the fall of 1825, Gauss took his ailing wife on a health trip to spas in southern Germany; but the travel and the hot weather had a very bad effect on his own health, and he was sick most of the winter. Distrusting doctors and never consulting one until the last few months of his life, he treated himself very sensibly by a very simple life, regular habits, and the avoidance of travel, for which he had never cared anyway. He resolved to drop direct participation in summer surveying and to spend the rest of his life "undisturbed in my study," as he had written Pfaff on 21 March 1825.

Apparently Gauss thought first of returning to a concentration on mathematics. He completed his work on least squares, geodesy, and curved surfaces as mentioned above, found new results on biquadratic reciprocity (1825), and began to pull together his long-standing ideas on elliptic functions and non-Euclidean geometry. But at forty-eight he found that satisfactory results came harder than before. In a letter to Olbers of 19 February 1826, he spoke of never having worked so hard with so little success and of being almost convinced that he should go into another field. Moreover, his most original ideas were being developed independently by men of a new generation. Gauss did not respond when Abel sent him his proof of the impossibility of solving the quintic equation in 1825, and the two never met, although Gauss praised him in private letters. When Dirichlet wrote Gauss in May 1826, enclosing his first work on number theory and asking for guidance, Gauss did not reply until 13 September and then only with general encouragement and advice to find a job that left time for research. As indicated in a letter to Encke of 8 July, Gauss was much impressed by Dirichlet's "eminent talent," but he did not seem inclined to become mathematically involved with him. When Crelle in 1828 asked Gauss for a paper on elliptic functions, he replied that Jacobi had covered his work "with so much sagacity, penetration and elegance, that I believe that I am relieved of publishing my own research." Harassed, overworked, distracted, and frustrated during these years, Gauss undoubtedly underestimated the value of his achievements, something he had never done before. But he was correct in sensing the need of a new source of inspiration. In turning toward intensive investigations in physics, he was following a pattern that had proved richly productive in the past.

In 1828 Alexander von Humboldt persuaded Gauss to attend the only scientific convention of his career, the Naturforscherversammlung in Berlin. Since first hearing of Gauss from the leading mathematicians in Paris in 1802, Humboldt had been trying to bring him to Berlin as the leading figure of a great academy he hoped to build there. At times negotiations had seemed near success, but bureaucratic inflexibilities in Berlin or personal factors in Göttingen always intervened. Humboldt still had not abandoned these hopes, but he had other motives as well. He wished to draw Gauss into the German scientific upsurge whose beginnings were reflected in the meeting; and especially he wished to involve Gauss in his own efforts, already extending over two decades, to organize worldwide geomagnetic observations. Humboldt had no success in luring Gauss from his Göttingen hermitage. He was repelled by the Berlin convention, which included a "little celebration" to which Humboldt invited 600 guests. Nevertheless, the visit was a turning point. Living quietly for three weeks in Humboldt's house with a private garden and his host's scientific equipment, Gauss had both leisure and stimulation for making a choice. When Humboldt later wrote of his satisfaction at having interested him in magnetism, Gauss replied tactlessly that he had been interested in it for nearly thirty years. Correspondence and manuscripts show this to be true; they indicate that Gauss delayed serious work on the subject partly because means of measurement were not available. Nevertheless, the Berlin visit was the occasion for the decision and also provided the means for implementing it, since in Berlin Gauss met Wilhelm Weber, a young and brilliant experimental physicist whose collaboration was essential.

In September 1829 Quetelet visited Göttingen and found Gauss very interested in terrestrial magnetism but with little experience in measuring it. The new field had evidently been selected, but systematic work awaited Weber's arrival in 1831. Meanwhile, Gauss extended his long-standing knowledge of the physical literature and began to work on problems in theoretical physics, and especially in mechanics, capillarity, acoustics, optics, and crystallography. The first fruit of this research was *Über ein neues allgemeines Grundgesetz der Mechanik* (1829). In it Gauss stated the law of least constraint: the motion of a system departs as little as possible from free motion, where departure, or constraint, is measured by the sum of products of the masses times the squares of their deviations from the path of free motion. He presented it merely as a new formulation equivalent to the well-known principle of d'Alembert. This work seems obviously related to the old meditations on least squares, but Gauss wrote to Olbers on 31 January 1829 that it was inspired by studies of capillarity and other physical problems. In 1830 appeared *Principia generalia theoriae figurae fluidorum in statu aequilibrii,* his one contribution to capillarity and an important paper in the calculus of variations, since it was the first solution of a variational problem involving double integrals, boundary conditions, and variable limits.

The years 1830–1831 were the most trying of Gauss's life. His wife was very ill, having suffered since 1818 from gradually worsening tuberculosis and hysterical neurosis. Her older son left in a huff and immigrated to the United States after quarreling with his father over youthful profligacies. The country was in a revolutionary turmoil of which Gauss thoroughly disapproved. Amid all these vexations, Gauss continued work on biquadratic residues, arduous geodesic calculations, and many other tasks. On 13 September 1831 his wife died. Two days later Weber arrived.

As Gauss and Weber began their close collaboration and intimate friendship, the younger man was just half the age of the older. Gauss took a fatherly attitude. Though he shared fully in experimental work, and though Weber showed high theoretical competence and originality during the collaboration and later, the older man led on the theoretical and the younger on the experimental side. Their joint efforts soon produced results. In 1832 Gauss presented to the Academy the *Intensitas vis magneticae terrestris ad mensuram absolutam revocata* (1833), in which appeared the first systematic use of absolute units (distance, mass, time) to measure a nonmechanical quantity. Here Gauss typically acknowledged the help of Weber but did not include him as joint author. Stimulated by Faraday's discovery of induced current in 1831, the pair energetically investigated electrical phenomena. They arrived at Kirchhoff's laws in 1833 and anticipated various discoveries in static, thermal, and frictional electricity but did not publish, presumably because their interest centered on terrestrial magnetism.

The thought that a magnetometer might also serve as a galvanometer almost immediately suggested its use to induce a current that might send a message. Working alone, Weber connected the astronomical observatory and the physics laboratory with a mile-long double wire that broke "uncountable" times as he strung it over houses and two towers. Early in 1833 the first words were sent, then whole sentences. This first operating electric telegraph was mentioned briefly by Gauss in a notice in the *Göttingische gelehrte Anzeigen* (9 August 1834; *Werke,* V, 424–425), but it seems to have been unknown to other inventors. Gauss soon realized the military and economic importance of the invention and tried unsuccessfully to promote its use by government and industry on a large scale. Over the years, the wire was replaced twice by one of better quality, and various improvements were made in the terminals. In 1845 a bolt of lightning fragmented the wire, but by this time it was no longer in use. Other inventors (Steinheil in Munich in 1837, Morse in the United States in 1838) had independently developed more efficient and exploitable methods, and the Gauss–Weber priority was forgotten.

The new magnetic observatory, free of all metal that might affect magnetic forces, was part of a network that Humboldt hoped would make coordinated measurements of geographical and temporal variations. In 1834 there were already twenty-three magnetic observatories in Europe, and the comparison of data from them showed the existence of magnetic storms. Gauss and Weber organized the Magnetische Verein, which united a worldwide network of observatories. Its *Resultate aus den Beobachtungen des magnetischen Vereins* appeared in six volumes (1836–1841) and included fifteen papers by Gauss, twenty-three by Weber, and the joint *Atlas des Erdmagnetismus* (1840). These and other publications elsewhere dealt with problems of instrumentation (including one of several inventions of the bifilar magnetometer), reported observations of the horizontal and vertical components of magnetic force, and attempted to explain the observations in mathematical terms.

The most important publication in the last category was the *Allgemeine Theorie des Erdmagnetismus* (1839). Here Gauss broke the tradition of armchair theorizing about the earth as a fairly neutral carrier of one or more magnets and based his mathematics on data. Using ideas first considered by him in 1806, well formulated by 1822, but lacking empirical foundation until 1838, Gauss expressed the magnetic potential at any point on the earth's surface by an infinite series of spherical functions and used the data collected by the world network to evaluate the first twenty-four coefficients. This was a superb interpolation, but Gauss hoped later to explain the results by a physical theory about the magnetic composition of the earth. Felix Klein has pointed out that this can indeed be done (*Vorlesungen über die Entwicklung der Mathematik im 19. Jahrhundert* [Berlin, 1926], pt. 1, p. 22), but that little is thereby added to the effective explanation offered by the Gaussian formulas. During these years Gauss found time to continue his geodesic data reduction, assist in revising the weights and measures of Hannover, make a number of electric discoveries jointly with Weber, and take an increasing part in university affairs.

This happy and productive collaboration was suddenly upset in 1837 by a disaster that soon effectively terminated Gauss's experimental work. In September, at the celebration of the 100th anniversary of the university (at which Gauss presented Humboldt with plans for his bifilar magnetometer), it was rumored that the new King Ernst August of Hannover might abrogate the hard-won constitution of 1833 and demand that all public servants swear a personal oath of allegiance to himself. When he did so in November, seven Göttingen professors, including Weber and the orientalist G. H. A. von Ewald, the husband of Gauss's older daughter, Minna, sent a private protest to the cabinet, asserting that they were bound by their previous oath to the constitution of 1833. The "Göttingen Seven" were unceremoniously fired, three to be banished and the rest (including Weber and Ewald) permitted to remain in the town. Some thought that Gauss might resign, but he took no public action; and his private efforts, like the public protest of six additional professors, were ignored. Why did Gauss not act more energetically? At age sixty he was too set in his ways, his mother was too old to move, and he hated anything politically radical and disapproved of the protest. The seven eventually found jobs elsewhere. Ewald moved to Tübingen, and Gauss was deprived of the company of his most beloved daughter, who had been ill for some years and died of consumption in 1840. Weber was supported by colleagues for a time, then drifted away and accepted a job at Leipzig. The collaboration petered out, and Gauss abandoned further physical research. In 1848, when Weber recovered his position at Göttingen, it was too late to renew collaboration and Weber continued his brilliant career alone.

As Gauss was ending his physical research, he published *Allgemeine Lehrsätze in Beziehung auf die im verkehrten Verhältnisse des Quadrats der Entfernung wirkenden Anziehungs- und Abstossungskräfte* (1840). Growing directly out of his magnetic work but linked also to his *Theoria attractionis* of 1813, it was the first systematic treatment of potential theory as a mathematical topic, recognized the necessity of existence theorems in that field, and reached a standard of rigor that remained unsurpassed for more than a century, even though the main theorem of the paper was false, according to C. J. de la Vallée Poussin (see *Revue des questions scientifiques,* **133** [1962], 314–330, esp. 324). In the same year he finished *Dioptrische Untersuchungen* (1841), in which he analyzed the path of light through a system of lenses and showed, among other things, that any system is equivalent to a properly chosen single lens. Although Gauss said that he had possessed the theory forty years before and considered it too elementary to publish, it has been labeled his greatest work by one of his scientific biographers (Clemens Schäfer, in *Werke,* XI, pt. 2, sec. 2, 189 ff.). In any case, it was his last significant scientific contribution.

Later Years. From the early 1840's the intensity of Gauss's activity gradually decreased. Further publications were either variations on old themes, reviews, reports, or solutions of minor problems. His reclusion is illustrated by his lack of response in 1845 to Kummer's invention of ideals (to restore unique factorization) and in 1846 to the discovery of Neptune by Adams, Le Verrier, and Galle. But the end of magnetic research and the decreased rate of publication did not mean that Gauss was inactive. He continued astronomical observing. He served several times as dean of the Göttingen faculty. He was busy during the 1840's in finishing many old projects, such as the last calculations on the Hannover survey. In 1847 he eloquently praised number theory and G. Eisenstein in the preface to the collected works of this ill-fated young man who had been one of the few to tell Gauss anything he did not already know. He spent several years putting the university widows' fund on a sound actuarial basis, calculating the necessary tables. He learned to read and speak Russian fluently, apparently first attracted by Lobachevsky but soon extending his reading as widely as permitted by the limited material available. His notebooks and correspondence show that he continued to work on a variety of mathematical problems. Teaching became less distasteful, perhaps because his students were better prepared and included some, such as Dedekind and Riemann, who were worthy of his efforts.

During the Revolution of 1848 Gauss stood guard with the royalists (whose defeat permitted the return of his son-in-law and Weber). He joined the Literary Museum, an organization whose library provided conservative literature for students and faculty, and made a daily visit there. He carefully followed political, economic, and technological events as reported in the press. The fiftieth anniversary celebration of his doctorate in 1849 brought him many messages and formal honors, but the world of mathematics was represented only by Jacobi and Dirichlet. The paper that Gauss delivered was his fourth proof of the fundamental theorem of algebra, appropriately a variation of the first in his thesis of 1799. After this celebration, Gauss continued his interests at a slower pace and became more than ever a legendary figure unapproachable by those outside his personal circle. Perhaps stimulated by his actuarial work, he fell into the habit of collecting all sorts of statistics from the newspapers, books, and daily observations. Undoubtedly some of these data helped him with financial speculations shrewd enough to create an estate equal to nearly 200 times his annual salary. The "star gazer," as his father called him, had, as an afterthought, achieved the financial status denied his more "practical" relatives.

Due to his careful regimen, no serious illnesses had troubled Gauss since his surveying days. Over the years he treated himself for insomnia, stomach discomfort, congestion, bronchitis, painful corns, shortness of breath, heart flutter, and the usual signs of aging without suffering any acute attacks. He had been less successful in resisting chronic hypochondria and melancholia which increasingly plagued him after the death of his first wife. In the midst of some undated scientific notes from his later years there suddenly appears the sentence "Death would be preferable to such a life," and at fifty-six he wrote Gerling (8 February 1834) that he felt like a stranger in the world.

After 1850, troubled by developing heart disease, Gauss gradually limited his activity further. He made his last astronomical observation in 1851, at the age of seventy-four, and later the same year approved Riemann's doctoral thesis on the foundations of complex analysis. The following year he was still working on minor mathematical problems and on an improved Foucault pendulum. During 1853–1854 Riemann wrote his great *Habilitationsschrift* on the foundations of geometry, a topic chosen by Gauss. In June 1854 Gauss, who had been under a doctor's care for several months, had the pleasure of hearing Riemann's probationary lecture, symbolic of the presence in Germany at last of talents capable of continuing his work. A few days later he left Göttingen for the last time to observe construction of the railway from Kassel. By autumn his illness was much worse. Although gradually more bedridden, he kept up his reading, correspondence, and trading in securities until he died in his sleep late in February 1855.

Mathematical Scientist. Gauss the man of genius stands in the way of evaluating the role of Gauss as a scientist. His mathematical abilities and exploits caused his contemporaries to dub him *princeps,* and biographers customarily place him on a par with Archimedes and Newton. This traditional judgment is as reasonable as any outcome of the ranking game, but an assessment of his impact is more problematic because of the wide gap between the quality of his personal accomplishments and their effectiveness as contributions to the scientific enterprise. Gauss published only about half his recorded innovative ideas (see Figure 1) and in a style so austere that his readers were few. The unpublished results appear in notes, correspondence, and reports to official bodies, which became accessible only many years later. Still other methods and discoveries are only hinted at in letters or incomplete notes. It is therefore necessary to reexamine Gauss as a participant in the scientific community and to look at his achievements in terms of their scientific consequences.

The personality traits that most markedly inhibited the effectiveness of Gauss as a participant in scientific activity were his intellectual isolation, personal ambition, deep conservatism and nationalism, and rather narrow cultural outlook. It is hard to appreciate fully the isolation to which Gauss was condemned in childhood by thoughts that he could share with no one. He must soon have learned that attempts to communicate led, at best, to no response; at worst, to the ridicule and estrangement that children find so hard to bear. But unlike most precocious children, who eventually find intellectual comrades, Gauss during his whole life found no one with whom to share his most valued thoughts. Kästner was not interested when Gauss told him of his first great discovery, the constructibility of the regular 17-gon. Bolyai, his most promising friend at Göttingen, could not appreciate his thinking. These and many other experiences must have convinced Gauss that there was little to be gained from trying to interchange theoretical ideas. He drew on the great mathematicians of the past and on contemporaries in France (whom he treated as from another world); but he remained outside the mathematical activity of his day, almost as if he were actually no longer living and his publications were being discovered in the archives. He found it easier and more useful to communicate with empirical scientists and technicians, because in those areas he was among peers; but even there he remained a solitary worker, with the exception of the collaboration with Weber.

Those who admired Gauss most and knew him best found him cold and uncommunicative. After the Berlin visit, Humboldt wrote Schumacher (18 October 1828) that Gauss was "glacially cold" to unknowns and unconcerned with things outside his immediate circle. To Bessel, Humboldt wrote (12 October 1837) of Gauss's "intentional isolation," his habit of suddenly taking possession of a small area of work, considering all previous results as part of it, and refusing to consider anything else. C. G. J. Jacobi complained in a letter to his brother (21 September 1849) that in twenty years Gauss had not cited any publication by him or by Dirichlet. Schumacher, the closest of Gauss's friends and one who gave him much personal counsel and support, wrote to Bessel (21 December 1842) that Gauss was "a queer sort of fellow" with whom it is better to stay "in the limits of conventional politeness, without trying to do anything uncalled for."

Like Newton, Gauss had an intense dislike of controversy. There is no record of a traumatic experience that might account for this, but none is required to explain a desire to avoid emotional involvements that interfered with contemplation. With equal rationality, Gauss avoided all noncompulsory ceremonies and formalities, making an exception only when royalty was to be present. In these matters, as in his defensive attitude toward possible wasters of his time, Gauss was acting rationally to maximize his scientific output; but the result was to prevent some interchanges that might have been as beneficial to him as to others.

Insatiable drive, a characteristic of persistent high achievers, could hardly in itself inhibit participation; but conditioned by other motivations it did so for Gauss. Having experienced bitter poverty, he worked toward a security that was for a long time denied him. But he had absorbed the habitual frugality of the striving poor and did not want or ever adopt luxuries of the parvenu. He had no confidence in the democratic state and looked to the ruling aristocracy for security. The drive for financial security was accompanied by a stronger ambition, toward great achievement and lasting fame in science. While still an adolescent Gauss realized that he might join the tiny superaristocracy of science that seldom has more than one member in a generation. He wished to be worthy of his heroes and to deserve the esteem of future peers. His sons reported that he discouraged them from going into science on the ground that he did not want any second-rate work associated with his name. He had little hope of being understood by his contemporaries; it was sufficient to impress and to avoid offending them. In the light of his ambitions for security and lasting fame, with success in each seemingly required for the other, his choice of career and his purposeful isolation were rational. He did achieve his twin ambitions. More effective communication and participation might have speeded the development of mathematics by several decades, but it would not have added to Gauss's reputation then or now. Gauss probably understood this well enough. He demonstrated in some of his writings, correspondence, lectures, and organizational activities that he could be an effective teacher, expositor, popularizer, diplomat, and promoter when he wished. He simply did not wish.

Gauss's conservatism has been described above, but it should be added here that it extended to all his thinking. He looked nostalgically back to the eighteenth century with its enlightened monarchs supporting scientific aristocrats in academies where they were relieved of teaching. He was anxious to find "new truths" that did not disturb established ideas. Nationalism was important for Gauss. As we have seen, it impelled him toward geodesy and other work that he considered useful to the state. But its most important effect was to deny him easy communication with the French. Only in Paris, during his most productive years, were men with whom he could have enjoyed a mutually stimulating mathematical collaboration.

It seems strange to call culturally narrow a man

with a solid classical education, wide knowledge, and voracious reading habits. Yet outside of science Gauss did not rise above petit bourgeois banality. Sir Walter Scott was his favorite British author, but he did not care for Byron or Shakespeare. Among German writers he liked Jean Paul, the best-selling humorist of the day, but disliked Goethe and disapproved of Schiller. In music he preferred light songs and in drama, comedies. In short, his genius stopped short at the boundaries of science and technology, outside of which he had little more taste or insight than his neighbors.

The contrast between knowledge and impact is now understandable. Gauss arrived at the two most revolutionary mathematical ideas of the nineteenth century: non-Euclidean geometry and noncommutative algebra. The first he disliked and suppressed. The second appears as quaternion calculations in a notebook of about 1819 (*Werke,* VIII, 357–362) without having stimulated any further activity. Neither the barycentric calculus of his own student Moebius (1827), nor Grassmann's *Ausdenunglehre* (1844), nor Hamilton's work on quaternions (beginning in 1843) interested him, although they sparked a fundamental shift in mathematical thought. He seemed unaware of the outburst of analytic and synthetic projective geometry, in which C. von Staudt, one of his former students, was a leading participant. Apparently Gauss was as hostile or indifferent to radical ideas in mathematics as in politics.

Hostility to new ideas, however, does not explain Gauss's failure to communicate many significant mathematical results that he did approve. Felix Klein (*Vorlesungen über die Entwicklung der Mathematik im 19. Jahrhundert,* pt. 1, 11–12) points to a combination of factors—personal worries, distractions, lack of encouragement, and overproduction of ideas. The last might alone have been decisive. Ideas came so quickly that each one inhibited the development of the preceding. Still another factor was the advantage that Gauss gained from withholding information, although he hotly denied this motive when Bessel suggested it. In fact, the Ceres calculation that won Gauss fame was based on methods unknown to others. By delaying publication of least squares and by never publishing his calculating methods, he maintained an advantage that materially contributed to his reputation. The same applies to the careful and conscious removal from his writings of all trace of his heuristic methods. The failure to publish was certainly not based on disdain for priority. Gauss cared a great deal for priority and frequently asserted it publicly and privately with scrupulous honesty. But to him this meant being first to discover, not first to publish; and he was satisfied to establish his dates by private records, correspondence, cryptic remarks in publications, and in one case by publishing a cipher. (See bibliography under "Miscellaneous.") Whether he intended it so or not, in this way he maintained the advantage of secrecy without losing his priority in the eyes of later generations. The common claim that Gauss failed to publish because of his high standards is not convincing. He did have high standards, but he had no trouble achieving excellence once the mathematical results were in hand; and he did publish all that was ready for publication by normal standards.

In the light of the above discussion one might expect the Gaussian impact to be far smaller than his reputation—and indeed this is the case. His inventions, including several not listed here for lack of space, redound to his fame but were minor improvements of temporary importance or, like the telegraph, uninfluential anticipations. In theoretical astronomy he perfected classical methods in orbit calculation but otherwise did only fairly routine observations. His personal involvement in calculating orbits saved others trouble and served to increase his fame but were of little long-run scientific importance. His work in geodesy was influential only in its mathematical by-products. From his collaboration with Weber arose only two achievements of significant impact. The use of absolute units set a pattern that became standard, and the Magnetische Verein established a precedent for international scientific cooperation. His work in dioptrics may have been of the highest quality, but it seems to have had little influence; and the same may be said of his other works in physics.

When we come to mathematics proper, the picture is different. Isolated as Gauss was, seemingly hardly aware of the work of other mathematicians and not caring to communicate with them, nevertheless his influence was powerful. His prestige was such that young mathematicians especially studied him. Jacobi and Abel testified that their work on elliptic functions was triggered by a hint in the *Disquisitiones arithmeticae.* Galois, on the eve of his death, asked that his rough notes be sent to Gauss. Thus, in mathematics, in spite of delays, Gauss did reach and inspire mathematicians. Although he was more of a systematizer and solver of old problems than an opener of new paths, the very completeness of his results laid the basis for new departures—especially in number theory, differential geometry, and statistics. Although his mathematical thinking was always concrete in the sense that he was dealing with structures based on the real numbers, his work contained the seeds of many highly abstract ideas that came later. Gauss, like Archimedes, pushed the methods of his time to the limit of their possibilities. But unlike his other ability peer, Newton, he did not initiate a profound new development, nor did he have the revolutionary impact of a number of his contemporaries of perhaps lesser ability but greater imagination and daring.

Gauss is best described as a mathematical scientist, or, in the terms common in his day, as a pure and applied mathematician. Ranging easily, competently, and productively over the whole of science and technology, he always did so as a mathematician, motivated by mathematics, utilizing every experience for mathematical inspiration. (Figure 2 shows some of the interrelations of his interests.) Clemens Schäfer, one of his scientific biographers, wrote in *Nature* (**128** [1931], 341): "He was not really a physicist in the sense of searching for new phenomena, but rather always a mathematician who attempted to formulate in exact mathematical terms the experimental results obtained by others." Leaving aside his personal failures, whose scientific importance was transitory, Gauss appears as the ideal mathematician, displaying in heroic proportions in one person the capabilities attributed collectively to the community of professional mathematicians.

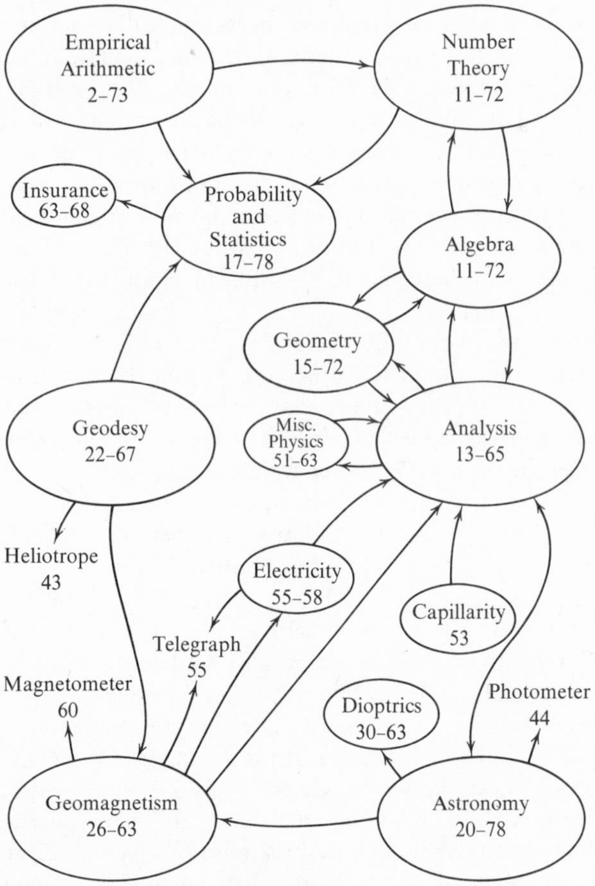

FIGURE 2. Main lines of development of Gauss's scientific ideas. Arrows suggest the most important directions of motivation and inspiration. Numerals indicate ages. His four most important inventions are given outside of any enclosing curves. The sizes of the ellipses suggest the weight of each field in his total effort, and the year span is indicative also of the number and variety of activities in each field. This figure should be compared with Figure 1.

BIBLIOGRAPHY

A complete Gauss bibliography would be far too large to include here, and the following is highly selective. Abbreviations used throughout are the following: *AMM: American Mathematical Monthly. AN: Astronomische Nachrichten. BA: Abhandlungen der (Königlichen) Bayerischen Akademie der Wissenschaften,* Mathematisch-naturwissenschaftliche Abteilung, II Klasse. *BAMS: Bulletin of the American Mathematical Society. BB: Bullettino (Bollettino) di bibliografia e di storia delle scienze matematiche (e fisiche)* (Boncompagni). *BSM: Bulletin des sciences mathématiques et astronomiques* (Darboux). *Crelle: Journal für die reine und angewandte Mathematik. DMV: Jahresbericht der Deutschen Mathematiker-vereinigung. FF: Forschungen und Fortschritte. GA: Abhandlungen der Akademie (K. Gesellschaft) der Wissenschaften zu Göttingen,* Mathematisch-naturwissenschaftliche Klasse. *GGM: Gauss-Gesellschaft Mitteilungen. GN: Nachrichten (Jahrbuch, Jahresbericht) der Gesellschaft der Wissenschaften zu Göttingen. HUB: Wissenschaftliche Zeitschrift der Humboldt-Universität Berlin,* Mathematisch-naturwissenschaftliche Reihe. *IINT: Trudy (Arkhiv) Instituta istorii nauki i tekhniki. IMI: Istoriko-matematicheskie issledovaniya. JMPA: Journal de mathématiques pures et appliquées* (Liouville). *LB: Berichte über die Verhandlungen der (Königlichen) Sächsischen Gesellschaft der Wissenschaften zu Leipzig. MA: Mathematische Annalen. MDA: Monatsberichte der Deutschen Akademie der Wissenschaften zu Berlin. NA: Nouvelles annales de mathématiques. NMM: National Mathematics Magazine.* OK: Ostwalds Klassiker der exacten Wissenschaften (Leipzig). *SM: Scripta mathematica. TSM: Scientific Memoirs, Selected from the Transactions of Foreign Academies and Learned Societies and From Foreign Journals* by Richard Taylor. *VIET: Voprosy istorii estestvoznaniya i tekhniki. Zach: Monatliche Correspondenz zur Beförderung der Erd- und Himmelskunde* (Zach). *ZV: Zeitschrift für Vermessungswesen.*

I. Original Works. All of Gauss's publications (including his fine reviews of his own papers) are reprinted in the *Werke,* published in 12 vols. by the Königliche Gesellschaft der Wissenschaften zu Göttingen (Leipzig–Berlin, 1863–1933). The *Werke* contains also a generous selection of his unpublished notes and papers, related correspondence, commentaries, and extensive analyses of his work in each field. The first 7 vols., edited by Ernst C. J. Schering, who came to Göttingen as a student in 1852 and taught mathematics there from 1858 until his death in 1897, contain Gauss's publications arranged by subject, as follows: I. *Disquisitiones arithmeticae* (1863; 2nd ed., with commentary, 1870). II. Number Theory (1863; 2nd ed., with the unpublished sec. 8 of the *Disquisitiones,* minor additions, and revisions, 1876). III. Analysis (1866; 2nd ed., with minor changes, 1876). IV. Probability, Geometry, and Geodesy (1873; 2nd ed., almost unchanged, 1880). V. Mathematical Physics (1867; unchanged 2nd ed., 1877). VI. Astronomy (1873). VII. *Theoria motus* (1871; 2nd ed., with new commentary by Martin Brendel and previously unpublished Gauss MSS, 1906).

After the death of Schering, work was continued under the aggressive leadership of Felix Klein, who organized a campaign to collect materials and enlisted experts in special fields to study them. From 1898 until 1922 he rallied support with fourteen reports, published under the title "Bericht über den Stand der Herausgabe von Gauss' Werken," in the *Nachrichten* of the Göttingen Academy and reprinted in *MA* and *BSM.* The fruits of this effort were a much enlarged Gauss Archive at Göttingen, many individual publications, and vols. VIII–XII of the *Werke,* as follows: VIII. Supp. to vols. I–IV (1900), papers and correspondence on mathematics (the paper on pp. 36–64 is spurious. See *Werke,* X, pt. 1, 137). IX. Geodesy (1903). Supp. to vol. IV, including some overlooked Gauss publications. X, pt. 1. Supp. on pure mathematics (1917), including the famous *Tagebuch* in which Gauss from 1796 to 1814 recorded mathematical results. Found in 1898 by P. Stäckel and first published by F. Klein in the *Festschrift zur Feier des hundertfünfzigjährigen Bestehens der Königlichen Gesellschaft der Wissenschaften zu Göttingen* (Berlin, 1901) and in *MA,* **57** (1903), 1–34, it was here reprinted with very extensive commentary and also in facsimile. A French trans. with commentary by P. Eymard and J. P. Lafon appeared in *Revue d'histoire des sciences et de leurs applications,* **9** (1956), 21–51. See also G. Herglotz, in *LB,* **73** (1921), 271–277. X, pt. 2. Biographical essays described below (1922–1933). XI, pt. 1. Supp. on Physics, Chronology, and Astronomy (1927). XI, pt. 2. Biographical essays described below (1924–1929). XII. Varia. *Atlas des Erdmagnetismus* (1929). A final volume, XIII, planned to contain further biographical material (especially on Gauss as professor), bibliography, and index, was nearly completed by H. Geppert and E. Bessel-Hagen but not published.

A. *Translations and Reprints.* The *Demonstratio nova* of 1799 together with the three subsequent proofs of the fundamental theorem (1815, 1816, 1849) were published in German with commentary by E. Netto under the title *Die vier Gauss'schen Beweise . . .* in OK, no. 14 (1890). The *Disquisitiones* (1801) is available in French (1807), German, with other works on number theory (1889; repr. New York, 1965), Russian (1959), and English (1966). Gauss's third published proof of the law of quadratic reciprocity (1808) is translated in D. E. Smith, *Source Book in Mathematics,* I (New York, 1929), 112–118. All his published proofs of this theorem are collected in *Sechs Beweise des Fundamentaltheorems über quadratische Reste,* E. Netto, ed., in OK, no. 122 (1901).

The *Theoria motus* (1809) was translated into English (1857), Russian (1861), French (1864), and German (1865). *Disquisitiones generales circa seriem* (1813) appeared in a German translation by H. Simon in 1888, and *Theoria attractionis* (1813) was translated in *Zach,* **28** (1813), 37–57, 125–234, and reprinted in OK, 19 (1890). The *Determinatio attractionis* (1818) was translated in OK, 225 (1927). The *Allgemeine Auflösung* (1825) was reprinted with related works of Lagrange in OK, 55 (1894). *Theoria combinationis* and supps. of 1823 appeared in French (by J. Bertrand, 1855), German (1887), and with other related work in *Abhandlungen zur Methode der kleinsten Quadrate,* translated by A. Börsch and P. Simon (Berlin, 1887), and in *Gauss's Work (1803–1826) on the Theory of Least Squares,* translated from French by H. F. Trotter (Princeton, N.J., 1957). The *Allgemeine Auflösung* of 1825 appeared in *Philosophical Magazine,* **4** (1828), 104–113, 206–215. *Disquisitiones generales circa superficies curvas* (1828) was translated into French in *NA,* **11** (1852), 195–252, and with notes by E. Roger (Grenoble, 1855); into German by O. Böklen in his *Analytische Geometrie des Raumes* (1884), and by Wangerin in OK, 5 (1889); into Russian (1895), Hungarian (1897); and English (1902). *Über ein neues allgemeines Grundgesetz* (1829) was translated in *NA,* **4** (1845), 477–479.

The *Intensitas vis magneticae* (1833) appears in the *Effemeridi astronomiche di Milano, 1839* (Milan, 1838); in OK, 53 (1894); and in W. F. Magie, *Source Book in Physics* (New York–London, 1935; repr., Cambridge, Mass., 1963), pp. 519–524. The *Allgemeine Theorie des Erdmagnetismus* of 1839 was promptly published in English in *TSM,* **2** (1841), 184–251, 313–316. The *Allgemeine Lehrsätze* (1840) was translated in *JMPA,* **7** (1842), 273–324, and reprinted in OK, 2 (1889). *Dioptrische Untersuchungen* (1841) appeared in English in *TSM,* **3** (1843), 490–498 (see also *Ferrari's Dioptric Instruments* [London, 1919]); and in French in *Annales de chimie,* **33** (1851), 259–294, and in *JMPA,* **1** (1856), 9–43. The *Untersuchungen über Gegenstände der höheren Geodäsie* (1844, 1847) was reprinted as OK, 177 (Leipzig, 1910).

Very little material from the *Nachlass* first printed in the *Werke* has been reprinted or translated. Parts of *Werke,* XI, pt. 1, on the arithmetic-geometric mean and modular functions appear in the OK, 255 (1927), translation of the *Determinatio attractionis* (1818). Some Gauss MSS and editor's commentary are translated from *Werke,* XII, by Dunnington in *Carl Friedrich Gauss, Inaugural Lecture on Astronomy and Papers on the Foundations of Mathematics* (Baton Rouge, La., 1937). Notes on Gauss's astronomy lectures by A. T. Kupffer are printed in A. N. Krylov, *Sobranie trudy* (Moscow–Leningrad, 1936), VI. The following selecta have appeared in Russian: *Geodezicheskie issledovania Gaussa . . .* (St. Petersburg, 1866); *Izbrannye trudy po zemnomu magnetizmu* (Leningrad, 1952); *Izbrannye geodezicheskie sochinenia* (Moscow, 1957).

B. *Correspondence.* Only the major collections are listed here. Many other letters have been published in journal articles and in bibliographies. G. F. J. A. von Auwers, *Briefwechsel zwischen Gauss und Bessel* (Leipzig, 1880). E. Schönberg and T. Gerardy, "Die Briefe des Herrn P. H.

L. von Bogulawski . . .," in *BA,* **110** (1963), 3–44. F. Schmidt and P. Stäckel, *Briefwechsel zwischen C. F. Gauss and W. Bolyai* (Leipzig, 1899). P. G. L. Dirichlet, *Werke,* II (Berlin, 1897), 373–387. C. Schäfer, *Briefwechsel zwischen Carl Friedrich Gauss und Christian Ludwig Gerling* (Berlin, 1927). T. Gerardy, *Christian Ludwig Gerling und Carl Friedrich Gauss. Sechzig bisher unveröffentlichte Briefe* (Göttingen, 1964). H. Stupuy, ed., *Oeuvres philosophiques de Sophie Germain* (Paris, 1879), pp. 298 ff.; and 2nd ed., pp. 254 ff. K. Bruhns, *Briefe zwischen A. v. Humboldt und Gauss* (Leipzig, 1877) (see also K.-R. Bierman, in *FF,* **36** [1962], 41–44, also in *GGM,* **4** [1967], 5–18). T. Gerardy, "Der Briefwechsel zwischen C. F. Gauss und C. L. Lecoq," in *GN* (1959), 37–63. W. Gresky, "Aus Bernard von Lindenaus Briefen an C. F. Gauss," in *GGM,* **5** (1968), 12–46. W. Valentiner, *Briefe von C. F. Gauss an B. Nicolai* (Karlsruhe, 1877). C. Schilling and I. Kramer, *Briefwechsel zwischen Olbers und Gauss,* 2 vols. (Berlin, 1900–1909). C. Pfaff, *Sammlung von Briefen, gewechselt zwischen Johann Friedrich Pfaff und . . . anderen* (Leipzig, 1853). P. Riebesell, "Briefwechsel zwischen C. F. Gauss und J. C. Repsold," in *Mitteilungen der mathematischen Gesellschaft in Hamburg,* **6** (1928), 398–431. C. A. Peters, *Briefwechsel zwischen C. F. Gauss und H. C. Schumacher,* 6 vols. (Altona, 1860–1865). T. Gerardy, *Nachtrage zum Briefwechsel zwischen Carl Friedrich Gauss und Heinrich Christian Schumacher* (Göttingen, 1969).

C. *Archives.* The MSS, letters, notebooks, and library of Gauss have been well preserved. The bulk of the scientific *Nachlass* is collected in the Gauss Archiv of the Handschriftenabteilung of the Niedersächsischen Staats- und Universitätsbibliothek, Göttingen, and fills 200 boxes. (See W. Meyer, *Die Handschriften in Göttingen* [Berlin, 1894], III, 101–113.) Theo Gerardy has for many years been working to arrange and catalog these materials. (See T. Gerardy, "Der Stand der Gaussforschung," in *GGM,* **1** [1964], 5–11.) Personal materials are concentrated in the municipal library of Brunswick. These include the contents of the Gauss Museum, removed from Gauss's birthplace before its destruction during World War II. (See H. Mack, "Das Gaussmuseum in Braunschweig," in *Museumskunde,* n.s. **1** [1930], 122–125.) Gauss's personal library forms a special collection in the Göttingen University Library. His scientific library was merged with the observatory library. There are also minor deposits of MSS, letters, and mementos scattered in the libraries of universities, observatories, and private collectors throughout the world. The best published sources on the Gauss archival material are Felix Klein's reports on the progress of the *Werke* mentioned above and in the yearly *Mitteilungen* of the Gauss-Gesellschaft (GGM), founded in Göttingen in 1962.

II. Secondary Literature. There is no full-scale biography of the man and his work as a whole, although there are many personal biographies and excellent studies of his work in particular fields.

A. *Bibliography.* No complete Gauss bibliography has been published. The best ones are in Poggendorff, VII A, supp., Lieferung 2 (1970), 223–238; and in Dunnington's biography (see below).

B. *Biography.* The year after Gauss's death, Sartorius von Waltershausen, a close friend of his last years, published *Gauss zum Gedächtniss* (Leipzig, 1856). An English trans. by his great-granddaughter, Helen W. Gauss, was published as *Gauss, a Memorial* (Colorado Springs, Colo., 1966).

Other sources based on personal acquaintance and/or more or less reliable contemporary evidence are the following: L. Hänselmann, *K. F. Gauss. Zwölf Capital aus seinem Leben* (Leipzig, 1878); I. M. Simonov, *Zapiski i vospominaniya o puteshestvii po Anglii, Frantsii, Belgii i Germanii v 1842 godu* (Kazan, 1844); A. Quetelet, in *Correspondance mathématique et physique,* **6** (1830), 126–148, 161–178, 225–239, repr. in A. Quetelet, *Sciences mathématiques et physiques chez les Belges* (Brussels, 1866); Ernst C. J. Schering, *Carl Friedrich Gauss' Geburtstag nach hundertjähriger Wiederkehr, Festrede* (Göttingen, 1877); M. A. Stern, *Denkrede . . . zur Feier seines hundertjährigen Geburtstages* (Göttingen, 1877); F. A. T. Winnecke, *Gauss. Ein Umriss seines Lebens und Wirkens* (Brunswick, 1877); Theodor Wittstein, *Gedächtnissrede auf C. F. Gauss zur Feier des 30 April 1877* (Hannover, 1877); R. Dedekind, *Gauss in seiner Vorlesungen über die Methode der kleinsten Quadrate. Festschrift . . . Göttingen* (Berlin, 1901), repr. in Dedekind, *Gesammelte mathematische Werke,* II (1931), 293–306; Moritz Cantor lecture of 14 November 1899, in *Neue Heidelberger Jahrbucher,* **9** (1899), 234–255; and Rudolf Borch, "Ahnentafel des . . . Gauss," in *Ahnentafeln berühmter Deutscher,* I (Leipzig, 1929), 63–65.

Most of the personal biographical literature is derivative from the above sources and is of the "beatification forever" type, in which fact and tradition are freely mixed. Only a few works of special interest are mentioned here. Heinrich Mack, *Carl Friedrich Gauss und die Seinen* (Brunswick, 1927), contains substantial excerpts from family correspondence and a table of ancestors and descendants. F. Cajori published family letters in *Science,* n.s. **9** (19 May 1899), 697–704, and in *Popular Science Monthly,* **81** (1912), 105–114. Other studies based on documents are T. Gerardy, "C. F. Gauss und seine Söhne," in *GGM,* **3** (1966), 25–35; W. Lorey, in *Mathematisch-physikalische Semesterberichte* (Göttingen), **3** (1953), 179–192; and Hans Salié, in the collection edited by Reichardt described below. The most complete biography to date is G. W. Dunnington, *Carl Friedrich Gauss, Titan of Science* (New York, 1955), a useful derivative compendium of personal information and tradition, including translations from Sartorius, Hänselmann, and Mack, the largest bibliography yet published, and much useful data on genealogy, friends, students, honors, books borrowed at college, courses taught, etc.

During the Third Reich two rather feeble efforts—L. Bieberbach, *C. F. Gauss, ein deutsches Gelehrtenleben* (Berlin, 1938); and E. A. Roloff, *Carl Friedrich Gauss* (Osnabrück, 1942)—were made to claim Gauss as a hero, but it is clear that Gauss would have loathed the fascists as the final realization of his worst fears about bourgeois politics. Neither author mentions that Gauss's favorite mathematician, whom he praised extravagantly, was Gotthold Eisenstein.

Erich Worbs, *Carl Friedrich Gauss, Ein Lebensbild* (Leipzig, 1955), makes an effort to relate Gauss realistically to his times. W. L. Schaaf, *Carl Friedrich Gauss, Prince of Mathematicians* (New York, 1964), is a popularization addressed to juveniles.

C. *Scientific Work.* The literature analyzing Gauss's scientific work is expert and comprehensive, although its fragmentation by subject matter gives the impression of dealing with several different men. Beginning in 1911, F. Klein, M. Brendel, and L. Schlesinger edited a series of eight studies under the title *Materialien für eine wissenschaftliche Biographie von Gauss* (Leipzig, 1911–1920), most of which were later incorporated in the *Werke.* On the occasion of the hundredth anniversary of Gauss's death, there appeared *C. G. Gauss Gedenkband,* Hans Reichardt, ed. (Leipzig, 1957), republished as *C. F. Gauss, Leben und Werk* (Berlin, 1960); and I. M. Vinogradov, ed., *Karl Friedrich Gauss, 100 let so dnya smerti, sbornik statei* (Moscow, 1956). These collections will be abbreviated as Klein, Reichardt, and Vinogradov, respectively, when individual articles are listed below.

Brief anniversary evaluations by mathematicians are the following: R. Courant and R. W. Pohl, *Carl Friedrich Gauss, Zwei Vorträge* (Göttingen, 1955)—Courant's lecture also appeared in *Carl Friedrich Gauss . . . Gedenkfeier der Akademie der Wissenschaften . . . Göttingen anlässlich seines 100ten Todestages* (Göttingen, 1955) and was translated in T. L. Saaty and J. F. Weyl, eds., *The Spirit and the Uses of the Mathematical Sciences* (New York, 1969), pp. 141–155; J. Dieudonné, *L'oeuvre mathématique de C. F. Gauss* (Paris, 1962), a talk at the Palais de la Découverte, 2 December 1961; R. Oblath, "Megemlékezés halálának 100-ik évfordulóján," in *Matematikai lapok,* **6** (1955), 221–240; and K. A. Rybnikov, in *VIET,* **1** (1956), 44–53.

The following selected titles are arranged by topic.

Algebra. A. Fraenkel, "Zahlbegriff und Algebra bei Gauss," (Klein, VIII), in *GN,* supp. (1920); "Der Zusammenhang zwischen dem ersten und dem dritten Gauss'schen Beweis des Fundamentalsatzes der Algebra," in *DMV,* **31** (1922), 234–238; A. Ostrowski, "Über den ersten und vierten Gauss'schen Beweis des Fundamentalsatzes der Algebra," in *Werke,* X, pt. 2, sec. 3 (1933), 3–18 (an enlarged revision of Klein, VIII [1920], 50–58); R. Kochendörfer, in Reichardt, pp. 80–91; and M. Bocher, "Gauss's Third Proof of the Fundamental Theorem of Algebra," in *BAMS,* **1** (1895), 205–209.

Analysis. A. I. Markushevich, "Raboty Gaussa po matematicheskomu analizu," in Vinogradov, pp. 145–216, German trans. in Reichardt, pp. 151–182; K. Schröder, "C. F. Gauss und die reelle Analysis," in Reichardt, pp. 184–191; O. Bolza, "Gauss und die Variationsrechnung," in *Werke,* X, pt. 2, sec. 5 (1922), 3–93; L. Schlesinger, "Fragment zur Theorie des arithmetisch-geometrischen Mittels" (Klein, II), in *GN* (1912), 513–543; *Über Gauss' Arbeiten zur Funktionentheorie* (Berlin, 1933), also in *Werke,* X, pt. 2, sec. 2 (1933), 3–210—an enlarged revision of Klein II which appeared in *GN* (1912), 1–140; H. Geppert, "Wie Gauss zur elliptischen Modul-funktion kam," in *Deutsche Mathematik,* **5** (1940), 158–175; E. Göllnitz, "Über die Gauss'sche Darstellung der Funktionen sinlemn x und coslemn x als Quotienten unendlicher Produkte," in *Deutsche Mathematik,* **2** (1937), 417–420; P. Gunther, "Die Untersuchungen von Gauss in der Theorie der elliptischen Funktionen," in *GN* (1894), 92–105, and in trans. in *JMPA,* 5th ser., **3** (1897), 95–111; H. Hattendorff, *Die elliptischen Funktionen in dem Nachlasse von Gauss* (Berlin, 1869); A. Pringsheim, "Kritisch-historische Bemerkungen zur Funktionentheorie," in *BA* (1932), 193–200; (1933), 61–70; L. Schlesinger, "Über die Gauss'sche Theorie des arithmetisch-geometrischen Mittels . . .," in *Sitzungsberichte der Preussischen Akademie der Wissenschaften zu Berlin,* **28** (1898), 346–360; and "Über Gauss Jugendarbeiten zum arithmetisch-geometrischen Mittel," in *DMV,* **20** (1911), 396–403.

Astronomy. M. Brendel, "Über die astronomischen Arbeiten von Gauss," in *Werke,* XI, pt. 2, sec. 3 (1929), 3–254, enlarged revision of Klein, vol. VII, pt. 1 (Leipzig, 1919); M. F. Subbotin, "Astronomicheskie i geodesicheskie raboty Gaussa," in Vinogradov, pp. 241–310; and O. Volk, "Astronomie und Geodäsie bei C. F. Gauss," in Reichardt, pp. 206–229.

Geodesy and Surveying. A. Galle, "Über die geodätischen Arbeiten von Gauss," in *Werke,* XI, pt. 2, sec. 1 (1924), 3–161; W. Gronwald *et al., C. F. Gauss und die Landesvermessung in Niedersachsen* (Hannover, 1955); T. Gerardy, *Die Gauss'sche Triangulation des Königreichs Hannover (1821 bis 1844) und die Preussischen Grundsteuermessungen (1868 bis 1873)* (Hannover, 1952); G. V. Bagratuni, *K. F. Gauss, kratky ocherk geodezicheskikh issledovanii* (Moscow, 1955); M. F. Subbotin, in Vinogradov (see under Astronomy); W. Gäde, "Beiträge zur Kenntniss von Gauss' praktisch-geodätischen Arbeiten," in *ZV,* **14** (1885), 53–113; T. Gerardy, "Episoden aus der Gauss'schen Triangulation des Königreichs Hannover," in *ZV,* **80** (1955), 54–62; H. Michling, *Erläuterungsbericht zur Neuberechnung der Gauss-Kruegerischen Koordinaten der Dreiecks- und Polygonpunkte der Katasterurmessung* (Hannover, 1947); "Der Gauss'sche Vizeheliotrop," in *GGM,* **4** (1967), 27–30; K. Nickul, "Über die Herleitung der Abbildungsgleichung der Gauss'schen Konformen Abbildung des Erdellipsoids in der Ebene," in *ZV,* **55** (1926), 493–496; and O. Volk, in Reichardt (see under Astronomy).

Geomagnetism. Ernst Schering, "Carl Friedrich Gauss und die Erforschung des Erdmagnetismus," in *GA,* **34** (1887), 1–79; T. N. Roze and I. M. Simonov, in *K. F. Gauss, Izbrannye trudy po zemnomu magnitizmu* (Leningrad, 1952), pp. 237–336; H.-G. Körber, "Alexander von Humboldts und Carl Friedrich Gauss' organisatorisches Wirken auf geomagnetischen Gebiet," in *FF,* **32** (1958), 1–8; and K.-R. Biermann, "Aus der Vorgeschichte der Aufforderung A. v. Humboldts an der Präsidenten der Royal Society . . .," in *HUB,* **12** (1963), 209–227.

Geometry. P. Stäckel, "C. F. Gauss als Geometer," in *Werke,* X, pt. 2, sec. 4 (1923), 3–121, repr. with note by L. Schlesinger from Klein, V (1917), which appeared also in *GN,* **4** (1917), 25–140; A. P. Norden, "Geometricheskie raboty Gaussa," in Vinogradov, pp. 113–144; R. C. Archibald, "Gauss and the Regular Polygon of Seventeen Sides," in *AMM,* **27** (1920), 323–326; H. Carslaw, "Gauss and Non-Euclidean Geometry," in *Nature,* **84,** no. 2134 (1910), 362; G. B. Halsted, "Gauss and non-Euclidean Geometry," in *AMM,* **7** (1900), 247, and on the same subject, in *AMM,* **11** (1904), 85–86, and in *Science,* **9,** no. 232 (1904), 813–817; and E. Hoppe, "C. F. Gauss und der Euklidische Raum," in *Naturwissenschaften,* **13** (1925), 743–744, and in trans. by Dunnington in *Scripta mathematica,* **20** (1954), 108–109 (Hoppe objects to the story that Gauss measured a large geodesic triangle in order to test whether Euclidean geometry was the "true" one, apparently under the impression that this would have been contrary to Gauss's ideas. Actually, Gauss considered geometry to have an empirical base and to be testable by experience.); V. F. Kagan, "Stroenie neevklidovoi geometrii u Lobachevskogo, Gaussa i Boliai," in *Trudy Instituta istorii estestvoznaniya,* **2** (1948), 323–389, repr. in his *Lobachevskii i ego geometriya* (Moscow, 1955), pp. 193–294; N. D. Kazarinoff, "On Who First Proved the Impossibility of Constructing Certain Regular Polygons . . .," in *AMM,* **75** (1968), 647; P. Mansion, "Über eine Stelle bei Gauss, welche sich auf nichteuklidische Metrik bezieht," in *DMV,* **7** (1899), 156; A. P. Norden, "Gauss i Lobachevskii," in *IMI,* **9** (1956), 145–168; A. V. Pogorelov, "Raboty K. F. Gaussa po geometrii poverkhnostei," in *VIET,* **1** (1956), 61–63; and P. Stäckel and F. Engel, *Die Theorie der Parallelinien* (Leipzig, 1895); "Gauss, die beiden Bolyai und die nichteuklidische Geometrie," in *MA,* **49** (1897), 149–206, translated in *BSM,* 2nd ser., **21** (1897), 206–228.

Miscellaneous. K.-R. Biermann, "Einige Episoden aus den russischen Sprachstudien des Mathematikers C. F. Gauss," in *FF,* **38** (1964), 44–46; E. Göllnitz, "Einige Rechenfehler in Gauss' Werken," in *DMV,* **46** (1936), 19–21; and S. C. Van Veen, "Een conflict tusschen Gauss en een Hollandsch mathematicus," in *Wiskunstig Tijdschrift,* **15** (1918), 140–146. The following four papers deal with the ciphers in which Gauss recorded some discoveries: K.-R. Biermann, in *MDA,* **5** (1963), 241–244; **11** (1969), 526–530; T. L. MacDonald, in *AN,* **241** (1931), 31; P. Männchen, in *Unterrichtsblätter für Mathematik und Naturwissenschaften,* **40** (1934), 104–106; and A. Wietzke, in *AN,* **240** (1930), 403–406.

Number Theory. P. Bachmann, "Über Gauss' Zählentheoretische Arbeiten" (Klein, I), in *GN* (1911), pp. 455–508, and in *Werke,* X, pt. 2, sec. 1 (1922), 3–69; B. N. Delone, "Raboty Gaussa po teorii chisel," in Vinogradov, pp. 11–112; G. J. Rieger, "Die Zahlentheorie bei C. F. Gauss," in Reichardt, pp. 37–77; E. T. Bell, "The Class Number Relations Implicit in the *Disquisitiones arithmeticae,*" in *BAMS,* **30** (1924), 236–238; "Certain Class Number Relations Implied in the *Nachlass* of Gauss," *ibid.,* **34** (1928), 490–494; "Gauss and the Early Development of Algebraic Numbers," in *NMM,* **18** (1944), 188–204, 219–223; L. E. Dickson, *History of the Theory of Numbers,* 3 vols. (Washington, D.C., 1919)—the indexes are a fairly complete guide to Gauss's extraordinary achievements in this field; J. Ginsburg, "Gauss' Arithmetization of the Problem of 8 Queens," in *SM,* **5** (1938), 63–66; F. Van der Blij, "Sommen van Gauss," in *Euclides* (Groningen), **30** (1954), 293–298; and B. A. Venkov, "Trudy K. F. Gaussa po teorii chisel i algebra," in *VIET,* **1** (1956), 54–60. The following papers concern an erroneous story, apparently started by W. W. R. Ball, that the Paris mathematicians rejected the *Disquisitiones arithmeticae:* R. C. Archibald, "Gauss's *Disquisitiones arithmeticae* and the French Academy of Sciences," in *SM,* **3** (1935), 193–196; H. Geppert and R. C. Archibald, "Gauss's *Disquisitiones Arithmeticae* and the French Academy of Sciences," *ibid.,* 285–286; G. W. Dunnington, "Gauss, His Disquisitiones Arithmeticae and His Contemporaries in the Institut de France," in *NMM,* **9** (1935), 187–192; A. Emch, "Gauss and the French Academy of Science," in *AMM,* **42** (1935), 382–383. See also G. Heglotz, "Zur letzten Eintragung im Gauss'schen Tagebuch," in *LB,* **73** (1921), 271–277.

Numerical Calculations. P. Männchen, "Die Wechselwirkung zwischen Zahlenrechnung und Zahlentheorie bei C. F. Gauss" (Klein, VI), in *GN,* supp. **7** (1918), 1–47, and in *Werke,* X, pt. 2, sec. 6 (1930), 3–75; and A. Galle, "C. F. Gauss als Zahlenrechner" (Klein, IV), in *GN,* supp. **4** (1917), 1–24.

Philosophy. A. Galle, "Gauss und Kant," in *Weltall,* **24** (1925), 194–200, 230, repr. in *GGM,* **6** (1969), 8–15; P. Mansion, "Gauss contre Kant sur la géométrie non-Euclidienne," in *Mathesis,* 3rd ser., **8,** supp. (Dec. 1908), 1–16, in *Revue néoscolastique,* **15** (1908), 441–453, and in *Proceedings of the Third* (*1908*) *International Congress of Philosophy in Heidelberg* (Leipzig, 1910), pp. 438–447; and H. E. Timerding, "Kant und Gauss," in *Kant-Studien,* **28** (1923), 16–40.

Physics. H. Falkenhagen, "Die wesentlichsten Beiträge von C. F. Gauss aus der Physik," in Reichardt, pp. 232–251; H. Geppert, "Über Gauss' Arbeiten zur Mechanik und Potentialtheorie," in *Werke,* X, pt. 2, sec. 7 (1933), 3–60; and C. Schäfer, "Gauss physikalische Arbeiten (Magnetismus, Elektrodynamik, Optik)," in *Werke,* XI, pt. 2, sec. 2 (1929), 2–211; "Gauss's Investigations on Electrodynamics," in *Nature,* **128** (1931), 339–341.

Probability and Statistics (*Including Least Squares*). B. V. Gnedenko, "O raboty Gaussa po teorii veroyatnostei," in Vinogradov, pp. 217–240; A. Galle, "Über die geodätischen Arbeiten von Gauss," in *Werke,* XI, pt. 2, sec. 6 (1924), 3–161; C. Eisenhart, "Gauss," in *International Encyclopedia of the Social Sciences,* VI (New York, 1968), 74–81; P. Männchen, "Über ein Interpolationsverfahren des jugendlichen Gauss," in *DMV,* **28** (1919), 80–84; H. L. Seal, "The Historical Development of the Gauss Linear Model," in *Biometrika,* **54** (1967), 1–24; T. Sofonea, "Gauss und die Versicherung," in *Verzekerings-Archive,* **32** (Aktuar Bijv, 1955), 57–69; and Helen M. Walker, *Studies in the History of Statistical Method* (Baltimore, 1931).

Telegraph. Ernst Feyerabend, *Der Telegraph von Gauss und Weber im Werden der elektrischen Telegraphie* (Berlin, 1933); and R. W. Pohl, "Jahrhundertfeier des elektromagnetischen Telegraphen von Gauss und Weber," in *GN* (1934), pp. 48–56, repr. in *Carl Friedrich Gauss, Zwei Vorträge* (Göttingen, 1955), pp. 5–12.

The author gratefully acknowledges many helpful suggestions and comments from Kurt-R. Biermann. Thanks are due also to the library staff at the University of Toronto for many services. The author claims undivided credit only for errors of fact and judgment.

KENNETH O. MAY

GAUTIER, ARMAND E.-J. (*b.* Narbonne, France, 23 September 1837; *d.* Cannes, France, 27 July 1920), *chemistry.*

Gautier, the son of Louis Gautier, a physician and landowner, studied chemistry at Montpellier under J. E. Bérard (a former assistant to Berthollet) and J. A. Béchamp. In contrast with his teachers, he favored the use of atomic representations, rather than equivalents, in chemical notation. He especially supported the ideas of Charles Gerhardt, who had taught at Montpellier until 1851. After receiving a medical degree in 1862, Gautier left Montpellier for the Paris laboratory of Adolphe Wurtz. His isolation in 1866 of the isonitriles (isomers of the nitriles), or carbylamines, as he called them, was an important contribution to the new chemical theories.

Gautier prepared his carbylamines in a double decomposition reaction between silver cyanide and a simple or compound ether. Despite the penetrating odor of the carbylamines, their formation had escaped earlier workers on cyanohydric ethers, since cyanogen compounds were believed to be completely analogous to halogen compounds; the production of isomers in a simple reaction of the cyanogen radical was unimaginable. Influenced, however, by Wurtz's researches on the "ammonia type," Gautier demonstrated that the isonitriles existed and were indeed amines, whereas ordinary nitriles were more like salts. He noted that the cyanogen carbon atom in the carbylamine permits polymerization into explosives as well as a direct union with sulfur or oxygen. Gautier's explanation illuminated analogous relations between the cyanic ethers and their isomers, and between the cyanates and fulminates. The use of silver cyanide with methyl or ethyl iodide to form the carbylamine suggested to Victor Meyer the reaction of these iodides with silver nitrate to produce nitrated aliphatics (nitromethane, nitroethane, etc.).

Gautier incorporated his researches on the carbylamines into his doctoral thesis ("Des nitriles des acides gras") in 1869 and so impressed Henri Sainte-Claire Deville that the young chemist was quickly appointed to the chemical laboratory of the École Pratique des Hautes-Études. In 1874 Gautier became director of the new laboratory of biological medicine at the Faculté de Médecine, and in 1884 he succeeded Wurtz in the chair of medical chemistry, a post which he held until 1912.

Gautier's researches in these years were prodigious. In 1873 he noticed the release of small quantities of volatile alkaloids during the bacterial fermentation of albuminous material. He demonstrated in 1882 that such alkaloids are constant products of the normal life of animal tissues and are eliminated from the healthy body in urine and saliva. He developed methods for the quantitative analysis of trace amounts of arsenic and demonstrated that such traces exist in healthy animals, especially in the skin. He further established the therapeutic value of arsenic compounds. Gautier analyzed iodine and free hydrogen in the air, iodine and fluorine in organic substances, the coloring matter of grapes, the composition of mineral waters, and chemical reactions related to volcanic phenomena.

He published numerous textbooks, the most significant of which was the three-volume *Cours de chimie minérale, organique et biologique* (1887–1892).

BIBLIOGRAPHY

I. ORIGINAL WORKS. In addition to the *Cours de chimie* (2nd ed., 1895–1897; Vol. II, 3rd ed., 1906), Gautier's texts include *Chimie appliquée à la physiologie, à la pathologie, et à l'hygiène,* 2 vols. (Paris, 1874); *La chimie de la cellule vivante,* 2 vols. (Paris, 1894–1898); and *L'alimentation et les régimes chez l'homme sain et chez les malades* (Paris, 1904; 3rd ed., 1908). An almost complete bibliography of Gautier's scientific and popular writings may be found in Lebon (see below).

II. SECONDARY LITERATURE. Ernest Lebon's biography, *Armand Gautier. Biographie, bibliographie analytique des écrits* (Paris, 1912), is the best single source of information about Gautier. An obituary notice in *Nature* (16 Sept. 1920), 85–86, is reprinted in *Journal of the Chemical Society* (London), **119,** pt. 1 (1921), 537–539. An *éloge* by Henri Deslandres, read at the Académie des Sciences (2 Aug. 1920), is reprinted in *Revue scientifique,* **58** (1920), 471–472.

MARY JO NYE

GAUTIER, PAUL FERDINAND (*b.* Paris, France, 12 October 1842; *d.* Paris, 7 December 1909), *astronomical instrumentation.*

Born into a family of modest means, Gautier was obliged to begin working at the age of thirteen. From the age of eighteen—when he was employed by M. L. F. Secrétan—until his death, he was occupied with construction of astronomical instruments.

Gautier's instruments were closely linked to the strides made by late nineteenth-century astronomy: many of the major refracting telescopes, astrographs, and transit instruments that he made from 1876 on are still used by the observatories, both in France and elsewhere, that commissioned them. His instruments performed perfectly; to the execution of precision screws, graduated circles, and telescopic mounts Gautier brought the unsurpassed competence that earned him recognition and membership in the Bureau des Longitudes in 1897.

Gautier supplied most of the double astrographs used in the international undertaking that produced the *Carte du ciel.* The mount for the first astrograph was built at his own expense, and the instrument's performance led to its adoption in 1887 as a prototype.

Among Gautier's accomplishments were all the equatorial telescopes of the *coudé* type. The classic *Atlas de la lune* of Loewy and Puiseux, compiled from 1896 to 1910, employed the instrument that he had built for the Paris observatory; the plates in this work compare favorably with the finest modern ones.

The career of this honest and unselfish man ended in undeserved failure. For the Paris Universal Exposition of 1900 Gautier constructed the largest refractor ever built. The lens, forty-nine inches in diameter, was mounted at the end of a horizontal tube more than 195 feet long and was joined to a large siderostat. The device operated at a huge financial loss and ruined Gautier. This instrument—which, with a few adjustments, might have played an important role in scientific research—was ultimately dismantled, and its components sold.

Gautier's most important work includes equatorial visual telescopes, double astrographs, reflectors, and *coudé* equatorial telescopes at leading observatories in France, Austria, Greece, the Netherlands, Vatican City, Spain, Algeria, Argentina, and Brazil.

BIBLIOGRAPHY

I. Original Works. Gautier published two technical memoirs in *Comptes rendus hebdomadaires des séances de l'Académie des sciences:* "Sur un procédé de construction des vis de haute précision . . .," in **112** (1891), 991–992; and "Construction d'un miroir plan de 2 mètres par des procédés mécaniques," in **128** (1899), 1373–1375. Gautier left to others the task of describing his instruments but drafted "Note sur le sidérostat à lunette de 60 mètres de foyer," in *Annuaire publié par le Bureau des longitudes* (1899), C1–C26.

II. Secondary Literature. On Gautier and his work, see H. Poincaré and B. Baillaud, "Funérailles de M. Paul Gautier," in *Annuaire publié par le Bureau des longitudes* (1911), D1–D11; and L. Vandevyver, "La grande lunette de 1900," in *Ciel et terre,* **19** (1899), 257–267.

Jacques R. Lévy

GAY, FREDERICK PARKER (*b.* Boston, Massachusetts, 22 July 1874; *d.* New Hartford, Connecticut, 14 July 1939), *bacteriology, pathology.*

Born into a prominent Boston family, Gay followed the tradition of attending the Boston Latin School and Harvard (B.A. 1897), where he developed a lifelong interest in art, music, and classical literature. At Johns Hopkins Medical School (1897–1901) the exceptional student attracted the attention of Simon Flexner, who made Gay his assistant and invited him to join the world tour of the Johns Hopkins Medical Commission for the study of bubonic plague and other diseases (1899). After one year in the Philippines investigating cholera and dysentery, Gay returned home via Paris, where he studied at the Pasteur Institute, was fascinated by the young and brilliant Jules Bordet, and became acquainted with the infant sciences of microbiology and immunology. After returning to America he was awarded the first fellowship of the recently established Rockefeller Institute (1901), serving from 1901 to 1903 as assistant demonstrator in pathology at the University of Pennsylvania, then headed by his mentor, Simon Flexner.

But pure pathology was not destined to retain Gay's exclusive attention. In 1903 he rejoined Bordet, now established in his own Pasteur Institute in Brussels, and for the next three years was deeply engrossed in the emerging problems of anaphylaxis, complement-fixation, and other aspects of immunology. In 1904 Gay married Catherine Mills Jones; they had three children. Returning to America in 1906, he served for one year as bacteriologist at the Danvers, Massachusetts, Insane Asylum, and from 1907 to 1909 was assistant and then instructor in pathology at Harvard Medical School. In 1909 Gay completed and published the first English translation of the classic *Studies in Immunology* by Bordet and his associates, an accomplishment that immediately brought him into national prominence.

In 1910 he accepted the position of professor of pathology at the University of California at Berkeley, a post he was to retain for thirteen years, with only a brief interruption for service in the army. At Berkeley he finally persuaded the authorities to establish a separate department of bacteriology, and it was as the department's first director that he spent his final two years in California. During World War I and later Gay served as a member of the medical section of the National Research Council, and in 1922 he was its chairman. He also served as chairman of the Council's Medical Fellowship Board from 1922 to 1926. In the latter year he traveled from one Belgian university to another as exchange professor.

In 1923 Gay had accepted his last academic position, as professor of bacteriology at the Columbia University College of Physicians and Surgeons. His monograph *Typhoid Fever* (New York, 1918) was already well-known, but at Columbia he produced his most famous work, *Agents of Disease and Host Resistance* (Springfield, 1935), the best exposition of the problems of bacteriology and immunology of the period. His humanistic interests also asserted themselves at this time; his last book, *The Open Mind* (Chicago, 1938), dedicated to the memory of his lifelong friend, the psychiatrist Elmer E. Southard, reveals the depth of his concern with current problems of psychology and sociology.

Gay's honors were many: Belgium accorded him the Order of the Crown for his work with the American Commission on Relief; George Washington University granted him an Sc.D. degree in 1932; and he was elected a member of the National Academy of Sciences a few months before his death. Membership in other learned societies included the Association of American Physicians, the American Association of Pathologists and Bacteriologists, the American Society for Experimental Pathology, the Society for Experimental Biology and Medicine, the Association of American Bacteriologists, and the American Association of Immunologists.

Any evaluation of Gay's wide and varied contributions to science and to society must deal with the unusual dichotomy of his interests. The influence of Bordet is evident in his studies on serum reactions (1905–1910) and on anaphylaxis (1905–1913). This led to a lasting concern with tissue immunity and especially with the roles played by the reticuloendothelial system and the clasmatocyte (histiocyte). As a bacteriologist he made substantial contributions to our knowledge of the carrier state in typhoid (1913–1919); hemolytic streptococcic infections (1919–1939); and viral diseases, especially the herpetic and encephalitic (1929–1939). Other specific entities with which he concerned himself included pneumonia, meningitis, influenza, and poliomyelitis. Always he explored the possibility of inducing antibody formation by the use of antigens, stressing the practical application of such reactions to the diagnostic problems of infectious disease. Among the multitude of related subjects on which Gay wrote are cowpox, tobacco mosaic, bacteriophage, protozoa, spirochetes, rickettsia, dental caries, Vincent's angina, bacterial mutation, chemotherapy, lysozyme, and the importance of hormones and vitamins in resistance to infection.

In all these areas his position is assured; yet he deserves special consideration as that relatively infrequent and unusual combination of scientist, social philosopher, and humanist. Gay was also a man of great sincerity and integrity. Possessed of a touch of compassion for the plight of humanity, he forged strong bonds of affection which made him a seminal influence in the lives of those who knew him well.

BIBLIOGRAPHY

On Gay or his work see J. M. Cattell and Jacques Cattell, eds., *American Men of Science* (New York, 1938), p. 508; A. R. Dochez, "Frederick Parker Gay 1874–1939," in *Biographical Memoirs. National Academy of Sciences,* **38** (1954), 99–116, with portrait and complete bibliography; and Claus W. Jungeblut, "Frederick Parker Gay," in *Science,* **20** (1939), 290–291.

MORRIS H. SAFFRON

GAY-LUSSAC, JOSEPH LOUIS (*b.* St. Léonard, France, 6 December 1778; *d.* Paris, France, 9 May 1850), *chemistry, physics.*

He was the eldest of five children of Antoine Gay, lawyer and *procureur royal* at St. Léonard, and Leonarde Bourigner. His father, to distinguish himself from others with the surname Gay in the Limoges region, had begun to call himself Gay-Lussac after the family property near St. Léonard. Joseph Louis, although baptized "Gay," adopted the same practice.

The comfortable social and economic position of the family was rudely disturbed by the Revolution. In September 1793, when Gay-Lussac was fourteen, his father was arrested as a suspect. The Abbé Bourdeix, who had been giving the son private lessons, fled the country. Joseph Louis was sent to a small private boarding school in Paris, where his lessons included mathematics and science. The opening of the École Polytechnique provided a splendid opportunity for an able boy without fortune. Gay-Lussac was successful in the competitive entrance examination and was admitted on 27 December 1797. Graduating on 22 November 1800, he followed the practice of many of the better students by entering the civil engineering school, the École Nationale des Ponts et Chaussées. In the winter of 1800–1801, the chemist Berthollet, impressed by the ability of the young man, took him to his country house at Arcueil as an assistant. Having already had an excellent mathematical education, Gay-Lussac received training in chemical research from Berthollet, who also played a key role in the professional advancement of his protégé. In 1808 Gay-Lussac married Geneviève Marie Josèphe Rojot; they had five children.

Gay-Lussac was successively *adjoint* (from 31 December 1802) and *répétiteur* (from 23 September 1804) at the École Polytechnique. On 31 March 1809 he was given the honorary title of professor of practical chemistry, but upon the death of Fourcroy he was appointed to succeed him as professor of chemistry (17 February 1810). On the creation of the Paris Faculty of Science in 1808, Gay-Lussac was appointed professor of physics; in 1832 he gave up this chair in favor of that of general chemistry at the Muséum National d'Histoire Naturelle. On 8 December 1806 Gay-Lussac obtained the coveted place of member of the first class of the Institute (physics section). He was already a member of the Société d'Arcueil and the Société Philomatique.

Nearly all of Gay-Lussac's life was devoted to pure and applied science, but he did have a brief political career. He was elected to the Chamber of Deputies in 1831, 1834, and 1837 but resigned on a matter of principle in 1838. On 7 March 1839, having earlier refused a title from Charles X, he was honored by Louis Philippe with nomination to the upper house.

Gay-Lussac's first major research was on the thermal expansion of gases.[1] It was carried out with the encouragement of Berthollet and Laplace in the winter of 1801–1802. There was conflicting evidence about the expansive properties of different gases when heated. Gay-Lussac improved on most earlier work by taking precautions to exclude water vapor from his apparatus and to use dry gases. After examining a variety of gases, including several soluble in water, and repeating each experiment several times, he concluded that equal volumes of all gases expand equally with the same increase of temperature. Over the range of temperature from 0°C. to 100°C. the expansion of gases was 1/266.66 of the volume at 0°C. for each degree rise in temperature. Similar research was carried out independently by Dalton at about the same time. Dalton's work, however, was considerably less accurate. About 1787 J. A. C. Charles had recognized the equal expansion of several gases but had never bothered to publish his findings. Although the quantitative law of thermal expansion is often called "Charles's law," Charles did not measure the coefficient of expansion; moreover, for soluble gases, he had found unequal expansion.

Gay-Lussac made an ascent in a hydrogen balloon with Biot on 24 August 1804. The primary objective of the ascent was to see whether the magnetic intensity at the earth's surface decreased with an increase in altitude.[2] They concluded that it was constant up to 4,000 meters. They also carried long wires to test the electricity of different parts of the atmosphere. Another objective was to collect a sample of air from a high altitude to compare its composition with that of air at ground level. Gay-Lussac made a second ascent, on 16 September 1804, but this time by himself, in order to lessen the weight of the balloon and thus reach a greater height.

He was able to repeat observations of pressure, temperature, and humidity and also make magnetic measurements. He had taken two evacuated flasks, which he opened to collect samples of air when he had attained an altitude of over 6,000 meters. His subsequent analysis of these samples showed that the proportion of oxygen was identical with that in ordinary air. Gay-Lussac reached a calculated height of 7,016 meters above sea level, a record not equaled for another half century.

One of Gay-Lussac's early collaborators was Alexander von Humboldt. Nearly ten years older than Gay-Lussac, Humboldt already had an international reputation as an explorer; yet he learned something about precision in scientific research from Gay-Lussac, who in turn had his horizons broadened by his German friend. They collaborated in an examination of various methods of estimating the proportion of oxygen in the air, particularly the use of Volta's eudiometer.[3] In this method the gas being tested (which was required to contain some oxygen) was sparked with hydrogen to form water vapor, which condensed.

The resulting contraction permitted an estimate of the proportion of oxygen in the sample. This method obviously presupposed a knowledge of the relative proportions by volume in which hydrogen and oxygen combine to form water; one of the principal objects of the work of Gay-Lussac and Humboldt was to determine the proportion with the greatest possible accuracy. They also determined the limiting proportions for an explosion to be possible. After carrying out a large number of experiments with an excess of first one gas and then the other, they calculated—making allowance for a slight impurity in the test oxygen—that 100 parts by volume of oxygen combined with 199.89 parts of hydrogen or, they said, in round numbers, 200 parts. Gay-Lussac clearly expressed his preference for volumes, pointing out that the presence of moisture, which would be difficult to estimate gravimetrically, did not alter the volumetric ratio. This memoir made a useful contribution to science not only for its accuracy but as a precursor of Gay-Lussac's famous research on the combining volumes of gases.

In March 1805 Gay-Lussac embarked on a year of European travel with Humboldt, going first to Rome and ending in Berlin. During this journey Gay-Lussac carried out various chemical analyses. Their principal object, however, was to record the magnetic elements at different points along their route.[4]

To obtain the magnetic intensity, the period of oscillation of a magnetized needle was determined. The magnetic intensity was then found to be proportional to the square of the number of oscillations made by the needle, displaced slightly from the magnetic meridian, in a given time. They did not think that magnetic intensity in any one place changed with time, since on taking readings at Milan on entering and leaving Italy at an interval of six months, they found no difference. A series of prolonged experiments to determine diurnal variation, both on Mount Cenis and in Rome, had not revealed any difference at different hours of the day and night. As regards the general accuracy of their readings, many of which were made under conditions that were far from ideal, they estimated that the greatest discrepancy between their angular readings could not have been more than ten minutes of arc. Their general conclusion was that the horizontal component of the earth's magnetic intensity increased from north (Berlin) to south (Naples) but that the total intensity decreased on approaching the equator.

In 1807 Gay-Lussac carried out a series of experiments designed principally to see whether there was a general relationship between the specific heats of gases and their densities.[5] He measured the change in the temperature of a gas (and thus heat capacity) as a function of density changes produced by the free expansion of the gas. From a modern viewpoint the importance of his work was his establishment of a basic principle of physics, since it follows from his experiments that (in modern terms) the internal energy of an ideal gas depends on the temperature only. He took two twelve-liter, double-neck flasks. To one neck a tap was fitted and to the other a sensitive alcohol thermometer. Each flask contained anhydrous calcium chloride to absorb all moisture. One of the flasks was then evacuated and the other filled with the gas under test. The flasks were then connected with a lead pipe, the taps opened, and the readings of the thermometers carefully noted. It was known that compression of gases was accompanied by evolution of heat and expansion by absorption of heat. Gay-Lussac, however, wished to find the relationship between heat absorbed and heat evolved in the two flasks, and from his experiments he drew the valuable conclusion that these were equal within the limits of experimental error. The change of temperature was, moreover, directly proportional to the change of pressure. This he found by connecting the flasks, equalizing the pressures by opening the tap (that is, reducing the pressure to half, since the volumes were equal), evacuating the second flask, and repeating this process until the temperature change was so slight as to make accurate measurement impossible.

Gay-Lussac's experiment with two connecting vessels was repeated nearly forty years later by Joule, who apparently knew nothing of the earlier work.

Probably Gay-Lussac's greatest single achievement is based on the law of combining volumes of gases, which he announced at a meeting of the Société Philomatique in Paris, on 31 December 1808. For Gay-Lussac himself, the law provided a vindication of his belief in regularities in the physical world, which it was the business of the scientist to discover. Gay-Lussac began his memoir by pointing out the unique character of the gaseous state.[6] For solids and liquids a particular increase in pressure would produce a change different in each case; it was only matter in the gaseous state that increased equally in volume for a given increase of pressure. His own statement was that "gases combine in very simple proportions . . . and . . . the apparent contraction in volume which they experience on combination has also a simple relation to the volume of the gases, or at least to one of them." He gives the following examples of the simple ratios of combining volumes of gases (modern symbols are used for brevity).

$$O:H = 1:2$$
$$HCl:NH_3 = 1:1$$
$$BF_3:NH_3 = 1:1 \text{ and } 1:2$$
$$CO_2:NH_3 = 1:1 \text{ and } 1:2$$
$$CO:O_2 = 2:1$$

Combinations

$$NH_3:N:H = 1:3$$
$$SO_3:SO_2:O_2 = 2:1$$
$$N_2O:N:O = 2:1$$
$$NO:N:O = 1:1$$
$$NO_2:N:O = 1:2$$

Analyses

These neat ratios do not, however, correspond exactly to his experimental results. He deduced his law from a few fairly clear cases (particularly the first few listed above) and glossed over discrepancies in some of the others. The simple reaction between hydrogen and chlorine, which is often used today as an elementary illustration of the law, was not discovered until 1809 and was included only as a footnote when this memoir was printed.

Gay-Lussac presented his law of combining volumes of gases as a natural consequence of his collaboration with Humboldt, with whom he had found that 100 parts by volume of oxygen combine with almost exactly 200 parts of hydrogen. That his work of January 1805 with Humboldt led naturally to the law of combining volumes may be logically true but historically the connection is less direct. One has to explain the interval of nearly four years between obtaining the first data and the announcement of the law. Probably something had happened earlier in the year 1808 that made Gay-Lussac turn his attention back to his earlier work and realize that the value he had obtained for the combining volumes of hydrogen and oxygen was more than a coincidence and was in fact only one example of a general phenomenon. In the autumn of 1808 Gay-Lussac and Thenard had discovered boron trifluoride. They were particularly impressed by one of the properties of this new gas, the dense fumes produced when it came into contact with the air; they compared these fumes with the fumes produced by the reaction of muriatic-acid gas and ammonia. It seems likely that Gay-Lussac, struck by the reaction of boron trifluoride with moist air, tried its reaction with other gases including ammonia. An obvious reaction for comparison would be that between hydrochloric-acid gas and ammonia. This reaction was given special prominence in the memoir on combining volumes of gases.

One of the points of strength of the memoir was that it took data from a wide variety of reputable sources. This was no suspect generalization based on the biased experimental work of its author. On the other hand, all the data had not, of course, been conveniently assembled for Gay-Lussac to publish. In many cases the analyses that had appeared in the chemical literature had given only the gravimetric composition, and Gay-Lussac, taking reliable data for the density, had to convert this to a volumetric ratio. A close examination of the provenance of the density data shows that much was derived from his associates in the Société d'Arcueil.

The influence of Berthollet is particularly prominent in Gay-Lussac's attempt to reconcile the opinions of Dalton, Thomson, and Wollaston on definite and multiple proportions with Berthollet's known conviction that compounds can always be formed in variable proportions except in special circumstances. It was possible to argue that the gaseous state provided such an exception, and Berthollet accepted Gay-Lussac's law. Considering the implications of the law for the atomic structure of matter, it would be reasonable to expect Dalton to have welcomed the law of combining volumes as additional evidence for his atomic theory. Dalton, however, refused to accept the accuracy of the results of the French chemist. The Italian physical chemist Avogadro, on the other hand, not only accepted Gay-Lussac's work but developed its implications for the relationship between the volumes of gases and the number of molecules they contain. His great debt to Gay-Lussac's memoir was explicit.

Although Berzelius and Gay-Lussac differed in the actual values given to "volume weights" (often by a factor of 2), Berzelius, especially in his earlier work, regarded Gay-Lussac's method of speaking of volumes as preferable to Dalton's atoms. It had the advantage of being based on more direct evidence, and there was no absurdity in dealing with half volumes, whereas there was a contradiction involved in speaking of "half atoms." The obvious disadvantage of translating "atom" as "volume" was that many compounds cannot exist in the gaseous state. Gay-Lussac himself was prepared to estimate the relative vapor density of mercury not by direct means but by calculation based on the weight combining with a given weight of oxygen in the solid state. Gay-Lussac later speculated about the proportion of "carbon vapor" in carbon compounds. His interest in volumes led him to devise an apparatus by which the vapor densities of liquids could be compared.[7] The vapor displaced mercury in a graduated glass tube immersed in a glass cylinder containing water which was heated. The apparatus was improved half a century later by A. W. Hofmann, and the method by which the volume of a given weight of a vaporized substance is found is now usually known as Hofmann's method.

The work of Volta inspired many chemists to investigate the chemical effects of the voltaic pile. Gay-Lussac and Thenard were among this number. They were influenced particularly by the news in the winter of 1807–1808 of Davy's isolation of potassium and sodium by the use of the giant voltaic pile at the Royal Institution. Napoleon ordered the construction of an even larger pile at the École Polytechnique and Gay-Lussac and Thenard were placed in charge of it. Their research, reported in part 1 of their *Recherches physico-chimiques* (1811), was basically a repetition of Davy's experiments. Although Davy seems to have exhausted the most obvious possibilities, Gay-Lussac and Thenard's report does contain the suggestion that the rate of decomposition of an electrolyte depends only on the strength of the current (and not, for example, on the size of the electrodes), and they used chemical decomposition as a measure of electric current thirty years before Faraday. The Institute's prize of 3,000 francs for work in the field of galvanism was awarded to Davy in December 1807 and to Gay-Lussac and Thenard in December 1809.

Gay-Lussac and Thenard's really important contribution stemming from Davy's work was their preparation (announced to the Institute on 7 March 1808) of potassium and sodium in reasonable quantities and by purely chemical means.[8] Davy's method of electrolysis, although spectacular, had produced only tiny amounts of the new metals. The two young Frenchmen, no doubt under the influence of Berthollet, had reasoned that the action of great heat should change the usual affinities. Thinking that the normal affinities of oxygen for iron and the alkali metals could thus be reversed, they fused the respective alkalies with iron filings subjected to a bright red heat in a bent iron gun barrel. The metal vapor distilled over into a receiver luted to the gun barrel. In this way they prepared samples of about twenty-five grams of each metal at a low cost.

They were then able to investigate the physical constants of potassium, finding its specific gravity to be 0.874 (modern value, 0.859 at 0°C.). Davy had been unable to produce a better result than 0.6. Gay-Lussac and Thenard also discovered the alloy of potassium and sodium that exists as a liquid at room temperature. They then began a program of research in which potassium was not the end product but a reagent used to make further discoveries. In particular, they investigated the reaction between potassium metal and various gases. They found that when potassium is strongly heated in hydrogen, it combines with it to form a gray solid, potassium hydride, which is decomposed by water. They proposed the use of heated potassium as a means of performing an accurate volumetric analysis of nitrous and nitric oxides. The data obtained in this way by Gay-Lussac about the composition of nitric oxide was used by him later as evidence for his law of combining volumes of gases. They found that heated potassium metal decomposed muriatic-acid gas, forming the muriate of potash and hydrogen. Unfortunately they were prevented from reaching the conclusion that the gas was a simple compound of hydrogen and the muriatic radical by the conviction that the reaction was really due to water vapor in the gas.

In a further memoir, Gay-Lussac and Thenard described an experiment in which potassium was heated in dry ammonia, forming a solid (KNH_2) and liberating hydrogen. Other related experiments seemed to indicate to them that potassium was not an element at all but a hydride, and they argued this at length with Davy. Despite their mistaken conclusions on this point, the French chemists deserve credit for their discovery of a new class of compounds, the amides of metals.

In their next memoir Gay-Lussac and Thenard made further use of potassium as a reagent, this time to decompose boric acid.[9] They were not, however, alone in this field, since in the early summer of 1808 Davy turned his attention to their method of using potassium as a reagent. In a memoir read to the Royal Society on 30 June 1808, Davy described in a footnote how he had ignited boric acid and heated the product with potassium in a gold tube; this process yielded a black substance, which he did not identify but which was later recognized to be boron. It was not until his fourth Bakerian lecture, read on 15 December 1808, that Davy made any claim to the discovery of a new substance. His experimental work was rather poor and hurried. He admitted that he had had a report that Thenard was investigating the decomposition of boric acid by potassium. In December 1808 Davy succeeded in decomposing boric acid. He doubted, however, whether the substance obtained was a "simple body."

Gay-Lussac and Thenard's discovery of boron was first announced in November 1808. On 20 June 1808 they had mentioned an olive-gray substance obtained by the action of potassium on fused boric acid, but it was not until 14 November that they claimed to have isolated a new element and discovered its properties. This is one case where the work of Gay-Lussac and Thenard is indubitably prior to that of Davy. Equal weights of potassium metal and fused boric acid were heated together in a copper tube, thus producing a mixture of potassium, potassium borate, and boron. The new element did not dissolve or react chemically with water; this property thus provided a method of separating it. Gay-Lussac and Thenard gave it the name *bore* ("boron") and noted the similarity of its properties to those of carbon, phosphorus, and sulfur. Boron was found to form borides similar to carbides.

Their success in decomposing boric acid and isolating its "radical" led Gay-Lussac and Thenard to apply their new reagent, potassium, to the isolation of other radicals. Although the natural limitations of their method prevented them from achieving their immediate objective, they made a number of interesting discoveries.[10] In the course of these experiments they tried to prepare pure "fluoric acid" by heating together a mixture of calcium fluoride and vitrified boric acid. Investigating the properties of their fluoric acid, they found it had no effect on glass (a well-known property of hydrofluoric acid), and they reasoned correctly that this must be because it was already combined with an element similar to the basis of silica, namely, the boron from the acid used in its preparation. They therefore named the gas fluoboric gas (boron trifluoride).

They were now ready to prepare true hydrofluoric

acid and attempt its decomposition. This difficult feat was not accomplished until 1886, but Gay-Lussac and Thenard managed to prepare nearly anhydrous acid by distilling calcium fluoride with concentrated sulfuric acid in a lead retort.

After an unsuccessful attempt to isolate the muriatic radical by the action of heated potassium on muriates (chlorides) of metals, they turned their attention to oxymuriatic acid (chlorine), hoping to decompose it by removing its supposed oxygen.[11] Potassium was useless, but they were even more surprised when they found that even strongly heated carbon would not decompose the gas. This was all the more unexpected since sunlight decomposed it so easily. This led them to carry out further experiments on the effect of light on chemical reactions. They prepared two mixtures of chlorine and hydrogen; one was placed in darkness and the other in feeble sunlight. The first mixture was still greenish-yellow in color after several days, but the second had reacted completely by the end of a quarter of an hour, judging by the disappearance of the color of the chlorine. The experiment was repeated with olefiant gas (ethylene) and oxymuriatic-acid gas, which were mixed and left for two days in total darkness. As soon as the mixture was exposed to bright sunlight, there was a violent explosion. This confirmed their hypothesis that the speed of the reaction was proportional to the intensity of the light.

Apart from their early contribution to photochemistry, Gay-Lussac and Thenard made a fundamental contribution to the realization that so-called oxymuriatic acid contained no oxygen and was an element. Their memoir, read at a meeting of the Institute on 27 February 1809, contains the following remark, the wording of which should be carefully noted:

> Oxygenated muriatic acid is not decomposed by charcoal, and it might be supposed from this fact and those which are communicated in this memoir, that this gas is a simple body. The phenomena which it presents can be explained well enough on this hypothesis; we shall not seek to defend it, however, as it appears to us that they are still better explained by regarding oxygenated muriatic acid as a compound body.

The explanation of this statement is provided by events at a meeting of the Société d'Arcueil. On the previous day, 26 February, Gay-Lussac and Thenard had read a first draft of their memoir. In the first reading the authors had suggested unequivocally that oxymuriatic gas was an element. Their patron, Berthollet, unfortunately persuaded them to alter their remarks to make this no more than a possibility—as in the above quotation. Because of the pressure he exerted on Gay-Lussac and Thenard, Davy is usually credited with the discovery of the elementary nature of chlorine, which he announced in 1810. He had been particularly impressed by the evidence of Gay-Lussac and Thenard that charcoal, even at white heat, could not affect the decomposition of oxymuriatic gas, a result which one would hardly expect in a gaseous oxide.

Another area in which the contributions of Gay-Lussac were eclipsed by Davy—at least, outside France—was in the understanding of the properties of iodine. We must avoid describing this as the "discovery" of iodine, since it was neither Gay-Lussac nor Davy but Courtois who was the first to study this substance. The details of the story would take considerable space to elaborate; here it is sufficient to do no more than describe the contributions of Gay-Lussac.

Courtois recognized iodine to be a distinctive substance from its purple vapor, but its compound with hydrogen was at first confused with hydrogen chloride. It was Gay-Lussac who gave it the name *iode* (from the Greek *ioeidēs,* "violet colored"). On 12 December 1813 an article appeared in *Le Moniteur* in which Gay-Lussac expressed his view that iodine was probably an element. But he allowed also for the possibility of its being a compound containing oxygen. He stressed the analogy of the properties of iodine with those of chlorine. He was able to prepare the related acid (HI) by the action of iodine on moist phosphorus. He had prepared successively potassium iodate and iodic acid by 20 December 1813; the former was also prepared independently by Davy. A large part of Davy's claim for the originality of his study of iodine depends on his complete honesty in claiming certain knowledge before that of Gay-Lussac and in particular in dating as 11 December a paper read to the Institute on 13 December (that is, the day following Gay-Lussac's publication).

Gay-Lussac's major publication on iodine was not ready to be read to the Institute until 1 August 1814,[12] by which time not only Davy but Vauquelin had explored the subject fairly extensively. Gay-Lussac, however, deserves full credit for his detailed study of hydrogen iodide, which he found to have a 50 percent hydrogen content by volume. He contrasted its thermal decomposition with the stability of hydrogen chloride. By the action of chlorine on iodine, he prepared, independently of Davy and at about the same time, iodine monochloride and trichloride. After further careful study of the properties of iodine, he prepared and examined a number of iodides and iodates. He prepared for the first time ethyl iodide by distilling together concentrated hydriodic acid with absolute alcohol.

The close analogy that he emphasized between chlorine and iodine led him to a further investigation of the former, and he discovered chloric acid by the action of sulfuric acid on a solution of barium chlorate. Later, in collaboration with Welter, he discovered dithionic acid ($H_2S_2O_6$).[13] He also showed that aqua regia contains chlorine (which attacks gold) and nitrosyl chloride (NOCl) and that both gases are evolved on heating.[14]

In 1809 Gay-Lussac established by purely empirical means the general principle that the weight of acid in salts is proportional to the oxygen in the corresponding oxide.[15] (Salts were then considered to be compounds of metallic oxides with "acids," that is, acid anhydrides.) Gay-Lussac used this principle (occasionally referred to as a law) to determine the composition of some soluble salts. The analysis of insoluble salts was comparatively straightforward, but there was little agreement about the composition of the majority of salts, those which were soluble and could not therefore be weighed as precipitates. For example, insoluble lead sulfate had been found by analysis to consist of lead, 100.00; oxygen, 7.29; and acid, 37.71. Knowing the proportions of oxygen in the corresponding oxides of lead and copper, soluble copper sulfate must therefore contain oxygen and acid in the same proportions as lead sulfate: copper, 100.00; oxygen, 24.57; acid, 127.09. This was in fairly close agreement with the value obtained experimentally by L. J. Proust.

An extension of Gay-Lussac's principle could be used to determine the composition of sulfites indirectly. Direct determination presented practical difficulties, because sulfites are easily oxidized by the atmosphere to sulfates. The principle could be used in reverse if the composition of the salt were known and if the weight of oxygen that would combine with a given weight of the metal were required. This was applicable to the newly isolated barium.

Among his other work in inorganic chemistry, Gay-Lussac investigated the thermal decomposition of sulfates.[16] Under suitable oxidizing conditions, he was able to convert the sulfides of zinc and iron to the sulfates. His thermal decomposition of sulfuric acid in a porcelain tube showed the volumetric composition of sulfur trioxide to be 100 parts sulfur dioxide and 47.79 parts oxygen. In 1808 Gay-Lussac was able to use this data to help establish his law of combining volumes of gases.

Gay-Lussac carried out research on sulfides. The most important part of this work for the subsequent history of qualitative analysis was his investigation of the precipitation of metal sulfides. It was generally considered that such metals as zinc, manganese, cobalt, and nickel could not be precipitated by passing hydrogen sulfide through solutions of their respective salts. Gay-Lussac successfully demonstrated that the sulfides of these metals could be precipitated if they were present as salts of acetic, tartaric, or oxalic acids (that is, weak acids) or, better, in the presence of an alkali, such as ammonia.[17]

In 1809 Gay-Lussac carried out a study of the combining volumes of nitric oxide and oxygen.[18] This was a more complex problem than he then realized, but he returned to it in 1816 after criticism of his earlier work by Dalton; this time his results were of permanent value.[19] He recognized five oxides of nitrogen, which he listed as follows:

	Vols. of Nitrogen	Vols. of Oxygen	Modern Formula
Oxide d'azote	100	50	N_2O
Gaz nitreux	100	100	NO
Acide pernitreux	100	150	N_2O_3
Acide nitreux	100	200	NO_2
Acide nitrique	100	250	N_2O_5

Lavoisier's oxygen theory of acids had been questioned by Berthollet, who had failed to find oxygen either in hydrogen sulfide or in prussic acid. Although both gave acid reactions, Berthollet was not fully satisfied that Lavoisier's theory was erroneous; it was therefore left to his pupil Gay-Lussac to demonstrate conclusively that there was a definite class of acids that, instead of containing oxygen, contained hydrogen. Gay-Lussac introduced the term "hydracid" to denote this class, which included hydrochloric acid, hydriodic acid, and hydrogen sulfide.[20] Gay-Lussac thus introduced the name hydrochloric acid (*acide hydrochlorique*) for what had been called muriatic acid. Yet, so firmly accepted was Lavoisier's idea of oxygen as an acidifying principle that Gay-Lussac was convinced that hydrogen had no connection with the acidic properties and was in fact a principle of alkalinity.[21] If, for example, a solution of hydrogen sulfide showed acidic properties, it would have to be attributed to the sulfur that it contained.

Gay-Lussac's important research on prussic acid began with his successful preparation in 1811 of the anhydrous acid by the action of hydrochloric acid on mercuric cyanide.[22] In 1815 he determined the physical constants of the acid, including its vapor density.[23] He expressed its composition as follows: one volume of carbon vapor, one-half volume hydrogen, one-half volume nitrogen. He also expressed this in gravimetric terms, his figures being reasonably accurate. When he heated mercuric cyanide, he found that it decomposed into mercury and an inflammable gas composed of carbon and nitrogen. He proposed for this gas the name *cyanogène* (from the Greek *kyanos*, "dark blue"). He carefully examined the new compound, establishing its composition and showing that it combined with alkalies to form salts (cyanides). He investigated the properties and composition of cyanogen chloride, previously discovered by Berthollet. He examined several compounds derived from cyanogen, including ferrocyanate, which he clearly recognized as a compound radical and which he would have written as $Fe(CN)_6$ with modern atomic weights.[24] He later analyzed Prussian blue and made suggestions about its composition.[25]

Gay-Lussac demonstrated the growth of crystals of ammonia alum over those of potash alum and suggested that "the molecules of the two alums have the same form."[26] This has sometimes been incorrectly interpreted as an anticipation of Mitscherlich's law of isomorphism.

Gay-Lussac's study of the solubility of salts is of considerable importance, since he was the first to construct a solubility curve showing the variation of solubility of various salts in water at different temperatures.[27] He recognized that the amount of solid has no influence on the ultimate solubility. He understood that the solubility of a salt in water at a given temperature is a constant in the presence of excess solute. He noticed the break in the solubility curve of hydrated sodium sulfate and that this occurs at the point of maximum solubility.

Gay-Lussac studied the effect of the material and form of different vessels on the constancy of boiling points of liquids.[28] He found that the vapor pressure of a solution is lower than that of the pure solvent, for example, a solution of sodium chloride with a specific gravity of 1.096 was 0.9 that of the vapor pressure of water.

Gay-Lussac, in considering the action of chlorine on alkalies, stated, "There is a general rule that in every case where the same elements can form compounds of different stability (but capable of existing simultaneously under the same given conditions), the first to be formed is the least stable."[29] This is a remarkably perceptive statement and is almost the "law of successive reactions" proposed by Ostwald in 1897.

As might be expected from a pupil of Berthollet, Gay-Lussac made several contributions to an understanding of chemical equilibrium and the realization of the relevance to a reaction of the mass of the reactants. He showed, for example, that the action of steam on heated iron is a reversible action.[30] Following Berthollet's ideas, Gay-Lussac considered that when sulfuric acid is added to a solution of borax, "the base is partitioned between the two acids . . . in proportion to the numbers of their atoms."[31] Toward the end of his career, Gay-Lussac wrote a long historical article on affinity. He considered the particles in a solution of different salts to be in state of random motion (*pêle-mêle*) at the moment of mixture. Eventually a situation of equilibrium was obtained, but any slight alteration of conditions could bring about a further exchange of the acid and basic parts of the salts in solution. He introduced the concept of permutation of the constituent part of salts (*équipollence*):

> At the moment of mixture of two neutral salts, two new salts are formed in certain ratios with the two original salts; and then according to whether one of the properties of insolubility, density, fusibility, volatility, etc. is greater for the new salts than for the original salts, there will be a disturbance of equilibrium and the separation of one or even several salts.[32]

Although Gay-Lussac is probably best known for his work in physical and inorganic chemistry, he also made a number of important contributions to organic chemistry. In January 1810 Gay-Lussac and Thenard developed the pioneer work of Lavoisier on the quantitative combustion analysis of organic compounds. Whereas Lavoisier had burned a few inflammable substances in oxygen gas, Gay-Lussac and Thenard greatly extended the generality of the method by the use of an oxidizing agent.[33] They at first proposed potassium chlorate, but as this was found to act too powerfully, Gay-Lussac suggested in 1815 that copper oxide was preferable and thereby established its use. They applied their method in 1810 to the analysis of twenty vegetable and animal substances. On the basis of these analyses, they divided vegetable substances into three classes according to the proportion of hydrogen and oxygen contained in them. One of these classes included compounds—such as starch, gum, and sugar—in which the proportion of oxygen to hydrogen was the same as in water. This classification was accepted by William Prout, who referred to this group as the saccharine class, later called carbohydrates.

Gay-Lussac's analysis of prussic acid in 1815 is particularly important because he drew attention to the existence of a radical (—CN) that is fully analogous to the chlorine in hydrochloric acid and the iodine in iodic acid, the essential difference being that "this radical is compound."[34] This was the first example of the analysis of a carbon-containing radical. If this had been generally considered as an organic radical, it might have anticipated the radical theory of organic chemistry of the 1830's.

In 1815 Gay-Lussac referred to prussic acid as a "true hydracid in which carbon and nitrogen *replace* [author's italics] chlorine in hydrochloric acid. . . ."[35] He later took the idea of replacement beyond the theoretical plane when he considered actual reactions in organic chemistry. When discussing the action of chlorine on oils and waxes, he observed that the chlorine removes part of the hydrogen from the oil-forming hydrochloric acid and also "part of the chlorine combines with the oil and takes the place of the hydrogen removed."[36] In 1834 Dumas began to develop the principle adumbrated by Gay-Lussac into a general theory of substitution in organic chemistry.

One of the consequences of Gay-Lussac's volumetric approach to chemistry was his conversion in 1815 of the gravimetric analysis of alcohol by Theodore de Saussure in terms of olefiant gas and water into a volumetric analysis.[37] This gave approximately equal volumes. Gay-Lussac confirmed that the sum of the vapor densities of olefiant gas and water is equal to the vapor density of absolute alcohol within the limits of experimental error. He therefore concluded that alcohol is composed of one volume of olefiant gas and one volume of water. By similar reasoning he concluded that "sulfuric ether" (diethyl ether) is composed of two volumes of olefiant gas and one volume of water. Gay-Lussac's work was the inspiration of the etherin theory of Dumas and Boullay in 1827.

Gay-Lussac also contributed to the early history of isomerism. In 1814 he remarked that acetic acid and *matière ligneuse* ("cellulose") have the same composition and concluded that it is the arrangement of the constituent particles of a compound which determines whether a substance has a neutral, acidic, or alkaline character.[38] In 1824, in his capacity as chemical editor of the *Annales de chimie et de physique,* he remarked that if Wöhler's analysis of silver cyanate was correct, it was identical with that of silver fulminate and that the explanation must lie in the different arrangement of the elements within the two compounds.[39] Later he showed experimentally that racemic acid (a name introduced by him) has the same composition as tartaric acid.[40]

We have left until now Gay-Lussac's vital work on volumetric analysis, since this belongs to the later part of his life, when he was largely occupied with applied science. French chemists made most of the basic contributions to the history of volumetric analysis. Some pioneer work was carried out by Henri Descroizilles, but the subsequent work of Gay-Lussac was even more influential. Although the French term *titre* was used about 1800, the concept of titration passed into general chemical practice from the method proposed by Gay-Lussac for estimating the purity of silver.

In 1824 Gay-Lussac extended earlier methods for the estimation of hypochlorite or chlorinated lime solution using indigo solution.[41] He later improved on the method by the use of standard solutions of certain reducing agents: arsenious oxide, mercurous nitrate, and potassium ferrocyanide.[42] His 1824 paper is important, as it contains the first use of the terms *pipette* and *burette* for the respective pieces of apparatus that have since become standard. Gay-Lussac's apparatus was an improvement on that used earlier by Descroizilles and Welter. Gay-Lussac's pipette had essentially the form of its modern counterpart, but his burette was more like a graduated cylinder with a connecting side arm. In a paper published in 1828 Gay-Lussac also used a one-liter volumetric flask.[43] In this paper he described *acide normale* ("normal acid") as a standard solution of 100 grams of sulfuric acid diluted to one liter. Gay-Lussac used litmus as an indicator and described accurately the color transition in different reactions. In 1829 he published a method for the determination of borax.[44] Sulfuric acid was added to a solution of the borax. The turning of the litmus present to the "color of onion skin" indicated the neutralization of the soda present in the borax. He even carried out an indicator correction, measuring the amount of acid required to change the color of the same amount of indicator as had been used in the titration.

Gay-Lussac made a major contribution to chemical analysis in 1832 when he introduced a volumetric method of estimating silver, which he justly claimed was much more accurate than the centuries-old method of cupellation.[45] He proposed two parallel procedures for this method, one gravimetric, which he said was the more accurate, and one volumetric, which had the advantage of simplicity. The principle of both methods was the precipitation of silver chloride. He prepared a standard solution of sodium chloride of such concentration that 100 milliliters precipitated rather less than one gram of silver. Another standard solution of sodium chloride one-tenth of the concentration of the first was also prepared. One gram of silver was accurately weighed and then dissolved in nitric acid; 100 milliliters of the concentrated sodium chloride solution was added, and the precipitate of silver chloride was allowed to settle. The dilute sodium chloride solution was then added in one-milliliter portions; after each addition, the flask was shaken and the precipitate allowed to settle. The procedure was continued until further addition caused no precipitation. This final excess of sodium chloride was found exactly by back-titrating with standard silver nitrate solution. It was characteristic of Gay-Lussac's standard solutions that they could be used only for specific analyses and for given weights of a sample, since the concentration of his solutions had no chemical basis related to equivalent weights. While, therefore, Gay-Lussac must be given credit for showing volumetric analysis to be convenient, rapid, and accurate, the establishment of a general system of volumetric analysis had to wait until the achievements of Fredrik Mohr in the next generation of chemists.

As early as 1807 Gay-Lussac had discussed the optimum temperature for the production of sulfuric acid in the lead chamber process.[46] His main contribution to this industry, however, was his suggestion of 1827 dealing with the spent gases discharged into the atmosphere at the end of the lead chamber process containing the expensive and noxious oxides of nitrogen. The latter were to be absorbed by passing them up a tower packed with coke over which trickled concentrated sulfuric acid. The adoption of this method had to wait until John Glover showed in 1859 that the oxides of nitrogen absorbed in the Gay-Lussac tower could be used again in the chamber if the acid, containing oxides of nitrogen, were passed through a second tower in which it could come into contact with water and sulfur dioxide. This released the oxides of nitrogen and simultaneously produced acid of the right concentration for use in the Gay-Lussac tower.

NOTES

1. "Sur la dilatation des gaz et des vapeurs," in *Annales de chimie,* **43** (1802), 137–175.
2. "Relation d'un voyage aérostatique," in *Journal de physique,* **59** (1804), 314–320, 454–461, written with J. B. Biot.
3. "Expériences sur les moyens eudiométriques et sur la proportion des principes constituants de l'atmosphère," *ibid.,* **60** (1805), 129–168.
4. "Observations sur l'intensité et l'inclinaison des forces magnétiques. . .," in *Mémoires de physique et de chimie de la Société d'Arcueil,* **1** (1807), 1–22, written with Humboldt.
5. "Premier essai pour déterminer les variations de température qu'éprouvent les gaz en changeant de densité. . .," *ibid.,* pp. 180–203.
6. "Mémoire sur la combinaison des substances gazeuses, les unes avec les autres," *ibid.,* **2** (1809), 207–234; translated in Alembic Club Reprint no. 4, pp. 8–24.
7. "Annonce d'un travail sur la densité des vapeurs de divers liquides," in *Annales de chimie,* **80** (1811), 218.
8. "Sur la décomposition de la potasse et de la soude," *ibid.,* **65** (1808), 325–326, written with Thenard; "Extrait de plusieurs notes sur les métaux de la potasse et de la soude," *ibid.,* **66** (1808), 205–217, written with Thenard.
9. "Sur la décomposition et la recomposition de l'acide boracique," *ibid.,* **68** (1808), 169–174, written with Thenard.
10. "Sur l'acide fluorique," *ibid.,* **69** (1809), 204–220, written with Thenard; "Des propriétés de l'acide fluorique et surtout de son action sur le métal de la potasse," in *Mémoires de physique et de chimie de la Société d'Arcueil,* **2** (1809), 317–331, written with Thenard.
11. "De la nature et des propriétés de l'acide muriatique et de l'acide muriatique oxigéné," *ibid.,* pp. 339–358, written with Thenard; translated in Alembic Club Reprint no. 13, pp. 34–48.
12. "Mémoire sur l'iode," in *Annales de chimie,* **91** (1814), 5–121.
13. "Sur un acide nouveau formé par le soufre et l'oxigène," in *Annales de chimie et de physique,* 2nd ser., **10** (1819), 312, written with Welter.
14. "Mémoire sur l'eau régale," *ibid.,* 3rd ser., **23** (1848), 203.
15. "Sur le rapport qui existe entre l'oxidation des métaux et leur capacité de saturation pour les acides," in *Mémoires de physique et de chimie de la Société d'Arcueil,* **2** (1809), 159–175.
16. "Sur la décomposition des sulfates par la chaleur," *ibid.,* **1** (1807), 215–251.
17. "Sur la précipitation des métaux par l'hydrogène sulfuré," in *Annales de chimie,* **80** (1811), 205–208.
18. "Sur la vapeur nitreuse, et sur le gaz nitreux considéré comme moyen eudiométrique," in *Mémoires de physique et de chimie de la Société d'Arcueil,* **2** (1809), 235–253.
19. "Sur les combinaisons de l'azote avec l'oxigène," in *Annales de chimie et de physique,* 2nd ser., **1** (1816), 394–410.
20. "Mémoire sur l'iode," *ibid.,* **91** (1814), 9, 148–149.
21. "Recherches sur l'acide prussique," *ibid.,* **95** (1815), 155.
22. "Note sur l'acide prussique," *ibid.,* **77** (1811), 128.
23. "Recherches sur l'acide prussique," *ibid.,* **95** (1815), 136–231.
24. "Sur l'acide des prussiates triples," *ibid.,* 2nd ser., **22** (1823), 320–323.
25. "Faits pour servir à l'histoire du bleu de Prusse," *ibid.,* **46** (1831), 73–80.
26. C. F. Bucholz and Meissner, "Expériences pour déterminer la quantité de strontiane contenue dans plusieurs espèces d'arragonite," *ibid.,* **2** (1816), 176.
27. "Premier mémoire sur la dissolubilité des sels dans l'eau," *ibid.,* **11** (1819), 296–315.
28. "Note sur la fixité du degré d'ébullition des liquides," *ibid.,* **7** (1817), 307–313.
29. "Sur les combinaisons du chlore avec les bases," *ibid.,* 3rd ser., **5** (1842), 302–303.
30. "Observations sur l'oxidation de quelques métaux," *ibid.,* 2nd ser., **1** (1816), 36–37.
31. "Sur la décomposition réciproque des corps," *ibid.,* **30** (1825), 291.
32. "Considérations sur les forces chimiques," *ibid.,* **70** (1839), 431.
33. "Sur l'analyse végétale et animale," in *Journal de physique,* **70** (1810), 257–266.
34. "Recherches sur l'acide prussique," in *Annales de chimie,* **95** (1815), 161.
35. *Ibid.,* 155 (my italics).
36. *Cours de chimie,* II, Leçon 28 (16 July 1828).
37. "Sur l'analyse de l'alcool et de l'éther sulfurique," in *Annales de chimie,* **95** (1815), 311–318.
38. "Mémoire sur l'iode," *ibid.,* **91** (1814), 149 n.
39. F. Wöhler, "Recherches analytiques sur l'acide cyanique," *ibid.,* 2nd ser., **27** (1824), 199–200 n.
40. *Cours de chimie,* II, Leçon 24, 1, 23.
41. "Instruction sur l'essai du chlorure de chaux," in *Annales de chimie et de physique,* 2nd ser., **26** (1824), 162–175.
42. "Nouvelle instruction sur la chlorométrie," *ibid.,* **60** (1835), 225–261.
43. "Essai des potasses du commerce," *ibid.,* **39** (1828), 337–368.
44. "Sur l'analyse du borax," *ibid.,* **40** (1829), 398.
45. *Instruction sur l'essai des matières d'argent par la voie humide* (Paris, 1832), *passim.*
46. "Sur la décomposition des sulfates par la chaleur," in *Mémoires de physique et de chimie de la Société d'Arcueil,* **1** (1807), 246.

BIBLIOGRAPHY

I. Original Works. Gay-Lussac was the author of *Recherches physico-chimiques, faites sur la pile, sur la préparation chimique et les propriétés du potassium et du sodium* . . ., 2 vols. (Paris, 1811), written with Thenard; and *Instruction sur l'essai des matières d'argent par la voie humide . . . publiée par la Commission des monnaies et médailles* (Paris, 1832). Although he himself never compiled elementary textbooks, the following, based on his lectures, were published: *Cours de chimie par M. Gay-Lussac, comprenant l'histoire des sels, la chimie végétale et animale* . . ., 2 vols. (Paris, 1828); and *Leçons de physique de la Faculté des sciences de Paris, recueillies et rédigées par M. Grosselin,* 2 vols. (Paris, 1828).

Gay-Lussac's most important research papers include "Sur la dilatation des gaz et des vapeurs," in *Annales de chimie,* **43** (1802), 137–175; "Relation d'un voyage aérostatique," in *Journal de physique,* **59** (1804), 314–320, 454–461, written with J. B. Biot; "Expériences sur les moyens eudiométriques et sur la proportion des principes constituants de l'atmosphère," *ibid.,* **60** (1805), 129–168, written with Humboldt; "Observations sur l'intensité et l'inclinaison des forces magnétiques, faites en France, en Suisse, en Italie, etc.," in *Mémoires de physique et de chimie de la Société d'Arcueil,* **1** (1807), 1–22, written with Humboldt; "Premier essai pour déterminer les variations de température qu'éprouvent les gaz en changeant de densité, et considérations sur leur capacité pour le calorique," *ibid.,* pp. 180–203; "Extrait de plusieurs notes sur les métaux de la potasse et de la soude," in *Annales de chimie,* **66** (1808), 205–217, written with Thenard; "Sur la décomposition et la recomposition de l'acide boracique," *ibid.,* **68** (1808), 169–174, written with Thenard; "Mémoire sur la combinaison des substances gazeuses, les unes avec les autres," in *Mémoires de physique et de chimie de la Société d'Arcueil,* **2** (1809), 207–234; "Sur l'acide fluorique," in *Annales de chimie,* **69** (1809), 204–220, written with Thenard; "De la nature et des propriétés de l'acide muriatique et de l'acide muriatique oxigéné," in *Mémoires de physique et de chimie de la Société d'Arcueil,* **2** (1809), 339–358, written with Thenard; "Sur l'analyse végétale et animale," in *Annales de chimie,* **74** (1810), 47–64, written with Thenard; "Mémoire sur l'iode," *ibid.,* **91** (1814), 5–121; "Recherches sur l'acide prussique," *ibid.,* **95** (1815), 136–231; "Sur l'analyse de l'alcool et de l'éther sulfurique," *ibid.,* pp. 311–318; "Sur les combinaisons de l'azote avec l'oxigène," in *Annales de chimie et de physique,* 2nd ser., **1** (1816), 394–410; "Premier mémoire sur la dissolubilité des sels dans l'eau," *ibid.,* **11** (1819), 296–315; "Instruction sur l'essai du chlorure de chaux," *ibid.,* **26** (1824), 162–176; "Essai des potasses du commerce," *ibid.,* **39** (1828), 337–368; "Considerations sur les forces chimiques," *ibid.,* **70** (1839), 407–434; and "Mémoire sur l'eau régale," *ibid.,* 3rd ser., **23** (1848), 203–229.

II. SECONDARY LITERATURE. On Gay-Lussac and his work, see D. F. J. Arago, "Biographie lue en séance de l'Académie des sciences le 20 décembre 1852," in *Oeuvres de François Arago, Notices biographiques,* 2nd ed., III (Paris, 1865), 1–112; E. Blanc and L. Delhoume, *La vie émouvante et noble de Gay-Lussac* (Paris, 1950); M. P. Crosland, "The Origins of Gay-Lussac's Law of Combining Volumes of Gases," in *Annals of Science,* **17** (1961), 1–26; and *The Society of Arcueil. A View of French Science at the Time of Napoleon I* (Cambridge, Mass., 1967); J. R. Partington, *A History of Chemistry,* IV (London, 1964), pp. 77–90; and F. Szabadváry, *History of Analytical Chemistry* (Oxford, 1966).

M. P. CROSLAND

GAYANT, LOUIS (*b.* Beauvais, France; *d.* Maastricht, Netherlands, 19 October 1673), *comparative anatomy.*

Gayant was trained in medicine and was serving as a military physician at the time of his death. He was recognized as one of the most able anatomists of his time and was closely associated with the anatomists in the Académie Royale des Sciences. By 1667 he was collaborating with Jean Pecquet, Claude Perrault, and others in the anatomical work published later in the *Mémoires.* This work was part of the scheme of research that Perrault proposed to the Academy soon after its founding. The exact portion of the work done by each man in the group of anatomists in the Academy cannot generally be determined because of the policy of dissecting and writing up the results anonymously.

Gayant's name seems to be associated firmly with only three pieces of anatomical work—all dating from 1667—although scattered references indicate that he participated regularly in the collective work of the Parisian anatomists. In February 1667 he dissected a female cadaver to demonstrate a number of venous valves which were already known but not universally accepted. In his demonstration the pertinent parts of the venous system were both inflated with air and injected with milk. The following month he conducted similar demonstrations, again at the Academy, in collaboration with Perrault and Pecquet.

During 1667 the transfusion of blood as a potential remedy was much discussed both in London and in Paris. That year at least seven transfusion experiments on dogs were performed by the Parisian anatomists. One of these was related to the Royal Society of London by a correspondent who witnessed Gayant perform it. The writer claims that the vigor of the recipient dog immediately improved. The Parisians reported, however, that all seven recipients died or were enfeebled and that coagulated blood was ordinarily found in their heart or veins. The donors all carried on well. On the basis of these results the Parlement of Paris prohibited blood transfusions "as a useless and dangerous remedy."

The dissection subjects of the Parisian anatomists, including Gayant, covered a wide range of vertebrates, primarily mammals. These included a few domestic animals for comparative purposes, many wild European forms, and as many foreign species as they could obtain, the latter often from the royal menagerie at Versailles. Specifically on which parts of this extensive project Gayant worked cannot be determined. There is no doubt, however, that until his death he was an important member of the group working in comparative anatomy in the Academy and that he contributed substantially to their series of publications.

BIBLIOGRAPHY

I. ORIGINAL WORKS. The three demonstrations with which Gayant was associated in 1667 are described in *Histoire de l'Académie royale des sciences,* **1** (Paris, 1733), 36–39. The letter to the Royal Society is in *Philosophical Transactions,* **26** (3 June 1667), 479–480. The collected works published by the Parisian anatomists, to which Gayant certainly contributed, are *Extrait d'une lettre . . . sur un grand poisson . . .* (Paris, 1667); *Description anatomique d'un cameleon . . .* (Paris, 1669); and *Mémoires pour servir à l'histoire naturelle des animaux* (Paris, 1671–1676).

II. SECONDARY LITERATURE. See "Louis Gayant," in *Biographie médicale,* IV (Paris, 1820–1825), 366.

For a discussion of the Parisian anatomists as a group see F. J. Cole, *A History of Comparative Anatomy* (London, 1944), pp. 393–442; and Joseph Schiller, "Les laboratoires d'anatomie et de botanique à l'Académie des sciences au XVIIe siècle," in *Revue d'histoire des sciences et de leurs applications,* **17** (1964), 97–114.

WESLEY C. WILLIAMS

GEER, CHARLES DE (*b.* Finspång, Sweden, 10 February 1720; *d.* Leufsta, Sweden, 8 March 1778), *entomology.*

De Geer grew up in Holland and returned to Sweden in 1739, where, at the age of nineteen, he was invited to become a member of the Swedish Academy of Sciences. He had not yet published any scientific work but, since he was one of the country's wealthiest men, the academy expected him to make generous donations after his election. Nothing came of that hope, but De Geer became one of the academy's most outstanding and widely known scientists. He resided in Leufsta castle, which still belongs to the De Geer family and contains his large and extremely valuable library. His position brought him into close contact with the royal court, and he was made master of the royal household.

After Linnaeus, De Geer was Sweden's most important and internationally known biologist in the eighteenth century. In contrast with Linnaeus, he was not primarily interested in descriptive systematics; he considered the study of "dead insects" both meaningless and useless. That did not prevent him from describing and naming several species, but such activity was a necessity; he had to name the previously unobserved species which he studied and whose biology he described. Otherwise, as he acknowledged, the biological description would be of little value. It is, however, of interest that in his seven-volume *Mémoires* he did not employ the binary Linnaean nomenclature until the third volume (1773).

Although De Geer lacked a particular interest in classification and cataloging, his enthusiasm for studying the life and metamorphosis of insects was great. His position gave him plenty of time for all kinds of nature studies, the only work which could not be left to his large staff of servants. In the field De Geer made his brilliant observations; he placed insect larvae in cages and studied their metamorphosis; and with the microscope—the best and most expensive English make—he made morphological observations and drawings of insects and their structures. He was an exceptional draftsman, which is reflected in his illustrations.

De Geer's scientific models were Leeuwenhoek, Swammerdam, and Réaumur. From the first two he drew the technique of using the microscope, and from the latter the method of biological observation. It is no coincidence that his monumental *Mémoires pour servir à l'histoire des insectes* (1752–1778) carries exactly the same title as Réaumur's equally large work (1734–1742). When the first volume was published in 1752, De Geer was accused, doubtless on the basis of the title of the work, of compilation and lack of independence; it was only a rehash of Réaumur. The great injustice of these accusations strongly disturbed De Geer; he announced that he would not continue the work and had the remaining part of the edition of the first volume destroyed. Not until nineteen years later, in 1771, was it possible to persuade him to resume communication of his experience by publishing the other volumes. From then on, the volumes appeared in unbroken sequence and received the notice and appreciation they deserved. The seventh and last volume appeared posthumously, in the fall of 1778. As already mentioned, De Geer did not use Linnaeus' binary nomenclature consistently; but a commentary introducing that principle of naming was published by Retzius in 1783 on the basis of De Geer's work. The work was translated into German by the entomologist J. A. E. Goeze, who published it, together with an extensive and valuable commentary, in 1776–1783.

De Geer published about twenty entomological works, the majority in the *Handlingar* of the Royal Academy of Sciences. His first article, published in 1740, was a short and very valuable treatise on Collembola. His smaller articles were always of high quality; the majority were published in more or less revised form in the *Mémoires.* He also published excellent studies on protozoa, which testified to the author's abilities as well as to the quality of his microscope.

De Geer was in close contact with the greatest entomological authorities of his time, as the library at Leufsta shows. After his death his microscope and collections were turned over to the academy; the insect collections are now in the entomological department of the Swedish Museum of Natural History in Stockholm.

De Geer's importance for biological research and for the technique of observing nature is much greater than the quite limited literature about him would indicate. Torbern Bergman, himself one of the great Swedish scientists of the eighteenth century, gave fine testimony about De Geer's merits in the obituary that he read before the Academy of Sciences in 1778.

BIBLIOGRAPHY

I. Original Works. De Geer's writings include "Rön och Observation öfver små Insecter som kunna håppa i högden," in *Kungliga Svenska vetenskapsakademiens handlingar* (1740), pp. 265–281; "Beskrifning på en märkwärdig Fluga kallad Ichneumon ater, antennis ramosis," *ibid.,* pp. 458–463; "Beskrifning på en Insect af ett nytt slägte kallad Physapus," *ibid.* (1744), pp. 1–9; "Om maskar funne på snön om vintern," *ibid.* (1749), pp. 76–78; and *Mémoires pour servir à l'histoire des insectes,* 7 vols. (Stockholm, 1752–1778), translated into German by J. A. E. Goeze as *Des Herrn Baron Karl de Geer Abhandlungen zur Geschichte der Insecten,* 7 vols. (Leipzig–Nuremberg, 1776–1783).

II. Secondary Literature. See Torbern Bergman, *Åminnelse-Tal öfer Hof-Marschalken, Högvälborne Friherren Herr Carl De Geer, hållet 19 Decemb. 1778* (Stockholm, 1779); F. Bryk, in S. Lindroth, ed., *Swedish Men of Science 1650–1950* (Stockholm, 1952), pp. 113–121; and A. J. Retzius, *Caroli De Geer genera et species insectorum et generalissimi auctoris scriptis extraxit, digessit, latine quand. partem reddidit, et terminologiam insectorum Linneanam addidit* (Leipzig, 1783).

Bengt-Olof Landin

GEER, GERHARD JAKOB DE (*b.* Stockholm, Sweden, 2 October 1858; *d.* Saltsjöbaden, Sweden, 23 July 1943), *geology, geochronology.*

Geer belonged to one of the leading noble families in Sweden. Originally from Belgium, they settled in Sweden at the beginning of the seventeenth century, and many of them have since then been important in politics and economics. Both his father, Louis de Geer, and his older brother, Gerhard Louis de Geer, were prime ministers of Sweden (1858–1870, 1875–1880 and 1920–1921, respectively), and his father was the leading politician in Sweden in the last half of the nineteenth century. Geer himself was also involved in politics and was a member of the Swedish parliament from 1900 to 1905.

Geer grew up in a home which was a center for both the political and the cultural life of Stockholm. He received his master's degree in geology from Uppsala in 1879, having been appointed to the Swedish Geological Survey in 1878. After a few years of ordinary geological mapping, Geer turned his concentration to what was to be his lifetime interest, the study of Quaternary (Pleistocene) geology. The first main problem was that of raised beaches. Shorelines much above sea level were known both in Scandinavia and in other regions, but the complicated system by which they were uplifted isostatically was not understood. The rise of the land is highest where the ice was thickest and the depression largest. The uplift decreases in all directions from the center of glaciation. Superposed on this is the eustatic change in sea level, due partly to the melting of inland ice. This complicated system was discovered and elegantly described by Geer, who also coined the term "marine limit" (the highest shoreline of the sea at any particular locality). The summary of his work, published in 1896, was one of the classic works in Scandinavian geology.

In order to explain glacial phenomena Geer traveled to Spitsbergen, where glaciers somewhat similar to the Quaternary ones still exist. He took part in and led expeditions in 1882, 1896, 1899, 1901, and 1908, among them the Swedish-Russian meridian expedition, which he led. Geer introduced terrestrial photogrammetry as an aid in his studies, and it was later used by most other Arctic expeditions, in order to increase the precision of both geological and geodetical observations. In 1897 Geer became professor at the University of Stockholm and was its president from 1902 to 1910. At Stockholm he established the varve chronology. Varves are annual, cyclic sediments consisting of summer and winter bands of silt and clay deposited by glacial meltwater in fresh or brackish water. They vary in thickness, and Geer early had the idea that these variations could be used by correlating various sections through varve sequences. In 1904–1905 he had his students measure all varves in a 200-kilometer-long north-south section near Stockholm; they found that the last ice in the area had melted away over a period of 800 years and that they could pinpoint the position of the ice margin for every year. This system was soon extended from Scania to the mountains of central Scandinavia, where it covered a period of 15,000 years. Geer used the final stage of the melting of the inland ice as his zero year; later studies by his assistant Ragnar Lidén made in the Angerman River, where varves are formed today, showed that the zero year was 6739 B.C. Geer's varve method is cumbersome and restricted to the few areas where varves are found, but it gives an unprecedented accuracy in age determinations. Geer became world-famous when he presented his results at the International Geological Congress at Stockholm in 1910, but his final paper on the subject, "Geochronologica Suecica," did not appear until 1940.

In 1924 Geer retired and became head of the Institute of Geochronology at the University of Stockholm. After several years of travel he and a number of assistants tried to extend his system on a global scale. These "teleconnections" were not generally accepted, since it seemed unlikely that the variations in meltwater and sediment volume should be synchronous all over the globe. Geer worked intensely during his last years to refine his method and to prove his long-distance correlations. After his death studies by isotope methods (carbon 14) have shown that some of his correlations, especially those with North America, were remarkably precise.

BIBLIOGRAPHY

I. ORIGINAL WORKS. Complete bibliographies of Geer's more than 200 scientific publications are in Nilsson and in Post (see below). Geer's most important works were *Om Skandinaviens geografiska utveckling efter istiden* (Stockholm, 1896), written in unusually clear and lucid Swedish but not a popular book and not easily accessible to non-Scandinavians; and "Geochronologica Suecica, Principles," *Kungliga Svenska vetenskapsakademiens handlingar,* 3rd ser., **18**, no. 6 (1940).

II. SECONDARY LITERATURE. The best biographies of Geer are E. Nilsson, "Gerhard de Geer, geokronologen," in *Levnadsteckningar över Kungliga Svenska vetenskapsakademiens ledamoter,* **172** (1969), 213–250; and L. von Post, "H. J. de Geer," in *Svensk biografisk lexikon,* X (1931), 564–567.

NILS SPJELDNAES

GEGENBAUR, KARL (*b.* Würzburg, Germany, 21 August 1826; *d.* Heidelberg, Germany, 14 June 1903), *anatomy.*

For a detailed study of his life and work, see Supplement.

GEHLEN, ADOLF FERDINAND (*b.* Bütow, Germany, 15 September 1775; *d.* Munich, Germany, 15 July 1815), *chemistry.*

For a detailed study of his life and work, see Supplement.

GEIGER, HANS (JOHANNES) WILHELM (*b.* Neustadt an der Haardt [now Neustadt an der Weinstrasse], Rheinland-Pfalz, Germany, 30 September 1882; *d.* Potsdam, Germany, 24 September 1945), *physics.*

Geiger developed a variety of instruments and techniques for the detection and counting of individual charged particles. He was the eldest of the five children of Wilhelm Ludwig Geiger, professor of philology at Erlangen from 1891 to 1920. His only brother, Rudolf, became professor of meteorology at Munich. Geiger passed his *Abitur* at the Erlangen Gymnasium in 1901. After a brief period of military service he studied physics both at Munich and at Erlangen. He took his preliminary examination in 1904 and then began his research under Eilhard Wiedemann. In July 1906 Geiger defended his inaugural dissertation and received his doctorate from the University of Erlangen. He then took a position in England, followed by a series of appointments in Germany.

Geiger married Elisabeth Heffter in 1920; they had three sons. He completed his *Habilitationsschrift* at Berlin in 1924. Geiger was awarded the Hughes Medal by the Royal Society on 30 November 1929 "for his invention and development of methods of counting alpha and beta particles,"[1] and the Duddell Medal by the Physical Society (London) in 1938 for his contributions to scientific instrumentation. Geiger was elected to the Leopoldina in 1935 and to the Preussische Akademie der Wissenschaften in 1937.

Geiger was a perfectionist, always trying to obtain the most from both his students and his experiments. His enthusiastic and warmhearted nature inspired others to emulate his methods and share his goals. He was a talented lecturer, popular with both his colleagues and the public.

In 1906 Geiger was assistant to Arthur Schuster at Manchester. Ernest Rutherford, who succeeded Schuster in 1907, persuaded Geiger to remain at Manchester and continue research on radioactivity. In 1908, working out the probability variations and statistical error factor, Geiger extended the experimental confirmation of the 1905 theoretically predicted "Schweidler fluctuations" for the case of radioactive disintegrations.

In 1908 Geiger and Rutherford investigated the charge and nature of the α particle. They devised an electrical technique in order to count the individual α particles and compare results with those obtained by Erich Regener, who used the scintillation technique. Their ionization chamber was a cylinder at low pressure with a thin wire stretched coaxially (Fig. 1). The wall of the cylinder had an entrance window at one end and was at high negative potential to the wire. An α particle entering parallel to the wire generated a secondary avalanche, according to the 1900 collision principle of John S. Townsend, multiplying the primary ionization effect a thousandfold. The resulting voltage step on the central wire was measured by a sensitive electrometer. With this proto-"Geiger counter" they estimated that the total number of α particles emitted per second from the radium C (actually radium C′) present in one gram of radium in equilibrium was 3.4×10^{10}. From this value and a determination of the total charge in a beam of α particles, they established that the α particle was doubly charged. This led directly to the confirmation by Rutherford and T. Royds that α particles were doubly charged helium atoms.

The beam of α particles was observed to spread. Geiger investigated this scattering effect and was joined in 1909 by Ernest Marsden. Using a scintillation detector, they observed the number of particles scattered at various angles of incidence. They detected α particles reflected at angles sufficiently large to make inadequate a statistical interpretation based upon multiple scattering. On preliminary evidence Rutherford was led to propose in 1911 that this effect was due to single scattering from compact nuclei. He theoretically predicted the behavior of a set of scattering parameters based upon a nuclear model of the atom. Geiger and Marsden undertook a further series of experiments and verified the predicted behavior of these parameters by July 1912.[2]

In 1910 Geiger examined α particles from a variety of radioactive substances and noted a linear relationship between the maximum range and the third power of the velocity of expulsion. Following up the 1907 suggestion of Rutherford, Geiger and John Michael Nuttall empirically established in 1911–1912 what seemed an essentially linear relationship between the half-value period, on the one hand, and the maximum range or energy of disintegration, on the other, for α particles from various materials. Later, in 1921, Geiger revised this empirical Geiger-Nuttall rule, noting that actinium-X did not fit the

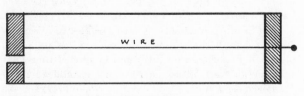

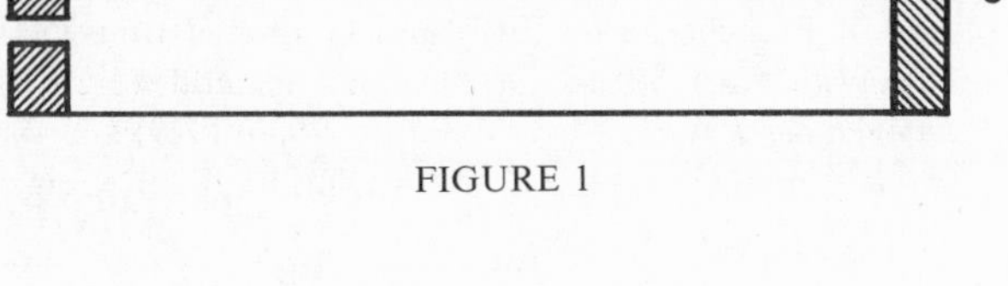

FIGURE 1

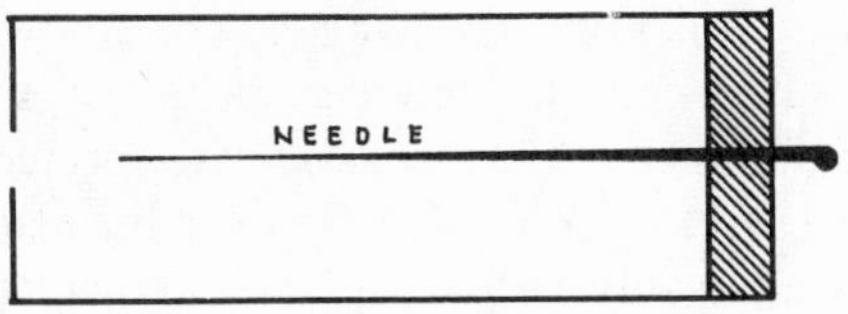

FIGURE 2

straight-line curve, and in 1928 George Gamow and others partially superseded this empirical rule altogether with a physical explanation of α disintegration in terms of the probability of α penetration of potential barriers.

In October 1912 Geiger, having turned down a call to Tübingen, took up the newly established position of director of the laboratory for radium research at the Physikalisch-Technische Reichsanstalt in Berlin. In addition to measuring radium samples, he continued experiments on the counting of α particles. Varying the form and dimensions of the central electrode, he found an arrangement which came to be known as the *Spitzenzähler* or "point counter," since "the whole working of the apparatus depends on the point of the needle" (Fig. 2).[3] The great advantage of this device was that in addition to α particles, it could, for the first time, count β particles as well as other types of radiation. Geiger noted that at ordinary pressure the size of the voltage step was proportional to the intensity of the incident radiation, whereas "the deflections *at low pressure* are all equal and independent of the intensity of the primary ionization."[4]

In November 1913 Geiger was joined by Walther Bothe, who investigated α scattering, and by James Chadwick, who counted β particles. In 1914 Chadwick was led by his investigations to note the presence of the continuous β spectrum in addition to the known line spectrum.

After the war Geiger returned to the Reichsanstalt. The 1924 statistical interpretation by Niels Bohr, H. A. Kramers, and J. C. Slater of the 1923 Compton effect stimulated Bothe and Geiger to devise, by that June, a technique to test its validity.[5] Using two *Spitzenzähler* in what was most likely the first coincidence experiment,[6] completed by April 1925, they noted that approximately every eleventh captured quantum was coincident to within 10^{-4} seconds of a recoiled electron.[7] This result, while unintelligible on the statistical interpretation, reconfirmed the validity of classic conservation principles for single atomic events.

In 1925 Geiger took his first teaching position as professor of physics at the University of Kiel. In addition to teaching and directing a large research team at the Institute of Physics, Geiger developed with

Walther Müller the counting device for which his name is best known. The Geiger-Müller counter was based upon the 1908 coaxial-wire principle (see Figure 1) and followed directly from the clarification by Geiger in July 1928 of an anomaly which Müller had encountered in his research.[8] The sensitivity of the counter was greatly improved so that it normally had to be shielded from background radiation. The recovery time was reduced through rapid quenching of the secondary avalanche. The construction of the central wire was improved so as to extend the operational lifetime for periods of months, and the signal could be amplified so as to trigger a mechanical register. In general, the device was designed to be compact, portable, and functional, and thus to meet a variety of laboratory requirements in particle detection and counting. The gradual production of these practical Geiger-Müller counters from 1928 marks the introduction of modern electrical devices into radiation research.

In October 1929 Geiger accepted a call to the University of Tübingen as professor of physics and director of research at the Institute of Physics. He continued to improve the counter, which by 1928 had already been extended in application to the study of canal rays. After noting that counters placed in separate rooms at the Institute periodically registered simultaneous bursts of radiation—the first detection of cosmic ray showers[9]—in 1931 Geiger refused a call to Lenard's chair at Heidelberg and began a series of investigations on cosmic radiation which he continued throughout the remainder of his career.

In October 1936 Geiger accepted the chair of physics at the Technische Hochschule in Berlin. While directing a large research team studying artificial radioactivity and the products of nuclear fission, he continued to make full use of his counting device, with which he had made possible the investigation of cosmic radiation. In 1937 Geiger and Otto Zeiller used nine such counting tubes in a circular arrangement to determine the angular distribution of a cosmic ray shower. His last lecture, given in April 1942, was on cosmic rays.

The war years brought a severe recurrence of a rheumatic condition, suffered during his front-line duty as an artillery officer in World War I, and contributed to his increasing absence from the Institute. However, it did not prevent him from going to the Institute even during 1944.[10] He also continued as editor of *Zeitschrift für Physik,* which he had taken over from Karl Scheel in 1936.[11]

In June 1945 Geiger was forced to abandon his home and possessions in Babelsberg and flee to nearby Potsdam, where he died shortly afterward.

NOTES

1. *Nature,* **124** (1929), 767.
2. Hans Geiger and Ernest Marsden, "Die Zerstreuungsgesetze der alpha Strahlen bei grossen Ablenkungswinkeln," in *Sitzungsberichte der Akademie der Wissenschaften zu Wien,* Math.-nat. Kl., Abt. II-a, **121** (1912), 2361–2390.
3. Geiger letter to Ernest Rutherford, 5 May 1913; Cambridge University Library Add. MSS 7653/G31.
4. *Ibid.*
5. Walther Bothe and Hans Geiger, "Ein Weg zur experimentellen Nachprüfung der Theorie von Bohr, Kramers und Slater," in *Zeitschrift für Physik,* **26** (1924), 44.
6. Professor Walther Gerlach informed me privately in Apr. 1971 that this was the first coincidence experiment.
7. Walther Bothe and Hans Geiger, "Über das Wesen des Comptoneffekts; ein experimenteller Beitrag zur Theorie der Strahlung," in *Zeitschrift für Physik,* **32** (1925), 639.
8. C. Schmidt-Schönbeck, *300 Jahre Kieler Universität,* p. 142.
9. Private confirmation by Walther Gerlach, Apr. 1971.
10. Private confirmation by Walther Gerlach, Apr. 1971.
11. Geiger was editor for eight years and issued the twenty vols. from **104** (1937) to **123** (1944); the partially complete last vol. was terminated in Oct. 1944.

BIBLIOGRAPHY

I. Original Works. A nearly complete bibliography of Geiger's writings is in M. von Laue, "Nachruf auf Hans Geiger," in *Jahrbuch der Deutschen Akademie der Wissenschaften zu Berlin: 1946–1949* (1950), pp. 150–158. In this bibliography, no. 46 should read "(1924)" instead of "(1927)" and the pagination of no. 61 is pp. 109–122. Besides the articles and scientific papers in Laue's bibliography, Geiger wrote "Erscheinungen bei sehr starken Strömen in Entladungsröhren," in *Comptes rendus du Premier Congrès International pour l'Étude de la Radiologie et de l'Ionisation, tenu a Liège, Septembre 1905* (Brussels, 1906), pp. 41–45, also published separately (Erlangen, 1905), an abstract of which is in *Physikalische Zeitschrift,* **6** (1905), 913–914; "Demonstrationsversuch zur Erläuterung der Temperaturverhältnisse in den Schichten des positiven Lichtes," in *Verhandlungen der Deutschen physikalischen Gesellschaft,* **8** (1906), 116–118, also published separately (Brunswick, 1906); "Die Kernstruktur der Atome und ihre experimentelle Begründung," in *Zeitschrift des Vereins deutscher Ingenieure,* **66** (1922), 221–225; "Der Einfluss der Atomphysik auf unser Weltbild," in *Deutschland in der Wende der Zeiten,* the open lectures for the summer semester of 1933 at the University of Tübingen (Stuttgart–Berlin, 1934), pp. 107–121; and "Memories of Rutherford in Manchester," in *Nature,* **141** (1938), 244, as well as "Some Reminiscences of Rutherford During His Time in Manchester," in J. Chadwick, ed., *The Collected Papers of Lord Rutherford,* II (London, 1963), 295–298.

With Walter Makower, Geiger published *Practical Measurements in Radio-Activity* (London, 1912), trans. and repub. in French (Paris, 1919) and German (Brunswick, 1920). With Karl Scheel he was joint general editor of *Handbuch der Physik,* 24 vols. (Berlin, 1926–1929) and the separately published subject index (Berlin, 1929). Geiger was also editor of vols. XXII–XXIV, dealing with the structure of matter and the nature of radiation. Geiger and Scheel extensively revised these three vols. in 1933, each of which appeared in two pts., and Geiger edited both pts. of XXII and XXIII. His own article "Durchgang von alpha Strahlen durch Materie," in XXIV (1927), 137–190, dealing with α radiation and detection principles, was revised, expanded, and reissued in XXII, pt. 2 (1933), 155–242.

Geiger contributed "Die Radioaktivität" to Leo Graetz, *Handbuch der Elektrizität und des Magnetismus,* III (Leipzig, 1914), 1–130. Written in 1913, the article contains an updated account of the relevant literature to the end of that year. Geiger was also instrumental in reworking the 13th and 14th eds. of Friedrich Kohlrausch, *Lehrbuch der praktischen Physik* (Leipzig–Berlin, 1921, 1923).

Extensive correspondence between Geiger and Rutherford from 1911 to 1937 is at Cambridge University Library, Add. MSS 7653/G.

II. SECONDARY LITERATURE. Biographical material is in M. von Laue, "Nachruf," which was included in his *Gesammelte Schriften und Vorträge,* III (Brunswick, 1961), 204–212; M. von Laue and R. W. Pohl, "Hans Geiger," in *Zeitschrift für Physik,* **124** (1947), 1; E. Stuhlinger, "Hans Geiger," in *Zeitschrift für Naturforschung,* **1** (1946), 50–52; and T. I. Williams, *A Biographical Dictionary of Scientists* (London, 1969), p. 211. Ewald Fünfer, who took his doctorate under Geiger at Tübingen, contributed the article in *Neue deutsche Biographie,* VI (Berlin, 1964), 141–142. Some early details are in the "Lebenslauf" of Geiger's inaugural dissertation (1906). See also Max Pollerman, in *Röntgen-Blätter,* **11** (1958), 33–35; and the brief account in *Reichshandbuch der Deutschen Gesellschaft,* I (Berlin, 1930), 528.

A brief account of Geiger's early research is in James Chadwick, "The Rutherford Memorial Lecture, 1953," in *Proceedings of the Royal Society,* **224A** (1954), 441–443. Valuable background information on Geiger is in A. S. Eve, *Rutherford* (Cambridge, 1939); and in L. Badash, ed., *Rutherford and Boltwood: Letters on Radioactivity* (New Haven, 1969), *passim.*

Physical descriptions of Geiger's work are given in Walter Dreblow, "Das Geiger-Müllersche Zählrohr," in *Kosmos* (Stuttgart), **47** (1951), 481–485; W. Christoph and W. Hanle, "Zum Mechanismus des Geiger-Müllerschen Zählrohrs," in *Physikalische Zeitschrift,* **34** (1933), 641–645; and Ewald Fünfer, *Zählrohre und Szintillationzähler,* 2nd ed. (Karlsruhe, 1959), pp. 1–5, which also contains a discussion of his work.

C. Schmidt-Schönbeck, *300 Jahre Physik und Astronomie an der Kieler Universität* (Kiel, 1965), pp. 136–146, focuses on Geiger's scientific work at Kiel.

Geiger's techniques and instrumentation are discussed in detail in W. Bothe, "Die Geigerschen Zählmethoden: Herrn Professor Hans Geiger zu seinem 60. Geburtstage am 30 September 1942," in *Naturwissenschaften,* **30** (1942), 593–599. The early work of Geiger is considered in A. T. Krebs, "Hans Geiger: Fiftieth Anniversary of the Publication of His Doctoral Thesis, 23 July 1906," in *Science,* **124** (1956), 166.

A full treatment of Geiger's work in its scientific context can be found in K. W. F. Kohlrausch, *Radioaktivität,* vol. XV of W. Wien and F. Harms, eds., *Handbuch der Experimentalphysik* (Leipzig, 1928), *passim.* The work for which he was awarded the Hughes Medal is considered in "Hughes Medal, Awarded to Professor Hans Geiger," in *Nature,* **124** (1929), 893.

An extensive bibliography containing over 300 references between 1913 and 1947 on Geiger and proportional counters was assembled by M. Healea, "Geiger and Proportional Counters," in *Nucleonics,* **1** (Dec. 1947), 68–75. Additional source material is listed in T. S. Kuhn, ed., *Sources for History of Quantum Physics* (Philadelphia, 1967), p. 164.

THADDEUS J. TRENN

GEIKIE, ARCHIBALD (*b.* Edinburgh, Scotland, 28 December 1835; *d.* Haslemere, Surrey, England, 10 November 1924), *geology.*

Geikie was the son of James Stuart Geikie, an Edinburgh businessman who was also a composer and music critic. His mother, Isabella Thom, was the daughter of a captain in the merchant marine. After three years at Black's School he went in 1845, at the age of ten, to Edinburgh High School, where he remained for four years. The education there was almost entirely classical, which was fortunate for Geikie, who showed a remarkable quality of mind and a great zest for study, and took full advantage of it to lay the foundation for his outstanding achievements in the literary exposition of science. Holiday pursuits, mostly of a scientific nature, suddenly became concentrated on geology when, with some of his schoolmates, Geikie found fossils in the limestone quarries of Burdiehouse, a few miles south of Edinburgh. His father introduced him to some of the professors and savants of the city; of these Robert Chambers, the publisher, and John Fleming, the distinguished naturalist, were particularly helpful and encouraging. Geikie himself eagerly read every book on geology he could find—Hugh Miller's *Old Red Sandstone* was his chief inspiration—and rambled among the strata and old volcanic rocks of Edinburgh and its environs.

In 1850 Geikie started a banking career, but he found the legal work that this involved "unspeakably dull." In 1851 he spent a holiday on the Isle of Arran and published an article, "Three Weeks in Arran by a Young Geologist," in an Edinburgh newspaper. This secured an introduction to Hugh Miller, who befriended him. His chief benefactor was the writer and lecturer on chemistry, George Wilson. Wilson introduced Geikie to Alexander Macmillan, head of the publishing firm, who became Geikie's intimate friend. Another eminent man to give Geikie encouragement was the geologist James David Forbes, a founder of the British Association.

In the summer of 1853 Andrew Ramsay, who held a responsible position in the Geological Survey of Great Britain, came to Scotland. Geikie was introduced to him and Ramsay held out hope that a place might sometime be found for him on the Survey. His banking career having been finally abandoned, it was decided that Geikie should meanwhile enter Edinburgh University. He matriculated in November 1854 as a student of classics and literature, and at the end of the session he had gained the reputation of being one of the best scholars of his year. He was then forced to leave the university owing to a financial crisis in the family. In 1855 he was recommended, by both Hugh Miller and Ramsay, to Sir Roderick Murchison, who had succeeded Sir Henry de la Beche as head of the Geological Survey. He was immediately appointed to that service as an assistant in the mapping of the Lothian counties. Between 1856 and 1859 Geikie was surveying on his own. In 1859 he visited London for the first time and was introduced into London learned circles, particularly by Leonard Horner and Charles Lyell.

During the next eight years Geikie vigorously carried out his official work in the field and also undertook highly significant researches in his holiday periods. In his spare time he wrote geological works and prepared papers for reading at the meetings of scientific societies. Geikie made several prolonged official excursions into various parts of Britain and traveled abroad to the Auvergne and to Norway. All the time he was thus widening and deepening his knowledge and experience. He was called on to deliver a course of lectures at the School of Mines in London and was also an examiner in the University of London. In 1861 he was elected to the Royal Society of Edinburgh, and he became a fellow of the Royal Society of London in 1865.

In 1867 Geikie was appointed director of the newly constituted Scottish branch of the Geological Survey; and for the next few years he was busy finishing his own personal mapping, superintending his staff, and making official and semiofficial visits abroad. He was taken seriously ill in the Lipari Islands in 1870, the same year Murchison founded a chair of geology at Edinburgh University and desired that Geikie be the first professor. After some difficulty in official circles, largely over the question of this post and that of the director of the Survey in Scotland being held by the same person, Geikie was appointed in 1871. In that year he married Alice Gabrielle Pignatel, whom he had met at Alexander Macmillan's house. She was a descendant of the Pignatelli family, southern Italians who had migrated into France some generations before and had settled in Lyons as merchants. The couple moved into a house that Geikie had already bought for himself on Castle Hill in Edinburgh.

Geikie was able to combine his professorial duties, which lasted from November to March, with the winter work of the Survey directed from Edinburgh. He threw himself enthusiastically into the conduct of his classes and excursions, drawing the necessary diagrams himself and introducing the newest techniques. In the evenings he was kept busy with his literary work, particularly with the large biography of Murchison which he had undertaken (Murchison had died in the autumn of 1871 and was succeeded by Ramsay), the preliminary work on his great textbook, and preparing a memoir (on the Old Red Sandstone) to be read before the Royal Society of Edinburgh. With the Geological Survey his most important charge, his life during the 1870's was fuller than ever. In the summer of 1879 he made a prolonged journey through the United States, meeting the geologists who had become famous for their explorations of the far west.

Ramsay, in failing health, retired as the head of the Geological Survey at the end of 1881, and Geikie was appointed to succeed him in this post, the highest in the profession. He and his family therefore moved to London. Reluctantly he had to relinquish his post as professor at Edinburgh, to which his brother James succeeded. Living in London enabled him to participate directly in the concerns of the learned scientific societies. In 1883 he was elected to the council of the Geological Society, which in 1881 had awarded him its Murchison Medal; and in 1885 he was elected to the council of the Royal Society, becoming its foreign secretary in 1889. In 1890 he was elected president of the Geological Society, and in 1891 he was knighted. Geikie was given the Geological Society's highest award, the Wollaston Medal, in 1895; and in 1896 he received the Royal Society's Royal Medal.

In 1901 Geikie, having reached the age of sixty-five, retired from the directorship of the Geological Survey and found relaxation and refreshment in turning to interests other than geological—largely English and classical literature. He was a member of the Classical Association from the time of its foundation in 1904 and in 1910 was elected its president—an extraordinary position to be held by a leading scientist. At the same time he continued to pursue his geological writing, translating, and editing. He was called upon to preside for the second time over the Geological

Society of London during the centenary celebrations in 1907 and was appointed its foreign secretary in 1908, an honor to which he was annually reelected until his death. In 1907 he was created Knight Commander of the Bath.

The most important and engrossing work that occupied Geikie during the years of his retirement was the conduct of the affairs of the Royal Society. In 1903 he became one of its two secretaries for five years and in 1908 was elected president, the only geologist ever so honored.

Geikie's natural genius, combined with his prodigious capacity for hard and sustained work, is clearly and abundantly revealed in his published writings, which, beginning in 1849, extend over a period of seventy-five years. His first was a schoolboy translation of a piece by Ovid into English verse (inserted in Stevens' *History of the High School of Edinburgh*), and the last was his autobiography, *A Long Life's Work*. His main publications fall under the following classifications:

1. The geological treatises setting forth the results of research, published in the journals of learned societies. Examples are those, mentioned below, concerning ancient volcanism, the Old Red Sandstone, and glaciation.

2. His contributions to the official Geological Survey memoirs. These are somewhat scattered and mixed with the contributions of his colleagues, some being published long after most of his own work concerning them had been finished. He was the main author of the first edition of the memoir on the Edinburgh neighborhood (1861) and of the memoirs on Fife (1900, 1902). He also was the originator and planner of the great series of stratigraphical monographs (on the Pliocene, Cretaceous, Jurassic, and Scottish Lower Paleozoic) published during his directorship.

3. Books on special themes. Two are outstanding and are considered below: *The Scenery of Scotland* (1865) and *Ancient Volcanoes* (1897).

4. Textbooks. While pursuing his researches in particular areas and on particular subjects, Geikie kept before him the whole panorama of geological science and produced a series of incomparable textbooks. The first was a largely rewritten edition (1872) of Joseph Jukes's *Student's Manual of Geology*. Then came (1873) two very small "primers," *Physical Geography* and *Geology*. They had an enormous success, immediate and continuing, and were translated into most European languages. *Field Geology* (1876), *Class-book of Physical Geography* (1877), and *Class-book of Geology* (1886) followed. All these works ran to many editions. In 1882 appeared the first edition of *Text-book of Geology*, which, in its successive editions of 1885, 1893, and 1903, served as a standard work which carried on the function of Lyell's famous *Principles of Geology*. It was based on a long article contributed to the *Encyclopaedia Britannica* in 1879. A storehouse of geological facts, a mine for the extraction of clear definitions and explanations, an authoritative exposition of established principles, and, with its copious notes and references, a worldwide guide to the records of geological discovery, the two-volume edition of 1903 is still indispensable, notwithstanding all the new information and techniques that have been made available during the years since its publication.

5. Biographies of geologists, annotated editions and translations, and histories of geology. Geikie wrote several well-known biographical and historical books. The memoirs of Murchison (1875) and Ramsay (1895), enlivened by contemporary letters and diaries, illuminate the progress of geology during the middle decades of the nineteenth century. He had previously written the greater part of the life of Edward Forbes (begun by George Wilson), the eminent naturalist and geologist (1861), and had communicated an obituary memoir of James David Forbes to the Edinburgh Geological Society (1869). His *Founders of Geology* was, as first published in 1897, the text of six lectures delivered at Johns Hopkins University, Baltimore. It was recast and greatly enlarged for the second edition of 1905, which treats the history of geology as revealed in the lives and work of the masters, both British and foreign. This is still the only work on its subject. The autobiography, written in his old age, shows an undiminished power to instruct, charm, and entertain.

Geikie's erudition was specially brought into play in the production of four works of editorship and commentary: (1) part of the third volume of Hutton's *Theory of the Earth* of 1795, the manuscript of which was found in the library of the Geological Society of London (1899); (2) a new translation of Faujas de Saint-Fond's *Voyage en Angleterre, en Écosse et aux Îles Hébrides* of 1797 (1907); (3) *Charles Darwin as Geologist*, a Cambridge University Rede lecture (1909); and (4) an appreciation of the work of John Michell, the eighteenth-century scientific savant who had been Woodwardian professor of geology at Cambridge (1918). These are all enriched with copious notes which illuminate the more obscure corners of the history of geology.

6. Belles-lettres. Geikie wrote innumerable essays and reviews—geological, geographical, biographical,

autobiographical, literary, historical, and educational. Fortunately, many of these were reprinted to form the two books *Geological Sketches at Home and Abroad* (1882) and *Landscape in History and Other Essays* (1905).

7. *Scottish Reminiscences* (1904). This book stands rather apart from his other publications. Here, more than anywhere else in his writing, Geikie's wit and humor and powers as a raconteur are allowed full play.

Geikie's fame as a geologist rests very largely on his work in the field of volcanic action in past geological times. He was born among the crags that mark the sites of some of these old volcanoes (of Carboniferous age) and was led in boyhood to interest himself in their structure and history. Little had been done before on these rocks beyond the recognition of their volcanic nature and the description of some details of local structure (chiefly by Charles Maclaren in 1839). As a result of his survey of the Lothians (1855–1859), Geikie was able to recognize a long series of eruptions through Devonian (Old Red Sandstone) and Carboniferous times. He summarized these results in a paper read before the British Association at Aberdeen (1859), which was expanded to form one read before the Royal Society of Edinburgh in 1861. In 1860 Geikie began his survey of the county of Fife. He tells us that he learned more here than he did anywhere else regarding the details of volcanic action as preserved in the earth's crust. The results were not published in official memoirs until much later: 1900 and 1902. His enthusiasm for this vast subject increased as his official work and holiday excursions took him to other parts of Scotland and the British Isles and to central France. He read his first paper on the Tertiary volcanic rocks of Scotland to the Royal Society of Edinburgh early in 1867. Later in 1867, in his presidential address to the Geological Section of the British Association at Dundee, on the history of volcanic action in the British Isles, Geikie made the first attempt to group in chronological order the sequence of eruptions in this westernmost part of Europe. His visits to the Eifel district of Germany in 1868 and to Naples and the Lipari Islands in 1870 extended his personal knowledge of recent, or comparatively recent, volcanic activity.

In 1879 the Royal Society of Edinburgh published a large memoir describing the volcanic history of the Carboniferous period in the basin of the Firth of Forth, containing in condensed form the results of Geikie's researches in that region during nearly a quarter of a century. In 1888 the same society published an even longer memoir, on the history of volcanic action during the Tertiary period in the British Isles. Geikie's journey in 1879 to western America, where Richthofen had shown the great volcanic plains to be due to massive fissure eruptions, caused him to advocate a similar origin for the volcanic rocks forming the plateaus of Scotland, Northern Ireland, the Faeroe Islands, and Iceland.

Geikie's presidential addresses to the Geological Society of London in 1891 and 1892 gave accounts of the history of volcanic action in the British Isles, and in 1896 this society published an extensive paper on the Tertiary basalt plateaus of northwestern Europe in which the results of the latest exploration were described.

Finally, in 1897 there appeared, in two large volumes, Geikie's masterpiece, *The Ancient Volcanoes of Great Britain.* Here we have a complete and detailed exposition of the essentials of igneous geology (other than the deeply plutonic). It is illustrated with a wealth of examples, described in word, diagram, and picture. As in all Geikie's writings, the subject is given depth by constant reference to the history of investigation. Exhaustive as this was of the knowledge of the time, Geikie himself was the foremost in realizing that its publication, far from closing the subject, opened up still wider horizons; for in 1895, two years before its appearance, he had launched a new campaign by the Geological Survey into the territory of the Tertiary volcanoes of Scotland by sending Alfred Harker to Skye. This campaign produced spectacular results during the next thirty years.

Apart from his work on the igneous rocks associated with the Old Red Sandstone strata, Geikie did important work on these strata themselves. He was the first to recognize a widespread unconformity throughout Scotland between an upper and a lower group (1860). His most important paper was that published by the Royal Society of Edinburgh on the Old Red Sandstone of Scotland, particularly on that of the northern region (1878). Further accounts were projected but did not materialize. In this paper he suggested that the Old Red Sandstone was deposited in separate lake basins, to which he gave names, the chief ones in Scotland being "Lake Orcadie" in the north and "Lake Caledonia" in the Central Valley. In each of these basins he considered the upper divisions to be equivalent in time; the same was true of the lower divisions. These large questions on which Geikie expressed his views are still not settled. It is considered that the general nature of the deposits certainly indicates a "Continental" origin, but probably not entirely a lacustrine one. The conception of separate basins of deposition is, however, taken to be valid. The general opinion now, based chiefly on the evidence of the fossil fish faunas, is that a tripartite time classification of the system is appropriate, at least in Scotland, a suggestion that had been put forward by Murchison in 1859. The lower division in "Orcadie" is mainly, if not entirely, Middle Old Red Sandstone, while the lower division in "Caledonia" is Lower Old Red Sandstone.

During his directorship of the Geological Survey, Geikie's most important operation was his direction of a vigorous and large-scale exploration of the extreme northwestern Highlands of Scotland. It had become realized that here lay a key to the unlocking of a knowledge of the structure and geological history of Scotland, but very different interpretations of what was to be seen on the ground had been put forward by some of the foremost geologists of the day. The official attack on the problem began in 1883 and lasted for about ten years. An interim report was given in 1888, and the complete description was finally published in the great Survey memoir of 1907. This memoir contains a detailed account of the history of research and ideas (with full documentation), particularly of the period before the Survey took over. Flett (1937) and Bailey (1952) provide commentaries, but each is rather disconnected.

Murchison, during the period of his directorship, had made geological excursions into the region, accompanied at one time (1859) by Ramsay and at another, during his most prolonged excursion (1860), by Geikie. Murchison had no doubt of the correctness of an interpretation which he expounded in full in 1861—essentially it was that there was an undisturbed upward succession of formations—and both Ramsay and Geikie agreed with this interpretation. Others, particularly James Nicol, Charles Callaway, and Charles Lapworth, had detected the great dislocations along what later came to be called the Moine thrust belt. Geikie sent his team onto the ground (1883) on the assumption that the Murchisonian interpretation would be found to be the correct one, and he proclaimed this assumption in his official report for that year. But the surveyors soon found that this view could not be sustained and that the interpretations given by Nicol, Callaway, and Lapworth were, on the main point at issue, correct. Geikie at once visited the ground, with every disposition to support Murchison's view, but he became entirely convinced that his surveyors were right. He immediately announced the important news in an article written by himself and his two chief surveyors, Benjamin Peach and John Horne, which was published in *Nature* in November 1884. His report for that year, published in 1885, contained the official announcement of the firm establishment as a known fact of what is perhaps the most striking geological feature in the structure of Britain, as well as a frank admission of his previous adherence to what had proved to be an erroneous assumption.

During the years 1861–1865, Geikie became, as he put it, "rather obsessed with glacial problems." The existence of a former "ice age" during which glacial conditions had been much more widespread than at the present time had been realized during the 1830's by geologists in the Alpine region; foremost among them was Louis Agassiz, whose chief publication appeared in 1840. It was shown that the Alpine glaciers had extended far beyond their present limits. At the same time the superficial deposits of stony clay, which in Britain had hitherto been generally called "diluvium" in the vague belief that they were relics of a universal flood, were being accounted for on the supposition that they had been transported and dropped by floating ice while the land was submerged beneath the sea. In the latter part of 1840, when Agassiz came to Scotland, he recognized the clear signs of the previous existence of land glaciers and succeeded at once in convincing such leading British geologists as William Buckland and Charles Lyell. All three gave their views to the Geological Society in November 1840. But the floating ice theory persisted and was the favored theory when three geologists—T. F. Jamieson, Andrew Ramsay, and Geikie—became independently interested in the matter; and each in his own way showed that it was untenable. Geikie investigated the deposits all over the southern counties of Scotland and gave a full description and discussion in a paper published by the Geological Society of Glasgow in 1863. At about this time it was decided that these superficial deposits (the "drifts") should be officially mapped. They had hitherto been regarded only as a nuisance obscuring the underlying rocks; now it was realized that they were not only of great interest in themselves but that the facts of their distribution were of great practical importance to agriculture. To carry out the mapping in Scotland a few new recruits were required, and among those appointed was Archibald's younger brother, James. Archibald Geikie had to initiate the new men into the mapping of the drifts, but after this had been done he abandoned his glacial work; it was taken up by his brother, who became one of the foremost authorities on this branch of geology. On his trip to arctic Norway in 1865 he, as he tells us, "caught the ice, as it were, in the very act of doing the work of which I had hitherto only seen the ancient results."

Geikie had an abiding interest in that earth science now called geomorphology, the study of landforms, but this interest was greatest during the early 1860's, when he was also especially interested in glacial geology. To some extent these two interests overlapped. In both fields there had been much doubt and argument during the preceding few decades, and in both it was Geikie who was among the foremost in settling the matter. In 1860 he made his tour with Murchison to the northwest Highlands of Scotland (primarily to study structure), and in 1861 he visited the Auvergne district of France (primarily to study volcanicity). On both these tours he was greatly impressed with the effects of erosion by weathering agents and the action of rivers (and, long ago, of ice in Scotland). The thesis he established was that the present relief of the land surface is the result of the subaerial erosion ("denudation") of a more or less even or gently curved surface which had been uplifted from beneath the sea. The sculpturing of the land is chiefly the result of the differential erosion of hard and soft rocks. This was in contrast with the thesis that valleys and hills and escarpments are due to the marine dissection of a land mass rising from beneath the sea. The subaerial erosion theory still left uncertain when the land surface was uplifted and what its height and form had been: these uncertainties remain today. Geikie's conclusions were given in his book *The Scenery of Scotland,* first published in 1865, which combines the virtues of a thoroughly scientific treatise with those of a popular account.

BIBLIOGRAPHY

I. Original Works. Among Geikie's more important writings are *The Geology of the Neighbourhood of Edinburgh,* Memoirs of the Geological Survey of Great Britain (London, 1861); "On the Chronology of the Trap Rocks of Scotland," in *Transactions of the Royal Society of Edinburgh,* **22** (1861), 633-653; "On the Phenomena of the Glacial Drift of Scotland," in *Transactions of the Geological Society of Glasgow,* **1** (1863), 1-190; *The Scenery of Scotland* (London, 1865); *Geology,* in the series Science Primers (London, 1873); *Life of Sir Roderick Murchison* (London, 1875); *Outlines of Field Geology* (London, 1876); "On the Old Red Sandstone of Western Europe," in *Transactions of the Royal Society of Edinburgh,* **28** (1878), 345-452; "On the Carboniferous Volcanic Rocks of the Basin of the Firth of Forth," *ibid.,* **29** (1879), 437-518; *Geological Sketches at Home and Abroad* (London, 1882); *Text-book of Geology* (London, 1882; 4th ed., 1903); "The History of Volcanic Action During the Tertiary Period in the British Isles," in *Transactions of the Royal Society of Edinburgh,* **35** (1888), 23-184; "The History of Volcanic Action in the British Isles," printed as "Proceedings. Anniversary Address of the President," in *Quarterly Journal of the Geological Society of London,* **47** (1891), 63-122, and **48** (1892), 60-179; *Memoir of Sir Andrew Crombie Ramsay* (London, 1895); "The Tertiary Basalt-Plateaux of North-western Europe," in *Quarterly Journal of the Geological Society of London,* **52** (1896), 311-406; *The Ancient Volcanoes of Great Britain* (London, 1897); *The Geology of Fife,* Memoirs of the Geological Survey of Great Britain (London, 1902); *Scottish Reminiscences* (Glasgow, 1904); *The Founders of Geology* (London, 1905); and *A Long Life's Work: An Autobiography* (London, 1924).

II. Secondary Literature. On Geikie or his work, see E. B. Bailey, *Geological Survey of Great Britain* (London, 1952), *passim;* E. B. Bailey and D. Tait, *Edinburgh's Place in Scientific Progress* (Edinburgh, 1921), pp. 89-91; R. J. Chorley *et al., The History of the Study of Landforms* (London, 1964), *passim;* "Eminent Living Geologists: Sir Archibald Geikie," in *Geological Magazine,* **27** (1890), 49-51; J. S. Flett, *The First Hundred Years of the Geological Survey of Great Britain* (London, 1937), *passim;* "A Century of Geology, 1807-1907: The Geological Society of London," in *Geological Magazine,* **44** (1907), 1-3; B. N. Peach and J. Horne, "The Scientific Career of Sir Archibald Geikie," in *Proceedings of the Royal Society of Edinburgh,* **45** (1926), 346-361; H. H. Thomas, in *Dictionary of National Biography, 1922-1930* (Oxford, 1937), pp. 332-334; and H. B. Woodward, *The History of the Geological Society of London* (London, 1908), *passim.*

Obituary notices include J. R. B. and J. H., in *Proceedings of the Royal Society,* **3A** (1926), xxiv-xxxix; and **99B** (1926), i-xvi; H. D., in *Proceedings of the Geologists' Association,* **36** (1925), 191-192; and A. S., in *Quarterly Journal of the Geological Society of London,* **81** (1925), "Proceedings," lii-lx.

John Challinor

GEIKIE, JAMES (*b.* Edinburgh, Scotland, 23 August 1839; *d.* Edinburgh, 1 March 1915), *geology.*

James Geikie was the son of James Stuart Geikie and Isabella Thom and the brother of Archibald Geikie. After leaving Edinburgh High School, for a few years he divided his time between working in a printer's office and attending the University of Edinburgh. Under the supervision of his brother, he joined the Geological Survey in 1861 as one of the men recruited to map the glacial deposits ("drifts") of parts of central Scotland. He devoted himself with sustained ardor to this work, with the result that the study of Pleistocene geology in general, and the glacial deposits in particular, became his lifework. In these fields he became the leading British authority. His official work in the mapping and investigation of the Paleozoic rocks and the superficial deposits overlying them in the areas allotted to him was of the highest quality but is hardly given full expression in the Survey publications.

It is on his unofficial papers and his books, *The Great Ice Age* (1874) in particular, that Geikie's reputation rests. This work was dedicated to Andrew Ramsay, the director general of the Geological Survey, who had already shown the effects of land ice and to whom he owed much as teacher and friend.

A second edition appeared in 1877, and in 1894 a third edition was published, extensively revised in accordance with new knowledge and with the advance in Geikie's own opinions. His book *Prehistoric Europe* (1880) supplemented it. In *The Great Ice Age* Geikie put forward the hypothesis that the glacial period as a whole had been interrupted by mild episodes or interglacial periods. This hypothesis was suggested to him by evidence in Scotland, where (as in the rest of Britain) the evidence is not very definite; thus he was at first hesitant. But support of a more conclusive nature was forthcoming from the Continent, and Geikie became a progressively stronger advocate for the existence of interglacial periods. His fundamental contention—now generally accepted—was strikingly supported by Albrecht Penck and Eduard Bruckner in their description of the glacial phenomena of the Alpine valleys published in 1909 in a volume dedicated to Geikie. He further taught that man lived in Europe throughout the glacial period, a theory that also has gained acceptance.

Geikie succeeded his brother Archibald as Murchison professor of geology at the University of Edinburgh in 1882. He had left the Geological Survey with great reluctance but enthusiastically took up the work of geological and geographical education. In 1884 he was one of the founders of the Royal Scottish Geographical Society and was its president from 1904 to 1910. For many years he was editor of its magazine. Geikie conducted his university teaching, both in the classroom and in the field, with great success and showed administrative ability within the university. For his students he wrote *Outlines of Geology* (1886; 4th ed., 1903) and *Structural and Field Geology* (1905). The latter was particularly successful and has been brought up to date in a sixth edition, published in 1953. He retired from his professorship in June 1914.

Geikie joined the Geological Society of London in 1873. He was awarded the Murchison Medal in 1889 and in the same year received the Brisbane Medal of the Royal Society of Edinburgh. He was elected a fellow of the Royal Society of London in 1875 and was president of the Royal Society of Edinburgh at the time of his death.

In 1875 Geikie married Mary Johnston, whose family lived in the region of the Cheviot Hills. A man of great activity and many interests, he published *Songs and Lyrics by Heinrich Heine,* translated from the German, in 1887.

BIBLIOGRAPHY

I. Original Works. A full list of Geikie's writings is in Newbigin and Flett (see below). Among the more important are "On the Buried Forests and Peat Masses of Scotland," in *Transactions of the Royal Society of Edinburgh,* **24** (1867), 363–384; *The Great Ice Age* (London, 1874); *Prehistoric Europe* (London, 1880); "On the Geology of the Faroe Islands," in *Transactions of the Royal Society of Edinburgh,* **30** (1882), 217–269; *Outlines of Geology* (London, 1886); *Fragments of Earth Lore* (Edinburgh, 1893); *Earth Sculpture* (London, 1898); *Structural and Field Geology* (Edinburgh, 1905); *Mountains: Their Origin, Growth and Decay* (Edinburgh, 1913); and *Antiquity of Man in Europe* (Edinburgh, 1914).

II. Secondary Literature. On Geikie or his work, see "Eminent Living Geologists: James Geikie," in *Geological Magazine,* **50** (1913), 241–248; J. H., in *Proceedings of the Royal Society,* **B91** (1920), "Obituary Notices," xxxiii–xxxv; J. Horne, "The Influence of James Geikie's Researches on the Development of Glacial Geology," in *Proceedings of the Royal Society of Edinburgh,* **36** (1917), 1–25; M. I. Newbigin and J. S. Flett, *James Geikie: The Man and the Geologist* (Edinburgh, 1917); and an obituary notice in *Quarterly Journal of the Geological Society of London,* **72** (1916), liii–lv.

JOHN CHALLINOR

GEISER, KARL FRIEDRICH (*b.* Langenthal, Bern, Switzerland, 26 February 1843; *d.* Küsnacht, Zurich, Switzerland, 7 May 1934), *mathematics.*

Geiser was the son of Friedrich Geiser, a butcher, and Elisabeth Geiser-Begert. Following graduation from the Polytechnikum in Zurich and the University of Berlin, where the influence of his great-uncle, Jakob Steiner, was of help to him, Geiser became *Dozent* in 1863. In 1873 he became professor at the Zurich Polytechnikum (later renamed the Eidgenössische Technische Hochschule), where he remained until his retirement.

Geiser made an outstanding contribution to the development of the Swiss system of higher education. Acquainted with many persons in the fields of politics and economics as well as with important mathematicians in the neighboring countries, and a close adviser of the chairman of school supervisors, Geiser worked effectively within the professoriate to attract first-rate teachers. There devolved upon him, above all, the instruction of candidates for the teaching of algebraic geometry, differential geometry, and invariant theory.

Geiser's scientific works are concerned especially with algebraic geometry. He explained the relation of the twenty-eight double tangents of the plane quadric to the twenty-seven straight lines of the cubic surface. An involution that he discovered bears his name. Minimal surfaces also engaged his attention: he investigated the intersection of an algebraic minimal surface with an infinite plane and determined all the algebraic minimal surfaces. In addition, Geiser edited Jakob Steiner's unpublished lectures and treatises. He was organizer and president of the first International Congress of Mathematicians, held at Zurich in 1897.

BIBLIOGRAPHY

I. Original Works. Geiser's major works are *Einleitung in die synthetische Geometrie* (Leipzig, 1869); and *Zur Erinnerung an Jakob Steiner* (Schaffhausen, 1874). His papers are listed in the articles by Kollros and by Meissner and Scherrer (see below).

Die Theorie der Kegelschnitte, pt. 1 of Jakob Steiner's *Vorlesungen über Geometrie,* was compiled and edited by Geiser (Leipzig, 1867).

II. Secondary Literature. See the following obituary notices: A. Emch, in *National Mathematics Magazine,* **12,** no. 6 (1938), 287–289, with portrait; L. Kollros, in *Verhandlungen der Schweizerischen naturforschenden Gesellschaft,* **115** (1934), 522–528, with list of publications and portrait; and E. Meissner and F. R. Scherrer, in *Vierteljahrsschrift der Naturforschenden Gesellschaft in Zürich,* **79** (1934), 371–376, with list of publications.

J. J. Burckhardt

GEISSLER, JOHANN HEINRICH WILHELM (*b.* Igelshieb, Thuringia, Germany, 26 May 1815; *d.* Bonn, Germany, 24 January 1879), *glassmaking, technology.*

Geissler's father, Johann Georg Jacob Geissler, was a maker of glass beads and a burgomaster. His mother, Johanne Rosine Eichhorn, was the daughter of a glassmaker. He was descended from other craftsmen active in the Thüringer Wald and in Böhmen, and two of his brothers worked as mechanicians, one in Berlin and the other in Amsterdam. Comparatively little is known of Geissler's life. He began working while very young and, having learned glassblowing in the duchy of Saxe-Meiningen, he practiced this trade at several universities, including Munich. He is said to have worked in the Netherlands for some eight years; he settled at The Hague in 1839 and is on census rolls of 1845 but not of 1849, although his workshop in Bonn is said to have been founded by him in 1841. In that year his brother, Friedrich Wilhelm Florenz, went to Amsterdam and made glass for the Gymnasium Illustre, especially for the physicist V. S. van der Willigen.

Geissler finally settled as a mechanic at the University of Bonn in 1852 (or earlier) and established a workshop for producing chemical and physical instruments. He provided many instruments for the mechanician W. H. Theodor Meyer and the physicist Julius Plücker, as well as for the mineralogist H.P.J. Vogelsang and the physiologist Eduard Pflüger. Later he was associated with Franz Müller, who succeeded him as owner of the workshop. On the fiftieth anniversary of the University of Bonn in 1868 he was awarded an honorary doctorate for his work.

Talented both in making instruments and in comprehending their physical bases, Geissler learned much from his association with the scientists at the university. He became an indispensable participant in the experimental work that was being conducted there.

The first account of Geissler's activity dates from 1852, when, with Julius Plücker, at Bonn, he constructed his famous standard thermometers. They differed from the thermometers then in use by their thin glass, by the application of capillarity, and by their high precision. For calibrating he used his new glass balance that had a sensitivity of 0.1 mg. of mercury. In 1863 Geissler constructed a maximum thermometer based on Casella's minimum thermometers. Also in 1852 Geissler, at the invitation of a Bonn industrialist, constructed an instrument for measuring the alcoholic strength of wine. This "vaporimeter" measured the pressure of vapors of alcohol and air against mercury. Plücker improved the apparatus by eliminating the air and was thus stimulated to investigate vapors scientifically. Geissler also used the instrument to measure the strength of liquid ammonia.

In 1858 it was stated that Plücker relied on Geissler's dexterity in using "Geissler's tubes," as Plücker called them—although, according to Plücker, Geissler was not the first to make such tubes. Geissler, in turn, stated in 1858 that he had made such tubes since 1857 and had sent many of them to Daniel Rühmkorff in Paris and to Bence Jones in London. There is a second invention connected with these tubes. The difficulty in obtaining a vacuum with the piston pumps then in use caused Geissler to construct a mercury air pump about 1855. Demonstrated to a wider public in 1858, it was an improvement on the idea of using Torricelli's vacuum for evacuation, which the theosopher Emanuel Swedenborg had described in 1722 and many others after him had tried to use. Geissler's pump, entirely of glass and thick rubber, was operated by manually moving a second tube up and down and therefore was slow, though effective.

Through use of this pump and his aptitude for glassblowing, Geissler was able to make rather small glass tubes with electrodes melted into the ends and filled with rarefied gases. By using these tubes Plücker was able to study discharges in very rarefied gases. The new and most interesting phenomenon, the stripes in the discharge light (*Schichtung im elek-*

trischen Licht), previously observed in the "electrical egg" by Rühmkorff and Jean Quet, could now, by means of "Geissler's tubes," be studied in detail. These tubes provided a much better vacuum and, in contrast with the "electrical egg," were not dependent on a pump. (John Gassiot had already tried to produce such a vacuum, and in 1856 V. S. van der Willigen had obtained the phenomenon using tubes constructed by Geissler's brother in Amsterdam.) At the thirty-ninth meeting of the Deutsche Naturforscher und Ärzte, held at Giessen in 1864, Geissler demonstrated his mercury pump; "Geissler's tubes" were shown there in experiments by J. C. Poggendorff to demonstrate induced currents. On the whole, the technology of "Geissler's tubes" helped to introduce a new branch of physics which led directly to the discovery of the cathode rays.

In addition, the thermometer tubes enabled Geissler to construct in 1852 an instrument for measuring the expansion of freezing water and ice. In 1858 Geissler suggested to Justus von Liebig that the chemical nature of gases could be identified by means of the discharge in "Geissler's tubes"; this was further implemented by Vogelsang and Geissler in 1868, when they described a vacuum tube in which liquids occluded in minerals could be identified chemically by means of the then new technique of spectral analysis. About 1860, in the inner of these tubes, Geissler converted white phosphorus into the red form "by electricity," as he put it. In 1873 he demonstrated the phenomenon before Anton von Schrötter at the world exhibition in Vienna, where he was awarded the Golden Cross of Merit in Art and Science.

BIBLIOGRAPHY

Descriptions of Geissler's work, by himself and his collaborators, are in *Annalen der Physik und Chemie,* **162** (1852), 233–279; **168** (1854), 199–200; **179** (1858), 88–106; **199** (1864), 657–658; **201** (1865), 153–158; **202** (1865), 222, 227; **211** (1868), 332–335; and **228** (1874), 171–173; and "Sitzungsberichte der Niederrheinischen Gesellschaft für Natur- und Heilkunde zu Bonn," in *Verhandlungen des naturhistorischen Vereines der preussischen Rheinlande und Westfalens,* **23** (Bonn, 1866), 12–14; W. H. T. Meyer, *Beobachtungen über das geschichtete electrische Licht* (Berlin, 1858).

There is an undated letter to an unknown correspondent in the Staatsbibliothek Preussischer Kulturbesitz, Berlin. Three letters to R. A. C. E. Erlenmeyer, dated 14 Jan. 1869, 9 June 1870, and 24 Mar. 1871, are in the Deutsches Museum, Munich. In the Bayerische Staatsbibliothek, Munich, are two letters to Justus von Liebig, one without date and one dated 2 Feb. 1858.

On Geissler's life and work, see also *Amtlicher Bericht über die 39. Versammlung Deutscher Naturforscher und Ärzte in Giessen im September 1864* (Giessen, 1865), pp. 81–86; *Amtlicher Bericht über die Wiener Weltausstellung im Jahre 1873,* 3 vols. (Brunswick, 1874–1875), II, 504 and III, 1, 221; *Bericht über das fünfzigjährige Jubilaeum der Rheinischen Friedrich-Wilhelms-Universität* (Bonn, 1868); *Dr. H. Geissler's Nachfolger, Gedenkblatt zur Erinnerung an Heinrich Geissler, Dr. phil., Glastechniker . . ., zur Feier des 50 jährigen Bestehens der Firma seinen Freunden mit beigeheftetem Bildnisse gewidmet* (Bonn, 1890); A. W. von Hofmann, in *Berichte der Deutschen chemischen Gesellschaft,* **12** (1879), 147–148; W. Huschke, *Forschungen über die Herkunft der Thüringischen Unternehmerschicht des 19. Jahrhunderts,* supp. 2 to *Tradition* (Baden-Baden, 1962), 34–35; H. Schimank, in *Lichttechnik* (Berlin), **6** (1954), 364; and in *Technikgeschichte in Einzeldarstellungen,* **19** (1971), 37–38; and A. Wissner, in *Neue deutsche Biographie,* VI (Berlin, 1964), 59.

HANS KANGRO

GEITEL, F. K. HANS (*b.* Brunswick, Germany, 16 July 1855; *d.* Wolfenbüttel, Germany, 15 August 1923), *experimental physics.*

Geitel studied from 1875 to 1877 at Heidelberg and from 1877 until 1879 at Berlin, where he took the examination for secondary-school teaching. From 1880 to 1920 he taught mathematics and physics in Wolfenbüttel. He published almost all his works in collaboration with Elster. Following the latter's death in 1920, Geitel published a paper on the photoelectric effect in very thin films of potassium, a topic which, like his earlier individual efforts, had been of interest to both (1922). Geitel wrote several comprehensive reports on atmospheric electricity, radioactivity, and photoelectric methods of measurement. Of particular note is "Die Radioaktivität der Erde und der Atmosphäre," in *Handbuch der Radiologie.*

In 1899 Geitel received a Ph.D. *honoris causa* from the University of Göttingen and in 1915 a doctorate in engineering *honoris causa* from the University of Brunswick. Following his retirement he became honorary professor at Brunswick. In 1910 Geitel represented Germany's physicists (and Otto Hahn its chemists) on the International Radium Standard Commission in Paris.

BIBLIOGRAPHY

Geitel's writings include *Über die Anwendung der Lehre von den Gasionen auf die Erscheinungen der atmosphärischen Elektrizität* (Brunswick, 1901); *Bestätigung der Atomlehre durch die Radioaktivität* (Brunswick, 1913); "Die Radioaktivität der Erde und der Atmosphäre," in *Handbuch der Radiologie,* I (Leipzig, 1920), 399–457; "Photoelektrische Messmethoden," in *Handbuch der biologischen*

Methoden (Berlin–Vienna, 1921), pp. 1–38; and "Die Proportionalität von Photostrom und Beleuchtung an sehr dünnen Kaliumschichten," in *Annalen der Physik*, **67** (1922), 420–427.

There is an obituary notice by R. Pohl, in *Naturwissenschaften*, **12** (1924), 685–688.

WALTHER GERLACH

GELFOND, ALEXANDR OSIPOVICH (*b.* St. Petersburg [now Leningrad], Russia, 24 October 1906; *d.* Moscow, U.S.S.R., 7 November 1968), *mathematics*.

Gelfond was the son of Osip Isaacovich Gelfond, a physician who also did work in philosophy. From 1924 to 1927 he studied in the division of mathematics of the department of physics and mathematics at Moscow University; later he took a postgraduate course (1927–1930) under A. J. Khintchine and V. V. Stepanov. In 1929–1930 Gelfond taught mathematics at Moscow Technological College, and from 1931 until his death he was at Moscow University, where for a number of years he held the chair of analysis. He later held the chair of the theory of numbers, to which was subsequently added the history of mathematics. From 1933 he also worked in the Soviet Academy of Sciences Mathematical Institute. He became professor of mathematics in 1931 and doctor of mathematics and physics in 1935; he was elected corresponding member of the Academy of Sciences of the U.S.S.R. in 1939 and corresponding member of the International Academy of the History of Science in 1968.

Most important in Gelfond's scientific work were the analytical theory of numbers and the theory of interpolation and approximation of functions of a complex variable. Studies in both fields were closely related; he used and improved methods of the theory of functions in working on the problems of the theory of transcendental numbers.

In 1748 Euler had expressed the idea that logarithms of rational numbers with rational bases are either rational or transcendental. Generalizing that statement, among the famous twenty-three problems that Hilbert posed in 1900, was the hypothesis of the rationality or transcendence of logarithms of algebraic numbers with algebraic bases; i.e., he presumed the transcendence of a^b, where a is any algebraic number not 0 or 1 and b is any irrational algebraic number. For thirty years no approach to a solution of this, the seventh of Hilbert's problems, could be found. In 1929 Gelfond established profound connections between the growth and other properties of an entire analytic function and the arithmetic nature of its values when the values of argument belonged to a given algebraic field. This enabled him to find, proceeding from the expansion of the exponential function a^z, a being an algebraic number not 0 or 1, into the interpolating series of Newton,

$$a^z = \sum_{n=0}^{\infty} A_n (z - x_0)(z - x_1) \cdots (z - x_n),$$

where $x_0, x_1, x_2, \cdots$ are integers of an algebraic field $K(\sqrt{-D})$, $D > 0$, a solution of the problem in a particular case: the number a^b, where $b = i\sqrt{D}$ and D is a positive integer that is not a perfect square, is transcendental.

In 1930 R. O. Kuzmin extended Gelfond's method to real $b = \sqrt{D}$, and in 1932 C. L. Siegel applied it to the study of the transcendence of the periods of elliptic functions. Soon after, Gelfond consolidated his method with new ingenious ideas and, introducing linear forms of exponential function into consideration, confirmed in 1934 Hilbert's hypothesis in its entirety. His methods and results led to the most important contributions to the theory of transcendental numbers since Hermite's demonstration of the transcendence of e (1873) and K. L. F. Lindemann's of π (1882).

Applying his method to functions of p-adic variables, Gelfond made a number of new discoveries. Among them is the theorem that if α, β, γ are real algebraic numbers and at least one of them is not an algebraic unit, with γ being not equal to 2^n (n is a rational integer), the equation $\alpha^x + \beta^y = \gamma^z$ can possess only a finite number of solutions in rational integers x, y, z (1940). The further development of the method enabled Gelfond to solve a number of problems of mutual algebraic independence of numbers and to construct new classes of transcendental numbers. A considerable part of his discoveries in the theory of transcendental numbers is described in his monograph *Transtsendentnye i algebraicheskie chisla* (1952). Gelfond also wrote on other problems of the theory of numbers, including the diophantine approximations, the distribution of fractional parts of functions, and elementary methods of analytic theory.

In the theory of functions of a complex variable, Gelfond conducted numerous studies on problems of convergence of interpolation processes depending upon the density of a set of basic points of interpolation and upon the properties of the function to be approximated; on necessary and sufficient conditions for the determination of an entire analytical function on its given values or some other element; and on corresponding methods for the construction of functions. These studies were to a great extent summed up in *Ischislenie konechnykh raznostey* (1952).

Gelfond also promoted the history of mathematics, brilliantly characterizing Euler's work and his investigations in the theory of numbers. For many years he was the chairman of the scientific council that refereed theses on the history of physics and mathematics for the Soviet Academy of Sciences Institute of the History of Science and Technology.

Gelfond, creator of a large scientific school in the Soviet Union, profoundly influenced the advance of the theory of transcendentals and the theory of interpolation and approximation of functions of a complex variable.

BIBLIOGRAPHY

I. ORIGINAL WORKS. Gelfond's writings include "Sur les nombres transcendants," in *Comptes rendus hebdomadaires des séances de l'Académie des sciences,* **189** (1929), 1224–1228; "Sur le septième problème de Hilbert," in *Izvestiya Akademii nauk SSSR,* **7** (1934), 623–630; "Sur la divisibilité de la différence des puissances de deux nombres entiers par une puissance d'un idéal premier," in *Matematicheskii sbornik,* **7 (49)** (1940), 7–26; *Ischislenie konechnykh raznostey* ("Calculus of Finite Differences"; Moscow–Leningrad, 1952; 3rd ed., 1967), translated into German as *Differenzenrechnung* (Berlin, 1958); *Transtsendentnye i algebraicheskie chisla* (Moscow, 1952), translated into English as *Transcendental and Algebraic Numbers* (New York, 1960); and *Elementarnye metody v teorii chisel* (Moscow, 1962), written with Y. V. Linnik.

Complete bibliographies of Gelfond's works are in Linnik and Marcushevich and Pjatetsky-Shapiro and Shidlovsky (see below).

II. SECONDARY LITERATURE. On Gelfond or his work, see Y. V. Linnik and A. I. Marcushevich, "Alexandr Osipovich Gelfond," in *Uspekhi matematicheskikh nauk,* **11,** no. 5 (1956), 239–248; *Matematica v SSSR za sorok let* ("Forty Years of Mathematics in the U.S.S.R."), 2 vols. (Moscow, 1959), index; *Matematica v SSSR za tridtsat let* ("Thirty Years of Mathematics in the U.S.S.R."; Moscow–Leningrad, 1948), index; I. I. Pjatetsky-Shapiro and A. B. Shidlovsky, "Alexandr Osipovich Gelfond," in *Uspekhi matematicheskikh nauk,* **22,** no. 3 (1967), 247–256; and I. Z. Shtokalo, ed., *Istoria otechestvennoy matematiki* ("History of Native Mathematics"), III (Kiev, 1968), index.

A. P. YOUSCHKEVITCH

GELLIBRAND, HENRY (*b.* London, England, 17 November 1597; *d.* London, 16 February 1636), *navigation, mathematics.*

Gellibrand was the son of a graduate of All Souls College, Oxford. He became a commoner of Trinity College, Oxford, in 1615, a few weeks after his father's death. After graduating in arts (B.A., 1619, M.A., 1623) he took holy orders, and before 1623 he held a curacy at Chiddingstone, Kent. Gellibrand was introduced to mathematics by one of Sir Henry Savile's lectures, and he had at least enough geometry to set up a sundial on the east side of his college quadrangle. When the professorship of astronomy at Gresham College, London, was vacated following the death of Edmund Gunter, Gellibrand was elected to the chair on 2 January 1627. He completed the second volume of his sponsor Henry Briggs's *Trigonometria Britannica* (left unfinished at his death in 1630) and saw it through the press in 1633.

By this time Gellibrand's Puritanism had brought him into conflict with William Laud, then bishop of London. Gellibrand and his servant were cited by Laud before the Court of High Commission in 1631 for the publication of an almanac in which the saints and martyrs from John Foxe's *Book of Martyrs* replaced those permitted by the Church of England. They were acquitted on the grounds that this was not the first almanac of its kind, and the case was later cited against Laud at his own trial in 1643.

Gellibrand's most widely appreciated scientific discovery, which he should share with John Marr, was that of the secular change in the magnetic variation (declination). It was announced, without much comment, in *A Discourse Mathematicall on the Variation of the Magneticall Needle, Together With Its Admirable Diminution Lately Discovered* (1635). His predecessor, Gunter, had noticed that the variation at Limehouse in 1622 differed from the value found by William Borough in 1580, but he ascribed the difference to an error on Borough's part. In 1633 some rough observations of his own and John Marr's convinced Gellibrand that the value was now even less, but not until 1634 was he sufficiently confident to make a categorical assertion of its secular change. As his main evidence he referred to an appendix to Edward Wright's *Certaine Errors in Navigation . . .* (1599, 1610). This contains a compendium of recorded values of variation at various places made by a number of physicists and navigators the world over. (Henry Bond, editor of *Tapp's Seaman's Kalendar,* spent many years elaborating upon Gellibrand's findings and argued that despite its change, variation could even now be used by sailors to determine terrestrial longitudes. This would have been easier, of course, granted constant variation.)

Gellibrand's position at Gresham College drew him into matters of mathematical navigation, and an example of his attempts at solving the problem of longitude is a three-page appendix to *The Strange and Dangerous Voyage of Captain Thomas James* (1633). James, a gentleman mariner who voyaged in 1631 to seek the Northwest Passage, had by prior arrangement observed at Charlton Island, James Bay, a lunar eclipse also observed by Gellibrand at Gresham.

James's position in longitude was thus calculated (79°30′ west of Gresham, being 15′ too low).

The essentially practical quality of Gellibrand's work, which is of very slight mathematical interest, may also be judged from four works: his "Treatise of Building of Ships," a manuscript mentioned by Anthony à Wood as belonging to Edward, Lord Conway; his textbook *An Institution Trigonometrical;* a longer Latin work translated by John Newton, *An Institution Trigonometrical . . . With the Application . . . to Questions of Astronomy and Navigation* (1652); and *An Epitome of Navigation. . .* (1674). This last and posthumous book (written after 1631 and before 1634) contains a number of logarithmic tables, including trigonometrical ones, and has an appendix on the use of the cross-staff, quadrant, and nocturnal in navigation. That it was found valuable is suggested by the appearance of later editions, in 1698 (by Euclid Speidell), 1706 and subsequently (by J. Atkinson), and 1759 (by William Mountaine under the title *A Short and Methodical Way to Become a Complete Navigator*).

Gellibrand's work was mainly derivative, leading influences on it having been Wright's *Certaine Errors* and Richard Norwood's *Trigonometrica* (1631). It can be said that he was a reasonably good calculator and a competent writer of textbooks which helped to raise English standards of navigation to new heights.

BIBLIOGRAPHY

I. Original Works. Besides works mentioned in the text, Gellibrand wrote "Astronomia lunaris . . .," composed between 20 December 1634 and 22 January 1635. This belonged to Sir Hans Sloane but is not indexed in the catalog of the Sloane Collection in the British Museum. He also added a preface to and published *Sciographia, or the Art of Shadows* (London, 1635), written by J(ohn) W(ells), a Roman Catholic of Hampshire. A Latin oration, "In laudem Gassendi astronomiae," delivered in Christ Church Hall, Oxford, is now Brit. Mus. Add. MS 6193, f. 96.

II. Secondary Literature. The two main sources for Gellibrand's life are Anthony à Wood, *Athenae Oxonienses,* rev. and enl. ed. (Oxford, 1721); and John Ward, *The Lives of the Professors of Gresham College* (London, 1740), pp. 81–85, 336. Gellibrand's work on navigation has received little attention from historians, but for some discussion of navigation in his time see D. W. Waters, *The Art of Navigation in England in Elizabethan and Early Stuart Times* (London, 1958), *passim;* and E. G. R. Taylor, *The Mathematical Practitioners of Tudor and Stuart England* (Cambridge, 1954), pp. 138, 164, 165, 175.

J. D. North

GELMO, PAUL JOSEF JAKOB (*b.* Vienna, Austria, 17 December 1879; *d.* Vienna, 22 October 1961), *chemistry.*

Gelmo attended the Technische Hochschule in Vienna from 1898, obtaining an engineering diploma in 1903 and a doctorate in 1906. From 1904 to 1909 he was an assistant there to Wilhelm Suida. For twenty-eight years (1910–1938) he was chief chemist for the Austrian State Printing Office. In 1929 he became lecturer, and in 1954 professor, of the chemistry and technology of cellulose and paper at the Technische Hochschule.

Gelmo made his only noteworthy contribution to science while serving as assistant to Suida. Engaged in research with azo compounds and their usefulness as synthetic dyes, he prepared several new sulfonamides. One of his syntheses was sulfonanilamide (para-aminobenzenesulfonamide). After his work was published in 1908, I. G. Farbenindustrie used the new compound as a constituent in azosulfonamide dyes, but no one suspected that sulfonanilamide had curative powers. In 1932 Gerhard Domagk demonstrated the effectiveness of prontosil, a dye containing a sulfonamide group, in controlling streptococcal infections, which discovery led to the development of the sulfonamides as medicinals. Gelmo's sulfonanilamide came to be the most widely used of the sulfa drugs, and its commercial manufacture was accomplished essentially by his method.

BIBLIOGRAPHY

Gelmo's preparation of sulfonamides is presented in "Über Sulfamide der p-Amidobenzolsulfonsäure," in *Journal für praktische Chemie,* **77** (1908), 369–382.

Brief notices in Poggendorff, VIIa, pt. 2 (1957), 183; and *Who's Who in Austria* (1955), p. 136, constitute the secondary literature.

Albert B. Costa

GEMINUS (*fl.* Rhodes [?], *ca.* 70 B.C.), *astronomy, mathematics.*

Geminus' name is Latin, but his works and manner are patently Greek—the forms Γεμῖνος and Γεμεῖνος, also found in the manuscripts, are probably false analogies based on true Greek forms such as Ἀλεξῖνος and Ἐργῖνος. He was author of an *Introduction* (*Isagoge*) *to Astronomy* (still extant) and of a work on mathematics (lost, except for quoted extracts from it). Nothing is known of the circumstances of his life, but his date and place of work may be inferred from internal evidence in the *Isagoge.* In chapter 8, sections 20–24 of the Manitius edition, Geminus corrects a widespread Greek view that the Egyptian festival of Isis coincided with the winter solstice; he explains that although this was so 120 years ago, in his own time there was a whole month's difference between the two dates, since every four years the Egyptian calendar (based on a "year" of twelve months of thirty days each plus five additional days)[1] became out of step with the solar year by one day. The festival of Isis took place from the seventeenth to the twentieth day of the Egyptian month Athyr, and a papyrus fragment tells us that in the calendar of Eudoxus of Cnidus the winter solstice occurred on 20 or 19 Athyr. By Julian reckoning the winter solstice in Eudoxus' time (*ca.* 350 B.C.) occurred on 25 December or 28 December, and the first years in which these Julian dates can coincide with 19 Athyr are 185 B.C. and 197 B.C.[2] Hence, the papyrus presumably was written at this time; and subtracting the 120 years mentioned by Geminus, we obtain a date for the *Isagoge* of 65 or 77 B.C., which agrees with other evidence indicating a date about 70 B.C.[3]

We have no definite evidence about where Geminus was born or worked, but the commonly held opinion that his place of work was Rhodes may be correct. It is the "clima" of Rhodes that he uses to illustrate his account of various astronomical phenomena (e.g., I, 10; I, 12; III, 15; V, 25); in XVII, 4, he refers to Mt. Atabyrius,[4] i.e., the modern Mt. Attaviros, in the center of Rhodes, without feeling it necessary to specify its location, whereas in the same passage he is careful to explain that Mt. Cyllene is in the Peloponnesus; and Rhodes had a reputation in the last two centuries B.C. as a center for those subjects (philosophy, astronomy, and mathematics) with which Geminus was concerned, Panaetius, Posidonius, and Hipparchus all having worked there.

On the other hand, the choice of Rhodes as a typical example may simply have been dictated by its position on the best-known and most central parallel of latitude, 36°N. (Geminus himself says [XVI, 12] that all globes were constructed for this "clima," which for practical purposes was regarded as the latitude of Greece as well),[5] or Geminus may merely have used the examples he found in his sources, in this case almost certainly Hipparchus (see below), just as Ptolemy in the *Almagest* (II, 3 and 4), some 200 years later, was to use the same example from the same source. Similarly, Geminus may have taken the examples of Mt. Cyllene and Mt. Atabyrius straight from Dicaearchus (who is cited for their heights in XVII, 5); and even though two of his chief authorities, Hipparchus and Posidonius, worked in Rhodes, it does not necessarily follow that Geminus did.

The *Isagoge* is an early example of an elementary astronomical handbook written to popularize the main ideas in the technical treatises of the scientists; it belongs to the same tradition as the *De motu circulari corporum caelestium* of Cleomedes, and there are many similarities in style and arrangement between the two works, although, as might be expected from its later date, Cleomedes' work is fuller and less elementary than its precursor. One interesting difference is that Geminus includes a chapter (*Isagoge,* II) on the astrological "aspects" of the zodiacal signs, i.e., their arrangement in pairs, triplets, quadruplets, etc., according to which the astrologers calculated the signs' influence on human affairs; Cleomedes has no such chapter and, in fact, does not mention astrological doctrines at all. Geminus gives a simplified description of basic astronomy as known in the time of Hipparchus, omitting most of the mathematics and giving (I, 23 f.) little information about the planets apart from their zodiacal periods (thirty years for Saturn, twelve for Jupiter, two and a half for Mars, one year each for Mercury, Venus, and the sun,[6] and $27\frac{1}{3}$ days for the moon); there is no mention of epicycles, but the eccentricity of the sun's path relative to the earth is carefully described (I, 31 ff.) and the Hipparchian values for the four astronomical seasons are given (I, 13 f.)—$94\frac{1}{2}$, $92\frac{1}{2}$, $88\frac{1}{8}$, and $90\frac{1}{8}$ days, respectively, starting from the vernal equinox.[7]

Chapter III describes the main constellations; chapters IV and V describe the chief circles of the celestial sphere; and chapter VI explains the variations in the lengths of day and night at different latitudes. Chapter VII (which is based largely on Aratus and, almost certainly, on Hipparchus' commentary on Aratus' astronomical poem entitled *Phaenomena*) deals with the rising of the zodiacal signs, and chapter VIII with the length of the lunar month, for which a figure of $29\frac{1}{2} + 1/33$ days is given (rounded off from the accurate Hipparchian value of 29 days, 12 hours, 44 minutes, 3 seconds);[8] this last chapter is especially valuable for its account of how the Greeks developed an astronomically based calendar with a scientific system of intercalation.[9] Chapter IX explains the phases of the moon, chapters X and XI solar and lunar eclipses, and chapter XII the general motions of the planets. Chapters XIII and XIV deal with the risings and settings and courses of the fixed stars, and chapters XV and XVI with the zones of the terrestrial globe, delineated according to the estimates of Eratosthenes, which Hipparchus also accepted.[10]

Chapter XVII discusses sensibly the principles on which the "parapegmata" (astronomical calendars containing weather prognostications connected with the risings and settings of certain stars and constellations)[11] were based. Chapter XVIII deals with the "exeligmus" (ἐξελιγμός), or shortest period containing a whole number of synodic months, of anomalistic months, and of days (cf. *Almagest,* IV, 2); this chapter, far more technical than the others and out of keeping with the elementary character of the rest of the book, may well be an unrelated fragment.[12] Finally, there is an astronomical calendar, or "parapegma," which begins with Cancer and is evidently based on figures for the astronomical seasons which are not Hipparchian;[13] it seems probable that this was not part of the original treatise but represents older material.

Geminus' exposition is usually sound and clear and includes some intelligent criticism, e.g., of the notion held "by many philosophers" that the planetary bodies do not in fact exhibit two opposite motions (the diurnal and the zodiacal) but only seem to do so because they revolve at different speeds (*Isagoge,* XII, 14 ff.); this idea, says Geminus, "is not in accordance with observed phenomena" (XII, 19, *ἀσύμφωνός ἐστι τοῖς φαινομένοις*). He also gives a shrewd appreciation of the limitations of parapegmata, points out that weather forecasting based on observation of the rising and setting of various stars is by no means an exact science but a rough codification of general trends, and asserts firmly that stellar risings do not cause changes in the weather but merely indicate them (*οὐκ αὐταὶ παραίτιοί εἰσι τῶν περὶ τὸν ἀέρα μεταβολῶν, ἀλλὰ σημεῖα ἔκκεινται,* XVII, 11; see the whole of this chapter, especially 6–41); this last assertion contrasts strangely with the belief underlying chapter II.

There are, of course, some errors and infelicities. The chapter which gives a rational discussion of parapegmata (XVII) also contains an absurdly exaggerated view of the restricted range of atmospheric phenomena, according to which no wind or rain is experienced at the top of a mountain under 10,000 feet high (XVII, 3–5). In chapters X and XI no mention is made that, for an eclipse to take place, the moon must be at a node; and in XVI, 13, it is wrongly stated that the magnitudes of eclipses are the same for people living on the same parallel of latitude. There are also minor errors in the description of a star's evening rising (XIII, 13) and morning setting (XIII, 16), which may be the result of scribal errors in the transmission of the text (cf. Manitius, Anmerkung 25, 26); but Manitius' theory (pp. 246–248) that our present text represents a Byzantine compilation from an epitome of Geminus' original work, although it cannot be disproved, rests on very slender evidence.[14]

A work on mathematics (known only from extracts quoted by later writers) is also attributed to Geminus; and although it has been thought that this is not the same man as the author of the *Isagoge,* there can, in fact, be little doubt of the identity of the two.[15] The title of the work was probably *Theory of Mathematics* (Θεωρία τῶν μαθημάτων),[16] and it must have extended to at least six books, since Eutocius quotes from the sixth. Our chief source for its contents is Proclus,[17] who quotes extensive extracts from it; parallel quotations appear in the scholia to book I of Euclid's *Elements*[18] and in the collection of writings attributed to Hero of Alexandria;[19] and there are isolated quotations elsewhere.[20] There is also an Arabic commentary on Euclid by al-Nayrīzī[21] which contains extracts from a commentary on the *Elements* by Simplicius, who quotes a certain "Aghanis" on the definition of parallels; from similarities with what we know from Proclus of Geminus' views on this subject, it has been suggested that Aghanis is actually Geminus, but there are grave objections to such an identification, which must therefore remain doubtful.[22] A Latin translation of this Arabic text by Gerard of Cremona is extant.[23]

The *Theory of Mathematics* apparently dealt with the logical subdivisions of the mathematical sciences, discussing the philosophical principles of their classification, distinguishing carefully between such terms as "hypothesis" and "theorem," "postulate" and "axiom," and paying particular attention to accurate definitions not only of the various branches of mathematics but also of concepts such as "line," "surface," "figure," and "angle." It seems to have been a more substantial work than the *Isagoge* and to have contained some very pertinent criticism of Euclid's postulates, particularly the fifth, the so-called parallel postulate, for which Geminus believed he had found a proof.[24]

We learn from Simplicius that Geminus wrote an exegesis on the *Meteorologica* of Posidonius;[25] Simplicius cites Alexander of Aphrodisias as transcribing a long extract from an "epitome" of Geminus' work (ἐκ τῆς ἐπιτομῆς τῶν Ποσειδωνίου Μετεωρολογικῶν ἐξηγήσεως), but an epitome of an exegesis sounds unlikely and it is tempting to excise the word ἐπιτομῆς as an otiose gloss that has crept into the text. The extract discusses the different aims of physics and astronomy and has obvious relevance to a work on meteorology, which has affinities with both these sciences. Simplicius ends his citation with the following: "In this manner, then, Geminus also, or rather Posidonius in Geminus, expounds the difference . . . ." (*οὕτω μὲν οὖν καὶ ὁ Γεμῖνος ἤτοι ὁ παρὰ τῷ Γεμίνῳ Ποσειδώνιος τὴν διαφορὰν . . . παραδίδωσιν*). From this it has been implied that Geminus did little else but reproduce the opinions of Posidonius.

Such an implication certainly overestimates Geminus' debt to Posidonius. There is no doubt that both writers subscribed to Stoic views of the universe, and both were concerned to combat the attacks on the validity of the mathematical sciences, which, as we learn from Proclus and Sextus Empiricus, were mounted by both Skeptic and Epicurean philosophers;[26] but Geminus shows his independence of Posidonius in several respects. In *Isagoge* XVI, it is Eratosthenes' estimate of 252,000 stades that is taken as the basis of the division of the earth into zones and not Posidonius' figure of 240,000 (Cleomedes, *De motu circulari,* I, 10) or 180,000 (Strabo, *Geography,* 95),[27] neither of which is mentioned (nor, in fact, is Posidonius named in the entire treatise). Chapters VIII and XVIII, on the calendar and the length of the lunar month, almost certainly owe nothing to Posidonius, as there is no evidence that he did any work on calendrical problems; and there are other indications that Geminus, although he must have been well acquainted with Posidonius' opinions and was probably Proclus' chief authority for the latter,[28] did not hesitate to differ from the latter in following other sources (particularly Eratosthenes and Hipparchus for geography and astronomy) or putting forward his own views, as in his criticism of Euclid's postulates.

NOTES

1. On this, see O. Neugebauer, *The Exact Sciences in Antiquity,* 2nd ed. (Providence, R.I., 1957), pp. 81, 94.
2. 25 December according to W. Kubitschek, *Grundriss der antiken Zeitrechnung* (Munich, 1928), p. 109; 28 December according to Böckh, cited by Manitius in his ed. of *Elementa,* p. 264. See also "Synchronistic Table," in E. J. Bickerman, *Chronology of the Ancient World* (London-Ithaca, N.Y., 1968), p. 150.
3. For details, see Manitius ed. of *Elementa,* Anmerkung 16, pp. 263-266.
4. The Σαταβύριον of the MSS must be corrected to Ἀταβύριον; see D. R. Dicks, *Geographical Fragments of Hipparchus* (London, 1960), p. 30.
5. See V, 48; Dicks, *op. cit.,* pp. 123, 130, 176.
6. See D. R. Dicks, *Early Greek Astronomy to Aristotle* (London, 1970), notes 174, 345.
7. See Ptolemy, *Almagest,* III, 4.
8. *Ibid.,* IV, 2.
9. See Dicks, *Early Greek Astronomy,* pp. 86 f.
10. See Dicks, *Geographical Fragments,* p. 148.
11. See Dicks, *Early Greek Astronomy,* pp. 84 f.
12. See Manitius ed. of *Elementa,* p. 278.
13. *Ibid.,* Anmerkung 34.
14. See Tittel, "Geminos I," cols. 1031-1032.
15. *Ibid.,* cols. 1029-1030.
16. See Eutocius, *Commentaria in Conica I,* in *Apollonii Pergaei quae graece exstant,* J. L. Heiberg, ed., II (1893), 170, 25.
17. *Commentarii in primum Euclidis elementorum librum,* G. Friedlein, ed. (Leipzig, 1873).
18. *Euclidis opera omnia,* J. L. Heiberg and H. Menge, eds., V (Leipzig, 1888), 81, 4; 82, 28; 107, 20.
19. *Heronis Alexandri reliquiae,* F. Hultsch, ed. (Berlin, 1864), nos. 5-14, 80-86.
20. See Tittel, *op. cit.,* cols. 1039-1040.
21. *Codex Leidensis 399,1,* R. O. Besthorn, J. L. Heiberg, G. Junge, J. Raeder, and W. Thomson, eds., 3 pts. (Copenhagen, 1893-1932).
22. T. L. Heath, *History of Greek Mathematics,* II, 224, accepts it; but the same scholar, in *The Thirteen Books of Euclid's Elements,* 2nd ed. (Cambridge, 1925), pp. 27-28, rejects it. Compare A. I. Sabra, "Thabit Ibn Qurra on Euclid's Parallels Postulate," in *Journal of the Warburg and Courtauld Institutes,* **31** (1968), 13.
23. *Euclidis opera omnia. Supplementum: Anaritii in decem libros priores Elementorum Euclidis commentarii,* M. Curtze, ed. (Leipzig, 1899).
24. For details see Heath, *History of Greek Mathematics,* II, 223-231.
25. *Simplicii in Aristotelis Physicorum libros IV priores commentaria,* H. Diels, ed. (Berlin, 1882), pp. 291-292; this passage is also printed by Manitius in his ed. of the *Isagoge* as Fragmentum I, pp. 283-285.
26. Proclus, G. Friedlein, ed., pp. 199 f., 214 ff.; Sextus Empiricus, *Adversus mathematicos,* H. Mutschmann-J. Mau, eds., I, 1 ff.; compare the whole of III.
27. See E. H. Bunbury, *History of Ancient Geography,* II (London, 1879), 95-96; Dicks, *Geographical Fragments,* p. 150.
28. See Tittel, *op. cit.,* col. 1042.

BIBLIOGRAPHY

K. Manitius edited the *Gemini Elementa astronomiae* (Leipzig, 1898); chs. I, III-VI, VIII-XVI have been published by E. J. Dijksterhuis as *Gemini Elementorum astronomiae,* no. 22 in the series Textus Minores (Leiden, 1957).

See T. L. Heath, *History of Greek Mathematics,* II (Oxford, 1921; repr. 1960), 222-234; and Tittel, "Geminos I," in *Real-Encyclopädie,* Halbband XIII (1910), cols. 1026-1050.

D. R. Dicks

GEMINUS (also known as **Lambrit** or **Lambert**), **THOMAS** (*b.* Lixhe, Belgium, *ca.* 1510; *d.* London, England, June 1562), *medicine.*

Geminus—his assumed name may indicate he was the twin of his brother Jasper Lambrit—migrated about 1540 to England, where he practiced the arts of engraving, printing, and instrument making, the last possibly with the assistance of Humphrey Cole. The unique copper-engraved anatomical figure of a woman (*ca.* 1540), now in the Wellcome Historical Medical Library (*Catalogue of Printed Books,* I [London, 1962], no. 290), was probably the work of Geminus, as were the *Compendiosa totius anatomie delineatio* (1545) and the unique copy of *Morysse and Damashin Renewed and Encreased. Very Profitable for Goldsmiths and Embroiderars* (London, 1548), now in the Landesmuseum, Münster. Geminus both engraved and printed a map entitled *Nova descriptio Hispaniae* (London, 1555), on four sheets, and printed *Britanniae insulae . . . nova descriptio* (London, 1555); the unique copies of both are now in the Bibliothèque Nationale, Paris. He also printed Leonard Digges's

Prognostication of Right Good Effect in 1555 and a second edition in 1556, and he was possibly responsible for the diagram of the signs of the zodiac on the title page; he also brought out Digges's *Boke Named Tectonicon* (1562). In addition, he produced and engraved several astrolabes: one with the arms of the duke of Northumberland, Sir John Cheke, and Edward VI, dated 1552 (now in the Royal Belgian Observatory, Brussels), two about 1555 (National Maritime Museum, Greenwich, and Museo di Storia delle Scienze, Florence), and another for Queen Elizabeth (Museum of the History of Science, Oxford).

Geminus' most important work was the series of handsome, copper-engraved anatomical figures, most of them plagiarized from Vesalius' *Fabrica* and a few from his *Epitome.* Upon being presented with a set of these engravings in 1544, Henry VIII urged Geminus to issue them in the form of a book. This was done in the following year, under the title *Compendiosa totius anatomie delineatio,* published in London by J. Herford rather than by Geminus, who apparently had not yet established his own press. The illustrations were accompanied by the Latin text of Vesalius' *Epitome,* slightly defective in its concluding chapter as the result of verbal compression, and by the Latin text of Vesalius' descriptions (*indices*) of his illustrations. It appears likely that this first plagiarism of the major Vesalian texts and illustrations was intended as a treatise to accompany the anatomical lectures given at the recently (1540) organized United Company of Barber-Surgeons of London.

Although Geminus' book introduced Vesalian anatomy to England, it appears to have been too advanced for the surgeons, who, moreover, because of guild rather than university training, were unable to comprehend the Latin text. In consequence of what was probably a disappointing sale, the *Compendious Anatomy* was published again in 1553 ("Imprynted at London by Nycholas Hyll . . . for Thomas Geminus"), with an English "Treatyse" substituted for the Latin text of the *Epitome* and the Vesalian descriptions of the illustrations translated into English. The translations and the new text were the work of Nicholas Udall, the new text being basically the same as that employed by Thomas Vicary in his *Anatomie of Mans Bodie* (1548), i.e., a fourteenth-century compilation mostly representative of Henry of Mondeville's surgical anatomy, known today through the existence of a late fifteenth-century manuscript copy (Wellcome MS. no. 564). To this Udall added some sections from Ludovicus Vassaeus' Galenic *In anatomen corporis humani tabula quatuor* (1540) and a few fragments from Guy de Chauliac. The result therefore was essentially a medieval anatomical text factually denied by the accompanying Vesalian illustrations and their Vesalian descriptions; it could have been of little use for anatomical instruction despite the relatively low level of anatomical studies in England at that time. It was probably because of the spectacular Vesalian illustrations rather than the text that another edition of the *Compendious Anatomy* seems to have been called for in 1559, this time with some but very slight editorial assistance from Richard Eden ("Imprinted at London within the blacke fryars: by Thomas Gemini. Anno salutis. 1559").

Despite the questionable value of the text, Geminus' plagiarized illustrations were of considerable influence and were plagiarized in turn for Raynold's *Byrth of Mankynde* (London, 1545, and certain succeeding editions), William Bullein's *Government of Health* (London, 1558, 1559), Vicary's *Profitable Treatise of the Anatomie of Mans Body* (London, 1577), and Banester's *Historie of Man Sucked From the Sappe of the Most Approved Anathomistes* (London, 1579). In 1560 or shortly thereafter Geminus' plates were acquired by the Parisian printer André Wechsel and, with the editorial assistance of Jacques Grévin, were reproduced with Latin and French texts (1564, 1565, 1569) borrowed from Geminus' first edition of 1545. In turn these Parisian editions led to still others in France, Germany, and the Netherlands as late as the mid-seventeenth century.

Aside from these activities very little is known of Geminus' life. During the reign of Henry VIII he received wages as a royal surgeon, although there is no indication of his ever having had the necessary training, except perhaps for some mechanical skill and whatever he may have learned of anatomy from his plagiarism of the Vesalian illustrations and texts. Indeed, in 1555 he was penalized by the College of Physicians of London for practicing medicine without a license and undertook to print 200 copies of a proclamation against quackery for the college in place of his fine. No copy of this proclamation is known to exist today. Geminus' printing and engraving activities, located in Blackfriars, appear to have been financially successful, as is indicated by the distribution of his possessions according to his will, dated 22 May 1562 (O.S.).

BIBLIOGRAPHY

All of Geminus' works are today very rare. For bibliographical details of those pertaining to anatomy, see Harvey Cushing, *A Bio-bibliography of Andreas Vesalius,* 2nd ed.

(Hamden, Conn., 1962), pp. 121–130, 131–132, 135–136. The 1553 ed. of the *Compendiosa totius anatomie delineatio* has been published in a facs. ed. (London, 1959); the intro. to it by C. D. O'Malley contains the fullest account of Geminus and his activities. There is also a facs. ed. of the illustrations, curiously entitled *Andreas Vesalius* (Geneva, 1964). The accompanying explanatory text unfortunately contains many errors of fact.

C. D. O'MALLEY

GEMMA FRISIUS, REINER (*b.* Dokkum, Netherlands, 1508; *d.* Louvain, Belgium, 1555), *geography, mathematics.*

Gemma Frisius was a native of Friesland; hence his nickname Frisius. He received his medical degree at Louvain, practiced medicine there, and taught later at its medical faculty. Although he was a practicing physician, he is remembered for his contributions to geography and mathematics, his avocations.

At the age of twenty-one Gemma Frisius published *Cosmographicus liber Petri Apiani mathematici* . . . (Antwerp, 1529), an edition of Peter Apian's *Cosmography,* "carefully corrected and with all errors set to right." In 1530 he published at Antwerp his first original work, *Gemma Phrysius de principiis astronomiae & cosmographiae* . . ., which was translated into several languages and reprinted numerous times. The Spanish Netherlands was in close contact with court and business circles in Spain, and Brussels was an ideal place to gather current information on the discoveries. Gemma Frisius designed globes and astronomical instruments that were well known and much sought after throughout Europe. Several of them still survive and are of key importance in tracing the growth of knowledge of the newly discovered lands. Some of Gemma Frisius' globes were completed by Gerard Mercator, who had attended mathematical lectures that Gemma Frisius gave at his home.

Gemma Frisius made two significant contributions to the earth sciences. In a chapter added to the 1533 Antwerp edition of the *Cosmographicus,* entitled "Libellus de locorum describendorum ratione," he was first to propose—and illustrate—the principle of triangulation as a means of carefully locating places and accurately mapping areas. Twenty years later, in the 1553 Antwerp edition of *De principiis astronomiae,* he added a chapter entitled "De novo modo investigandi latitudinem regionis absq. meridiani vel loci solis cognitione," in which he was the first to suggest in explicit terms the use of portable timepieces to measure longitude by lapsed time. Although this important idea could not be put into practice until after the invention of optical instruments and accurate portable timepieces, the credit for first suggesting it rests with Gemma Frisius.

BIBLIOGRAPHY

The basic reference work, which includes the text of the few items of Gemma Frisius' surviving correspondence, is Fernand van Ostroy, "Biobibliographie de Gemma Frisius, fondateur de l'école belge de géographie . . .," in *Mémoires de l'Académie royale des sciences . . . de Belgique,* Classe des Lettres, 2nd ser., **11** (1920). The original text of the method of measuring longitude is reproduced in A. Pogo, "Gemma Frisius, His Method of Determining Longitude . . .," in *Isis,* **22** (1935), i–xix, 469–485. A brief biographical sketch and an appraisal of Gemma Frisius' work is George Kish, "Medicine · Mensura · Mathematica; The Life and Works of Gemma Frisius, 1508–1555," James Ford Bell lecture no. 4 (1967), published by the Associates of the James Ford Bell Collection, University of Minnesota Library.

GEORGE KISH

GENTH, FREDERICK AUGUSTUS (*b.* Wächtersbach, Hesse, Germany, 17 May 1820; *d.* Philadelphia, Pennsylvania, 2 February 1893), *chemistry, mineralogy.*

Genth exhibited a keen interest in natural history at an early age. After three years at the Hanau Gymnasium, in 1839 he entered the University of Heidelberg, where he studied chemistry, geology, and mineralogy under Leopold Gmelin, J. R. Blum, and K. C. Leonhard. From 1841 to 1843 he attended the University of Giessen, where he worked under Fresenius, Kopp, and Liebig. In 1844 he continued his chemical studies under Bunsen at the University of Marburg, receiving his doctorate there in 1845. He remained at Marburg as *Privatdozent* and Bunsen's assistant for three years. In 1848 he immigrated to the United States, making his home first in Baltimore and then in Philadelphia. After occupying several positions, establishing one of the first commercial analytical laboratories in America, and engaging in the instruction of special students, in 1872 he became professor of chemistry at the University of Pennsylvania, a post he held until 1888, when he returned to consulting work and research.

Genth's European background and education supplied him with technical skills possessed by few scientists in the United States during his lifetime, and he holds a place in the foremost rank of pioneer mineralogists in America. He was a chemist almost without peer, especially in the field of analysis. His best-known research involved the ammonia-cobalt bases (cobalt ammines), developed jointly with Oliver Wolcott Gibbs. His original memoir on this topic (1851) contained the first distinct recognition of the existence of perfectly defined and crystallized salts of the cobalt ammines. His joint monograph with

Gibbs (1856) described thirty-five salts of four bases—roseocobalt, purpureocobalt, luteocobalt, and xanthocobalt—and for the first time distinguished roseo salts from purpureo salts.

Genth served as chemist for the Second Geological Survey of Pennsylvania and chemist to the Board of Agriculture of Pennsylvania; his analyses of fertilizers did much to develop the state's agricultural industry. His chief chemical contributions to mineralogy are contained in fifty-four papers describing 215 mineral species; he himself discovered twenty-four new minerals. His contributions to chemistry and mineralogy total 102.

BIBLIOGRAPHY

I. ORIGINAL WORKS. Genth's original memoir on cobalt ammines is in *Keller-Tiedemann's Nordamerikan Monatsbericht,* **2** (1851), 8–12; Gibbs and Genth's classic "Researches on the Ammonia-Cobalt Bases," described by Genth's student E. F. Smith as "among the finest chemical investigations ever made in this country," appears in *American Journal of Science,* 2nd ser., **23** (1856), 234, 319, and **24** (1856), 86, and as a separate publication in the series Smithsonian Contributions to Knowledge (Washington, D.C., 1856).

II. SECONDARY LITERATURE. The constitution of the cobalt ammines was not understood until Alfred Werner proposed his coordination theory in "Beitrag zur Konstitution anorganischer Verbindungen," in *Zeitschrift für anorganische Chemie,* **3** (1893), 267–330, of which an English trans. is in G. B. Kauffman, *Classics in Coordination Chemistry,* I, *Selected Papers of Alfred Werner* (New York, 1968), pp. 9–88. On Genth's life see especially his student E. F. Smith, *Chemistry in America* (New York, 1918), pp. 261–263, and "Mineral Chemistry," in *Journal of the American Chemical Society,* **48,** no. 8A (1926), 71–75. Additional data are in George F. Barker, "Obituary Notice: Frederick Augustus Genth," in *Proceedings of the American Philosophical Society,* **40** (1901), x–xxii, and "Memoir of Frederick Augustus Genth 1820–1893," in *Biographical Memoirs. National Academy of Sciences,* **4** (1902), 201–231; W. M. Myers and S. Zerfoss, "Frederick Augustus Genth: 1820–1893, Chemist-Mineralogist-Collector," in *Journal of the Franklin Institute,* **241** (1946), 341–354; H. S. van Klooster, "Liebig and His American Pupils," in *Journal of Chemical Education,* **33** (1956), 493–497; and W. H. Wahl, H. F. Keller, and T. R. Wolf, "A Memoir of Frederick Augustus Genth," in *Journal of the Franklin Institute,* **135** (1893), 448–452.

GEORGE B. KAUFFMAN

GENTZEN, GERHARD (*b.* Greifswald, Germany, 24 November 1909; *d.* Prague, Czechoslovakia, 4 August 1945), *logic, foundations of mathematics.*

Gentzen was a born mathematician. As a boy he declared his dedication to mathematics, and his short life constituted a realization of that promise. He benefited from the teaching of such renowned scholars as P. Bernays, C. Carathéodory, R. Courant, D. Hilbert, A. Kneser, E. Landau, and H. Weyl and, at the age of twenty-three, received his doctorate in mathematics. In 1934 he became one of Hilbert's assistants and held that position until 1943, with the exception of a two-year period of compulsory military service from 1939 to 1941, when he was requested to take up a teaching post at the University of Prague. He died at Prague of malnutrition three months after his internment by the liberating authorities in May 1945.

Gentzen combined in rare measure an exceptional inventiveness and the talent for coordinating diverse existing knowledge into a systematic conceptual framework. He invented "natural deduction" in order to create a predicate logic more akin to actual mathematical reasoning than the Frege-Russell-Hilbert systems, then used P. Hertz's "sentences" to transform his natural calculus into a "calculus of sequents." Thus he succeeded in making classical logic appear as a simple extension of intuitionist logic and in enunciating his *Hauptsatz* (chief theory), which he had discovered while studying more closely the specific properties of natural deduction. A formalization of elementary number theory based on sequents and his ingenious idea of using restricted transfinite induction as a metamathematical technique enabled Gentzen to carry out the first convincing consistency proof for elementary number theory, in spite of the limitations imposed on such proofs by Gödel's theorem. He eventually proved directly the nonderivability in elementary number theory of the required transfinite induction up to ϵ_0. In view of subsequent developments, Gentzen's consistency proof must be considered as the most outstanding single contribution to Hilbert's program.

The *Hauptsatz* says that in both intuitionist and classical predicate logic, a purely logical sequent can be proved without "cut" (*modus ponens,* in Hilbert-type systems). A corollary is the subformula property, to the effect that the derivation formulas in a cut-free proof are compounded in the sequent proved. This entails, for example, the consistency of classical and intuitionist predicate logic, the decidability of intuitionist propositional logic, and the nonderivability of the law of the excluded middle in intuitionist predicate logic. Gentzen succeeded in sharpening the *Hauptsatz* for classical logic to the midsequent theorem (Herbrand-Gentzen theorem) for sequents whose formulas are prenex, by proving that any such sequent has a cut-free proof consisting of two parts, the first part quantifier-free and the second consisting essentially of instances of quantification. The last quantifier-free sequent in the proof is the "midsequent" and corresponds closely to a "Herbrand tautology."

Among the consequences of the midsequent theorem are the consistency of arithmetic without induction, Craig's interpolation lemma, and Beth's definability theorem. Recent extensions of the *Hauptsatz* to stronger deductive systems, including infinitary logic, have yielded partial results at the second stage of Hilbert's program in the form of consistency proofs for subsystems of classical analysis. Only a few days before his death, Gentzen had in fact announced the feasibility of a consistency proof for classical analysis as a whole.

BIBLIOGRAPHY

Gentzen's writings include "Über die Existenz unabhängiger Axiomensysteme zu unendlichen Satzsystemen," in *Mathematische Annalen,* **107** (1932), 329–350; "Untersuchungen über das logische Schliessen," in *Mathematische Zeitschrift,* **39** (1935), 176–210, 405–431, his inaugural dissertation, submitted to the Faculty of Mathematics and Natural Science of the University of Göttingen in the summer of 1933; "Die Widerspruchsfreiheit der reinen Zahlentheorie," in *Mathematische Annalen,* **112** (1936), 493–565; "Die Widerspruchsfreiheit der Stufenlogik," in *Mathematische Zeitschrift,* **41,** no. 3 (1936), 357–366; "Der Unendlichkeitsbegriff in der Mathematik," in *Semester-Berichte, Münster in Westphalen,* 9th semester (Winter 1936/1937), pp. 65–80; "Unendlichkeitsbegriff und Widerspruchsfreiheit der Mathematik," in *Travaux du IXe Congrès International de Philosophie,* VI (Paris, 1937), 201–205; "Die gegenwärtige Lage in der mathematischen Grundlagenforschung," in *Forschungen zur Logik und zur Grundlegung der exakten Wissenschaften,* n.s. **4** (1938), 5–18, also in *Deutsche Mathematik,* **3** (1939), 255–268; "Neue Fassung des Widerspruchsfreiheitsbeweises für die reine Zahlentheorie," in *Forschungen zur Logik und zur Grundlegung der exakten Wissenschaften,* n.s. **4** (1938), 19–44; "Beweisbarkeit und Unbeweisbarkeit von Anfangsfällen der transfiniten Induktion in der reinen Zahlentheorie," in *Mathematische Annalen,* **119,** no. 1 (1943), 140–161, his Ph.D. *Habilitation* thesis, submitted to the Faculty of Mathematics and Natural Science of the University of Göttingen in the summer of 1942; and "Zusammenfassung von mehreren vollständigen Induktionen zu einer einzigen," in *Archiv für mathematische Logik und Grundlagenforschung,* **2,** no. 1 (1954), 1–3.

For a detailed account of Gentzen's life, extensive cross-references to his papers, and a critical appraisal of germane subsequent developments, see M. E. Szabo, *Collected Papers of Gerhard Gentzen,* in the series Studies in Logic (Amsterdam, 1969); of particular interest are the trans. of two articles Gentzen submitted to *Mathematische Annalen* but withdrew before publication (of which galley proofs are privately owned), "Über das Verhältnis zwischen intuitionistischer und klassischer Arithmetik" (1933) and sections 4 and 5 of "Die Widerspruchsfreiheit der reinen Zahlentheorie" (1935).

MANFRED E. SZABO

GEOFFROY, CLAUDE JOSEPH (*b.* Paris, France, 8 August 1685; *d.* Paris, 9 March 1752), *chemistry, botany.*

Geoffroy the Younger (le Cadet) was the second son of Matthieu François Geoffroy and Louise de Vaux, and the brother of Étienne François Geoffroy. He qualified as an apothecary in 1703 and took over the family pharmacy on his father's death in 1708. Highly esteemed in his profession, he was appointed inspector of the pharmacy at the Hôtel-Dieu (the Paris hospital) and in 1731 he served as a Paris alderman (*échevin*).

In 1707 Geoffroy, who had studied botany under J. P. de Tournefort and made a long field excursion in the south of France in 1704–1705, was elected to the Académie des Sciences as a botanist. He was already interested in chemistry and in his first research tried to find a chemical explanation of the colors of plants (1707). He discovered that the oil obtained by macerating and distilling thyme reacted with vinegar, potash, and other substances of vegetable origin to form colors similar to those in flowers and leaves, and this supported the belief that plants consisted of a limited number of principles combined in different ways and obtainable by simple processes such as distillation and fermentation.

After publishing a few botanical papers, Geoffroy transferred to the chemical section of the Academy in 1715. Much of his subsequent research arose from his pharmaceutical work, a good example being his discovery that sedative salt (boric acid), a medicament normally prepared in small quantities by subliming a mixture of borax and iron vitriol (ferrous sulfate), could be made on a larger scale by treating borax with diluted oil of vitriol (sulfuric acid) and crystallizing it (1732). This research was important in the development of theoretical as well as practical chemistry, for Geoffroy demonstrated the presence of a common constituent in borax, soda, and common salt, all of which yielded Glauber's salt (sodium sulfate) on treatment with sulfuric acid.

Geoffroy's son, Claude François Geoffroy (*ca.* 1728–1753; incorrectly called N. Geoffroy in *Nouvelle biographie générale*), succeeded him in his profession and was elected to the chemical section of the Academy in 1752.

BIBLIOGRAPHY

I. ORIGINAL WORKS. About sixty papers by Geoffroy were published in *Histoire et mémoires de l'Académie royale des sciences.* A complete list is given by P. Dorveaux (see below).

II. SECONDARY LITERATURE. A general account of Geoffroy's life and work is J. P. Grandjean de Fouchy, "Éloge de M. Geoffroy," in *Histoire de l'Académie royale des sciences* (1752, pub. 1756), 153–164. Further information is given by P. Dorveaux, "Claude-Joseph Geoffroy," in *Revue d'histoire de la pharmacie,* **3** (1932), 113–122, bib. on pp. 119–122. Dorveaux also gives an account of his son, "Claude François Geoffroy," *ibid.,* 122–126. There seems to be no connection between the Geoffroy family and that of Étienne and Isidore Geoffroy Saint-Hilaire, the naturalists, according to G. Planchon, "La dynastie des Geoffroy, apothicaires à Paris," in *Journal de pharmacie et de chimie,* 6th ser., **8** (1898), 289–293, 337–345 (esp. 344–345).

W. A. SMEATON

GEOFFROY, ÉTIENNE FRANÇOIS (*b.* Paris, France, 13 February 1672; *d.* Paris, 6 January 1731), *chemistry, medicine.*

Known as Geoffroy the Elder (l'Aîné) to distinguish him from his brother Claude Joseph, he was the son of Matthieu François Geoffroy, a wealthy pharmacist who had been a Paris alderman, and Louise de Vaux, daughter of a well-known surgeon. Such scientists as Wilhelm Homberg and J. D. Cassini visited their home, giving demonstrations and lectures that supplemented Geoffroy's education. His father, the fourth in a respected dynasty of pharmacists, hoping that Geoffroy would eventually take over the family business, sent him to Montpellier in 1692 for a year to learn pharmacy from a colleague, Pierre Sanche, whose son came to Paris. While in Montpellier, Geoffroy attended courses at the medical school; and although he qualified as a pharmacist in 1694 after his return to Paris, his real ambition was to become a physician. With his father's consent he therefore turned to the study of medicine.

While still a student Geoffroy was chosen as medical adviser by the comte de Talland, French ambassador extraordinary to England; and in 1698 he spent several months in London, where he became friendly with Hans Sloane. He was made a fellow of the Royal Society, of which Sloane was secretary; and in January 1699, after his return to Paris, he was elected to the Académie des Sciences as the student of Homberg; he became an *associé* later in 1699 and *pensionnaire* in 1715. When first elected, he offered to keep the Academy informed of scientific developments in England, and his correspondence with Sloane became a valuable medium for the transmission of scientific news between the two countries.

On his way home from London, Geoffroy had visited Holland; and in 1700 he made another long journey, to Italy. He eventually graduated M.D. at Paris in 1704 and began to practice a few years later. He acquired a considerable reputation and was often consulted by other physicians.

Geoffroy succeeded J. P. de Tournefort as professor of medicine at the Collège Royal (now the Collège de France) in 1709 and retained the chair until his death; but his lecturing career had begun in 1707, when he first deputized for G.-C. Fagan, professor of chemistry at the Jardin du Roi. Until 1710 he shared this duty with Louis Lemery and Claude Berger; then Berger acted alone until his death in 1712, when Fagan retired completely from the chair and Geoffroy was appointed. Geoffroy normally lectured on materia medica for two or three hours immediately after his two-hour lecture on chemistry, a feat that earned the praise of Bernard de Fontenelle; the comments of the students are not available.

In 1726 Geoffroy was elected dean of the Paris Faculty of Medicine, and after the customary two-year period he was reelected, serving until 1729, at a time when there was a serious dispute between the physicians and surgeons. The strains of this office, together with his chairs and his practice, weakened his health. He retired from the Jardin du Roi in 1730, and within a year he died of consumption at the age of fifty-eight. His son, Étienne Louis Geoffroy, became well known as a naturalist and was elected to the Institut de France in 1798.

A new Paris pharmacopoeia, *Codex medicamentarius seu pharmacopoeia parisiensis,* was published by the Faculty of Medicine in 1732 under the deanship of H. T. Baron. Largely the work of Geoffroy, it contained many chemical remedies in addition to the traditional galenicals, as did Geoffroy's unfinished book on materia medica, based on his lectures. The part that he had dictated, containing medicaments from the mineral kingdom and part of the vegetable kingdom, was published in Latin as *Tractatus de materia medica* in 1741 and was translated into French in 1743. Geoffroy's treatment of the vegetable kingdom was interesting. Exotic plants were not usually imported whole, so he classified them under such headings as roots, barks, and leaves, since these were the parts used in medicine; but he described the whole plant in the case of those native to France. Almost always he included the results of qualitative and quantitative analysis by distillation, recording the nature and amount of each oil, phlegm, salt, or earth obtained; and he endeavored to relate the medicinal properties to the products of analysis. This approach to the study of vegetable remedies, with the implication that the products of distillation were originally present as such in the plant, had been introduced by earlier chemists at the Academy; and many such analyses are recorded in its minute books. By the end of his life, though, Geoffroy had lost faith in the method, according to the editors of the supplement to his *Materia medica,* who excluded these analytical results.

Geoffroy's first publication, a study of heat effects observed when saline substances were mixed (1700), is of interest as an early attempt to use the thermometer in chemistry; but his results were inconclusive and it is clear that his air thermometer responded too slowly to temperature changes. He soon entered a field of experimental chemistry which he related to a theory of matter.

Homberg had "decomposed" common sulfur into an acid, a bituminous substance, and an earth. Geoffroy found in 1704 that it could be re-formed by heating oil of vitriol (sulfuric acid) and turpentine; after distillation iron, detected with a magnet, was present in the residue. In 1705 Geoffroy also found iron in the ashes of all vegetable matter, although it was not detectable in the original plant: he believed that the iron had been formed during these processes, a "sulfurous principle" being common to vegetable matter and metals and giving metals their properties of fusibility and ductility. Louis Lemery objected to this theory and argued that the iron was present all the time in the oil of vitriol or turpentine, and in the vegetable matter that had been burned (*Mémoires de l'Académie royale des sciences* for 1707 [1708], 5–11). He claimed that Geoffroy's reasoning was unsound, for in some circumstances—when dissolved in acid and then crystallized, for example—iron could not be detected with a magnet although it was certainly present (*Histoire de l'Académie royale des sciences* for 1708 [1709], 61–65). Yet Geoffroy persisted in his belief, and in 1720 he identified his "sulfurous principle" with Georg Stahl's phlogiston.

On fermentation, urine produced volatile alkali; and in 1717 Geoffroy considered that the acid in urine had been converted into alkali. He also believed that alkali could be formed from mineral acids; he explained these changes, as well as the formation of iron from vegetable matter, by a theory which was elaborated in his *Materia medica* but is also mentioned in some of his earlier publications.

Geoffroy recognized three "very simple substances": fire, which could exist only in combination with the others; water, composed of hard, smooth, oval or wedge-shaped particles that dissolved solids by forcing their particles apart; and earth, composed of irregular particles with many pores between them. These three combined to form two "principles," salt and sulfur, which were the usual products of analysis. Salt existed in two main forms, acid and alkali, which were interconvertible because they differed in the way their constituent fire, water, and earth were combined: the particles of acids were pointed at both ends; those of alkalies were spherical with projecting points that joined together, forming a porous globule into which acid particles could enter. Sulfur was formed by the combination of salt with more fire, water, and earth; this combination could take place in vegetables, or animals, or beneath the ground, where, according to the proportions of the constituents, the product was one of a variety of substances, such as petroleum, coal, common sulfur, or a metal.

It was well known before Geoffroy's time that certain substances could displace others from compounds; but in 1718 he advanced the first general proposition that if two substances in combination are approached by a third with which one of them has a greater relation (*rapport*), then that one will combine with the third, leaving the other free. He accompanied this with a sixteen-column table in which, using symbols, he showed the order of displacement of some common substances. The first column referred to compounds of mineral acids, with which fixed alkali (soda and potash were not yet distinguished) had the greatest relation, followed by volatile alkali (ammonia), absorbent earth (chalk and such), and metals. Since the order in which the metals displaced each other was not the same for all acids, the next three columns were devoted to the individual acids and their reactions with metals. There followed columns for absorbent earth, fixed alkali, volatile alkali, metals in combination with acids, and common sulfur; and then six columns for the "compounds" of the metals with each other and one for water in relation to salt and alcohol.

No details were given by Geoffroy of the experiments on which his table was based, and in 1720 he had to reply to some criticisms. For example, one critic challenged his statement that absorbent earth came below volatile alkali in the first column, for it was well known that lime expelled volatile alkali from sal ammoniac (ammonium chloride). Geoffroy replied that although it was formed by heating chalk, lime was not itself a pure absorbent earth; rather, it contained sharp and caustic particles of alkali, which might have been formed from acid in the wood that was burned when the lime was made, or perhaps from "aluminous vitriolic acid" present in the original chalk. This opinion was criticized by Louis Lemery, who, like his father, Nicolas Lemery, believed that lime owed its causticity to fire particles (*Histoire de l'Académie royale des sciences* for 1720 [1722], 33). Thus it is easy to understand why Geoffroy's table was not elaborated until after about 1750, when ideas on the nature of acids, alkalies, and earths were more clearly defined.

In 1718 and again in 1720 Geoffroy referred only to "rapport" and did not use the words "affinity" or "attraction." There have been suggestions that he was influenced by Newton's theory that chemical reactions were caused by attraction between particles, but his detailed account of pointed and porous particles that combine by interlocking seems to make it clear that his ideas were akin to those of Descartes, Pierre Gassendi, Nicolas Lemery, and Nicolaas Hartsoeker, and that he did not belong to the Newtonian school of chemists.

BIBLIOGRAPHY

I. ORIGINAL WORKS. According to Fontenelle, Geoffroy was the principal author of *Codex medicamentarius seu pharmacopoeia parisiensis* (Paris, 1732). The first version of his work on materia medica to be published was *A Treatise of the Fossil, Vegetable and Animal Substances, That Are Made Use of in Physick* (London, 1736), a partial English trans. by G. Douglas of a MS of Geoffroy's lectures, which were delivered in Latin at the Collège Royal; this contains a short account of the animal kingdom, which is not in the Latin and French eds., and an English version of Fontenelle's "Éloge." The Latin text was published (by Étienne Chardon de Courcelles, according to Dorveaux) as *Tractatus de materia medica,* 3 vols. (Paris, 1741); vol. I includes the Latin texts of five of Geoffroy's medical theses and the French texts of Fontenelle's "Éloge" and Geoffroy's papers written in 1713, 1718, and 1720. A French trans. (by A. Bergier, according to Dorveaux) appeared as *Traité de matière médicale,* 7 vols. (Paris, 1743; new ed. [unaltered], 1757). Vol. I contains Fontenelle's "Éloge," Geoffroy's papers written in 1713, 1718, and 1720, and a French trans. of one of his medical theses: "Question, si l'homme a commencé par être ver." The Latin and French eds. of *Materia medica* stop where Geoffroy's MS ended, at the word "Melilotus" in the alphabetical list of indigenous plants. The vegetable kingdom was completed in *Suite de la matière médicale de M. Geoffroy, par M***, docteur en médecine,* 3 vols. (Paris, 1750); the authors of this were apparently the men who published an account of the animal kingdom in *Suite de la matière médicale de M. Geoffroy, par Mrs Arnault de Nobleville & Salerne, médecins d'Orléans,* 7 vols. (Paris, 1756–1757). They claimed to follow Geoffroy's order but added new material and acknowledged their indebtedness to Bernard de Jussieu and others.

Seventeen papers read by Geoffroy to the Académie des Sciences are listed in Poggendorff, I, 873–874. The most important, to which reference has been made above, are "Observations sur les dissolutions et sur les fermentations que l'on peut appeller froides," in *Mémoires de l'Académie royale des sciences* for 1700 (1703), 110–121; "Manière de recomposer le souffre commun par la réunion de ses principes, et d'en composer de nouveau par le mêlange de semblables substances, avec quelques conjectures sur la composition des métaux," *ibid.,* for 1704 (1706), 278–286; "Problème de chimie: Trouver des cendres qui ne contiennent aucunes parcelles de fer," *ibid.,* for 1705 (1706), 362–363; "Éclaircissemens sur la production artificielle du fer, & sur la composition des autres métaux," *ibid.,* for 1707 (1708), 176–188; "Expériences sur les métaux, faites avec le verre ardent du Palais Royal," *ibid.,* for 1709 (1711), 162–176; "Observations sur le vitriol et le fer," *ibid.,* for 1713 (1716), 170–188; "Du changement des sels acides en sels alkalis volatiles urineux," *ibid.,* for 1717 (1719), 226–238; "Table des différens rapports observés en chymie entre différentes substances," *ibid.,* for 1718 (1719), 202–212; and "Éclaircissemens sur la table inserée dans les Mémoires de 1718, concernant les rapports observés entre différentes substances," *ibid.,* for 1720 (1722), 20–34. Some of his letters to Sloane were printed, in part, in *Philosophical Transactions of the Royal Society* and are listed in P. H. Maty, *A General Index to the Philosophical Transactions* (London, 1787) pp. 633–634.

II. SECONDARY LITERATURE. A general account of Geoffroy's life is in Bernard de Fontenelle, "Éloge de M. Geoffroy," in *Histoire de l'Académie royale des sciences* for 1731 (1733), 93–100. Additional information is given by P. Dorveaux, "Étienne-François Geoffroy," in *Revue d'histoire de la pharmacie,* **2** (1931), 118–126; J. P. Contant, *Enseignement de la chimie au Jardin Royal des Plantes de Paris* (Cahors, 1952), pp. 55–57; and J. Torlais, "Le Collège Royal," in R. Taton, ed., *Enseignement et diffusion des sciences en France au XVIII*e *siècle* (Paris, 1964), pp. 261–286. Geoffroy's relations with British scientists (with extracts from his letters to Sloane which are now in the British Museum and the Royal Society) are discussed by I. B. Cohen, "Isaac Newton, Hans Sloane and the Académie Royale des Sciences," in I. B. Cohen and R. Taton, eds., *Mélanges Alexandre Koyré* (Paris, 1964), I, 61–116; Cohen's description of Geoffroy as "one of Newton's chemical disciples" is disputed by W. A. Smeaton, "E. F. Geoffroy Was not a Newtonian Chemist," in *Ambix,* **18** (1971), 212–214. A good account of tables of affinity is given by A. M. Duncan, "Some Theoretical Aspects of Eighteenth-Century Tables of Affinity," in *Annals of Science,* **18** (1962), 177–194, 217–232.

W. A. SMEATON

GEOFFROY, ÉTIENNE LOUIS (*b.* Paris, France, 2 October 1725; *d.* Chartreuve, near Soissons, France, 12 August 1810), *zoology, medicine.*

Geoffroy was the son of Étienne François Geoffroy, dean of the Faculty of Medicine of Paris and professor of medicine at the Collège de France, and the grandson of the apothecary Matthieu François

Geoffroy. His father died when the boy was five, and Étienne was brought up by his mother. After a brilliant career at the *collège* of Beauvais, he went to Paris to study medicine. There he attended the courses of Antoine Ferrein (anatomy), G. F. Rouelle (chemistry), Bernard de Jussieu (botany), and Jean Astruc (practical medicine). Geoffroy's thesis for the *licence,* which he defended in 1746, dealt with the manner in which the fetus is nourished. Received as a doctor in 1748, he henceforth applied himself to medical practice while pursuing research in zoology.

In 1762 Geoffroy published a work on the insects of the Paris area in which he used new criteria of classification: absence or presence, number, form, and texture of the wings; and distribution of the various orders according to the number of tarsomeres in the tarsi. The latter criterion attracted the attention of Linnaeus, who often quoted Geoffroy. In 1767 Geoffroy published a volume on the terrestrial and aquatic gastropods of the Paris area in which he used the characteristics of the animal and not, as was customary, those of the shell. His study on the auditory organ in man, the reptiles, and the fishes (1778) is an important work in comparative anatomy.

Geoffroy was a modest and unselfish scientist who did not seek honors; he declined Astruc's proposal that he succeed the latter in the chair of medicine at the Collège de France. He was elected an associate member of the Academy of Sciences on 24 April 1798.

Geoffroy was also the author of a Latin poem on hygiene (1771) and of a *Manuel de médecine pratique* (1800), which he wrote on his farm in the village of Chartreuve, near Soissons, where he had retired. He was also the mayor of this small town.

Geoffroy had several sons, of whom the best-known was René Claude Geoffroy, a physician and naturalist who traveled to Senegal and to Santo Domingo and became a member of the Academy of Medicine.

BIBLIOGRAPHY

I. Original Works. Geoffroy's principal writings are *Histoire abrégée des insectes qui se trouvent aux environs de Paris . . .*, 2 vols. (Paris, 1762); *Traité sommaire des coquilles tant fluviatiles que terrestres qui se trouvent aux environs de Paris* (Paris, 1767); *Hygieine, sive ars sanitatem conservandi* (Paris, 1771), also translated into French by P. Delaunay (Paris, 1774); *Dissertation sur l'organe de l'ouïe 1) de l'homme, 2) des reptiles, 3) des poissons* (Amsterdam-Paris, 1778); and *Manuel de médecine à l'usage des chirurgiens et des personnes charitables . . .* (Paris, 1800).

There are three letters from Geoffroy to Antoine-Laurent de Jussieu (1797–1798) in the archives of the Académie des Sciences, Paris.

II. Secondary Literature. See the unsigned "Notice sur M. Et. L. Geoffroy, docteur régent et professeur de l'ancienne Faculté de médecine de Paris . . .," in *Bibliothèque médicale* (1810); P. Delaunay, *Le monde médical parisien au dix-huitième siècle* (Paris, 1906), pp. 425–430; and E. Lamy, "Deux conchyliologistes français du XVIIIe siècle; les Geoffroy oncle et neveu," in *Journal de conchyliologie,* **73** (1929), 129–132.

Jean Théodoridès

GEOFFROY SAINT-HILAIRE, ÉTIENNE (*b.* Etampes, France, 15 April 1772; *d.* Paris, France, 19 June 1844), *zoology.*

Geoffroy's father, a procurator at the tribunal of Etampes, a small town near Paris, had little money and fourteen children. Étienne, the youngest, received as a child the surname Saint-Hilaire, which he later joined to his family name. His extraordinary career (professor at the Muséum at twenty-one) was furthered by priests who were captivated by his lively intelligence, his unusual imagination, and a sort of inner fire that added to his physical charm. Thanks to the cultivated *grand seigneur* the Abbé de Tressan, he became a canon at the age of fifteen with prospects for a splendid career in the church. He was introduced to natural history by the agronomist Abbé A. H. Tessier in Etampes and later by the ornithologist Brisson and Antoine de Jussieu at the Collège de Navarre in Paris, where Geoffroy was on a scholarship. With the outbreak of the Revolution, ecclesiastical careers were jeopardized; obeying his father's orders, he studied law, and then, pursuing his own desires, he began medical studies. In 1792 he was a *pensionnaire libre* at the Collège du Cardinal Lemoine in Paris. There he won the affection of that institution's most illustrious member, Abbé René Just Haüy, one of the founders of crystallography. In Haüy's simply furnished room he met all the famous scientists of the period. Consumed with enthusiasm for mineralogy, he became a student of the venerable Daubenton at the Collège de France.

While retaining a deep attachment to the priests who had supported his career, Geoffroy embraced revolutionary ideas. He frequented the clubs and committees and adopted a philosophical deism and a generous humanitarianism that he preserved for the rest of his life. At the beginning of the Terror (August 1792), Haüy was imprisoned because he was a priest; by actions as courageous as they were romantic, Geoffroy attempted to free him. Finally Haüy was liberated; in recognition of Geoffroy's efforts, Daubenton—a great friend of Haüy—had him named demonstrator in zoology at the Jardin des Plantes, replacing the count de Lacépède, who had been forced to flee (March 1793). In June 1793 the Jardin des Plantes became the Muséum d'Histoire Naturelle; and it was then, owing to his patrons, that Geoffroy, barely twenty-one years old, was named, in the absence of Lacépède, professor of quadrupeds, cetaceans, birds, reptiles, and fish. He became an intimate friend of Lamarck—his elder by almost thirty years—a botanist promoted to the study of insects, worms, and crustaceans. Each of them eagerly explored his new field.

At this period the Abbé Tessier, Geoffroy's former patron, recommended to him a poor young man living in Normandy who was making excellent drawings of careful dissections of fish and invertebrates; he was Georges Cuvier. Geoffroy was extremely friendly to him upon his arrival in Paris, and for one year (1795) they lived and worked together. In a note on tarsiers they stated that these animals constitute a link between the ape and the bat in the great chain of being. Then, following Buffon, they envisioned the possibility of deriving all species from a single type. Cuvier later renounced these audacious ideas, especially after the return to religious beliefs marked by Napoleon's coronation as emperor by the pope (1804). To the contrary, Geoffroy persisted on the "philosophical" road, which was also Lamarck's. In 1796 he began to study, perhaps with the latter, modifications of species due to the environment.

When Bonaparte organized the famous Egyptian campaign, he requested the assistance of numerous scientists. Cuvier avoided leaving, but Geoffroy accepted enthusiastically, and from 1798 to 1801, in the midst of adventures in which he often risked his life, he made many scientific observations. He proceeded up the Nile as far as Aswan. The English allies of the Egyptians were victorious but Geoffroy succeeded in rescuing from the English his important natural history collections. Cuvier, in his absence, had become in everyone's eyes France's leading naturalist.

Returning to Paris, Geoffroy devoted himself from 1802 to 1806 to descriptive zoology and classification, despite his predilection for great theoretical views. He pursued the research on the marsupials that he had begun in 1796. He also composed a large catalog of the mammal collections of the Muséum, the printing of which he stopped suddenly at page 272 in 1803, perhaps as a result of differences with Cuvier; the work remained unfinished. In 1807 he entered the Académie des Sciences, where Cuvier had dominated in natural history since 1796.

The study and publication of the rich material that he had gathered in Egypt proceeded very slowly in the sumptuous work *Description de l'Égypte par la Commission des sciences* (1808–1824). In the Egyptian tombs Geoffroy had found mummified animals more than three thousand years old. They were identical to existing species, and Cuvier saw in this fact the proof of the fixity of species. For Lamarck, on the other hand, this fixity was not demonstrable. In relation to geological ages, which Lamarck calculated in hundreds of millions of years in his *Hydrogéologie* (1802), three thousand years are but a moment; much too short a period for the evolution of creatures to be perceptible. Although Geoffroy does not seem to have accepted Lamarck's views on the duration of geological epochs, he continued to believe in the nonfixity of species. In the following years it was by comparative anatomy, teratology, and then paleontology that he strove to prove that species are transformed in the course of time, the simpler ones engendering the more complex.

Since Aristotle, the unity of plan (that is, the unity of anatomical structure) of vertebrates as a whole had been recognized. Buffon had proclaimed it as early as 1753. Today it seems quite obvious, but it was contested in Geoffroy's time, particularly by Cuvier. For the latter, the fish's fin bore no relation to the mammal's paw, each having been created separately by God. Fifteen years of work, beginning in 1806, enabled Geoffroy to establish two fundamental principles of comparative anatomy: (1) the principle of anatomical connections, which allows one to trace an organ from species to species despite its transformations; and (2) the principle of balance (that is, of the equilibration of the organs), which manifests itself in a reduction in the size of organs when a neighboring organ hypertrophies. The unity of the vertebrate plan that Geoffroy proposed implies a sort of kinship among the vertebrates, the more complex having issued from the simpler—in other words, the mammals having descended from the fish. In order to demonstrate this relationship, Geoffroy turned to comparative embryology.

Haüy greatly admired Daubenton's nephew, the anatomist Félix Vicq d'Azyr, with whose audacious ideas Geoffroy was undoubtedly acquainted. Vicq d'Azyr had observed in the human embryo the transitory appearance of the intermaxillary bone, which persists in the adult ape and is thus an indication of a kinship between man and ape. Furthermore, Cuvier had certainly presented to Geoffroy the ideas of his former professor and friend Karl Kielmeyer of the University of Stuttgart. Kielmeyer had shown that vertebrates, in the course of their embryonic life, go through phases recalling their supposed ancestors; hence, the human embryo possesses the preliminary forms of branchial fissures typical of the fish. Geoffroy, in turn, following J. H. F. Autenrieth, a disciple of Kielmeyer, demonstrated that the disposition of the centers of ossification of the fetal cranium conforms to the general plan of the vertebrate series, of which the prototype is found among the fish. Antoine Serres, a friend and disciple of Geoffroy, later developed this notion of the recapitulation by the embryo of certain characteristics of the supposed ancestors.

In the scientific language of the early nineteenth century, the word *evolution* designated the sum of the transformations undergone by an embryo. Girou de Buzareingnes, taking up Kielmeyer's and Serres's hypothesis of embryonic recapitulation, declared in 1828 that the embryological evolution of an individual follows the path of "the evolution of the animal kingdom itself." In 1831 Geoffroy adopted this new meaning of *evolution,* which implies a transformation of the species in the course of geologic time. The term was then promulgated by an admirer of Geoffroy, Frédéric Gérard, in the *Dictionnaire universel d'histoire naturelle* (see "Espèce," V [1844]; and "Géographie zoologique," VI [1845]), which was distributed throughout the world.

Geoffroy was confronted with the great problem of how the transition from the plan of the invertebrates to that of the vertebrates was accomplished. Carried away by his imagination, he supposed that the carapace of insects corresponds to the vertebra. This hypothesis, which contained only a small element of truth (the vertebrates and the insects are formed by more or less condensed metameres), rendered Geoffroy slightly ridiculous. In 1829 two young researchers, Laurencet and P. S. Meyranx, proposed an ingenious interpretation to account for a transition from cephalopods to fish. Geoffroy used it as an opportunity to attack Cuvier at the Academy. Thus there began the famous controversy of 1830 that so excited Goethe. (A full account of the controversy is in the article on Cuvier.)

It appears that Geoffroy, following the path of the botanists of the preceding century, saw in the study of monsters a means of explaining certain sudden transformations of species. From 1802 to 1840 he devoted more than fifty reports to descriptive teratology. Moreover, his *Essai de classification des monstres* (1821) marks the debut of scientific teratology. Between 1832 and 1837 his son, Isidore, regrouped and completed his father's publications, under the latter's direction, to form the first scientific treatise on teratology. Geoffroy went even further. According to Cuvier, it would seem that Geoffroy sought, by intervening in the development of the chicken embryo, to maintain the fish stage or to obtain the transition to the mammalian stage. He failed, but his attempts make him the founder of experimental embryology (1825–1826).

In 1824 a new way appeared for Geoffroy to demonstrate the transition from reptiles to mammals. In that year Cuvier introduced into the second edition of his *Recherches sur les ossements fossiles* a study, done a little too hastily, of the remains of a "crocodile" discovered near the city of Caen. Geoffroy, who had studied the living Egyptian crocodile extensively, announced that the Caen animal was in reality very different from the crocodile; he named it *Teleosaurus.* It presented, he stated, characteristics intermediate between those of saurians and mammals (1825). Although modern studies have somewhat modified Geoffroy's interpretation, it does nevertheless mark the starting point of evolutionary paleontology. Thereafter Geoffroy was obsessed by paleontological problems. In 1833 he studied the fossil mammals of the Perrier bed (old Pleistocene) in the Massif Central. He established that all the species of Perrier have disappeared from nature and that certain of them constitute "intermediate links" in the great "progressive" series of living beings. He also studied the fossil remains of the Oligocene deposit of St.-Gérand-le-Puy, near Vichy. The few lines that he wrote on each species demonstrate his profound knowledge of vertebrate osteology, and present-day science confirms the majority of his interpretations concerning St.-Gérand.

True to the hypotheses that had guided his researches in experimental embryology, he attributed the variations between species to physicochemical changes in the environment in the course of geologic ages, changes that, he presumed, had influenced not the adults, as Lamarck thought, but the embryos. It is regrettable that in paleontology Geoffroy never followed up his projects with detailed and illustrated memoirs in support of his theories, which after his death were challenged by the hypothesis of multiple creations put forward by Alcide Dessalines d'Orbigny. Multiple creation conflicted little with the Bible and contributed greatly to the progress of geology by justifying the creation of periods defined by their respective faunas. It was not until the beginning of 1859, seven months before the publication of Darwin's *Origin of Species,* that the young Albert Gaudry was able to demonstrate, through the study of the fossil mammals of Greece, that Geoffroy's "intermediate" species and "missing links" were tangible realities.

Starting around 1834, Geoffroy's writings became increasingly theoretical and vague, infused with a kind of grandiose cosmic poetry born of the concept of a unitary universe. Thereafter, the Academy published only the titles of his communications. In July 1840 he became blind as the result of a cataract, and by 1842 his mental powers had begun to fail. The news of his death was received with sorrow by a great many Parisians who had loved his enthusiasm and his liberal ideas.

In France, and perhaps even more in English-speaking countries, Geoffroy's work is often ranked below that of Cuvier, his implacable adversary. Geoffroy's awkward style and sometimes bizarre ideas harmed him considerably; yet Cuvier himself recognized that Geoffroy possessed a great talent for description and classification. Moreover, Geoffroy revitalized comparative anatomy in France and created scientific teratology, experimental embryology, and the concept of paleontological evolution. When Cuvier died in 1832, Geoffroy was only sixty years old; he could have tried for one last time to make his ideas prevail among younger naturalists. But already the fire of his genius was dimming. He and his friend Lamarck lived too early to be completely understood. Indeed, Geoffroy used to say that innovators, like Christ, wear a crown of thorns.

Nevertheless, in judging Geoffroy only on the basis of his publications, one risks underestimating his influence. His contemporaries assure us that he was bolder and clearer in his speech than in his writings. Much loved by his students, he put forth his ideas for forty-seven years in his courses at the Muséum and for thirty-two years in those at the Sorbonne. His home was frequented by the leading liberal thinkers of Paris. Balzac, who long esteemed Cuvier, ultimately concluded that Geoffroy was superior. Michelet admired Geoffroy and Lamarck equally: each had taught that the natural sciences and the human sciences ought to be closely joined, since man, by his origins, remains tied to the animal world.

Like Haüy and Lamarck, Geoffroy pursued the great, if somewhat mystical, idea of the fundamental unity of the universe, life, and human thought.

BIBLIOGRAPHY

I. Original Works. T. Cahn (see below) gives a bibliography of 259 titles. Isidore Geoffroy Saint-Hilaire (see below) classified 321 titles by subject matter and provided references to analyses and criticisms provoked by the works listed. Additional information may be found in the *Catalogue of Scientific Papers* of the Royal Society, which lists 247 titles.

Geoffroy's personal papers and MSS remained in the possession of his family until about 1950. Since then they have periodically appeared for sale in lots (on auction at the Hôtel Drouot and by Parisian autograph dealers); the library of the Muséum has been able to purchase a few of them.

Geoffroy's principal works are *Catalogue des mammifères du Muséum* (Paris, 1803), a very rare work, the printing of which was never completed and a copy of which is possessed by the library of the Muséum; "Considérations sur les pièces de la tête osseuse des vertébrés," in *Annales du Muséum d'histoire naturelle,* **10** (1807), 332–365; "Sur les déviations organiques provoquées et . . . les incubations artificielles," in *Mémoires du Muséum d'histoire naturelle,* **13** (1825), 289–296, in *Archives générales de médecine,* **13** (1826), 289, and in *Journal complémentaire des sciences médicales,* **24** (1826), 256; the article "Monstre," in *Dictionnaire classique d'histoire naturelle,* XI (Paris, 1827), 108–152, which bears the inexact signature "G.N."; *Principes de philosophie zoologique discutés en mars 1830 à l'Académie* (Paris, 1830), of which there is an analysis by Goethe (see below); and *Recherches sur les grands sauriens trouvés à l'état fossile* (Paris, 1831), repr. in *Mémoires de l'Académie des sciences,* **12** (1833), 1–138.

II. Secondary Literature. On his life and work, see I. E. Amlinsky, *Zhoffrua Sent-Iler i ego borba protiv Kyuvier* ("Geoffroy Saint-Hilaire and His Struggle Against Cuvier"; Moscow, 1955); F. Bourdier, "Geoffroy Saint-Hilaire Versus Cuvier: The Campaign for Paleontological Evolution (1825–1838)," in C. J. Schneer, ed., *Toward a History of Geology* (Cambridge, Mass., 1969), pp. 36–61; T. Cahn, *La vie et l'oeuvre d'Étienne Geoffroy Saint-Hilaire* (Paris, 1962); Isidore Geoffroy Saint-Hilaire, *Vie, travaux et doctrine scientifique d'Étienne Geoffroy Saint-Hilaire* (Paris, 1847); J. W. von Goethe, in *Jahrbuch für wissenschaftlichen Kritik,* nos. 52–53 (1830), and nos. 51–53 (1832); and Jean Rostand, "É. Geoffroy Saint-Hilaire et la tératogenèse expérimentale," in *Revue d'histoire des sciences et de leurs applications,* **17** (1964), 41–50.

Regarding Geoffroy's influence on historians and reformers, see R. van der Elst, *Michelet naturaliste* (Paris, 1914), and the works of Geoffroy's contemporaries, such as P. H. Buchez, Pierre Leroux, and Jean Raynaud.

Franck Bourdier

GEOFFROY SAINT-HILAIRE, ISIDORE (*b.* Paris, France, 16 December 1805; *d.* Paris, 10 November 1861), *zoology.*

The only son of Étienne Geoffroy Saint-Hilaire, Isidore wanted to become a mathematician; but his father saw in him the continuator of his work and engaged him in his laboratory as an *aide-naturaliste* in 1824, when he was only nineteen. In 1830 Isidore gave a course of lectures at the Athénée which attracted considerable attention. It dealt with a new subject: the interrelations of animal species and their relations with the environment. While undertaking extensive research on mammals and birds, he published in 1832 the first of three large volumes on monsters.

In 1833 Geoffroy Saint-Hilaire entered the Academy of Sciences, at the age of twenty-seven. For his candidacy, he published a notice on his works (1824–1833) which reveals their astonishing scope. Teaching, and especially administrative duties, subsequently reduced his scientific activity. He replaced his father as professor of comparative anatomy at the Faculté des Sciences in 1837, became inspector of the Académie de Paris in 1840, and replaced his father, who had become blind, as professor at the Muséum d'Histoire Naturelle in 1841. He assumed the considerable duties of inspector general of education in 1844 but gave them up in 1850, when he was named professor of zoology at the Sorbonne. His brilliant career was darkened by the death of his wife in 1855 and of the last of his sisters in 1860. The attacks of an undetermined illness grew increasingly severe, and he died in 1861, cared for by his aged mother, in the same room at the museum in which he had been born. He was only fifty-five.

Unlike his father, who possessed a vivid and intense imagination, was rash in both thought and action, and was given to making abstruse remarks, Isidore hid his feelings, was cold and reflective, and enjoyed precise reasoning and lucid exposition. He continued his father's work, which he strengthened and made more exact, although he sometimes dissembled its audacious aspects in the face of the all-powerful opposition of the partisans of Georges Cuvier. Was he a continuator without originality, as his biographers have implied? In truth, his work is too little known for this position to be upheld. His important views on the persistence of infantile characteristics among the primates and on "parallel" evolution appear to be original.

Although the idea of seeking laws governing the formation of monsters was his father's, Isidore Geoffroy Saint-Hilaire nonetheless grouped and brought into accord, judiciously and critically, a great number of scattered facts. In 1832 he coined the word *teratology,* to designate the science of monsters. His work on the description and classification of the mammals, especially of the apes, was original and successful. In 1832, taking up and refining the ideas of Buffon, the full significance of which had perhaps not been grasped, he showed that, in proportion to the entire body, the brain of young apes is larger than in adult apes and that young apes also possess relatively greater intelligence and adaptability. Geoffroy Saint-Hilaire believed that through the persistence of infantile characteristics certain apes possess a large brain and great possibility for adaptation throughout their lives. Long before L. Bolk enunciated his theory of neoteny (1921), Geoffroy Saint-Hilaire suggested that the adult human's large brain and potential for adaptation might likewise represent the persistence of an infantile form. In the same year, refining the notion of a genealogical tree of species, originated by Lamarck, he attempted to establish what he termed a "parallel" classification of beings, in which both the evolution of the phyla and their adaptive convergences are allowed for.

Primarily a theorist, Geoffroy Saint-Hilaire nevertheless took an interest in practical problems. For example, his duties as director of the menagerie of the Muséum d'Histoire Naturelle led him to experiments on hybridization among mammals and among birds. In 1856 he conducted an active campaign, with hippophagic banquets, to encourage the consumption of horsemeat, neglected until then because of traditional prejudice. Above all, however, he sought to develop the acclimatization of useful animals (1849) and founded two organizations which are still active: the Société d'Acclimatation and the Jardin d'Acclimatation in the Bois de Boulogne, Paris.

In almost all of his works Geoffroy Saint-Hilaire gave considerable space to the history of science. The large volume that he devoted to the life and work of his father remains a model of biography, although discretion sometimes made him tone down his father's conceptions concerning evolution. In 1859 he published *Résumé des vues sur l'espèce organique,* in which he quietly reminded Darwin of his predecessors in France: Buffon, Lamarck, and Étienne Geoffroy Saint-Hilaire.

BIBLIOGRAPHY

I. Original Works. A list of Geoffroy Saint-Hilaire's works was published in 1862, but it is both incomplete and inaccurate. It is preferable to refer to the printed catalog of the Bibliothèque Nationale, vol. LVI, cols. 130–136, for the individual publications and to Royal Society, *Catalogue of Scientific Papers,* II, 832–837, for the articles in scientific periodicals (125 titles). A large portion of his work is, however, to be found in dictionaries and nonscientific periodicals. The *Dictionnaire classique d'histoire naturelle,* 16 vols. (Paris, 1822–1830), contains a number of his articles on mammals beginning with vol. VII; see also X, 63–73, 199–206, 372–375; XI, 102–107; XII, 512–520; XV, 129–151; XVI, 141–149. A list of his many articles published in the *Gazette médicale,* the *Revue encyclopédique,* the *Encyclopédie moderne,* and the *Revue des deux-mondes,* among others, has never been compiled.

His chief works are *Histoire générale . . . des anomalies . . . ou Traité de tératologie,* 4 vols. (Paris, 1823–1837); *Description des mammifères . . . famille des singes* (Paris, 1839); *Essai de zoologie générale* (Paris, 1841); *Vie, travaux . . . d'Étienne Geoffroy Saint-Hilaire* (Paris, 1847); *Domestication et naturalisation* (Paris, 1854); and *Histoire*

GERARD OF BRUSSELS

naturelle générale des règnes organiques, 3 vols. (Paris, 1854–1862), an undertaking of grandiose intentions which was never completed.

II. SECONDARY LITERATURE. See A. de Quatrefages de Bréau, "Éloge historique de M. Geoffroy Saint-Hilaire," in *Bulletin de la Société impériale d'acclimatation,* **9** (1862), 257–278; and "Éloge historique par J. B. Dumas," in *Mémoires de l' Académie des sciences,* 2nd ser., **38** (1873), 178–212, delivered at the Institut de France. Other, more brief, *éloges* are by Edouard Drouyn de Lhuys, Henri Milne-Edwards, Charles Delaunay, Émile Blanchard, and Nicolas Joly. The article in Hoeffer, ed., *Nouvelle biographie générale,* XX (Paris, 1857), 54–55, recounts the main facts of his administrative career, but no extended work has been devoted to him.

FRANCK BOURDIER

GERARD OF BRUSSELS (*fl.* first half of the thirteenth century), *geometry.*

Gerard played a minor but not unimportant role in the development of kinematics and the measure of geometrical figures. His career remains obscure except for his having written a treatise entitled *Liber de motu,* which remains in six manuscripts. Four of these date from the thirteenth century. Written sometime between 1187 and 1260, the *Liber de motu* quotes the translation of Archimedes' *De quadratura circuli* ("On the Measurement of the Circle") by Gerard of Cremona; the translation was completed before the translator died in 1187. On the other hand, the *Liber de motu* is mentioned in the *Biblionomia* of Richard of Fournival, who died in 1260.

Gerard seems to have known the *Liber philotegni de triangulis* of Jordanus de Nemore, whose exact dating is as difficult to determine as that of Gerard but who can be placed, with some confidence, in the early decades of the thirteenth century. The similarity in their names suggests that Gerard may be identified with the unknown mathematician Gernardus who wrote an arithmetical tract *Algorithmus demonstratus.* That Gerard is referred to as *magister* in the title of *Liber de motu* and his apparent knowledge of Jordanus suggest a university milieu for this work—perhaps the University of Paris.

The *Liber de motu* contains thirteen propositions, in three books. In these propositions the varying curvilinear velocities of the points and parts of geometrical figures in rotation are reduced to uniform rectilinear velocities of translation. The four propositions of the first book relate to lines in rotation, the five of the second to areas in rotation, and the four of the third to solids in rotation. Gerard's proofs are particularly noteworthy for their ingenious use of an Archimedean-type *reductio* demonstration, in which the comparison of figures is accomplished by the comparison of their line elements. In this latter technique Gerard assumed that if the ratio of the elements of two figures taken in pairs is the same, then the ratio of the totalities of the elements of the figures is the same. Such a technique resembles the procedure followed in Archimedes' *Method,* which Gerard could not have read. The proposition most influential on later authors was the first: "Any part as large as you wish of a radius describing a circle . . . is moved equally as its middle point. Hence the radius is moved equally as its middle point."[1] This is similar in a formal way to the rule for uniform acceleration, which appears to have originated with William of Heytesbury at Merton College, Oxford, in the 1330's.[2] This rule asserted that a body which is uniformly accelerated traverses the same space in the same time as a body which moves with a uniform velocity equal to the velocity that is the mean between the initial and final velocities of the accelerating body. Gerard's proposition concerns itself with movements that uniformly vary over some part or all of the linear magnitude rotating, while Heytesbury's rule concerns instantaneous velocities that uniformly vary through some period of time. The "middle velocity" is used in both rules to convert the movements to uniformity.

Gerard's influence on Thomas Bradwardine, the founder of the Merton school of kinematics, is evident, for Bradwardine knew and quoted Gerard's tract. Furthermore, Nicole Oresme's *De configurationibus qualitatum,* written in the 1350's, shows some possible dependency on the *De motu.*[3]

NOTES

1. *Liber de motu,* M. Clagett, ed., p. 112.
2. For a discussion of the Merton rule, see M. Clagett, *Science of Mechanics,* ch. 5.
3. M. Clagett, *Nicole Oresme and the Medieval Geometry of Qualities and Motions* (Madison, Wis., 1968), p. 466.

BIBLIOGRAPHY

The *Liber de motu* has been edited by M. Clagett, "The *Liber de motu* of Gerard of Brussels," in *Osiris,* **12** (1956), 73–175. See M. Clagett, *Science of Mechanics in the Middle Ages* (Madison, Wis., 1959; repr. 1961), ch. 3; G. Sarton, *Introduction to the History of Science,* II (Baltimore, 1931), 629; and V. Zubov, "Ob 'Arkhimedovsky traditsii' v srednie veka (Traktat Gerarda Bryusselskogo 'Odvizhenii')" ("The Archimedean Tradition in the Middle Ages [Gerhard of Brussels' Treatise on Motion]"), in *Istoriko-matematicheskie issledovaniya,* **16** (1965), 235–272.

MARSHALL CLAGETT

GERARD OF CREMONA (*b.* Cremona, Italy, 1114 [?]; *d.* Toledo, Spain, 1187), *transmission of knowledge.*

For a detailed study of his life and work, see Supplement.

GERARD OF SILTEO (SILETO) (*fl.* thirteenth century), *astronomy.*

Gerard was a Dominican friar about whom little is known except that he composed a *Summa de astris.* He is cited twice by Dominican chroniclers as from Silteo and once as from Sileto, but neither location is known. J. Quétif and J. Échard list him as belonging to a German province (*Scriptores ordinis,* II, 918), whereas M. Grabmann refers to him as an Italian (*Mittelalterliches Geistesleben,* II, 397). One manuscript of his work is preceded by a letter from the Dominican Gerard of Feltre, who is identified as the author of the work, to another Dominican called John, noted marginally (and in a different hand) as John of Vercelli, master general of the order from 1264 to 1283; perhaps Silteo or Sileto was a hamlet near Feltre, in the Italian Alps east of Trent and north of Padua. An early list gives the date 1291 for Gerard, which is possibly the year of his death.

The *Summa de astris* is divided into three parts, the first of which is concerned with astronomy, the second with astrology, and the third with a critical refutation of astrological excesses. Part 1 comprises twenty-three distinctions and deals with classical topics of medieval astronomy at approximately the level of the *Rudimenta* of al-Farghānī and the *Sphere* of Sacrobosco; the chief source cited is the Arab astrologer Abū Maʿshar. The final distinction, dealing with comets, has been edited and analyzed by Thorndike, who notes that Gerard saw and described the comet of 1264 (probably writing soon after that date) and that he otherwise borrowed extensively from Albertus Magnus. Generally, Gerard's discussion of the comet of 1264 is inferior to that of another Dominican, Giles (Aegidius) of Lessines; there seems to be no connection between the two. Gerard's criticisms of judicial astrology "may have had some influence on the subsequent attacks upon astrology by Nicolas Oresme, Henry of Hesse, and Pico della Mirandola" (Thorndike, p. 187).

BIBLIOGRAPHY

Lynn Thorndike, *Latin Treatises on Comets Between 1238 and 1368 A.D.* (Chicago, 1950), pp. 185–195, apart from the Latin text of the section of *Summa de astris* on comets, lists the distinction headings of the entire work. For biographical details, see Jacques Quétif and Jacques Échard, *Scriptores ordinis praedicatorum,* 2 vols. (Paris, 1719–1721; repr. New York, 1959), I, 725b; and Martin Grabmann, *Mittelalterliches Geistesleben,* 3 vols. (Munich, 1925–1956), II (1936), 397.

WILLIAM A. WALLACE, O.P.

GERARD, JOHN (*b.* at or near Nantwich, Cheshire, England, 1545; *d.* Holborn, London, England, February 1612), *botany, pharmacy, horticulture.*

Gerard belonged to a branch of the family of Gerard of Ince in Lancashire. He received a grammar school education at Willaston (Wistaston), Cheshire, and was apprenticed at the age of sixteen to a London barber-surgeon, Alexander Mason, for the customary seven years. Some time thereafter he traveled, presumably as a ship's surgeon, aboard a merchant ship of the Company of Merchant Adventurers in London trading in the Baltic, for he stated later that he had been in Denmark, Sweden (Swenia), Poland, and Russia (Muscovia). He then settled in London and probably carried on his profession of barber-surgeon while developing his horticultural interests.

By 1577 he had become superintendent of the gardens belonging to William Cecil, Lord Burleigh, at the Strand, London, and at Theobalds, Hertfordshire, a post he held for the next twenty-one years. He possessed a garden of his own at Holborn, London, so well stocked in 1597, according to George Baker, surgeon to Queen Elizabeth, with "all manner of strange trees, herbes, rootes, plants, flowers, and other such rare things, that it would make a man woonder, how one of his degree, not having the purse of another, could ever accomplish the same." He added, "Upon my conscience, I do not thinke for the knowledge of plants, that he is inferior to any." In 1596 Gerard issued a catalog of his plants, the first such in England, followed by a second edition in 1599. This period was one of horticultural expansion in England, many new plants being introduced from abroad through the powerful influence of Cecil and others. Gerard undoubtedly acquired a detailed first-hand knowledge of them, which is reflected in his *Herball.* His standing as a barber-surgeon, which necessitated a knowledge of medicinal plants, and as a practical gardener led to his appointment from 1586 to 1603 or 1604 as curator of a physic garden belonging to the College of Physicians of London. In 1597 he was elected junior warden of the Barber-Surgeon's Company and in 1608 master.

The Herball or Generall Historie of Plantes, first published in 1597, is the best-known and most often quoted herbal in the English language. Its lasting repute is due not so much to its originality and accuracy, which are ofttimes questionable, as to its entertaining Elizabethan descriptive style, its interspersed anecdotes and comments, its antique remedies, and its woodcuts.

It occupies 1,392 pages, plus introductory matter and index, and has nearly 2,200 woodcut illustrations, most of which had already been used by Tabernaemontanus (Bergzabern), whose woodblocks had been obtained from Frankfurt am Main. The work is divided into three books. The first (pp. 1–176) deals with monocotyledons, described as "Grasses, Rushes, Corne, Flags, Bulbose, or Onion-rooted plants"; the second (pp. 177–1076), with "all sorts of herbes for meate, medicine, or sweete smelling use"; and the third (pp. 1077–1392), with "trees, shrubs, bushes, fruit-bearing plants, Rosins, Gums, Roses, Heath, Mosses, Mushroms, Corall, and their severall kindes." These books are divided into numerous short chapters, each dealing with a small group of plants and setting forth "the kindes, description, place, time, names, nature, and vertues, agreeing with the best received opinions."

At the beginning Gerard genially states his intent: "Now with our friendly labors we will accompagnie thee, and lead thee through a grasse plot [i.e., an account of the *Gramineae*], little or nothing of many Herbarists heertofore touched. . . . Then little by little conduct thee through most pleasant gardens, and other delightfull places where any herbe or plant may be found, fit for meate or medicine." Such a vast work was necessarily compiled from other works, and much of it came from Dodoens' *Stirpium historiae pemptades sex* (1583). About 1584 a young London physician and Cambridge graduate, Robert Priest, was requested by the London printers and booksellers Bonham and John Norton (who later published Gerard's *Herball*) to translate Dodoens' Latin work into English, and they retained his services until 1590, but this translation had evidently not been completed when he died in 1596 or 1597.

The fate of Priest's manuscript is not known. Gerard in his preface "to the courteous and well-willing Readers" stated that "Doctor *Priest,* one of our London Colledge, hath (as I heard) translated the last edition of *Dodonaeus,* which meant to publish the same, but being prevented by death, his translation likewise perished." Stephen Bredwell, however, in his preface to the first edition of Gerard's *Herball* implied that it then still existed. Johnson in 1633 declared, presumably on the authority of Mathias de L'Obel, that "this translation became the ground-worke whereupon Mr *Gerard* built up this work," thus directly accusing Gerard of dishonestly concealing his major source. The whole truth of this matter can never be known. It would seem probable, as indicated by Jeffers, that Gerard, with the help of L'Obel, was engaged in compiling a book about plants before Priest began his translation of Dodoens; that Gerard's book had not reached a state fit for publication when Priest relinquished his task; and that Norton then requested Gerard to produce a work of like character which became the *Herball.*

To what extent Gerard was indebted to Priest's work is quite uncertain. Although this book is probably not so gross an example of successful piracy and plagiarism as it is sometimes considered, Gerard's honesty has certainly been much questioned and little defended since the adverse comments and accusations rendered in the preface to the second edition (1633) by its editor and reviser Thomas Johnson (1604–1644): "His chiefe commendation is, that he, out of a propense good will to the publique advancement of this knowledge, endeavoured to performe therein more than he could well accomplish; which was partly through want of sufficient learning." The care bestowed by Johnson in correcting what Raven calls "the errors of Gerard's book, the misplaced pictures, the confused species, the blunders of fact" and in adding much new material made his edition (often cited as *Ger. emac.,* i.e., *Gerardus emaculatus*) a popular and standard work, which proved of especial value in promoting the study of the British flora well into the eighteenth century. Yet, the *Herball* as published contains so much that undoubtedly came from Gerard himself, and its production, even with the possible aid of Priest's translation, was so massive a task that it seems charitable to credit him with the whole. It remains a valuable source of information about the plants available in western European gardens at the end of the sixteenth century and about the Latin and vernacular names then applied to them.

BIBLIOGRAPHY

I. Original Works. The two eds. of *Catalogus arborum, fruticum ac plantarum tam indigenarum, quam exoticarum in horto Johannis Gerardi* (London, 1596; 2nd ed., 1599) are both reprinted in *A Catalogue of Plants Cultivated in the Garden of John Gerard, in the Years 1596–1599, Edited With Notes, References to Gerard's Herball, the Addition of Modern Names, and a Life of the Author,* B. D. Jackson, ed. (London, 1876). Gerard's major work is *The Herball or Generall Historie of Plantes Gathered by John Gerard, Master in Chirurgie* (London, 1597; repr. 1598); extracts from the "very much enlarged and amended" ed. by Thomas Johnson (London, 1633) are in Marcus Woodward, *Gerard's Herball, the Essence Thereof Distilled* (London, 1927; repr., 1964).

II. Secondary Literature. The best source of biographical information is in Jackson (see above), supplemented by R. H. Jeffers, *The Friends of John Gerard*

(*1545–1612*), *Surgeon and Botanist* (Falls Village, Conn., 1967). There is an excellent chapter on Gerard, particularly in relation to the British flora, in C. E. Raven, *English Naturalists From Neckam to Ray* (Cambridge, 1947), pp. 204–217.

WILLIAM T. STEARN

GERASIMOVICH, BORIS PETROVICH (*b.* Kremenchug, Russia, 19 March 1889; *d.* Moscow, U.S.S.R., October 1937), *astrophysics.*

Gerasimovich's father, a physician, was director of a district hospital. Gerasimovich attended the Poltava Gymnasium but did not graduate, having been expelled for participation in the revolutionary movement. Only in 1909, after passing the examination as an extern, did he receive his "certificate of maturity." In 1910 he studied at the Faculty of Physics and Mathematics of Kharkov University, where his teachers in astronomy were the director of the astronomical observatory, Ludwig Struve, and the astrometrist N. N. Yevdokimov.

Gerasimovich received a prize in 1911 for his student composition "Aberratsia sveta" ("Aberration of Light"). After graduating from the university in 1914, he remained to prepare for an academic career. In 1916 he was a probationer at Pulkovo Observatory, studying astrophysics under A. A. Belopolsky and Sergei Kostinsky. Having passed his master's degree examination, in 1917 Gerasimovich became a *Privatdozent* at Kharkov University. From 1920 to 1933 he was senior astronomer at the observatory, and from 1922 he was also professor of astronomy. At the same time Gerasimovich taught mathematics and mechanics at a number of higher educational institutions in Kharkov. In 1931 he was invited to head the astrophysics section of the Pulkovo Observatory, and in 1933 he was appointed director of the observatory.

In 1924 Gerasimovich made a scientific trip to England and France, and from 1926 to 1929 he was visiting professor at Harvard Observatory, where both independently and in collaboration with Harlow Shapley, Otto Struve, Willem Luyten, and Donald Menzel he conducted a number of scientific investigations. In 1926, 1932, and 1935 Gerasimovich participated in the Copenhagen Congress of the German Astronomical Society, and in Cambridge, Massachusetts, and Paris sessions of the General Assembly of the International Astronomical Union.

Gerasimovich's range of scientific interests was very broad, and there are about 170 publications in his bibliography. Among them are works on photometrical and spectral research on variable stars (about eighty works), planetary nebulas, emission stars, scientific works in the field of theoretical astrophysics, stellar astronomy, the structure of the Galaxy, stellar statistics, celestial mechanics, astrometry, solar physics, and other problems. His research on semiregular variable stars, which he conducted on materials from the rich collection of photographic plates of the Harvard Observatory, has retained its great value.

Gerasimovich was a pioneer in the study of planetary nebulas, which are expanded clouds thrown out at the time of the explosions of certain types of nonstationary stars. He studied the turbulent movement in gas nebulas and investigated the varied forms of the planetary nebulas as figures of equilibrium, which can accept masses of gas under the influence of the forces of gravity of the central star and the forces of light repulsion (light pressure). Gerasimovich also studied the processes of ionization of planetary nebulas, determined the luminosity of their nuclei (the central stars), and came to the important conclusion that the masses of their central stars are small. This hypothesis was confirmed by the later research of others.

Gerasimovich was one of the first to emphasize the important role of computation of interstellar light absorption (which weakens the visible brightness of stars and causes their reddening) in the study of the structure of the Galaxy. In particular he used an original method of studying the apparent change of the mean distance of variable stars of the Cepheid type from the galactic plane as a function of their distance from the sun for an estimate of the value of the interstellar absorption of light.

Gerasimovich was responsible for an important investigation of the dynamics of the stellar system as the site of the simultaneous action of regular and irregular forces. In this work the appearance of the Milky Way and its insufficient brilliance in the direction of the constellation Sagittarius (where the dynamic center of the Galaxy is found) again led him to the belief in the essential role of the interstellar substratum, which forms a substantial condensation in space and at the same time causes a weakening of the brightness of the Milky Way.

With the American astronomer W. Luyten, Gerasimovich determined in 1927 the altitude of the sun over the base plane of the Galaxy as thirty-four parsecs (contemporary determinations give fifteen–twenty).

The study of the sun and the organization of and participation in expeditions to observe total solar eclipses occupied a special place in Gerasimovich's scientific work. In the later years of his life, in addition to his other responsibilities, he was president of the

Commission for the Study of the Sun of the Astronomical Council of the Soviet Academy of Sciences and president of the special commission of the Soviet Academy of Sciences for the preparation of all expeditions to observe the total eclipse of 19 June 1936. This was the first eclipse of the sun for which, on Gerasimovich's initiative, the whole program's photographic observations were organized in a unified way, using six uniform, standard coronagraphs placed along the zone of visibility of the total phase of the eclipse. As a result, very valuable data on the movement of matter in the solar corona were obtained.

Gerasimovich's monograph *Solnechnaya fizika* ("Solar Physics," in Ukrainian, 1933; 2nd ed., in Russian, 1935) is an excellent description of the physics of the sun, summing up the achievements of Soviet and foreign scientists in the field. Another of his monographs, *Vselennaya pri svete teorii otnositelnosti* ("The Universe in Light of the Theory of Relativity," 1925), was of great importance in popularizing the theory of relativity and Einstein's cosmological ideas. An outstanding role in the preparation of Soviet astronomers of the following generations was played by *Kurs astrofiziki i zvezdnoy astronomii* ("Course in Astrophysics and Stellar Astronomy"), which contained, among other works, a number of his original articles and was published under his direction in 1934 and 1936.

Gerasimovich's scientific activity was recognized by awards in the Soviet Union (1924, 1926, 1936), the United States (1928), and France (1934). He was elected a member of the All-Union Astronomical-Geodesical Society, the American and German astronomical societies, the Royal Astronomical Society, the American Association of Observers of Variable Stars, and the International Astronomical Union.

BIBLIOGRAPHY

I. Original Works. Gerasimovich's writings include *Vselennaya pri svete teorii otnositelnosti* ("The Universe in Light of the Theory of Relativity"; Kharkov, 1925); "On the Radiative and Mechanical Equilibrium of Spherical Planetary Nebulae," in *Astronomische Nachrichten,* **225** (1925), 89; "Ionization in Nebular Matter," in *Harvard Reprints. Harvard College Observatory,* **38** (1927); "On the Distance of the Sun From the Galactic Plane," in *Proceedings of the National Academy of Sciences of the United States of America,* **13** (1927), 387-390, written with Willem Luyten; "On the Luminosities of the Nuclei of Planetary Nebulae," in *Publications of the Astronomical Society of the Pacific,* **39** (1927), 19; and "On the Spectroscopic Absolute Magnitude Effect," in *Circular. Astronomical Observatory of Harvard College,* **311** (1927), 1-11.

For the works on semiregular variable stars, see "V Vulpeculae," *ibid.,* **321** (1927), 1-11; "The Photographic Light Curves of R Scuti," *ibid.,* **323** (1928), 1-3; "Secular Changes in the Mean Period of R Scuti (1795-1927)," *ibid.,* **333** (1928), 1-5; "V Ursae Minoris and SW Persei," *ibid.,* **338** (1929), 1-9; "R Sagittae," *ibid.,* **340** (1929), 1-2, written with L. Hufnagel; "A General Study of RV Tauri Variables," *ibid.,* **341** (1929), 1-15; and "On Variables of the Intermediate Group," *ibid.,* **342** (1929), 1-9.

See also "Spectrophotometric Temperature of Early Stars," *ibid.,* **339** (1929), 1-27; "On the Photographic Absolute Magnitudes of the Nuclei of Planetary Nebulae," in *Bulletin. Harvard College Observatory,* **864** (1929), 9-14; "The Nuclei of Planetary Nebulae," in *Observatory,* **54** (1931), 108; "Probability Problems Connected With the Discovery of Variable Stars in a Photographic Way," in *Doklady Akademii nauk SSSR,* **4,** nos. 5-6 (1931), 43-45; "Rayleighsche Streung und anomale Sterntemperaturen," in *Zeitschrift für Astrophysik,* **4** (1932), 265-281; "Nonstatistic Hydrogen Chromospheres and the Problem of B Stars," in *Monthly Notices of the Royal Astronomical Society,* **94** (1933), 737-765; *Kurs astrofiziki i zvezdnoy astronomii* ("Course in Astrophysics and Stellar Astronomy"), II (Moscow-Leningrad, 1936), chs. 3, 6-12; "The Zero Point of the Cepheids' Period-Luminosity Relation," in *Observatory,* **57** (1934), 22-23; "B Spectrum Variables," *ibid.,* **58** (1935), 115-124; *Solnechnaya fizika* ("Solar Physics"; 2nd ed., Kharkov, 1935); "Cosmic Absorption and the Galactic Concentration of Classical Cepheids," in *Tsirkular Glavnoi astronomicheskoi observatorii v Pulkove,* no. 10 (1936), 9-11; "On the Behavior of Absorption Lines in the Spectrum of P Cygni," *ibid.,* no. 17 (1936), 13-15; "The System of Polaris," *ibid.,* no. 19 (1936), 739; "A Unitary Model of the Galactic System," in *Nature,* **137** (1936), 739; and "On the Illumination of a Planet Covered With a Thick Atmosphere," in *Izvestiya Glavnoi astronomicheskoi observatorii v Pulkove,* no. 127 (1937), 1-32.

II. Secondary Literature. On Gerasimovich or his work, see *Astronomia v SSSR za 40 let 1917-1957* ("Astronomy in the U.S.S.R. for Forty Years"; Moscow, 1960), pp. 54, 120, 287, 294, 332; *Razvitie astronomii v SSSR* ("The Development of Astronomy in the U.S.S.R."; Moscow, 1967), pp. 206, 215-217, 219; Y. G. Perel, "B. P. Gerasimovich," in *Astronomichesky kalendar na 1964 g.* ("Astronomical Calendar for 1964"; Moscow, 1936), pp. 256-258; and O. Struve, "About a Russian Astronomer," in *Sky and Telescope,* **16,** no. 8 (1957), 379-381.

P. G. Kulikovsky

GERBERT, also known as **Gerbert d'Aurillac,** later **Pope Sylvester II** (*b.* Aquitaine, France, *ca.* 945; *d.* Rome, 12 May 1003), *mathematics.*

Gerbert received his early education at the Benedictine convent of Saint Géraud in Aurillac. He left it in 967 in the company of Borel, count of Barcelona. In Catalonia he continued his studies under Atto, bishop of Vich; he concentrated on mathematics, probably on the works of such authors as Boethius, Cassiodorus, and Martianus Capella. How much Moorish science Gerbert was able to study as far north as Vich is uncertain. In 970 he accompanied Borel and Atto to Rome, where he attracted the attention of Pope John XIII and, through him, of Otto I, Holy Roman Emperor, who was then residing in Rome.

This was the beginning of Gerbert's career, which was based not only on his intellectual gifts but also on his allegiance to the Saxon imperial house and its political dream—the restoration of the empire of Charlemagne, ruled in harmony by emperor and pope. Gerbert was assigned to Adalbero, the energetic and learned archbishop of Rheims; there he reorganized the cathedral school with such success that pupils began to flock to it from many parts of the empire. Equal attention was paid to Christian authors and to such pagan writers as Cicero and Horace; great pains were taken to enrich the library.

For many years experts have tried, without reaching full agreement, to date the many existing mathematical manuscripts dating from the tenth to the thirteenth centuries and ascribed to Boethius or Gerbert or their pupils. From what most authorities believe are transcripts of Boethius and Gerbert themselves, it seems that in arithmetic some Pythagorean number theory was taught in the spirit of Nicomachus, and in geometry, some statements (without proofs) of Euclid together with the mensuration rules of ancient Roman surveyors; the art of computing was taught with the aid of a special type of abacus. For his lessons in astronomy Gerbert constructed some armillary spheres.

Among Gerbert's pupils were Robert, son of Hugh Capet (later Robert II of France); Adalbold, later bishop of Utrecht; Richer of Saint-Remy, who wrote Gerbert's biography; and probably also a certain Bernelinus, the Paris author of a *Liber abaci* that mentions Gerbert as pope and may well represent his teachings. Gerbert's influence probably extended to other cathedral or monastic schools, especially in Lorraine. This school of training in the quadrivium (music, geometry, arithmetic, astronomy), which is also represented by the *Quadratura circuli* of Franco of Liège (*ca.* 1050), indicates the vivid interest in mathematics that was beginning to appear in western Europe. The only works available, however, were poor remains of Greek knowledge transmitted in the later Roman period. These prepared the way for Arabic science; a work entitled *De astrolabia,* which shows Arabic influence and of which the earliest manuscript is from the eleventh century, has occasionally been ascribed to Gerbert.

In 983 Otto II, a great admirer of Gerbert, appointed him abbot of Bobbio in the Apennines, but by 984 he was back in Rheims. From then on, he took an active part in the political schemes among the Saxons, Carolingians, and Capets; he and Adalbero were deeply involved on the side of the emperor. The Carolingian dynasty came to an end, and in 987 Gerbert assisted in the coronation of Hugh Capet as king of France. In 991 he became archbishop of Rheims, but in 997 he left his see amid controversy and intrigue. He followed the court of young Otto III through Germany to Italy. At Magdeburg between 994 and 995 he constructed an *oralogium,* either a sundial or an astrolabe, for which he took the altitude of the pole star. In 998 Gerbert became archbishop of Ravenna; and in 999, through Otto's influence, he was the first Frenchman to be elected pope. A lover of arts and sciences, Otto hoped that emperor and pope would revive the Carolingian Renaissance. Significantly, Gerbert assumed the name Sylvester II, Sylvester I having been pope at the time of Constantine and, thus, a participant in the first holy alliance of pope and emperor.

The great scheme, however, came to naught with the death of Otto in 1002 and of Gerbert the following year. Legendary ascriptions to Gerbert of supernatural and demonic powers (which even found their way into Victor Hugo's *Welf, castellan d'Osbor*) testify to the impression that his learning made on posterity.

Information about Gerbert's life is in the "Historiae" written from 996 to 998 by his pupil Richer, in 224 published letters, and in contemporary chronicles. Many theological and scientific writings testify to his work and influence. Among those that seem to be authentic are *Regulae de numerorum abaci rationibus* (also called *Libellus de numerorum divisione*), *De sphaera,* sections of a *Geometria,* a letter to Adalbold on the area of an isosceles triangle, and a *Libellus de rationali et ratione uti* (997 or 998) with considerations on the rational and the use of reason. A text that Olleris entitled *Regula de abaco computi* and ascribed to Gerbert is ascribed to Heriger by Bubnov. The authenticity of the *Geometria* has been the subject of much controversy, often in connection with that of Boethius' work of the same title.

The abacus connected with Gerbert was a board with as many as twenty-seven columns, combined in groups of three. From left to right they were headed by the letters *C* (*centum,* hundred), *D* (*decem,* ten), and *S* or *M* (*singularis* or *monad,* one); other columns (and other letters) were for higher decimal units. Numbers were expressed by counters (apices) which carried symbols equivalent to our 1, 2, ... 9 (which may indicate some Arabic influence), so that 604, for instance, was expressed by an apex with 6 in the *C* column and an apex with 4 in the *S* column. There was no apex for zero. With such an apparatus Gerbert and his school were able to perform addition, subtraction, multiplication, and even division, something considered complicated. This art of computation probably remained confined to ecclesiastical schools, never replacing older forms of reckoning, and went out of fashion with the gradual introduction of Hindu-Arabic numerals. A letter from Adalbold to Gerbert "de ratione inveniendi crassitudinem sperae" mentions the equivalent of $\pi = 22/7$, which was probably considered as exact. For $\sqrt{3}$ Gerbert accepted 26/15 (at another place 12/7), and for $\sqrt{2}$, 17/12.

Low as the level of Gerbert's mathematical knowledge was, it surpassed that of his monastic contemporaries and their pupils. This is shown in eight letters exchanged between two monastic friends of Adalbold, edited by P. Tannery and Abbé Clerval (see *Mémoires scientifiques,* volume 5).

BIBLIOGRAPHY

I. Original Works. Gerbert's extant work can be found in *Oeuvres de Gerbert,* A. Olleris, ed. (Paris-Clermont-Ferrand, 1867); *Lettres de Gerbert,* J. Havet, ed. (Paris, 1889); and *Gerberti Opera mathematica,* N. Bubnov, ed. (Berlin, 1899). An added document is found in H. Omont, "Opuscules mathématiques de Gerbert et de Hériger de Lobbes," in *Notices et extraits des manuscrits de la Bibliothèque nationale et autres bibliothèques,* **39** (1909), 4–15.

II. Secondary Literature. Works on Gerbert include Moritz Cantor, *Vorlesungen über Geschichte der Mathematik,* 3rd ed., I (Leipzig, 1907), 848–878; O. G. Darlington, "Gerbert the Teacher," in *American Historical Review,* **52** (1947), 456–476, with titles of the articles published at the time of Gerbert's millennary commemoration in 1938; J. Leflon, *Gerbert, humanisme et chrétienté au Xe siècle* (Abbaye Saint Wandrille, 1946); F. Picavet, *Gerbert, un pape philosophe* (Paris, 1917); P. Tannery, ed., *Mémoires scientifiques,* V (Toulouse-Paris, 1922), arts. 5, 6, and 10; M. Uhlirz, *Untersuchungen über Inhalt und Datierung der Briefe Gerberts von Aurillac, Papst Sylvester II* (Göttingen, 1957); and J. M. Millás Vallicrosa, *Nueve estudios sobre historia de la ciencia española* (Barcelona, 1960).

Richer's "Historiae" were published in R. Latouche, *Richer, Histoire de France (888–995)* (Paris, 1937), with French trans., and in *Monumenta Germaniae historica, Scriptorum,* III, G. H. Pertz, ed. (Hannover, 1839). See also A. J. E. M. Smeur, "De verhandeling over de cirkelkwadratuur van Franco van Luik van omstreeks 1050," in *Mededelingen van de K. Vlaamsche academie voor wetenschappen, letteren en schoone kunsten van België,* Klasse der wetenschappen, **30,** no. 11 (1960).

D. J. Struik

GERBEZIUS, MARCUS, also known as **Marko Gerbec** (*b.* St. Vid, near Stična, Slovenia, 24 October 1658; *d.* Ljubljana, Slovenia, 9 March 1718), *medicine.*

Gerbezius was born into a family in modest circumstances, and it was only through a government scholarship that he was able to obtain a higher education. He first studied philosophy in Ljubljana, then medicine in Vienna, Padua, and Bologna, where he obtained the doctorate in philosophy and medicine in 1684. Gerbezius is one of the forty former students of the University of Padua whose portraits hang in the historic Sala dei Quaranta.

After returning to his native country Gerzebius was named chief physician of the province of Carniola and became the most sought-after practitioner in Ljubljana. Barely four years following receipt of his doctorate he was admitted to the Academia Leopoldina Naturae Curiosorum, to which he sent, from 1689 until his death, a great many medical, meteorological, and zoological observations. Gerbezius was also a founding member of the Academia Operosorum in Ljubljana (1701). In 1712–1713 he was president of this small learned society, which played quite a large role in the cultural development of Slovenia.

Although attracted to Bologna by the teaching of Marcello Malpighi, Gerbezius was not converted to the iatromechanist doctrine; nor was he fully aware of the proper importance of the orientation toward anatomy of contemporary Italian medicine. His own views are a mixture of Dutch and German iatrochemical ideas with English neo-Hippocratic ideas. Gerbezius stressed the importance of a minute clinical examination devoid of preconceptions. He published the first detailed observation of an auriculoventricular block (1692). It occurred in a ninety-year-old woman suffering from spells of dizziness and fainting. Gerbezius described the particulars of her pulse so well that it is possible to make a retrospective diagnosis of the Adams-Stokes syndrome. In 1717 Gerbezius observed two patients afflicted with the same illness—one with a complete and permanent block, the other with an intermittent block. George Cheyne described this syndrome in 1733, as did G. B. Morgagni in 1761. It must be emphasized that Morgagni cited Gerbezius' publications with praise and recognized their priority.

Gerbezius also observed hypertrophy of the myocardium, exanthematous typhus, malaria, removal of the spleen, mercury poisoning among miners, the harmful effect of wine on children, and the treatment of biliary disorders with mineral waters. In a series of publications he set forth, year by year, the relationships between meteorological and terrestrial factors, on the one hand, and clinical and epidemiological aspects of diseases current in Ljubljana, on the other. He confirmed the majority of Thomas Sydenham's conclusions and, emphasizing the importance of social factors, gave them even a broader meaning.

Gerbezius also carried out experimental investigations on the physical and chemical properties of the air and on fermentation. In his view, alcoholic and acetic fermentation were chemical processes induced by certain minuscule particles, "volatile bodies," which escape from organic matter and are found suspended in the atmosphere.

BIBLIOGRAPHY

I. Original Works. Gerbezius' principal works are *Intricatum extricatum medicum, seu tractatus de morbis complicatis* (Ljubljana, 1692; 2nd ed., Frankfurt am Main, 1713); *Chronologia medica:* I (Ljubljana, 1699); II (Ljubljana, 1700); III (Ljubljana, 1702); IV (Augsburg, 1705); V (Frankfurt, 1710); 2nd ed., I–V (Frankfurt, 1713)—the following years were published in *Appendix ephemeridorum naturae curiosorum* (1712–1718); and *Vindiciae physico-medicae aurae Labacensis oder gründliche Verthädigung der laybacherischen Lufft* (Ljubljana, 1710). In addition Gerbezius published seventy-nine articles in *Miscellanea Academiae naturae curiosorum;* a list of these articles can be found in J. J. Manget, *Bibliotheca scriptorum medicorum veterum et recentiorum* (Geneva, 1731). The first description of the auriculoventricular block is in "Pulsus mira inconstantia," in *Miscellanea Academiae naturae curiosorum,* dec. 2, yr. 10 (1692), observatio 63, pp. 115–118. An English trans. of the cardiological fragments is in R. H. Major, *Classic Descriptions of Disease,* 3rd ed. (Springfield, Mass., 1945), pp. 326–327.

II. Secondary Literature. A detailed study of Gerbezius' life and work is still lacking. All the previous publications on this subject are summarized in I. Pintar, "Dr. Marko Gerbec," in *Razprave. Slovenska akademija znanosti in umetnosti,* classis IV, pars medica, **3** (1963), 1–40. See also H. Tartalja, "Der slowenische Arzt Dr. Marko Gerbec als Vorgänger der Fermentationslehre," in *Vorträge der Hauptversammlung der Internationalen Gesellschaft für Geschichte der Pharmazie* (*Rotterdam, 1963*) (Stuttgart, 1965), pp. 173–180; and N. Flaxman, "The History of Heart-Block," in *Bulletin of the Institute of the History of Medicine,* **5** (1937), 115–130.

M. D. Grmek

GERGONNE, JOSEPH DIAZ (*b.* Nancy, France, 19 June 1771; *d.* Montpellier, France, 4 May 1859), *geometry.*

Gergonne's father, a painter and architect, died when Joseph was twelve years old. Joseph studied at the religious *collège* of Nancy, did some private tutoring, and in 1791 became a captain in the National Guard. In 1792 he joined the volunteers to fight the Prussians. He saw action at Valmy, and later that year went to Paris as secretary to his uncle. After a year he was in the army again, this time as secretary to the general staff of the Moselle army. In 1794, after a month at the Châlons artillery school, Gergonne received a commission as lieutenant. Sent to the army in the east Pyrenees, he participated in the siege of Figueras in Catalonia. After the Treaty of Basel in 1795, Gergonne was sent with his regiment to Nîmes, where he obtained the chair of transcendental mathematics at the newly organized École Centrale. He then married, settled down, and began his mathematical career under the influence of Gaspard Monge, the guiding spirit of the École Polytechnique in Paris.

Not finding a regular outlet for mathematical papers in the existing journals, such as the *Mémoires* of the Academy of Sciences or the *Journal de l'École polytechnique,* Gergonne began to publish (1810) the *Annales de mathématiques pures et appliquées,* the first purely mathematical journal. It appeared regularly every month until 1832 and was known as the *Annales de Gergonne.* His colleague J. E. Thomas-Lavernède was coeditor of the first two volumes. Gergonne continued editing the journal after he had accepted, in 1816, the chair of astronomy at the University of Montpellier. In 1830 he became rector at Montpellier and discontinued publishing his *Annales* after twenty-one volumes and a section of the twenty-second had appeared. In these volumes alone he had published more than 200 papers and questions, dealing mainly with geometry but also with analysis, statics, astronomy, and optics.

By 1831 the *Annales* had ceased to be the only wholly mathematical journal. In 1825 there appeared at Brussels A. Quetelet's *Correspondance mathématique et physique* (1825–1839), and in 1826 at Berlin A. L. Crelle's *Journal für die reine und angewandte Mathematik.* In 1836 J. Liouville continued Gergonne's work in France through his *Journal de mathématiques pures et appliquées.* The latter two journals are still being published.

Although Gergonne had given up his journal, he continued to teach after 1830. It is said that during the July Revolution of that year, when rebellious students began to whistle in his class, he regained their sympathy by beginning to lecture on the acoustics of the whistle. He retired in 1844, and during the last years of his life suffered from the infirmities of advanced age.

Gergonne's *Annales* played an essential role in the creation of modern projective and algebraic geometry. It offered space for many contributors on these and other subjects. The journal contains papers by J. V. Poncelet, F. Servois, E. Bobillier, J. Steiner, J. Plücker,

M. Chasles, C. J. Brianchon, C. Dupin, and G. Lamé; in volume **19** (1828–1829) there is an article by E. Galois. The geometry papers stressed polarity and duality, first mainly in connection with conics, then also with structures of higher order. Here the terms "pole," "polar," "reciprocal polars," "duality," and "class" (of a curve) were first introduced. After Poncelet, in his monumental *Traité des propriétés projectives des figures* (1822), had given the first presentation of this new geometry in book form, a priority struggle developed between Gergonne and Poncelet. The result was that Poncelet switched to other journals, including Crelle's.

The discovery of the principle of duality in geometry can be said to have started with C. J. Brianchon, a pupil of Monge, who in 1806 derived by polar reciprocity, from Pascal's theorem, the theorem now named for him. This method of derivation was used by several contributors to the *Annales,* together with the polarity method typical of spherical trigonometry. In his *Traité*, Poncelet stressed polar reciprocity. Then, in three articles in the *Annales* (**15–17** [1824–1827]), Gergonne generalized this method into the general principle that every theorem in the plane, connecting points and lines, corresponds to another theorem in which points and lines are interchanged, provided no metrical relations are involved (*géométrie de la règle*).

In his "Considérations philosophiques sur les élémens de la science de l'étendue" (*Annales,* **16** [1825–1826], 209–232) Gergonne used the term "duality" for this principle and indicated the dual theorems by the now familiar device of double columns. He applied his principle first to polygons and polyhedrons, then to curves and surfaces; it is here that he made the now accepted distinction between curves of degree m and of class m (instead of "order" for both). These papers led to the controversy between him and Poncelet, which was partly based on the way Gergonne edited the papers for the *Annales.* In the meantime, however, A. F. Moebius had introduced duality for the plane in full generality in *Der barycentrische Calcul* (Leipzig, 1827).

One subject of contention between Gergonne and Poncelet was that Poncelet was the foremost representative of the synthetic (i.e., the purely geometric) method, while Gergonne believed in analytic methods. True, Gergonne said, the methods of analytic geometry were often clumsy, but this was only due to lack of *adresse.* He illustrated this point in "Recherche du cercle qui en touche trois autres sur un plan" (*Annales,* **7** [1816–1817], 289–303), in which he gave an elegant analytic solution of this, the "Apollonian," tangent problem. Then, in his third article on duality (*Annales,* **17** [1826–1827], 214–252), following ideas developed by Gabriel Lamé in a study published in 1818 (*Examen des différentes méthodes employées pour résoudre les problèmes de la géométrie*) of which Lamé already had had an abstract published in the *Annales* (**7** [1816–1817], 229–240), Gergonne showed the power of what we now call the "abbreviated" notation, in which, for instance, the pencil of circles in the plane is represented by $C_1 + \lambda C_2 = 0$. This method was fully developed by J. Plücker in his *Analytisch-geometrische Entwicklungen* (1828–1831).

In 1834 Plücker solved a problem which to both Gergonne and Poncelet had seemed something of a paradox. Poncelet (*Annales,* **8** [1817–1818], 215–217) had found that from a point outside a curve of degree m there can be drawn $m(m - 1)$ tangents to the curve. Gergonne missed this fact until (*Annales,* **18** [1827–1828], 151) he corrected himself on several points and introduced for the polar reciprocal of a curve of order m the term "curve of class m," which is therefore of order $m(m - 1)$. But the reciprocal of this curve is the original one, and this seems therefore of order $m(m - 1)\{m(m - 1) - 1\}$, which is greater than m except when $m = 2$. Poncelet had already stated that the answer was to be found in the fact that the polar curve was not fully general. Plücker gave the precise answer by means of his formulas on the number of singularities of a plane curve (*Journal für die reine und angewandte Mathematik,* **12** [1834], 105 ff.).

Among the many other theorems discovered by Gergonne is the following (*Annales,* **16** [1825–1826], 209–232): If two plane curves C_m of degree m intersect in such a way that mp points of intersection are on a C_p, then the $m(m - p)$ other points of intersection are on a C_{m-p}. This leads to a simple proof of Pascal's theorem by considering the six sides of the hexagon inscribed in a conic alternately as two C_3.

Gergonne liked to season his papers with "philosophic" remarks. In one such remark he said, "It is not possible to feel satisfied at having said the last word about some theory as long as it cannot be explained in a few words to any passerby encountered in the street" (M. Chasles, *Aperçu historique* . . . [Paris, 1889], p. 115).

BIBLIOGRAPHY

I. Original Works. Almost all of Gergonne's papers are in the *Annales,* and a bibliography is in Lafon (see below). The more important ones are mentioned in the text. Those on differential geometry include "Demonstration des principaux théorèmes de M. Dupin sur la courbure des surfaces," in *Annales,* **4** (1813–1814), 368–378; and "Théorie élémentaire de la courbure des lignes et des surfaces courbes," *ibid.*, **9** (1818–1819), 127–196. On statics, see "Démonstrations des deux théorèmes de géométrie," *ibid.*, **11** (1820–1821), 326–336. He returned to one of his old loves in an address at Lille: "Notes sur le principe de dualité en géométrie," in *Mémoires de l'Académie des sciences et lettres de Montpellier pour 1847*, Section des Sciences.

II. SECONDARY LITERATURE. A. Lafon, "Gergonne, ses travaux," in *Mémoires de l'Académie de Stanislas*, **1** (1860), xxv–lxxiv, includes a bibliography of Gergonne's works. For further information, see E. Kötter, "Die Entwicklung der synthetischen Geometrie von Monge bis auf Staudt (1847)," in *Jahresbericht der Deutschen Mathematiker-vereinigung*, **5**, no. 2 (1901), with details on the controversy between Poncelet and Gergonne (pp. 160–167). The documents in this case were reprinted by Poncelet in his *Traité des propriétés projectives des figures*, II (Paris, 1866), 351–396.

See also C. B. Boyer, *History of Analytic Geometry* (New York, 1956), ch. 9; and *A History of Mathematics* (New York, 1968), ch. 24; M. Chasles, *Aperçu historique sur l'origine et le développement des méthodes en géométrie* (Paris, 1837; 3rd ed., 1889); and *Rapport sur le progrès de la géométrie* (Paris, 1870), pp. 54–60; and H. de Vries, *Historische Studien*, II (Groningen, 1934), 114–142.

D. J. STRUIK

GERHARDT, CHARLES FRÉDÉRIC (*b.* Strasbourg, France, 21 August 1816; *d.* Paris, France, 19 August 1856), *chemistry.*

Gerhardt's father, Samuel Gerhardt, who came from a family of brewers, was born in Switzerland. As a young man he moved to Strasbourg, where he found employment in a bank and married an outstanding beauty of the town, Charlotte Henriette Weber. Samuel Gerhardt's position in the banking house of Turkheim gave his family the benefits of a prosperous and cultured home. Like many inhabitants of Strasbourg, the Gerhardts spoke and wrote French and German with almost equal facility. As was expected of the sons of the bourgeoisie, young Gerhardt attended the lycée, where he showed unusual ability. In 1825 Gerhardt *père* gave financial backing for the exploitation of a patent for white lead. The partner who was to supply the technical knowledge withdrew, and Gerhardt was left to run a factory, the scientific aspect of which was quite outside his competence. It was this situation which convinced Gerhardt to provide an education for his son Charles which would prepare him for the management of the factory. In 1831 young Gerhardt accordingly entered the newly founded Polytechnicum at Karlsruhe, where he followed intermediate courses in chemistry, physics, and mathematics. In 1833 his father decided to encourage the other aspect of his plan for Charles by sending him to a commercial college in Leipzig. Even there, however, he had lodgings in the house of the chemist Otto Erdmann, who encouraged his scientific interests.

A long paper on the revision of the formulas of natural silicates which Gerhardt wrote in 1834 was accepted for publication by the *Journal für praktische Chemie;* and in 1835, before his nineteenth birthday, his further research had won him the honor of election as corresponding member of the Société d'Histoire Naturelle de Strasbourg. Having seen the attraction of pure science, he came into open conflict with his father, who wanted him to return to the family chemical factory. After a violent quarrel the son left home to join a regiment of lancers. Here, too, he was unhappy and managed to borrow the 2,000 francs necessary to buy himself out. Realizing that his vocation was chemistry, Gerhardt went to Giessen, where Liebig was beginning to build up a reputation, and was enrolled in Liebig's course for 1836–1837.

To earn money for his studies, Gerhardt undertook the translation of one of Liebig's works into French and in so doing helped his own career. In April 1837 he left Liebig to make a final attempt to reconcile himself with his father. Yet he could not settle down to a life of commerce. To make his mark in chemistry he left for Paris. Arriving in October 1838, he enrolled in the course given by Dumas in the Faculty of Sciences. For three years he studied with Dumas and finally became his assistant.

Gerhardt's hard work and brilliant research won him the degrees of licentiate and doctor, both in April 1841 (his thesis was on helenin). Within a few days and on the recommendation of Dumas, Gerhardt was nominated to a vacancy in the Faculty of Sciences in Montpellier. In fact Gerhardt was only *chargé de cours* in 1841 and had to wait three years for nomination to the rank of titular professor. He soon found that the facilities for research were very limited and that it was difficult to settle down so far from Paris and Strasbourg. He went to Paris as often as possible and finally obtained leave of absence to work there. When in 1851 a request for further leave was refused, Gerhardt resigned. He did so the more easily as he was then, with the help of borrowed money, establishing his own private school for practical chemistry. This was not a financial success, but in 1854 he was able to secure a further university appointment. There were two vacancies for chairs of chemistry at Strasbourg, in the Faculty of Sciences and the School of Pharmacy, and both were offered to him. Although reluctant to leave Paris, Gerhardt was glad to return to his native city. Above all, his position in French chemistry was now recognized, and his financial problems were at an end. In 1844 Gerhardt had married a Scottish girl, Jane Sanders, whose brother was studying at the University of Montpellier. Gerhardt thus learned to speak and write English as well as French and German.

In 1844 there began a close friendship with Laurent, professor of chemistry at Bordeaux. They had much in common: zeal for a new approach to organic chemistry with poor facilities available for research, and above all, isolation from the center of power in Paris because of the remoteness of their provincial teaching posts. Wurtz justly commented: "In the history of science the great figure of Gerhardt cannot be separated from that of Laurent: their work was done in collaboration, their talent was complementary, their influence was reciprocal." Most commentators have agreed that Gerhardt had the merit of clarity. Yet he himself remarked how vital an impact was made on him by the profusion of ideas which poured from the pen and the lips of his friend.

Gerhardt was attracted several times in his career to scientific journalism. He was a collaborator in the first issues (1840) of Quesneville's *Revue scientifique et industrielle,* and it is typical of his literary zeal that he should produce a new journal from his association with Laurent. Their *Comptes rendus mensuels des travaux chimiques,* although a help in publicizing their own work, was not well received and lasted only from 1845 to 1851.

In national and academic politics Gerhardt was numbered among the radicals. He became bitterly opposed to Dumas, who had come to typify the scientific establishment. Gerhardt's position was not helped by his readiness to speculate, his lack of tact, and his dogmatism. He was involved in many disputes, even with his protector Liebig. Disputes which began in organic chemistry quickly descended to personalities, and it was characteristic of the organization of French science in the mid-nineteenth century that Gerhardt was not an active member of any important scientific society. On 21 April 1856 he was at last honored by election as a correspondent of the Institute, but within four months he was dead. Gerhardt's tragic death in his fortieth year, following a career of banishment to the provinces, did not prevent him from becoming one of the seminal figures in the history of nineteenth-century chemistry.

Gerhardt was sufficiently impressed by the substitution theories of Laurent and Dumas, which had invaded organic chemistry in the late 1830's, that he was prepared to regard each molecule as a unitary structure or "single edifice" within which substitution of different "residues" could occur. He did this in opposition to the more conservative chemists headed by Berzelius, who supported a dualistic theory, according to which all compounds were interpreted as consisting of an electropositive part and an electronegative part. In the case of many organic compounds this interpretation involved the arbitrary grouping of atoms without supporting evidence.

A major problem confronting chemists in the early 1840's was whether it was possible to ascertain the arrangement of atoms in a compound. Gerhardt reacted violently against the empiricist principle that the arrangement of the atoms could be inferred from a compound's mode of formation or from its reactions. He maintained that we cannot infer arrangements from reactions; all we can ever know are the reactions. So, whereas the view of Berzelius was that each compound had a rational formula and there remained only the practical difficulty of discovering what it was, Gerhardt's view became the exact opposite: We could never know the arrangement of atoms but only the reactions of compounds. Any formula must be based on a particular reaction. If an aldehyde behaves in some reactions like an oxide and in others like a hydride, it must be given two different formulas according to the occasion. Gerhardt took his operational definition of a formula to the logical conclusion and stated that a compound has "as many rational formulas as [it has different] reactions."[1] Consequently his chemistry has a positivist flavor. A chemical formula for Gerhardt was simply equivalent to a particular reaction of a compound and thus had little explanatory value.

A considerable part of Gerhardt's claim to our attention is connected with his use of certain formulas in chemistry. Like Lavoisier, he felt that chemistry could be successfully pursued only if it were based on a rational and systematic language. It was not merely that formulas are a reflection of our basic concepts but, more, that "our formulas *are* our ideas." It is not surprising, therefore, to find Gerhardt insisting on the importance of writing chemical equations: "The only approach which is at the same time rigorous and easy and which can be reconciled with the individual opinions of all chemists is that which consists in expressing reactions by equations from which all purely hypothetical entities are excluded."[2] Gerhardt was one of the first to make systematic use of equations in chemistry.

Gerhardt's most conspicuous contribution to the development of organic chemistry was his homologous series. His earliest publications were characterized by attempts to arrange organic compounds in series of increasing complexity: his "ladder of combustion," rising from water and carbon dioxide at the foot to albumin and fibrin at the summit, was an analogue of the biologists' ladder of nature. Another biological analogy was to underlie the application of his homologous series when they were refined in 1843:

Gerhardt presupposed a principle of plenitude in organic chemistry which dictated that hitherto undocumented members of any series must exist. In addition, the concept of homology itself was of biological origin, deriving from Cuvier. For Gerhardt, however, it did not carry that structural connotation which it had for Cuvier. On this subject Gerhardt simply asserted: "We call substances homologues when they exhibit the same chemical properties and when there are analogies in the relative proportions of their elements."[3]

Drawing on the work of Dumas—who, in 1842, had observed that a whole series of acids could be generated by the formula $(C^4H^4)_n\ O^4$ [$(CH_2)_n\ O_2$ in modern notation]—and also of Kopp, who had investigated "a great regularity in the physical properties of analogous organic compounds," Gerhardt generalized the concept of homologous series and introduced it into his *Précis de chimie organique* of 1844. He did so with particular reference to the four known alcohols, since he could demonstrate a significant numerical relation between their empirical formulas: They could be written in the forms [$(CH^2) + H^2O$]; [$(CH^2)^2 + H^2O$]; [$(CH^2)^5 + H^2O$]; and [$(CH^2)^{16} + H^2O$]. Furthermore, their respective oxidation, sulfonation, and halogenation products could all be denoted by formulas in which the characteristic (CH_2) unit recurred. The solution which Gerhardt found to the problem of prediction was then explicit in his enthusiastic conclusion: provided one knew how properties varied regularly along a series, "it would suffice to know the composition, the properties and the mode of formation of a single product obtained [from one of the above compounds] in order to be able to predict the composition, properties and mode of formation of all substances similar to this first product."[4]

Gerhardt systematically showed how one could argue from the reactions of one compound to those of another on the basis of a formal numerical analogy displayed by their respective empirical formulas. His enthusiasm for this system of classification led to his being accused of doing algebra rather than chemistry. Nevertheless, on this basis Gerhardt not only forecast the existence of many new compounds, such as those required to complete the alcohol series [$(CH^2)^n + H^2O$], but also predicted the properties of many others, such as the boiling point (140°C.) of propionic acid. Within the space of twenty years organic compounds had been removed from what Wöhler had described as a primeval forest and had been transplanted in decorous straight lines. Within the next few years the carbon-carbon bonds of Kekulé were to explain the significance of the recurrent CH_2 unit; and in retrospect the only serious shortcoming of Gerhardt's understanding of homology was its failure to do justice to structural isomerism.

If the concept of homology was Gerhardt's most notable contribution, his most notorious was a reform of the presuppositions then underlying the determination of chemical equivalents. As a consequence of the prevalent disregard for Avogadro's hypothesis, current equivalents were not based on equal volumes of vapor. Accordingly, Berzelius saw nothing wrong in writing water as H^2O and acetic acid as $C^4H^8O^4$, in order that the latter might be considered the hydrate of an oxide ($C^4H^6O^3 + H^2O$) analogous to an inorganic acid; compare sulfuric acid ($SO^3 + H^2O$). Similarly, Gmelin's alternative system allowed an organic acid to be envisaged as an anhydride plus water ($C^4H^3O^3 + HO$). But in both cases there was an inconsistency, and it was Gerhardt who faced the consequences of removing it. The inconsistency was this: if H^2O represented an equivalent of water corresponding to two volumes of vapor, how could the same equivalent of water be preformed within an organic acid if the overall equivalent of the acid corresponded to four volumes of vapor? To eliminate the inconsistency, it would be necessary to represent the water participating in organic reactions by H^4O^2 (Berzelius' system) or by H^2O^2 (Gmelin).

Consequently, in his famous paper read before the Paris Academy of Sciences in September 1842, Gerhardt enumerated a host of organic reactions in order to demonstrate that when water was produced or utilized in such reactions, it was in quantities which could be represented only by H^4O^2, on a four-volume system. From similar considerations with respect to the participation of carbon dioxide in organic reactions, Gerhardt argued that the only way to achieve consistency was either to double all two-volume inorganic formulas or to halve all four-volume organic formulas. But this was a particularly drastic measure—since it destroyed almost all the current constitutional analogies between inorganic and organic compounds—and such was the dogmatic and precocious tone of its advocate that Gerhardt's revision met constant hostility.

It was not until February 1845 that even the sympathetic Laurent finally agreed to the innovation, one corollary of which merits special attention. If all organic formulas corresponding to four volumes of vapor really had to be divided by two, then no four-volume formula could be tolerated if it included an odd number of atoms. Both Laurent and Gerhardt were therefore obliged to instigate a program of reanalysis in cases where four-volume formulas failed to conform to their scheme; and the implication that their contemporaries, particularly Liebig, had been incompetent did much more to increase their professional alienation during the 1840's. It has often been said that Gerhardt's standardization constituted a revival of Avogadro's hypothesis, but this is not strictly true. Nothing could be further from Avogadro's hypothesis than Gerhardt's conclusion that "atoms, equivalents, and volumes are synonymous. . . ." Certainly it was a corollary of Avogadro's hypothesis that molecular formulas should be standardized in the way Gerhardt had chosen, but Gerhardt himself was preoccupied with the corollary. Simplification and the elimination of the internal inconsistency had been ends in themselves, and it was left to Laurent and others to clarify further the relationship between atoms, equivalents, and molecules.

Another notable, although less well-known, contribution of Gerhardt's was his redefinition of acids. Since the standardization of inorganic and organic formulas, effected by Gerhardt, strictly precluded the preexistence of water in the molecule of a monobasic acid, some alternative convention for the formulation of acids was required. During the 1830's Liebig had become dissatisfied with the (anhydride + water) model but had not been prepared to introduce the alternative hydrogen theory in inorganic chemistry, even though he had commended it for the organic domain. Gerhardt's view of chemistry, however, was dominated by the attempt to introduce organic concepts into inorganic chemistry, and he felt no compunction in introducing a universal definition of acidity based on hydrogen. The idea that an acid could be defined with reference to its displaceable hydrogen appealed to Gerhardt for the additional reason that salt formation could then be construed as a displacement reaction rather than as an addition reaction.

In this way one of the main props of the prevalent electrochemical theory was removed. Hitherto, acid, base, and salt had often been defined in terms of each other, so it was an obvious merit of Gerhardt's definition that it broke the circle. The essential conceptual advance consisted in the obliteration of the artificial distinction between "oxacids" and "hydracids." In deference to their heritage from Lavoisier, chemists had been obliged to create a special class for acids, such as hydrochloric, which contained no oxygen. These were the "hydracids." Long after Lavoisier's erroneous explanation of acidic properties was obsolete, the classification of acids still paid lip service to it. A conceptual switch was necessary to recognize hydracids as the rule and to transpose the oxacids accordingly. Pursuing this transposition to its conclusion, Gerhardt was able to refine Liebig's criteria for the establishment of acid basicity: the diagnostic value of acid and double salts assisted in the determination of the number of replaceable hydrogen atoms in a given acid. The dibasicity of sulfuric acid was at last publicized; and when, in 1856, Alexander Williamson expressed the respective basicities of nitric, sulfuric, and phosphoric acids as NO_3H; SO_4H_2; PO_4H_3, he added that the "labors of Messrs. Laurent and Gerhardt greatly contributed to the establishment of these results which are uncontroverted."

During the 1830's the attempt to model the structure of organic compounds on the dualistic structure of inorganic compounds led to the postulation of a large number of hypothetical radicals, supposedly analogues of the inorganic elements. According to Liebig's famous definition, organic chemistry differed from inorganic chemistry in that it dealt with compound rather than simple radicals. Ethyl chloride, for example, could be envisaged as a salt in which the composite ethyl radical played a role analogous to the potassium of potassium chloride. As complex a compound as cacodyl chloride was regarded by Bunsen as $(C^4H^{12}As^2)Cl$, with the implication that the complex radical $(C^4H^{12}As^2)$ should be as capable of isolation as the inorganic elements. Bunsen was convinced that he had isolated the free cacodyl radical.

In the 1840's Kolbe and Frankland isolated what they thought were the methyl and ethyl radicals and thus appeared to corroborate the analogy between metal and radical, but there was a disconcerting feature of this corroboration. If one bowed before Gerhardt's insistence that molecular formulas should all refer to the same volume of vapor, it was impossible to equate what Bunsen had isolated with the hypothetical constituent of the cacodyl compounds, just as it was also impossible to equate Kolbe's species with the hypothetical methyl. The equivalent vapor densities of the isolated species corresponded to the dimers $(C^8H^{24}As^4)$ and dimethyl, respectively. How were these results to be interpreted? It was a clear case of circular verification: if one accepted the dualistic approach to organic chemistry, then Kolbe's work confirmed it; if one accepted Gerhardt's presuppositions, it did not. Eventually the inert character of the Kolbe-Frankland hydrocarbons, together with their respective boiling points, testified in Gerhardt's favor; and by 1851 Frankland himself was admitting that what he had taken to be methyl and ethyl were in reality stable dimers. Gerhardt's ideas were, therefore, instrumental in preventing a serious misinterpretation of hydrocarbon chemistry, as they were also in drawing attention to the legitimacy of postulating diatomic molecules X_2 (compare $(CH^3)_2$) in contradistinction to the tenets of electrochemical theories.

One of Gerhardt's principal claims to fame was his "type" theory. The concept of a chemical "type" has a long and intricate history. Chemists had long given similar compounds similar names (compare the "pyrites" of iron and copper), and when Berzelius had eventually represented the sulfates, selenates, and chromates by the formulas $MO.SO^3$, $MO.SeO^3$, and $MO.CrO^3$, he had recognized more than a superficial resemblance. The discovery of isomorphism by Mitscherlich and of chlorine substitution within organic compounds by Laurent and Dumas culminated in Dumas's "type theory" (1838–1840), which purported to explain the common properties of parent and chlorine derivative with reference to a common spatial arrangement of their constituents: acetic and trichloracetic acids, for example, belonged to the same "chemical" type. Impressive as Dumas's theory was, it had at least two outstanding defects. First, since there turned out to be no rigid distinction between substitutions with and without retention of properties, Dumas's division between "chemical" and "mechanical" types—which had been designed to cater to such a distinction—began to appear arbitrary. Second, during the 1840's, when the central problem became one of classification, his types proved to be too specific. They might illuminate the relation between any one acid and its chlorine derivatives, but there was no obvious way of correlating the types of different parent acids. It seemed that what was required was to expand the concept of "type" for an economic classification and for an understanding of all substitution reactions (irrespective of a change in properties), and yet escape the problems associated with the ever-increasing number of conflicting opinions about the precise arrangement of atoms within a given compound.

It was Gerhardt who provided a solution to this problem when, in his definitive exposition of a "new type theory" (1853–1856), he illustrated how one could envisage organic compounds as substitutionary derivatives of a minimal number of inorganic compounds: water, ammonia, hydrogen, and hydrogen chloride. Several chemists contributed the empirical foundation for this new theory. Williamson, for example, was able to prepare mixed ethers which admirably conformed to the water type—compare

$$\left.\begin{matrix}H\\H\end{matrix}\right\}O \quad \text{and} \quad \left.\begin{matrix}CH^3\\C^2H^5\end{matrix}\right\}O$$

—while Hofmann showed that the amines could be subsumed under ammonia as an all-embracing type—compare

$$\left.\begin{matrix}H\\H\\H\end{matrix}\right\}N \quad \text{and} \quad \left.\begin{matrix}R\\R'\\R''\end{matrix}\right\}N.$$

It was, in fact, in the context of establishing the utility of the water type that Gerhardt himself made what was his most prestigious contribution to practical chemistry. According to the water type theory, acetic acid could be written as $\left.\begin{matrix}C^2H^3O\\H\end{matrix}\right\}O$, and by a further substitution of an acyl group for a hydrogen atom there should result a compound $\left.\begin{matrix}C^2H^3O\\C^2H^3O\end{matrix}\right\}O$. Gerhardt's triumph was to prepare acetic anhydride by the reaction of acetyl chloride with sodium acetate. Furthermore, by producing mixed anhydrides, he established—against contemporary opinion—that two equivalents of a monobasic acid were involved in the process; compare

$$\left.\begin{matrix}H\\H\end{matrix}\right\}O, \quad \left.\begin{matrix}RCo\\RCo\end{matrix}\right\}O, \quad \left.\begin{matrix}RCo\\R'Co\end{matrix}\right\}O.$$

Gerhardt's type theory dominated the organic chemistry of the late 1850's, not simply because of its comprehensiveness but also because it could be extended in a number of profitable directions. The introduction of the methane type completed a series which was highly suggestive in the context of emerging ideas on valency:

$$HCl'; \quad \left.\begin{matrix}H\\H\end{matrix}\right\}O''; \quad \left.\begin{matrix}H\\H\\H\end{matrix}\right\}N'''; \quad \left.\begin{matrix}H\\H\\H\\H\end{matrix}\right\}C^{IV}.$$

Moreover, this theory was highly flexible, since types could be conjugated, condensed, or multiplied in order to accommodate more elusive species, such as ammonium hydroxide:

$$\begin{matrix}\left.\begin{matrix}H\\H\\H\end{matrix}\right\}N,\\ \left\{\begin{matrix}H\\H\end{matrix}\right. O\end{matrix} \quad \text{glycine} \quad C^2H^2 \begin{matrix}\left.\begin{matrix}H\\H\end{matrix}\right\}N\\ \left.\begin{matrix}O\\H\end{matrix}\right\}O\end{matrix}, \quad \text{and glycol} \quad \left.\begin{matrix}C^2H^4\\H^2\end{matrix}\right\}O^2.$$

Although the purely formal nature of Gerhardt's types prevented their earning a permanent place in the body of chemical theory, at the time of their inception they exerted a powerful unifying influence on the development of chemistry. In two quite different senses Gerhardt had contributed to the unification of chemical theory. In the first place, by introducing the radicals, such as ethyl, into types such as water, Gerhardt was able to achieve some kind of rapprochement between radical and type concepts which had hitherto been in opposition. Second, by subsuming all organic compounds under four inorganic types, he was advocating analogies of unprecedented generality between organic and inorganic compounds.

Gerhardt, like Laurent, was convinced of the unity of chemical theory; and when Wurtz (1862) sought a proof of the artificiality of the inorganic-organic dichotomy, it was to Gerhardt's theory of types that he appealed.

Gerhardt will occupy a permanent position in the history of chemistry for his services to organic classification, for his concept of homology, for his preparation of acid anhydrides, and for his reform of equivalents. His unitary emphasis, while remaining indispensable for the comprehension of organic compounds, was eventually superseded in inorganic chemistry as ionic concepts marked the culmination of a return to a more mechanistic approach. Indeed, shortly after the death of Gerhardt chemistry was to change its sights. A new program, explicitly hostile to Gerhardt's positivist construction of chemistry, was promulgated by Kekulé and Scott-Couper. Reductionist in intent, it focused attention once more on the elements themselves and on the individual atoms, with the object of so elucidating the nature of chemical bonding that the properties of any compound could be demonstrated to follow from those of its constituent elements. Questions concerned with the real arrangement of atoms in a molecule and with what held them together could not be bypassed for long, and with the resuscitation of these questions certain features of Gerhardt's unitary chemistry were quietly forgotten: no longer was it reasonable to regard all reactions as double decompositions, and no longer could all the metals be regarded as diatomic M_2. Nevertheless, whenever chemical philosophers have gathered together, there have been those, like Benjamin Brodie, who have expressed their gratitude to those "great chemists, Laurent and Gerhardt who implanted in the science the germ of a more abstract philosophy, which it has ever since retained."

NOTES

1. Grimaux and Gerhardt, *Charles Gerhardt, sa vie . . .*, p. 490.
2. *Précis de chimie organique*, I, viii–ix.
3. *Annales de chimie et de physique*, 3rd ser., **8** (1843), 245.
4. *Revue scientifique et industrielle*, **14** (1843), 588.

BIBLIOGRAPHY

I. Original Works. Gerhardt's books are *Précis de chimie organique*, 2 vols. (Paris, 1844–1845); *Introduction à l'étude de la chimie par le système unitaire* (Paris, 1848); and *Traité de chimie organique*, 4 vols. (Paris, 1853–1856).

His major research papers are the following: "Sur la constitution des sels organiques à acides complexes, et leurs rapports avec les sels ammoniacaux," in *Annales de chimie*, 2nd ser., **72** (1839), 184–215; "Recherches chimiques sur les huiles essentielles," *ibid.*, 3rd ser., **1** (1841), 60–111; "On the Chemical Classification of Organic Substances," in *Revue scientifique et industrielle*, **7** (1841), 104; **8** (1842), 300; **10** (1842), 145; **12** (1843), 592; **14** (1843), 580; "Considérations sur les équivalents de quelques corps simples et composés," in *Annales de chimie*, **7** (1843), 129–143, and **8** (1843), 238–245; "Recherches sur la salicine," *ibid.*, **8** (1843), 215–229; "Recherches sur les alcalis organiques," *ibid.*, **7** (1843), 251–253; "Recherches chimiques sur l'essence de valériane et l'essence d'estragon," *ibid.*, pp. 275–295, also in *Annalen der Chemie*, **45** (1843), 29–41; "Action de l'acide sulfurique sur les matières," in *Comptes rendus hebdomadaires des séances de l'Académie des sciences*, **16** (1843), 458–460; "Sur les combinaisons de l'acide sulfurique avec les matières organiques," *ibid.*, **17** (1843), 312–317; "Recherches concernant les alcalis organiques," *ibid.*, **19** (1844), 1105–1107; "Sur la génération de l'éther," in *Revue scientifique*, 2nd ser., **3** (1844), 304–310; "Sur le point d'ébullition des hydrogènes carbonés," in *Annales de chimie*, **14** (1845), 107–114, also in *Journal für praktische Chemie*, **35** (1845), 300–305; "Sur une nouvelle classe de composés organiques," in *Annales de chimie*, **14** (1845), 117–125, and **15** (1845), 88–96; "Observations sur la formation des formules chimiques," in *Journal de pharmacie*, **8** (1845), i–viii; "Sur l'identité de l'essence d'estragon et de l'essence d'anis," in *Comptes rendus hebdomadaires des séances de l'Académie des sciences*, **20** (1845), 1440–1444; "Sur la loi de saturation des corps copulés," *ibid.*, pp. 1648–1657; "Sur les mellonures," *ibid.*, **21** (1845), 679–681; "Introduction à l'étude de la chimie," in *Journal de pharmacie*, **14** (1848), 63–67; "Recherches sur les anilides," in *Annales de chimie*, **24** (1848), 163–207; "Remarques sur les combinaisons des acides avec les alcalis organiques," in *Comptes rendus mensuels des travaux chimiques*, **5** (1849), 160–170; "Recherches sur les phénides, nouvelle classe de composés organiques," *ibid.*, pp. 429–437; "Sur la composition des mellonures et de leurs dérivés," *ibid.*, **6** (1850), 104–111, also in *Comptes rendus hebdomadaires des séances de l'Académie des sciences*, **30** (1850), 318–319; "Remarques sur un travail de M. Hofmann sur les radicaux, etc.," in *Comptes rendus mensuels des travaux chimiques*, **6** (1850), 233–236; "Remarques sur un travail de M. Williamson relatif aux éthers," *ibid.*, pp. 361–364; "Sur la constitution des composés organiques," *ibid.*, **7** (1851), 65–84; "Sur la basicité des acides," *ibid.*, pp. 129–156, also in *Journal für praktische Chemie*, **53** (1851), 460–488; "Recherches sur les acides organiques anhydres," in *Annales de chimie*, **37** (1853), 285; "Note sur la théorie des amides," in *Comptes rendus hebdomadaires des séances de l'Académie des sciences*, **37** (1853), 280–284; "Addition aux recherches sur les acides anhydres," *ibid.*, **36** (1853), 1050–1069; "Sur les amides," in *Annales de chimie*, **46** (1856), 129–172; and "Recherches sur les amides," *ibid.*, **53** (1858), 302–313.

Many of Gerhardt's most revealing articles were published in *Comptes rendus mensuels des travaux chimiques* between 1846 and 1852. For his correspondence, see M. Tiffeneau, ed., *Correspondance de C. Gerhardt* (Paris, 1918).

II. Secondary Literature. On Gerhardt or his work,

see E. Grimaux and C. Gerhardt, *Charles Gerhardt, sa vie, son oeuvre, sa correspondance* (Paris, 1900); J. Jacques, "Onze lettres inédites de Charles Gerhardt à J. B. Dumas," in *Bulletin de la Société chimique de France,* **156** (1856), 1315–1324; C. de Milt, "Auguste Laurent. Guide and Inspiration of Gerhardt," in *Journal of Chemical Education,* **28** (1951), 198–204; J. F. H. Papillon, *La vie et l'oeuvre de C. F. Gerhardt* (Paris, 1863); and J. R. Partington, *History of Chemistry,* IV (London, 1964), 405–424 and *passim.*

M. P. CROSLAND
J. H. BROOKE

GERMAIN, SOPHIE (*b.* Paris, France, 1 April 1776; *d.* Paris, 27 June 1831), *mathematics.*

Sophie Germain, France's greatest female mathematician prior to the present era, was the daughter of Ambroise-François Germain and Marie-Madeleine Gruguelu. Her father was for a time deputy to the States-General (later the Constituent Assembly). In his speeches he referred to himself as a merchant and ardently defended the rights of the Third Estate, which he represented. Somewhat later he became one of the directors of the Bank of France. His extensive library enabled his daughter to educate herself at home. Thus it was that, at age thirteen, Sophie read an account of the death of Archimedes at the hands of a Roman soldier. The great scientist of antiquity became her hero, and she conceived the idea that she too must become a mathematician. After teaching herself Latin and Greek, she read Newton and Euler despite her parents' opposition to a career in mathematics.

The Germain library sufficed until Sophie was eighteen. At that time she was able to obtain the lecture notes of courses at the recently organized École Polytechnique, in particular the *cahiers* of Lagrange's lectures on analysis. Students at the school were expected to prepare end-of-term reports. Pretending to be a student there and using the pseudonym Le Blanc, Sophie Germain wrote a paper on analysis and sent it to Lagrange. He was astounded at its originality, praised it publicly, sought out its author, and thus discovered that M. Le Blanc was Mlle. Germain. From then on, he became her sponsor and mathematical counselor.

Correspondence with great scholars became the means by which she obtained her higher education in mathematics, literature, biology, and philosophy. She wrote to Legendre about problems suggested by his 1798 *Théorie des nombres.* The subsequent Legendre-Germain correspondence was so voluminous that it was virtually a collaboration, and Legendre included some of her discoveries in a supplement to the second edition of the *Théorie.* In the interim she had read Gauss's *Disquisitiones arithmeticae* and, under the pseudonym of Le Blanc, engaged in correspondence with its author.

That Sophie Germain was no ivory-tower mathematician became evident in 1807, when French troops were occupying Hannover. Recalling Archimedes' fate and fearing for Gauss's safety, she addressed an inquiry to the French commander, General Pernety, who was a friend of the Germain family. As a result of this incident, Gauss learned her true identity and accorded even more praise to her number-theoretic proofs.

One of Sophie Germain's theorems is related to the baffling and still unsolved problem of obtaining a general proof for "Fermat's last theorem," which is the conjecture that $x^n + y^n = z^n$ has no positive integral solutions if n is an integer greater than 2. To prove the theorem, one need only establish its truth for $n = 4$ (accomplished by Fermat himself) and for all values of n that are odd primes. Euler proved it for $n = 3$ and Legendre for $n = 5$. Sophie Germain's contribution was to show the impossibility of positive integral solutions if x, y, z are prime to one another and to n, where n is any prime less than 100. In 1908 the American algebraist L. E. Dickson generalized her theorem to all primes less than 1,700, and more recently Barkley Rosser extended the upper limit to 41,000,000. In his history of the theory of numbers, Dickson describes her other discoveries in the higher arithmetic.

Parallel with and subsequent to her pure mathematical research, she also made contributions to the applied mathematics of acoustics and elasticity. This came about in the following manner. In 1808 the German physicist E. F. F. Chladni visited Paris, where he conducted experiments on vibrating plates. He exhibited the so-called Chladni figures, which can be produced when a metal or glass plate of any regular shape, the most common being the square or the circle, is placed in a horizontal position and fastened at its center to a supporting stand. Sand is scattered lightly over the plate, which is then set in vibration by drawing a violin bow rapidly up and down along the edge of the plate. The sand is thrown from the moving points to those which remain at rest (the nodes), forming the nodal lines or curves constituting the Chladni figures.

Chladni's results were picturesque, but their chief effect on French mathematicians was to emphasize that there was no pure mathematical model for such phenomena. Hence, in 1811 the Académie des Sciences offered a prize for the best answer to the following challenge: Formulate a mathematical theory of elastic surfaces and indicate just how it agrees with empirical evidence.

Most mathematicians did not attempt to solve the problem because Lagrange assured them that the mathematical methods available were inadequate for the task. Nevertheless, Sophie Germain submitted an anonymous memoir. No prize was awarded to anyone; but Lagrange, using her fundamental hypotheses, was able to deduce the correct partial differential equation for the vibrations of elastic plates. In 1813 the Academy reopened the contest, and Sophie Germain offered a revised paper which included the question of experimental verification. That memoir received an honorable mention. When, in 1816, the third and final contest was held, a paper bearing her own name and treating vibrations of general curved as well as plane elastic surfaces was awarded the grand prize—the high point in her scientific career.

After further enlargement and improvement of the prize memoir, it was published in 1821 under the title *Remarques sur la nature, les bornes et l'étendue de la question des surfaces élastiques et équation générale de ces surfaces.* In that work Sophie Germain stated that the law for the general vibrating elastic surface is given by the fourth-order partial differential equation

$$N^2\left[\frac{\partial^4\rho}{\partial {s_1}^4} + 2\frac{\partial^4\rho}{\partial {s_1}^2\partial {s_2}^2} + \frac{\partial^4\rho}{\partial {s_2}^4} - \frac{4}{S^2}\left(\frac{\partial^2\rho}{\partial {s_1}^2} + \frac{\partial^2\rho}{\partial {s_2}^2}\right)\right] + \frac{\partial^2\rho}{\partial t^2} = 0.$$

Here N is a physical constant if the "surface" is an elastic membrane of uniform thickness. The generality is achieved because S, the radius of mean curvature, varies from point to point of a general curved surface. The very concept of mean curvature $(1/S)$ was created by Sophie Germain.

The notion of the curvature of a surface generalizes the corresponding concept for a plane curve by considering the curvatures of all plane sections of the surface through the normal at a given point of the surface and then using only the largest and smallest of those curvatures. The extremes, called the principal curvatures, are multiplied to give the Gaussian total curvature at a point and are added to give the mean curvature. Sophie Germain, however, defined the mean curvature as half the sum, that is, the arithmetic mean, of the principal curvatures. Her definition seems more in accordance with the term "mean." Moreover, she indicated that her measure is a representative one, an average in the statistical sense, by demonstrating that if one passes planes through the normal at a point of a surface such that the angle between successive planes is $2\pi/n$ where n is very large (thus yielding sample sections in many different directions), the arithmetic mean of the curvatures of all the sections is the same as the mean of the two principal curvatures, a fact that remains true in the limit as n gets larger and larger. Also, while the Gaussian curvature completely characterizes the local metric geometry of a surface, the mean curvature is more suitable for applications in elasticity theory. A plane has zero mean curvature at all points. Hence $4/S^2 = 0$ in Germain's differential equation, and it reduces to the equation which she and Lagrange had derived for the vibration of flat plates. The same simplification holds for all surfaces of zero mean curvature, the so-called minimal surfaces (such as those formed by a soap film stretched from wire contours).

In later papers Sophie Germain enlarged on the physics of vibrating curved elastic surfaces and considered the effect of variable thickness (which emphasizes that one is, in fact, dealing with elastic solids).

She also wrote two philosophic works entitled *Pensées diverses* and *Considérations générales sur l'état des sciences et des lettres,* which were published posthumously in the *Oeuvres philosophiques.* The first of these, probably written in her youth, contains capsule summaries of scientific subjects, brief comments on the contributions of leading mathematicians and physicists throughout the ages, and personal opinions. The *État des sciences et des lettres,* which was praised by Auguste Comte, is an extremely scholarly development of the theme of the unity of thought, that is, the idea that there always has been and always will be no basic difference between the sciences and the humanities with respect to their motivation, their methodology, and their cultural importance.

BIBLIOGRAPHY

I. ORIGINAL WORKS. Among Sophie Germain's scientific writings are *Remarques sur la nature, les bornes et l'étendue de la question des surfaces élastiques et équation générale de ces surfaces* (Paris, 1826); *Mémoire sur la courbure des surfaces* (Paris, 1830); *Oeuvres philosophiques de Sophie Germain* (Paris, 1879); and *Mémoire sur l'emploi de l'épaisseur dans la théorie des surfaces élastiques* (Paris, 1880).

II. SECONDARY LITERATURE. On Sophie Germain or her work, see L. E. Dickson, *History of the Theory of Numbers* (New York, 1950), I, 382; II, 732–735, 757, 763, 769; M. L. Dubreil-Jacotin, "Figures de mathématiciennes," in F. Le Lionnais, *Les grands courants de la pensée mathématique* (Paris, 1962), pp. 258–268; and H. Stupuy, "Notice sur la vie et les oeuvres de Sophie Germain," in *Oeuvres philosophiques de Sophie Germain* (see above), pp. 1–92.

EDNA E. KRAMER

GERMANUS, HENRICUS MARTELLUS (*fl.* Florence, Italy, 1480–1496[?]), *geography.*

Henricus Martellus was probably Heinrich Hammer and assuredly was of German birth, since he referred to himself as "Germanus." He is a mysterious personality of whom no mention has ever been found except for the remarkable maps that he signed with his full name. It is established that he worked in Florence in the closing decades of the fifteenth century and was closely associated with the printer, engraver, and map publisher Francesco Rosselli.

Germanus' contribution is in the maps that he drew, remarkable not only for their high artistic quality but also for the new geographical concepts that they represented. His works include two sets of maps drawn to illustrate Ptolemy's *Geography,* five codices of an *Insularium,* or Book of Islands, and a large world map (43″ by 75″).

Roberto Almagià states that Germanus was the first mapmaker to append to the traditional set of maps illustrating the work of Ptolemy a set of maps showing the world of his time, the "tabulae modernae." Of these the most important are the world maps added to several of his *insularia* and the large world map now in the Yale University Library. These maps show the world on the eve of Columbus' voyages: the continent of Africa as reported by the Portuguese, an open Indian Ocean, a jumbled—but in places recognizable—eastern coast of Asia, and, on the Yale world map, Japan, identified as "Zipango."

There can be little doubt that Germanus' world maps served as the model for Martin Behaim's celebrated 1492 globe, the oldest surviving globe in the Western world: these two are the only "new" world maps prior to 1500 to be graduated in longitudes and latitudes. Further, it is highly probable that Germanus' map, or a copy thereof, inspired the geographic ideas of Columbus. According to Almagià, it can best explain the geographic premises of all of Columbus' voyages and would fully support his convictions, his conjectures, and his projects. The influence of Germanus' large world map, in all likelihood circulated in printed form throughout Europe, is evident in nearly all of the important maps of the Columbian age; and it is a landmark in the mapping of our world.

BIBLIOGRAPHY

On Germanus or his work, see Roberto Almagià, "I mappamondi di Enrico Martello e alcuni concetti geografici do Cristoforo Colombo," in *Bibliofilia,* **43,** nos. 8–10 (1940), 288–311, which has a list of Germanus' maps; and Marcel Destombes, ed., *Mappemondes, A.D. 1200–1500,* vol. I of Monumenta Cartographica Vetustioris Aevi (Amsterdam, 1964), pp. 229–233.

GEORGE KISH

GESELL, ARNOLD LUCIUS (*b.* Alma, Wisconsin, 21 June 1880; *d.* New Haven, Connecticut, 29 May 1961), *psychology.*

Trained in pedagogy, psychology, and medicine, Gesell developed a systematic program of research in human growth and development during many years of work with normal and problem children at Yale University's Clinic of Child Development; and through his associates, students, and a multitude of publications, he disseminated his conclusions for practical application and elaboration, initiating a new concept in child care.

Gesell was the oldest of the five children of Gerhard and Christine Giesen Gesell. His mother taught elementary school in the small town where he was born and raised. After graduation from high school in 1896, he went to the Stevens Point Normal School to train as a teacher, then taught for a short time at the Stevens Point High School.

Gesell next went to the University of Wisconsin, where he received the B.Ph. in 1903 with a thesis on higher education in Ohio and Wisconsin. He was principal of the high school in Chippewa Falls, Wisconsin, the following year; but having come under the influence of Joseph Jastrow, professor of psychology at Wisconsin, he enrolled in Clark University, Worcester, Massachusetts, where G. Stanley Hall, pioneer in child psychology, introduced him to this then-new field of investigation. There Gesell earned the Ph.D. in 1906 with a thesis on jealousy.

For the next two years Gesell taught at the California State Normal School in Los Angeles, where, on 18 February 1909, he married Beatrice Chandler. The following summer he went to study at the Pennsylvania Training School for Feeble-Minded Children, where Lightner Witmer (who founded this institution as well as the country's first psychological clinic at the University of Pennsylvania) was director. The Gesells also spent several weeks that summer at the Training School for Feeble-Minded Children in Vineland, New Jersey, where Henry Goddard, director of psychological research, was investigating the application of Binet tests to feebleminded children.

Gesell considered this visit to Vineland as the beginning of his professional interest in mentally defective children; and he later for several years conducted summer courses with Goddard at New York University, in which they trained special teachers for defective children. In 1910 he studied anatomy at the University of Wisconsin; and the following year, having joined the department of education at Yale University, he enrolled at the same time as a medical student there. The dean of the medical school, George Blumer, provided him with space in the New Haven Dispensary to study retarded children. Thus the Clinic of Child Development originated in 1911, while Gesell was still pursuing his medical degree. He received the M.D. in 1915 and was made professor in the Yale Graduate School of Medicine.

From 1915 to 1919 Gesell served as school psychologist for the Connecticut State Board of Education. This entailed identifying handicapped children and devising individualized programs for them. In 1918 he surveyed mental conditions in the elementary schools of New Haven, and from 1919 to 1921 he served on the Governor's Commission on Child Welfare. In 1924 he initiated the use of cinematography in psychological research and established, in 1925, the Photographic Library of Yale Research Films of Child Development, supervising for many years the production of still and motion pictures at Yale. With the cooperation of Louise Ames and Frances L. Ilg, Gesell issued a nationally syndicated column on child studies. Generous funds granted in 1926 by the Laura Spelman Rockefeller Memorial Foundation and other private foundations supported his research and enabled him to establish a nursery which provided for the observation and guidance of children as well as for aiding parents in caring for them. Here, in 1930, he devised a one-way observation dome for research and teaching of child behavior, a sort of "candid camera" technique, by means of which he could observe and record infant behavior without being seen.

From 1928 to 1948 Gesell was attending pediatrician at the New Haven Hospital. When he became professor emeritus of child hygiene upon his retirement in 1948, he directed the Yale Child Vision Research Project for two years; from 1948 to 1952 he also served as research associate on the Harvard Pediatric Study. In 1950 the Gesell Institute of Child Development was founded, superseding the Yale Clinic of Child Development, and here Gesell served as consultant and lecturer in the School for Social Research for the rest of his life. He was a member of the National Research Council (1937–1940), the American Psychological Association, the National Academy of Sciences, and the American Association for the Advancement of Science. The American Academy of Pediatrics decided in 1934 that a requirement for membership would be certification by the American Board of Pediatrics; an exception—and the only exception—was made for Gesell in 1948 because of his outstanding contributions in the field of child development. Clark University conferred an honorary D.Sc. in 1930, and the same degree was awarded him in 1953 by the University of Wisconsin.

Gesell's significance lies in his development of new methods in the study of children. He placed particular emphasis on the preschool years, a period that had previously received only cursory attention. His studies led him to conclusions about the psychological care of infants and the guidance of children that exerted an important influence on the attitudes and practices of nursery schools, kindergartens, and elementary schools. In addition, he inspired a group of active disciples who are continuing his work, and had a talent for popularizing and gaining support for his ideas. Some of his concepts related to predictive measurement of mental development in children have been adopted into current pediatrics.

BIBLIOGRAPHY

I. Original Works. Gesell's writings include *The First Five Years of Life* (New York, 1940); *Developmental Diagnosis* (New York, 1941; 2nd ed., rev. and enl., 1947), written with Catherine S. Armatruda, for medical students and practitioners, with translations into several other languages; *Infant and Child in the Culture of Today* (New York, 1943), written with Janet Learned and Louise B. Ames, which presents the significance of a democratic culture for the psychological welfare of infants and young children, and is based on studies of the relationship between the pressures of natural growth, which Gesell called "maturation," and the pressure of the social order, termed "acculturation"; and *The Child From Five to Ten* (New York, 1946), written with Frances Ilg, which supplements *The First Five Years of Life,* as both complement *Infant and Child in the Culture of Today.* An extensive bibliography is included by Miles, in his memoir listed below.

II. Secondary Literature. On Gesell's life and work, see Walter R. Miles, "Arnold Lucius Gesell," in *Biographical Memoirs. National Academy of Sciences,* **37** (1964), 55–96. See also *Who's Who in America,* **31** (1960–1961), 1066; and the obituary in *Journal of the American Medical Association,* **177** (1961), 75.

Samuel X. Radbill

GESNER, KONRAD (*b.* Zurich, Switzerland, 26 March 1516; *d.* Zurich, 13 March 1565), *natural sciences, medicine, philology.*

The godson and protégé of the Protestant reformer Ulrich Zwingli, Gesner was destined from early childhood to study theology. He attended the Carolinum in his native Zurich and later entered the Fraumünster seminary. After the death of his godfather and protector in 1531 at the Battle of Kappel, Gesner left Zurich; the following year he was at the Strasbourg Academy, where he attended the courses of Wolfgang Capito and soon became a Hebrew scholar. Theological studies no longer held much interest for him, however; and he turned to medicine, studying first at Bourges, then at Paris, and later at Basel, from which he received his doctorate in 1541. Meanwhile he was pursuing his studies of ancient languages. Such was his reputation that the government of Bern appointed him the first occupant of the chair of Greek, which he held from 1537 to 1540, at the newly founded Lausanne Academy.

On the advice of his close friend Christophe Clauser, then chief physician of Zurich, Gesner traveled to Montpellier to carry on work in botany. He settled permanently in Zurich, where he was named chief physician and was later elevated to *canonicus,* a position that substantially improved his financial status. Gesner was an ardent traveler: he explored the Alps and the Adriatic coast, bringing back from his many excursions documents that he used in preparing his treatises on botany and zoology. In 1555 Gesner climbed—under difficult conditions—Mont Pilate, overlooking Lake Lucerne, and brought back useful data on Alpine flora. He died during the plague epidemic that began in Brazil in 1560 and reached Zurich in 1565.

Two dominant poles of interest can be discerned in Gesner's work. At times they oriented him toward letters, but more often they directed him to the natural sciences.

In 1535 Gesner compiled a Greek-Latin dictionary, and from 1537 to 1540 he taught Greek at Lausanne. He published several treatises on philology, notably one in which he transcribed the Lord's Prayer in twenty-two languages. He devoted several years to the preparation of a treatise, the four-volume *Bibliotheca universalis* (1545–1555), an index to Greek, Latin, and Hebrew writers that earned him fame and marks him as the founder of bibliography and brought him into correspondence with all the scholars of his time.

But natural history remained his first interest. Fascinated by botany as a youth, Gesner continued his studies in that field at Lausanne and Montpellier. He never succeeded, however, in publishing the monumental treatise on which he had worked throughout his life. This *Opera botanica,* for which he himself drew nearly 1,500 plates, was published in two volumes from 1551 to 1571 through the efforts of C. Schmiedel. Gesner was virtually the only botanist of his time to grasp the importance of floral structures as a means of establishing a systematic key to the classification of vegetable life. He was also the first to stress the nature of seeds, which enabled him to establish the kinship of plants that seemed extremely dissimilar. Later, Linnaeus would frequently acknowledge his own debt to Gesner.

Zoology also attracted Gesner, who patterned his *Historia animalium* on a work published a few years earlier by Aelian. This massive work of more than 4,500 pages received immediate acclaim; even Georges Cuvier later delighted in recognizing its enduring interest. The attempt of the treatise to regroup animals recalls the principal themes that Gesner defended in proposing a classification of the vegetable kingdom according to flowering and nonflowering plants, vascular and nonvascular plants, and so on. Gesner was also drawn to animal physiology and pathology, and he is considered by some the founder of veterinary science.

Gesner's interests extended to the study of paleontology, in which he wrote several memoirs on vegetable forms no longer extant. He is also considered the first naturalist to have sketched fossils. In addition, he studied crystallography and was one of the first to include printed plates of crystals in his works.

BIBLIOGRAPHY

Works concerning Gesner are J. C. Bay, "Conrad Gesner: The Father of Bibliography," in *Papers of the Bibliographical Society of America,* **10,** no. 2 (1916), 53–86; H. Escher, "Die *Bibliotheca universalis* K. Gesners," in *Vierteljahrsschrift der Naturforschenden Gesellschaft in Zürich,* **79** (1934), 174–194; H. Günther, "K. Gesner als Tierarzt," thesis (Leipzig, 1933); W. Ley, *K. Gesner. Leben und Werk* (Munich, 1929); and K. Müller, *Der polyhistor Konrad Gesner als Freund und Förderer erdkundlicher Studien,* doctoral diss. (Munich, 1912).

P. E. PILET

GESSNER (GESNER), JOHANNES (*b.* Zurich, Switzerland, 18 March 1709; *d.* Zurich, 6 May 1790), *botany, geology.*

Gessner was the son of Christophe Gessner, pastor of the Reformed Church of Zurich for many years, and Esther Maag, a member of a very distinguished Zurich family. For more than four centuries the Gessner family gave Switzerland theologians, physicians, and, above all, naturalists. One of Gessner's ancestors was Konrad Gesner, whose highly regarded *Historia animalium* earned its author an international reputation. Gessner's brother Johann Jakob (1704–1787) was a well-known theologian who taught Hebrew at the Carolinum and wrote extensively on numismatics.

After receiving a substantial education in Zurich, Gessner went to Leiden to study medicine. Among his teachers there was the famous Dutch physician and botanist Hermann Boerhaave. In Leiden, Gessner also met his fellow Swiss, Albrecht von Haller, and the two became friends. Boerhaave and Haller stimulated his interest in botany, which soon became his favorite area of research. Gessner next went to Paris and then to Basel, where he was initiated into higher mathematics by Johann I Bernoulli. He also became friendly with the latter's son Daniel, who later introduced probability theory into medicine. Gessner earned his medical degree in 1729, and the following year began to practice in his native city. In 1742 he was in Basel, teaching mathematics. He founded the Société de Physique in 1757 in Zurich, where he remained for the rest of his life.

Accomplished in medicine and physics as well as in botany and mathematics, Gessner was undoubtedly one of the last of the great humanists. He maintained an imposing correspondence with most of the scientists of his time, in particular with Linnaeus. One of the first to adopt the latter's system of classification, he did much to popularize it.

Gessner established his reputation as a naturalist primarily through his writings in systematic botany. His first important work was *Dissertationes de partium vegetationis et fructificationis structura* (1743). It was soon followed by *Dissertationes physicae de vegetabilibus* (1747) and the memoir *De Ranunculo bellidifloro et plantis degeneribus* (1753), in which he skillfully defended Linnaeus' conceptions. In *De petrificatorum variis originibus praecipuarum telluris mutationem testibus* (1756) Gessner showed some recognition of the real nature of fossil plants and in this regard can be considered one of the founders of paleobotany. Moreover, he devoted fourteen years (1759–1773) to the publication of an eleven-part treatise that summarized contemporary knowledge of plants, *Phytographia sacra generalis et specialis.*

Following Haller's example, Gessner specialized in the study of Alpine flora. From his very numerous excursions in the Alps and the Forealps he brought back many new species that now bear his name. Gessner was an innovator in his botanizing, since he was quite probably the first to describe plant habitats; for example, he provided altimetric data obtained with the aid of a barometer.

Toward the end of his life Gessner concentrated on geological observations. He was interested in the formation of mountain chains on the European continent and estimated the era and duration of their formation with great care. Gessner's research led him to attack the brief chronologies—based mainly on theological considerations—that were generally accepted at the time. A brilliant advocate of the principle of geochronological extrapolation, his work foreshadowed modern geophysics. Finally, his extremely precise observations of the mineral springs of the Alps were long authoritative.

The recipient of many honors, a member of countless scientific societies, and a correspondent of most of the European academies, Gessner was, in his own lifetime, considered one of the greatest naturalists of the age. Yet, shortly after his death he was somewhat forgotten, and new plants that he had been the first to describe were attributed, often wrongly, to his illustrious ancestor Konrad Gesner. He was also confused with Johann Matthias Gessner, a German pedagogue, humanist, and botanist, whose books were widely distributed. In addition, Gessner's memoirs on Alpine flora in particular could hardly withstand the inevitable comparison with those of Haller. It is only very recently, notably with the publication in 1949 of Gessner's correspondence with Linnaeus, that his originality and importance have finally gained recognition.

BIBLIOGRAPHY

I. Original Works. Gessner's works are *Dissertationes de partium vegetationis et fructificationis structura* (Zurich, 1743); *Dissertationes physicae de vegetabilibus* (Zurich, 1747); *De Ranunculo bellidifloro et plantis degeneribus* (Zurich, 1753); *De petrificatorum variis originibus praecipuarum telluris mutationem testibus* (Zurich, 1756); *Phytographia sacra generalis et specialis* (Zurich, 1759–1773); and *Tabulae phytographica analysin generum plantarum exhibentes,* with commentary and edited by C. S. Schinz (Zurich, 1795–1826).

II. Secondary Literature. On Gessner's life and work, see G. R. de Beer, "The Correspondence Between Linnaeus and Johannes Gessner," in *Proceedings of the Linnean Society of London,* **161** (1948–1949), 225; H. K. Hirzel, *Denkrede auf Johannes Gessner* (Zurich, 1790); and Rudolf Wolf, *Biographien zur Kulturgeschichte der Schweiz,* I (Zurich, 1858), 281–322.

P. E. Pilet

GEUTHER, ANTON (*b.* Neustadt, near Coburg, Germany, 23 April 1833; *d.* Jena, Germany, 23 August 1889), *chemistry.*

Geuther was the son of Christian Friedrich Geuther, a master weaver, brewer, and farmer who was also municipal treasurer of his native city. His mother was Anna Cordula Eichhorn. In accordance with his father's wishes, Geuther learned the weaver's trade and after his apprenticeship attended the Realschule in Coburg and, later, the one in Saalfeld. At Saalfeld he was more attracted by the scientific than by the commercial and technical subjects and thus, following the certificate examination, decided to study science. He entered the University of Jena, where among his teachers were H. W. F. Wackenroder (chemistry) and Matthias Schleiden (botany). He went to Göttingen in 1853 where, except for a semester in Berlin (the winter of 1853–1854), he remained for ten years. He attended lectures on mineralogy, physics, organic chemistry, and philosophy but, most important, he was for years an assistant to Friedrich Wöhler. He received his doctorate in 1855 and then advanced through various posts in Wöhler's institute, becoming successively lecture assistant, private assistant, head assistant, *Privatdozent* (1857), and associate professor (1862).

In 1863 Geuther went to the University of Jena as a full professor. In the same year he married Amalie Agnes Sindram, the daughter of Wilhelm Sindram, director of a hospital at Göttingen. They had one son and one daughter. Geuther remained in Jena for the rest of his life, achieving success both as a researcher and as a teacher. Great demands were made on Geuther's idealism, for although his summerhouse had been equipped for chemical research through the patronage of Grand Duchess Sophie of Saxe-Weimar, it was never adequate to his needs. A new structure had already been agreed to when, in 1889, he contracted typhus—and he did not live to see it built.

Under Wöhler's influence Geuther's years at Göttingen were devoted primarily to inorganic chemistry. Geuther was a strict adherent of J. J. Berzelius' dualistic, electrochemical conception; the substitution theory, which was rapidly gaining prominence, appeared to him insufficient "if it is a question of real insight and reduction to general principles." Geuther interpreted his extensive investigations of double compounds in the light of the dualistic theory and discussed the constitution of these compounds in a manner that suggests Alfred Werner's interpretation of complex compounds.

In Jena, where organic chemistry took precedence in his work, Geuther made his most important discovery, the synthesis of acetoacetic ester. The starting point for this achievement was his investigation of the constitution of alkyl compounds; among them was acetic acid, which, as the result of a then-common but false assumption concerning the atomic weights of carbon and oxygen, Geuther thought to be dibasic. Through the reaction of metallic sodium and acetic ester, he hoped to obtain the dibasic sodium salt of acetic acid; instead the result was acetoacetic ester. Geuther determined the composition of this previously unknown substance and ascertained its great reactivity. Moreover, from the color reaction with ferric chloride characteristic of phenoloid compounds and from the green color of the copper salts, he inferred the presence of an acidifying hydroxyl group in the molecule. A long controversy with Edward Frankland and Baldwin Duppa, who suspected that a ketonic form was involved, was not settled until 1911, when Geuther's successor Ludwig Knorr demonstrated that under normal conditions both substances exist in the compound. As the first example of a keto-enol tautomerism, acetoacetic ester was of great significance in the development of theoretical organic chemistry.

BIBLIOGRAPHY

I. Original Works. Lists of Geuther's publications may be found in Poggendorff, vols. III, IV, and VI. The most important are *Lehrbuch der Chemie* (Jena, 1869); "Untersuchungen über die einbasischen Säuren," in *Nachrichten von der Gesellschaft der Wissenschaften zu Göttingen* (1863), p. 281; "Untersuchungen über einbasische Kohlenstoffsäuren, über die Essigsäure," in *Jenaische Zeitschrift für Medizin und Naturwissenschaft,* **2** (1866), 388; and "Über die Constitution des Acetessigesters (Aethyldiacetsäure) und über diejenige des Benzols," in *Justus Liebigs Annalen der Chemie,* **219** (1883), 119–128.

II. Secondary Literature. Works by his pupils that show Geuther's immediate influence include C. Duisberg, "Beiträge zur Kenntniss des Acetessigesters," in *Justus Liebigs Annalen der Chemie,* **213** (1882), 133–181; and Wilhelm Wedel, "Über einige Abkömmlinge des Acetessigesters," *ibid.,* **219** (1883), 71–119.

On Geuther and his work see C. Duisberg and K. Hess, in *Berichte der Deutschen chemischen Gesellschaft,* **63A** (1930), 145–157, with portrait; C. Liebermann, *ibid.,* **22** (1889), 2388; and *Neue deutsche Biographie,* vol. VI.

Grete Ronge

GHETALDI (GHETTALDI), MARINO (*b.* Ragusa, Dalmatia [now Dubrovnik, Yugoslavia], 1566 [1568?]; *d.* Ragusa, 11 April 1626), *mathematics.*

Ghetaldi was born to a patrician family originally from Taranto, Italy. Ragusa was then an independent republic and very jealous of its Latinism. Ghetaldi spent only the latter part of his life (from 1603) there, holding various public and legal positions. As a young man, after his education in Ragusa, he had moved to Rome and then traveled extensively through Europe, returning to Rome briefly in 1603.

Ghetaldi lived the peripatetic life of a scholar participating in the intense scientific awareness of early seventeenth-century Italian culture, a last flowering of the Renaissance spirit. Galileo was its most notable example. Archimedes and Apollonius were its inspiration. In Rome Ghetaldi came under the influence of Christoph Clavius, famous as teacher and editor of Euclid. He then went to Antwerp to study with Michel Coignet. Thence he moved to Paris, where he associated with Viète, who entrusted him with an unpublished manuscript to revise and edit, although Ghetaldi had as yet published nothing of his own.

Ghetaldi's first publications appeared at Rome in 1603 and were part of the beginning of research on Archimedes. The first, *Promotus Archimedis,* dealt with the famous problem of the crown; it also included tables that Ghetaldi calculated from experiments on the specific weights of certain substances, with results that were, for the time, remarkably accurate. For this, and for research on burning glasses, a topic then of great interest, he also became known as a physicist. In his second work, *Nonnullae propositiones de parabola,* Ghetaldi treated parabolas which he had obtained as sections of a right circular cone of any proportions.

From the analysis of Apollonius' known work, Ghetaldi turned to the task of reconstructing the content of his lost works. He followed the example of his master Viète, who had attempted such reconstruction in his two books of 1600, *Tactionum* (Περὶ ἐπαφῶν), and was consequently nicknamed Apollonius Gallus. Ghetaldi took over and completed that work, although on less restricted problems, as *Supplementum Apollonii Galli* (1607). Ghetaldi later concentrated his attention on the last of Apollonius' books mentioned by Pappus, Περὶ νεύσεων (*Inclinationum libri duo*) and solved the four problems that were supposed to form the first book. The problems of insertion, as they were called, consisted of constructing certain segments with their extremes touching arcs of a circle or other given figure; the book was entitled *Apollonius redivivus seu restituta Apollonii Pergaei inclinationum geometria* (1607). Later, Ghetaldi reexamined the problem which, according to Pappus, made up the second book of *Inclinationum;* although it was rather complex, involving insertions between two semicircles, Ghetaldi declared he had needed only a few days to complete it. Published in 1613, it was entitled *Apollonius redivivus seu restitutae Apollonii Pergaei de inclinationibus geometriae, liber secundus.*

Meanwhile, Ghetaldi had produced a pamphlet with the solutions of forty-two geometrical problems, *Variorum problematum collectio* (1607). The method used in some of the solutions suggests that he was already applying methods of algebra to geometry, such as first-degree and second-degree problems, determinate or not, which he later treated specifically in a volume that appeared after his death, *De resolutione et de compositione mathematica, libri quinque* (1630). Because of this work, possibly his most significant, Ghetaldi has been considered the precursor of analytic geometry—a hypothesis difficult to support, especially in the light of the methods used by Descartes and Fermat.

Ghetaldi wrote in Latin, and his works were well and widely known—some for a long time. Pierre Herigone, for instance, included in the first volume of his *Cursus mathematicus* (1634) the first of Ghetaldi's two works devoted to the problems of insertion, translating it in a notation anticipating modern mathematical logic.

Ghetaldi was held in great esteem not only as a scientist, but also as a man. While still young he had been offered a chair at the University of Louvain, which he did not accept; and in 1621 his name was included in a list of scientists proposed for membership in the flourishing new Accademia dei Lincei. He was not nominated, however, because he returned to Ragusa without notice and the Academy did not know his whereabouts.

In letters of that time Ghetaldi was described as having "the morals of an angel" and Paolo Sarpi, his close friend, called him "a Ragusan gentleman of discernment." For his exceptional skill and intelligence Ghetaldi was good-naturedly called "a mathematical demon." Later, in Ragusa, he was even called a magician and gained the reputation of being a sorcerer because he made frequent astronomical observations and experimented with burning glasses; another explanation attributes the sobriquet to his using a nearby cave popularly called "the magician's den" for his research.

Ghetaldi had met Sarpi in Venice before 1600, during his frequent peregrinations between Rome, Padua, and Venice. In Rome his teacher Clavius had introduced him to another Jesuit scholar, Christopher Grinberg, author of a treatise on trigonometry and, later, famous as one of the four Jesuits whom Robert Cardinal Bellarmine consulted in April 1611 on the value of Galileo's *Sidereus nuncius.* Ghetaldi must certainly have met Grinberg again in Padua, where Grinberg lived from 1592 to 1610, and later the two maintained a correspondence, as shown by a letter of 1608 and another of 1614, which accompanied the second part of Ghetaldi's *Apollonius redivivus . . . liber secundus* and in which Ghetaldi declared he was sending the volume "as a sign of reverence and in memory of our old friendship."

In June 1606 the government of Ragusa charged Ghetaldi with a mission to the sultan of Constantinople. The task absorbed him considerably, and to it must be attributed the break in his scientific work that coincides with this period. The mission must have had its dangers, since rumors of his death began to circulate. So persistent were these rumors that even J. E. Montucla, in his *Histoire des mathématiques,* gave Ghetaldi's date of death as about 1609, "in the course of his mission to the [Sublime] Porte."

BIBLIOGRAPHY

Ghetaldi's writings were collected as *Opera omnia,* Žarko Dadić, ed. (Zagreb, 1968). Among his works are *Promotus Archimedes seu de variis corporum generibus gravitate et magnitudine comparatis* (Rome, 1603); *Nonnullae propositiones de parabola* (Rome, 1603); *Apollonius redivivus seu restituta Apollonii Pergaei inclinationum geometria* (Venice, 1607); *Supplementum Apollonii Galli seu exsuscitata Apollonii Pergaei tactionum geometriae pars reliqua* (Venice, 1607); *Variorum problematum collectio* (Venice, 1607); *Apollonius redivivus seu restitutae Apollonii Pergaei de inclinationibus geometriae, liber secundus* (Venice, 1613); and *De resolutione et compositione mathematica, libri quinque* (Rome, 1630).

See also A. Favaro, "Amici e corrispondenti de Galileo Galilei," in *Atti del Istituto veneto di scienze, lettere ed arti,* **69,** 303–324; E. Gelcich, in *Abhandlungen zur Geschichte der Mathematik,* **4,** 191–231; and H. Wieleitner, "Marino Ghetaldi," in *Bibliotheca mathematica,* **13,** 242–247.

LUIGI CAMPEDELLI

GHINI, LUCA (*b.* Croara d'Imola, Italy, *ca.* 1490; *d.* Bologna, Italy, 4 May 1556), *botany.*

A prominent pioneer in the creation of the first botanical gardens in sixteenth-century Italy and in the collection of the earliest herbaria, Ghini exerted his influence primarily through correspondence and teaching, for he wrote little and published nothing in his lifetime. His career reflects the growth and emancipation of botanical research within university medical schools.

His father, Ghino Ghini, was a notary in Imola; this profession may have been in the family, for Ghini's only son, Galeazzo, was also a notary. Ghini was sent to study medicine at Bologna, where he was appointed to read "medicina practica" in 1527. During the next decade the title of his post grew more specifically botanical: in 1535 it was noted "let him lecture on Simples" (i.e., botany as herbal therapeutics); these lectures led to a course on Galen's book *On Simples* (1537), then an associate chair "on Simples," and finally a professorial chair (1539). In 1544 he was invited to become professor of simples at Pisa, where he stayed until 1554. Nevertheless, he remained attached to Bologna, where he had married Gentile Sarti in 1528 and had been granted citizenship in 1535; he spent his vacations there and maintained a house, close to that of his wife's family, with a garden for his private work, where he could try to grow seeds sent him from abroad. Among his successes was "Medica" (*Medicago sativa*) from Spain.

While teaching at Bologna, Ghini introduced, probably for the first time, the herbarium or *hortus siccus,* the technique of pressing and drying plants which could then be attached to cards and filed as a source of reference more reliable than an illustration. His collection was also used for the dissemination of knowledge, for when inquiries were addressed to him, he could send a labeled card to exemplify his answer. For instance, in reply to an appeal by Pietro Mattioli, Ghini mentions enclosing specimens of two varieties of "lesser Horminum" (*Salvia sclarea*) treated in this way. The two oldest surviving herbaria were assembled by Gherardo Cibo da Roccacontrada and Michele Merini, who had been Ghini's pupils. Another pupil, John Falconer, compiled one much admired at the time.

Shortly after his arrival at Pisa, Ghini became actively involved in the creation of the botanical garden there, which disputes with Padua the title of the oldest in Europe set up as an aid to university teaching and research, as opposed to herb gardens intended purely for the immediate supply of medicinal plants. In a letter of July 1545, Ghini describes two expeditions to the mountains, in search of plants for the garden, the site of which was already being cleared. He also became its first prefect and therefore was responsible for the original collection. Ulisse Aldrovandi owned a catalog of the 610 plants that were in the garden in Ghini's time. Ghini had much to do also with the foundation in 1545 of another botanical garden, at Florence, capital of the duchy to which Pisa then belonged.

In 1554 Ghini returned to lecture at Bologna, where he died two years later. His influence was to be felt not only through the new institutions and techniques he helped to establish but also through his pupils, among them some of the outstanding naturalists of the next generation. While he was holidaying at Bologna in 1549, Aldrovandi studied with him, later claiming that his love for botany dated from that time. The affiliation was sustained by correspondence and the exchange of specimens; Aldrovandi also visited Ghini at Pisa, attended his lectures there, and went botanizing with him in the hills behind Lucca. Andrea Cesalpino studied under him at Pisa and succeeded him as prefect of the botanical garden in 1554. Luigi Anguillara, first prefect of the Padua botanical garden, was another pupil, as were two

English herbalists of the new school, William Turner and Falconer.

In 1551 Mattioli asked Ghini's help in the identification of a number of Dioscorides' plants on which he had no information. Ghini's reply, his "Placiti" on these plants, demonstrates his methods. The context obliged him to start with the accounts of Dioscorides or Pliny, then relate them to actual plants known to him; the leaves were his preferred indicator. To help him in these inquiries he procured specimens of the flora of Greece and the Levant from merchants and asked Greek soldiers or his Greek maid about the modern Greek names, in order to compare them with those in classical sources. Luckily, one of Ghini's brothers spent some years in Crete and could supply him with seeds or branches. Besides Crete, Ghini refers to receipt of material from Egypt, Syria, Spain, Sicily, and Calabria; and even "papyrus" leaves from the island of São Tomé, used for wrapping sugarloaves, were not unworthy of his investigation. Certainly he was far from being merely a bookish scholar: the "Placiti" often recall his collecting expeditions in the Apennines, along the Tuscan shore, and on a sail round Elba, where he admired the abundance of *Medicago marina.*

The "Placiti" is our only evidence on Ghini's researches. Although he is supposed to have begun compiling a pictorial herbal on plants of which there were as yet no illustrations, he abandoned it when Mattioli published his own commentaries on Dioscorides, to which Ghini had in effect contributed. Another manuscript, now lost, discussed the kindred topic of plants known to practicing apothecaries but not included in the written tradition of materia medica.

BIBLIOGRAPHY

Ghini's only published works—and those long after his death—were minor medical tracts. Much more important is the letter to Mattioli, published as "I placiti di Luca Ghini intorno a piante descritte nei commentarii al Dioscoride di P. A. Mattioli," G. B. de Toni, ed., in *Memorie del R. Istituto veneto di scienze, lettere ed arti,* **27,** no. 8 (1907). Toni's commentary has been used for the identifications in this article.

Toni is also the author of papers touching on aspects of Ghini's work, which is summarized in his "Luca Ghini," in A. Mieli, ed., *Gli scienziati italiani,* I (Rome, 1921), 1-4. See also A. Chiarugi, "Le date di fondazione dei primi orti botanici del mondo," in *Nuovo giornale botanico italiano,* **60** (1953); and "Nel quarto centenario della morte di Luca Ghini," in *Webbia,* **13** (1957), 1-14; and L. Sabbatani, "Alcuni documenti su la vita di Luca Ghini," in *Atti e memorie della R. Accademia di scienze, lettere ed arti* (Padua), n.s. **39** (1923), 243-248.

A. G. KELLER

GHISI, MARTINO (*b.* Soresina, Italy, 11 November 1715; *d.* Cremona, Italy, 11 May 1794), *medicine.*

Ghisi, who is unjustly forgotten by medical historians and on whom there is very little biographical information, was an obscure provincial doctor to whom we owe one of the first—if not the first—descriptions of diphtheria to be complete and valid both clinically and anatomicopathologically. Probably a handicap to recognition was that his ideas and observations were disseminated not from a university chair but in a small pamphlet with a limited circulation.

After completing his secondary education, Ghisi studied under Paolo Valcarenghi, a doctor of some renown who had founded a practical school of medicine in Cremona; he subsequently moved to Florence, where he graduated from the university. He returned to Cremona to practice and in 1747-1748 combated an epidemic which struck a large number of children and adolescents in the Cremona region. Ghisi made careful clinical and meteorological observations on the epidemic, publishing the results in a pamphlet entitled *Lettere mediche del Dottor M. Ghisi.* Of particular note is the section entitled "Istoria delle angine epidemiche," the first truly complete scientific description of diphtheria.

Ghisi began with a precise account of climatic and meteorological conditions prior to and during the epidemic—in accordance, apparently, with the Hippocratic tradition—but his attention was mainly centered on the clinical framework of the illness. He described in particular detail the diphtheric paralysis of the velum palatinum and the tumefaction of the submaxillary glands.

Ghisi was also interested in examining and describing the diphtheric membrane, which some patients would expel in coughing and which Ghisi compared to the fibrous crusts that formed in blood extracted by bleeding. He did not neglect the anatomicopathological aspect of the epidemic, even though he was able to conduct only one autopsy; this, thanks to his great knowledge of normal and pathological anatomy, was sufficient for him to compare accurately the diagnostic features and pathological alterations detected in the lungs and pleura of patients suffering from pneumonia and pleurisy with those found in diphtheria. He showed quite clearly that the bronchial and pulmonary edema caused by diphtheria resulted in a strain of the right side of the heart.

Ghisi limited himself to clinical and anatomico-pathological observations that could be made directly and objectively, and deliberately refrained from giving an opinion on the etiologic-pathogenic causes of diphtheria (which would in any case have been impossible to identify at that time). He confined himself to emphasizing the small amount of data that he had been able to collect, at the same time steadily refusing to classify it according to any of the several systems then in vogue.

BIBLIOGRAPHY

Ghisi's only publication is *Lettere mediche del Dottor M. Ghisi* (Cremona, 1749). The first letter deals with various illnesses cured by mercury; the second contains the history of epidemic angina in 1747 and 1748.

Secondary literature includes A. Caccia, *Elogio del celebre medico Martino Ghisi* (Cremona, 1794); and C. Castellani, "La 'Lettera medica' di Martino Ghisi relativa alla 'Istoria delle angine epidemiche,'" in *Rivista di storia della medicina,* **2** (1960), 163–188, which includes the text of the letter.

CARLO CASTELLANI

GIARD, ALFRED (*b.* Valenciennes, France, 8 August 1846; *d.* Paris, France, 8 August 1908), *botany, zoology, embryogeny, general biology.*

Giard was an extraordinarily gifted child who, by the age of fifteen, had already acquired, under the influence of his father, an extensive knowledge of insects and plants. Following secondary studies at the *lycée* in Valenciennes, he entered the École Normale Supérieure (1867), where he was named *préparateur* in 1871. He defended his doctoral thesis on the compound ascidians in 1872, then was successively professor at the Faculté des Sciences of Lille (1875), lecturer at the École Normale Supérieure (1887), and professor at the Faculté des Sciences of Paris, holding the chair of evolution of living organisms from 1888 until his death following a short illness. From 1882 to 1885 he sat in the Chamber of Deputies as the member from Valenciennes; but, failing to win reelection in 1885, he gave up politics. He was elected to the Académie des Sciences in 1900.

Giard was a morphologist, a phylogenist, an ethologist—a complete naturalist who was endowed with a remarkable memory and possessed prodigious factual knowledge. Moreover, he had the ability to rank facts and coordinate them to bring out the ideas of general biology.

In 1874, with his own funds, he founded the biological station at Wimereux in order to introduce his students to marine and terrestrial flora and fauna. He was a great laboratory director, and he rapidly formed a brilliant school of zoology in Lille.

Giard was the opposite of a specialist. He was a remarkable observer and the variety of his observations stimulated him to study diverse animals. He discovered the Orthonectida (parasites of the Ophiurida) in 1877, and a member of the Turbellaria (*Fecampia*), a parasite of the higher crustaceans; with J. Bonnier he carried out research on the crustaceans, notably on the Epicaridea (parasitic isopods) and on the Bopyridae.

Giard investigated several problems of general biology: regeneration (hypotypic regeneration), metamorphosis, sexuality, experimental parthenogenesis, merogenesis, hybridization, autotomy, convergence, mimetism, and anhydrobiosis. He defined poecilogony (in the same species animals will develop differently, according to their environment) and parasitic castration (all the morphological or physiological phenomena involved in the organization of a living being are a result of the presence of a parasite acting indirectly or directly on the genital function of the host).

Never an advocate of technique—be it injections or histological sections or preparations—Giard considered the examination of living creatures in their environment to be superior to that of materials that were preserved or cut in pieces. One ought always to begin with examination.

Giard was rapidly able to free himself from the tenor of instruction he had received, especially from J. H. Lacaze-Duthiers, who for a long time opposed his nomination to Paris. He became a convinced follower of transformism, a doctrine opposed by his contemporaries, and his courses were filled with new ideas already widespread abroad. The transformist hypotheses overturned the general classification of animals. Giard was among the first to bring together the mollusks and the Annelida, Brachiopoda, Bryozoa, and Gephyrea; in 1876 he united them under the name Gymnotoca—the name was forgotten, but the grouping was recognized by Emil Hatschek, who termed its members the Trochozoa.

In accepting transformism as fact and interpreting nature accordingly, Giard was under the influence of Ernst Haeckel. He thought that Lamarckism and Darwinism complemented each other. The primordial cause of variation resided in the actions of external agents, which constituted the primary factors of evolution (a Lamarckian idea); natural selection intervened only as a secondary factor of great power (a Darwinian idea). Yet Giard preferred Lamarckism to Darwinism and strove to glorify Lamarck. Heredity, sexual selection, and physiological selection were also secondary factors. He did not accept particulate theories of heredity, and he rejected all theories based on unverifiable internal tendencies, such as the orthogenesis conceived by Teodor Eimer.

Giard created new biological terms, some of which became classic. He was also greatly interested in scientific societies and attempted to guide their activity. In 1878 he became editor of the *Bulletin scientifique du Nord;* ten years later this local journal became the *Bulletin scientifique de la France et de la Belgique.*

BIBLIOGRAPHY

I. Original Works. Giard's writings include "Étude critique des travaux d'embryogénie relatifs à la parenté des Vertébrés et des Tuniciers," in *Archives de zoologie expérimentale,* **1** (1872), 233–288; "Deuxième étude critique des travaux d'embryogénie relatifs à la parenté des Vertébrés et des Tuniciers; recherches nouvelles du professeur Kuppfer," *ibid.,* 307–428; "Recherches sur les Ascidies composées ou Synascidies," *ibid.,* 501–704, his doctoral thesis; "Principes généraux de biologie," the introduction to T. H. Huxley's *Éléments d'anatomie comparée des Invertébrés* (1876); "Sur l'organisation et la classification des Orthonectidea," in *Bulletin scientifique du Nord,* **11** (1879), 338–341; "Nouvelles remarques sur les Entonisciens," in *Comptes rendus hebdomadaires des séances de l'Académie des sciences,* **102** (1886), 1173–1176, written with J. Bonnier; "Sur un Rhadocoele nouveau, parasite et nidulant (*Fecampia erythrocephala*)," *ibid.,* **103** (1886), 499–501; "La castration parasitaire et son influence sur les caractères extérieurs du sexe mâle chez les Crustacés décapodes," in *Bulletin scientifique du Nord,* **18** (1887), 1–28; "Contribution à l'étude des Bopyriens," in *Travaux de l'Institut de zoologie de Lille et du Laboratoire de zoologie maritime de Wimereux,* **5** (1887), written with J. Bonnier; "Leçon d'ouverture des cours d'évolution des êtres organisés," in *Bulletin scientifique,* **20** (1889), 1–26; "Sur la signification des globules polaires," *ibid.,* 95–103; and "Les facteurs de l'évolution, leçon d'ouverture du cours d'évolution des êtres organisés, 2ème année," in *Revue scientifique,* **44** (1889), 641–648.

Later works are "Prodrome d'une monographie des Epicarides du golfe de Naples," in *Bulletin scientifique du Nord,* **22** (1890), 367–391, written with J. Bonnier; "Le principe de Lamarck et l'hérédité des modifications somatiques, leçon d'ouverture du cours d'évolution des êtres organisés," in *Revue scientifique,* **46** (1890), 705–713; "L'anhydrobiose ou ralentissement des phénomènes vitaux sous l'influence de la déshydratation progressive," in *Comptes rendus de la Société de biologie,* **66** (1894), 497–500; "La direction des recherches biologiques en France et la conversion de M. Yves Delage," in *Bulletin scientifique du Nord,* **27** (1896), 432–458; *Titres et travaux scientifiques* (Paris, 1896); "Coup d'oeil sur la faune et note sur la flore du Boulonnais," in *Boulogne et le Boulonnais* (Paris, 1899); "Parthénogenèse de la macrogamète et de la microgamète des organismes pluricellulaires," in *Volume cinquantenaire de la Société biologique* (Paris, 1899), pp. 654–667; "Les faux hybrides de Millardet et leur interprétation," in *Comptes rendus de la Société de biologie,* **55** (1903), 779–782; "Les tendances actuelles de la morphologie et ses rapports avec les autres sciences," in *Bulletin scientifique du Nord,* **39** (1905), 455–486; "La poecilogonie," *ibid.,* 153–187; "L'évolution dans les sciences biologiques," *ibid.,* **41** (1907), 427–458; and "L'éducation du morphologiste," in *La méthode dans les sciences: Morphologie* (Paris, 1908), pp. 149–175.

II. Secondary Literature. There is a notice on Giard's life and works, with complete bibliography, by F. Le Dantec and M. Caullery in *Bulletin scientifique de la France et de la Belgique,* **42** (1909), i–lxxiii. Obituaries include those by H. Piéron, in *Scientia,* **5** (1909), 1–4; P. Pelseneer, in *Annales de la Société royale zoologique et malacologique de Belgique,* **43** (1908), 220–227; E. Rabaud, in *Bibliographie anatomique,* **18** (1909), 285–290; H. Fischer, in *Journal de conchyliologie,* **56** (1909), 294–301; and M. Caullery, in *Revue du mois,* **6** (1908), 385–399.

Andrée Tétry

GIBBS, JOSIAH WILLARD (*b.* New Haven, Connecticut, 11 February 1839; *d.* New Haven, 28 April 1903), *theoretical physics.*

Gibbs was the only son among the five children of Josiah Willard Gibbs and Mary Anna Van Cleve Gibbs. His father was a noted philologist, a graduate of Yale and professor of sacred literature there from 1826 until his death in 1861. The younger Gibbs grew up in New Haven and graduated from Yale College in 1858, having won a number of prizes in both Latin and mathematics. He continued at Yale as a student of engineering in the new graduate school, and in 1863 he received one of the first Ph.D. degrees granted in the United States. After serving as a tutor in Yale College for three years, giving elementary instruction in Latin and natural philosophy, Gibbs left New Haven for further study in Europe. By this time both his parents and two of his sisters were dead, and Gibbs traveled with his two surviving older sisters, Anna and Julia. He spent a year each at the universities of Paris, Berlin, and Heidelberg, attending lectures in mathematics and physics and reading widely in both fields. These European studies, rather than his earlier engineering education, provided the foundation for his subsequent career.

Gibbs returned to New Haven in June 1869. He never again left America and rarely left even New Haven except for his annual summer holidays in northern New England and a very occasional journey to lecture or attend a meeting. Gibbs never married and lived all his life in the house in which he had grown up, less than a block away from the college buildings, sharing it with Anna, Julia, and Julia's family. In July 1871, two years before he published his first scientific paper, Gibbs was appointed professor of mathematical physics at Yale. He held this position without salary for the first nine years, living on his inherited income. It was during this time that he wrote the memoirs on thermodynamics that constitute his greatest contribution to science. Gibbs had no problem about declining a paid appointment at Bowdoin College in 1873, but he was seriously tempted to leave Yale in 1880, when he was invited to join the faculty of the new Johns Hopkins University at Baltimore. Only then did Yale provide a salary for Gibbs, as tangible evidence of the esteem in which he was held by his colleagues and of his importance to the university, but this salary was still only two-thirds of what Johns Hopkins had offered him. Gibbs stayed on at Yale nevertheless and continued teaching there until his death, after a brief illness, in the spring of 1903.

Gibbs's first published paper did not appear until he was thirty-four years old, and it displays his unique mastery of thermodynamics. If there are even earlier signs of Gibbs's intellectual power, they must be sought in his previous engineering work. His doctoral thesis, "On the Form of the Teeth of Wheels in Spur Gearing," certainly shows Gibbs's unusually strong geometrical ability. He generally preferred "the niceties of geometrical reasoning" to analytical methods in his later work, and this is true in his thesis. The style of this early work also shows the same "austerity," the same "extreme economy (one might almost say parsimony) in the use of words,"[1] that made his later memoirs so difficult to read. Some of his engineering work, such as the design of an improved railway car brake, for which he received a patent in 1866, is hard to relate to the concerns of the future master of theoretical physics—but this is not true of all of it. After his return from Europe, Gibbs designed a new form of governor for steam engines by suitable mounting of a second pair of massive balls on the simple Watt governor. This new arrangement was planned to increase the responsiveness of the system to a change in the engine's running speed. Although Gibbs went no further with this invention than having a model of it built in the department workshop, it is interesting nevertheless: the problems of dynamic equilibrium and stability of this particular mechanical device foreshadow the related questions of equilibrium and stability that he would soon raise and answer for general thermodynamic systems.

When Gibbs first turned his attention to thermodynamics in the early 1870's, that science had already achieved a certain level of maturity. Rudolf Clausius had taken the essential step in 1850, when he argued that two laws and not just one are needed as the basis of a theory of heat. Only a year before that, William Thomson had been writing about the "very perplexing question," and the associated "innumerable" and "insuperable" difficulties, of choosing *the* correct axiom for the theory.[2] Should one hold fast to Carnot's postulate (that heat must pass from a hot body to a colder one when work is done in a cyclic process), even though Carnot's results seemed to depend on his use of the caloric theory of heat? Or should one accept the interconvertibility of heat and work, since James Joule's new experimental evidence clearly favored the mechanical theory of heat? Clausius showed that, despite the apparent need to choose one law or the other, both were necessary and both could be maintained without contradiction. One had only to drop Carnot's inessential requirement that heat itself be conserved. This change did have one major implication. The proof of Carnot's theorem (that the maximum motive power of heat depends solely on the temperatures between which the heat is transferred) now had to appeal to a new axiom: that heat "everywhere exhibits the tendency to annul temperature differences, and therefore to pass from a *warmer* body to a *colder* one."[3] Clausius' memoir demonstrated how one could develop a thermodynamics starting with both the equivalence of heat and work and his new axiom. These two laws of thermodynamics were restated in slightly different form a year later by Thomson, who proceeded to apply them to a variety of physical problems, including thermoelectricity.

Clausius tried as hard as he could to find the essence of the second law of thermodynamics, since he felt unable at first to "recognize . . ., with sufficient clearness, the real nature of the theorem."[4] This search led finally in 1865 to his most concise and ultimately most fruitful formulation of the two laws, the formulation Gibbs later used as the motto of his greatest work: "The energy of the universe is constant. The entropy of the universe tends to a maximum."[5] The two basic quantities, internal energy and entropy, were, in effect, defined by the two laws of thermodynamics. The internal energy U is that function of the state of the system whose differential is given by the equation expressing the first law,

$$dU = đQ + đW, \qquad (1)$$

where $đQ$ and $đW$ are, respectively, the heat added to the system and the external work done on the system in an infinitesimal process. For a simple fluid the work $đW$ is given by the equation

$$đW = -PdV, \tag{2}$$

where P is the pressure on the system and V is its volume. Neither the heat $đQ$ nor the work $đW$ is the differential of a function of state, and the inexactness or nonintegrability of these differentials is indicated by the symbol $đ$, whose use for this purpose goes back to Carl Neumann's lectures in the early 1870's.[6] The entropy S is that state function whose differential is given by the equation

$$dS = \frac{đQ}{T}, \tag{3}$$

valid for reversible processes, where T is the absolute temperature. For irreversible processes equation (3) is replaced by the inequality

$$dS > \frac{đQ}{T}. \tag{4}$$

The power and importance of the entropy concept were certainly not evident to Clausius' contemporaries upon the publication of his 1865 paper. Clausius himself considered it to be a summarizing concept and thought that the true physical significance of the second law was better expressed in terms of the disgregation, a concept he sought to interpret mechanically. Entropy plays no particular role in the thermodynamics texts by Georg Krebs (1874) and Carl Neumann (1875). The word was picked up by Peter Guthrie Tait in his *Sketch of Thermodynamics* (1868), but he completely changed its meaning, using it to denote available energy rather than the quantity Clausius had intended. Tait's misinterpretation was taken up and repeated by James Clerk Maxwell in his *Theory of Heat* (1871). The confusion and uncertainty about the thermodynamic significance of entropy were only aggravated by the bitter priority disputes between Clausius and Tait (on behalf of Thomson) that raged in the early 1870's. The basic structure of modern thermodynamics was implicitly present in the work of both Clausius and Thomson, but it was certainly not clearly visible to most writers on the subject.

It was in this context that Gibbs's first scientific paper, "Graphical Methods in the Thermodynamics of Fluids," appeared in 1873. His mastery and his quiet assurance in this paper are as remarkable as his scientific insight. Gibbs assumed from the outset that entropy is one of the essential concepts to be used in treating a thermodynamic system, along with energy, temperature, pressure, and volume. He immediately combined the first three equations given above to obtain the form

$$dU = TdS - PdV, \tag{5}$$

a relation that contains only the state variables of the system, the process-dependent heat and work having been eliminated. As Gibbs pointed out, an equation expressing the internal energy of the system in terms of its entropy and volume could appropriately be called its fundamental equation; for equation (5) would then allow one to determine the two equations of state, expressing temperature and pressure as functions of the pair, volume and entropy. These remarks were the starting point for Gibbs's later work, but in this first paper he limited himself to a discussion of what could be done with geometrical representations of thermodynamic relationships in two dimensions.

James Watt's indicator diagram, in which pressure and volume are plotted on the two coordinate axes, had been in use for thermodynamic purposes since Émile Clapeyron's memoir of 1834. But Gibbs showed how other choices for the coordinate variables would produce representations even more useful for thermodynamic purposes; the temperature-entropy diagram, for example, had many advantages in the study of cyclic processes. The form of the basic equation (5), expressing both laws of thermodynamics, suggested that the volume-entropy diagram might be best suited for general thermodynamic considerations, and Gibbs discussed it in more detail. He also showed how some of the interrelations among the curves describing, respectively, states of equal pressure, equal temperature, equal energy, and equal entropy were independent of how the thermodynamic diagram was constructed and followed directly from the stability of equilibrium states.

In his second paper, which appeared later in 1873, Gibbs extended his geometrical discussion to three dimensions by analyzing the properties of the surface representing the fundamental thermodynamic equation of a pure substance. The thermodynamic relationships could be brought out most clearly by constructing the surface using entropy, energy, and volume as the three orthogonal coordinates. Gibbs pointed out that, as a consequence of equation (5), the temperature and pressure of the body in any state was determined by the plane tangent to the surface at the corresponding point, since one has the equations

$$T = \left(\frac{\partial U}{\partial S}\right)_V \tag{6a}$$

and

$$-P = \left(\frac{\partial U}{\partial V}\right)_S. \tag{6b}$$

This way of representing the thermodynamic properties of a body in thermodynamic equilibrium could be used just as well when different parts of the body were in different states (for example, a mixture of liquid and gas or of two different crystalline forms of the same pure substance). Gibbs showed how one could use the thermodynamic surface to discuss the coexistence of the various phases (liquid, solid, and gas) of a pure substance and the stability of these states under given conditions of temperature and pressure. One feature of particular interest was the critical point—the state at which liquid and gas become identical—a phenomenon discovered experimentally in carbon dioxide by Thomas Andrews only a few years earlier.

These early papers, as well as Gibbs's major memoir on thermodynamics that soon followed them, appeared in the *Transactions of the Connecticut Academy of Arts and Sciences,* a new and relatively obscure journal whose nonlocal circulation consisted largely of exchanges with other learned societies, including some 140 outside the United States. Gibbs did not count on finding his potential readers among those who checked the contents of the *Transactions;* he sent copies of his papers to an impressive list of scientists in many countries, a list that probably included all those he thought might really read and understand his work.[7] One of them was James Clerk Maxwell, who proved to be Gibbs's most enthusiastic and most influential reader. He immediately accepted Gibbs's clarification of what Clausius had intended by the term "entropy," correcting the error in his own *Theory of Heat* accordingly and informing Tait about his mistake.

Maxwell found Gibbs's use of geometric rather than algebraic arguments particularly attractive, since he too preferred geometric insight to calculations, even when others found algebraic procedures decidedly simpler. He was sufficiently impressed by Gibbs's paper on the thermodynamic surface to include a discussion of this subject in the fourth edition of *Theory of Heat* (1875) and actually to construct a model of the thermodynamic surface for water, which he sent to Gibbs. He talked about Gibbs's work to his colleagues at Cambridge and recommended it to his friends. "Read Prof. J. Willard Gibbs on the surface whose coordinates are Volume Entropy and Energy," he wrote to Tait, and then added for the benefit of his rather chauvinistic friend, "He has more sense than any German."[8] Maxwell even started to generalize Gibbs's thermodynamics of a pure substance to include the case of heterogeneous mixtures. This proved to be quite unnecessary and was dropped when he received a set of galley proofs of Gibbs's new memoir containing this generalization and a great deal more.

"On the Equilibrium of Heterogeneous Substances" contains Gibbs's major contributions to thermodynamics. In this single memoir of some 300 pages he vastly extended the domain covered by thermodynamics, including chemical, elastic, surface, electromagnetic, and electrochemical phenomena in a single system. The basic idea had been foreshadowed in his two earlier papers, in which Gibbs had directed his attention to the properties characterizing the equilibrium states of simple systems rather than to the heat and work exchanged in particular kinds of processes. In the abstract of his memoir that Gibbs published in the *American Journal of Science* in 1878, he began by stating the simple but profound idea underlying his work:

> It is an inference naturally suggested by the general increase of entropy which accompanies the changes occurring in any isolated material system that when the entropy of the system has reached a maximum, the system will be in a state of equilibrium. Although this principle has by no means escaped the attention of physicists, its importance does not appear to have been duly appreciated. Little has been done to develop the principle as a foundation for the general theory of thermodynamic equilibrium.[9]

Gibbs formulated the criterion for thermodynamic equilibrium in two alternative and equivalent ways. "For the equilibrium of any isolated system it is necessary and sufficient that in all possible variations of the state of the system which do not alter its energy [entropy], the variation of its entropy [energy] shall either vanish or be negative [positive]."[10] The bracketed form immediately indicates that thermodynamic equilibrium is a natural generalization of mechanical equilibrium, both being characterized by minimum energy under appropriate conditions. The consequences of this criterion could then be worked out as soon as the energy of the system was expressed in terms of the proper variables. Gibbs's first and probably most significant application of this approach was to the problem of chemical equilibrium. The result of his work was described by Wilhelm Ostwald as determining the form and content of chemistry for a century to come, and by Henri Le Chatelier as comparable in its importance for chemistry with that of Antoine Lavoisier.

The simplest case is that of a homogeneous phase—a liquid or gas, for example—containing n independent chemical species $S_1, \cdots, S_n$ whose masses $m_1, \cdots, m_n$ can be varied. Gibbs modified the basic equation (5) to include the change of internal energy due to a change in the mass of any of the chemical components by writing it in the form

$$dU = TdS - PdV + \sum_{i=1}^{n} \mu_i \, dm_i. \quad (7)$$

Here dm_i is the change in mass (conveniently expressed as the number of moles) and the new quantity μ_i is the (chemical) potential of the ith chemical species. The chemical potential is related to the energy by the equation

$$\mu_i = \left(\frac{\partial U}{\partial m_i}\right)_{S,V,m_j'}, \quad (8)$$

where the subscript m_j' means that μ_i represents the rate of change of energy with respect to the mass of the ith component in this phase, the masses of all other components being held constant along with entropy and volume.

In a heterogeneous system composed of several homogeneous phases the fundamental equilibrium condition leads to the requirement that temperature, pressure, and the chemical potential of each independent chemical component must have the same values throughout the system. From these general conditions Gibbs derived the phase rule, that cornerstone of physical chemistry, which specifies the number of independent variations δ in a system of r coexistent phases having n independent chemical components:

$$\delta = n + 2 - r. \quad (9)$$

Gibbs also showed how to obtain the specific conditions for equilibrium when chemical reactions could take place in the system. Instead of one's attention being restricted to a set of independent chemical components, all the relevant chemical species are considered. Suppose, for example, that a reaction of the type

$$\sum_j a_j A_j = 0 \quad (10)$$

can occur; here the a_j's are integers, the stoichiometric coefficients, and the A_j's stand for the chemical symbols of the reacting substances. (An illustration would be the reaction $H_2 + Cl_2 - 2\,HCl = 0$, where $a_1 = 1$, $a_2 = 1$, $a_3 = -2$ and the corresponding A_j are respectively H_2, Cl_2, and HCl.) The equilibrium condition that Gibbs derived for such a reaction has the simple form

$$\sum_j a_j \mu_j = 0, \quad (11)$$

obtained by replacing the chemical symbols A_j with the chemical potential μ_j of the corresponding substance in the reaction equation (10). Since the potentials could in principle be determined from experimental data, the equilibrium conditions were really established by equation (11).

The requirement that the energy have a minimum and not just a stationary value at equilibrium was used by Gibbs to explore the stability of equilibrium states. This stability depends ultimately on the second law of thermodynamics and manifests itself in the unique sign of certain properties of all substances; the heat capacity at constant volume, for example, must be positive, and the isothermal derivative of pressure with respect to volume must be negative for any substance. The most interesting aspect of Gibbs's investigation of stability was his theory of critical phases, those situations where the distinction between coexistent phases vanishes and the stability is of a lower order than that usually found.

Gibbs's memoir showed how the general theory of thermodynamic equilibrium could be applied to phenomena as varied as the dissolving of a crystal in a liquid, the temperature dependence of the electromotive force of an electrochemical cell, and the heat absorbed when the surface of discontinuity between two fluids is increased. But even more important than the particular results he obtained was his introduction of the general method and concepts with which all applications of thermodynamics could be handled.

Although Maxwell responded immediately to Gibbs's work and influenced a number of his English colleagues to apply Gibbs's results if not his methods, it took a little longer for Continental scientists to appreciate Gibbs. Such figures as Hermann von Helmholtz and Max Planck independently developed thermodynamic methods for chemical and electrochemical problems in the 1880's, quite unaware of Gibbs's prior work. This situation changed gradually—Ludwig Boltzmann referred to Gibbs in 1883—but it was Wilhelm Ostwald's German translation of Gibbs's papers in 1892 that made his ideas more readily available to German chemists.

Gibbs wrote no other major works on thermodynamics itself, restricting himself to a few small applications and developments of his extensive memoir. He rejected all suggestions that he write a treatise that would make his ideas easier to grasp. Even Lord Rayleigh thought the original paper "too condensed and too difficult for most, I might say all, readers."[11] Gibbs responded by saying that in his own view the memoir was instead "too *long*" and showed a lack of "sense of the value of time, of [his] own or others, when [he] wrote it."[12]

During the 1880's Gibbs seems to have concentrated on optics and particularly on Maxwell's electromagnetic theory of light. He was giving lectures on Maxwell's theory at Yale at least as early as 1885, and he published a series of papers in the *American Journal of Science* on double refraction and dispersion, that is, on the behavior of light as it passes through material media. Two aspects of Gibbs's optical work are of more than technical interest. He emphasized that a theory of dispersion requires one to treat the local irregularities of the electric displacement due to the atomic constitution of the medium. Since he was writing before H. A. Lorentz's theory of electrons (the first version of which did not appear until 1892), Gibbs had to make assumptions of a different kind from those of later theories, and he missed the essential contribution of the atomic structure of the medium—the frequency dependence of the dielectric constant. In the last two papers of this series, published in 1888 and 1889, Gibbs appeared as a defender of the electromagnetic theory of light against the latest versions of purely mechanical theories. These were based on special elastic ethers still being proposed by William Thomson. Gibbs showed that although such theories might account for the phenomena, they required rather artificial assumptions as to internal forces, while Maxwell's theory was "not obliged to invent hypotheses."[13]

Gibbs's reading of Maxwell's *Treatise on Electricity and Magnetism* led him to a study of quaternions, since Maxwell had used the quaternion notation to a limited extent in that work. Gibbs decided, however, that quaternions did not really provide the mathematical language appropriate for theoretical physics, and he worked out a simpler and more straightforward vector analysis. He wrote a pamphlet on this subject which he had printed in 1881 and 1884 for private distribution to his classes and to selected correspondents. No real publication of Gibbs's version of vector analysis took place until 1901, when his student Edwin B. Wilson prepared a textbook of the subject based on Gibbs's lectures. In 1891 Gibbs defended his use of vectors rather than quaternions against an attack by Tait, who was the great exponent of—and crusader for—William Rowan Hamilton's quaternions. Gibbs more than held his own in the ensuing controversy over quaternions, debating both Tait and his disciples in the pages of *Nature,* on minor matters of notation and on the "deeper question of notions underlying that of notations."[14]

During the 1890's the classic goal of the physicist—the explanation of natural phenomena in mechanical terms—was seriously questioned and sharply criticized. Among the most outspoken critics were such men as Ernst Mach, Pierre Duhem, and Wilhelm Ostwald, who rejected the concept of atomism along with that of mechanism. One of the spokesmen for the group who called themselves energeticists was Georg Helm, who in 1898 wrote a treatise on the historical development of energetics. In his book Helm claimed Gibbs as a fellow energeticist, pointing to Gibbs's writings on thermodynamics as a sign that he was free of any prejudice in favor of atomistic mechanical explanations. To Helm, Gibbs's thinking proceeded directly from the two laws of thermodynamics "without any hankering or yearning after mechanics"; his writings were "not decked out with molecular theories."[15] While it is true that Gibbs's papers on thermodynamics were based only on the two laws and required no assumptions about the molecular structure of matter, it is equally true that Gibbs believed in and constructed a (statistical) mechanical explanation of thermodynamics itself. He certainly did not share the scientific values of the energeticists.

Gibbs had carefully studied the writings of Maxwell and Boltzmann on the kinetic theory of gases. This is evident from his obituary notice of Clausius, written in 1889, in which he commented perceptively on a peculiar feature of Clausius' work in this field. Clausius never really accepted the statistical point of view. "In reading Clausius we seem to be reading mechanics; in reading Maxwell, and in much of Boltzmann's most valuable work, we seem rather to be reading in the theory of probabilities."[16] Maxwell had introduced statistical methods in his first paper on gases in 1860 and had emphasized the essentially statistical nature of the second law of thermodynamics with the help of the "Maxwell demon." Boltzmann then developed all the essential features of a theoretical explanation of the second law based on a combination of mechanics and the laws of probability applied to a large assemblage of molecules in a gas. Gibbs had already paid his own respects to this fundamental insight in his memoir on heterogeneous equilibrium, when he argued that "the impossibility of an uncompensated decrease of entropy seems to be reduced to improbability."[17]

During the academic year 1889–1890 Gibbs announced "A short course on the a priori Deduction of Thermodynamic Principles from the Theory of Probabilities,"[18] a subject on which he lectured repeatedly during the 1890's. He referred to this subject in a letter to Lord Rayleigh in 1892:

> Just now I am trying to get ready for publication something on thermodynamics from the *a priori* point of view, or rather on "Statistical Mechanics" of which the principal interest would be in its application to thermodynamics—in the line therefore of the work of Maxwell and Boltzmann. I do not know that I shall have anything particularly new in substance, but shall

be contented if I can so choose my standpoint (as seems to me possible) as to get a simpler view of the subject.[19]

In fact Gibbs did not publish anything more than a very brief abstract on this subject (1884) until 1902, when his book *Elementary Principles in Statistical Mechanics Developed With Special Reference to the Rational Foundation of Thermodynamics* appeared as one of the Yale Bicentennial series.

Gibbs thought of his book as offering a more general approach to statistical mechanics than that used by Boltzmann or Maxwell. Individual results previously obtained by others could now assume their proper places in the logical structure Gibbs gave to the subject. He considered an ensemble of systems, that is, a large number of replicas of the physical system of interest—which might be anything from a molecule to a sample of gas or a crystal. The replicas were all identical in structure but differed in the values of their coordinates and momenta. The ensemble was then characterized by its probability density ρ in phase space, where $\rho\, dq_1 \cdots dq_N dp_1 \cdots dp_N$ is the fractional number of systems in the ensemble whose coordinates $\{q_i\}$ and momenta $\{p_j\}$ lie in the intervals $\{q_j, q_j + dq_j\}$ and $\{p_j, p_j + dp_j\}$, respectively, at time t. The phase point representing any individual system moves with time, and so the probability density ρ at any point in the $2N$-dimensional phase space varies in a way determined by the mechanical equations of motion of the system.

If the average behavior of a system in the ensemble was to describe the behavior of the actual physical system, then a physical system in equilibrium had to be described by a stationary ensemble, one whose probability density ρ was constant in time. Gibbs analyzed several such stationary ensembles but found the one he called "canonical" to be most useful. In a canonical ensemble the probability density ρ is given by the equation

$$\rho(q_1 \cdots p_N) = \exp\{(\psi - E)/\Theta\}, \qquad (12)$$

where $E(q_1 \cdots p_N)$ is the energy of the system having coordinates and momenta $q_1 \cdots p_N$, and ψ, Θ are constants in phase space. Gibbs showed that the energy of such an ensemble has a sharply peaked distribution, if the systems have many degrees of freedom; only a very small fraction of the systems in the canonical ensemble have energies appreciably different from the average.

The principal theme of Gibbs's book is the analogy, as he describes it, between the average behavior of a canonical ensemble of systems and the behavior of a physical system obeying the laws of thermodynamics. When this analogy is worked out, the modulus Θ of the canonical distribution is proportional to the absolute temperature, with a universal proportionality constant k,

$$\Theta = kT. \qquad (13)$$

The average energy $\bar{E}$, where $\bar{E}$ satisfies the equation

$$\bar{E} = \frac{\int E\rho\, dq_1 \cdots dp_N}{\int \rho\, dq_1 \cdots dp_N}, \qquad (14)$$

is identified with the thermodynamic internal energy U. The second parameter of the distribution, ψ, is fixed by the condition that ρ is a probability density, so one has the equation

$$\psi = -\Theta \ln \{\int \exp(-E/\Theta)\, dq_1 \cdots dp_N\} \qquad (15)$$

and ψ is also related to the energy U (or $\bar{E}$) and the entropy S by the equation

$$\psi = U - TS, \qquad (16)$$

a result Gibbs obtained by analyzing the meanings of heat and work in the ensemble.

Gibbs was very much aware of the gaps in his statistical mechanics. He had supplied a "rational foundation" for thermodynamics in statistical mechanics to the extent that thermodynamic systems could be treated as if they were conservative mechanical systems with a finite number of degrees of freedom. He could not incorporate the phenomena of radiation that were of so much interest at the turn of the century, nor could he surmount the long-standing difficulties associated with the theorem of the equipartition of energy. For these reasons he disclaimed any attempts "to explain the mysteries of nature" and put his work forward as the statistical "branch of rational mechanics."[20] He was also dissatisfied with the effort he had made in the twelfth chapter of his book to explain the irreversibility of nature embodied in the second law. His argument in this chapter was almost completely verbal rather than mathematical, and his statements were carefully qualified. Gibbs's manuscript notes suggest that he was still struggling with the problem of irreversibility and the nature of the entropy of systems not in equilibrium.

Despite these difficulties Gibbs's work in statistical mechanics constituted a major advance. His methods were more general and more readily applicable than Boltzmann's and eventually came to dominate the whole field. Gibbs did not live to see the real successes of statistical mechanics, for his fatal illness came within a year of the publication of his book.

NOTES

1. Everett O. Waters, "Commentary Upon the Gibbs Monograph 'On the Form of the Teeth of Wheels in Spur Gearing,'" in L. P. Wheeler, E. O. Waters, and S. W. Dudley, eds., *The Early Work of Willard Gibbs in Applied Mechanics* (New York, 1947), p. 43.
2. William Thomson, "An Account of Carnot's Theory of the Motive Power of Heat," in *Transactions of the Royal Society of Edinburgh,* **16** (1849), 541.
3. Rudolf Clausius, "On the Moving Force of Heat and the Laws of Heat Which May Be Deduced Therefrom," in *Annalen der Physik,* **79** (1850), 368, 500. Trans. into English by T. Archer Hirst as *The Mechanical Theory of Heat* (London, 1867), p. 45.
4. Clausius, "On a Modified Form of the Second Fundamental Theorem in the Mechanical Theory of Heat," in *Annalen der Physik,* **93** (1854), 481. Translation, *The Mechanical Theory of Heat,* p. 111.
5. Clausius, "On Several Convenient Forms of the Fundamental Equations of the Mechanical Theory of Heat," in *Annalen der Physik,* **125** (1865), 353. Translation, *The Mechanical Theory of Heat,* p. 365.
6. Carl Neumann, *Vorlesungen über die mechanische Theorie der Wärme* (Leipzig, 1875), p. ix.
7. The list is reprinted as app. IV in Lynde Phelps Wheeler, *Josiah Willard Gibbs* (New Haven, 1952).
8. James Clerk Maxwell to Peter Guthrie Tait, 13 Oct. 1874.
9. Gibbs, abstract of "Equilibrium of Heterogeneous Substances," in *American Journal of Science,* 3rd ser., **16** (1878), 441; *Scientific Papers,* I, 354.
10. *Ibid.*
11. Lord Rayleigh to J. W. Gibbs, 5 June 1892.
12. Gibbs to Lord Rayleigh, 27 June 1892.
13. Gibbs, "A Comparison of the Electric Theory of Light and Sir William Thomson's Theory of a Quasi-Labile Ether," in *American Journal of Science,* 3rd ser., **37** (1889), 144; *Scientific Papers,* II, 246.
14. Gibbs, "On the Role of Quaternions in the Algebra of Vectors," in *Nature,* **43** (1891), 511; *Scientific Papers,* II, 155.
15. Georg Helm, *Die Energetik* (Leipzig, 1898), p. 146.
16. Gibbs, "Rudolf Julius Emanuel Clausius," in *Proceedings of the American Academy of Arts and Sciences,* **16** (1889), 458; *Scientific Papers,* II, 265.
17. Gibbs, "On the Equilibrium of Heterogeneous Substances," in *Transactions of the Connecticut Academy of Arts and Sciences,* **3** (1875–1878), 108, 343; *Scientific Papers,* I, 167.
18. Henry A. Bumstead to Edwin B. Wilson, 22 Dec. 1915.
19. Gibbs to Lord Rayleigh, 27 June 1892.
20. Gibbs, *Elementary Principles in Statistical Mechanics* (New Haven, 1902), pp. ix–x.

BIBLIOGRAPHY

I. Original Works. Gibbs's scientific papers are repr. in *The Scientific Papers of J. Willard Gibbs,* H. A. Bumstead and R. G. Van Name, eds., 2 vols. (New York, 1906; repr. 1961). Vol. I contains the papers on thermodynamics; all others are in vol. II. There is also his *Elementary Principles in Statistical Mechanics* (New Haven, 1902; repr. New York, 1960). His work on vector analysis is in Edwin B. Wilson, *Vector Analysis Founded Upon the Lectures of J. Willard Gibbs* (New York, 1901). Gibbs's engineering work is reprinted in *The Early Work of Willard Gibbs in Applied Mechanics,* compiled by Lynde P. Wheeler, Everett O. Waters, and Samuel W. Dudley (New York, 1947). See also Edwin B. Wilson, "The Last Unpublished Notes of J. Willard Gibbs," in *Proceedings of the American Philosophical Society,* **105** (1961), 545–558.

Gibbs's notes, correspondence, and MSS are collected in the Beinecke Rare Book and Manuscript Library of Yale University.

II. Secondary Literature. There is extensive treatment of Gibbs's writings in F. G. Donnan and Arthur Haas, eds., *A Commentary on the Scientific Writings of J. Willard Gibbs,* 2 vols. (New Haven, 1936). The official biography is Lynde P. Wheeler, *Josiah Willard Gibbs. The History of a Great Mind* (New Haven, 1951; rev. ed., 1952). The appendixes include a bibliography of writings on Gibbs, a catalog of Gibbs's scientific correspondence, his mailing lists for reprints, the text of his first unpublished paper, and family information.

A more popularly written biography, valuable for period background and a poet's insight, is Muriel Rukeyser, *Willard Gibbs* (New York, 1942; repr. 1964).

Shorter accounts may be found in Henry A. Bumstead, "Biographical Sketch," repr. in Gibbs's *Scientific Papers,* I, xi–xxvi, and in J. G. Crowther, *Famous American Men of Science* (New York, 1937), pp. 229–297.

Two recent articles are Martin J. Klein, "Gibbs on Clausius," in Russell McCormmach, ed., *Historical Studies in the Physical Sciences,* I (Philadelphia, 1969), pp. 127–149; and Elizabeth W. Garber, "James Clerk Maxwell and Thermodynamics," in *American Journal of Physics,* **37** (1969), 146–155.

Martin J. Klein

GIBBS, (OLIVER) WOLCOTT (*b.* New York, N.Y., 21 February 1822; *d.* Newport, Rhode Island, 9 December 1908), *chemistry.*

Gibbs's career epitomizes much of the development of chemistry in America. He received his M.D. in 1845 from the College of Physicians and Surgeons with a dissertation on chemical classification. He then studied in Germany and France and, while in Berlin, was particularly influenced by Heinrich Rose. After fourteen years (1849–1863) teaching elementary students at what is now City College of the City University of New York, he became Rumford professor at Harvard in 1863. Until 1871, when the Lawrence Scientific School's laboratory was combined with the Harvard College laboratory, Gibbs trained a good number of professional chemists by the German practice of research as a method of teaching.

Gibbs had neither laboratory nor chemistry students from 1871 until his retirement in 1887. He did, however, lecture in the physics department on heat and spectroscopy. Publicly, this was ascribed to economy; privately, it was explained by some as President Charles Eliot's revenge for not getting the

Rumford professorship himself. Recent scholars explain the event as part of the policy of progressively attenuating the scientific schools at both Yale and Harvard in favor of a unified liberal arts undergraduate and graduate faculty.

Gibbs specialized in analytic and inorganic chemistry. His work on the platinum metals (1861–1864) and the development of the electrolytic method for the determination of copper are probably his principal contributions to the former. Gibbs was particularly interested in the structure of complex inorganic acids and their derivatives, especially those of tungsten, molybdenum, and vanadium.

BIBLIOGRAPHY

I. Original Works. Gibbs's personal papers are in the Franklin Institute, Philadelphia. A good bibliography of his published works is F. W. Clarke, "Biographical Memoir of Wolcott Gibbs, 1822–1908," in *Biographical Memoirs. National Academy of Sciences,* **7** (1910), 1–22.

II. Secondary Literature. Clarke's memoir remains the best biographical account. Gibbs, who was a member of the "Lazzaroni" around Alexander Dallas Bache, is mentioned in studies of such contemporaries as Agassiz, Asa Gray, Bache, and Joseph Henry—but hardly enough to illuminate his career. A recent work on the professionalization of chemistry is Edward A. Beardsley, *The Rise of the American Chemical Profession, 1850–1900,* University of Florida Monographs, Social Sciences, no. 23 (Gainesville, Fla., 1964).

Nathan Reingold

GIESEL, FRIEDRICH OSKAR (*b.* Winzig, Silesia, Germany, 20 May 1852; *d.* Brunswick, Germany, 14 November 1927), *commercial chemistry.*

Giesel was an organic chemist who distinguished himself principally through his pioneering researches in radiochemistry. A physician's son who retained lifelong medical interests, Giesel pursued a career in chemistry. He studied from 1872 to 1874 at the Königliche Gewerbeakademie in Berlin. After a period of varied research Giesel received his doctorate from Göttingen in 1876. He then collaborated at the Gewerbeakademie until 1878 with Carl Liebermann, with whom he continued to publish jointly until 1897. Concentrating upon alkaloid research, they achieved a partial synthesis of cocaine and patented the technique in 1888. Working at Buchler & Co., a *Chininfabrik* in Brunswick, Giesel had introduced, by 1882, alkaloid extraction with benzol homologues.

In addition to this main line of research Giesel developed the use of radioactive luminous compounds and published over thirty papers on radioactivity between 1899 and 1909. A past master at the art of extracting and preparing pure substances in phytochemistry, after the Curies' 1898 discovery of polonium, he applied his craft to radiochemistry. By 1900 he had developed an improved method of fractional crystallization, producing a greater concentration of radium salts in a shorter time, by using bromide instead of chloride. One direct result of his highly influential efforts, by which pure radium bromide became commercially available for research, was the 1903 verification by William Ramsay and Frederick Soddy of the production of helium from radium. Giesel was the first to observe the decomposition of water by radium salts.

When his close friends and nearby colleagues Julius Elster and Hans Geitel obtained inconclusive results regarding magnetic influence upon Becquerel rays, Giesel provided a key to these rays' non-X-ray character by his decisive proof of their magnetic deflectability in October 1899. Three years later, using a zinc sulfide screen as a detector of alpha radiation, Giesel was able to isolate an emanating substance allied with lanthanum but free from thorium. He provisionally named his substance emanium (proven to be pure actinium by Otto Hahn and Otto Sackur in 1904) to distinguish it from André Debierne's 1899 thorium-contaminated actinium preparation. In 1903 Debierne also found the gaseous emanation (actinon) in his own actinium.

Giesel noted, as he had with radium in 1899, that the activity of his emanium increased with time. He thus proposed in 1904, by analogy with the 1902 analysis of Rutherford and Soddy, that an intermediate substance was the direct cause of the emanation. By 1905 this intermediate substance was named both by Giesel and by another, independent researcher, Tadeusz Godlewski. Giesel called it "emanium X," but Godlewski's terminology, actinium X, is the name that has survived.

Giesel was elected to the Leopoldina in 1903 and received the honorary title of professor (1903), as well as that of doctor of engineering (1916), all of which indicated the high esteem he enjoyed for his many contributions to science. Particular gratitude was expressed by Rutherford in a letter to Giesel dated 3 March 1904:

> I have followed with great interest your researches on radioactivity and I feel that I, as well as the scientific world, owe a debt of gratitude to you for your enterprise in preparing pure radium bromide for use of outside scientists. But for your aid, I feel confident most of us would have to be content with Barium chloride of Paris manufacture of activity about 20,000 [Rutherford Collection, Cambridge University Library, Add MSS 7653/G79].

The *Altmeister* of radium research in Germany, Giesel succumbed to radiation-induced lung cancer.

BIBLIOGRAPHY

I. ORIGINAL WORKS. A nearly complete list of Giesel's works is part of Otto Hahn, "Friedrich Giesel," in *Physikalische Zeitschrift,* **29** (1928), 353-357. Richard Lucas, *Bibliographie der radioaktiven Stoffe* (Leipzig, 1908), pp. 33-35, is a valuable supplement to Hahn's list.

Ferdinand Henrich, *Chemie und chemische Technologie radioaktiver Stoffe* (Berlin, 1918), contains a communication from Giesel (p. 344) concerning Buchler & Co.'s commercial provision of pure radium salts and a table (p. 283), beginning with 1902, indicating the rapidly increasing price per milligram of pure hydrated radium bromide. Some of Giesel's unpublished correspondence and other MS material is at Buchler & Co. in Brunswick, the Deutsches Museum in Munich, and the Darmstaedter Collection, Staatsbibliothek, Berlin.

II. SECONDARY LITERATURE. The following are partially derivative accounts: S. Loewenthal, "Leben und Werk des Professor Dr. Fritz Giesel," in *Braunschweigisches Magazin,* **36** (1930), 33-38; "Friedrich Giesel und die Radiumfabrikation," in Walther Buchler, *Dreihundert Jahre Buchler* (Brunswick, 1958), pp. 115-122.

Giesel's successful deflection experiment is considered by Lawrence Badash in "An Elster and Geitel Failure: Magnetic Deflection of Beta Rays," in *Centaurus,* **11** (1966), 236-240. Stefan Meyer and Egon von Schweidler, using similar equipment but different experimental technique, could not initially confirm that the effect they had observed was also due to deflection. Correspondence among Giesel, Elster and Geitel, and Meyer and von Schweidler dealing with this research during October and November 1899 was published by S. Meyer, "Zur Geschichte der Entdeckung der Natur der Becquerelstrahlen," in *Die Naturwissenschaften,* **36** (1949), 129-132.

Giesel's achievements concerning actinium, actinium X, and actinon are discussed in M. E. Weeks, *Discovery of the Elements,* 5th ed. (Easton, Pa., 1945), pp. 499-501; and H. W. Kirby, "The Discovery of Actinium," in *Isis,* **62** (1971), 290-308.

THADDEUS J. TRENN

GILBERT, GROVE KARL (*b.* Rochester, New York, 6 May 1843; *d.* Jackson, Michigan, 1 May 1918), *geology, geomorphology.*

Gilbert received the A.B. at the University of Rochester in 1862, having taken only one course in geology, which was taught by Henry A. Ward; he subsequently worked for the Ward Natural Science Establishment, which prepared and sold scientific materials to educational institutions, from 1863 to 1868. In 1869 he joined the second geological survey of Ohio as a volunteer assistant to J. S. Newberry. From 1871 to 1874 he was "geological assistant" on G. M. Wheeler's geographical and geological survey, conducted west of the 100th meridian.

On 2 December 1874 Gilbert joined John Wesley Powell's Rocky Mountain geographical and geological survey, which five years later, on Powell's recommendation, was combined with the other federal surveys to form the U.S. Geological Survey. Thus began the long and fruitful association of Powell, Gilbert, and Clarence Edward Dutton. Powell's fecundity in ideas found its effective foil in Gilbert's accurate observation and suspended judgment.

Powell's doctrine of subaerial erosion and baselevel was developed by Gilbert with emphasis on lateral planation in *Report on the Geology of the Henry Mountains* (1877). Importing these ideas into humid regions, W. M. Davis formulated the concept of geographic cycles. Thus were founded the fundamental principles of a new subscience, geomorphology, although that name, introduced by Powell, did not come into general use until the 1930's.

According to W. W. Rubey (p. 497), the essence of Gilbert's ideas was the concept of graded streams—the concept that, either by cutting down their beds or by building them up with sediment, streams tend always to make for themselves channels and slopes that, over a period of years, will transport exactly the load of sediment delivered into them from above. From 1907 to 1909, at Berkeley, California, Gilbert gratified his desire for quantitative data by conducting flume experiments on the transportation of debris by running water. The 1905-1908 investigation of hydraulic-mining debris and its sedimentary effects in the Sacramento River drainage system and in San Francisco Bay is a dispassionate account of the great power of man as a geologic agent.

Gilbert explained the structure of the Great Basin as the result of extension. The individual "basin ranges" are the eroded upper parts of tilted blocks, which were displaced along faults as "comparatively rigid bodies of strata." Gilbert analyzed Powell's diastrophism into orogeny, or mountain formation, and epeirogeny, or regional displacement. He described Lake Bonneville, the gigantic Pleistocene ancestor of Great Salt Lake, and related the displaced Bonneville shorelines and the displaced proglacial shorelines of the Great Lakes to epeirogenic isostatic rebound.

Gilbert studied the Henry Mountains in 1875 and 1876. He was the first to establish that an intrusive body may deform its host rock. He emphasized that the crust of the earth is "as plastic in *great masses* as wax is in small." But he exaggerated the fluidity of magma, and his laccoliths are now interpreted as "tongue-shaped masses . . . injected radially as satellites from stocks" (Hunt *et al.*, p. 142).

Gilbert was the very antithesis of a temperamental, erratic genius. He was scrupulous in giving credit due others, careless about receiving his own. In his presidential address to the Society of American Naturalists in December 1885, entitled "The Inculcation of Scientific Method," he stressed the importance of inventing and testing multiple hypotheses, maintaining: "The great investigator is primarily the man who is rich in hypotheses."

From January 1889 until August 1892 Gilbert served as chief geologist of the U.S. Geological Survey. His brilliant presidential address to the Philosophical Society of Washington in December 1893 gave cogent argument for the impact origin of craters on the moon. In 1899 he was a member of the Harriman expedition to Alaska.

BIBLIOGRAPHY

I. Original Works. The B. D. Wood and G. B. Cottle bibliography that follows the Mendenhall memorial (see below), pp. 45–64, has 400 entries and is nearly complete. Gilbert's writings include *Report on the Geology of the Henry Mountains,* U.S. Geographical and Geological Survey of the Rocky Mountain Region (Washington, D.C., 1877; 2nd ed., 1880); *Lake Bonneville,* Monographs of the United States Geological Survey, no. 1 (Washington, D.C., 1890); *The Transportation of Débris by Running Water,* United States Geological Survey Professional Paper no. 86 (Washington, D.C., 1914); *Hydraulic-Mining Débris in the Sierra Nevada,* Professional Paper no. 105 (Washington, D.C., 1917); and *Studies of Basin-Range Structure,* Professional Paper no. 153 (Washington, D.C., 1928).

II. Secondary Literature. W. C. Mendenhall, "Memorial to Grove Karl Gilbert," in *Bulletin of the Geological Society of America,* **31** (31 Mar. 1920), 26–45, includes a portrait and lists Gilbert's honors and biographical notices. W. M. Davis, "Biographical Memoir. Grove Karl Gilbert, 1843–1918," in *Biographical Memoirs. National Academy of Sciences,* **21** (1926), 5th memoir, presented 1922, includes pictures of Gilbert. See also Joseph Barrell, "Grove Karl Gilbert, an Appreciation," in *Sierra Club Bulletin,* **10,** no. 4 (Jan. 1919), 397–399; and, in the same number, p. 438, a letter from E. C. Andrews, Australia, dated 30 Apr. 1913. The references cited in text are W. W. Rubey, "Equilibrium-Conditions in Debris-Laden Streams," in *Transactions of the American Geophysical Union,* **13** (June 1933), 497–505; and C. B. Hunt, assisted by P. Averitt and R. L. Miller, *Geology and Geography of the Henry Mountains Region,* United States Geological Survey Professional Paper no. 228 (Washington, D.C., 1953).

Ronald K. DeFord

GILBERT, L. W. For an account of his work, see the biography of **Lawes, J. B.**

GILBERT, WILLIAM (*b.* Colchester, Essex, England, 1544; *d.* London, England, 30 November 1603), *magnetism, electricity.*

Gilbert was born into a rising, middle-class family that had only recently acquired its well-to-do status. His great-grandfather, John Gilbert, had married Joan Tricklove, the only daughter of a wealthy merchant from Clare, Suffolk. Their son, William Gilbert of Clare, became a weaver and eventually sewer of the chamber to Henry VIII. This William married Margery Grey, and among their nine children was Jerome Gilbert. Jerome, who had some knowledge of law, moved from Clare to Colchester in the 1520's, became a free burgess and recorder there, and married Elizabeth Coggeshall. The oldest of their five children was William Gilbert of Colchester. After Elizabeth's death Jerome married Jane Wingfield, and after her death he married a third time. Little is known of this third marriage other than that the woman's name was Margery.

Nothing is known of Gilbert's early life and education. In May 1558 he was matriculated as a member of St. John's College, Cambridge, where he received his A.B. in 1561, his M.A. in 1564, and his M.D. in 1569. During this time he was appointed pensioner (1558), fellow of Mr. Symson's foundation (1561), mathematical examiner of St. John's College (1565 and 1566), and senior bursar (1569 and 1570). Seven months after receiving his M.D. he was elected a senior fellow of his college.

Frequently writers have stated that after receiving his doctor's degree, Gilbert went abroad to study. This is possible, but evidence for it is lacking; nothing is known of his life from the time he left Cambridge until he settled in London sometime in the mid-1570's. There he practiced medicine, obtained a grant of arms in 1577, and sometime before 1581 became a member of the Royal College of Physicians. By 1581 Gilbert was one of the prominent physicians in London, and for the rest of his life he was consulted by influential members of the English nobility. In 1600 he became physician to Elizabeth I and after her death was appointed physician to James I.

While in London, Gilbert was active in the Royal College and held several offices in that organization. In 1588 he was one of the four College physicians requested by the Privy Council to care for the health of the men in the Royal Navy. In 1589 he was assigned the topic "Philulae" for the College's *Pharmacopoeia,* and later in that year and again in

1594 he was mentioned among the examiners for this book on drugs. From 1582 on, Gilbert was an officer of the College and held the following positions: censor (1582, 1584–1587, 1589–1590); treasurer (1587–1594, 1597–1599); consiliarium (1597–1599); elect (1596–1597). In 1600 he was elected president.

Gilbert never married. He lived in London at Wingfield House (presumably a legacy from his stepmother), St. Peter's Hill. The house served as a laboratory but probably was not, as is sometimes stated, a center for the meetings of a scientific group. Little is known about Gilbert's life in London, for upon his death, presumably from the plague, he left his books, instruments, globes, and minerals to the Royal College of Physicians for their library. The Royal College, with its library, and Wingfield House were destroyed by the Great Fire in 1666.

Sometime during his life, presumably in the decade following his years at Cambridge, Gilbert studied magnetic phenomena. The results of these studies were published in 1600 under the title *De magnete, magneticisque corporibus, et de magno magnete tellure; physiologia nova, plurimis & argumentis, & experimentis demonstrata.* The book was an attempt to explain the nature of the lodestone and to account for the five movements connected with magnetic phenomena. It was well received both in England and on the Continent and was republished in 1628 and again in 1633.

Gilbert's other writings were not published until almost half a century after his death. His younger half brother, William Gilbert of Melford, collected and possibly edited his brother's papers and presented them, under the title *De mundo nostro sublunari philosophia nova,* to Prince Henry of England. Francis Bacon and Thomas Harriot were both acquainted with these writings, which were published at Amsterdam in 1651. The *De mundo* is, in part, an extension of the cosmological ideas Gilbert introduced in the last section of the *De magnete;* it is dependent on the latter work for much of its vocabulary and basic assumptions but lacks its finish and completeness. It is Gilbert's work in the *De magnete* that gives him a place in the history of science.

During the fifteenth century the widespread interest in navigation had focused much attention on the compass. Since at that time the orientation of the magnetic needle was explained by an alignment of the magnetic poles with the poles of the celestial sphere, the diverse areas of geography, astronomy, and phenomena concerning the lodestone overlapped and were often intermingled. Navigators had noted the variation from the meridian and the dip of the magnetic needle and had suggested ways of accounting for and using these as aids in navigation. The connection between magnetic studies and astronomy was less definite; but so long as the orientation of the compass was associated with the celestial poles, the two studies were interdependent to some extent. There were suggestions in Thomas Digges and Nicolas Rymers that perhaps the magnetic property was somehow innate in the earth, but these were slight hints or passing remarks. Gilbert provided the only fully developed theory dealing with all five of the then known magnetic movements and the first comprehensive discussion of magnetism since the thirteenth-century *Letter on the Magnet* of Peter Peregrinus.

Gilbert divided his *De magnete* into six books. The first deals with the history of magnetism from the earliest legends about the lodestone to the facts and theories known to Gilbert's contemporaries. The nature, properties, and behavior of the lodestone are discussed and ways of demonstrating them are suggested. Throughout the book Gilbert marked his own discoveries and experiments with asterisks; larger symbols were used for the more important discoveries and experiments, smaller asterisks for the less important ones. In the last chapter of book I, Gilbert introduced his new basic idea which was to explain all terrestrial magnetic phenomena: his postulate that the earth is a giant lodestone and thus has magnetic properties. The assertion is supported by a comparison of the earth and a lodestone (each has poles and an equator; each draws objects to itself), by an appeal to experience (lodestones are found in all parts of the earth; iron, the prime magnetic substance, lies deep within the earth), by a denial of the Aristotelian elements (elemental earth has never been found), and by Gilbert's repeated statements that this new idea is so.

The remaining five books of the *De magnete* are concerned with the five magnetic movements: coition, direction, variation, declination, and revolution. Before he began his discussion of coition, however, Gilbert carefully distinguished the attraction due to the amber effect from that caused by the lodestone. This section, chapter 2 of book II, established the study of the amber effect as a discipline separate from that of magnetic phenomena, introduced the vocabulary of electrics, and is the basis for Gilbert's place in the history of electricity.

Gilbert's distinction between magnetic phenomena and the amber effect was based upon the difference between their causes. He used a material cause to explain the amber effect and a formal one for magnetic attraction. That is, substances which had been formed from the fluid and humid matter in the earth would, after they had become solid, behave as amber does when it is rubbed. Gilbert's explanation was that the fluidity was never completely lost, and thus such substances emitted an effluvium which seized small particles and pulled them inward. Magnetic materials were those substances which shared in the specific, primary form of the earth. This form, implanted in the globe by the Creator, gave the earth its magnetic property. All parts of the earth which maintained a principal share in this form, i.e., lodestones and iron, were magnetic bodies. Unlike the electrics, magnetics did not depend on the emission of effluvia to draw bodies to themselves.

Having distinguished the magnetic and amber effects, Gilbert presented a list of many substances other than amber which, when rubbed, exhibit the same effect. These he called electrics. All other solids were nonelectrics. To determine whether a substance was an electric, Gilbert devised a testing instrument, the versorium. This was a small, metallic needle so balanced that it easily turned about a vertical axis. The rubbed substance was brought near the versorium. If the needle turned, the substance was an electric; if the needle did not turn, the substance was a nonelectric.

After disposing of the amber effect, Gilbert returned to his study of the magnetic phenomena. In discussing these, Gilbert relied for his explanations on several assumptions: (1) the earth is a giant lodestone and has the magnetic property; (2) the magnetic property is due to the form of the substance; (3) every magnet is surrounded by an invisible orb of virtue which extends in all directions from it; (4) pieces of iron or other magnetic materials within this orb of virtue will be affected by and will affect the magnet within the orb of virtue; and (5) a small, spherical magnet resembles the earth and what can be demonstrated with it is applicable to the earth. This small spherical magnet he called a terrella.

Gilbert was more negative than positive in his assertions about the form which accounts for the magnetic property. He tried to distinguish it from the commonly accepted forms of his time. Thus he denied that this form was the formal cause of Aristotle's four causes, or the specific cause alchemists associated with mixtures, or the secondary form of the philosophers, or the propagator of generative bodies. Yet when he attempted to describe or define this form, he could assert only that there is a primary, radical, and astral form that is unique to each body and that orders its own proper globe; for the earth this form was the anima of the earth and was associated with the magnetic property.

One of the effects of this primary form was the surrounding of the magnetic body with an orb of virtue. The orb extended in all directions from the body, and its extent and strength depended on the perfection and purity of the magnetic body. Magnetics within the orb would be attracted to the body; those outside would be unaffected. Thus Gilbert used this orb to eliminate the necessity for attraction at a distance in regard to the magnet just as he had used the effluvium in his explanation of the amber effect. Yet he was unable or unwilling to account for the magnetic effect solely in terms of substance, as he had done for the electrics. The primary form, once accepted, went beyond a material explanation and so, for Gilbert, provided another essential difference between the two phenomena. Once this was established as a fundamental part of his theory, he was free to discuss the five magnetic movements.

In discussing coition Gilbert was careful to distinguish magnetic coition from other attractions. For him magnetic coition was a mutual action between the attracting body and the attracted body. At the beginning of the *De magnete* he explained several terms that were necessary for understanding his work. One of these was "magnetic coition," which he said he "used rather than attraction because magnetic movements do not result from attraction of one body alone but from the coming together of two bodies harmoniously (not the drawing of one by the other)" (P. Fleury Mottelay, *William Gilbert of Colchester . . . on the Great Magnet of the Earth* [Ann Arbor, 1893], p. liv).

The coition occurred only if the bodies were within the orb of virtue of the magnet, and the action was dependent upon the size and purity of the magnet and the object. Larger and purer magnets were stronger than smaller and less pure ones. The removal of part of a lodestone would weaken it, while the addition of an iron cap would strengthen the orb of virtue.

Book III of the *De magnete* contains Gilbert's explanation of the orientation taken by a lodestone that is balanced and free to turn, that is, the behavior of the magnetic compass. Since the earth was a giant lodestone, it was surrounded by an orb of virtue; and magnetic substances within this orb behaved as they did in the orbs of small magnets. Thus the orientation of the compass was simply an alignment of the magnetic needle with the north and south poles of the earth. Gilbert gave numerous demonstrations of this with the terrella as well as directions for magnetizing iron.

By the end of the sixteenth century, navigators were well acquainted with variations from the meridian in the orientation of the compass. Thus, after discussing orientation, Gilbert turned in book IV to the variations in that orientation. Here he again used the comparison of the phenomena that can be demonstrated with the terrella and those that occur on the surface of the globe. Just as a very small magnetic needle will vary its orientation if the terrella on which it is placed is not a perfect sphere, so will the compass needle vary its orientation on the surface of the earth according to the proximity or remoteness of the masses of earth extending beyond the basic spherical core. Also, the purity of these masses (the amount of primary magnetic property retained by them) will affect the orientation of the compass just as stronger lodestones have greater attractive powers than weaker ones.

The next magnetic movement that Gilbert discussed was declination, the variation from the horizontal. This phenomenon had been described by Robert Norman in his book on magnetism, *The New Attractive* (1581). Although Norman had also given an effective means of constructing the compass needle so that it would not dip but would remain parallel to the horizontal, he had made no attempt to account for this strange behavior. As with the other magnetic effects of the compass, Gilbert explained declination in terms of the magnetic property of the earth and the experiments with the terrella. The small needle placed on the terrella maintained a horizontal position only when placed on the equator. When moved north or south of this position, the end of the needle closer to one pole of the terrella dipped toward that pole. The amount of dip increased as the needle was moved nearer the pole, until it assumed a perpendicular position when placed on the pole. A compass on the earth, according to Gilbert, behaved in a similar manner.

In discussing the variations from the meridian and the horizontal, Gilbert suggested practical applications of his theory. Navigators of the period were concerned with determining the longitude and latitude of their positions on the open seas. Since the deviation from the meridian was constant at a given point, Gilbert thought that if the seamen would record these variations at many points, an accurate table of variation for various positions could be compiled and the problem would be solved. He included detailed instructions for the construction of the instruments necessary for this task.

Gilbert thought that the variations from the horizontal could be obtained by means of experimentation with the terrella, since the dip depended on the position of the needle between the equator and the pole rather than on the configuration of the surface of the magnet. He does not seem to have had much data from navigators in this regard, as he did concerning the variation from the meridian, and was satisfied with his theoretical considerations.

The final book of the *De magnete,* book VI, deals with rotation and in this section Gilbert expounded his cosmological theories. Without discussing whether the universe is heliocentric or geocentric, Gilbert accepted and explained the diurnal rotation of the earth. From the time of Peter Peregrinus' *Letter on the Magnet,* written in the thirteenth century, rotation had been considered one of the magnetic movements. The assumption was that a truly spherical, perfectly balanced lodestone, perfectly aligned with the celestial poles, would rotate on its axis once in twenty-four hours. Since the earth was such a lodestone, it would turn upon its axis in that manner and thus the diurnal motion of the earth was explained. The theory was taken from Peter's *Letter;* the application to the earth was Gilbert's addition.

In advancing his theory Gilbert denied the existence of the solid celestial spheres, stated that the fixed stars were not equally distant from the earth, and accounted for the precession of the equinoxes and the tides in terms of the magnetic property of the earth. These statements were in general weakly, if at all, supported and were not well developed. Much of the criticism directed by Bacon and others against Gilbert's writing was based upon the sixth book of the *De magnete,* where Gilbert extended to the cosmos his magnetic theory and the results obtained from his experiments.

Throughout the *De magnete,* Gilbert discussed and usually dismissed previous theories concerning magnetic phenomena and offered observational data and experiments which would support his own theories. Most of the experiments are so well described that the reader can duplicate them if he wishes, and the examples of natural occurrences which support his theory are well identified. Where new instruments are introduced (for example, the versorium, to be used in identifying electrics), directions for their construction and use are included. The combination, a new theory supported by confirming evidence and demonstrations, is a pre-Baconian example of the new experimental philosophy which became popular in the seventeenth century.

Gilbert's other writings, those in the *De mundo,* do not follow this pattern. When the younger William Gilbert collected his half brother's papers for presentation to Prince Henry and eventual publication, he divided them into two sections. The first of these, "Physiologiae nova contra Aristotelem," is an expansion of the cosmology of the *De magnete;* the second,

"Nova meteorologia contra Aristotelem," follows the general pattern of Aristotle's *Meteorology.* There is nothing in the two works to indicate that William Gilbert of Colchester considered the two to be one work. Internal evidence indicates that the "Nova meteorologia" was written during the 1580's and left unfinished, while the "Physiologia nova" must have been written after the early 1590's. Also, since it is assumed in the "Physiologia nova" that the reader is familiar with the content of the *De magnete,* it appears that much of this work was written after the major portion of the *De magnete* was completed.

At the beginning of the "Physiologia nova" Gilbert denied the existence of the four terrestrial elements—earth, water, air, and fire—and replaced them with one element, earth. This earth was the one substance from which all terrestrial bodies were made; its primary attribute was its magnetic property; solids not exhibiting this property were degenerate forms of the element; and moist fluid substances on the earth were effluvia of this basic element. The surface of the globe consisted primarily of these degenerate forms and effluvia. The lodestones and iron were purer forms of this one element.

Gilbert also postulated a similar structure for all of the heavenly globes. Each consisted of a substance with a primary form and effluvia surrounding it. He then placed a void between the effluvia from one globe and that from the next. While the general scheme was the same for all, each globe or type of globe had its own distinguishing characteristics. Gilbert gave a more detailed description of the moon than of any other celestial body. This "Companion of the Earth," as he called it, was described as a miniature earth and possessed seas, continents, and islands. These Gilbert named and charted; the lighter parts of the moon were assumed to be bodies of water, the darker parts land masses. Since the moon was within the orb of virtue of the earth, there was a mutual attraction between the two bodies. Because the earth was larger, it held the moon in its power and thus the moon revolved around it. The lesser effect of the moon on the earth was seen in the tides.

The sun was designated as the center for the orbits of the five wandering stars and was the cause of motion for all the globes within its orb of virtue. Although the earth was located within this orb, Gilbert excluded it from those bodies affected by the sun. There are indications that he considered the planets to be earthlike bodies with continents and seas, but this was never definitively stated. The fixed stars were placed in the same category as the sun, the light-giving bodies, while moon, planets, and earth belonged to the group of light-reflecting bodies. The causes for the differences were not stated.

From the structure of the earth and the other globes, Gilbert moved to the structure of the universe. While he repeated his belief, expressed in the *De magnete,* that the earth had a diurnal rotation and that the fixed stars were not all equally distant from the earth, and while he discussed the motions of the earth according to Copernicus and Giordano Bruno, he did not affirm or deny the heliocentric system. At times he dismissed the system as not pertinent to the topic he was discussing; at other times he indicated that it would be taken up in another place. Gilbert dismissed the third motion described in the *De revolutionibus* as "no motion." This treatment of the motions of the earth is only one of the many indications that the *De mundo* was left in a fragmentary state.

Scattered throughout the latter part of the "Physiologia nova" are references to and statements about spices, twilight, putrefaction, the polarity of magnets, the buoyancy of a leaden vessel, the comparative densities of solid and liquid forms of the same substance, and light. All of these are mere statements or partial discussions. It seems as if the younger William Gilbert included everything he found, regardless of its relevance to the rest of the papers or its internal completeness.

The second part of the *De mundo,* the "Nova meteorologia," contains Gilbert's discussion of comets, the Milky Way, clouds, winds, the rainbow, the origin of springs and rivers, and the nature of the sea and tides. Most of these are summaries of other theories with Gilbert's ideas interspersed among them.

Comets, Gilbert considered, could be either above or below the moon. They were wandering bodies without polarity and with uncertain paths. He listed the various positions the vapor of a comet might take but said nothing about the centers of comets or the causes of their motions.

Several theories and mythological explanations for the Milky Way were reviewed and denied by Gilbert; then the hypothesis that the Milky Way is a collection of stars so numerous and so far from the earth as to appear to be a mist or cloud was given but was neither accepted nor denied. The section ends with a suggestion that the reader look at the Milky Way through a "specillis." The instrument is not described, and it is uncertain whether Gilbert meant a lens, a small mirror, or some other instrument.

Clouds, in Gilbert's meteorology, were exhalations and effluvia from the earth which rose to varying heights according to the density of their content. Some methods were given for estimating the heights of clouds, but there was little new information in this section.

Like the clouds, winds were part of the effluvia of the earth. They were described as expanding and swollen exhalations which escaped from the interior of the earth in search of more room in the region above the earth. The specific properties of any wind were determined by the location and circumstances of its origin and also by the positions of various stars at the time. Gilbert mentioned a "Table of Winds" he had composed, but this table was missing from the manuscript used for the printed edition. The editor inserted the table from Francis Bacon's "Historia ventorum," but since Bacon had four secondary winds and Gilbert mentioned five, it is unlikely that the two tables were similar.

In the section on the rainbow Gilbert included elaborate drawings showing the position and colors of both primary and secondary rainbows and the conditions necessary for the rainbow to be visible; he discussed the necessity for moisture, a dense object, and proper conditions in the air for the rainbow and digressed a little on the subject of mirror images. Again all the explanations are general and incomplete.

The last part of the "Meteorologia" concerns water phenomena—springs, rivers, the sea, and tides. Gilbert considered water to be a humor from the earth, and the motions of springs and rivers were explained in terms of water returning to its source; the tides were the results of the combined actions of the diurnal motion of the earth and the magnetic coition between the earth and the moon.

Throughout the "Nova meteorologia" Gilbert included numerous examples of specific instances of the phenomena he was describing. Some of these observations were his own, some he had received from others. There is an indication of an interest in astrology and, as in the *De magnete,* a concern for observational data to support his ideas. It appears that at one time Gilbert planned a detailed study of meteorology that would replace the existing theories, but he never completed the project.

The *De mundo* did not have the influence of the *De magnete,* since Gilbert's cosmology was less acceptable than either his magnetic theory or his electric theory. Gilbert's contemporaries generally praised the earlier work both for its content and for its methodology, and the idea of the earth's magnetism was incorporated into arguments for the support of the Copernican theory. Johann Kepler tried to use Gilbert's magnetic theory, with its orb of virtue, as a motive force for his astronomical theory but needed so many *ad hoc* postulates to do so that others found this use of magnetism unacceptable. Kepler also expressed interest in seeing Gilbert's theory of the void in the *De mundo,* but we do not know whether he did so.

Certainly the *De magnete* was the far more influential of Gilbert's books. The theory of the magnetic orb of virtue and the explanation of the amber effect in terms of an emitted effluvium provided mechanistic explanations for these phenomena and a starting point for the study of the two disciplines in the following centuries.

BIBLIOGRAPHY

I. ORIGINAL WORKS. Gilbert's writings are *De magnete, magneticisque corporibus, et de magno magnete tellure; physiologia nova, plurimis & argumentis, & experimentis demonstrata* (London, 1600), Eng. trans., P. Fleury Mottelay, *William Gilbert of Colchester . . . on the Great Magnet of the Earth* (Ann Arbor, 1893); and *De mundo nostro sublunari philosophia nova,* collected by his half brother, William Gilbert of Melford (Amsterdam, 1651).

II. SECONDARY LITERATURE. On Gilbert or his work, see Suzanne Kelly, *The De mundo of William Gilbert* (Amsterdam, 1965); and Duane H. D. Roller, *The De magnete of William Gilbert* (Amsterdam, 1959).

SUZANNE KELLY

GILES (AEGIDIUS) OF LESSINES (*b.* Lessines [now Hainaut, Belgium], *ca.* 1235; *d.* 1304 or later), *astronomy, natural philosophy.*

Giles entered the Dominican order, possibly at the priory of Valenciennes, and in all likelihood studied under Albertus Magnus at Cologne and under Thomas Aquinas at Paris during the latter's second professorship there (1269–1272). He was one of the first to develop, not merely expound, Thomistic doctrine, particularly on the unicity of substantial form (*De unitate formae,* completed July 1278). His *De usuris,* written between 1278 and 1284, is the most complete study of usury in the Middle Ages. He composed a letter to Albert asking his judgment on fifteen points of doctrine, thirteen of which were condemned by Étienne Tempier, bishop of Paris, on 10 December 1270; this elicited a reply from Albert, the important *De quindecim problematibus.* Giles wrote also a number of theological treatises and *De concordia temporum,* a concordance of historical chronology that ends with the year 1304—from which is conjectured the date of his death.

Works of scientific interest include a lost treatise, *De geometria;* a work on twilights, *De crepusculis;* and the classic *De essentia, motu et significatione cometarum* ("On the Nature, Movement, and Significance of Comets"), occasioned by a comet that was seen from the latter part of July to early October 1264. The work depends heavily on Aristotle's *Meteorologia,* which Giles knew in a translation made from the Greek in 1260 by his fellow Dominican, William of Moerbeke, and which shows Giles's awareness of problems of textual criticism. Giles cites classical authors as well as al-Bitrūjī, Abu Maʿshar, Robert Grosseteste, and Albertus Magnus, among others; evidently "he had access to a remarkably extensive library"[1] and used his sources intelligently. The treatise is divided into ten chapters: the first seven, concerned with the nature, causes, and properties of comets, are astronomical and meteorological in intent; and the last three, dealing with the significance of comets, are chiefly astrological. The final chapter includes a history of comets and their sequels; apart from those of antiquity, only the comets of 840, 1062 or 1066, 1222, 1239, and 1264 are mentioned. Incidental details of the comet of 1264, based on Giles's own observations, were used by him to falsify theories proposed by others; they were sufficiently precise to enable Richard Dunthorne, working from a manuscript of Giles's treatise in 1751, to compute the orbit of the comet.[2] Both Giles and Dunthorne were assailed by "an enlightened eighteenth-century *philosophe,*" Alexandre Guy Pingré, whose own work is criticized by Thorndike.[3]

NOTES

1. Thorndike, p. 95.
2. *Philosophical Transactions of the Royal Society,* **47** (1753), 282.
3. Pp. 97–99.

BIBLIOGRAPHY

The Latin text of Giles's treatise on comets, together with a critical intro., is in L. Thorndike, *Latin Treatises on Comets Between 1238 and 1368 A.D.* (Chicago, 1950), pp. 87–184. F. J. Roensch, *Early Thomistic School* (Dubuque, Iowa, 1964), lists all of Giles's works, summarizes his philosophical thought, and provides a bibliographical guide.

WILLIAM A. WALLACE, O.P.

GILES (AEGIDIUS) OF ROME (*b.* Rome, Italy, before 1247; *d.* Avignon, France, 22 December 1316), *physics, astronomy, medicine.*

Often called, probably mistakenly, Giles Colonna, he joined the Hermits of St. Augustine while very young. He pursued his studies in Paris where he was a disciple of Thomas Aquinas and became *baccalarius sententiarius* in 1276. In March 1277 Étienne Tempier, the bishop of Paris, delivered his famous condemnation of Aristotelianism and Averroism. His teaching and writings having thus been censured, Giles was obliged to leave the city. He did not return for several years. In 1285 he received the *licentia docendi* in Paris at the request of Pope Honorius IV, after having retracted several of his theses. From 1285 to 1291 he taught theology.

The Hermits of St. Augustine revealed exceptional confidence in deciding as early as 1287 that his opinions should be admitted and upheld throughout the order, and they chose him for their general on 6 January 1292. On 25 April 1295 Giles was named archbishop of Bourges by Pope Boniface VIII. He died during a stay at the papal court at Avignon.

Although mainly a philosopher and theologian, Giles frequently dealt with problems relating to natural philosophy, notably in his commentaries on Aristotle. Moreover, he did so in a style distinctive enough to place him in the first rank of those thinkers who have made a positive contribution to the scientific thought of their time (see Maier, *Die Vorläufer Galileis,* p. 2). One of the first theses that Giles defended was the unity of substantial form, which he presented—without, however, daring to apply it to man—in his early commentary on the *De anima,* written before 1275. He returned to it in his *Theoremata de corpore Christi* and then, in 1278, in his *Contra gradus formarum.* But it is chiefly in his commentary on the *Physics,* written around 1277, that he considered scientific problems.

Among Giles's theses that have attracted the attention of more recent historians of science are those relating to quantity, which led him to admit the existence of natural *minima* below which concrete material substance cannot exist and which thus imply an atomistic theory of matter. The study of movement induced him to investigate the nature of a vacuum, to which he attributed a kind of suction force, observable with the aid of the clepsydra, the cupping glass, or the siphon. He arrived at a curious theory according to which only the resistance of the material medium, and not the distance traversed, enables movement to occur in time: movement in a vacuum would be *non in tempore.* His observations on the accelerated motion of falling bodies have similarly been noted: he observed that the speed of a freely falling body depends not on the proximity to its destination but on the traversed distance from its point of departure.

Several of these theories reappear in his later works, mainly in the *Quodlibeta* (1286–1291) and the *Expo-*

sitio and *Quaestiones* on the *De generatione et corruptione.* The latter two became classics, and were often utilized by such fourteenth-century physicists as Buridan and Marsilius of Inghen, who considered Giles the *communis expositor* of the *De generatione.*

Giles was also interested in other questions, which he often dealt with in short treatises that are difficult to date. Especially noteworthy are *De materia coeli,* which takes the position—against Aristotle, Thomas Aquinas, and the majority of contemporary scholars—that celestial matter is identical to that of the sublunary world; *De intentionibus in medio,* on the nature of light and its propagation; and *De formatione corporis humani in utero,* an embryological treatise inspired by Ibn Rushd. Giles developed his cosmological views to their fullest at the end of his career, in his commentary on the second book of the *Sententiae* of Peter Lombard and in his *In hexaemeron,* both finished during his episcopacy. Undoubtedly influenced by the censure of 1277, he admitted the possibility of a plurality of worlds. Furthermore, he renounced Aristotle's theory of homocentric spheres in favor of that of eccentrics and epicycles, inherited from Ptolemy and Simplicius.

BIBLIOGRAPHY

I. ORIGINAL WORKS. It is impossible to give a complete list here of the very numerous works that Giles has left us. For that, one should consult the bibliographies by Lajard, Boffito, Glorieux, and Bruni (see below). Early eds. of the majority of Giles's writings have recently been reproduced (18 vols., Frankfurt am Main, 1964–1968). A list of modern eds. whose introductions are of the most interest or which concern Giles's scientific thought follows.

De erroribus philosophorum: P. Mandonnet, ed., in *Siger de Brabant,* 2 vols. (Louvain, 1908), II, 3–25; and J. Koch, ed., with English trans. by J. O. Riedl (Milwaukee, 1944); Koch text repr. (Milan, 1965).

De ecclesiastica potestate: G. Boffito, ed., with intro. by G. M. Oxilia (Florence, 1908); R. Scholz, ed. (Weimar, 1929; repr., Aalen, 1961).

Theoremata de esse et essentia: E. Hocedez, ed. (Louvain, 1930); English trans. by M. V. Murray (Milwaukee, 1953).

De plurificatione intellectus possibilis: H. Bullotta Barracco, ed. (Rome, 1957).

Quaestio de natura universalis: G. Bruni, ed., in *Collezione di testi filosofici inediti,* II (Naples, 1935).

Other, previously unpublished "Quaestiones" were published by Bruni, in *Analecta augustiniana,* **17** (1939), no. 1, 22–66; no. 2, 125–157; no. 3, 197–207, 229–245; and by V. Cilento, in *Medio evo monastico e scolastico* (Milan, 1961), pp. 359–377.

II. SECONDARY LITERATURE. For his biography and literary and doctrinal history, see G. Bruni, *Le opere di Egidio Romano* (Florence, 1936); "Saggio bibliografico sulle opere stampate di Egidio Romano," in *Analecta augustiniana,* **24** (1961), 331–355; "Rari e inediti egidiani," in *Giornale critico della filosofia italiana,* **40** (1961), 310–323; P. Glorieux, *Répertoire des maîtres en théologie de Paris au XIIIe siècle,* 2 vols. (Paris, 1933–1934), II, 293–308; E. Hocedez, "Henri de Gand et Gilles de Rome," in *Richard de Middleton* (Louvain, 1925), pp. 459–477; "Gilles de Rome et saint Thomas," in *Mélanges Mandonnet,* 2 vols. (Paris, 1930), I, 385–410; "La condamnation de Gilles de Rome," in *Recherches de théologie ancienne et médiévale,* **4** (1932), 34–58; F. Lajard, "Gilles de Rome, religieux augustin théologien," in *Histoire littéraire de la France,* XXX (Paris, 1888), 421–566; J. S. Makaay, *Der Traktat des Ägidius Romanus über die Einzigkeit der substantiellen Form* (Würzburg, 1924); P. Mandonnet, "La carrière scolaire de Gilles de Rome," in *Revue des sciences philosophiques et théologiques,* **4** (1910), 481–499; N. Mattioli, *Studio critico sopra Egidio Romano Colonna* (Rome, 1896); and Z. K. Siemiatkowska, "Avant l'exil de Gilles de Rome, au sujet d'une dispute sur les theoremata de esse et essentia de Gilles de Rome," in *Mediaevalia philosophica Polonorum,* **7** (1960), 3–48.

Further information on Giles's MSS has been provided by F. Pelster, in *Scholastik,* **32** (1957), 247–255; and for Polish MSS by W. Sénko, in *Mediaevalia philosophica Polonorum,* **7** (1960), 22–24, and **11** (1963), 146–151; in *Augustiniana,* **12** (1962), 443–450; and by Z. K. Siemiatkowska, in *Mediaevalia philosophica Polonorum,* **11** (1963), 5–22.

Giles's scientific thought is discussed in P. Duhem, *Études sur Léonard de Vinci,* II (Paris, 1909); *Le système du monde,* IV, VI–X (Paris, 1954–1959); A. Maier, *Die Vorläufer Galileis im 14. Jahrhundert* (Rome, 1949); *Zwei Grundprobleme der scholastischen Naturphilosophie,* 2nd ed. (Rome, 1951); *An der Grenze von Scholastik und Naturwissenschaft,* 2nd ed. (Rome, 1952); *Metaphysische Hintergründe der spätscholastischen Naturphilosophie* (Rome, 1955); and G. Sarton, *Introduction to the History of Science,* II, pt. 2 (Baltimore, 1931), 922–926.

JEAN CHÂTILLON

GILL, DAVID (*b.* Aberdeen, Scotland, 12 June 1843; *d.* London, England, 24 January 1914), *astronomy.*

Her Majesty's astronomer at the Cape of Good Hope and one of the foremost practical astronomers of his generation, Gill was the eldest surviving son of a well-established watch- and clockmaker in the city of Aberdeen. His father intended that David should follow him in the family business and educated him accordingly. After two years at Marischal College of the University of Aberdeen, where he attended classes conducted by James Clerk Maxwell, Gill was sent for another two years to learn the fundamentals of clockmaking in Switzerland, Coventry, and Clerkenwell. There is no doubt that this somewhat informal training was extremely valuable to him in his later career, both for the experience and knowledge of fine mechanisms that he acquired and for the mastery of the French language and of business methods.

Gill duly succeeded his father and ran the business for ten years. His days were given to clocks but his evenings and other free time to social duties, to rifle shooting—in which he was in the national-championship class—and, in ever increasing amount, to astronomy. His first astronomical project was undertaken soon after his return to Aberdeen; this was the provision of a reliable time service for Aberdeen based on astronomical observations made with a portable transit instrument set up in a small observatory at King's College.

Spurred on by the success of his time service and his delight in making precise observations, he soon acquired an instrument that made possible a wider range of astronomical work—a twelve-inch reflector. His main objective in its use was the measurement of the parallaxes, or distances, of stars, with the micrometric method that Struve had employed to find the distance of Vega. This was, at the time, one of the most interesting and difficult problems of practical astronomy, and it is intriguing to imagine what Gill would have made of it. He never completed it with this instrument, however, because at about this time he received an invitation to become private astronomer to Lord Lindsay, an invitation which he accepted with alacrity although it involved giving up his business and consequently entailed a heavy financial sacrifice. When Gill later returned to the measurement of stellar parallaxes, it was with a heliometer, a far more powerful instrument for the purpose.

Lord Lindsay was building an observatory at Dun Echt, about a dozen miles from Aberdeen, and it was Gill's job to help with the planning and to supervise the building. This was no small task as Lord Lindsay desired to have an observatory second to none and furnished with the best instruments available. The Dun Echt observatory later became the nucleus of the Royal Observatory on Blackford Hill, Edinburgh, to which it was removed in 1894. The work of fitting out the observatory gave Gill the opportunity of meeting and becoming friendly with most of the leading European astronomers and instrument makers and of acquiring much firsthand experience of practical details that was to be invaluable to him in his later work at the Cape observatory. It was also at Dun Echt that he first encountered and mastered a heliometer, which was to become his own special instrument. Heliometers, although potentially very accurate, require great dexterity of hand and eye to operate, skills that Gill had highly developed through astronomical observation, shooting, and watchmaking.

Gill remained at Dun Echt from 1872 to 1876, during which time he went on an expedition to Mauritius, where, with Lord Lindsay and others, he observed the 1874 transit of Venus. The object of the many transit of Venus expeditions of that year was to determine the distance of the sun and the associated constants, which must be accurate if the data computed in nautical almanacs are to be reliable. The method used was that originally proposed by Halley—combining the observed times of transit of Venus across the face of the sun as observed from a number of places as widely scattered across the earth as possible. As the last such transit had occurred in 1769, that of 1874 was eagerly anticipated, and several nations prepared elaborate expeditions to observe it. While on Mauritius, Gill used the Dun Echt heliometer to observe a near approach of the minor planet Juno and was able from relatively few observations to deduce a value of the solar parallax that was fully as reliable as that deduced from all the elaborate transit-of-Venus expeditions put together. The method he used was to measure the parallactic displacement of Juno resulting from the diurnal movement of the place of observation between the early evening and the late morning. Such observations are most effective when the place of observation is close to the equator and the object observed is close to opposition.

This method of determining the solar parallax and the related astronomical constants was clearly worth pursuing. Thus, in 1877 Gill and his wife went on a private expedition sponsored by the Royal Astronomical Society to Ascension Island, where he spent six months observing a near approach of Mars. The instrument he used was the same one that he had used in Mauritius—the four-inch heliometer lent to him by Lord Lindsay for the purpose. Gill was living in London, working up the results of this expedition, when in 1879 he was appointed Her Majesty's astronomer at the Cape of Good Hope. Before sailing for the Cape he toured the major European observatories, renewing his acquaintance with most of the leading astronomers and laying the foundations for future cooperative schemes, particularly those to determine the solar parallax.

The Royal Observatory at Cape Town had been founded in 1820 and was intended to make observations in the southern hemisphere strictly comparable with those made at Greenwich. For this purpose it had been supplied with similar instruments, but by 1879 they were in a very poor state of repair and largely obsolete. Moreover, many observations had not been fully reduced or published.

Gill's first work at the Cape was to clear away these arrears of reduction and publication and to recondition the various instruments. He paid particular attention to the Airy transit circle, the twin of that on longitude zero, which had been installed at the Cape in 1855 and with which the meridian observations—the main work of the observatory—were made. This instrument was not reversible and therefore, in Gill's opinion, was not really suitable for the determination of fundamental star positions. Nevertheless, Gill improved it as much as he could and kept it in active use until near the end of his term of office, when it was replaced by a fine reversible transit circle constructed by Troughton and Simms to Gill's own design. In 1900 this design was revolutionary, but it was so good that it has provided the pattern for most of the transit circles that have since been made.

Gill closely supervised observations with the transit circle but did most of his personal observing on the heliometers. His first heliometer was the four-inch instrument that he had bought from Lord Lindsay, the second, a seven-inch one made by Repsold of Hamburg and installed in 1887. This was probably the best—and certainly the most widely used—heliometer ever made. With it, and in cooperation with a number of northern observatories, he determined the solar parallax by systematic observations of three minor planets, Iris, Victoria, and Sappho. The value he deduced (8.80 arc seconds) was used in the computation of all almanacs until 1968, when it was replaced by 8.794 arc seconds derived by radar echo methods and by observations of Mariner space probes. Gill also used the heliometers to measure the distances of a score of the brighter and nearer southern stars and obtained results of which the accuracy was later confirmed by photographic observation.

Photographs of the bright comet of 1882 drew Gill's attention to the possibility of accurately charting and measuring star positions by means of photography. The immediate outcome was the *Cape Photographic Durchmusterung,* which gives the approximate positions and brightness of nearly half a million southern stars and which was the first major astronomical work to be carried out photographically.

While work on the *Durchmusterung* was still in progress, Gill became involved with the Paris astronomers, to whom he had sent copies of the 1882 comet photographs, in the initiation of the *Carte du ciel* astrographic project. A much larger and more ambitious undertaking, it aimed at preparing a photographic chart of the whole heavens showing stars to the fourteenth magnitude and a catalog giving precise positions for all stars to the eleventh magnitude—that is, for over two million stars. This vast project was divided among a dozen observatories but was too big for many of them; thus the catalog for the whole sky was not completed until 1961. The Cape observatory undertook a major section of this work, and a suitable telescope, the astrographic refractor, was acquired and made ready for use by 1892; all the necessary plates had been obtained by 1900.

The astrographic refractor proved to be an extremely useful all-round instrument. The British engineer and astronomical amateur Frank McClean used it with an objective prism to obtain the spectra of the brighter southern stars. A few years later he offered as a gift to the observatory a very fine, large modern telescope, fully equipped with a powerful spectrograph, which was installed in 1901. The first major program completed with it was a determination of the solar parallax from the observed radial velocities of a series of stars near the ecliptic. These radial velocities differ throughout the year because of the earth's motion around the sun; the amplitude of the variation in velocity is directly connected to the linear size of the earth's orbit.

Apart from his astronomical work, Gill acted as the organizer of geodetic and boundary surveys throughout southern Africa as well as of projects to determine the longitude and latitude of its various ports. His most ambitious project was for a triangulation of the thirtieth meridian of east longitude from South Africa to Norway, a total arc of 105°, the longest observable meridian in the world. Gill made himself responsible for the southern end of this arc, the survey of which as a whole was not completed until after the end of World War II. He was knighted on 24 May 1900.

On account of his own health and that of his wife, Gill retired from the Cape at age 63, two years before he need have done. On his arrival in 1879 he had found a small, rather run-down, dispirited institution; when he left in 1906 the Cape observatory was generally recognized as one of the best equipped in the world with a large, young, keen staff fully engaged in important astronomical projects. Throughout his directorate there was a constant stream of visiting astronomers and volunteer assistants, some of whom stayed for lengthy periods, quite often as house guests. Among them were Auwers, Kapteyn, De Sitter, Elkin, Newcomb, Franklin Adams, Bryan Cookson, McClean, and Agnes Clarke. On his retirement Gill and his wife went to live in London, where they were able to keep in close touch with astronomers and scientists from all over the world. Gill enjoyed good health until December 1913, when he caught pneumonia, which proved fatal.

No account of Gill's astronomical work would be

complete without some reference to the man himself and the very high esteem in which he was held by his contemporaries. Sir Arthur Eddington, who knew him well during his retirement, wrote:

> By his widespread activity, his close association with all the great enterprises of observational astronomy, and by the energy and enthusiasm of his character, he had come to hold an almost unique position in astronomical counsels. . . . By his individual achievements and by his leadership he has exerted an incalculable influence on the progress of all that pertains to precision of observation. . . . Those who came into contact with him felt the charm of his personality. In some indefinable way he could inspire others with his enthusiasm and determination. Enjoying a life crowded with activity, surrounded by an unusually wide circle of friends, he was ever eager to encourage the humblest beginner. It was no perfunctory interest that he displayed. He was quick to discern any signs of promise, and no less outspoken in his criticism; but whether he praised or condemned, few could leave him without the truest admiration and affection for his simple-hearted character (obituary, *Monthly Notices of the Royal Astronomical Society,* **75** [1915], 236).

BIBLIOGRAPHY

I. Original Works. Gill's *History and Description of the Cape Observatory* (London, 1913), written during his retirement, contains a full account of his work. A complete list of his numerous scientific papers and of the very many honors bestowed upon him will be found in the full-length biography by George Forbes, *David Gill, Man and Astronomer* (London, 1916), which is more concerned with the personal details of his life than with his astronomical work. In a long introduction to his wife's book (see below) Gill outlined the history and general methods of obtaining the solar parallax.

II. Secondary Literature. Gill was fortunate in those who wrote his obituary notices. Of these the most outstanding are Frank Dyson, in *Proceedings of the Royal Society of London,* **91A** (1915), xxvi–xlii; Arthur Eddington, in *Monthly Notices of the Royal Astronomical Society,* **75** (1915), 236–247; and J. C. Kapteyn, in *Astrophysical Journal,* **40** (1914), 161–172.

A charming account of the Ascension expedition is given by Mrs. Gill, *Six Months in Ascension: An Unscientific Account of a Scientific Expedition* (London, 1878).

R. H. Stoy

GILL, THEODORE NICHOLAS (*b.* New York, N.Y., 21 March 1837; *d.* Washington, D.C., 25 September 1914), *ichthyology.*

His youthful interest in the Fulton Fish Market led Gill to a life's work in fishes and other animals despite the preference of his father, James Darrell Gill, for his son to become a minister. His mother, Elizabeth Vosburgh Gill, died when the boy was nine. Visits to the market and interest in natural history continued even after Gill had begun studying law, and a scholarship from the Wagner Free Institute of Science in Philadelphia enabled him to continue his preferred interests. Through William Stimpson he was introduced to Spencer F. Baird, who arranged for the Smithsonian Institution to publish Gill's report on the fishes of New York when he was only nineteen (1856). Almost his only fieldwork was an expedition to the West Indies in 1858, when he made collections especially of the freshwater fishes of Trinidad.

Gill became librarian of the Smithsonian Institution in 1862; and when the books were given to the Library of Congress in 1866, he went with them as assistant librarian until 1874. From 1860 he held various appointments at Columbian College (now George Washington University), including that of professor of zoology from 1884 to 1910. The college recognized his merit by awarding him the M.A. (1865), M.D. (1866), Ph.D. (1870), and LL.D. (1895). He was elected to the National Academy of Sciences, was a fellow and president (1897) of the American Association for the Advancement of Science, a member of many other scientific societies, and a founder of the Cosmos Club.

A bachelor, Gill lived and studied in cluttered offices in the Smithsonian throughout most of his scientific career. One of Baird's close-knit coterie in the U.S. Fish Commission, he was an outstanding taxonomist and synthesizer of scientific literature. His classifications of fishes, based primarily on skeletal structure, were especially valuable at the family and order levels and formed a major basis for the classification adopted and promulgated by David Starr Jordan. Many of Gill's papers were brief and succinct analyses of the genera of fishes, group by group. He was less keen in the recognition and description of fish species. His publications on the habits and life histories of fishes brought together the scattered observations of many workers. His taxonomic studies on birds and on mollusks have been generally superseded. Gill was unusually generous with advice and knowledge to colleagues and visitors at the Smithsonian Institution.

BIBLIOGRAPHY

I. Original Works. Gill's publications consisted of a very large number of relatively short papers (with no single extensive monograph) which constituted a major contribution, primarily to ichthyology. Dall's biography of Gill (cited below) contains an almost complete bibliography.

II. SECONDARY LITERATURE. A full account of Gill's life and accomplishments is W. H. Dall, "Biographical Memoir of Theodore Nicholas Gill," in *Biographical Memoirs. National Academy of Sciences,* **8** (1916), 313–343. The same account, without the bibliography, appeared in *Smithsonian Report for 1916* (Washington, D.C., 1917), pp. 579–586. Brief references to Gill's contributions to ichthyology are found in C. L. Hubbs, "History of Ichthyology in the United States After 1850," in *Copeia,* no. 1 (1964), 46–48; and in David Starr Jordan, *The Days of a Man,* vol. I (Yonkers, N.Y., 1922).

ELIZABETH NOBLE SHOR

GIORGI, GIOVANNI (*b.* Lucca, Italy, 27 November 1871; *d.* Castiglioncello, Italy, 19 August 1950), *electrical theory, electrical engineering, mathematics.*

Giorgi's father was an eminent jurist, who served as president of the Council of State and senator of the kingdom. From him Giorgi inherited a respect for scholarship and an austere way of life. Giorgi's dedication to the doctrines of physics and their applications began early and lasted throughout his life; his more than 350 publications include works on engineering, pure physics, mathematical physics, electricity, magnetism, natural sciences, chemistry, and philosophy.

Giorgi took the degree in civil engineering from the Institute of Technology in Rome when he was twenty-two; his most important technological achievements include projects in steam-generated electrical traction, innovations in urban trolley systems, and pioneering concepts in hydroelectric installations (integral utilization of rivers) and distribution networks (as, for example, the secondary three-phase network with the fourth wire, used by him for the first time in Rome's municipal installation). The work in large part coincided with his tenure as director of the Technology Office of the city of Rome from 1906 to 1923.

Giorgi's teaching activities further reflect the scope of his interests. From 1913 to 1927 he taught courses in the Physics and Mathematics Faculty of the University of Rome, at the School of Aeronautics, and in the School of Engineering; he was later titular professor of mathematical physics and, by annual contract, head of the department of rational mechanics at the universities of Cagliari and Palermo. From 1934 he was professor of electrical communications at the University of Rome and in 1939 he became associate professor at the Royal Institute of Higher Mathematics. In addition to teaching and practical engineering, he did original scientific work (particularly in mathematics) and wrote popular treatments of scientific and technological subjects.

Giorgi's chief fame, however, arises from his concept of a new absolute system of measurement to be simultaneously applicable to all electrical, magnetic, and mechanical units. In a letter to the English periodical *Electrician,* dated 28 March 1895 and published in April 1896, Giorgi took issue with the French physicist Alfred Cornu about the rationality of retaining the c.g.s. system of Wilhelm Weber and the English physicists, standardized in 1898. Giorgi held that the system, whose basic energy unit was the erg—one gram cm./sec.^{2}, or one centimeterdyne —was ill-adapted to current physics, given the connection between electrical and magnetic phenomena long since revealed by the researches of Oersted and Ampère.

Giorgi then devoted considerable time to the systematization of electrical units, and on 13 October 1901 presented to a meeting of the Italian Electrical Engineering Association a report entitled "Unità razionali di elettromagnetismo"—the cornerstone of his subsequent work. In this paper he proposed a consistent measurement system based on the meter, the kilogram, and the mean solar second (and hence called the M.K.S. system, as well as the Giorgi International System). The Giorgi system, of which the basic energy unit is the joule (one kg. meter^2/sec.^{2}, or one meternewton), is adaptable to electrical, magnetic, and mechanical units; is entirely composed of the standard units of mechanics; and requires no conversion factors since it is applicable to both electrostatic and electromagnetic systems. It therefore offers fewer irrationalities and greater convenience than the c.g.s. system because of its establishment of a single basic unit of appropriate size for each application.

Giorgi's proposals were supported by Silvanus Thompson in England, Fritz Emde in Germany, and the U.S. Bureau of Standards, among others, but it was not until June 1935 that the plenary session of the International Electrical Engineering Commission, meeting in Scheveningen, Netherlands, and in Brussels, unanimously recommended the adoption of the new system of units to supersede the c.g.s. system. In October 1960 the General Conference of Weights and Measures confirmed the International System, based on the meter, the kilogram, and the second, as well as the ampere, kelvin, and candle. It is interesting to note that Giorgi himself had proposed the ohm or some other such unit as a fourth standard.

A half century thus elapsed between Giorgi's letter to *Electrician* and the final adoption of a system based upon his principles. The Giorgi system is the clear manifestation of his versatility and of his abilities as a synthesizer.

BIBLIOGRAPHY

I. Original Works. Giorgi reprinted several of his works that are most important to reforms in the study of electrical engineering and the system of units—together with biographical data and a bibliography to December 1948 that lists more than 300 publications—in *Verso l'elettrotecnica moderna* (Milan, 1949).

His textbooks include *Lezioni di costruzioni elettromeccaniche* (Rome, 1905); *Lezioni di meccanica generale (superiore)* (Rome, 1914); *Lezioni di fisica matematica (elettricità e magnetismo)* (Cagliari, 1926); *Lezioni di fisica matematica* (Rome, 1927); *Compendio delle lezioni di meccanica razionale* (Rome, 1928); *Lezioni di meccanica razionale*, 2 vols. (Rome, 1931–1934); *Lezioni del corso di communicazioni elettriche* (Rome, 1934–1939); *Meccanica razionale* (Rome, 1946); *Compendio di storia delle matematiche* (Turin, 1948); *Aritmetica per scuole medie* (Rome, 1948); and *Verso l'elettrotecnica moderna* (Milan, 1949).

His scientific popularizations include *Le ferrovie a trazione elettrica* (Bologna, 1905); *Che cos'è l'elettricità?*, no. 8 in Collezione Omnia (Rome, 1928); *Metrologia elettrotecnica antica e nuova* (Milan, 1937), a repr. of three arts. published in *Energia elettrica*, **14**, nos. 3–5 (Mar.-May, 1937); *L'etere e la luce (dall'etere cosmico alle moderne teorie della luce)*, no. 32 in Collezione Omnia (Rome, 1939); and *La frantumazione dell'atomo* (Rome, 1946).

In addition, Giorgi wrote 37 papers on the new system of measurement, 32 on machinery and electrical installations, 14 on electrical traction, 45 on general electrical engineering, 93 on theories in mathematics and mathematical physics, 19 on the history of science, and 27 articles for the *Enciclopedia italiana Treccani*.

II. Secondary Literature. A very good summary of Giorgi's life and work was given by Basilio Focaccia at the commemoration ceremony in Rome on 26 April 1951 and was published in *Elettrotecnica*, **38** (1951).

Mario Loria

GIRARD, ALBERT (*b.* St. Mihiel, France, 1595; *d.* Leiden, Netherlands, 8 December 1632), *mathematics.*

Girard's birthplace is fixed only by the adjective *Samielois* that he often added to his name, an adjective the printers of St. Mihiel often applied to themselves in the seventeenth century. The city belonged at that time to the duchy of Lorraine. The exact date of Girard's birth is subject to dispute. That of his death is known from a note in the *Journal* of Constantijn Huygens for 9 December 1632. The place of death is only conjectured.

Girard was undoubtedly a member of the Reformed church, for in a polemic against Honorat du Meynier he accused the latter of injuring "those of the Reformed religion by calling them heretics." This explains why he settled—at an unknown date—in the Netherlands, the situation of Protestants being very precarious in Lorraine.

The respectful and laudatory tone in which he speaks of Willebrord Snell in his *Trigonometry* leads one to suppose that Girard studied at Leiden. According to Johann Friedrich Gronovius, in his *éloge* of Jacob Golius, in 1616 Girard engaged in scientific correspondence with Golius, then twenty years old.

When Golius succeeded Snell at Leiden in 1629, Constantijn Huygens wrote to him to praise the knowledge of Girard (*vir stupendus*), particularly in the study of refraction. On 21 July of the same year Pierre Gassendi wrote from Brussels to Nicholas de Peiresc that he had dined at the camp before Bois-le-Roi with ". . . Albert Girard, an engineer now at the camp." We thus know definitely that Girard was an engineer in the army of Frederick Henry of Nassau, prince of Orange; yet the only title that he gives himself in his works is that of mathematician.

The end of Girard's life was difficult. He complains, in his posthumously published edition of the works of Stevin, of living in a foreign country, without a patron, ruined, and burdened with a large family. His widow, in the dedication of this work, is more precise. She is poor, with eleven orphans to whom their father has left only his reputation of having faithfully served and having spent all his time on research on the most noble secrets of mathematics.

Girard's works include a translation from Flemish into French of Henry Hondius' treatise on fortifications (1625) and editions of the mathematical works of Samuel Marolois (1627–1630), of the *Arithmetic* of Simon Stevin (1625), and of Stevin's works (1634). He also prepared sine tables and a succinct treatise on trigonometry (1626; 1627; 2nd ed., 1629) and published a theoretical work, *Invention nouvelle en l'algèbre* (1629). Although in the preface to the trigonometric tables (1626) he promised that he would very soon present studies inspired by Pappus of Alexandria (plane and solid loci, inclinations, and determinations), no such work on these matters appeared. Likewise, his restoration of Euclid's porisms, which he stated he "hopes to present, having reinvented them," never appeared.

Contributions to the mathematical sciences are scattered throughout Girard's writings. It should be said at the outset that, always pressed for time and generally lacking space, he was very stingy with words and still more so with demonstrations; thus, he very often suggested more than he demonstrated. His notations were, in general, those of Stevin and François Viète, "who surpasses all his predecessors in algebra." He improved Stevin's writing of the radicals by proposing that the cube root be written not as $\sqrt{③}$ but as $\sqrt[3]{\ }$ (*Invention nouvelle,* 1629) but, like Stevin, favored fractional exponents. He had his own symbols for $>$ and $<$, and in trigonometry he was one of the first to utilize incidentally—in several very clear tables—the abbreviations sin, tan, and sec for sine, tangent, and secant.

In spherical trigonometry, following Viète and like Willebrord Snell, but less clearly than Snell, Girard made use of the supplementary triangle. In geometry he generalized the concept of the plane polygon, distinguishing three types of quadrilaterals, eleven types of pentagons, and sixty-nine (there are seventy) types of hexagons (*Trigonométrie,* 1626). With the sides of a convex quadrilateral inscribed in a circle one can construct two other quadrilaterals inscribed in the same circle. Their six diagonals are equal in pairs. Girard declared that these quadrilaterals have an area equal to the product of the three distinct diagonals divided by twice the diameter of the circle.

Girard was the first to state publicly that the area of a spherical triangle is proportional to its spherical excess (*Invention nouvelle*). This theorem, stemming from the optical tradition of Witelo, was probably known by Regiomontanus and definitely known by Thomas Harriot—who, however, did not divulge it. Girard gave a proof of it that did not fully satisfy him and that he termed "a probable conclusion." It was Bonaventura Cavalieri who furnished, independently, a better-founded demonstration (1632).

In arithmetic Girard took up Nicolas Chuquet's expressions "million," "billion," "trillion," and so on. He "explains radicals extremely close to certain numbers, such that if one attempted the same things with other numbers, it would not be without greatly increasing the number of characters" (*Arithmétique de . . . Stevin,* 1625). He gave, among various examples, Fibonacci's series, the values 577/408 and 1393/985 for $\sqrt{2}$, and an approximation of $\sqrt{10}$. One should see in these an anticipation of continuous fractions. They are also similar to the approximation 355/113 obtained for π by Valentin Otho (1573) and by Adriaan Anthoniszoon (1586) and to the contemporary writings of Daniel Schwenter.

In the theory of numbers Girard translated books V and VI of Diophantus from Latin into French (*Arithmétique de . . . Stevin*). For this work he knew and utilized not only Guilielmus Xylander's edition, as Stevin had for the first four books, but also that of Claude Gaspar Bachet de Méziriac (1621), which he cited several times. He gave fourteen right triangles in whole numbers whose sides differ from unity. For the largest the sides are on the order of 3×10^{10} (*ibid.,* p. 629).

Girard stated the whole numbers that are sums of two squares and declared that certain numbers, such as seven, fifteen, and thirty-nine, are not decomposable into three squares; but he affirmed, as did Bachet, that all of them are decomposable into four squares (*ibid.,* p. 662). The first demonstration of this theorem was provided by Joseph Lagrange (1772). Girard also contributed to problems concerning sums of cubes by improving one of Viète's techniques (*ibid.,* p. 676).

In algebra, as in the theory of numbers, Girard showed himself to be a brilliant disciple of Viète, whose "specious logistic" he often employed but called "literal algebra." In his study of incommensurables Girard generally followed Stevin and the tradition of book X of Euclid, but he gave a very clear rule for the extraction of the cube root of binomials. It was an improvement on the method of Rafael Bombelli and was, in turn, surpassed by that which Descartes formulated in 1640 (*Invention nouvelle*).

Unlike Harriot and Descartes, Girard never wrote an equation in which the second member was zero. He particularly favored the "alternating order," in which the monomials, in order of decreasing degree, are alternately in the first member and the second member. That permitted him to express, without any difficulty with signs, the relations between the coefficients and the roots. In this regard he stated, after Peter Roth (1608) and before Descartes (1637), the fundamental algebraic theorem: "Every equation in algebra has as many solutions as the denominator of its largest quantity" (1629).

A restriction immediately follows this statement, but it is annulled soon after by the introduction of solutions which are "enveloped like those which have $\sqrt{-}$." From this point of view, Girard hardly surpassed Bombelli, his rare examples treating only equations of the third and fourth degrees. For him the introduction of imaginary roots was essentially for the generality and elegance of the formulas. In addition, Girard gave the expression for the sums of squares, cubes, and fourth powers of roots as a function of the coefficients (Newton's formulas).

Above all, Girard thoroughly studied cubic and biquadratic equations. He knew how to form the discriminant of the equations $x^3 = px + q$, $x^3 = px^2 + q$, and $x^4 = px^3 + q$. These are examples of the "determinations" that he had promised in 1626. The first equation is of the type solved by Niccolò Tartaglia and Girolamo Cardano, the second relates to book II of the *Sphere* of Archimedes, and the third to Plato's problem in the *Meno.* With the aid of trigonometric tables Girard solved equations of the third degree having three real roots. For those having only one root he indicated, beside Cardano's rules, an elegant method of numerical solution by means of trigonometric tables and iteration. He constructed equations of the first type geometrically by reducing them, as Viète did, to the trisection of an arc of a circle. This trisection was carried out by using a hyperbola, as Pappus had done. The figure then made evident the three roots of the equation.

Girard was the first to point out the geometric significance of the negative numbers: "The negative solution is explained in geometry by moving backward, and the minus sign moves back when the + advances." To illustrate this affirmation he took from Pappus a problem of intercalation that Descartes later treated in an entirely different spirit (1637). This problem led him to an equation of the fourth degree. The numerical case that he had chosen admitted two positive roots and two negative roots; he made the latter explicit and showed their significance.

BIBLIOGRAPHY

I. ORIGINAL WORKS. Girard's two books are *Tables des sinus, tangentes et sécantes selon le raid de 100,000 parties* . . . (The Hague, 1626; 1627; 2nd ed., 1629), which also appeared in Flemish but had the Latin title *Tabulae sinuum tangentium et secantium ad radium 100,000* (The Hague, 1626; 1629); and *Invention nouvelle en l'algèbre* (Amsterdam, 1629; repr. Leiden, 1884). The repr. of the latter, by D. Bierens de Haan, is a faithful facs., except for the notation of the exponents, in which parentheses are substituted for the circles used by Girard and Stevin. However, the parentheses had been used by Girard in the *Tables.*

Girard was also responsible for trans. and eds. of works by others: *Oeuvres de Henry Hondius* (The Hague, 1625), which he translated from the Flemish; Samuel Marolois's *Fortification ou architecture militaire* (Amsterdam, 1627), which he enlarged and revised, and also issued in Flemish as *Samuel Maroloys, Fortification* . . . (Amsterdam, 1627), and *Géométrie contenant la théorie et practique d'icelle, necessaire à la fortification* . . ., 2 vols. (Amsterdam, 1627–1628; 1629), which he revised and also issued in Flemish as *Opera mathematica ofte wis-konstige, Wercken* . . . *beschreven door Sam. Marolois* . . . (Amsterdam, 1630); and Simon Stevin's *L'arithmétique* (Leiden, 1625), which he revised and enlarged, and *Les oeuvres mathématiques de Simon Stevin* (Leiden, 1634), also revised and enlarged.

II. SECONDARY LITERATURE. On Girard or his work, see several articles by Henri Bosmans in *Mathesis,* **40** and **41** (1926); Antonio Favaro, "Notizie storiche sulle frazioni continue," in *Bullettino di bibliografia e di storia delle scienze matematiche e fisiche,* **7** (1874), 533–596, see 559–565; Gino Loria, *Storia delle matematiche,* 2nd ed. (Milan, 1950), pp. 439–444; Georges Maupin, "Étude sur les annotations jointes par Albert Girard Samielois aux oeuvres mathématiques de Simon Stevin de Bruges," in *Opinions et curiosités touchant le mathématique,* II (Paris, 1902), 159–325; Paul Tannery, "Albert Girard de Saint-Mihiel," in *Bulletin des sciences mathématiques et astronomiques,* 2nd ser., **7** (1883), 358–360, also in Tannery's *Mémoires scientifiques,* VI (Paris, 1926), 19–22; and G. A. Vosterman van Oijen, "Quelques arpenteurs hollandais de la fin du XVIème et du commencement du XVIIème siècle," in *Bullettino di bibliografia e di storia delle scienze matematiche e fisiche,* **3** (1870), 323–376, see 359–362.

See also *Nieuw Nederlandsch Woordenboek,* II (1912), cols. 477–481.

JEAN ITARD

GIRARD, PIERRE-SIMON (*b.* Caen, France, 4 November 1765; *d.* Paris, France, 30 November 1836), *hydraulic engineering.*

Educated at Caen, Girard was admitted to the École des Ponts et Chaussées at the age of twenty-one and in 1789 was appointed to the grade of engineer in the Corps des Ponts et Chaussées. His first subject of investigation, to which he later returned, was the strength of wood as a structural material, yet he won the 1790 competition of the Académie des Sciences on the theory and practice of canal and harbor lock construction. In 1798 he was among the scientific experts in many fields called to take part in Napoleon's expedition to Egypt, where he remained until 1803, after the last troops had left. At first assigned to the port of Alexandria, he soon undertook an extensive study of the surface elevation and bed characteristics of the Nile; this study eventually broadened to cover material on Egypt's agriculture, commerce, and industry, all to be included in the comprehensive report on the expedition, of which he was one of eight authors.

Upon Girard's return to France, Napoleon appointed him director of the Paris water supply, with the special task of connecting the Seine and Ourcq rivers with a ship canal to serve the capital. This led him to study the resistance of the flow of water through pipes and open channels, the most essential contribution of which was the attention that it called to an important analysis, buried since 1768 in the files of the Corps des Ponts et Chaussées, by Antoine de Chézy. The first barges reached Paris from the Ourcq in 1813, but the overthrow of Napoleon and the restoration of the monarchy delayed completion of the 100-kilometer canal until 1820. Girard's account of the project, including the causes of certain objectionable effects on the groundwater level in urban districts, is to be found in his major treatise, *Mémoire sur le canal de l'Ourcq* . . ., a two-volume work plus atlas (1831–1843).

Girard was elected to the first class of the Institut National des Sciences et des Arts in 1815—this class became the Académie des Sciences of the Institute the following year—and served as its president in 1830. Despite his having rallied to Napoleon during the Hundred Days, Girard retained his post as water commissioner until 1831, and in the latter period he was promoted to the grade of *officier* in the Legion of Honor. The day of his death, 30 November, is given incorrectly in several references.

BIBLIOGRAPHY

A complete list of Girard's writings is in *Nouvelle biographie générale* (see below), which refers to a projected collection of his works, but no trace of the latter can be found. His major work is *Mémoire sur le canal de l'Ourcq* . . ., 2 vols. plus atlas (Paris, 1831–1843).

Biographies are in *Nouvelle biographie générale,* XX (Paris, 1857), 661–668; and *Grand dictionnaire universel du XIXe siècle,* VIII (Paris, 1872), 1268. See also Charles Richet (Girard's great-grandson), "Pierre-Simon Girard . . .," in *Comptes rendus de l'Académie des sciences,* **197** (11 Dec. 1933), 1481–1486.

HUNTER ROUSE

GIRAUD-SOULAVIE, J. L. See **Soulavie, J. L. Giraud.**

GIRTANNER, CHRISTOPH (*b.* St. Gall, Switzerland, 7 December 1760; *d.* Göttingen, Germany, 17 May 1800), *medicine, chemistry.*

Girtanner's father, Hieronymus, was a banker; his mother, Barbara Felicitas, was the daughter of the burgomaster Christoph Wegelin. He studied first at Lausanne and then at Göttingen where he obtained his doctorate in 1782 with a thesis on chalk, quicklime, and the matter of fire. He studied pediatrics at St. Gall, and then visited Paris, Edinburgh, and London before returning to Göttingen in 1787, the year he met Georg Lichtenberg. After further travels in 1788–1789, he settled in Göttingen, and in 1793 became a privy councillor to the duke of Saxe-Coburg. In 1790 he had married Catherine Maria Erdmann; their two sons both became naturalists. Girtanner was of a contentious disposition and published antirevolutionary works.

Girtanner was attracted by the Brunonian theory and studied Lavoisier's work on oxygen which he believed might be the principle of irritability. In 1790 he suggested this possibility in Rozier's *Observations sur la physique* and was accused of plagiarizing John Brown. He then wrote critical expositions of the views of Brown and of Erasmus Darwin. Meanwhile he had also published a book on pediatrics and another on venereal disease, arguing forcibly for the American origin of syphilis.

Girtanner was an early convert to Lavoisier's doctrines, and in 1791 published the first German version of the new chemical nomenclature. But his term for nonacidic oxides, *Halbsäure,* proved unacceptable, and his scheme for distinguishing such acids as sulfuric and sulfurous was unsuccessful. In 1792 he published his *Anfangsgründe der antiphlogistischen Chemie,* a textbook modeled upon Lavoisier's, which saw three editions and was used by Berzelius. According to Lavoisier, muriatic acid (hydrogen chloride) must, like all acids, be an oxide. Girtanner thought he had proved it to be an oxide of hydrogen, and nitrogen another oxide which could be prepared from steam. But unlike contemporary Germans who believed that water was thus proved the basis of all gases, he refused to accept that his experiments entailed a return to the phlogiston principle.

BIBLIOGRAPHY

I. ORIGINAL WORKS. Girtanner's writings include *Dissertatio inauguralis chemica de Terra Calcarea cruda et calcinata* (Göttingen, 1782); *Abhandlung über die venerische Krankheit,* 3 vols. (Göttingen, 1788–1789), in which the first vol. is practical, the others bibliographical; "Mémoires sur l'irritabilité," in *Observations sur la physique,* **36** (1790), 422; **37** (1790), 139; *Neue chemische Nomenklatur für die Deutsche Sprache* (Berlin, 1791); *Anfangsgründe der antiphlogistischen Chemie* (Berlin, 1792; 2nd ed., 1795; 3rd ed., 1801); *Abhandlung über die Krankheiten der Kinder* . . . (Berlin, 1794), Italian trans., 2 vols. (Genoa, 1801); *Ueber das Kantische Prinzip für die Naturgeschichte* . . . (Göttingen, 1796); *Ausfürliche Darstellung des Brownischen Systemes der praktischen Heilkunde* . . ., 2 vols. (Göttingen, 1797–1798); Russian trans., *Iogona brovno sistema,* 3 vols. (St. Petersburg, 1806–1807); *Ausfürliche Darstellung des Darwinischen Systemes der praktischen Heilkunde* . . ., 2 vols. (Göttingen, 1799); "Sur l'analyse de l'azote," in *Annales de chimie,* **33** (1799), 229–231; **36** (1800), 3–40; a trans. is in *Philosophical Magazine,* **6** (1800), 152–153, 216–217, 335–354.

II. SECONDARY LITERATURE. For works about Girtanner, see M. P. Crosland, *Historical Studies in the Language of Chemistry* (London, 1962), pp. 207–210; G. W. A. Kahlbaum and A. Hoffman, *Die Einführung der Lavoisierischen Theorie im Besonderen in Deutschland* (Leipzig, 1897); *Neue deutsche Biographie,* VI (Berlin, 1964), 411–412; and J. R. Partington, *A History of Chemistry,* III (London, 1962), 589–590.

DAVID M. KNIGHT

GLADSTONE, JOHN HALL (*b.* London, England, 7 March 1827; *d.* London, 6 October 1902), *chemistry.*

Financially independent for the latter part of his life, Gladstone devoted much time to research as well as to philanthropic and religious work; in science he is best-known for his application of optical phenomena to chemical problems.

His father, John Gladstone, a junior partner in the firm of Cook and Gladstone, wholesale drapers, married a cousin, Alison Hall, whose father also owned a drapery business. John Hall was the eldest of their three sons. The boys were all educated at home under tutors and showed an early interest in natural science. At seventeen Gladstone wished to enter the Christian ministry but was dissuaded and entered University College, London, where he attended Thomas Graham's lectures and worked in his laboratory. He gained a gold medal for original research and in 1847 went to work under Justus Liebig at Giessen, from which he graduated Ph.D. He returned to London in 1848 and in 1850 became lecturer in chemistry at St. Thomas' Hospital, where he stayed for two years. In 1853 Gladstone was elected fellow of the Royal Society, and from 1874 to 1877 he was Fullerian professor of chemistry at the Royal Institution. He was a founder member of the Physical Society and its first president (1874–1876), and president of the Chemical Society from 1877 to 1879. Gladstone was married twice: in 1852 to May Tilt—she and their only son died in 1864—and in 1869 to Margaret King (niece of Lord Kelvin), who died in 1870, leaving a daughter.

In an early paper (1853) Gladstone arranged all the known elements in the order of their "atomic weights" (actually, equivalents), thus anticipating John Newlands and others in pointing out certain peculiarities and drawing attention to some surprising relationships existing between the atomic weights of related elements, including some relationships observed earlier by Johann Döbereiner. He did not mention Döbereiner, but acknowledged the work of Leopold Gmelin who, in 1843, had drawn attention to and enlarged upon Döbereiner's observations. (Gladstone's contribution to the evolution of the periodic table is assessed by J. W. van Spronsen in *The Periodic System of Chemical Elements* [Amsterdam–London–New York, 1969], pp. 76–78 and *passim.*)

In 1855 he carried out the first quantitative investigation of equilibria in homogeneous systems, particularly using solutions of various ferric salts and thiocyanates, choosing these reactions because of the red color of the ferric thiocyanate thus formed. (Gladstone's results were later examined mathematically by E. J. Mills, on the basis of the law of mass action—see *Philosophical Magazine,* **47** [1874], 241–247.) Since the reaction never went to completion in any one direction, the inadequacy of prevailing ideas on chemical affinity was demonstrated.

Gladstone's important pioneering work on refractivity, in collaboration with T. P. Dale, began in 1858 with the measurement of the decrease in the refractive indexes of a number of liquids with increase in temperature. Observations of this in connection with accompanying changes of density subsequently led them to the formulation of what they called the specific refractive energy (now called specific refractive index—$\frac{n-1}{d}$, where n is the refractive index and d is the density), which they found to be approximately constant for a given liquid. Hans Landolt termed the product of this and the atomic weight of an element the refraction equivalent, and Gladstone subsequently measured it for a number of elements, finding it to be additive in compounds. (Refractivity is both additive and constitutive and has subsequently been of importance in organic analysis, particularly to resolve structure.)

In a series of researches with Alfred Tribe the copper-zinc couple was introduced and used in a number of organic preparations. His work on essential oils in his refractivity experiments led Gladstone to analyze them, and he discovered a number of terpenes.

Gladstone was deeply involved in a number of religious movements (particularly the Y. M.C.A.) and in educational reform.

BIBLIOGRAPHY

I. Original Works. About 200 papers by Gladstone (of which approximately one-third are collaborative) are listed in the Royal Society, *Catalogue of Scientific Papers,* II (London, 1868), 909–911; VII (London, 1877), 783–784; X (London, 1894), 2–3; XV (Cambridge, 1916), 327–328. The lists are not entirely reliable and contain a few duplications. The papers mentioned in the text are "On the Relations Between the Atomic Weights of Analogous Elements," in *Philosophical Magazine,* **5** (1853), 313–320 (not listed in the above); "On Circumstances Modifying the Action of Chemical Affinity," in *Philosophical Transactions of the Royal Society,* **145** (1855), 179–223—see also "Some Experiments Illustrative of the Reciprocal Decomposition of Salts," in *Journal of the Chemical Society,* **9** (1857), 144–156, and "Additional Notes on Reciprocal Decomposition Among Salts in Solution," *ibid.,* **15** (1862), 302–311; "On the Influence of Temperature on the Refraction of Light," in *Philosophical Transactions of the Royal Society,* **148** (1858), 887–894; "Researches on the Refraction, Dispersion and Sensitiveness of Liquids," *ibid.,* **153** (1863), 317–343; "Researches on Refraction-equivalents," in *Proceedings of the Royal Society,* **16** (1868), 439–444; "On the Refraction-equivalents of the Elements," in *Philosophical Transactions of the Royal Society,* **160** (1870), 9–32; "On Essential Oils," in *Journal of the Chemical Society,* **17** (1864), 1–21; **25** (1872), 1–12; **49** (1886), 609–623; and "Researches on the Action of the Copper-Zinc Couple on Organic Bodies," *ibid.,* **26** (1873), 445–452, 678–683, 961–970; **27** (1874), 208–212, 406–410, 410–415, 615–619; **28** (1875), 508–514; **35** (1879), 107–110; **47** (1885), 448–456, written with A. Tribe. Gladstone published a biography of Faraday, whom he knew well, *Michael Faraday* (London, 1872; 2nd ed., 1873); and, from articles which had appeared in *Nature, The Chemistry of the Secondary Batteries of Planté and Faure* (London, 1883), written with A. Tribe.

Gladstone also wrote a pamphlet on spelling reform, several pamphlets on religious matters, and some hymns.

II. SECONDARY LITERATURE. A biography is W. A. Tilden, "John Hall Gladstone," in *Journal of the Chemical Society,* **87** (1905), 591–597. Obituary notices are T. E. T., in *Proceedings of the Royal Society,* **75** (1905), 188–192; and W. C. R. A., in *Nature,* **66** (1902), 609–610.

E. L. SCOTT

GLAISHER, JAMES (*b.* Rotherhithe, England, 7 April 1809; *d.* Croydon, England, 7 February 1903), *meteorology.*

Glaisher seems to have been largely self-educated and to have acquired his interest in science on visits to Greenwich observatory. In 1833 he attracted the attention of George Airy, who appointed him assistant at Cambridge observatory; when Airy became astronomer royal in 1835, Glaisher soon followed him to Greenwich. In 1838 a magnetic and meteorological department was formed at Greenwich with Glaisher as superintendent, a post he held until his retirement at the statutory age in 1874. This appointment determined the course of Glaisher's life. He effectively organized meteorological observations and climatological statistics in the United Kingdom; and although more than 120 papers appeared under his name, his importance in the history of his chosen science lies chiefly in the great energy and persistence that he displayed in this work.

Glaisher's first extensive scientific paper was on the radiation of heat from the ground at night (1847), and in the same year he published his *Hygrometrical Tables Adapted to the Use of the Dry and Wet Bulb Thermometer,* which, although entirely empirical in construction, remained in use by British meteorologists for almost a century. His most spectacular activity, which brought him to the attention of the public, was a series of scientific balloon ascents with the aeronaut Henry Coxwell in 1862, under the auspices of the British Association for the Advancement of Science.

Glaisher was elected a fellow of the Royal Society in 1849 and took a leading part in the founding of the British (now the Royal) Meteorological Society in 1850. He was the first president of the Royal Microscopical Society (1865–1869), president of the Photographic Society for more than twenty years, and a member of the council of the Royal Aeronautical Society from its foundation in 1866 until his death.

BIBLIOGRAPHY

A bibliography compiled by W. Marriott is in *Quarterly Journal of the Royal Meteorological Society,* **30** (1904), 1–28, together with an account of Glaisher's scientific work. His writings include "Radiation of Heat at Night From the Earth . . .," in *Philosophical Transactions of the Royal Society,* **137** (1847), 119–216; *Tables Adapted to the Use of the Dry and Wet Bulb Thermometer* (London, 1847; 9th ed., 1902); and "Account of Meteorological and Physical Observations in Balloon Ascents," in *Report of the British Association for the Advancement of Science* (1862), 376–503.

W. E. K. MIDDLETON

GLAISHER, JAMES WHITBREAD LEE (*b.* Lewisham, Kent, England, 5 November 1848; *d.* Cambridge, England, 7 December 1928), *mathematics, astronomy.*

Glaisher was the eldest son of James Glaisher, an astronomer who was also interested in the calculation of numerical tables. His given names were derived from those of his father and his father's colleagues in the founding of the British Meteorological Society, S. C. Whitbread and John Lee.

Glaisher attended St. Paul's School, London (1858–1867), and Trinity College, Cambridge, where he graduated as second wrangler in 1871. Elected to a fellowship and appointed an assistant tutor at Trinity, he remained there the rest of his life. He never married.

A tall, slim, upright man who retained good health until his last few years, Glaisher enjoyed walking, bicycling, collecting, travel (often in the United States), and teaching as well as mathematical research and participation in the meetings of scientific societies. He became an authority on English pottery, writing parts of several books on the subject and leaving his fine collection to the Fitzwilliam Museum, Cambridge. Glaisher was active in the British Association for the Advancement of Science, as president in 1900 and as a member of several committees. He was the "reporter," as well as a member—along with A. Cayley, G. G. Stokes, W. Thomson, and H. J. S.

Smith—of the Committee on Mathematical Tables. Its 175-page *Report,* containing much historical and bibliographical data, appeared in 1873.

Glaisher's honors included memberships in the councils of the Royal Society (for three different periods), the London Mathematical Society, and the Royal Astronomical Society (from 1874 until his death), as well as the presidency of the last two societies. Cambridge University awarded him the new D.Sc. degree in 1887, and Trinity College of Dublin and Victoria University of Manchester awarded him honorary D.Sc. degrees. Glaisher was an honorary fellow of the Royal Society of Edinburgh, of the Manchester Literary and Philosophical Society, and of the National Academy of Sciences, Washington. He was awarded the De Morgan Medal of the London Mathematical Society in 1908 and the Sylvester Medal of the Royal Society in 1913.

Glaisher's first paper typified three of his continuing interests: special functions, tables, and the history of mathematics. It was written while he was an undergraduate and was communicated to the Royal Society by Arthur Cayley in 1870. It dealt with the integral sine, cosine, and exponential functions and included both tables which he had calculated and much historical matter. Glaisher's first astronomical paper also typified his interest: "The Law of the Facility of Errors of Observations and on the Method of Least Squares," published in the *Memoirs of the Royal Astronomical Society* for 1872. This paper was inspired by a historical note in an American journal giving Robert Adrain credit for the independent discovery of Gauss's law of errors. A. R. Forsyth labels it, along with a paper on Jacopo Riccati's differential equation and one on the history of plus and minus signs, as "classical."

Glaisher published nearly 400 articles and notes but never a book of his own. The nearest he came was the *Report* noted above, the *Collected Mathematical Papers of Henry John Stephen Smith,* which he edited, and volumes VIII and IX of the *Mathematical Tables* of the British Association for the Advancement of Science, published in 1940. The latter were revisions and extensions of number theoretical tables (divisors, Euler's ϕ function and its inverse, and others) which he had completed in 1884.

Glaisher served as editor of two journals, *Messenger of Mathematics* (1871–1928) and *Quarterly Journal of Mathematics* (from 1878 until his death). G. H. Hardy wrote, "A generation of well known English mathematicians began their careers as authors in the *Messenger,*" and stated that Glaisher was ". . . underestimated as a mathematician. He wrote a great deal of very uneven quality, and he was old-fashioned, but the best of his work is really good." He applied to number theory, especially to representations by sums of squares, the properties of special functions, especially elliptic modular functions.

Glaisher's interest in students and publications affected American mathematics. He befriended an American student at Cambridge, Thomas S. Fiske, and took him to meetings of the London Mathematical Society. When he returned to Columbia University, Fiske organized the New York Mathematical Society (later the American Mathematical Society) in 1888 and copied the format of the *Messenger* when the *Bulletin of the New York Mathematical Society* was initiated.

Forsyth's characterization of Glaisher as "a mathematical stimulus to others rather than a pioneer" seems sound.

BIBLIOGRAPHY

I. ORIGINAL WORKS. For lists of papers see Poggendorff, III, 524–525; IV, 502; V, 427–428; VI, 900.

For Glaisher's contributions to number theory, see the author index in Leonard Eugene Dickson, *History of the Theory of Numbers* (New York, 1934). "On Riccati's Equation and its Transformations and on Some Definite Integrals Which Satisfy Them," is in *Philosophical Transactions of the Royal Society of London,* **172,** pt. 3 (1882), 759–828. His article on the history of plus and minus signs appeared in *Messenger of Mathematics,* vol. **51** (1922).

II. SECONDARY LITERATURE. A. R. Forsyth published a biography in *Journal of the London Mathematical Society,* **4,** pt. 2, no. 14 (Apr. 1929), 101–112, repr. in *Proceedings of the Royal Society,* **126A,** no. A802 (22 Jan. 1929), i–xi, with a portrait facing p. i. Forsyth also wrote the biography in *Dictionary of National Biography. 1922–1930* (London, 1937), pp. 339–340, which records that there is a pencil drawing of Glaisher by Francis Dodd in Trinity College, Cambridge.

See also H. H. Turner, "James Whitbread Lee Glaisher," in *Monthly Notices of the Royal Astronomical Society,* **89** (Feb. 1929), 300–308; and G. H. Hardy, "Dr. Glaisher and the Messenger of Mathematics," in *Messenger of Mathematics,* **58** (1929), 159–160.

PHILLIP S. JONES

GLANVILL, JOSEPH (*b.* Plymouth, England, 1636; *d.* Bath, England, 4 November 1680), *theology, apologetics, history and philosophy of science.*

Little is known of Glanvill's early life. His father was a merchant; his family and early education, Puritan. He matriculated at Exeter College, Oxford, in 1652; obtained the B.A. in 1655; studied at Lincoln College both before and after taking the M.A. in 1658; and was ordained in 1660. The most important of Glanvill's ecclesiastical livings was the abbey church at Bath, which he held from 1666 until his death. He was elected fellow of the Royal Society on 14 December 1664 and was the first secretary of a Somerset affiliate established in 1669.

Neither experimenter nor theorist, Glanvill made a few minor contributions to natural history. In number 11 of the *Philosophical Transactions of the Royal Society,* Robert Boyle gave a set of general headings for the natural history of a country, and in number 19 he followed it up with a long list of inquiries concerning the procedures used in mines and the geographical characteristics of mining regions. Glanvill sent in two sets of concise replies for the Mendip lead mines near Bath, obtained through interviews with miners and local residents. Later, in response to queries from Henry Oldenburg, he provided a report on the medicinal springs at Bath, again confined to factual observations except for one modest theoretical suggestion (for which he quickly apologized).

Glanvill's principal contribution to the work of the Royal Society was to defend it against its critics. In a series of much-discussed works he argued that the new experimental philosophy was beneficial in practical terms, had already advanced knowledge beyond what antiquity could claim and would rapidly advance it still further, and was harmless—indeed, it was helpful—to the cause of religion. In the process he produced one of the earliest histories, and one of the earliest philosophies, of science.

While still at Oxford (where he was almost certainly familiar with John Wilkins' "Invisible College," although there is no record of his attending its meetings), Glanvill wrote an elaborate essay, published in 1661, called *The Vanity of Dogmatizing.* This was originally intended to be a preface, defending the use of reason in religion and attacking sectarians and enthusiasts, to a projected book on the immortality of the soul. The preface was to begin with a criticism of dogmatism in general and would lead into an attack on dogmatism and disputatiousness in religion. Throughout his career Glanvill was a prominent apologist for latitudinarian Anglicanism as well as for the new philosophy, and his two lines of apologetic endeavor were frequently intertwined. The fate of the intended preface suggests that defense of the new philosophy was a genuine and independent concern of Glanvill's and no mere adjunct or instrument of his theological apologetics, for the philosophical part grew to book length, while the sectaries were disposed of in two chapters at the end. There Glanvill argues that "confidence in opinions" has led to acrimonious disputes about obscure doctrines, while the essentials of religion—devotion to God and practical love of neighbor—are ignored. The philosophical study of nature, on the other hand, promotes piety both by teaching us to admire more justly the work of the Divine Architect and by elevating the mind above sensual concerns. (The virtues traditionally ascribed to quasi-mystical, world-scorning philosophers are here—with incongruously traditional rhetoric—credited to such men as "those illustrious Heroes, *Cartes, Gassendus, Galilaeo, Tycho, Harvey, More, Digby.*" But of course Glanvill had to counter the claim of the enthusiasts that "vain philosophy" turns men's thoughts from heaven to earth. In later works he chose to sidestep that charge.)

The book begins with a speculative discussion of Adam's knowledge before the Fall. Glanvill reasons that a being created in God's image would have senses that could perceive the hidden causes of things, as well as the wonders revealed by Galileo's telescope. The "circumference" of his senses must have been "the same with that of natures activity." But the Fall brought us very low; our ignorance is almost total. We cannot understand how the soul is united with and moves the body; we can give no account of sensation or memory; we cannot explain how plants and animals are formed, nor what holds the parts of material objects together. Not even the ingenious hypotheses of Descartes and Henry More—most admirable of philosophers—will do. The causes of our ignorance are many. Truth lies deeply hidden; our senses are weak; they deceive us or, rather, present misleading impressions, so that our precipitate judgment errs. Our attempts to imagine things which cannot be imagined, the mind's liability to fatigue in close reasoning, and such affectional factors as personal vanity and reverence for antiquity—all these lead to hasty judgment, the source of all error. The mention of antiquity occasions a denunciation of Aristotelianism: it delights in controversy, its terms are ambiguous, its occult qualities explain nothing, its astronomy is silly, it has led to no useful inventions or discoveries, it is inconsistent both with itself and with true divinity. In all these regards we can expect better things from the "*Neoterick* endeavours" now under way.

The influence of Descartes (whether direct or through Henry More) is plain, although it is also plain that Glanvill has picked and chosen among Cartesian doctrines. In particular he ignores Descartes's claims for certainty and follows that strand in his physical writings which claims only to offer useful hypotheses and calls for experiments.

The next section of *The Vanity of Dogmatizing,* where Glanvill tries to show by an analysis of causality that we can have no certain knowledge of nature, begins to seem more like a crude anticipation of Hume. To have "science" in the dogmatist's sense, we would need "knowledge of things in their true, immediate, necessary causes." We have no immediate perception of causal connections; at best we observe constant concomitances. To know that a causal connection is necessary, we would have to know that alternatives are impossible; but what is impossible on one set of hypotheses (for instance, those of Aristotle, or Descartes, or common sense) will often be possible on another, and there are phenomena (e.g., sympathetic cure of wounds or control of another's thoughts) which are impossible in all known thought systems yet are real. We do not know the true causes of things, the "first springs of natural motions"; and since even the proximate causes we know are often very dissimilar to their effects, the invisible "first springs" are probably quite unlike anything with which we are familiar. The argument is not logically tight. It is meant to be rhetorically persuasive, and much of it really aims only to show that no one is in a position to claim certain knowledge of nature. We can have certainty in mathematics, but it is about notions of our creation and not the world, and in the essentials of religion, which are "as demonstrable as Geometry" (although Glanvill does not tell how).

The Vanity of Dogmatizing was promptly attacked by Thomas White, a Catholic Aristotelian, as destructively skeptical and as, by its endorsement of the mechanical philosophy, an aid to Hobbesian atheism. Glanvill replied in 1664 by issuing a revised version, with additional essays directed at White and a long prefatory address to the Royal Society, the whole titled *Scepsis scientifica.* The way he had advocated is just that followed by the Royal Society: accumulating factual information (which only a theory-obsessed dogmatist could dispute) about natural phenomena while prudently refraining from premature theorizing. Moreover, we cannot guard against Hobbesian misuse of the "mechanical hypothesis" by appeal to a discredited Scholasticism; the only way is to show, as the virtuosos are showing, that when well worked out, the hypothesis provides overwhelming evidence for a wise and benevolent Designer.

The address won Glanvill election to the Royal Society and a reputation as a potentially valuable apologist. When Thomas Sprat's *History of the Royal Society* failed to silence the critics, Oldenburg encouraged Glanvill to write a supplementary defense, which appeared in 1668 under the title *Plus ultra.* Its main theme is that the experimental philosophy, and the Royal Society in particular, have accomplished more to advance useful knowledge in a few years "than all the *Philosophers* of the *Notional way,* since *Aristotle* opened his *Shop* in *Greece.*" The principal ways of advancing knowledge are by enlarging natural history and by improving communications. Under the former heading Glanvill includes "*investigation* of the *Springs* of *Natural Motions* as well as *fuller Accounts* of the . . . more *palpable Phaenomena.*" Recent additions to our knowledge of palpable phenomena are briefly cataloged; the emphasis is on the aids to "*deep Research*" provided by modern achievements in instrumentation and in chemistry, anatomy, and especially mathematics (under which he includes astronomy and optics). A rather detailed survey of these achievements is given, stressing experiment rather than theory. (While premature hypothesizing is continually deplored, Glanvill has no clear and consistent doctrine on the role of hypotheses in research.) As to communications, he mentions printing and the compass but dwells particularly on the Royal Society itself as a vehicle for cooperative efforts along the lines laid out by "the excellent Lord *Bacon.*"

Glanvill's answer to the challenge "What have they done?" is twofold. It is unreasonable to expect too much too soon; to clear away the rubble of Peripatetic philosophy and establish organized inquiry with a sound method is a creditable work for one generation. But of course he has pointed to many accomplishments, claiming credit for the Royal Society and its members and sympathizers where he can. The contributions of Boyle are reviewed as a particularly strong recommendation.

As for the charge of irreligion, Glanvill cites all the prelates and other pious men who are members and repeats the argument that the new philosophy provides the best proofs for the Deity. Investigations into the works of nature are, indeed, religious duties, for they enable us to discover the means God has provided for alleviating man's lot. They help to banish degrading superstitions, and they promote a religious temper of equanimity, charity, and modesty. To the charge that the new philosophy turns men from scriptural revelation to nature, he replies by (1) asserting that (considering the variety of revelations that are claimed) a solid natural theology must be established first and (2) simply affirming his reverence for the Scriptures.

Further controversies embroiled Glanvill, most notably that with Henry Stubbe, but the main points in his argument remained the same (and were repeatedly employed by other apologists). In his later years he wrote primarily on specifically religious and religiopolitical questions, and above all to combat disbelief in witches. As a pastor he observed that incredulity as to evil spirits usually led, if not to outright atheism, at least to religious indifference and scorn for the Bible. Further, he found that many unphilosophical worldlings, unimpressed by abstruse arguments for the existence of God, were shaken in unbelief by well-attested accounts of demonic activities. As early as 1666 he published a book on the subject, with his membership in the Royal Society advertised on the title page. Encouraged by Henry More (who edited and expanded the final version, *Saducismus triumphatus,* after the author's death), he published a succession of enlarged editions. In the 1668 version (only) he proposed investigation of the spirit world and its laws as a suitable project for the Royal Society.

Glanvill's argument has two steps. First, he tried to show that there is nothing absurd or inconceivable in the idea that there are evil spirits who act in the world. Those who say this is impossible can actually show only that we do not understand how it is done. But—and here Glanvill referred to the argument of *Scepsis scientifica*—there are many familiar phenomena whose causes we do not know. Matters of fact can be established only by sense or credible testimony; our inability to understand them is no ground for denying them. He buttressed this line of argument by offering conjectural natural accounts—in some cases vaguely mechanical—of how the spirits might work. He thought these explanations to be probably inadequate (much more likely the spirit world is governed by its own laws, of which we as yet have no inkling) but sufficient to show that the events in question are not impossible. The second step, of course, was to show that there are well-attested cases. To this end he offered a number of narratives, with detailed accounts of how he (or the source of his information) had observed the phenomena and tested for trickery and other purely natural sources of them. Bizarre as his occupation with witchcraft may now seem, it was consistent with his understanding of science and acceptable to most of his Royal Society colleagues.

BIBLIOGRAPHY

Glanvill's contributions to the *Philosophical Transactions of the Royal Society* are "Answers to Some of the Inquiries Formerly Published Concerning Mines," in **2** (1667), 525–527; "Additional Answers to the Queries of Mines," in **3** (1668), 767–771; and "Observations Concerning the Bath-Springs," in **4** (1669), 977–982.

Jackson I. Cope, *Joseph Glanvill: Anglican Apologist* (St. Louis, 1956; 2nd ed., 1958), is an excellent study and gives a complete list of Glanvill's works. See also Richard F. Jones, *Ancients and Moderns: A Study of the Rise of the Scientific Movement in Seventeenth-Century England* (St. Louis, 2nd ed., 1961), chs. 8 and 9; Henry G. van Leeuwen, *The Problem of Certainty in English Thought, 1630–1690* (The Hague, 1963), pp. 71–89; and Richard S. Westfall, *Science and Religion in Seventeenth-Century England* (New Haven, 1958), *passim.*

On special topics see Richard H. Popkin, "Joseph Glanvill: A Precursor of David Hume," in *Journal of the History of Ideas,* **14** (1953), 292–303; and "The Development of the Philosophical Reputation of Joseph Glanvill," *ibid.,* **15** (1954), 305–311; and Moody E. Prior, "Joseph Glanvill, Witchcraft, and Seventeenth-Century Science," in *Modern Philology,* **30** (1932), 167–193.

WILLIAM H. AUSTIN

GLASER, CHRISTOPHER (*b.* Basel, Switzerland, *ca.* 1615; *d.* Paris, France, 1672 [?]), *pharmacy, chemistry.*

Little is known about Glaser's early life, but he seems to have been trained as a pharmacist in his native city, and references in his published work indicate that he traveled in eastern Europe to observe mining practice. Sometime prior to 1662 he settled in Paris, where he opened an apothecary's shop in the Faubourg Saint-Germain. Here he prospered, becoming apothecary in ordinary to Louis XIV and to the king's brother, the duke of Orleans. He also enjoyed the patronage of Nicolas Fouquet, the ill-fated superintendent of finances. In 1662 he was appointed demonstrator in chemistry at the Jardin du Roi in Paris in succession to Nicolas Le Fèvre. The following year he published his only contribution to the literature of chemistry, *Traité de la chymie,* a textbook for his course. His most noted pupil in Paris was Nicolas Lemery.

The events of Glaser's later life are likewise elusive. In 1672 he was implicated in the famous Brinvilliers poison case when evidence came to light that the marquise de Brinvilliers and her accomplice Gaudin de Sainte-Croix had used a recipe of Glaser's to prepare the poison with which they disposed of the marquise's father (1666) and two brothers (1669–1670). At this point Glaser disappeared from public life in France. If the preface by the printer to the 1673 edition of Glaser's *Traité* is to be believed, Glaser died before completing the revisions for this new edition, which received the approbation of the Paris Faculty of Medicine on 15 October 1672. At her interrogation in 1676 the marquise de Brinvilliers alleged that Glaser had indeed prepared poison for Sainte-Croix but that he had been dead for a long time. One source maintains, however, that Glaser returned to Basel, where he died in 1678 (see C. de Milt, "Christopher Glaser").

In the series of French chemical manuals of the seventeenth century, that of Glaser appeared between the more famous works of Le Fèvre and Lemery. Whereas Le Fèvre's textbook drew on the Paracelsian-Helmontian tradition for its theoretical content and Lemery attempted a corpuscularian interpretation of the processes he described, Glaser largely eschewed theory and was content with a straightforward, concise recital of chemical operations and recipes. In spite of considerable competition, Glaser's textbook enjoyed some success. The fourteen editions recorded between 1666 and 1710 include one English and five German versions. The work is divided into two books: book I briefly describes the utility, definitions, principles, operations, and apparatus of chemistry; book II is devoted to a description of medicinal preparations drawn from the mineral, vegetable, and animal kingdoms. The section devoted to mineral remedies is by far the largest. Little is novel in these preparations, although Glaser displays individual refinements of technique. His recipe for a *sel antifebrile* (potassium sulfate made by heating saltpeter and sulfur and recrystallizing from water) became uniquely identified with him and was later known as *sel polychrestum Glaseri.* The naturally occurring mixed sulfate of sodium and potassium ($3K_2SO_4$: Na_2SO_4) was named glaserite in his honor.

Due to his influence on Lemery, Glaser's importance for the development of chemistry was greater than the contents of his book at first indicate. Although Fontenelle in his *éloge* of Lemery states that Lemery, finding Glaser obscure and secretive, abandoned studies with him after two months in 1666, the early editions of Lemery's highly successful *Cours de chymie* bear a remarkable resemblance both in organization and content to Glaser's textbook. There seems little doubt that Glaser's modest work served as a model for at least the practical part of the most popular chemical textbook of the late seventeenth century.

BIBLIOGRAPHY

I. Original Works. For the various eds. and reprs. of Glaser's textbook see Partington, de Milt, and Neville in the works cited below. The first ed. has the title *Traité de la chymie, enseignant par une briève et facile méthode toutes ses plus nécessaires préparations* (Paris, 1663). The most important subsequent eds. (Paris, 1668, 1673) both contain the author's additions and corrections. An English trans., based on the 1668 ed., is *The Compleat Chymist, or A New Treatise of Chymistry* (London, 1677). Two separate German translations are *Chimischer Wegweiser* (Jena, 1677), and *Novum laboratorium medico-chymicum* (Nuremberg, 1677). The Jena vers. was reprinted several times, the last in 1710.

II. Secondary Literature. Works on Glaser and his *Traité* are H. Lagarde, "Christopher Glaser, professeur de chimie au Jardin des Plantes, apothicaire du roi, fournisseur de la Brinvilliers," in *Mémoires de la Société d'émulation du Doubs,* 6th ser., **5** (1890), 407–421; H. Metzger, *Les doctrines chimiques en France du début du XVIIe à la fin du XVIIIe siècle,* repr. (Paris, 1969), pp. 82–86; C. de Milt, "Christopher Glaser," in *Journal of Chemical Education,* **19** (1942), 53–60; R. G. Neville, "Christopher Glaser and the *Traité de la Chymie,* 1663," in *Chymia,* **10** (1965), 25–52; J. R. Partington, *A History of Chemistry,* III (London, 1962), 24–26; and J. Read, *Humour and Humanism in Chemistry* (London, 1947), pp. 114–115.

Documents relating to Glaser and the Brinvilliers case are in F. Ravaisson, *Archives de la Bastille,* IV (Paris, 1870), 237, 244, 250; VII (Paris, 1874), 44–46. An extensive bibliography on Glaser and the Brinvilliers affair is given in J. Ferguson, *Bibliotheca Chemica,* I (Glasgow, 1906), 321.

Owen Hannaway

GLASER, JOHANN HEINRICH (*b.* Basel, Switzerland, 6 October 1629; *d.* Basel, 5 February 1679), *anatomy, botany, surgery.*

Glaser's father had acquired a sound reputation as a painter and engraver in Basel, and it was there that his son began his studies. By 1645 he seemed committed to philosophy, but in 1648 he went to Geneva, where he studied medicine (he later practiced at Heidelberg). Afterward Glaser settled at Paris, where he became interested in the work of the botanists at the Muséum d'Histoire Naturelle. Following the resignation of his close friend, Felix Platter, he was considered for the chair of physics at the University of Basel. The chair went to someone else, however, and Glaser turned decisively to medicine.

His thesis, *De dolore colico,* submitted in July 1650, attracted the attention of the medical world, since in it Glaser considered anatomical and morphological data, as well as physiological. He returned to Basel and, in 1661, presented for his doctorate a classical dissertation, *Disputatio de rheumatismo.* In 1662 he began a medical practice that soon brought him international fame, and in 1665 he became full professor of Greek. Two years later, Glaser achieved his goal of being named professor of anatomy and botany at the Faculté de Médecine at Basel. In order to be prepared for this important post, he had published, in collaboration with J. J. Spörlin, the memoir *Positiones de respiratione ex Hippocrate et Galeno depromptae* (1661) and his *Theses opticae* (1664). In 1668 Glaser was named doctor-in-chief of the large municipal hospital at Basel, the crowning achievement of his career. He died of a fever contracted while caring for a patient.

Even more as a teacher than as a doctor, Glaser achieved a great reputation. The fame of the Basel hospital and of its doctors, many of whom had been his pupils, spread rapidly. Glaser particularly owed his fame to his clinical teaching and to the novelty of his methods. He introduced the application of theory through clinical teaching, spending hours with students at the bedsides of patients. Glaser was one of the first physicians to introduce hospital rounds, and many of his pupils later adopted this new conception of clinical teaching. He also was an innovator in surgery.

At Basel, Glaser held public dissections followed by surgical demonstrations. With his students he regularly examined the corpses of patients who had died in his hospital. He noted all his observations in memoranda that show how advanced he was in comparison with his colleagues. Glaser owes his lasting fame, however, to his work on the brain, the nerves, and the bones of the head. *Tractatus de cerebro* (1680) was a compilation of the numerous original observations that he had accumulated on the cerebral system. It is a classic that treats the anatomy, both normal and pathological, and the physiology of the central nervous system.

In memory of Glaser the fissure of the temporal bone through which the tympanic cords pass is known as the Glaserian petrotympanic fissure. Glaser was one of the first to carry out frequent dissections of animals, and he thereby discovered many anatomical details before they were found in man. Undoubtedly he was a great practitioner and certainly a master surgeon of his time.

BIBLIOGRAPHY

I. Original Works. Glaser's writings include *De summo hominis bono morale,* his diss. in philosophy (Basel, 1648); *De dolore colico,* his diss. in medicine (Paris, 1650); *Disputatio de rheumatismo,* his doctoral diss. (Basel, 1661); *Positiones de respiratione ex Hippocrate et Galeno depromptae,* written with J. J. Spörlin (Basel, 1661); *Theses opticae* (Basel, 1664); and *Tractatus de cerebro* (Basel, 1680).

II. Secondary Literature. Works on Glaser are H. Buess, *Recherches, découvertes et inventions de médecins suisses,* E. Kaech, trans. (Basel, 1946); A. Burckhardt, *Geschichte des medizinischen Fakultät zu Basel* (Basel, 1917); F. Husner, *Verzeichnis der Basler medizinischen Universitätsschriften von 1575–1829* (Basel, 1942); and Franciscus Pariz, *Sancta merx viri nobilissimi J. Henrici Glaseri* (Basel, 1675).

P. E. Pilet

GLAUBER, JOHANN RUDOLPH (*b.* Karlstadt, Germany, 1604; *d.* Amsterdam, Netherlands, March 1670), *chemistry, medicine, metallurgy.*

Glauber was the son of a barber, Rudolph Glauber von Hundsbach, and his second wife, Gertraut Gosenberger. Unlike most iatrochemists, he did not attend a university but instead set out in quest of spagyric wisdom, visiting laboratories in Paris, Basel, Salzburg, and Vienna. At one time he earned his living by casting metallic mirrors, and in 1635 he went to work as a court apothecary in Giessen. There he married Rebecca Jacobs but soon divorced her on grounds of infidelity; in 1641 he married Helene Cornelius, who bore him eight children.

The political uncertainties of the Thirty Years' War persuaded Glauber to leave Germany about 1639. Although his biographers often claim that he returned in the 1640's, Glauber himself tells of settling in Amsterdam and remaining there, except for brief stays in Utrecht and Arnhem, until 1650. During these years he invented his famous distillatory furnaces, which made it possible to obtain high temperatures and to heat substances under a variety of conditions. One of the furnaces had a chimney and may have been the first so equipped. Encouraged by these technical improvements, Glauber began to speak of himself as a chemical philosopher and, in a burst of creative activity, completed most of the practical work for which he is famous.

With the end of political strife Glauber happily returned to Germany to work in the wine industry in Wertheim and Kitzingen—at least this was his ostensible profession and the source of his livelihood. His main interest continued to be alchemy, but he found it prudent to conceal his activities because of the hostility to goldmakers. He also set aside one hour each day to administer free medicines, especially his *panacea antimonialis* (probably antimony pentasulfide). In 1655 Glauber again left Germany for Amsterdam, this time never to return. The move was undoubtedly related to a bitter dispute with Christopher Farner, who had stolen some of his processes and had slandered his work and character. Amsterdam was also more receptive to Glauber's religious beliefs; although born a Catholic, he argued that men would be judged by their deeds rather than by the idiosyncrasies of a particular sect.

In Amsterdam, Glauber outfitted what was surely the most impressive laboratory in Europe. Samuel Sorbière, a visitor to the laboratory in 1660, described it as "magnificent." There were workrooms both inside and outside the house, and the walls were covered with vessels and instruments of Glauber's own invention. Even the garden was utilized for agricultural experiments. After 1662 Glauber was plagued with ill health and was eventually bedridden for months at a time. He continued to write prolifically, but with more time for contemplation he began to emphasize the esoteric side of alchemy and to regret his years of toil in the laboratory. He believed that he had finally found the "secret fire of Artephius" and the material of the philosophers' stone. He died in 1670, poor, lonely, and embittered, and was buried in the Westerkerk, Amsterdam.

Glauber was an independent worker, boastful of his own achievements and suspicious of others. He had little to do with other chemists, and there is no evidence to suggest that he corresponded with important contemporaries. Since he refused to be associated with a patron, he was forced to live entirely on the sale of his products. His chief vehicle for luring customers was his writings, and he filled them with exaggerated claims—suggesting, indeed, that his inventions would usher in a kind of chemical apocalypse. Critics quickly charged Glauber both with revealing too much about alchemy and with peddling useless processes. As the criticism mounted, he withdrew even more into himself, taking comfort in the contrast of his own virtue with the pride and greed of other men.

Glauber was more influenced by the metallurgical tradition than other iatrochemists were, and it was undoubtedly from Agricola, Vannoccio Biringuccio, and Lazarus Ercker that he derived much of his practical good sense. On the other hand, alchemy, particularly that of Paracelsus, J. I. Hollandus, Michael Sendivogius, and J. B. van Helmont, determined his goals and his perception of his work. Glauber's own influence was widespread. The *Furni novi philosophici* (1646–1649) was quickly translated into Latin, English, and French and went through many editions; major compilations of his works appeared in Latin, English, and German. Robert Boyle, Nicholas Le Fèvre, and Johann Kunckel were all impressed by his labors, and Hermann Boerhaave spoke especially highly of him. In the eighteenth century his name continued to be associated with many processes, and even today hydrated sodium sulfate is familiarly known as Glauber's salt.

Glauber gave the best account of his practical work in the *Furni novi philosophici,* a book written with a clarity and an honesty almost unprecedented in early chemistry. With it he established his reputation as a master of laboratory skills. He carefully described the materials and dimensions for the construction of the furnaces and gave instructions for the necessary accessory equipment: vitrified earthen vessels to withstand the increased temperatures, a large quantity of cupels and crucibles, improved condensing apparatus, and jars with mercury seals or ground glass stoppers to store corrosive and volatile liquids.

The range of distillable substances was increased tremendously with these furnaces, and Glauber put into them almost anything he could lay hands on. From the mineral kingdom he prepared the mineral acids (hydrochloric, nitric, and sulfuric) in concentrated form and with them made chlorides, nitrates, and sulfates. He was probably the first to distill coal and obtain (with the help of hydrochloric acid) benzene and phenol. From the animal kingdom he distilled the "superfluities": hair, horns, feathers, silk, and urine. He extracted the aromatic oils of plants by first soaking their parts in salt water or hydrochloric acid, and he obtained acroleins by distilling burned clay balls presoaked in the fatty oils. The dry distillation of wood yielded wood vinegar, with which he produced metal acetates and acetone. The distillation of salt of tartar (potassium carbonate), effected by adding powdered flints, particularly intrigued him. Liquor of flints (potassium silicate) was obtained as a by-product, and the metallic trees that he grew by adding metal salts were a source of great delight to him.

Glauber's efficient production of such important chemical reactants as the mineral acids is particularly noteworthy since they are essential for other processes. He described several ways in which each can be prepared, realizing that the products are similar, although the methods by which they are prepared are different. He recognized, for example, that the spirit of sulfur produced by burning sulfur under a bell jar is of similar nature to the oil of vitriol distilled from green vitriol and that the vitriol used in his recommended recipe for hydrochloric acid functions as a catalyst. His preparation of nitric and hydrochloric acids by applying sulfuric acid to saltpeter and common salt, respectively, was long kept secret because of the purity obtainable.

The *Pharmacopoea spagyrica* (1654–1668) and *Dess Teutschlands-Wohlfahrt* (1656–1661) were more typical of Glauber's style than was the earlier *Furni.* Written intermittently over a period of several years, they lack both organization and a consistent point of view. Descriptions of processes are often squeezed between lengthy digressions or are obscured by metaphors and references to classical mythology.

The *Pharmacopoea spagyrica* is a collection of the medical preparations that Glauber found most reliable. Indeed, most of the products of Glauber's laboratory found eventual use in medicine. Like other iatrochemists, he complained about the sorry assortment of substances to be found in most apothecary shops while boasting of the high standards met by his own work. He believed that the most effective remedies were those prepared from the mineral kingdom, and he reported extensive work with chlorides, antimony and sulfur compounds, gold preparations, and a "magnesia of Saturn."

Although he preferred mineral remedies, Glauber nevertheless devoted considerable space in the *Pharmacopoea* to proving his skill in more traditional areas. He suggested a new way to prepare essences of herbs by separating and recombining their oils, spirits, and salts. By soaking plant substances in nitric or sulfuric acid and then adding potash, he precipitated fine powders that may well have been the alkaloids strychnine, brucine, and morphine. Frequently manifest in his choice of materials was the time-honored assumption that unpleasant substances yield the best medicines. He therefore praised the virtues of excrements and gave recipes using worms, beetles, and venomous toads.

The final sections of the *Pharmacopoea* show Glauber's immersion in esoteric alchemy in later life. His revelation of a "secret sal armoniack" (ammonium sulfate) was followed by the revelation of an even grander "most secret sal armoniack" (ammonium nitrate?). The latter was claimed to be the celebrated alchemical substance that Adam brought out of the Garden of Eden. Man thus carried within himself the means to transform the natural world—but in such a loathsome place that his pride kept him from finding it. In spite of the deliberate obscurity, it seems likely that Glauber prepared his "most secret" salt by combining ammonia and saltpeter, made from excrement and urine.

Glauber displayed a good sense of economic feasibility as well as his love for his homeland in *Dess Teutschlands-Wohlfahrt,* a work encouraging Germans to make better use of their natural resources and to become economically self-sufficient. He gave recipes for wine and beer concentrates that are both stable and easily exported and he mentioned a secret press for the efficient extraction of niter from wood. He proceeded to point out that niter can then be used in the extraction of metals, particularly gold and silver, and that these precious metals, in turn, could be directed into foreign trade. He dedicated a variety of other items to the fatherland: new medicines, a fertilizer of salt and lime, a seed preparation, and various techniques for processing metals. Finally, since all this was futile without adequate protection from the Turks, he disclosed a new weapon: a missile containing "fiery water" (a fuming acid, or perhaps essential oils to be ignited by nitric acid).

Glauber also devoted considerable attention to transmutation in *Dess Teutschlands-Wohlfahrt.* Although he sometimes used the word loosely, he usually meant to refer to two operations distinguished as "universal" and "particular" transmutation. The "universal" transmutation was effected through the philosophers' stone, which Glauber did not claim to have prepared in its final form. "Particular" transmutation, on the other hand, was effected through salts; and he claimed to be a master of these. In our terms, such operations usually involve the extraction of components present in the original material. Glauber believed that spiritual substances were transmuted into corporeal bodies, presumably because he could not detect components that vanished in the fire unless they were first fixed with salt.

Glauber's interest in the transmutation of metals and in industrial chemistry distinguished him from Paracelsus and other iatrochemists, who were more narrowly concerned with the preparation of chemical medicines. In the most general sense Glauber sought to perfect nature for the enhancement of human life—to render useless things useful through the release of their hidden virtues. Such changes were effected in his laboratory primarily through the "ripening" powers of salts.

Since art imitates nature, the role of salt in Glauber's laboratory corresponded to its role in the macrocosm. The sun was the fountain of all maturation and perfection in the natural world, and its fire was carried by an aerial salt to the earth below, where it was responsible for the growth of all things. This explained why gold and spices and sweet wine, the ripest of growths, came from southern lands, where sun and salt are most abundant. Sulfurous salts were operative in mines, and the active force of fertilizer was the salt it contained. Animals derived salt from the air they breathed and from their food. Glauber was by no means unusual among metallurgists in attributing growth to minerals; nor was he unusual, in the seventeenth century, in believing that the sun, operating through a universal salt, underlay the unity of all living things. His laboratory skill in preparing and handling salts, however, predisposed him to describe the role of the universal salt more specifically than did many of his contemporaries.

In the early parts of the *Miraculum mundi* (1653–1660) Glauber specified that the universal salt is niter. The claim was less preposterous than it sounds, since he was not referring to a single substance but to a family of substances: niter in its crude form (saltpeter); the "spirit" of niter (nitric acid), obtained through distillation; and "fixed niter" (potassium carbonate), the residue when niter is deflagrated with charcoal. Glauber's contention that niter was universally present in nature was grounded upon his ability to produce it from a variety of different sources and his realization that vegetable alkalies were similar to his "fixed nitre." (Even in the eighteenth century it was not always understood that these substances have the same chemical composition.) When Glauber called niter a universal dissolvent, he sometimes referred only to the fixed salt (alkahest: "Alkali est"), but usually he intended the term to apply to niter in its three forms. What one form did not dissolve, one of the others could. Even stones could be dissolved, since powdered flints fused with potassium carbonate yielded liquor of flints. He gave numerous uses for the ripening powers of niter, from the fertilization of grape vines to the removal of facial wrinkles and the coloring of shoe leather. As his critics were quick to note, Glauber had reduced the mysteries of alchemy to a rather mundane level.

The work with niter illustrates rather well that although Glauber generally had a better sense of chemical composition than his contemporaries, the animistic categories of alchemy still had a strong hold over his conception of matter. On the one hand, he displayed a good understanding of the acid and base constituents of salt: not only did he make potassium carbonate and nitric acid out of saltpeter, but he also took the further step of combining these two to yield saltpeter. (Boyle described a similar experiment in his *Essay on Nitre,* denying that it had been inspired by Glauber.) On the other hand, he regarded the constituents of saltpeter as spirit and body and described the three forms of niter as though they were preformed in one another and elaborated through sexual procreation.

In 1658 the *Tractatus de natura salium* appeared, and in 1660 a second part was added to the *Miraculum mundi.* Only then did Glauber recognize the significance of his "sal mirabile" (Glauber's salt) and begin to utilize it, not very successfully, in the central position that niter formerly held. It was produced in its most interesting form as a by-product of his secret process for hydrochloric acid: from common salt and sulfuric acid. Hence he considered it to be common salt brought to its highest degree of purity, and he argued plausibly that common salt is everywhere present in nature. Glauber drew on the analogy of microcosm and macrocosm and Harvey's discovery of the circulation of the blood to demonstrate the circulation of salt in the macrocosm. It was further argued that salts could be generated out of one another and that all were forms of the primordial common salt. Glauber therefore saw no incompatibility between his previous focus on niter and his new commitment to "sal mirabile." The applications suggested for the new salt in art, alchemy, agriculture, and medicine were as numerous as those for niter. One worth noting was the use of "sal mirabile" in its anhydrous form to remove excess water from oils, mineral acids, vinegar, and poor-quality wines.

Since the light (heat) of the sun was ultimately responsible for all changes on earth, Glauber was greatly intrigued by optical phenomena, particularly those associated with mirrors and colored glass. He had once made metallic mirrors for a living and claimed to own one of the finest in Europe. In the *Furni* he gave a careful description both of the casting procedure and of the speculum metal itself: an alloy of copper, arsenic, brass, and tin. He experimented on metals with these mirrors and was able to melt lead with a mirror two or three spans in diameter. The role of the sun intrigued Glauber, for he believed that its rays were concentrated by the mirror and subsequently materialized as the lead gained weight. He believed that a like process was responsible for the generation of metals in nature (an explicit account is given in *Operis mineralis,* pt. 2). Astral rays were concentrated into the center of the earth, where a fiery vacuum was produced, and were then turned back to be materialized in the bowels of the earth. Glauber also described hermetic medicines in optical terminology: the most efficacious substances were those whose circumferences (virtues) had been concentrated into their original centers.

Glauber's fascination with colored glass was closely tied to a rather attractive interpretation of the making of the philosophers' stone. The sulfur (tincture, soul) of a metal was its color, and this must be isolated and fixed in order to effect transmutations. He argued that distillates, however subtle, remain composed of the three Paracelsian principles: salt, sulfur, and mercury. For the isolation of sulfur alone, metals must be reduced to ashes in the fire and returned to their origin for rebirth. Since their origin was sand, and since glass was made from sand, the true colors of metals would be revealed when their ashes were added to glass. The colors were then to be extracted by a sulfurous menstruum to yield the universal medicine. Glauber conceded failure in this last step, but in the course of his labors he related much useful information on the coloring of glass and rediscovered the process for ruby glass, which had been lost for many years.

Since Glauber conceived of God as eternal light, the coloring of glass was weighty with symbolic implications for him. On the last day, he believed, our bodies will be reduced to ashes, from which we will arise with clarified bodies to stand before God, who is himself pure light, and will be revealed in our true colors.

Glauber has justly been called the best practical

chemist of his day and the first industrial chemist. His instructions for the improvement of laboratory technique were instrumental in preparing the way for the chemical revolution of the next century. In his own estimation, however, the final goal of his labors was the perfection of the material world, capped by the preparation of the philosophers' stone. Glauber attempted to renew the hermetic art by tying it to specific aspects of laboratory practice, but in so doing he interpreted the symbols of alchemy so concretely as to destroy their esoteric appeal. Later alchemists understandably found him too mundane, while chemists failed to appreciate his hermetic conception of the world.

BIBLIOGRAPHY

I. Original Works. The complete list of Glauber's works is available in J. R. Partington, *A History of Chemistry,* II (London, 1961), 343–347. His major works—*Furni novi philosophici oder Beschreibung einer newerfundener Destillirkunst* (Amsterdam, 1646–1649); *Miraculum mundi oder Ausführliche Beschreibung der wunderbaren Natur, Art, und Eigenschafft des grossmächtigen Subiecti* . . . (Amsterdam, 1653–1660); *Pharmacopoea spagyrica oder Gründlicher Beschreibung, wie man aus den Vegetabilien, Animalien, und Mineralien . . . gute, kräfftige und durchdringende Arztneyen zurichten und bereiten soll* (Amsterdam, 1654–1668); *Dess Teutschlands-Wohlfahrt* (Amsterdam, 1656–1661)—consist of several pts. and appendixes published separately and at different times. German compilations appeared in 1658–1659—*Opera chymica, Bücher und Schrifften* . . . and *Continuatio operum chymicorum* . . .—and in 1715—the much abbreviated *Glauberus concentratus, oder Kern der Glauberischen Schrifften* . . ., available in a facs. repr. (Ulm, 1961). Christopher Packe, ed., *The Works of the Highly Experienced and Famous Chymist, John Rudolph Glauber* . . . (London, 1689), includes almost all his writings, translated into English. The translation is generally reliable, even though often translated from the Latin collected ed. rather than from the original German. Much of the moralizing and polemics has been omitted.

II. Secondary Literature. P. Walden, "Glauber," in Günther Bugge, ed., *Das Buch der grossen Chemiker,* I (Berlin, 1929), 151–172, gives the best assessment of Glauber's practical work; a shortened English trans. of Walden's article can be found in Eduard Farber, ed., *Great Chemists* (New York, 1961), pp. 115–134. Glauber's biography was in some confusion until the twentieth century, even though it can be reconstructed fairly completely from his own apologetic writings. Kurt F. Gugel, *Johann Rudolph Glauber 1604–1670, Leben und Werk* (Würzburg, 1955), has compiled the recent literature to give the fullest account of Glauber's life; Gugel also gives an extensive bibliography, but his account of Glauber's practical work is wholly derivative from Walden. Erich Pietsch, *Johann Rudolph Glauber* (Munich, 1956), attempts to make Glauber's theory of salt and fire respectable by explicating it from the standpoint of modern energy concepts. A more historical appraisal of his theory and motivation is that of H. M. E. de Jong, "Glauber und die Weltanschauung der Rosenkreuzer," in *Janus,* **56** (1969), 278–304; however, there is little reason to believe that Glauber was a Rosicrucian.

Kathleen Ahonen

GLAZEBROOK, RICHARD TETLEY (*b.* West Derby, Liverpool, England, 18 September 1854; *d.* Limpsfield Common, England, 15 December 1935), *physics.*

The eldest son of Nicholas Smith Glazebrook, a surgeon, and Sarah Anne Tetley, Glazebrook was educated at Dulwich College until 1870, then Liverpool College, and in 1872 entered Trinity College, Cambridge. He received his B.A. as fifth wrangler in 1876 and his M.A. in 1879. After working under Maxwell at the Cavendish Laboratory from 1876 until Maxwell's death in 1879, he stayed on under Rayleigh and in 1880 was appointed demonstrator (with Napier Shaw). Glazebrook was a college lecturer in mathematics and physics (1881–1895) and university lecturer in mathematics (1884–1897).

Although he was disappointed in not being elected to succeed Rayleigh when the latter resigned in 1884, Glazebrook remained at the Cavendish Laboratory and was appointed assistant director in 1891. In 1895 he took on additional duties as senior bursar of Trinity College. He resigned these last positions to become principal of University College, Liverpool, in 1898, with the understanding that he might leave if offered the directorship of the National Physical Laboratory, then being established. This in fact occurred, and he left the college on the last day of 1899, taking up his new position on the first day of the new year. He remained in this post until his retirement in 1919. Glazebrook was elected to the Royal Society in 1882 and received numerous other honors, including presidencies of the Physical Society (1903–1905), the Optical Society (1904–1905, 1911–1912), the Institution of Electrical Engineers (1906), the Faraday Society (1911–1913), and the Institute of Physics (1919–1921).

Glazebrook's initial work under Maxwell was in optics, with considerable attention to electrical measurements. When Rayleigh became a member of the reconstituted British Association Committee on Electrical Standards in 1881, Glazebrook assisted him; and in 1883 he became secretary of the committee, a position he was to hold until 1913, when the work of the committee was taken over by the National Physical Laboratory. Glazebrook became increasingly interested in the precise measurement of electrical standards. This specialty, together with his talent as an administrator, made him an obvious candidate to head the National Physical Laboratory when it was formed.

As director of the new laboratory Glazebrook continued to press for the determination of the fundamental units for both scientific and industrial purposes. In 1909 work was begun in the field of aeronautics, leading to efforts that were greatly accelerated during the war.

Glazebrook was an accomplished experimentalist, and he wrote several physics textbooks which enjoyed widespread use. His true vocation, however, was scientific administration, as he demonstrated in leading the National Physical Laboratory through its first two decades.

BIBLIOGRAPHY

I. ORIGINAL WORKS. Glazebrook's textbooks, each of which went through several editions, include *Physical Optics* (London, 1883); *Laws and Properties of Matter* (London, 1893); *Heat* (Cambridge, 1894); and *Mechanics* (Cambridge, 1895). Two of his articles of particular interest are "Life and Works of James Clerk Maxwell," in *Cambridge Review,* **1** (1879), 70, 98–99, 118–120; and "The Aims of the National Physical Laboratory of Great Britain," in *Popular Science Monthly,* **60** (Dec. 1901), 124–144, reprinted in *Smithsonian Institution Annual Report* (1901), pp. 341–357.

A list of Glazebrook's pre-1900 papers is in the Royal Society, *Catalogue of Scientific Papers.* A bibliography of his books and papers is in Poggendorff, III, 526; IV, 504; V, 42; VI, 903–904. His correspondence is in the Public Record Office; the Royal Society; and the Forbes papers, University Library, St. Andrews, Fife.

II. SECONDARY LITERATURE. Biographical information appears in Rayleigh and F. J. Selby, *Obituary Notices of Fellows of the Royal Society of London,* **2** (1936–1938), 29–56, with portrait; *Proceedings of the Physical Society of London,* **48** (1936), 929–933; and W. C. D. Dampier, *Dictionary of National Biography, 1931–1940* (London, 1949), pp. 343–344.

BERNARD FINN

GLEICHEN-RUSSWORM, WILHELM FRIEDRICH VON (*b.* Bayreuth, Germany, 14 January 1717; *d.* Schloss Greifenstein, Bonnland, Hammelburg, Germany, 16 June 1783), *microscopy.*

Gleichen-Russworm was the elder son of Heinrich von Gleichen and Caroline von Russworm. He received little formal education and in 1734, after some years as a page at the court of Prince Thurn und Taxis in Frankfurt, he decided to make his career in the forces of the margrave of Bayreuth. He married Antoinette Heidloff in 1753 and they had seven children, of whom only two daughters survived to adulthood. Gleichen-Russworm remained in the army until 1756, when he resigned his commission in order to devote himself to the management of the Greifenstein estates, inherited from his mother in 1748.

His first published writings appeared after his departure from Bayreuth, in the periodical *Fränkische Sammlung aus der Naturlehre, Arzneigelahrtheit, Ökonomie und der damit verbundenen Wissenschaften;* they deal, *inter alia,* with natural history, physics, and chemistry but are, for the most part, quite fanciful. These articles involved Gleichen-Russworm in a certain amount of controversy, with the result that his subsequent writings were much less extravagant, although he did go on to publish, in 1782, a highly imaginative account of the origin and structure of the earth, which is now of interest only for its faint adumbration of evolutionary theory.

In the summer of 1760 Gleichen-Russworm made the acquaintance of Martin Ledermüller, who had already begun publication of his *Mikroskopische Gemüths- und Augenergötzungen* (1759–1762); it was this work which led Gleichen-Russworm to concentrate on microscopy. Ledermüller visited Schloss Greifenstein in 1762, and Gleichen-Russworm continued to benefit from his advice until the former took offense at certain criticisms of his work which appeared in *Geschichte der gemeinen Stubenfliege* (1764).

Gleichen-Russworm was particularly interested in the processes of fertilization in plants and animals, and in 1763 he published the first fascicle of *Das neueste aus dem Reiche der Pflanzen.* This work contains fifty-one colored plates illustrating numerous details of floral structure and various pollens; in addition, his interest in the construction of the microscope is reflected in the six plates devoted to the different modifications and accessories which he designed for the instrument. His account of the pollen of *Asclepias syriaca* L. in *Auserlesene mikroskopische Entdeckungen* (1777–1781) contains what appears to be the first observation of a pollen tube, although he remained unaware of its significance.

In 1778 Gleichen-Russworm made his most important contribution to science. In *Abhandlung über die Saamen- und Infusionsthierchen* he described the technique of phagocytic staining, which he had developed from earlier reports of the use of dyes as coloring agents for plant and animal tissues. In order to study the nutrition of a colony of ciliates, he added water colored with carmine and observed the subsequent staining of the food vacuoles, of which he provided an illustration. This technique did not become generally known until described by a number of nineteenth-century biologists, notably Christian Gottfried Ehrenberg, Theodor Hartig, and Joseph von Gerlach.

BIBLIOGRAPHY

I. ORIGINAL WORKS. Gleichen-Russworm's writings include *Das neueste aus dem Reiche der Pflanzen, oder mikroskopische Untersuchungen und Beobachtungen der geheimen Zeugungstheile der Pflanzen in ihren Blüthen, und der in denselben befindlichen Insekten,* 3 fascs. (Nuremberg, 1763–[?]1766); *Geschichte der gemeinen Stubenfliege* (Nuremberg, 1764); *Auserlesene mikroskopische Entdeckungen bey den Pflanzen, Blumen und Blüthen, Insekten und andere Merkwürdigkeiten,* 6 fascs. (Nuremberg, 1777–[?]1781); *Abhandlung über die Saamen- und Infusionsthierchen, und über die Erzeugung; nebst mikroskopischen Beobachtungen des Saamens der Thiere, und verschiedener Infusionen* (Nuremberg, 1778); and *Von Entstehung, Bildung, Umbildung und Bestimmung des Erdkörpers* (Dessau, 1782).

II. SECONDARY LITERATURE. Works on Gleichen-Russworm's life and career include (in chronological order): M. A. Weikard, *Biographie des Herrn Wilhelm Friedrich von Gleichen* (Frankfurt, 1783); Ascherson, "Wilhelm Friedrich von G. genannt Rusworm (Russworm)," in *Allgemeine deutsche Biographie,* IX (Leipzig, 1879), 226–228; Carl Willnau [Carl W. Naumann], *Ledermüller und v. Gleichen-Russworm. Zwei deutsche Mikroskopisten der Zopfzeit* (Leipzig, 1926); John R. Baker, "The Discovery of the Uses of Colouring Agents in Biological Microtechnique," in *Journal of the Quekett Microscopical Club,* 4th ser., **1,** no. 6 (1943), p. 12, rev. separate publication (London, 1945); Friedrich Klemm, "Wilhelm Friedrich Gleichen gen. v. Russwurm," in *Neue deutsche Biographie,* VI (Berlin, 1964), 447–448; and Frans A. Stafleu, *Taxonomic Literature* (Utrecht–Zug, 1967), p. 172.

MICHAEL E. MITCHELL

GLISSON, FRANCIS (*b.* England, 1597 [?]; *d.* London, England, 16 October 1677), *medicine, philosophy.*

According to tradition and evidence from the portraits in his books of 1672 and 1677, Francis Glisson was born in 1597. Upon matriculation in Gonville and Caius College, Cambridge, at Michaelmas 1617, Rampisham, Dorset, where he had been taught by Allot, was given as Glisson's home and eighteen as his age. The latter may be doubted in view of some inconsistencies in other matriculation entries. His father, William, was born in Bristol and was designated as "gentleman" in the son's Cambridge matriculation. His mother, Mary, was the daughter of John Hancock of Kingsweston, Somerset. Exactly when the family moved to Rampisham is uncertain, as is the place of Glisson's birth.

Glisson's academic career remained connected with Cambridge: B.A. in 1620–1621, M.A. and junior fellowship in 1624; Greek lecturer in 1625–1626; dean in 1629; and senior fellow 1629–1634. In 1634 he also completed his medical studies with the M.D. degree. Two years later, he was appointed regius professor of physic (John Wallis was among his students), a position he held until his death. There exists an isolated reference to Maria, daughter of Thomas Morgan, as the wife of Glisson (R. M. Walker, "Francis Glisson and his Capsule").

In the year of his medical graduation, Glisson was admitted as a candidate by the Royal College of Physicians of London. With the possible exception of practice in Colchester during the Civil War (contested by Walker), London remained the seat of his professional and scientific life. The College of Physicians made him a fellow in 1635, councilor from 1666 on, and president in 1667, 1668, and 1669. One of the scientific pillars of the College, he was also made a reader in anatomy and appointed to give the Gulstonian lecture in 1640. Thomas Wharton, in his *Adenographia,* mentions "his most faithful friend," Glisson, as his helper in dissecting. He belonged to the "Invisible College," and was an early member of the Royal Society, elected 4 March 1660/1661.

Around 1645 a group of the fellows of the College began to exchange notes on rickets, thought to have but recently spread in England, and Glisson, G. Bate, and A. Regemorter were assigned to publish a book on the subject. The investigation of the essential nature of the disease fell to Glisson, who impressed his co-workers so much that they entrusted him with drafting the whole book, into which their own observations and possibly those of authors like Daniel Whistler (cf. ch. 13) were incorporated. *De rachitide* appeared in 1650 with Glisson as the author, Bate and Regemorter as his associates, and with five additional contributors. It is hence hard to tell how much of the classic anatomical and clinical descriptions of the disease belongs to Glisson alone. He claimed originality specifically for chapters 3–14. These are concerned mainly with the nature of the disease, which he believed to be a cold and humid distemper in which the indwelling spirit (*spiritus insitus*) of the parts primarily affected (spinal cord and peripheral nerves) was deficient and torpid. This emphasis on an inner principle was to remain throughout Glisson's life.

In *De rachitide,* as well as his other publications, Glisson incorporated empirical findings into a scholastic framework of reasoning, trying to lay a broad basis for argumentation while discussing any problem encountered on the way. Thus this work dwells on such subjects as regulation of the circulation of the blood (which was assumed as a matter of course), mechanisms of nervous function, and the nature of hereditary disease. An English translation of the book appeared in 1651, testifying to the interest it aroused.

Until the Glisson papers in the British Museum, sporadically used by various biographers, are edited, Glisson's intellectual biography must rely mainly on his published works, the prefaces of which present a running commentary on their history and interconnection. Glisson's second work, the *Anatomia hepatis* (1654), rested largely on observations made in 1640, when he had lectured on the fine structure of the liver. The work begins with *Prolegomena quaedam ad rem anatomicam universe spectantia* ("Some Prolegomena Referring to Anatomy Generally"), where he tries to reconcile the Aristotelian doctrine of the elements with that of the chemists. In this work he advocates very advanced anatomical methods such as use of the microscope and injection of colored liquids.

In the *Anatomia hepatis* proper, a section of the book of the same title, Glisson denies the continuity of the branches of the portal vein into those of the hepatic veins. He contends that the branches cross, and that the blood carried in the portal vein is separated in the liver. Its bilious fraction is sucked up by the biliary vessels, because of an attraction which Glisson variously calls similar, magnetic, or natural, and which does not differ essentially from Galen's "attractive faculty." The remaining blood is attracted by the hepatic veins. The ramifications of the portal vein, together with the bile ducts, are encased in fibrous tissue, which Glisson calls *capsula communis,* now known as "Glisson's capsule."

The book ends with a chapter on the lymphatics. Stimulated by ideas of his friend George Ent, Glisson elaborated a theory which he revised in his last medical work, the *Tractatus de ventriculo et intestinis* (1677). The theory presented itself as follows: The nerves carry a nutritive juice (*succus nutritivus*) secreted by the brain between cortex and medulla from particles of the arterial blood. The psychic spirits are the "fixed spirits" of this juice, which serves nutrition rather than the function of body fibers. As a chemical substance, the psychic spirits cannot flow fast enough to assure simultaneity of events in the brain and the peripheral parts. Nerve action is transmitted by a vibration of the nerves (caused by localized contraction of the brain), and the muscle fibers then contract because of irritability, a property which they share with all fibers of the body.

In evidence of the independence of muscle contraction from any material influx, Glisson cited the experiment which Goddard had described and performed before the Royal Society in 1666. An arm was placed in a tube which was closed at one end and provided with a gauge. The tube was sealed around the arm and then filled with water. When the muscles were contracted, the gauge registered a fall of the water level rather than a rise.

Glisson had used the word "irritability" once before, in the *Anatomia hepatis,* where it connoted the ability of a part to become irritated, that is, to perceive an irritant and to try to rid itself of it. At that time he thought of irritation as being dependent on the presence of nerves. By 1677, however, natural irritability was a property attributed to almost all living parts of the body including the blood (an idea implicit in Harvey's theory), a property independent of the nerves. Irritability presupposed perception of the irritating object, appetite to attain it (if pleasant) or to flee it (if unpleasant), and motion to realize the appetite.

In sense organs connected with the brain, natural perception was elevated to sensitive, that is, conscious, perception, and it became psychic where the fibers followed commands coming from the brain. But these higher forms of perception, depending on organization, did not supersede natural perception, without which the fibers could not perceive messages from the brain. This metaphysical doctrine of natural perception and its interdependence with appetite and all motion (unless accidentally imparted) needed philosophical elaboration.

Glisson maintained that the first draft of the *Tractatus de ventriculo et intestinis* was written around 1662 but was set aside in favor of the *Tractatus de natura substantiae energetica* (1672), dedicated to Anthony Ashley Cooper, Lord Shaftesbury, whose family Glisson had long served as physician. The work attempts to prove there is life in all bodies. In so-called inanimate bodies it is specified by their forms, whereas in plants and animals life is modified to become the vegetative soul and the sensitive soul, respectively. In animals the implanted life (*vita insita*) is duplicated and triplicated by the influx of the blood (*vita influens*) and by the psychic regulations.

This philosophical work, even more than Glisson's medical books, has a strictly scholastic form of argumentation; large parts are a running debate with Francisco Suarez, whom Glisson held in the highest esteem. Among other modern authors, Glisson pays particular attention to Bacon, Scaliger, Harvey, and Descartes. He often refers to the *vis plastica,* which he identifies with van Helmont's *archeus.* Although the terminology is reminiscent of the Cambridge Platonists, it should not be overlooked that Glisson's metaphysics was fundamentally hylozoistic and thus hardly acceptable to Ralph Cudworth, who thought of "plastic nature" as incorporeal.

Glisson's doctrine of irritability acquired fame because in later years Haller traced the origin of the term back to Glisson. But in limiting irritability to muscle contractility, Haller defined it experimentally, depriving the concept of its broad biological significance.

The doctrine of irritability does not exhaust the content of the *Tractatus de ventriculo et intestinis,* which, apart from the treatise indicated by the title, also contains a treatise on skin, hair, nails, fat, abdominal muscles, peritoneum, and omentum. Together the *Anatomia hepatis* and the *Tractatus de ventriculo et intestinis* constitute a monumental work on general anatomy and on anatomy and physiology of the digestive organs. Moreover, in the latter treatise, Glisson goes far beyond the stomach and intestinal tract. Apart from discussing the theory of digestion (there is even an appendix on fermentation), Glisson manages to include theories of embryogenesis (in which the relationship to Harvey is particularly interesting). Aware of his discursiveness, Glisson in his apology referred to "the allurement and sweetness of speculation" (p. 333).

In the battle between the ancients and the moderns Glisson belongs to neither side. In a peculiar manner all his own, he adhered to the scholasticism of his formative years (possibly sustained by his professorship in Cambridge) combining it with Helmontian chemistry, Harvey's heritage, and the new science as represented by the Royal Society.

BIBLIOGRAPHY

I. Original Works. For the Glisson papers in the British Museum, see *Index to the Sloane Manuscripts in the British Museum* (London, 1904), pp. 217 ff. The following are the first eds. of his published works: *De rachitide, sive morbo puerili, qui vulgo the rickets dicitur, tractatus, opera primo ac potissimum Francisci Glissonii . . . adscitis in operis societatem Georgio Bate et Ahasvero Regemortero* (London, 1650); *Anatomia hepatis, cui praemittuntur quaedam ad rem anatomicam universe spectantia et ad calcem operis subjiciuntur nonnulla de lymphae ductibus nuper reperta* (London, 1654); *Tractatus de natura substantiae energetica, seu de vita naturae, ejusque tribus primis facultatibus . . .* (London, 1672); and *Tractatus de ventriculo et intestinis. Cui praemittitur alius, De partibus continentibus in genere; et in specie, de iis abdominis* (London–Amsterdam, 1677). The *Opera medico-anatomica, in unum corpus collecta . . .*, 3 vols. in a single pub. (Leiden, 1691), does not contain the *Tractatus de natura substantiae energetica.*

II. Secondary Literature. Although the literature on Glisson is considerable (he is discussed in almost all histories of medicine, biology, and science), there is no comprehensive monograph on his life and work. The main biographical sketches are John Aikin, *Biographical Memoirs of Medicine in Great Britain* (London, 1780), pp. 326–338; William Munk, *The Roll of the Royal College of Physicians of London,* I (London, 1878), 218–221; John Venn, *Biographical History of Gonville and Caius College 1349–1897,* I (Cambridge, 1897), 236 f.; and Norman Moore, *Dictionary of National Biography,* VII, 1316–1317.

R. Milnes Walker, "Francis Glisson and his Capsule," in *Annals of the Royal College of Surgeons of England,* **38,** no. 2 (1966), 71–91, adds many details to Glisson's biography and suggests that "he was born in 1598 or 1599, and probably in Bristol" (p. 77) and ascribes his alleged sojourn in Colchester (1640–1648) to a confusion with his younger brother, Henry, who was practicing medicine there (p. 78). Glisson's work on the liver is presented clearly and in detail by Nikolaus Mani, *Die historischen Grundlagen der Leberforschung,* II (Stuttgart, 1967), 104–120. For Glisson's relation to traditional medicine and his concept of irritability, see Walter Pagel, "The Reaction to Aristotle in Seventeenth-Century Biological Thought," in E. Ashworth Underwood, ed., *Science, Medicine, and History. Essays . . . in Honour of Charles Singer,* I (Oxford, 1953), 489–509; Owsei Temkin, "The Classical Roots of Glisson's Doctrine of Irritation," in *Bulletin of the History of Medicine,* **38,** no. 5 (1964), 297–323, where older literature on Glisson's philosophical and biological concepts is cited; and Walter Pagel, "Harvey and Glisson on Irritability," *ibid.,* **41,** no. 6 (1967), 497–514.

On Glisson's relationship to the London College of Physicians and the Royal Society, see Charles C. Gillispie, "Physick and Philosophy: A Study of the Influence of the College of Physicians of London Upon the Foundation of the Royal Society," in *Journal of Modern History,* **19** (1947), 210–225; and C. Webster, "The College of Physicians: 'Solomon's House' in Commonwealth England," in *Bulletin of the History of Medicine,* **41,** no. 5 (1967), 393–412. On the much debated question of the interrelationship of Glisson's *De rachitide* and Daniel Whistler's Leiden dissertation of 1645, *De morbo puerili anglorum,* see Edwin Clarke, "Whistler and Glisson on Rickets," *ibid.,* **36,** no. 1 (1962), 45–61, with ample literature.

Owsei Temkin

GMELIN, JOHANN GEORG (*b.* Tübingen, Germany, 10 August 1709; *d.* Tübingen, 20 May 1755), *botany, natural history, geography.*

Johann Georg Gmelin's father (also called Johann Georg), apothecary, chemist, and academician in Tübingen, was the founder of the older branch of the Gmelin family, which included several distinguished scholars and scientists. The younger Johann Georg was extremely gifted and was early encouraged in his scientific endeavors by his father, who had a natural history collection and a laboratory. In their travels, the elder Gmelin also introduced his son to the study of the Württemberg mineral springs. From the time Gmelin was fourteen he was able to follow university lectures. He held his first disputation when he was seventeen and a year later, in 1727, graduated in medicine. Among his teachers were the philosopher and mathematician Georg Bernhard Bilfinger and the botanist and anatomist Johann Georg Duvernoy; both went to St. Petersburg in 1725 and thus determined the destination of young Gmelin's first scientific voyage.

In St. Petersburg, with the help and guidance of his teachers, Gmelin was allowed to attend meetings of the Academy of Sciences. In 1728 he was offered a fellowship and in 1730 permitted to lecture at the Academy. He became professor of chemistry and natural history in 1731, and then academician. In 1733, when he had intended to return home, Gmelin took part instead in an imperial scientific expedition to eastern Siberia with the historian Gerhard Friedrich Müller and the astronomer Louis Delisle de la Croyère. Müller was to survey archives and records, Delisle de la Croyère to determine geographical coordinates, and Gmelin to study the natural history of the territories to be visited. They were supported by a party of six students, two painters, two hunters, two miners, four land surveyors, and twelve soldiers. They were expected to join, by land, the sea expedition to Kamchatka led by Captains Bering and Chirikov.

Gmelin's expedition left St. Petersburg on 8 July 1733 for Tobolsk, which they expected to reach early in 1734 and where they hoped to make a lengthy stay. They proceeded eastward with many side expeditions, exploring territories along the Irtysh, Ob, and Tom rivers, through Krasnoyarsk to Yeniseysk (January 1735) and then through Irkutsk to the Chinese (now Mongolian) frontier at Kyakhta. In 1735 they thoroughly explored the Transbaikal region proceeding through Selenginsk and Nerchinsk, then along the Lena River to the north. In September 1735 they reached Yakutsk (130° east) from which they undertook numerous expeditions.

In November 1736 a fire destroyed most of Gmelin's equipment, instruments, books, collections, and drawings. Facing additional difficulties, Gmelin and Müller realized they could not succeed in joining the Bering-Chirikov expedition and so received permission to continue explorations on their return journey. They left Yakutsk in May 1737 to explore the regions along the Angara and Tunguska rivers. At Yeniseysk they met Georg Wilhelm Steller, a bold and tough explorer who was sent from St. Petersburg to join them. Gmelin, however, sent him to the east with a small party. (Steller thus succeeded in joining Bering and distinguished himself by reaching the Alaskan coast; he was one of the few survivors of the disastrous winter of 1741–1742 on Bering Island, and went on to explore Kamchatka.)

Gmelin meanwhile traveled to the north along the Yenisey River to 66°N. latitude, then turned to the south and reached Krasnoyarsk in February 1740. Müller separated from Gmelin's party, which next explored the region between the Yenisey and Ob, the Baraba Steppe, and then advanced to the southwest to the Ishim and Wagai steppes and to the Caspian Sea. Eventually they explored the mines in the Ural Mountains. The party reached St. Petersburg on 28 February 1743 after nine and one-half years of travel.

Upon his return Gmelin resumed his academic functions at the Academy and worked on the scientific accounts of his journey. His four-volume *Flora sibirica* (1747–1769) contains descriptions of 1,178 species and illustrations of 294 of these. Although primarily a botanist, Gmelin had a good knowledge of other natural sciences of his time and with his travels contributed to the knowledge of the zoology, geography, geology, ethnography, and natural resources (e.g., location of coal, iron, salt, and mica) of the explored regions. He used the barometer to determine altitude and was the first to find (from the average of J. J. Lerche's eleven-month barometric pressure observation in Astrakhan) that the level of the Caspian Sea is below that of the Mediterranean and Black seas. Greatly astonishing the world's scientists, in January 1735 he recorded at Yeniseysk the lowest temperatures observed anywhere up to that time. In addition, he made another important finding in parts of eastern Siberia where a subsurface layer of soil, several feet thick, remained frozen even in summer. Gmelin attempted to measure its thickness.

In his preface to the *Flora sibirica,* Gmelin gave a remarkable overall picture of the nature of central Siberia, pointing out that western Siberia looks very much like eastern Europe, but that after crossing the Yenisey River he had the impression of being in another continent. Once on the other side, he saw rivers with clear water, new forms of plants and animals, a strange landscape with strange people—in short, a new world. Thus the Yenisey River seemed to him the natural frontier between Europe and Asia, an idea which had not occurred to any geographer before him. As a whole, the results of Gmelin's expedition represent the most important early contribution to the natural history and geography of the vast Siberian mainland.

In 1747 Gmelin was granted a year's leave from the Academy of Sciences and returned to Tübingen, where he married and remained until his death. In 1749 he became professor of medicine, botany, and chemistry at the University of Tübingen. In his inaugural lecture Gmelin reported that he had observed, in his St. Petersburg garden, the appearance of five or six new forms of the plant genus *Delphinium* from two original species brought from Siberia. He, with other leading scientists of the time, tried to reconcile, in the ensuing debate, such transmutations with belief in the original creation of all species and with the accepted Linnaean position on the fixity of species. He corresponded with Linnaeus, Haller, and Steller on this and other matters of scientific interest.

BIBLIOGRAPHY

I. ORIGINAL WORKS. Gmelin's principal scientific work, considered to be a masterpiece of scientific survey, is the *Flora sibirica sive historia plantarum Sibiriae,* 4 vols. (St. Petersburg, 1747–1769); the preface contains a short account of Gmelin's travels and results of his explorations. Vols. III and IV of this work were edited after his death by his nephew, Samuel Gottlieb Gmelin, who also worked as an explorer in Asia for the Russian Academy of Sciences. The most remarkable among Gmelin's shorter academic treatises is the *Sermo academicus De novarum vegetabilium post creationem divinam exortu* (Tübingen, 1749).

Gmelin's second major work, *Reise durch Sibirien von dem Jahr 1733 bis 1743,* 4 vols. (Göttingen, 1751–1752), is an adaptation of his travel notebooks for general publication. It contains a wealth of information, but makes rather dull reading. It was published in an abridged French version, *Voyage en Sibérie contenant la description des moeurs et usages des peuples de ce pays . . .,* 2 vols. (Paris, 1767), and in Dutch. Its publication in Russia was banned because of the work's severe criticism of the Russian bureaucracy for its inefficiency, incompetence, and even malevolence.

For Gmelin's correspondence with Linnaeus, Haller, Steller, and others see T. Plieninger, ed., *Johannis Georgii Gmelini reliquiae quae supersunt* (Stuttgart, 1861). Several vols. of MS notes from Gmelin's travels have been preserved in the archives of the Academy of Sciences in Leningrad. Their description is in D. J. Litvinov, *Bibliografia flory Sibiri* (St. Petersburg, 1909), pp. 53–64.

II. SECONDARY LITERATURE. Genealogical tables of the Gmelin family and other valuable information are in Moritz Gmelin, *Stammbaum der Familie Gmelin* (Karlsruhe, 1877); 2nd ed. by Edward Gmelin in 2 vols.: *Jungere Tübinger Linie* (Munich, 1922), and *Ältere Stuttgarter Linie und ältere Tübinger Linie* (Munich, 1929). M. Gmelin also published a short biography in *Allgemeine deutsche Biographie,* IX (1879), 269–270.

Another short biography is Eyries, *Biographie universelle,* J. F. Michaud, ed. (1856), pp. 644–646. Much information is in F. A. Golder, *Bering's Voyages, an Account of the Efforts of the Russians to Determine the Relations of Asia and America,* 2 vols. (New York, 1922–1925); R. Grandmann, *Johann Georg Gmelin, 1709–1755. Der Erforscher Sibiriens. Ein Gedenkbuch,* Otto Gmelin, ed. (Munich, 1911), which contains a German trans. of the preface to the *Flora sibirica,* a selection from the *Reise durch Sibirien,* and selections from Gmelin's letters; and L. Stejneger, *Georg Wilhelm Steller, the Pioneer of Alaskan Natural History* (Cambridge, Mass., 1936). See also P. Pekarsky, *Istoria imperatorskoy Akademii Nauk,* I (St. Petersburg, 1870), 431–457.

Gmelin's contributions to Siberian geology are reported by V. A. Obruchev in his *Istoria geologicheskovo issledovania Sibiri,* I (Leningrad, 1931).

VLADISLAV KRUTA

GMELIN, LEOPOLD (*b.* Göttingen, Germany, 2 August 1788; *d.* Heidelberg, Germany, 13 April 1853), *chemistry.*

Leopold Gmelin was the third and youngest son of Johann Friedrich Gmelin, professor variously of philosophy, medicine, chemistry, botany, and mineralogy at Tübingen and a distinguished historian of chemistry. (It was through the elder Gmelin's efforts that a student chemistry laboratory was built at the university in 1783.) The family had been physicians, ministers, teachers, scientists, and apothecaries from the beginning of the sixteenth century.

Gmelin's early education was at the hands of a private tutor, in addition to which he attended his father's lectures at the university. He then attended the Göttingen Gymnasium, from which he graduated in 1804. The following summer his father sent him to work in the family apothecary shop in Tübingen, in accordance with long-standing tradition. At the same time he attended lectures on materia medica and pharmacology given by Ferdinand Gmelin (his cousin) and on medicine by K. F. Kielmeyer (husband of his cousin Lotte Gmelin). Both lecturers were professors of medicine at the University of Tübingen. He also met a number of other medical students and professors—including Justinus Kerner, Ludwig Uhland, and J. H. F. Autenrieth—with whom he was to maintain professional contact.

Johann Friedrich Gmelin died in November 1804; on his return to Göttingen in that year Gmelin worked with F. X. Stromeyer, his father's successor at the university. He passed his examinations in 1809, then returned to Tübingen to study with his former teachers until Easter 1811. He simultaneously began his doctoral researches on the black pigmentation of cattle eyes, a study that he was to continue in the laboratory of Nicolas J. Jacquin in Vienna later in 1811. He was awarded the medical doctorate by Göttingen in 1812; he had also qualified himself as a chemist and had studied mathematics with Bernhard Thibaut.

Gmelin then decided to travel in Italy for a year to broaden his command of the natural sciences. He was particularly concerned with mineralogy and geology, and therefore concentrated his interest in the regions of Mt. Vesuvius and San Marco. He published his geological findings in 1815.

Upon his return to Göttingen he undertook the analysis of the mineral haüynite under the guidance of Stromeyer. At the same time he began his academic career; he was appointed docent at Heidelberg in fall of 1813, and soon thereafter, in 1814, became extraordinary professor. In a letter of that year, addressed to his mother, he stated that "medicine in Heidelberg is deplorably organized—but soon it will be better."

Gmelin's cousin Christian Gottlob Gmelin received his medical degree in the academic year 1814; together they then went to Paris to study and work in Vauquelin's laboratory. They stayed in Paris until spring 1815; in addition to their laboratory work they attended lectures by Gay-Lussac, Thenard, Vauquelin, and occasionally those of Haüy himself.

When Gmelin returned to Heidelberg he replaced F. K. Nägele on the faculty. F. Tiedemann became teacher of anatomy and physiology in the same year. M. J. von Chelius came to Heidelberg in 1817, and these men together set about to establish scientific method in the curriculum. Gmelin was appointed director of the Chemical Institute—which still, however, remained part of the physical institute within the medical faculty. In 1817 he was made full professor, having refused an offer to succeed Klaproth in Berlin.

It is possible that Gmelin was influenced in his decision to stay in Heidelberg by his wife, Luise Maurer, whom he had married on 1 October 1816. She was a singer and the daughter of the pastor of the nearby Kirchheim church. (Certainly Gmelin turned down attractive offers not only from Berlin but also, later, from Göttingen.) They had four children.

In 1818 the Chemical Institute was transferred to its own quarters in a former Dominican cloister, an installation that also included an apartment for Gmelin. This move made the institute virtually independent of the medical faculty, and thus fulfilled one of Gmelin's long-range plans. In a letter to his mother (28 February 1818) Gmelin described the auditorium of the new facility as being roomy and having elevated benches so that all the students could see the experiments, and added that the laboratory had running water and that there were four additional rooms, including a large one that could house the mineral collections. He further noted that he had thirty students in chemistry but only four in medicine.

Although Gmelin devoted a great deal of time in these early years to improving the teaching of chemistry, he also—and more importantly—made extensive laboratory studies that embraced physiology, organic chemistry, inorganic chemistry, and mineralogy, in addition to purely theoretical studies. He published papers on almost all these subjects, as well as teaching and publishing his great *Handbuch,* which first appeared in three volumes in 1817 and 1819. Tiedemann, Friedrich Wöhler, and Leonhard were his occasional collaborators. (It is interesting to note that Gmelin persuaded Wöhler, who was enrolled at Heidelberg as a medical student, to relinquish medicine and take up chemistry; and it was through Gmelin's efforts that upon his graduation in 1823 Wöhler went to work with Berzelius.)

The *Handbuch der theoretischen Chemie* was Gmelin's masterwork. The first edition bore that title; the fourth edition, of 1843–1852, had grown to five volumes (expanded to ten by 1870) and was entitled simply *Handbuch der Chemie.* Gmelin was solely responsible for the first three multivolume editions, and was sole author of the first four volumes of the five-volume fourth edition, the fifth being compiled by Karl List and Karl Kraut.

Little is known about how or when Gmelin decided to start work on the project that became the *Handbuch.* As early as 1808 Berzelius had begun work on a textbook of several volumes but had himself realized that it could not be an all-inclusive systematic presentation. Indeed, Gmelin's father had noted the difficulty involved in such a work as early as 1780. Gmelin sought the complete, objective presentation of the prevailing state of chemistry. His father had found the science in a state of flux, with each author altering his textbook to reflect his own ideas; it was Gmelin's task to unify it through his own knowledge and—more important—the existing literature. He planned, then, to adduce all pertinent facts, arrange them by element and compound, and give appropriate references. It was necessary for him to bring calm, scholarship, and a critical eye to the data at his disposal; it was likewise necessary that he avoid speculation, which he considered to be hazardous as well as demanding of an inappropriate amount of time and effort. He kept a card-file index, and it is said of him that whenever he found that a compound did not exist as a separate entity or that it was identical to another named substance, he would remark, "Thank God, that there is one less acid."

Gmelin was unable to objectify chemistry completely, however, and some confusion about atomic weights, equivalents, and molecular theories and compounds is evident in his book. He constantly sought means to simplify or resolve these conflicts, not always with success; some of the formulas he gave reflect such irresolution. Nor did he escape the charge of supporting certain theories above others, despite his announced intention to avoid personal advocacy.

The first edition of the *Handbuch* reported on only forty-eight elements; two volumes of this edition were devoted to inorganic chemistry and one to organic. By the fourth edition (1843), fifty-five elements were discussed and the work had grown to nine volumes, of which three were devoted to inorganic chemistry and six to organic—thus demonstrating the growth of interest in organic substances and the increase in their known number.

Gmelin was aware from the time of the first edition that the major problem that he must confront would be in the treatment of organic substances. He maintained that inorganic and organic compounds must be distinguished from each other and began working toward their definition. He first suggested that while simple inorganic compounds are composed of two elements, simple organic compounds require three, and accordingly considered methane, cyanogen, and other like compounds as inorganic. In addition, inorganic compounds could be created by the chemist out of their constituent elements, while organic compounds required a plant or animal for their synthesis, the chemist being able to produce only minor modifications in them.

In the first three editions of his book Gmelin used the terms stoichiometric number, combining weight, chemical equivalent, or mixing weight to obtain equivalents. He accepted Döbereiner's idea of triads, opposed Berthollet's theory of affinities, and accepted Laurent's nucleus theory as a basis for the systematization of organic compounds (a system that Beilstein was in turn to adopt in arranging organic compounds in his *Handbuch*). He devised a system in which compounds were assigned formulas on the basis of equivalents present, and suggested smaller values for them. By the fourth edition Gmelin had adopted the atomic hypothesis and had proposed that the chemical definition of an organic substance might be that it always includes in its composition carbon and hydrogen, with the frequent addition of oxygen or nitrogen or both.

Although the *Handbuch* may quite properly be considered Gmelin's masterwork, he did a considerable amount of original research throughout his career. With Tiedemann he did pioneering work in the chemistry of digestion, reported in their two-volume *Die Verdauung nach Versuchen* (Heidelberg–Leipzig, 1826); in this work they identified choline in bile cholesterol, hematin in blood, and taurine, which Gmelin had found in ox gall in 1824 (it was later synthesized by Kolbe)—to mention but a few of their discoveries. They also studied saliva and changes in the blood. By himself Gmelin prepared potassium ferricyanide (red prussiate of potash, or Gmelin's salt); cobalticyanides, platinocyanides, croconic acid (which resulted when potassium carbonate and coal were heated); rhodizonic acid; formic acid (by distilling alcohol with manganese dioxide and dilute sulfuric acid); uric acid; and selenium. In addition he developed a test for bile pigments.

Gmelin designed and described some chemical apparatus—a drying tube for gases, a straight tube condenser, and an inverted flask to contain water for washing precipitates—and introduced the terms "racemic acid," "ester," and "ketone" into the literature. He suggested that minerals should be classified by form and composition, and reported a number of experiments on galvanism.

Gmelin was highly regarded as a teacher. He was an engaging person with a friendly face surrounded by an aureole of snow-white hair—his friends compared him to a blossoming cherry tree. His stature as a scientist won him membership in many learned societies. He resigned from the Heidelberg faculty in 1851, because of failing health, and sought to obtain the appointment of Robert Bunsen as his successor. His efforts were rewarded when Bunsen became director of the Chemical Institute in 1852. Gmelin died the following year.

The fifth edition of the *Handbuch* was under way at the time of Gmelin's death. It appeared in three volumes and five parts (1871–1886), under the editorship of Karl Kraut. In this edition the organic section of the work was dropped and the remainder entitled *Handbuch der anorganische Chemie.* In 1922 the Deutsche Chemische Gesellschaft assumed the obligation to continue the monumental work; the eighth edition, now entitled *Gmelins Handbuch der anorganische Chemie,* began publication in 1924 and is still being published. The book maintains the same authoritative position that it has always had and is a fitting tribute to Gmelin's skill and scholarship.

BIBLIOGRAPHY

I. ORIGINAL WORKS. Poggendorff provides a list of Gmelin's individual writings, in addition to those cited in the text.

II. SECONDARY LITERATURE. For works about Gmelin and his life, see E. Beyer and E. H. E. Pietsch, "Leopold Gmelin—Der Mensch, sein Werk und seine Zeit," in *Berichte der Deutschen chemischen Gesselschaft,* **72** (1939), 5–33; Eduard Farber, ed., *Great Chemists* (New York, 1961), pp. 453–463; A. Ladenburg, *History of Chemistry* (Edinburgh, 1886); *Lectures on the History of the Development of Chemistry Since the Time of Lavoisier* (Edinburgh, 1886), nos. 347 and 682, both works trans. by L. Dobbin; M. Nikolas, "Das Werk von Friedrich Tiedemann und Leopold Gmelin—die Entwicklung der Ernährungslehre in der ersten Hälfte des 19. Jahrhunderts," in *Gesnerus,* **13** (1956), 190–214; and J. R. Partington, *A History of Chemistry,* vol. IV (London, 1964).

On the occasion of an anniversary celebration at the Gmelin Institute see E. H. E. Pietsch, *Die Familie Gmelin und die Naturwissenschaften; Ein Ruckblick auf drei Jahrunderte* (Frankfurt, 1964); and *Kinder und Jugenderinnerungen der Julie G. Mayer geb. Gmelin (1817–1896), der Tochter Leopold Gmelin* (Frankfurt, 1965). Also see P. Walden, "The Gmelin Dynasty," trans. by R. E. Oesper, in *Journal of Chemical Education,* **31** (1954), 534–541.

CLAUDE K. DEISCHER

GOBLEY, NICOLAS-THÉODORE (*b.* Paris, France, 11 May 1811; *d.* Bagnères-de-Luchon, France, 1 September 1876), *chemistry.*

As a youth Gobley was apprenticed to the eminent pharmacist and chemist Pierre Robiquet, whose son-in-law he later became. After studying pharmacy in Paris and completing an internship in hospital pharmacy, in 1837 he purchased a pharmacy on the rue du Bac, which he directed until 1861. Despite heavy professional obligations, Gobley found time for chemical pursuits and in due course achieved a reputation as a distinguished chemist. From 1842 to 1847 he served as *professeur agrégé* at the School of Pharmacy, and from 1850 until his death he was a member of the editorial board of the prestigious *Journal de pharmacie et de chimie.* In 1861 he was elected to the Academy of Medicine, and in 1868 he was named a member of the Council on Hygiene and Health of the Department of the Seine.

Gobley's most significant work concerned the chemistry of phosphatides. He investigated the fatty matter in egg yolk, milt and fish eggs, venous blood, bile, and brain tissue; and in 1845 he discovered a fatty substance containing phosphorus which in 1850 he named lecithin (from the Greek *lekithos,* egg yolk). Gobley was unable to elucidate the exact chemical composition of lecithin, which he obtained in impure form, but he noted that its hydrolysis yielded fatty acids as well as glycerophosphoric acid. In 1844 Gobley found phosphorus in oil from the ray's liver and recommended this oil as a more palatable substitute for cod liver oil.

Gobley collaborated with the physiologist J. L. M. Poiseuille in a study of blood levels of urea and its secretion from the kidneys, the results of which were published in 1859. He invented an instrument called the *élaïomètre* to test the purity of oils by determining their density and first described the device in 1843. He also carried out research on biliary calculi and vanillin.

BIBLIOGRAPHY

I. ORIGINAL WORKS. A listing of Gobley's scientific papers is in the Royal Society of London, *Catalogue of Scientific Papers (1800–1863),* II (London, 1868), 924–925; VII (London, 1877), 790; X (London, 1894), 11; and in A. Goris, *Centenaire de l'internat en pharmacie des hôpitaux et hospices civils de Paris* (Paris, 1920), pp. 404–405. Gobley's most important publications are "Note sur l'élaïomètre, nouvel instrument d'essai pour les huiles d'olives," in *Journal de pharmacie et de chimie,* 3rd ser., **4** (1843), 285–297; "Mémoire sur l'huile de foie de raie," *ibid.,* **5** (1844), 306–310; "De la présence du phosphore dans l'huile de foie de raie," *ibid.,* **6** (1844), 25–26; "Sur l'existence des acides oléique, margarique et phosphoglycérique dans le jaune d'oeuf," in *Comptes rendus hebdomadaires des séances de l'Académie des sciences,* **21** (1845), 766–769; "Recherches chimiques sur le jaune d'oeuf," in *Journal de pharmacie et de chimie,* 3rd ser., **9** (1846), 1–15, 81–91, 161–174; **11** (1847), 409–417; **18** (1850), 107–119; "Recherches chimiques sur la laitance de carpe," *ibid.,* **19** (1851), 406–421; "Recherches chimiques sur les matières grasses du sang veineux de l'homme," *ibid.,* **21** (1852), 241–254; "Recherches sur la nature chimique et les propriétés des matières grasses contenues dans la bile," *ibid.,* **30** (1856), 241–246; "Recherches sur le principe odorant de la vanille," *ibid.,* **34** (1858), 401–405; "Examen chimique d'un calcul biliaire, suivi de considérations sur les différentes phases de sa formation, et sur les meilleurs dissolvants des calculs biliaires," *ibid.,* **40** (1861), 84–91; "De l'action de l'ammoniaque sur la lécithine," *ibid.,* 4th ser., **12** (1870), 10–13; "Sur la lécithine et la cérébrine," *ibid.,* **19** (1874), 346–354; "Recherches chimiques sur le cerveau," *ibid.,* **20** (1874), 98–102, 161–166; and "Recherches sur l'urée,'" in *Comptes rendus hebdomadaires des séances de l'Académie des sciences,* **49** (1859), 164–167, written with J. L. M. Poiseuille.

II. SECONDARY LITERATURE. For additional information on Gobley's life and work, see "Discours prononcé par M. le Dr. Delpech, au nom de l'Académie de médecine," in *Journal de pharmacie et de chimie,* 4th ser., **24** (1876), 329–333; *Centenaire de l'École supérieure de pharmacie de l'Université de Paris, 1803–1903* (Paris, 1904), p. 348; E.

Bourquelot, *Le centenaire du Journal de pharmacie et de chimie, 1809–1909* (Paris, 1910), pp. 71–72; J. R. Partington, *A History of Chemistry,* IV (London–New York, 1964), 485; and D. L. Drabkin, *Thudicum, Chemist of the Brain* (Philadelphia, 1958), p. 173.

ALEX BERMAN

GODDARD, ROBERT HUTCHINGS (*b.* Worcester, Massachusetts, 5 October 1882; *d.* Baltimore, Maryland, 10 August 1945), *physics, rocket engineering.*

After the advent of ballistic missiles and space exploration, Goddard became posthumously world-famous as one of three scientific pioneers of rocketry. Like the Russian hero Konstantin Tsiolkovsky and the German pioneer Hermann Oberth, Goddard worked out the theory of rocket propulsion independently; and then almost alone he designed, built, tested, and flew the first liquid-fuel rocket on 16 March 1926 near Auburn, Massachusetts. Although Goddard seriously studied experimental physics throughout his life, whether teaching or doing applied research for the government, he began to dream of astronautics in 1899 and rocket engineering remained his prime preoccupation.

Raised by his old-line Yankee family in middle-class suburbs of Boston, Goddard was a studious child whose academic development was thwarted by ill health. He graduated from Worcester's South High School in 1904 and from Worcester Polytechnic Institute in 1908. Beginning graduate work in physics immediately at nearby Clark University, he obtained the M.A. and Ph.D. there in 1910 and 1911, respectively. Under the tutelage of A. G. Webster, Goddard studied radio devices, particularly the thermionic valve, electromagnetism in solids, and both solid and liquid propulsion for reaction engines. Following a year's research at Princeton (1912–1913), he returned to Clark to teach and rose to a full professorship by 1919.

Having explored the mathematical practicality of rocketry since 1906 and the experimental workability of reaction engines in laboratory vacuum tests since 1912, Goddard began to accumulate ideas for probing beyond the earth's stratosphere. His first two patents in 1914, for a liquid-fuel gun rocket and a multistage step rocket, led to some modest recognition and financial support from the Smithsonian Institution. During World War I, Goddard led research on tube-launched rockets that became the bazookas of World War II, and during the latter war he worked primarily on jet-assisted takeoff (jato) and variable-thrust rockets for aircraft, barely living to see evidence of the German V-2 rockets and to hear of Hiroshima.

The publication in 1919 of his seminal paper "A Method of Reaching Extreme Altitudes" gave Goddard distorted publicity because he had suggested that jet propulsion could be used to attain escape velocity and that this theory could be proved by crashing a flash-powder missile on the moon. Sensitive to criticism of his moon-rocket idea, he worked quietly and steadily toward the perfection of his rocket technology and techniques. With an eye toward patentability of demonstrated systems and with the aid of no more than a handful of technicians, Goddard achieved a series of workable liquid-fuel flights starting in 1926. Through the patronage of Charles A. Lindbergh, the Daniel and Florence Guggenheim Foundation, and the Carnegie and Smithsonian institutions, the Goddards and their small staff were able to move near Roswell, New Mexico. There, during most of the 1930's, Goddard demonstrated, despite many failures in his systematic static and flight tests, progressively more sophisticated experimental boosters and payloads, reaching speeds of 700 miles per hour and altitudes above 8,000 feet in several test flights. Among Goddard's successful innovations were fuel-injection systems, regenerative cooling of combustion chambers, gyroscopic stabilization and control, instrumented payloads and recovery systems, guidance vanes in the exhaust plume, gimbaled and clustered engines, and aluminum fuel and oxidizer pumps.

Although his list of firsts in rocketry was distinguished, Goddard was eventually surpassed by teams of rocket research and development experts elsewhere, particularly in Germany. By temperament and training Goddard was not a team worker, yet he laid the foundation from which team workers could launch men to the moon. Early in the 1960's the National Aeronautics and Space Administration named its first new physical facility at Greenbelt, Maryland, after Goddard; and the government awarded his estate one million dollars for all rights to the collection of over 200 Goddard patents.

BIBLIOGRAPHY

I. ORIGINAL WORKS. Goddard's writings include "A Method of Reaching Extreme Altitudes," in *Smithsonian Miscellaneous Collections,* **71,** no. 2 (1919), and "Liquid-Propellant Rocket Development," *ibid.,* **95,** no. 3 (1936), both reprinted in Goddard's *Rockets* (New York, 1946). See also *Rocket Development: Liquid-Fuel Rocket Research, 1929–1941,* Esther C. Goddard and G. Edward Pendray, eds. (New York, 1948); "An Autobiography," in *Astronautics,* **4** (Apr. 1959), 24–27, 106–109; and *The Papers of Robert H. Goddard,* Esther C. Goddard and G. Edward Pendray, eds., 3 vols. (New York, 1970), based on a voluminous MSS collection at Robert H. Goddard Memorial Library. Clark University, Worcester, Massachusetts. Microfilm and artifacts of Goddard's work are in the Goddard Wing of the Roswell, New Mexico, Museum and Art Center.

II. SECONDARY LITERATURE. On Goddard or his work, see Wernher von Braun and Frederick I. Ordway, III, *History of Rocketry and Space Travel,* rev. ed. (New York, 1969), pp. 40–59; Eugene M. Emme, ed., *The History of Rocket Technology* (Detroit, 1964), pp. 19–28; Bessie Z. Jones, *Lighthouses of the Skies: The Smithsonian Astrophysical Observatory, Background and History, 1846–1955* (Washington, D.C., 1965), pp. 241–276; Milton Lehman, *This High Man: The Life of Robert H. Goddard* (New York, 1963), the authorized biography; and Shirley Thomas, *Men of Space: Profiles of the Leaders in Space Research, Development, and Exploration,* I (Philadelphia, 1960), 23–46.

LOYD S. SWENSON, JR.

GODFREY, THOMAS (*b.* Bristol Township, Pennsylvania, 1704; *d.* Philadelphia, Pennsylvania, December 1749), *technology.*

Godfrey's major contribution was his invention of the double reflecting quadrant which became generally known as Hadley's quadrant and is, essentially, the navigational sextant used today. It quickly replaced other instruments for measuring elevation.

Godfrey produced his instrument in October 1730 and had it tested in Delaware Bay and on a voyage to Jamaica. James Logan, the most learned man in Pennsylvania, sent a description of the device to the astronomer royal, Edmond Halley, but received no reply and was soon surprised to find in the *Philosophical Transactions of the Royal Society* an account of an almost identical instrument invented by John Hadley, a fellow of the Royal Society. Fearing that Godfrey had unjustly lost credit for his invention, Logan collected affidavits on the chronology of the invention, obtained reports from Jamaica, and wrote again to Halley as well as to several of his friends in the Royal Society. Godfrey, too, fowarded a presentation of his case. The society heard these papers and published Logan's account in the next volume of *Philosophical Transactions.* Hadley clearly had the priority of publication, but Godfrey's invention was solely his own in a day when identical independent inventions were not easily accepted.

Godfrey was an important member of a small intellectual circle in Philadelphia. A glazier by trade, he developed an impressive command of mathematics and, with the help of Logan and Logan's extensive library, learned and used Latin. He was a founding member of Benjamin Franklin's 1727 Junto and a director of the Library Company of Philadelphia from its establishment in 1731. The 1743 American Philosophical Society included Godfrey as its "Mathematician."

Godfrey published almanacs from 1729 to 1736. He also contributed mathematical questions and answers, astronomical data, and general essays to the *Pennsylvania Gazette* and the *Pennsylvania Journal.* In 1740 he advertised instruction in navigation, astronomy, and mathematics. To fix the longitude of Philadelphia on his 1755 *General Map of the Middle British Colonies,* Lewis Evans used astronomical observations that he made with Godfrey.

BIBLIOGRAPHY

Godfrey issued *An Almanack for the Year 1730* (Philadelphia, 1729) and other annual almanacs until *The Pennsylvania Almanack for 1737* (Philadelphia, 1736). He made occasional contributions to the *Pennsylvania Gazette* and the *Pennsylvania Journal.*

On the quadrant, the key writings are Godfrey's letter to the Royal Society (9 Nov. 1732), in the Royal Society library (microfilm copy in American Philosophical Society Library), and James Logan, "An Account of Mr. T. Godfrey's Improvement of Davis's Quadrant," in *Philosophical Transactions of the Royal Society,* **38** (1733–1734), 441–450. Both publications and other Logan letters appear also in *American Magazine,* **1** (1757–1758), 475–480, 529–534. Other related Logan correspondence is in the Royal Society library and in the Logan Papers of the Historical Society of Pennsylvania.

Nathan Spencer, "Essay of a Memorial of Thomas Godfrey, September 8, 1809," MS., American Philosophical Society, is helpful. Frederick B. Tolles, *James Logan and the Culture of Colonial Pennsylvania* (Boston, 1957), pp. 202–204, is a brief but understanding account of Logan.

BROOKE HINDLE

GODIN, LOUIS (*b.* Paris, France, 28 February 1704; *d.* Cádiz, Spain, 11 September 1760), *astronomy.*

The son of François Godin, a lawyer in the Parlement, and Elisabeth Charron, Louis received his early training at the Collège de Beauvais. Although his courses in humanities were intended as a background for legal studies, he turned thereafter to philosophy and ultimately to astronomy, in which he received instruction under Joseph Delisle at the Collège Royal.

Having entered the Academy of Sciences in 1725, Godin presented his first memoir there the following year. Inspired by an appearance of a meteor which had frightened many people, Godin addressed himself to such transient phenomena, offering, for example, both a history and a physical explanation of displays of northern lights. It was partially the superiority of that historical analysis that led the Academy to involve Godin in its own historical project. For the next few years Godin concerned himself with editing the eleven volumes of the Academy's *Mémoires* from 1666 to 1699, the writing of its *Histoire* for nineteen of those years, and the preparation of a four-volume index of the materials included in this basic collection (*Histoire et les Mémoires de l'Académie Royale des Sciences*) from 1666 to 1730.

As time-consuming as these activities were, they did not prevent Godin from engaging in astronomical work. In addition to observing some eclipses at the royal observatory, he brought out, in 1727, an appendix to Philippe de La Hire's astronomical tables, a work which indicated his suitability for assuming, in 1730, the preparation of the Academy's annual ephemeris, the *Connaissance des temps;* he continued this task until 1735. Meanwhile, Godin had obtained his own observational site, where he viewed various eclipses of 1731, 1732, and 1733 and duly reported the observations to the Academy. The observation dealing with the lunar eclipse of 1732 was more than a simple report, since it offered a comparison with corresponding observations elsewhere and utilized these data to deduce longitudinal differences between observation sites. Moreover, his concern with the phenomenon in general led him to propose a method for the determination of lunar parallax by means of lunar eclipses.

Of Godin's other works of this period, about half were devoted to various instrumental and observational problems. These included a memoir and a later addendum on the construction, verification, and placing of a mural quadrant in the plane of the meridian, a description of a commodious observational tower, a means of determining the height of the pole independently of refraction, and a method for observing the variation of the magnetic needle at sea. The other half dealt with various aspects of planetary theory and positional changes of standard reference lines and points. Included here were memoirs concerned with the problem of the place of greatest reduction from the ecliptic to the equator and with a method for determining planetary nodes, with the apparent movements of the planets in epicycles, and with the diminution of the obliquity of the ecliptic and its amount. In none of these works was Godin responsible for any new insight or basic improvement.

Similar judgment would also apply to the one remaining memoir of this period, the 1733 paper on a means for tracing parallels of latitude. But because it contained reflections on the proportions of these circles in differing figures of the earth, this memoir led Godin soon thereafter to propose that the Academy send an expedition to the equator to resolve the issue between the "Cassinians" and the "Newtonians" with their respective views of the earth's prolateness or oblateness. Having accepted this plan, the Academy logically named Godin to undertake this task, along with Pierre Bouguer and Charles de La Condamine. He went first to England to consult with Edmond Halley and other astronomers; there he was received into the Royal Society and furnished with several instruments. As it turned out, however, Godin contributed little to the expedition.

Despite great and various difficulties, the members of the expedition did ultimately measure an arc of about three degrees in Ecuador, a province of the Spanish viceroyalty of Peru. Two slightly different figures for the length of a degree were arrived at by Bouguer and La Condamine, each of whom published an account of the voyage after returning to Paris. On the basis of his separate effort undertaken with Jorge Juan and Antonio de Ulloa, the two Spanish naval officers whose collaboration was one of the costs of Spain's cooperation, Godin produced still another figure. Because the later-dispatched but earlier-completed expedition to Lapland had already resolved the basic issue in favor of oblateness, these equatorial figures immediately served only as verifications, although subsequently they were employed in the calculations establishing the metric system.

Godin never published his account of the voyage, despite subsequent claims that he was working on it, but he did accomplish other works during this period. La Condamine related Godin's 1737 experiments on the speed of sound, and Godin himself reported to the Academy on the length of the seconds pendulum observed at Santo Domingo on the way to Ecuador and on a lunar eclipse viewed in Quito in 1737. Finally, in 1738, he submitted a memoir on a method for determination of solar parallax.

Bouguer and La Condamine left Peru in 1743; Godin stayed on, as professor of mathematics at the University of San Marcos, until 1751. After a year in Paris, during which he fruitlessly sought the return of his academic place and pension, he went to Spain and became the director of the Academy of Naval Guards at Cádiz. Although he returned to Paris briefly in 1756, reentering the Academy in "veteran" status and participating in a base-line verification, the preparation of a mathematics course for his Cádiz students was the principal occupation of his last years. Like his expedition account, a planned astronomical bibliography and a collection of astronomical observations remained unrealized.

Godin's 1728 marriage to Rose-Angélique le Moyne produced a son and a daughter, both of whom predeceased him. Godin died in 1760, following an attack of apoplexy.

BIBLIOGRAPHY

I. Original Works. Godin's only publication independent of Academy sponsorship was his *Appendice aux tables astronomiques de Lahire* (Paris, 1727). Under the aegis of the Academy, he constructed five vols. of the *Connaissance des temps,* drew up and published the four-volume *Table alphabétique des matières contenues dans l'Histoire et les Mémoires de l'Académie royale des sciences* . . . (Paris, 1734), in the preparation of which collection he participated and presented many papers. His first contribution was "Sur le météore qui a paru le 19 octobre 1726," in the *Mémoires* for 1726, 287-302. His reports of eclipses may be seen in the *Mémoires* as follows: lunar (1729), 9-11, 346-349; (1731), 231-236; (1732), 484-494; (1733), 195-197; (1739), 389-392; solar (1726), 330-331; (1733), 149-150. His suggestions for lunar and solar parallax determinations appeared in the *Mémoires* as "Sur la parallaxe de la lune" (1732), 51-63; and "Méthode de déterminer la parallaxe du soleil par observation immédiate" (1738), 347-360.

Godin's pendulum observation, "La longueur du pendule simple, qui bat les secondes du temps moyen, observée à Paris et en petit Goave en l'île Saint-Domingue," was in *Mémoires* (1735), 505-521. Most of his other instrumental and observational offerings were also in the *Mémoires:* "Du quart de cercle astronomique fixe" (1731), 194-222; "Addition qu'il faut faire aux quarts-de-cercle fixes dans le méridien" (1733), 36-39; "Méthode nouvelle de trouver la hauteur de pôle" (1734), 409-416; "Méthode d'observer la variation de l'aiguille aimantée en mer" (1734), 590-593; his tower description, however, appeared in M. Gallon, ed., *Machines et inventions approuvées par l'Académie royale des sciences depuis son établissement jusqu'à présent, avec leurs descriptions,* 7 vols. (Paris, 1735-1777), VI, 49-52.

Godin's remaining contributions to the *Mémoires* were "Solution fort simple d'un problème astronomique d'où l'on tire une méthode nouvelle de déterminer les noeuds des planètes" (1730), 26-33; "Des apparences du mouvement des planètes dans un épicycle" (1733), 285-293; "Méthode pratique de tracer sur terre un parallèle par un degré de latitude donnée; et du rapport du même parallèle dans le sphéroïde oblong et dans le sphéroïde aplati" (1733), 223-232; and "Que l'obliquité de l'écliptique diminue, et de quelle manière; et que les noeuds des planètes sont immobiles" (1734), 491-502.

II. Secondary Literature. The "official" *éloge* for the Academy was written by Grandjean de Fouchy, another Delisle student and Godin's friend, and appeared in the *Histoire de l'Académie* . . . (1760), 181-194. Although mentioning, and lauditorily analyzing, many of his memoirs and other works, this *éloge* does not provide explicit citations; better for the latter, although weak on analysis, are several subsequent biographical treatments: J. M. Quérard, *La France littéraire ou Dictionnaire bibliographique des savants* . . ., 10 vols. (Paris, 1827-1839), III, 391; J. F. Michaud, ed., *Biographie universelle,* 45 vols. (Paris, 1843-1858), XVII, 23; and Niels Nielsen, *Géomètres français du dix-huitième siècle* (Paris, 1935), pp. 192-195. The best general account of his astronomical work, with fair bibliographical information, is J. B. J. Delambre, *Histoire de l'astronomie au dix-huitième siècle* (Paris, 1827), pp. 331-336; he also provides a separate treatment of Godin's arc-measurement venture in G. Bigourdan, ed., *Grandeur et figure de la terre* (Paris, 1912), pp. 85-145.

Recent treatments of the problem of the shape of the earth are the brief but general account of Seymour L. Chapin, "The Size and Shape of the World," in *UCLA Library Occasional Papers,* no. 6 (1957), 1-7; and the large-scale account of the mid-1730's expeditions by Tom B. Jones, *The Figure of the Earth* (Lawrence, Kans., 1967), esp. ch. 6.

On Godin's observational site, see G. Bigourdan, *Histoire de l'astronomie d'observation et des observatoires en France,* II (Paris, 1930), 42-47.

Seymour L. Chapin

GODWIN-AUSTEN, ROBERT ALFRED CLOYNE (*b.* Guildford, England, 17 March 1808; *d.* Guildford, 25 November 1884), *geology.*

Son of Sir Henry Edmund Austen of Shalford House, Guildford, and Anne Amelia Bate, Godwin-Austen was educated in France and subsequently at Oriel College, Oxford, taking his B.A. in 1830 and being elected to a fellowship of his college. He was also a student at Lincoln's Inn. His interest in the discipline to which he was to devote his life was kindled by William Buckland at Oxford, and among his early friends he numbered Charles Lyell, Leonard Horner, and Roderick Murchison, who sponsored, also in 1830, his election to the Geological Society of London. In 1833 Godwin-Austen married Maria Elizabeth Godwin, only daughter and heiress of General Sir Henry Thomas Godwin, who commanded the British army in Burma. Upon the death of his father-in-law in 1854, Austen added the name of Godwin to his own by royal license.

Godwin-Austen is remembered among geologists for his contributions to the stratigraphy of southern England, as one of the first European paleogeographers, and for his prediction that a coalfield would be discovered beneath the younger rocks of Kent. His first original work was devoted to the limestones and slaty rocks of southeast Devon, where he had settled after his marriage. Henry de la Beche, who in 1835 founded the Geological Survey of Great Britain, encouraged the young man by relying upon him for the geological lines on the map covering the district between Dartmouth and Chudleigh. Austen was, however, sufficiently independent of mind to resist the introduction, proposed by Adam Sedgwick, Murchison, and William Lonsdale, of the Devonian system.

After 1840, when he moved to Chilworth manor house, near Guildford, Godwin-Austen began to devote his considerable energies to the geology of Surrey. Here his interests included the fossil faunas of the Cretaceous rocks, the origin of the phosphatic deposits, and the succession in the Tertiary sands; his work on the structure of the Weald led him to conclude that the folding postdated the deposition of the lower Tertiaries. Now he was beginning to view the stratigraphical data in a wider context, to derive a picture of seas advancing and retreating over western Europe. Pursuing these conceptions, Godwin-Austen visited the coalfields of northern France and studied the structure of the Ardennes. In 1856 he produced what remains his best-known paper, suggesting a possible extension of the coal measures beneath southeast England. Maintaining, on theoretical grounds, that the coal-bearing strata of England, France, and Belgium once formed part of a continuous formation, he traced its breakup by folding and erosion, calling attention to the probability that in the east-west belt between the Ardennes and Bristol, coal measures basins other than those at the two extremities should exist. Godwin-Austen's views attracted interest, and in his last paper, published in 1879, he was still advocating them. They were not, however, vindicated until six years after his death, when a borehole drilled at the foot of Shakespeare Cliff near Dover proved coal measures beneath the chalk and led to the development of the Kent coalfield.

Godwin-Austen was also a pioneer in the elucidation of the history of the English Channel and among the first marine geologists. He was elected a fellow of the Royal Society in 1849. In awarding him the Wollaston Medal, premier award of the Geological Society of London, Murchison said in 1862 that he was "pre-eminently the physical geographer of bygone periods," a description amply justified by the essay on the European seas, begun by his friend Edward Forbes and completed by Godwin-Austen.

BIBLIOGRAPHY

I. Original Works. A comprehensive list of Godwin-Austen's writings is given in the article by Woodward cited below. Among them are "On the Valley of the English Channel," in *Quarterly Journal of the Geological Society of London,* **6** (1850), 69–97; "On the Possible Extension of the Coal-Measures Beneath the South-Eastern Part of England," *ibid.,* **12** (1856), 38–73; *The Natural History of European Seas,* begun by E. Forbes, edited and completed by Godwin-Austen (London, 1859); and "On Some Further Evidence as to the Range of the Palaeozoic Rocks Beneath the South-East of England," in *Report of the British Association for the Advancement of Science for 1879* (1879), pp. 227–229.

II. Secondary Literature. On Godwin-Austen or his work, see T. G. Bonney, "Anniversary Address of the President," in *Quarterly Journal of the Geological Society of London,* **41** (1885), 37–39; J. G. O. Smart, G. Bisson, and B. C. Worssam, "Geology of the Country Around Canterbury and Folkestone," in *Memoirs of the Geological Survey* (1966), pp. 16–30; and H. Woodward, "Robert Alfred Cloyne Godwin-Austen," in *Geological Magazine,* n.s. decade 3, **2** (1885), 1–10.

K. C. Dunham

GOEBEL, KARL (*b.* Billigheim, Baden, Germany, 8 March 1855; *d.* Munich, Germany, 9 October 1932), *botany.*

Although his full style was Karl Immanuel Eberhard Ritter von Goebel, he called himself simply Karl Goebel throughout his life. He was one of that group of independent German investigators who, in the latter half of the nineteenth century, revitalized botany and made it a wide-ranging experimental science. Goebel brought this activity well into the twentieth century; indeed, the *Organographie der Pflanzen,* his major work, was not fully published in its final form until 1933 (the year following his death).

Intended by his family for the church, Goebel was educated at the Evangelical College of Blaubeuren and thence, at the age of eighteen, went to study theology and philosophy at Tübingen. There he came under the influence of Wilhelm Hofmeister and realized his true inclination toward science. After some mental conflict—since he did not wish to disappoint his mother—he persuaded her of his interest and devoted himself to botany. At this time he also began his extensive botanical travels. Hofmeister fell ill before Goebel completed his training, and in 1876 he transferred to Strasbourg to study with Heinrich Anton de Bary. Here he took his doctorate.

Goebel then worked for a short time at the biological station at Naples. The following year Julius von Sachs appointed him his assistant at Würzburg, and he qualified as *Privatdozent.* He thus had the advantage of contact with three of the outstanding botanical figures of his time—he received inspiration from Hofmeister in the widest aspects of the newly arising morphology; from de Bary in plant anatomy and mycology; and from Sachs in physiology.

After four years as Sachs's assistant Goebel was appointed professor at Rostock and in 1887 at Marburg. In 1891 he moved to Munich, where he was professor of botany and later general director of the State Scientific Collections, retiring emeritus in 1931.

Goebel's principal administrative achievement in Munich was the removal of the botanical laboratories and gardens from their cramped quarters near the main railway station in the center of town to the edge of the Bavarian royal park at Nymphenburg. The gardens and greenhouses were his particular concern; through the years he enriched them with specimens collected on his many journeys (which took him to the Rockies, the Andes, the New Zealand Alps, and the Indian Ghats, among other places). Under his supervision the installation became second in Germany only to that in Berlin. An acute contemporary noted that Goebel had planned the greenhouses and gardens with such thought and consideration that, although their unity bore his unmistakable imprint, his assistants had not thought their ideas disregarded. Goebel also contributed several new editions of the guide to the collections. He wished to provide students and researchers in the institute itself with spacious, practical working and teaching laboratories, and there are indications that its vast, ornate entrance hall, with its marble and polychrome mosaics, was not of his planning or even desiring.

As a botanist, Goebel drew upon that great wealth of data accumulated in the late nineteenth century through use of the compound light microscope. One of the great problems of the time was to decide how this great assembly of facts could best be codified and studied, and it was Goebel's contribution to see and industriously apply a profitable method to the existing corpus of information and to his own collections. That he early established a reputation as a botanist of wide knowledge and great objectivity is testified to by Sachs's decision to ask Goebel to assist him in the preparation of a new edition of his textbook, entrusting him with the sections on systematics and special morphology.

Goebel preferred objective research to speculation. For him this meant observation and simple experimentation on the great variety of living plants. To a friend he expressed regret that he did not have the knowledge of the exact sciences necessary to carry his experimental studies to the biochemical level. He was, however, impatient of gadgetry and the niceties of preparation and rarely used a microtome for his sections.

An unfortunate by-product of Darwinism among botanists had been an excessive preoccupation with phylogenetic speculation. This Goebel despised. He once said, for example, that concern about the "natural system" of seed plants seemed about as hopeless as attempting to return to its original paper bags the confetti scattered during the Munich carnival. His attitude was best expressed in his introduction to the *Organographie:* "I take exactly the same view as Herbert Spencer. . . . He says 'Everywhere structures in great measure determine functions; and everywhere functions are incessantly modifying structures. In nature the two are inseparable co-operators; and science can give no true interpretation of nature without keeping their co-operation constantly in view.'"

The parts of plants might therefore be modified during their individual life by the effects of the surroundings upon their functions, as when a spiny plant, grown in a moist atmosphere under a bell jar, became leafy. Such changes were open to experimental measurement and proof. Nevertheless, Goebel clearly realized that organ primordia are inherited with properties that "belong to the capacity of the plant itself." The dependence of metamorphosis on both racial and individual characteristics and experiences would remain true, he taught, even if a general theory of descent were abandoned. Plants consist of operating and adjustable organs, and their study is an organography.

By the middle of the nineteenth century plant studies, which up until then had been mainly observational, had begun to harden into a rigid formalism. The significance of Goebel's organography for botanical science lay in the fact that it provided one of the main bridges from the achievements of observation to the fully fledged experimental science of the twentieth century. Earlier attempts had been premature; organography itself was transitional because methods were not yet in existence to enable it to be carried to its logical conclusion. Goebel, however, lived long enough to see the first developments of experimental plant physiology and biochemistry, although not perhaps their coordination with the subtler levels of structure, to which his organography had pointed.

Goebel's success as a teacher resulted from his clarity and impartiality, but he is said to have underrated his didactic powers—although adding, "If an angel from heaven came down to give the botany lectures, the medics would still not turn up." Yet the records show that many completed the full fifty hours prescribed. He gave freely of his time to his pupils and received many advanced students from abroad.

His aloofness in the lecture hall and laboratory appears to have been a pedagogic device which Goebel deemed useful. With his students in the field, or even during evening discussions, he was more relaxed; and those botanists who have left records of meeting him on his travels have all done so with affectionate admiration.

Beyond the vast knowledge of his special subject, Goebel had a cultivated and philosophic mind. He quoted freely from the Bible, although with age he became increasingly cool toward the church. His contemporaries regarded Goebel as the exponent of an extreme materialistic view of living things, yet he thought highly of Henri Bergson's concept of *élan vital,* could speak of the Logos in nature, and held Hegelian viewpoints to which he had been introduced as a student at Tübingen. The objectivity of his ideas and their freedom from the rigidity and speculation that were simultaneously besetting the older schools made his influence on later work very considerable. He died as the result of a fall suffered while botanizing in his native Swäbische Alb.

BIBLIOGRAPHY

I. Original Works. Goebel published more than 200 works, many of which appeared in *Flora,* which he edited until 1932. A full list of Goebel's publications is in the obituary by Karsten (see below). His principal work, *Organographie der Pflanzen,* had several eds.: 1st ed., 2 vols. (Jena, 1898-1901), English trans. (Oxford, 1900-1905); 2nd ed., 3 vols. (Jena, 1915-1923); 3rd ed., 3 vols. (Jena, 1928-1933).

II. Secondary Literature. An obituary notice is G. Karsten, in *Berichte der deutschen botanischen Gesellschaft,* **50** (1932), 131-162. Otto Renner, "Erinnerungen an K. Goebel," in *Flora,* **131** (1936), v-xi, is an excellent sketch of Goebel as man and scientist.

W. O. James

GOEDAERT, JOHANNES (*b.* Middelburg, Netherlands, *ca.* 19 March 1617; *d.* Middelburg, February 1668),[1] *entomology.*

Goedaert was the son of Pieter Goedaert and Judith Pottiers. (The family name is variously spelled Goedhart or Goedaerdt or latinized as Goedartius or Goedardus.) The occupation of the elder Goedaert and the religion of the family are unknown, but it is quite probable that they were members of the Dutch Reformed Church.[2] Little is known of Goedaert's life. He probably did not receive a secondary education. He apparently did not know Latin, and wrote his only book in Dutch; the Latin translation, which is the best known, was the work of others (see below). He certainly did not attend a university.

Goedaert is remembered as a painter, more particularly as a watercolorist, whose subjects were mainly birds and insects. According to his biographer C. de Waard, it appears that he had some knowledge of chemistry and pharmacy; it is reported that he knew how to make a remarkable extract of *Artemisia absinthium* and how to eliminate the tendency of antimony to cause vomiting. Goedaert lived all his life in Middelburg. He married Clara de Bock and by her had one daughter and one son, Johannes, who became a surgeon.

One of the earliest authors on entomology, Goedaert was the first to write on the insects of the Netherlands. More important, he was the first to base his discussions entirely on firsthand observation instead of making the traditional appeal to authority, citing and paraphrasing the work of predecessors. In his only work, *Metamorphosis naturalis,* he describes his observations of and experiments with insects made between 1635 and 1658.

Basically, Goedaert's technique was to catch "worms" (larvae) in the field and to rear them, feeding them with their natural nutrients and observing and recording their metamorphosis, until finally the mature animal could be observed and drawn. In this way, he studied the life cycles of a variegated collection of butterflies, bees, wasps, flies, and beetles. Goedaert's pioneering work is not without its faults. He made no attempt to devise a system of insect classification such as Swammerdam would do as early as 1669, and although aware that most of his "worms" originated from eggs, he believed some were produced by spontaneous generation. The year of his death saw the publication of Redi's *Esperienze intorno alla generatione degli insetti,* in which the possibility of spontaneous generation was denied for the first time. Goedaert's fieldwork was not sufficiently extensive to enable him to solve the problem of the ichneumon wasps. He reported that of two identical caterpillars, one yielded a beautiful butterfly and the other no less than eighty-two little flies. He also made anatomical errors, for example when he related the position of a caterpillar's legs to the position of the pupa in the cocoon.

Goedaert published two volumes of his book during his lifetime, in 1662 and in 1667. A third, posthumous volume was edited by Johannes de Mey from his papers at the request of his widow. De Mey also translated the first and third volumes into Latin, adding commentaries of his own on insects and comets, mostly the kind of material that Goedaert has been praised for omitting. The second volume was translated into Latin by P. Veezaerdt, who abstained from comment but added a chapter of philosophical speculations on insects. The zoologist M. Lister produced an English translation in which he tried to organize the contents of the book, and it is therefore difficult to compare it with the original. He also edited another Latin edition. Finally, a French translation was published in 1700. Several authors have offered identifications of the insects described by Goedaert.

The faults in Goedaert's work were recognized soon after his death. Swammerdam spent three folio pages criticizing him,[3] but he also added a few words of praise: " . . . but at the same time we own with satisfaction that this author alone observed and discovered, in the space of a few years, more singularities in the caterpillar kind, than had been done by all the learned men who treated the subject before him."

NOTES

1. Dates according to C. de Waard; the date given for birth is day of baptism. A. Schierbeek gives the birth year as 1620. P. J. Meertens states (p. 472, n. 280) that Goedaert was buried in Middelburg on 15 Jan. 1668.
2. It will never be possible to ascertain these points; the archives of Middelburg were destroyed, together with the city hall, in May 1940.
3. Jan Swammerdam, *The Book of Nature* (London, 1758), pp. 14–17, *passim.* This is Thomas Flloyd's trans. of the *Biblia naturae.* Goedaert is mentioned many times and sometimes criticized in this and in other of Swammerdam's works.

BIBLIOGRAPHY

I. Original Works. The bibliography of Goedart's only book is somewhat complicated; it is detailed in Kruseman's paper (see below). A summary account follows:

Metamorphosis naturalis, ofte historische beschrijvinge van den oirspronk, aerdt, eygenschappen ende vreemde veranderinghen der wormen, rupsen, maeden, vliegen, witjens, byen, motten en diergelijke dierkens meer; niet uit eenige boeken, maar aleenlyck door eygen ervarentheid uytgevonden, beschreven ende na de konst afgeteykent door Johannum Goedaerdt, 3 vols. (Middelburg, vol. I, 1662; vol. II, 1667; vol. III, 1669), carried the imprint of J. Fierens. This edition was reissued in 1700 (probably the same sheets of the 1662–1669 edition) but with a French title page as well as the original Dutch one. The French title page has the imprint of Adrian Moetiens of The Hague; there is an engraved frontispiece, which gives "Amsterdam, 1700."

Metamorphosis et historiae naturalis insectorum, autore Joanne Goedartio; cum commentariis D. Joannis de Mey . . . (Middelburg, 1662 [date of dedication]).

Metamorphoseos et historiae naturalis, pars secunda, De insectis, autore Joanne Goedartio, latine donata . . . a Paulo Veezaerdt (Middelburg, 1667 [date of preface]).

Metamorphoseos et historiae naturalis insectorum, pars tertia et ultima, autore Joanne Goedartio aucta observationibus et appendice D. Joannis de May (Middelburg [1669]).

Johannes Goedartius, Of Insects. Done Into English and Methodized, With the Addition of Notes by Martin Lister Esq. The Figures Etched Upon Copper by Mr. F. Pl. (York, 1682). The engraver was Francis Place (1647–1728). Only 150 copies were printed. See *Philosophical Transactions of the Royal Society,* **13** (1683), 22–23.

Johannes Goedartius, De insectis. In Methodum redactus cum notularum additione, opera M. Lister . . . item . . . (London, 1685). This translation is also "methodized." See *Philosophical Transactions,* **14** (20 Dec. 1684), 833–834.

Métamorphoses naturelles, ou histoire des insectes. Traduit en françois (Amsterdam–The Hague, 1700). It appears that undated copies exist. See *The History of the Works of the Learned,* III (1701), 597–602.

J. van Abcoude, in his *Naamregister van de . . . Nederduitsche boeken* (Rotterdam, 1773), p. 153, has under the name of Goedaert *Historie van den oorsprong der wormen* (n.p., n.d.) and *Historie van de bloedelooze dieren,* 3 vols. (Haarlem, n.d.). I could not confirm these two titles. The title of the second book is the same as that of one of Swammerdam's books, which, however, was never printed in three volumes. Both works are probably ghosts.

II. Secondary Literature. On Goedaert and his work, see P. de la Ruë, *Geletterd Zeeland* (Middelburg, 1741), pp. 61–64; C. de Waard, "Johannes Goedaert," in *Nieuw Nederlandsch Biografisch Woordenboek,* I (Leiden, 1911), 944–945; P. J. Meertens, *Letterkundig leven in Zeeland in de zestiende en de eerste helft der zeventiende eeuw* (Amsterdam, 1943); F. Nagtglas, *Levensberichten van Zeeuwen* (Middelburg, 1890–1893), pp. 267–268; A. Schierbeek, *Schouwburg der dieren* (The Hague [1943]), pp. 122–127; and G. Kruseman, "The Editions of Goedaert's Metamorphosis naturalis," in *Entomologische Berichten,* **16** (1956), pp. 46–48.

Works especially concerned with the identification of Goedaert's illustrations are F. S. Bodenheimer, *Materialien zur Geschichte der Entomologie bis Linné,* 2 vols. (Berlin, 1928), II, 368–372; H. P. Snelleman Cz., "Johannes Goedaert," in *Album der Natuur,* **26** (1877), 203–212; S. C. Snellen van Vollenhoven, "Determinatie der platen in het werk van Johannes Goedaert," *ibid.,* pp. 307–318; and A. Werneburg, *Beiträge zur Schmetterlingskunde,* I (Erfurt, 1864), p. 24 ff.

Peter W. van der Pas

GOEPPERT, HEINRICH ROBERT (*b.* Sprottau, Lower Silesia, Germany [now Szprotawa, Poland], 25 July 1800; *d.* Breslau, Germany [now Wroclaw, Poland], 18 May 1884), *paleobotany, botany.*

Goeppert, whose father owned a pharmacy, discovered his love of botany while still a schoolboy. In order to follow his inclination he left school early and worked for five years as a pharmacist. After finishing his education he entered the University of Breslau in 1821 to study medicine. In 1824 he went to the University of Berlin, where he earned his medical degree in 1825. He returned to Breslau in 1826 and established himself as a general practitioner, surgeon, and ophthalmologist. Goeppert soon realized however, that he would not be fully satisfied in this occupation. In 1827, therefore, he became *Privat-*

dozent at the Faculty of Medicine of the University of Breslau with a work on plant physiology. In the same year he became an assistant at the university's botanical garden, with which he was associated for more than fifty-six years. He was promoted to associate professor on the Faculty of Medicine in 1831 and to full professor in 1839. In 1852 Goeppert assumed the chair of botany and was appointed director of the botanical garden and museum. His lectures in these years covered many fields: pharmacology, toxicology, forensic chemistry, systematic botany, plant physiology, plant geography, and paleobotany. He was particularly interested in the cryptogams.

Besides his official duties and scientific studies Goeppert, who was extremely active in public life, participated in the promotion of the cultural and economic interests of the city of Breslau and of the province of Silesia. He was aided in this by his extraordinary organizational ability, as well as by his affability. He was especially concerned with the Schlesische Gesellschaft für Vaterländische Kultur, whose president he was from 1846 until his death. On the fiftieth anniversary of his doctorate, "old Goeppert," as he was called by the townspeople, was granted the honorary freedom of the city of Breslau. He was an honorary, corresponding, or regular member of more than a hundred learned societies and academies all over the world. Goeppert was married twice, first to the eldest daughter of his professor, Remer, and then—after her early death—to one of her younger sisters. He had one son and one daughter.

With the exception of a few medical topics, Goeppert's scientific publications were devoted to botany, especially paleobotany. His doctoral dissertation and *Habilitationsschrift* both dealt with plant physiology. He wrote other works in this field on the evolution of heat in living plants, especially during germination and blossoming, and on the influence of low temperatures on plants; in particular, he studied the problem of whether a plant exposed to cold dies at the moment of freezing or at thawing. He later resumed these investigations and collected them in a book (1883). In another series of works he considered the ecology, physiology, and pathology of forest trees and fruit trees, especially their reactions to mechanical interference and external injuries. For instance, he showed that in stands of spruces and silver firs the roots of all the trees grow together. Hence, if one trunk breaks off or is felled, the stump is nourished by the neighboring trees until the point of fracture or of cutting has grown over and healed. Goeppert also considered questions of plant anatomy and of descriptive botany. He published studies of the anatomical structure of the conifers, of several Casuarinaceae and Magnoliaceae and of tropical Balanophorales.

In 1833 Goeppert entered the field in which he was to accomplish his most distinguished work. Stimulated by Otto, an anatomist at the University of Breslau who had assembled a considerable collection of fossil animal remains found in Silesia, he began to examine this region's fossil plant remains. The two scientists issued a joint call to their fellow Silesians to assist this project by sending them fossil plants. Their appeal was very successful; Goeppert received rich and interesting materials from many areas. He studied both this material and his own collections with great industry and enthusiasm. The Carboniferous flora from the coal deposits of Upper and Lower Silesia provided his richest discoveries.

Goeppert's first paleontological work, "Die fossilen Farnkräuter," appeared in 1836. In it he discussed the Carboniferous ferns and compared them—following strict principles of comparative anatomy—with those of the modern period, thereby establishing his reputation as a paleobotanist. Five years later he began publication of *Gattungen der fossilen Pflanzen, vergliechen mit denen der Jetztwelt* (1841–1846). This large, illustrated work, with German and French texts, greatly advanced the knowledge of fossil plants. Among Goeppert's most important achievements was the demonstration that coal seams are formed from the same plants that are found in the clays and sandstones located above and below them. Furthermore, he showed that the coal seams had originated through the high pressures exerted by sedimentary coverings and through decomposition resulting from lack of air, and therefore were not structureless masses carbonized by fire. Goeppert's entry in the Haarlem Academy's prize competition concerning the question whether coal seams are autochthonous or allochthonous was awarded the double prize. His studies on the Silesian coal regions enabled Goeppert to give valuable advice on the seams that were worth mining. He generously provided this information to all who sought it.

Following his great success in the study of Carboniferous flora, Goeppert turned attention to the fossil plants of other stages of the earth's history and produced monographs on the fossil flora of almost all the geological periods. Among these are two masterpieces: *Die fossilen Coniferen* (1850) and *Die fossile Flora der Permischen Formation* (1863–1865). These works contain the results of his microscopic examination of various specimens, including chips and thin sections of siliceous trunks; this examination allowed him to provide the first detailed comparisons with the tissues of living woods.

Goeppert was especially attracted by the flora of the Tertiary. He described and reconstructed palm, yew, and plane forests and cypress stands from various fossil occurrences in Silesia. As in his work on the Paleozoic and Mesozoic, he also considered plant remains from other regions of Germany, as well as from the rest of Europe and from overseas. Thus he demonstrated that in the Tertiary deposits of central Europe the Japanese ginkgo, the Chilean *Libocedrus,* and the North American yew occur side by side, and that in the Tertiary the vegetation of Java had the same tropical character it has today. Goeppert took a special interest in the amber of east Prussia and throughout his life studied the plants in it. As early as 1837, for example, he realized that a certain species of conifer must have produced the resin of the east Prussian amber.

BIBLIOGRAPHY

I. ORIGINAL WORKS. A complete bibliography up to 1882 is in Goeppert's "Beiträge zur Pathologie und Morphologie fossiler Stämme," in *Palaeontographica,* **28** (1882), 141–145. A complete bibliography is in Conwentz (see below).

Goeppert's writings include "Die fossilen Farnkräuter," in *Nova acta Leopoldina,* **17** (1836), 1–258; *Die Gattungen der fossilen Pflanzen, vergliechen mit denen der Jetztwelt,* 6 pts. (Bonn, 1841–1846); *Die fossilen Coniferen, mit steter Berücksichtigung der lebenden* (Haarlem-Leiden, 1850); *Die fossile Flora der Permischen Formation* (Kassel, 1864–1865); and *Die Flora des Bernsteins und ihre Beziehungen zur Flora der Tertiärformation und der Gegenwart* (Danzig, 1883) and *Über das Gefrieren, Erfrieren der Pflanze und Schutzmittel dagegen* (Stuttgart, 1883), both written with Menge.

II. SECONDARY LITERATURE. See F. Cohn, "Heinrich Robert Göppert," in *Leopoldina,* **20** (1884), 196–199, 211–214; H. Conwentz, "Heinrich Robert Goeppert, sein Leben und Wirken," in *Schriften der naturforschenden Gesellschaft in Danzig,* n.s. **6** (1885), 253–285, with portrait, also in *Leopoldina,* **21** (1885), 135–139, 149–154; and K. Lambrecht and W. and A. Quenstedt, "Palaeontologi. Catalogus biobibliographicus," in *Fossilium catalogus,* **72** (The Hague, 1938), 166.

HEINZ TOBIEN

GOETHE, JOHANN WOLFGANG VON (*b.* Frankfurt am Main, Germany, 28 August 1749; *d.* Weimar, Germany, 22 March 1832), *zoology, botany, geology, optics.*

Born of middle-class parents—his father, Johann Kaspar Goethe, was a lawyer—Goethe obtained a degree in law at Strasbourg in 1771. He was summoned in 1775, on the basis of his literary fame, to the court of Weimar, where his duties soon included the supervision of mining in the duchy. He was raised to the nobility in 1782. After a sojourn in Italy (1786–1788) which constituted a decisive break with his turbulent youth, Goethe returned permanently to Weimar and established a lasting reputation as Germany's greatest poet. In religion he was never orthodox, although he did not deny God or immortality. Much of his theorizing in biology was based on belief in a Spinozistic God as Nature and on the conviction that his own mind could come to know the mind of this deity.

Goethe's first scientific paper (1784) claimed to demonstrate the presence of the intermaxillary (premaxillary) bone in man. It was published first in 1820, with a long postscript on the history of research on the problem and the controversy the manuscript had evoked. Long before Goethe it had been noted that, of the three sutures—external (facial), nasal, and palatal—which delimit the bone when it is present in the vertebrate upper jaw, the palatal is sometimes visible in human skulls, is more distinct in children than in adults, and can best be seen in embryos. Goethe was struck by the fact that in some mammals (for example, ruminants) the premaxilla is indisputably present even though the upper incisor teeth, which it normally supports, are absent. He inferred that if present even in such cases, it is unlikely to be absent in man, in whom upper incisors are well developed; and so he sought and found traces of the nasal and palatal sutures in human skulls.

J. C. Loder, the Jena anatomist, and later J. B. Spix accepted Goethe's inference that man has the bone, whereas Peter Camper, S. T. Sömmerring, and J. F. Blumenbach maintained that the inference would be justified only if the sutures were clearly visible. In fact the facial suture is never seen, and the two others are indistinct or absent. This rebuff led Goethe to regard the physicists' later rejection of his optical theories as yet another example of the impatience of the professional scientist with the amateur. His erroneous belief that Sömmerring and Blumenbach eventually accepted his findings arose because in his old age he no longer had clear memories of the controversy of the 1780's.

Goethe believed that to deny man the premaxilla would be to impugn the unity of nature. "Morphology" was his term for tracing out the unity underlying animal and plant diversity. He did not argue that similarities between genera are due to descent from common ancestors, for he understandably lacked the modern concept of specialization. Thus characters in apes and in sloths which are today attributed to a high degree of adaptation to arboreal conditions appeared to him as sheer lack of proportion. In botany Goethe found it difficult to divide some genera into distinct species with no transitional forms, since the classification was based on characters (particularly leaf structures) which were highly variable. This diversity suggested to him that species were in some way flexible, and he even allowed (following Georges Buffon) that differences in climate and food could lead to the evolution of one plant or animal species from another within the same genus. Thus he regarded an extinct species of bull, fossils of which were found near Stuttgart in 1820, as possibly the ancestor of the modern European and Indian bull. But to account for the unity of type pervading different genera he supposed that nature, regarded as a kind of creative artist, used a single archetype in constructing them; thus plants derive from "a supersensuous archetypal plant" (*Urpflanze*), which he thought of as an idea in the mind of nature, individual genera being modifications in one direction or another of this type.

Goethe thought that the biologist, by comparing a large number of plant and animal forms, can obtain a clear idea of the underlying archetypes. Having found at least traces of the premaxilla in cetaceans, amphibians, birds, and fishes, he inferred that a structure so widely distributed must be part of the vertebrate archetype and must therefore be represented in all vertebrates, including man.

Goethe also constructed his idea of the archetype from a study of function. A bone which is not only present in most vertebrates but also obviously serves an important feeding function (both when it supports upper incisor teeth which have a nipping action against the incisors of the lower jaw, and when it forms a toothless, hard pad against which the lower incisors bite) is likely, for both these reasons, to belong to the archetype. He stressed the stability of function and thought that a bone or organ which performs a function in one animal will be present to perform the same function in another—although he realized that in some few cases an organ functional in some animals may occur as a rudiment in others; and he emphasized that a functional organ may be drastically reduced if other structures are extended. This theory is in accordance with the principle of compensation that he derived from Aristotle, a *loi de balancement* (then being independently stated by Étienne Geoffroy Saint-Hilaire) which Goethe illustrated with the recession of the premaxilla in the walrus, whose canines are elongated into tusks.

The best-known of Goethe's examples illustrating the principle of compensation is the inverse development of horns and front teeth in the upper jaw. He said, for instance, that the lion, with upper incisors and canines, cannot have horns. Fossil evidence has since shown that there is no incompatibility, since some extinct horned ungulates have the full eutherian dentition. The connection between Goethe's principle of compensation and his idea of a vertebrate archetype appears in his criticism from his teleological standpoint of the grosser teleology of his day: that of the so-called physicotheologians, who supposed that all the organs of an animal were designed to be useful to it, for example, the horns of the ox for defense. Goethe countered by asking why Providence did not supply the sheep with horns, or, when they have horns, why they are curled round their ears so as to be useless. His view was that ruminants, with no upper incisors or canines, have horns because horns, or some alternative to them consistent with the principle of compensation, belong in the mammalian archetype.

Goethe extended his idea of unity of type to cover not only vertebrates but all animals. He pointed out, for instance, that insects, as well as vertebrates, have bodies consisting of three major divisions, each with its appropriate organs. He welcomed Geoffroy Saint-Hilaire's arguments that all animals are built upon a common plan, that all existing forms are modifications of a nonexistent *être abstrait.*

Goethe's views on the relationship between allegedly similar parts in different organisms are paralleled in his thought concerning the different parts of one and the same organism. Just as organisms consist of variations of a single type, so the type itself consists of a number of parts or segments, each of which is identical with the others. This, he said, is particularly clear in the case of plants: cotyledons, inflorescence, stamens, and pistils are all, he said (having observed transitional forms), variations of the foliage leaf. He did not mean that they develop from leaves during the growth of the plant or that they have evolved from leaves during the history of plants, but that an "ideal leaf" is the essential scheme which underlies them all. He attempted to give the metamorphosis a physical basis by arguing that forms more delicate than foliage leaves are produced by elaboration of the sap as it passes upward.

Goethe argued that the vertebral column preserves some indication of the underlying identity of the units which go to form the vertebrate archetype, and that the skull is really a series of bones which can be seen to be variations of vertebrae. Although Lorenz Oken was the first to publish such views, Goethe could prove that he had adumbrated them earlier in extant letters to friends. He summed up his services to morphology by saying that the recognition that man, too, possesses the premaxilla secured the admission that a single osteological type pervades all forms, and that the construction of the skull from vertebrae establishes the identity of all the segments of this osteological type.

The attribution of the premaxilla to man never attained the popularity of the vertebral theory of the skull (also closely connected with archetypal thinking), although Oken and Goethe were committed to both. After F. S. Leuckart's well-documented account of 1840 it was hardly possible to dispute that in man the premaxilla is eliminated during ontogeny. And so Richard Owen, who retained the premise of the vertebrate archetype—which he imagined as consisting of a number of modified vertebrae—did not find it necessary for the purpose to credit man with a premaxilla. The vertebral origin of the skull was finally refuted on an embryological basis by T. H. Huxley in 1858.

What Goethe sought in botany and zoology was nothing less than a theory that would explain all living forms. He had no interest in details for their own sake and undertook detailed study only because of his consciousness that he was working toward wide generalizations which far outran his observations. Although his theory posits "the original identity of all plant parts," he ignored the root and stem and studied only the lateral appendages of the annual herbs. This premature generalization was due neither to personal arrogance nor to an a priori method but to a conviction, religious in character, that he had penetrated to the mind of nature. This aspect of his work endeared Goethe to the *Naturphilosophen* of the early nineteenth century; and when they were discredited, his scientific reputation remained unaffected largely because Ernst Haeckel quite unjustifiably stamped him as one of the foremost precursors of Darwinism.

Goethe's concern with geology sprang from his superintending the reopening of the copper slate mines at Ilmenau in 1784. At that time most rocks were regarded as chemical precipitates from saline seas. Mountain chains such as the Harz, the Thuringian forest, and the Alps all have central cores of granite, which was therefore interpreted as an *Urgebirge,* a foundation against which all later deposits, precipitated from a universal ocean, rest: the granite is flanked by "transition rocks," believed to have been formed when the ocean had receded sufficiently to expose the highest granite. The steep inclination or dip of these transition strata was considered original, not the result of postdepositional tilting, and they were made partly of detritus (scree from the granite peaks) and partly of further chemical precipitate from the ocean; the chemical ingredients were believed sufficient to consolidate the gathering sediment with steep original dip on the submerged slopes. When the waters had retreated still further, the *Flöz,* or layered rocks, were deposited—steeply inclined where they rest against the mountain core but elsewhere mainly horizontal. The final retreat of the waters to their present level was accompanied by the deposition of recent gravels, often rich in mammalian remains.

Such a scheme underlies Goethe's geological thinking. In the Harz he saw granite in close contact with "transition" rock of an entirely different type (hornfels), and he envisaged the two as attracting each other as they crystallized. It is characteristic that whereas the modern geologist explains the facts by positing a long sequence of events (deposition of clay, intrusion of liquid granite, baking, cooling, and solidification), Goethe preferred to think in terms of events occurring more or less simultaneously.

It is an important part of his theory of rock origin that the joint planes which divide granite masses into blocks were original, not shrinkage cracks due to cooling or drying. Each block was, for Goethe, an original precipitated "crystal"; and the mountain mass was formed by piling them. Since an extra crystal would give an uneven top to this basement rock, later rocks would locally acquire a steep dip as they wrapped themselves around it. Goethe thus believed that the steep dip of the rocks leaning against the basement was original. If they had been originally horizontal, they could have become steeply inclined only as a result of considerable crustal dislocation; and he believed that nature produces her effects without violent disturbances, since there was no evidence in his day that cataclysms or catastrophes were then occurring. His geological thinking clearly lacked the crucial concepts of time and uplift.

Actual proof of relationships posited by the above theory seemed to be provided by the Ilmenau mines. We know that the commercial copper bed and parallel seams are there strongly upfolded by the contact with the Thuringian granite and porphyry. But to Goethe the steep inclination was original, the seam wrapping against an *Urgebirge* cliff. In explaining the vertical position of the strata without supposing any dislocation of the rocks, Goethe was, in 1785, in agreement with most professional geologists, although by the early nineteenth century they had revised this opinion and he had not.

If the steep limbs of *Flöz* beds were deposited in this steep position, then it was easier to regard the whole *Flöz* as a crystalline precipitate from water rather than as fragments carried and deposited (for particles in water tend to settle in horizontal layers). And so Goethe regarded nearly all *Flöz* horizons—limestones, sandstones, shales, and even conglomerates—as chemically deposited. Many quartz grains in the Thuringian Bunter sandstones are angular, which seemed to suggest that they had not been transported. These sandstones were also so thick that enormous periods of time would have been required to derive them by erosion of preexisting granites. And before the development of the polarizing microscope in the mid-nineteenth century, there was no decisive way of distinguishing the groundmass of a porphyry from the cement of a detrital rock. Field relationships encouraged Goethe to link the Thuringian porphyry with local red conglomerates, for as we now know, both are of Rotliegendes age.

Goethe's repugnance for theories involving terrestrial violence sometimes led him to pioneer a correct path. The most notable instance is his glacial interpretation of erratic blocks at a time when violent and catastrophic movement was being invoked to explain their remoteness from their parent rocks. He explained the Swiss erratics by arguing that the glaciers had extended to the lakes of Geneva and Lucerne at a time when the general sea level reached these lakes. The glaciers transported the boulders to the lakes, and they completed their journey on floating ice. He realized that the theory implied a cold climate, giving an ice sheet over most of northern Germany and floating ice when it melted. His failure to appreciate the time factor is well illustrated by this explanation of phenomena confined to the present-day land surface in terms of a change in sea level of 1,000 feet, which would point back to what he saw as the earliest stage of the earth's geological history. But his stress on the importance of glacier transport of the erratics was correct, and in 1841 Johann de Charpentier mentioned John Playfair and Goethe as pioneers of the idea.

Goethe's whole approach to rocks reflects the insistence on types which distinguishes his biological thinking. He could relate a conglomerate to a granite because he had in his mind an idea of a rock type of which the two were variations. His biological ideas proved useful because the likenesses he perceived could later be understood not in an archetypal way, but as genetic relationships, as due to common ancestry. But his rock analogies could not serve as a pointer to future development, since he linked rocks which are not genetically related at all.

Goethe's first publications on optics (1791) culminated in his *Zur Farbenlehre* (1810), his longest and, in his own view, best work, today known principally as a fierce and unsuccessful attack on Newton's demonstration that white light is composite. Goethe supposed that the pure sensation of white can be caused only by a simple, uncompounded substance. Not until 1826 did Johannes Müller establish that any nervous receptor, no matter how stimulated, can excite only a characteristic sensation peculiar to it.

Goethe propounded the ancient idea that colors arise from mixing light with darkness. He was aware that these normally mix to form gray but held that the intervention of a turbid medium produces color; that all bodies are to some extent turbid and hence may appear colored in daylight; and that even transparent refracting media are comparable with turbid ones. (This attempt to bring the color phenomena produced by prisms under the theory was further developed by Arthur Schopenhauer in 1816 but was designated "senseless" by Ernst Mach.) In 1827 H. W. Brandes pointed out that the color phenomena Goethe alleged are not shown by such turbid media as steam or water-saturated mist; and in 1852 Ernst Wilhelm von Brücke showed, in terms of the wave theory of light and on the basis of long-forgotten work by Thomas Young, that whether colors are produced depends on the size of the particles in the medium. But for Goethe the color effects of turbid media were an *Urphänomen,* an ultimate which cannot itself be explained—which is in fact not in need of explanation—but from which all that we observe can be made intelligible.

Goethe's chapter on physiological colors (those which depend more on the condition of the eye than on the illumination) is the most successful and also typifies his psychological approach to color. Color vision involves an exciting stimulus and a conscious sensation. Goethe was concerned with the latter, and he posited three primary sensations—yellow, blue, and purple (for him, the purest red). In his color circle these three primaries alternated with orange, violet, and green, each of which, he claimed, could be seen to be compounded of the two adjacent primaries. He admitted, however, that the eye can see no trace of another color in pure green, which he classed as mixed presumably because blue and yellow pigments together give green. The distinction between additive and subtractive mixing was not properly understood before Hermann von Helmholtz, and Goethe's color circle certainly confused a subjective or psychological classification with an objective one.

Violet was positioned in the circle above blue, as its intensified form, and orange likewise above yellow; purple was placed highest of all, as the fusion of these intensified forms of his two other primaries. By "purple" Goethe meant the color seen through a prism when spectral red and spectral violet are superposed by viewing a thin black strip on a white background. Although this purple was thus compounded, it was, Goethe insisted, as a sensation pure (facts which undermine his principal reason for rejecting Newton's view of white!); whereas spectral orange and violet—designated "pure" by the physicist in terms of wavelength—are impure sensations (the eye can see red and yellow in orange, and red and blue in violet). Later authorities have agreed with Goethe in taking purple in his sense as psychologically the purest red and in finding spectral red distinctly yellowish in comparison.

Goethe supposed that the eye, by virtue of its own vital activity, is impelled to change a given condition into its opposite. It cannot, he said (explaining the phenomena of simultaneous and successive contrast), remain for a moment in a specific state that has been evoked by an object presented to it; when offered one extreme, or one mean, it spontaneously posits the other. He extended this doctrine to all living substance and was convinced that reality must ultimately be explained in terms of polar opposites—a view which endeared him to F. W. J. Schelling and G. W. F. Hegel, and to the *Naturphilosophen* in general. He posited no neural mechanism to explain simultaneous and successive contrast and thought them sufficiently explained by reference to his principle of polarity. The phenomena are in fact to a large extent polar and have since been attributed by Ewald Hering to a neural mechanism which functions in a polar fashion.

The terms in which Goethe explained colors (light, darkness, and turbidity) can be readily visualized, and for him explanation was never adequate unless the explicans fulfilled this condition. He thus had no sympathy with mathematical physics. He insisted that concrete phenomena can be represented in numerical form only if some of their essential conditions are ignored, and that if we reason from such abstractions, we are bound to err. He argued that the student of nature must not transmute what he sees into concepts and these concepts into words, but must think only in terms of what he sees. A physicist would today find it quite impossible to implement such an injunction. Goethe's adherence to it explains why he was so much less successful with physical than with physiological optics.

BIBLIOGRAPHY

I. Original Works. Goethe's scientific writings are available in *Goethes Werke,* pt. 2, 13 vols. (Weimar, 1890–1904), edited by order of the Grand Duchess Sophie of Saxony. Another valuable (but as yet incomplete) ed. is *Goethe: Die Schriften zur Naturwissenschaft,* G. Schmid *et al.,* eds., pt. 1, text, 11 vols. (Weimar, 1947–1970); pt. 2, supplements and commentaries (Weimar, in progress). Details of other eds. are in *Goethes Werke,* Dorothea Kuhn *et al.,* eds., XIII (Hamburg, 1955), 598–600, 638–639.

II. Secondary Literature. The principal bibliographies are K. Goedeke, *Grundriss zur Geschichte der deutschen Dichtung aus den Quellen,* IV, pt. 5 (Berlin, 1960), 363–382, covering 1912–1950; H. Pyritz, *Goethe Bibliographie* (Heidelberg, 1965), pp. 483–528; M. Richter, *Das Schriftum über Goethes Farbenlehre* (Berlin, 1938); and G. Schmid, *Goethe und die Naturwissenschaften* (Halle, 1940).

Critical studies include A. Arber, "Goethe's Botany," in *Chronica botanica,* **10** (1946), 63–126; B. von Freyberg, *Die geologische Erforschung Thüringens in älterer Zeit* (Berlin, 1932); M. Gebhardt, *Goethe als Physiker* (Berlin, 1932); H. von Helmholtz, "Über Goethes naturwissenschaftliche Arbeiten," in *Populäre wissenschaftliche Vorträge* (Brunswick, 1876), I, 31–54; J. H. F. Kohlbrugge, "Historisch-kritische Studien über Goethe als Naturforscher," *Zoologische Annalen,* **5** (1913); R. Magnus, *Goethe als Naturforscher* (Leipzig, 1906); W. Ostwald, *Goethe, Schopenhauer und die Farbenlehre* (Leipzig, 1918); M. Semper, *Die geologischen Studien Goethes* (Leipzig, 1914); C. S. Sherrington, *Goethe on Nature and Science,* 2nd ed. (Cambridge, 1949); R. Trümpy, "Goethes geognostisches Weltbild," in *Eidgenössische technische Hochschule, kultur- und staatswissenschaftliche Schriften,* no. 127 (1968), 1–37; J. Walther, ed., *Goethe als Seher und Erforscher der Natur* (Halle, 1930); and G. A. Wells, "Goethe's Geological Studies," in *Publications of the English Goethe Society,* **35** (1965), 92–137; "Goethe's Scientific Method and Aims in the Light of His Studies in Physical Optics," *ibid.,* **38** (1968), 69–113; "Goethe and Evolution," in *Journal of the History of Ideas,* **28** (1967), 537–550; and "Goethe and the Intermaxillary Bone," in *British Journal for the History of Science,* **3** (1967), 348–361.

George A. Wells

GOETTE, ALEXANDER WILHELM (*b.* St. Petersburg, Russia, 31 December 1840; *d.* Heidelberg, Germany, 5 February 1922), *zoology.*

Goette was the son of Ernst Bernhard Goette, a physician and counselor of state in St. Petersburg, and the former Natalie Bagh. He studied medicine at the University of Dorpat from 1860 to 1865 and completed his training with an M.D. degree at the University of Tübingen under Franz Leydig. Goette then worked as an independent scholar and in 1872 qualified as a lecturer under the Strasbourg zoologist Oscar Schmidt, at the same time becoming an assistant in the Zoological Institute of the University of Strasbourg. Named an associate professor in 1877, he took the additional post in 1880 of director of the zoological collection of the Municipal Museum of Strasbourg. From 1882 to 1886 Goette was professor of zoology at the University of Rostock. He was called back to Strasbourg in 1886 as Schmidt's successor. In 1918 he left Strasbourg and spent his last years in Heidelberg.

Following several minor investigations in vertebrate embryology, Goette's principal work, *Die Entwicklungsgeschichte der Unke* (*Bombinator igneus*) *als Grundlage einer vergleichenden Morphologie der Wirbelthiere,* appeared in 1875. Along with a detailed description of the development of the organs of *Bombinator igneus,* he gave a detailed presentation of his ideas of the methods and problems of ontogenetic research. In opposition to the dominant phylogenetic interpretation of embryonic development, Goette emphasized the necessity of investigating purely ontological and physiological regularities as a basis for the understanding of morphological phenomena, thereby criticizing Ernst Haeckel's gastraea theory and the "biogenetic law," which said nothing about the causation involved in the events occurring during ontogenesis. Haeckel responded immediately with the polemic work *Ziele und Wege der heutigen Entwicklungsgeschichte* (Jena, 1875), in which he presented Goette as an opponent of Darwin's theory. Yet Goette had always acknowledged the theory of descent, although he was critical of the explanation of species transformation by means of the theory of selection, especially because of Darwin's (and Haeckel's) acceptance of the inheritance of acquired characteristics.

Goette sought to explain developmental processes through a particular "law of form" which ruled the world of living creatures. This conception superimposed purely mechanical operations upon a teleological and vitalistic interpretation of life itself. He viewed cell division as a purely chemicophysical process. With Wilhelm His and August Rauber, Goette was one of the pioneers in research in developmental physiology, which soon became a separate field of study in the "developmental mechanics" of Wilhelm Roux. Goette's own careful investigations on animal embryology remained purely descriptive. After 1875 they treated most invertebrate groups as well: sponges, coelenterates, worms, mollusks, and echinoderms.

Goette had a little-known dispute with August Weismann concerning the "duration of life" and the definition of death. Whereas Weismann accepted the concept of "natural death" only for multicell forms of life, Goette defended the position that death is the necessary concomitant of reproduction and that there is no absolute continuity of life.

Goette's reticence in the polemics over Darwinism, the cell theory, and conceptions of heredity soon caused his own views on these questions to recede into the background. Hence there are no assessments of his scientific work except for the short obituary by Karl Grobben. On the other hand, in accounts of zoology in the last decades of the nineteenth century his name is almost always mentioned. Besides his zoological writings, Goette published *Holbeins Totentanz und seine Vorbilder,* which shows his thorough knowledge of the history of art and culture.

BIBLIOGRAPHY

I. Original Works. Goette's writings include *Die Entwicklungsgeschichte der Unke* (*Bombinator igneus*) *als Grundlage einer vergleichenden Morphologie der Wirbelthiere* (Leipzig, 1875); *Über Entwicklung und Regeneration des Gliedmassenskeletts der Molche* (Leipzig, 1879); *Abhandlungen zur Entwicklungsgeschichte der Tiere,* 5 vols. (Leipzig, 1882–1890); *Über den Ursprung des Todes* (Leipzig, 1883); *Über Vererbung und Anpassung* (Strasbourg, 1898); *Lehrbuch der Zoologie* (Leipzig, 1902); and *Die Entwicklungsgeschichte der Tiere* (Berlin–Leipzig, 1921). A nonscientific work is *Holbeins Totentanz und seine Vorbilder* (Strasbourg, 1897).

II. Secondary Literature. See Karl Grobben, in *Almanach der Akademie der Wissenschaften in Wien,* **72** (1923), 171–173; Jürgen-Wilhelm Harms, in R. Dittler, *et al.,* eds., *Handwörterbuch der Naturwissenschaften,* V (Jena, 1934), 297; and Georg Uschmann, in *Neuė deutsche Biographie,* VI (1964), 579.

Hans Querner

GOHORY, JACQUES (*b.* Paris, France, 1520; *d.* Paris, 15 March 1576), *natural history, alchemy, medicine.*

Jacques Gohory was the eldest of six children born to Pierre de Gohory, an advocate to the Parlement of Paris, and his wife Catherine de Rivière. The family had strong links with the Parlement and Court of Paris, and Jacques, like his father and two of his younger brothers, became an advocate to the Paris Parlement. As a young man Gohory served on various ambassadorial missions, including periods in Flanders, England (1546–1549), and Rome (1554–1556).

Finding himself unsuited to legal or courtly life, he decided on his return from Rome to devote himself to the study and pursuit of poetry, music, the occult arts including alchemy, natural history, and medical philosophy. He retained his title of advocate to the Parlement, however, until his death.

Gohory's wide-ranging interests place him in the mainstream of French Renaissance culture which surrounded the courts of the later Valois monarchy. Indeed, as references in his works make clear, he was a close friend of members of the Pléiade and of Jean Antoine de Baïf's circle. From 1572 Gohory maintained a private academy which he called the Lycium Philosophal San Marcellin, at his home in the Faubourg Saint-Marcel. This academy was a rival to Baïf's royally chartered Academy of Poetry and Music founded two years earlier. Both academies were devoted to the encyclopedic cultivation of the arts in the Italian Neoplatonic tradition, but whereas Baïf's emphasized poetry and music, Gohory's laid stress on alchemy, botany, and the magical arts. The Lycium had a botanical garden and a chemical laboratory; games and music were played in the alleys of the garden. The site of Gohory's Lycium was close to that of the later Jardin du Roi, founded in 1626, but there was no formal connection between the two institutions.

Gohory is important as an early disseminator of Paracelsian ideas in France. In his writings he refers to his discussions on Paracelsus' teachings with such distinguished medical figures as Jean Fernel, Ambroise Paré, Jean Chapelain, Honoré Chastellan, and Leonardo Botal. His Lycium became a center for the preparation of chemical medicines. His *Compendium* (1568) of the philosophy and medicine of Paracelsus contains a brief life of Paracelsus, a summary of his principal doctrines, a catalogue of his works, and a commentary on his *De vita longa.* Gohory was critical of contemporary commentators on Paracelsus, particularly Gerard Dorn, who published an immediate rebuttal in 1568. He linked Paracelsus with the medieval magical and alchemical tradition through Artephius, Roger Bacon (from whom he said Paracelsus borrowed much), Peter of Abano, Albert the Great, Arnald of Villanova, Raymon Lull, and John of Rupescissa. Although he recognized Paracelsus' debt to the later Neoplatonic magical tradition, in particular by pointing to the relationship of Paracelsus' *De vita longa* to Marsiglio Ficino's *De triplici vita* (1489), he was critical of both Ficino and Giovanni Pico della Mirandola for their religious scruples which, he alleged, prevented them from becoming truly great *magi.*

Gohory's short monograph on tobacco, *L'instruction sur l'herbe petum* (1572), is one of the earliest on the subject and contains recipes for chemical preparations derived from the plant. It is also notable for its information about the author and his Lycium.

Gohory's numerous literary works include translations of Machiavelli's *The Prince* (1571) and of an anonymous account of the conquest of Peru (1545). During the last three years of his life he was royal historiographer.

BIBLIOGRAPHY

I. Original Works. The most complete guide to Gohory's published work is contained in Hamy's art. cited below. Works of philosophical and medical interest are *De usu et mysteriis notarum liber* (Paris, 1550), a wide-ranging discussion of the occult; *Theophrasti Paracelsi philosophiae et medicinae . . . compendium* (Basel, 1568), published under the pseudonym Leo Suavius; *Livre de la fontaine perilleuse . . . contenant la steganographie des mystères secrets de la science minérale* (Paris, 1572), an ed. and commentary on a medieval poem which Gohory believed to be an alchemical allegory; *Discours responsif à celui d'Alexandre de la Tourette sur les secrets de l'art chymique et confection de l'or potable* (Paris, 1575), by L.S.S. [Leo Suavius Solitaire], a reply to Tourette's treatise on potable gold published in 1575.

Works of botanical interest are *Devis sur la vigne, vin et vendages* (Paris, 1550), published under the pseudonym Orl. de Suave; *L'instruction sur l'herbe petum . . .* (Paris, 1572), a monograph on the tobacco plant. His trans. of the account of Pizarro's conquest of Peru is *L'histoire de la Terre-Neuve du Péru* (Paris, 1545).

II. Secondary Literature. A very full account of Gohory's life and work is contained in E.-T. Hamy, "Un précurseur de Guy de la Brosse. Jacques Gohory et le Lycium Philosophal de Saint-Marceau-lès-Paris (1571–1576)," in *Nouvelles archives du Muséum d'histoire naturelle,* 4th ser., **1** (1899), 1–26. Gohory's commentary on Paracelsus is discussed in D. P. Walker, *Spiritual and Demonic Magic From Ficino to Campanella* (London, 1958), pp. 96–106. See also L. Thorndike, *A History of Magic and Experimental Science,* V (New York, 1941), 636–640; and J. R. Partington, *A History of Chemistry,* II (London, 1961), 162–163. The account of Peru and the treatise on tobacco are dealt with in W. H. Bowen, "L'histoire de la Terre-Neuve du Péru. A Translation by Jacques Gohory," in *Isis,* **28** (1938), 330–340; and "The Earliest Treatise on Tobacco: Jacques Gohory's 'Instruction sur l'herbe petum,' " *ibid.,* 347–363. In these arts. Bowen refers to his Harvard University diss. on Gohory (n.d.).

Owen Hannaway

GOLDBACH, CHRISTIAN (*b.* Königsberg, Prussia [now Kaliningrad, R.S.F.S.R.], 18 March 1690; *d.* Moscow, Russia, 20 November 1764), *mathematics.*

The son of a minister, Goldbach studied medicine and mathematics at the University of Königsberg before embarking, sometime around 1710, on a series of travels across Europe. Everywhere he went, he formed acquaintances with the leading scientists of his day, laying the basis for his later success as first corresponding secretary of the Imperial Academy of Sciences in St. Petersburg. Among others, he met Leibniz in Leipzig in 1711, Nikolaus I Bernoulli and Abraham de Moivre in London in 1712, and Nikolaus

II Bernoulli in Venice in 1721. At Nikolaus II's suggestion, in 1723 Goldbach initiated a correspondence with Daniel Bernoulli which continued until 1730. Back in Königsberg in 1724, Goldbach met Jakob Hermann and Georg Bilfinger on their way to participate in the formation of the Imperial Academy and decided to follow them. Writing from Riga in July 1725, he petitioned the president-designate of the new academy, L. L. Blumentrost, for a post in that body. Among his references he named General James Bruce, commander of the imperial forces, with whom he had exchanged ideas on a problem in ballistics around 1718. Although at first informed that no places were open, Goldbach soon received the position of professor of mathematics and historian of the academy at a yearly salary of 600 rubles. In the latter capacity he acted as recording secretary from the first meeting until January 1728, when he moved to Moscow.

That move resulted from Goldbach's new post as tutor to Tsarevich Peter II and his distant cousin Anna of Courland. Introduced into court circles by Blumentrost as early as 1726, Goldbach was in a position to benefit from the split between Peter II and Prince Menshikov by replacing the tutors appointed by the prince. Peter's sudden death in 1730 ended Goldbach's teaching career but not his connections with the imperial court. He continued to serve Peter's successor Anna and returned to St. Petersburg and the Imperial Academy only when she moved the court there in 1732. While in Moscow in 1729, Goldbach began the exchange of letters with Leonhard Euler that would continue regularly until 1763.

Returning to the Imperial Academy in 1732, Goldbach quickly rose to a commanding position. Under the presidency of Baron Johann-Albrecht Korf, he was first designated corresponding secretary (1732) and later named a *Kollegialrat* and, together with J. D. Schuhmacher, was charged with the administration of the Academy (1737). At the same time he rose steadily in court and government circles. The two roles began to conflict seriously in 1740, when Goldbach requested release from administrative duties at the Academy; and his promotion to *Staatsrat* in the Ministry of Foreign Affairs in 1742 ended his ties to the Imperial Academy. In 1744 his new position was confirmed with a raise in salary and (in 1746) a grant of land; in 1760 he attained the high rank of privy councilor at 3,000 rubles annually. That same year he set down guidelines for the education of the royal children that served as a model during the next century.

Coupled with a vast erudition that equally well addressed mathematics and science or philology and archaeology, and with a superb command of Latin style and equal fluency in German and French, Goldbach's polished manners and cosmopolitan circle of friends and acquaintances assured his success in an elite society struggling to emulate its western neighbors. But this very erudition and political success prevented Goldbach's obvious talent in mathematics from attaining its full promise. Unable or unwilling to concentrate his efforts, he dabbled in mathematics, achieving nothing of lasting value but stimulating others through his flashes of insight.

Goldbach's mathematical education set the pattern for his episodic career. Rather than engaging in systematic reading and study, he apparently learned his mathematics in bits and pieces from the various people he met, with the result that later he frequently repeated results already achieved or was unable to take full advantage of his insights. As he himself related in a letter to Daniel Bernoulli, he first encountered the subject of infinite series while talking to Nikolaus I Bernoulli at Oxford in 1712. Unable to understand a treatise by Jakob I Bernoulli on the subject, loaned to him by Nikolaus, he dropped the matter until 1717, when he read Leibniz's article on the quadrature of the circle in the *Acta eruditorum.* His reawakened interest led to his own article "Specimen methodi ad summas serierum," which appeared in the *Acta* in 1720. Only afterward did Goldbach discover that the substance of his article formed part of Jakob I's *Ars conjectandi,* published in 1713. In his article "De divisione curvarum . . ." Goldbach frankly admitted that Johann I Bernoulli had already solved the problem in question but that he could not remember the solution and so was deriving it again. Often Goldbach's mathematical knowledge showed surprising bare spots. Impressed by his solution of several cases of the Riccati equation (in "De casibus quibus integrari potest aequatio differentialis . . ." and "Methodus integrandi aequationis differentialis . . ." and in correspondence),[1] Daniel Bernoulli encouraged him to extend his results to exponential functions. Goldbach replied that he knew nothing about exponential functions and did not want to give the impression that he did.

Of Goldbach's other published articles, the two on infinite series—"De transformatione serierum" and "De terminis generalibus serierum"—and the one on the theory of equations, "Criteria quaedam aequationum . . .," show the greatest originality. "De transformatione serierum," read to the Imperial Academy in 1725, contains a technique for transforming one series, *A,* into another series, *B,* having the same sum, through term-by-term addition of A to, or subtraction of A from, a series, C, of which the sum is zero. Adjustment of the technique leads to a similar transformation through multiplication of the given series by a series of which the sum is one. In reply to objections that the multiplicative method may involve a divergent series as unit multiplier,[2] Goldbach defended the use of such a series provided that it leads to a convergent result. "De terminis generalibus serierum," read in 1728, continues the work begun in "Specimen methodi ad summas serierum" (1720) by addressing the problem of determining the "general term" of any sequence;[3] that is, it seeks a function (either explicit or finitely recursive) that yields the nth term of the sequence for a given n. Goldbach shows that the general term can always be expressed as an infinite series and that the problem therefore reduces to one of finding a general formula for the sum of that series. The general term of an infinite sequence proves useful, he argues, both for interpolation of missing terms and for the determination of terms for noninteger indices. Although Goldbach and Daniel Bernoulli corresponded on the specific problem of determining the general term of the sequence $\{n!\}$, neither could offer a solution (Euler later provided one).

In the article "Criteria quaedam aequationum quarum nulla radix rationalis est" Goldbach begins from results contained in "Excerpta a litteris C. G. ad * * * Regiomonte datis" and applies further some of the number-theoretical results worked out in correspondence with Euler to obtain a technique for testing quickly whether an algebraic equation has a rational root. For equations of the form $x^n = P(x)$, where P is an algebraic polynomial of degree $n - 1$ or less, the technique rests basically on determining all integers m for which P can be expressed in the form $mxR(x) + r$ and then ascertaining whether r is an nth-degree residue *modulo m*. If no such residue exists, the equation in question has no rational root.

If, in the realm of analysis, Goldbach's native talent could not substitute for thorough training in the subject, that talent did come into full play in his correspondence with Euler on number theory, a field then still at a rudimentary stage of development. Here Goldbach could be provocative on a fundamental level, as "Demonstratio theorematis Fermatiani . . ." and "Criteria quaedam aequationum quarum nulla radix rationalis est" show. Calling attention in his correspondence to Pierre de Fermat's assertion that all numbers of the form $2^{2^n} + 1$ are prime, he stimulated Euler's disproof for the case $n = 5$ (Euler's memoir in fact immediately follows Goldbach's "Criteria . . ."). Not all of his suggestions led to such positive results. In 1742 Goldbach conjectured that all even numbers may be expressed as the sum of two primes (taking 1 as a prime where necessary). Euler agreed with the assertion but could offer no proof, nor has any proof of "Goldbach's conjecture" yet been found. Goldbach also stated that every odd number may be expressed as the sum of three primes; in the form given it by Edward Waring (which excludes 1 as a prime) this assertion also remains an unproved conjecture. The above are only the outstanding results of the prolix correspondence with Euler on number theory.[4] That correspondence as a whole marks Goldbach as one of the few men of his day who understood the implications of Fermat's new approach to the subject.

NOTES

1. The solution includes the full conditions for the integrability of binomial differentials usually credited to Euler. See Youschkevich, *Istoria matematiki v Rossii,* p. 96.
2. I.e., the unit multiplier may not share the same domain of convergence as the resultant series.
3. Goldbach uses the same Latin term, *series,* to denote both series and sequences.
4. For details, consult Leonard E. Dickson, *History of the Theory of Numbers,* 2nd ed. (New York, 1952), I and II, *passim.*

BIBLIOGRAPHY

I. ORIGINAL WORKS. Goldbach's writings include "Temperamentum musicum universale," in *Acta eruditorum,* **36** (1717), 114–115; "Excerpta a litteris C[hristiani]. G[oldbachi]. ad * * * Regiomonte datis," in *Actorum eruditorum supplementum,* **6** (1718), 471–472; "Specimen methodi ad summas serierum," in *Acta eruditorum,* **39** (1720), 27–31; "Demonstratio theorematis Fermatiani, nullum numerum triangularem praeter 1 esse quadrato-quadratum," in *Actorum eruditorum supplementum,* **8** (1724), 483–484; "De casibus quibus integrari potest aequatio differentialis $ax^m dx + byx^p dx + cy^2 dx = dy$ observationes quaedam," in *Commentarii Academiae scientiarum imperialis Petropolitanae,* **1** (1728), 185–197; "Methodus integrandi aequationis differentialis $aydx + bx^n dx + cx^{n-1}dx + ex^{n-2}dx = dy$ ubi n sit numerus integer positivus," *ibid.,* 207–209; "De transformatione serierum," *ibid.,* **2** (1729), 30–34; "De divisione curvarum in partes quotcunque quarum subtensae sint in data progressione," *ibid.,* 174–179; "De terminis generalibus serierum," *ibid.,* **3** (1732), 164–173; and "Criteria quaedam aequationum quarum nulla radix rationalis est," *ibid,* **6** (1738), 98–102.

For Goldbach's correspondence with Nikolaus II and Daniel Bernoulli and Leonhard Euler, see Paul-Henri Fuss, *Correspondance mathématique et physique de quelques célèbres géomètres du XVIIème siècle,* 2 vols. (St. Petersburg, 1843); for a more recent ed. of part of that correspondence, see *Leonhard Euler und Christian Goldbach, Briefwechsel, 1729–1764,* edited with introduction by A. P. Juškevič [Youschkevich] and E. Winter (Berlin, 1965).

II. Secondary Literature. Piotr P. Pekarskii, *Istoria imperatorskoi akademii nauk v Peterburge*, I (St. Petersburg, 1870), 155–172, contains the most complete biography of Goldbach and quotes heavily from his nonmathematical correspondence and papers now in the State Archives, Moscow. A. P. Youschkevich includes a fairly complete account of Goldbach's mathematical work in his *Istoria matematiki v Rossii* (Moscow, 1968), pp. 92–97. See also the eds. cited above and the works cited in the notes.

Michael S. Mahoney

GOLDBERGER, JOSEPH (*b.* Girált, Hungary, 16 July 1874; *d.* Washington, D.C., 17 January 1929), *epidemiology.*

The son of poor Jewish immigrants, Goldberger was brought to the United States at the age of six by his parents, Samuel and Sarah Gutman Goldberger, who settled on New York's Lower East Side. He attended the city's public schools and entered the College of the City of New York in 1890 as an engineering student. In 1892 his career plans changed, and Goldberger became a student at the Bellevue Hospital Medical School, graduating second in his class three years later. After placing first on the highly competitive Bellevue internship examination, he spent eighteen months at the hospital as intern and house physician. Following two unhappy years of private practice in Wilkes-Barre, Pennsylvania (1897–1899), he took and passed the examination for an assistant surgeon's post in the U.S. Public Health Service. Appointed in 1899, he remained in the Public Health Service until his death.

Public health was then dominated by the infectious diseases; and during the next fifteen years Goldberger received intensive on-the-job training in classic epidemiology, beginning with a traditional apprenticeship as quarantine physician. When not on field assignments, he accumulated valuable experience in parasitology and bacteriology at the Public Health Service's Hygienic Laboratory. By 1910 Goldberger played an increasingly responsible role in field investigations of yellow fever, typhus, and dengue—as well as other, less dramatic, ills. During these journeyman years he became successively a victim of yellow fever, dengue, and typhus. In the course of his investigations he acquired a reputation in the Public Health Service as one of its most gifted epidemiologists. Goldberger also developed a familiarity with conditions in the southern United States and—in his typhus work—with Mexico as well.

During these years Goldberger made several important epidemiological contributions. Perhaps most significant was his demonstration, with J. F. Anderson, that measles is transmissible to monkeys by a filter-passing virus and that the virus is present in buccal and nasal secretions. In his typhus studies, also in collaboration with Anderson, Goldberger was able to show that head as well as body lice could act as vectors and that "Brill's disease," described in New York City, was actually typhus. In another, less significant but impressively elegant, field investigation, he demonstrated the role of a straw mite in causing a dermatological ailment.

While in the midst of directing a detailed study of diphtheria in Detroit in the winter of 1913–1914, Goldberger was requested by Surgeon-General Rupert Blue to undertake the direction of an expanded antipellagra program. Work on this disease was, with one or two brief diversions, to fill the rest of Goldberger's life.

Essentially unknown to American clinicians before 1900, pellagra had seemingly spread rapidly during the century's first decade. Its unpleasant symptoms, its novelty, and its rapid increase in an era proud of its public health accomplishments tended to focus both lay and medical attention on this new and terrifying disease. As early as 1909 the Public Health Service established a special committee on pellagra. Although its most dramatic incidence was in certain southern orphanages, insane asylums, and cotton-mill villages, few areas in the South were completely free of the disease. Southern senators and representatives were instrumental in passing a special appropriation to underwrite the extended pellagra study which Goldberger was chosen to direct.

Traditional explanations of the disease, long familiar to physicians in Italy and other Mediterranean countries, centered on the role of a diet based largely upon corn. This theory—in the form that spoiled corn somehow provided an appropriate substrate for the growth of a toxin-producing microorganism—dominated the conjectures of physicians in the generation before 1910. But by 1914 medical opinion had shifted toward a belief that the disease was infectious—that pellagra was caused by some as yet undiscovered microorganism (possibly a protozoon spread by an insect vector).

A few writers, most notably the biochemist Casimir Funk, had suggested that pellagra might be the consequence of an inadequate or unbalanced diet. The idea was hardly novel in itself. Clinicians had known empirically for many years of the role of diet in the etiology of scurvy, beri beri, and possibly rickets as well. F. G. Hopkins' and E. Willcocks' demonstration in 1906 of the pathological effects of specific amino acid deficiencies was well known to knowledgeable American workers; only a year or so before Goldberger began his pellagra work, two American laboratories had almost simultaneously discovered the presence of an accessory food substance in butterfat (vitamin A).

Goldberger decided, almost as soon as he had been put to work on the problem, that pellagra was a consequence of improper diet. (The well-attested immunity of staff and administrators at pellagra-ridden asylums and orphanages seems to have been the most significant factor in determining his conviction; it has been pointed out that such immunity would have been difficult for a survivor of typhus and yellow fever to have ignored.) Goldberger then proceeded with great care and ingenuity to prove his original intuition. In three major steps he succeeded by 1916 in marshaling extremely strong evidence for his position. By supplementing diets in particular institutional populations, Goldberger almost completely eliminated the disease. In a critical experiment, moreover, he was able to induce symptoms of pellagra in five of eleven Mississippi prison-farm volunteers by providing them with an abundant but protein-deficient diet. (The other prisoners served as a control group.) In a final and almost dismayingly heroic experiment Goldberger and co-workers were unable to produce symptoms of pellagra in themselves through ingestion and injection of excreta, vomitus, nasal secretions, and material from the skin lesions of pellagrins.

By 1917 Goldberger had convinced America's medical elite of the correctness of his views. Indeed, as early as November 1915 the Public Health Service had issued a press release reporting the Mississippi prison-farm experiment and urging that pellagra could be prevented by an appropriate diet; yet throughout the 1920's many practicing physicians, especially in the American South, were unwilling to accept diet as a more than predisposing cause of pellagra. Chronic resentment toward the East and the well-financed Public Health Service seems to have contributed to this incredulity.

In the decade after World War I, Goldberger turned his efforts toward the identification of the constituent or constituents lacking in a pellagra-producing diet; it seemed to him most likely that the substance he sought was some amino acid component of such protective foods as meat and yeast. Influenced by earlier work on protein chemistry, he experimented with the use of particular amino acids, including even tryptophan, in experimental therapeutic trials. It is significant that Goldberger's efforts were guided not only by the biochemist's desire to isolate a particular substance or substances but also by the pragmatic epidemiologist's desire to find an inexpensive and readily available food which might prove effective in preventing the disease.

The most striking aspect of Goldberger's antipellagra work was its flexibility and sensitivity to social and economic context. Goldberger and his co-workers, most prominently statistician and economist Edgar Sydenstricker, exhaustively studied conditions in a number of self-contained mill villages, in several of which the incidence of pellagra was atypically high. They explored every environmental factor which might shape the daily life of the villagers; diet, they assumed, was a function both of custom and of economics. For example, mill communities in diversified farming areas without urban markets or good transportation would naturally have a more varied food supply than villages in cotton-growing areas with ready access to railroads and roads, facilities which would tend to siphon off none-too-abundant truck crops and fresh meats to towns and cities. In the scale and complexity of their work, in their dependence on team techniques and interdisciplinary studies, Goldberger and his co-workers were forerunners of a new idiom in the social approach to disease, one appropriate to the problems and techniques of the twentieth century.

On 19 April 1906 Goldberger married Mary Humphreys Farrar, the daughter of a prominent New Orleans family; they had four children. With a salary never adequate for comfort and a father gone for long periods on field investigations, the Goldbergers' domestic life was often troubled. Goldberger died of cancer on 17 January 1929.

BIBLIOGRAPHY

A well-selected collection of Goldberger's most important papers has been reprinted with a brief intro.: *Goldberger on Pellagra,* edited, with intro., by Milton Terris (Baton Rouge, La., 1964). The most important source for Goldberger's life and work is his papers, deposited at the Southern Historical Collection, University of North Carolina Library, Chapel Hill. The collection contains many letters exchanged between Goldberger and his wife while he was on assignments in the field. The General Subject File of the U.S. Public Health Service, RG 90, boxes 150–155 in the National Archives, are devoted to the Service's pellagra work and provide a detailed record of Goldberger's place in their antipellagra campaign.

There is a full-length, popular biography: Robert P. Parsons, *Trail to Light. A Biography of Joseph Goldberger* (Indianapolis–New York, 1943); although largely uncritical, it does utilize the Goldberger papers extensively. See also Solomon R. Kagan, "Joseph Goldberger," in *Medical Life,* **40** (1933), 434–445; W. H. Sebrell, "Joseph Goldberger (July 16, 1874–January 17, 1929)," in *Journal of Nutrition,* **55** (1955), 3–12; James M. Phalen, "Joseph Goldberger," in *Dictionary of American Biography,* VII

(New York, 1931), 363–364. For Goldberger's pellagra work in perspective, see E. V. McCollum, *A History of Nutrition. The Sequence of Ideas in Nutrition Investigations* (Boston, 1957), pp. 296–317. For a clear presentation of the social assumptions which Goldberger held but never formally articulated, see Edgar Sydenstricker, *Health and Environment* (New York–London, 1933).

CHARLES ROSENBERG

GOLDSCHMIDT, RICHARD BENEDICT (*b.* Frankfurt am Main, Germany, 12 April 1878; *d.* Berkeley, California, 24 April 1958), *zoology, general biology.*

Goldschmidt belonged to a very old German-Jewish family that had included scientists, artists, bankers, and industrialists. His father managed a coffeehouse combined with a wine trade and a confectionery. The young Goldschmidt, who had a wide circle of friends, lived in a well-to-do milieu. He attended the Gymnasium in Frankfurt and planned from the first year of secondary school to study the natural sciences: his native city possessed the famous Senckenberg Museum, a powerful attraction; and his teacher F. C. Noll was a zoologist.

Goldschmidt entered the University of Heidelberg in 1896, and among his professors were the great Otto Bütschli and Karl Gegenbaur. In 1898 he continued his studies at the University of Munich, where Richard Hertwig was teaching. In 1902, at Heidelberg, he defended his thesis on the maturation, fertilization, and embryonic development of the worm *Polystomum integerrimum.* A year later Goldschmidt became Hertwig's assistant and in 1904, a *Privatdozent;* he remained at Munich until 1913. In that year Theodor Boveri and Carl Correns organized the Kaiser Wilhelm Institute for Biology in Berlin; Goldschmidt was appointed director of the genetics department, a post that he was to hold until 1935.

Having received a grant from the Club Autour du Monde Goldschmidt went to Japan in order to continue his research. When World War I broke out he was in Honolulu and went from there to San Francisco. He was detained in the United States, where he worked at various universities. In 1917 he was placed in an internment camp and finally was repatriated to Germany. In 1935, when conditions for Jewish scientists had become impossible under the Nazi regime, Goldschmidt decided to leave Germany. He received offers from England and Turkey, but he accepted a professorship at the University of California and left for America in July 1936. He began a new life in Berkeley, where he remained until his death. He rapidly organized a laboratory and formed a group of students and friends.

A zoologist, biologist, and geneticist of exceptional ability, an original thinker, a great traveler, and an indefatigable worker, Goldschmidt produced more than 250 memoirs and articles and about twenty books; and it is difficult to present a comprehensive view of his total output. Very broad general knowledge combined with great specialization enabled him to interpret new facts and to study individual problems thoroughly. Three orientations emerge quite clearly. He was interested at first in morphological problems and in the cytology, fertilization, meiosis, histology, comparative anatomy, and embryology of the trematodes, nematodes (*Ascaris*), and the Acrania. From the time of his appointment at Munich he was concerned with many students who were preparing dissertations. In 1906 he provided them with a vehicle for publication by founding a new journal, *Archiv für Zellforschung.*

During the same period Goldschmidt undertook a series of researches on moths of the genus *Lymantria.* The work lasted for twenty-five years. He was interested in a problem of microevolution: industrial melanism. Through recognizing that the melanic mutant possesses a selective advantage, he became one of the pioneers of population genetics. Goldschmidt experimented on the genetics of sex determination from 1911 to 1920 and pointed out the existence of intersexuality (a term coined in 1915), which he distinguished from gynandromorphism. He succeeded in obtaining at will all the degrees of intersexuality, up to a complete inversion of the genetic sex into the opposite sex. To account for these appearances, he constructed a coherent theory in which a quantitative balance intervenes between the male and female sex factors.

Since the *Lymantria* also presented enormous geographic variation, Goldschmidt undertook (1918–1933) an analysis of the genetics of geographic variation. He accepted the neo-Darwinian proposal that a geographic race represents a nascent species, but the numerous crossings carried out among geographic races from all parts of the world modified his opinion. While on a visit in Ithaca, New York (1933), Goldschmidt realized that geographic variation entails only a microevolution in the species and that it could not be the source of true evolution. He postulated the existence of macromutants, produced by alteration of the early embryonic processes; these he called "hopeful monsters." In 1940 he pursued his critique of neo-Darwinian conceptions and argued for the existence of macroevolution carried out by means of macromutations.

The *Lymantria* became the subject of a new series of investigations on the theory of the gene. As early as 1916 Goldschmidt had fashioned a physiological

GOLDSCHMIDT

theory of heredity (one gene, one enzyme). He published it only in 1920 in a book which marks the beginning of physiological genetics. According to this theory it should be possible, by modifying the speeds of the chains of reactions, to produce insects among which the nonhereditary phenotype copies the phenotype of the mutations; these are the phenocopies (1935). With his students Goldschmidt was able to produce varied phenocopies. At this time he left the *Lymantria,* which had been widely studied, and selected the *Drosophila* for examination.

With this change in material the third major period of research began. Goldschmidt studied the physiological genetics of the *Drosophila* and established that in the vestigial series the genetically controlled clipping of the wings can be influenced by the introduction of dominance modifiers. He then proposed an unorthodox theory concerning the nature of the gene, rejecting its corpuscularity (1938). This position aroused violent reactions, but in 1951 Goldschmidt opened the symposium on the gene at Cold Spring Harbor, New York, with an exposition of his ideas. His last works concerned the podoptera effect; the homoeotic mutants of *Drosophila melanogaster,* Podoptera and Tetraltera, hold great morphological, genetic, and evolutionary interest.

An amateur of the history of science, Goldschmidt wrote biographies of biologists he had known throughout the world. In addition, he wrote popular articles and books on science. Goldschmidt had, in addition, refined and discriminating taste; he particularly loved music and oriental art.

BIBLIOGRAPHY

I. Original Works. Goldschmidt's articles include the following: "Zur Entwicklungsgeschichte der Echinococcusköpfchen," in *Zoologische Jahrbücher,* Anatomie, **13** (1900), 467–494; "Untersuchungen über die Eireifung, Befruchtung und Zelltheilung bei *Polystomum integerrimum,*" in *Zeitschrift für wissenschaftliche Zoologie,* **71** (1902), 397–444; "Der Chromidialapparat lebhaftfunktionierender Gewebzellen," in *Zoologische Jahrbücher,* Anatomie, **21** (1904), 1–100; "Amphioxides," in *Wissenschaftliche Ergebnisse der Deutschen Tiefsee-Expedition auf dem Dampfer "Valdivia" 1898–1899,* **12** (1905), 1–92; "Lebensgeschichte der Mastigamöben *Mastigella vitrea* n. sp. und *Mastigina setosa* n. sp.," in *Archiv für Protistenkunde,* supp. **1** (1907), 83–168; "Das Nervensystem von *Ascaris lumbricoides* und *megalocephala,*" in *Zeitschrift für wissenschaftliche Zoologie,* **90** (1908), 73–136, and **92** (1909), 306–357, repr. in *Festschrift R. Hertwig,* II (Jena, 1910), 254–354; "Die cytologische Untersuchungen über Vererbung und Bestimmung des Geschlechtes," in *Die Vererbung und Bestimmung des Geschlechtes* (Berlin, 1913), pp. 73–149; "A Preliminary Report on Some Genetic Experiments Concerning Evolution," in *American Naturalist,* **52** (1918), 28–50; "Untersuchungen über Intersexualität," in *Zeitschrift für induktive Abstammungs- und Vererbungslehre,* **23** (1920), 1–199; **29** (1922), 145–185; **31** (1923), 100–133; **49** (1929), 168–242; **56** (1930), 275–301; **67** (1934), 1–40; "Untersuchungen zur Genetik der geographischen Variation," in *Archiv für Entwicklungsmechanik der Organismen,* **101** (1924), 92–337; **116** (1929), 136–201; **126** (1932), 277–324, 591–612, 674–768; **130** (1933), 266–339, 562–615; "*Lymantria,*" in *Bibliotheca genetica,* **11** (1934), 1–185; "The Time Law of Intersexuality," in *Genetica,* **20** (1938), 1–50; "The Structure of Podoptera, a Homoeotic Mutant of *Drosophila melanogaster,*" in *Journal of Morphology,* **77** (1945), 71–103; "Ecotype, Ecospecies and Macroevolution," in *Experientia,* **4** (1948), 465–472; "Fifty Years of Genetics," in *American Naturalist,* **84** (1950), 313–340; "The Maternal Effect in the Production of the Beaded-Minute Intersexes in *Drosophila melanogaster,*" in *Journal of Experimental Zoology,* **117** (1951), 75–110; "The Podoptera Effect in *Drosophila melanogaster,*" in *University of California Publications in Zoology,* **55** (1951), 67–294, written with A. Hannah and L. K. Piternick; "Homoeotic Mutants and Evolution," in *Acta biotheoretica,* **10** (1952), 87–104; "Heredity Within a Sex Controlled Structure of *Drosophila,*" in *Journal of Experimental Zoology,* **122** (1953), 53–96; "Materials for the Study of Dominant Personality Traits," in *Folia hereditaria et pathologica,* **2** (1953), 267–295; "The Genetic Background of Chemically Induced Phenocopies in *Drosophila,*" in *Journal of Experimental Zoology,* **135** (1957), 127–202, and **136** (1957), 201–228, written with L. K. Piternick.

His books include *Zoologisches Taschenbuch für Studierende* (Leipzig, 1907; 6th ed., 1912), written with E. Selenka; *Einführung in die Vererbungswissenschaft* (Berlin, 1911; 5th ed., 1928); *Die quantitativen Grundlagen von Vererbung und Artbildung* (Berlin, 1920); *Mechanismus und Physiologie der Geschlechtsbestimmung* (Berlin, 1920); *Der Mendelismus* (Berlin, 1920); *Physiologische Theorie der Vererbung* (Berlin, 1927); *Die Lehre von der Vererbung* (Berlin, 1927; 4th ed., 1953); *Les problèmes de la sexualité* (Paris, 1932); *Physiological Genetics* (New York, 1938); *The Material Basis of Evolution* (New Haven, Conn., 1940); *Understanding Heredity: An Introduction to Genetics* (New York, 1952); *Theoretical Genetics* (Berkeley, Calif., 1955); *Portraits From Memory: Recollections of a Zoologist* (Seattle, Wash., 1956); and *In and Out of the Ivory Tower. The Autobiography of Richard B. Goldschmidt* (Seattle, Wash., 1960), with twenty-seven plates and a complete bibliography.

II. Secondary Literature. On Goldschmidt or his work, see A. Kühn, "Zum 70. Geburtstag Richard Goldschmidt am 12. April 1948," in *Experientia,* **4** (1948), 239–240; "R. B. Goldschmidt 1878–1958. Zoologo, geneticista, evolucionista," in *Revista de la Sociedad mexicana de historia natural,* **20** (1959), 185–193, with photo.; and a special vol. devoted to him of *Portugaliae acta biologica,* ser. A (1949–1951), published to honor his seventieth birthday: it contains a biography by

A. Quintanilha and twenty-seven memoirs contributed by European and American students and friends.

ANDRÉE TÉTRY

GOLDSCHMIDT, VICTOR (*b.* Mainz, Germany, 10 February 1853; *d.* Salzburg, Austria, 8 May 1933), *crystallography, harmonics.*

Born to a well-to-do family, Goldschmidt attended the Gymnasium in Mainz. He then entered the Freiberg Bergakademie and, after graduating, stayed on as an instructor in metallurgy, assaying, and blowpipe analysis under H. T. Richter (1875–1878). For graduate and research work he went to the universities of Munich, Prague, and Heidelberg; at the latter he obtained his Ph.D. under K. H. F. Rosenbusch in 1880, with a dissertation entitled "Ueber Verwendbarkeit einer Kaliumquecksilberjodidlösung bei mineralogischen und petrographischen Untersuchungen"; it concerned the determination of the specific gravity of minerals, a topic to which he returned in later papers.

From 1882 to 1887 Goldschmidt was at the University of Vienna; and these years, especially the work with Aristedes Brezina, appear to have determined his lifework. From Vienna he returned to Heidelberg, where in February 1888 he submitted "Ueber Projektion und graphische Kristallberechnung" as a *Habilitationsschrift* for a post in Rosenbusch's institute.

Also in 1888 Goldschmidt married Leontine von Portheim and settled in Heidelberg. His wife brought as a dowry a substantial part of the wealth which enabled him to work with little help from the university; she was also a very understanding companion who provided a homelike atmosphere for many of his co-workers and students. Except for a long journey to the Far East in 1894–1895 he spent almost all of his time in Heidelberg. In 1893 Goldschmidt was named associate professor, and somewhat later he became an honorary full professor. In 1916 he and his wife established the Eduard und Josefine von Portheim Stiftung, of which the Victor-Goldschmidt-Institut für Kristallforschung was a part.

Together with E. S. Fyodorov in St. Petersburg and Paul von Groth in Munich, Goldschmidt was the founder of modern crystallography. Until then that science's methods and mode of thought adhered rigidly to a purely geometric vision of crystals, with little or no interest in the physicochemical meaning of the wealth of geometric observations. The work of these three men opened the way and created the methods for Max von Laue's discovery of X-ray diffraction and for the discovery of the principles of crystal chemistry by Aleksandr Fersman, Victor Moritz, Goldschmidt, and Paul Niggli.

Goldschmidt's contribution centered mainly on a complete indexing and recording of mineral crystal forms, the final aim being to link these external variations of form to the physicochemical variations of composition and of physicochemical factors present during formation. He realized the vastness of the task and was pleased that he accomplished the mapping of most of the crystal forms available during his lifetime. The second *sine qua non* was his great skill in teaching and the enthusiasm he created in his students. Many students from various countries worked with him, including Fersman, William Nicol, Charles Palache, Friedrich Kolbeck, M. A. Peacock, and Ludwig Milch.

Goldschmidt's outstanding works form a sort of trilogy: *Index der Kristallformen der Mineralien* (1886–1891), *Kristallographische Winkeltabellen* (1897), and *Atlas der Kristallformen* (1913–1923). These works are a foundation of crystallography and are essential to much crystallographic work even today. They and the more than 100 papers on individual crystal forms or groups required the improvement of traditional methods, which were entirely inadequate, and the creation of new ones. Consequently, part of Goldschmidt's contribution to crystallography consisted of improvement of existing instruments and invention of new ones. The most important was the construction of the two-circle goniometer. His work required a great number of crystal models and much cutting and oriented polishing. In this work he was assisted by the skilled mechanic Stoe. Goldschmidt wrote many instruction booklets on the new methods and instruments. For about forty years—until he was past seventy-five—he taught courses in measurement and calculation of crystals, determinative mineralogy, and blowpipe analysis.

Other methods improved or initiated by Goldschmidt are the Goldschmidt symbols, the gnomonic projection, use of the position angles ϕ and ρ (borrowed from astronomy) to characterize crystal forms, the recognition of the importance of zones, and the mathematical periodicity of zone symbols from 0 to ∞ to a maximum number in the *Normalreihe* III:

$$N_3 = 0, 1/3, 1/2, 2/3, 1, 3/2, 2, 3, \infty.$$

Goldschmidt defined the task of crystallography in the first volume of the *Index* (1886) and made the definition the program for his own work in crystallography: "The main purpose of crystallography is to explore the molecular structures of solid substances and to determine the intensity of molecular forces and their manner of operation." Later in the *Index* he wrote: "Every surface is crystallographically possible, the perpendicular is the direction of molecular attraction." Thus, Goldschmidt hoped to gain insight into the atomic or molecular bond relations within the lattice, through the crystal form as the product of bond strength and bond direction. For his time this was most certainly an ingenious approach. As soon as X rays were applied to bond relations, the results confirmed most of Goldschmidt's findings.

But Goldschmidt was not satisfied with the geometric approach alone. He wanted to test the results by trying out the forces opposed to those active in crystal growth: he etched and dissolved crystals and compared the results. The statistical and geometric part of this work was excellent proof for his goniometrical work. But when attempting to interpret the resulting micromorphology dynamically, he made the mistake of applying analogies from erosion on the earth's surface. This revealed a weakness in his thinking: a rock is an aggregate and is subject to statistical laws different from those of the crystal lattice. Interest in intergrowth and related problems had not yet arisen. If it had—and if modern knowledge of phases and modern statistics had been available—an association of Goldschmidt and Rosenbusch would have been immensely fruitful. But such knowledge was not available; and, in addition, these men had very different personalities which would not allow a close friendship and cooperation.

Goldschmidt's work on crystal forms and on the forces active in the dissolution of crystals led him to extensive investigations of twinning, surface symmetries, accessories and vicinals, oblique surfaces, and multiple twinning; and the foundations were laid for the understanding of epitaxial overgrowth as a phenomenon related to unmixing or exsolution.

Among the monographs on individual crystal forms, the one on diamond written with Fersman is worthy of special mention. Fersman, who studied for almost two years with Goldschmidt, wrote in his obituary of the latter: "The three works, *Index, Winkeltabellen,* and *Atlas,* are henceforth basic materials for the study of crystals. Without them it is impossible to do crystallographic work. They translate the work of a complete century into a new language . . . the language of new, great ideas in . . . contemporary crystal chemistry. . . ."

Goldschmidt could not split himself into a scientific and a general personality; both parts of his life had to be a unit originating from the same source. Therefore his crystallographic thought—at least its pattern—extended, for him, without a break into the other domains of his personality: the aesthetic, the ethical, and perhaps the religious. Consequently he found excellent correspondence of the harmonic series of crystals with that in music, in fine arts, and with traits of human life in general. Attempts at such integrations were Goldschmidt's favorite philosophic themes and formed the subjects of some of his articles and books: *Ueber Harmonie und Complication* (1901), "Ueber harmonische Analyse von Musikstücken" (*Annalen der Naturphilosophie,* **3** [1904]), "Ueber Harmonie im Weltraum" (*ibid.,* **5**), "Beiträge zur Harmonielehre" (*ibid.,* **13** [1917]), and "Materialien zur Musiklehre" (*Heidelberger Akten der von-Portheim-Stiftung,* nos. 5, 8, 9, 11, 14, 15 [1923–1925]). These works showed that for Goldschmidt harmonic properties and symmetries occurred in all domains of human endeavor as a sort of pantheistic or mystic substratum. In the terms of his contemporary, C. G. Jung, these harmonic series and their ascending and descending differentiations ("complications") were archetypal properties of life.

BIBLIOGRAPHY

I. Original Works. Himmel's bibliography (see below) lists 180 articles or books, but this figure does not include numerous smaller articles and reviews. Goldschmidt's major works are *Index der Kristallformen der Mineralien,* 3 vols. (Berlin, 1886–1891); *Ueber Projektion und graphische Kristallberechnung* (Berlin, 1887); *Kristallographische Winkeltabellen* (Berlin, 1897); *Ueber Harmonie und Complication* (Berlin, 1901); *Der Diamant, eine Studie* (Heidelberg, 1911), written with A. Fersman; *Atlas der Kristallformen,* 9 vols. (Heidelberg, 1913–1923); and *Farben in der Kunst* (Heidelberg, 1919). In addition, Goldschmidt was founder of *Beiträge zur Krystallographie und Mineralogie,* of which he was editor from 1914 to 1926, and of the *Heidelberger Akten der von-Portheim-Stiftung* (1922).

II. Secondary Literature. See A. E. Fersman, "Victor Goldschmidt (10. February 1853 bis 8. Mai 1933)," in *Fortschritte der Mineralogie,* **37,** no. 2 (1959), 207–212, originally in *Reports of the Mineralogical Society of the USSR,* **87,** no. 6 (1958), 677; F. Herrmann, "Victor Goldschmidt," in *Neue deutsche Biographie,* vol. VI (1964); Hans Himmel, "Victor Goldschmidt zum Gedächtnis," in *Zentralblatt für Mineralogie, Geologie und Paläontologie,* sec. A (1933), 391–398; L. Milch, "Zum 75. Geburtstage von Victor Goldschmidt," in *Festschrift zum 75. Geburtstage von seinen Schülern und Freunden gewidmet* (Heidelberg, 1928); and P. Ramdohr, "Zum 100. Geburtstag von Victor Goldschmidt," in *Ruperto-Carola,* **5,** nos. 9–10 (1953), 160–161.

G. C. Amstutz

GOLDSCHMIDT, VICTOR MORITZ (*b.* Zurich, Switzerland, 27 January 1888; *d.* Oslo, Norway, 20 March 1947), *geochemistry, chemistry, mineralogy.*

Goldschmidt was the only son of the distinguished

GOLDSCHMIDT

physical chemist Heinrich Jacob Goldschmidt, who held professorships at Amsterdam, Heidelberg, and Oslo; his mother was Amelie Köhne. After secondary education at Heidelberg, Goldschmidt matriculated in 1905 at the University of Christiania (now Oslo) to study chemistry, mineralogy, and geology. During this year he obtained Norwegian citizenship. His university work was strongly influenced by W. C. Brøgger, the noted Norwegian petrologist and mineralogist, and by such earth scientists as Paul von Groth at Munich and Friedrich Becke at Vienna, in whose institutes he spent the winter terms of 1908 and 1911. Goldschmidt received the doctorate in 1911. Following two years as an instructor at the University of Christiania, in 1914 he was appointed full professor and director of its mineralogical institute.

Goldschmidt's doctoral thesis, "Die Kontaktmetamorphose im Kristianiagebiet," concerned the factors governing the mineral associations in contact-metamorphic rocks and was based upon samples collected in southern Norway. This investigation led to the mineralogical phase rule, which states that the maximum number of crystalline phases that can coexist in rocks in stable equilibrium is equal to the number of components. Goldschmidt continued these petrological studies on regional metamorphism as the first phase of his scientific career, until the middle of World War I. They culminated in the publication of five large reports with the common title *Geologisch-petrographische Studien im Hochgebirge des südlichen Norwegens,* published between 1912 and 1921.

In 1917 the Norwegian government called upon Goldschmidt to investigate the country's mineral resources, and he became chairman of the Government Commission for Raw Materials and director of the Raw Materials Laboratory. His dedication to these practical problems reflected his concern for the utilization of science for the benefit of society. These commitments involved finding local sources for previously imported chemicals, tasks which led Goldschmidt into the second phase of his scientific career—investigations seeking the factors governing the distribution of chemical species in nature.

The base for this geochemical work evolved from extensive crystallographic studies in the Oslo laboratory made by means of the newly developed X-ray techniques which utilized the discoveries of Max von Laue, W. H. Bragg, and W. L. Bragg. Goldschmidt and his associates worked out the crystal structures of 200 compounds of seventy-five elements to form the background for the elucidation of the laws of geochemical distribution. He was able to produce the first tables of atomic and ionic radii for many of the elements, and he investigated the substitution of one element for another in crystals and established patterns of elemental behavior in such processes. The complex formulas of such minerals as tourmaline and mica could be explained by the maintenance of charge neutrality for the positive and negative ions through substitutions based primarily on size. Goldschmidt related the hardness of crystals to their structures, ionic charges, and interatomic distances. This extensive work in geochemistry and mineralogy was published as the monographs *Geochemische Verteilungsgesetze der Elemente,* I-VIII.

In 1929 Goldschmidt became full professor in the Faculty of Natural Sciences at Göttingen and head of its mineralogical institute. Here he initiated geochemical investigations on germanium, gallium, scandium, beryllium, the noble metals, boron, the alkali metals, selenium, arsenic, chromium, nickel, and zinc. Analyses were performed on both terrestrial materials and extraterrestrial meteorites. A model of the earth was formulated in which elements were accumulated in various geological domains on the bases of their charges and sizes and the polarizabilities of their ions. The siderophilic elements, postulated to concentrate in the metallic liquid core of the earth, include iron, nickel, gold, and germanium. The lithophilic elements are enriched in the outer portions of the earth; silicon, magnesium, calcium, aluminum, and the alkalies are members of this class. A third group encompasses the chalcophilic elements, those which ally themselves to sulfur, such as lead and copper. The atmophilic elements have gaseous forms at the temperatures and pressures encountered in the earth's atmosphere and include the noble gases, nitrogen, oxygen, carbon, and hydrogen. Finally, there are the biophilic species, elements that are preferentially incorporated into organisms; carbon, hydrogen, oxygen, nitrogen, vanadium, calcium, and potassium fall within this group. A rather elegant verification of the first three categories is in Goldschmidt's study of the metallurgical products from the copper industry of the Mansfeld in Germany. Here the sulfide, pig iron, and silicate slags included elements that were predicted from his model of the earth.

Following a series of unpleasant confrontations with the emerging anti-Semitism of the Nazis, Goldschmidt abandoned his Göttingen chair in 1935 and returned to Oslo, where a similar position at the university was immediately offered to him. Here he collated his data on cosmic and terrestrial distributions of chemical elements in the ninth and final publication of the *Verteilungsgesetze* and entered into isotopic geology by considering the significances of the isotopic compositions of elements in minerals. While in Oslo, Goldschmidt reentered industrial work and developed techniques for utilizing Norwegian olivine rock in industrial refractories. The onset of World War II brought additional brushes with the Germans. He escaped concentration camps, although imprisoned several times, and, following periods of hiding, made his way to Sweden and then Great Britain. In the final phases of his scientific career at the Macaulay Institute for Soil Research and at Rothamsted, he applied his previously gained geochemical concepts to soil science. Goldschmidt's manuscripts for the definitive treatise on the science of geochemistry, which he had done so much to found, were edited after his death by A. Muir and were published in 1954.

The adversities and humiliations suffered by Goldschmidt at the hands of the Nazis were met with courage and wit. Under Nazi occupation in Norway and Germany, he carried a capsule of hydrocyanic acid for use as the final evasion of oppression. A university colleague in Oslo once asked Goldschmidt for a similar capsule. He replied, "This poison is for professors of chemistry only. You, as a professor of mechanics, will have to use the rope."

Goldschmidt stands as one of the pioneers in geochemistry who, utilizing the basic properties of matter, gave simple and beautiful explanations of the composition of our environment. He never married, but his students and associates provided him with warm personal friendships. His co-workers, such as Fritz Laves, T. F. W. Barth, and W. Zachariasen, became noted geochemists; and some of his students, including Theodor Ernst, H. Hauptmann, W. von Engelhardt, and C. Peters, became heads of university departments.

BIBLIOGRAPHY

I. ORIGINAL WORKS. The complete list of Goldschmidt's some 200 papers may be found in *Norsk geologisk tidsskrift,* **27** (1949), 143-163. In addition, see his posthumously published *Geochemistry,* Alex Muir, ed. (London, 1954).

II. SECONDARY LITERATURE. On Goldschmidt and his work see J. D. Bernal, "The Goldschmidt Memorial Lecture," in *Journal of the Chemical Society* (1949), pp. 2108-2114; Carl W. Correns, "Victor Moritz Goldschmidt," in *Naturwissenschaften,* **34** (1947), 129-131; and Ivar Oftedal, "Memorial to Victor Moritz Goldschmidt," in *Proceedings. Geological Society of America* (1948), pp. 149-154.

E. D. GOLDBERG

GOLDSTEIN, EUGEN (*b.* Gleiwitz, Upper Silesia [now Gliwice, Poland], 5 September 1850; *d.* Berlin, Germany, 25 December 1930), *physics.*

After attending Ratibor Gymnasium, Goldstein spent a year (1869-1870) at the University of Breslau. He then went on to the University of Berlin, where he worked with Helmholtz, taking his doctorate in 1881. He spent most of his exceptionally long professional career as a physicist at the Potsdam observatory. His first scientific paper was published in 1876, his last over fifty years later.

Almost all of Goldstein's published work was on topics which sprang naturally from his lifelong interest in electrical discharges in moderate to high vacuums. He is now known primarily as the discoverer, in 1886, of "Kanalstrahlen," as he called them—canal rays or positive rays, as they became known in English. He also made significant contributions to the study of cathode rays, which were discovered by Julius Plücker but named by Goldstein. Most of the rest of his work concerned various phenomena occurring in gaseous discharges.

In 1876 Goldstein showed that cathode rays could cast sharp shadows.[1] He was able to demonstrate that they were emitted perpendicularly to the cathode surface, a discovery that made it possible to design concave cathodes to produce concentrated or focused rays, which were useful in a wide range of experiments. But this same discovery cast some doubt on the idea then prevailing among German physicists that the rays consisted of some form of electromagnetic radiation. Further, Goldstein and others showed in 1880 that the rays could be bent by magnetic fields;[2] this discovery also gave aid and comfort to those physicists, predominantly British, who believed that the rays were streams of negative particles.

Sir William Crookes, for example, had suggested that the rays were charged "molecular torrents" rebounding from the cathode. To oppose this view, Goldstein conducted a series of experiments showing that cathode rays emitted light showing little if any Doppler shift and that they could traverse a distance some 150 times the mean free path for molecules at the pressures then being achieved in the discharge tubes.[3]

Over a span of many years Goldstein published several papers on other aspects of cathode rays. He showed (1895-1898) that they could make certain salts change color, that they could be "reflected" diffusely from anodes (1882), and that there was some evidence for electrostatic deflection of parallel beams. However, his "reflection" experiment may have been misleading: the "reflected" rays may well have been soft X rays produced in the anode by the impinging cathode rays (but of course X rays had not yet been discovered). An exceptionally clever experimentalist, Goldstein studied the effects of a wide range of cathode and anode configurations.

In 1886 Goldstein published his discovery of "Kanalstrahlen," rays which emerged from channels or holes in anodes in low-pressure discharge tubes.[4] His student Wilhelm Wien, who later became known primarily as a theoretical physicist, showed that the canal rays could be deflected by electric and magnetic fields, and that they had ratios of positive charge to mass approximately 10,000 times that of cathode rays.[5] Wien did not detect different ratios for different elements. The development of canal-ray apparatus into the important field of mass spectroscopy was, of course, carried out by others, notably J. J. Thomson and F. W. Aston.

Another of Goldstein's students, Johannes Stark, was able to show that light from canal-ray particles showed a Doppler shift.[6] This was the first clear-cut demonstration of an optical Doppler shift in a terrestrial source.

Goldstein continued to publish papers on various canal-ray topics, notably studies of the wavelengths of light emitted by various metals and oxides when they were struck by the rays. He found, for example, that the alkali metals, when hit by the rays, emitted their characteristic bright spectral lines, while they did not do so when hit by cathode rays. He also found that a constriction in a discharge tube could function as a source of positive rays.

In the last two decades of his life Goldstein devoted much attention to anode discharges and to the striations of the positive column in low-pressure discharge tubes. Such tubes present a wealth of beautiful and fascinating phenomena, and Goldstein's experimental virtuosity made it natural for him to pursue such topics. It is ironic that his work in these areas was of secondary importance and now is seldom mentioned in writings in the field, while his early work, and that of his students, was much more fundamental and lasting. But it is perhaps even more ironic that his last paper, published in 1928, reported detection of the synthesis of ammonia in discharge tubes containing various gases.[7] This virtually forgotten work foreshadowed an intriguing and interesting field of research that came to life over thirty years after Goldstein's death.

NOTES

1. *Monatsberichte der Königlichen Akademie der Wissenschaften zu Berlin* (1876), 284.
2. *Wiedemann's Annalen der Physik,* **11** (1880), 850.
3. *Philosophical Magazine,* **10** (1880), 234, originally in *Monatsberichte der Königlichen Akademie der Wissenschaften zu Berlin* (Jan. 1880).
4. "Über eine noch nicht untersuchte Strahlungsform an der Kathode inducirter Entladungen," in *Sitzungsberichte der Königlichen Akademie der Wissenschaften zu Berlin,* **39** (1886), 691.
5. "Deflection of Canal Rays," in *Berlin Physikalische Gesellschaft Verhandlungen,* **17** (1898), 10–12.
6. "Doppler Effect Exhibited by Canal Rays and the Spectrum of Positive Ions," in *Physikalische Zeitschrift,* **6** (1905), 892–897.
7. "Synthesis of Ammonia, Argon as Catalyst," in *Zeitschrift für Physik,* **47** (1928), 274.

BIBLIOGRAPHY

I. Original Works. Most of Goldstein's work was published in such journals as *Wiedemann's Annalen der Physik* and *Zeitschrift für Physik.* Specific references can be found in *Science Abstracts.* A collection of papers was reprinted as no. 231 of Ostwald's Klassiker der Exacten Wissenschaften (Leipzig, 1930).

II. Secondary Literature. As a tribute to Goldstein on his eightieth birthday, Rausch von Traubenberg wrote "Die Bedeutung der Kanalstrahlen für die Entwicklung der Physik," in *Naturwissenschaften,* **18** (5 Sept. 1930), 773–776. See also E. Rüchardt, "Zur Entdeckung der Kanalstrahlen vor fünfzig Jahren," and F. W. Aston, "Kanalstrahlen und Atomphysik," both in *Naturwissenschaften,* **24** (24 July 1936), 465–469. Goldstein's contributions to the understanding of cathode rays are briefly discussed in D. L. Anderson, *The Discovery of the Electron* (Princeton, 1964). A brief obituary note appeared in *Nature,* **127** (1931), 171.

David L. Anderson

GOLGI, CAMILLO (Corteno [now Corteno Golgi], Brescia, Italy, 7 July 1843; Pavia, Italy, 21 January 1926), *histology, pathology.*

Golgi's family was from Pavia; his father Alessandro was a doctor. Golgi read medicine at the University of Pavia, where, together with Giulio Bizzozero and Enrico Sertoli, he studied under Eusebio Oehl, distinguished as the first in Pavia to develop systematically studies of microscopic anatomy and histology.

After obtaining a degree in medicine in 1865, he worked for a short time in the psychiatric clinic directed by Cesare Lombroso, but his main interest was in the histological research he was conducting in the laboratory of experimental pathology directed by Bizzozero.

Golgi's first publications, which appeared between 1868 and 1871, included some works on clinical topics but were mainly devoted to the anatomy and pathological anatomy of the nervous system. In his papers on neurology he described the morphological features of the glial cells and showed the relationships between their prolongations and blood vessels.

In 1871 he gave a private course on clinical microscopy, but in 1872 financial difficulties forced him to interrupt his scientific career temporarily and accept the modest post of principal doctor of the Pio Luogo degli Incurabili at Abbiategrasso. Even there he managed, although with difficulty, to continue his microscopic research on the structure of the nervous system; later he was able to publish the results in important papers.

Having gained a certain degree of fame, he became in 1875 a lecturer in histology at the University of Pavia. In 1879 he obtained the chair of anatomy at the University of Siena, but the following year he returned to Pavia, first as professor of histology and later of general pathology; he continued to teach histology as well until his obligatory retirement in 1918. Around him flourished a group of notable scholars and researchers.

In 1906 he shared the Nobel Prize for medicine or physiology with Santiago Ramón y Cajal, famous also for his studies on the fine anatomy of the nervous system.

Golgi became a senator in 1900 and took an active part in public and university life, especially in Pavia, where he was dean of the Faculty of Medicine and president of the university. He also concerned himself with problems of public health and university administration. A member of numerous scientific societies and academies, Italian and foreign, he had contacts with such personalities as the Swiss anatomist Albert von Koelliker, and the Norwegian explorer and scientist Fridtjof Nansen.

In the course of his long life Golgi penetrated various fields of biology and medicine with equal success, but the areas of research in which he earned the greatest distinction were neuroanatomy (for which work he won the Nobel Prize), cytology, and malariology.

In the second half of the nineteenth century considerable progress was made in the study of histology and microscopic anatomy; until the work of Golgi, however, little headway had been made in the study of the nervous system because of a lack of appropriate techniques; and theories on the function of nerve cells and their extensions were nebulous and conflicting. Golgi invented a completely original method based on the coloration of cells and nerve fibers by means of the prolonged immersion of samples, previously hardened with potassium bichromate or ammonium bichromate, in a 0.5 to 1 percent solution of silver nitrate. This technique brings out clearly the features of the nerve elements. Under controlled conditions, based on the length of the period of hardening in the bichromate, the "black reaction" permits the controlled staining of certain nerve elements (for example, either the nerve fibers with their fine branches, or only the nerve or connective cells) or even only certain parts of one (fibers) or the other (cells), thus allowing a better study of their interrelationships.

From 1873 Golgi published many articles on the results of his systematic observations, using his new technique, on the fine anatomy of the various organs of the nervous system (the gray matter of the brain, the cerebellum, the olfactory lobes, etc.). On the basis of his observations Golgi formulated a theory based on the following fundamental points:

(1) The function of the nerve extensions, or axons, is exclusively one of transmission of nerve impulses.

(2) The function of the protoplasmic extensions, or dendrites, is predominantly trophic, as can be deduced, for example, from their frequent relationships with the pia mater.

(3) There are two types of nerve cells, differing according to the characteristics of the nerve extension of each: nerve cells of the first type are those with an axon that, although serving a more or less large number of lateral fibrils, nevertheless preserves its individuality and continues directly into the cylindraxis of a medullary fiber. Nerve cells of the second type are those with an axon that within a relatively short distance of its origin subdivides within an indeterminate distance, and with no demonstrable spatial limit. The cells of the first type probably have a motive or psychomotive function; those of the second, hypothetically a sensorial or psychosensorial function.

(4) In the gray matter of the nerve centers there is a diffused nerve network of extreme fineness, continuous over the entire nerve substance and made of nerve fibrils finely and thickly interlaced. Golgi would not pronounce dogmatically on the question of whether it was a network in the true sense, made of anastomosed fibrils derived from various nerve elements, or simply interlaced, functionally independent filaments of different origin. Golgi considered the diffused nerve network to be the mediating organ that effectuated connections between various parts of the nervous system or between various functional activities related to that system.

Golgi's hypotheses superseded those formulated in 1872 by Josef von Gerlach but were soon challenged by the contributions made by Ramón y Cajal to the neuron theory.

Some of Golgi's contributions to neuroanatomy deserve mention. He discovered the existence along the length of nerve fibers of numerous special apparatuses that support the myelin (the corneal spires); the existence of special terminal bodies of a sensitive nature in muscle tendons that had never previously been described and the importance of which has been confirmed by recent physiological research; and the critical examination of the theory of brain localizations.

In the field of cytology Golgi was the first to describe, in 1898, the existence in the cytoplasm of the nerve cell of a special small organ, in the shape of a fine and elegant network of anastomosed and interlaced threads. Later Golgi and his co-workers demonstrated that this endocellular structure, called Golgi's internal reticular apparatus, was given special attention by classical cytologists, who recognized its undoubted individuality and suspected its importance in the cellular economy; it is now the object of particular studies, because it is considered of fundamental importance in cytometabolic processes.

The discovery in 1880 of the malaric parasite by C. L. Alphonse Laveran was not immediately accepted but was received at first skeptically and with diffidence. Among Italians the theory of its existence was accepted and developed by Ettore Marchiafava and Angelo Celli, whose research on it achieved (1885) results important to the understanding of the development cycle of the parasite.

Golgi followed for some time, in Rome, the research of Marchiafava and Celli; then in Pavia, between 1885 and 1893, he did important research on malaria, arriving at the verification of the following fundamental facts:

(1) the existence of the cycle of monogamic development of the tertian and quartan forms of malaria;

(2) the existence of specific differences between the parasites of the two forms;

(3) the correspondence of the cyclic development of the malaric parasites with the periodic succession of the fever fits;

(4) the constant relationship of the single fits with the development, maturing, and reproduction of one generation of parasites;

(5) the correspondence of various species or varieties of malaric parasites with the various fundamental classical types of intermittent fever.

From this knowledge Golgi immediately derived results capable of practical application: by the examination of the blood of malaria patients carried out with methods that he suggested, it was possible to diagnose the different forms of the disease and to establish the sequence in the appearance of the fever fits. Furthermore, since the plasmodes display different degrees of sensitivity to quinine according to the stage of their development (the young forms derived immediately from the segmentation or sporulation process are the most sensitive to quinine), the most efficient way to prevent the appearance of the fever fit and progressively extinguish the infection is to give quinine a few hours before the fit, so that it can act on the new generation of the parasite. Also basically important for diagnosis was the observation that the entire nosogenic process of malaric fevers sometimes occurs not in the circulating blood but in the internal organs, so that it is only later that the parasites spread in the blood.

BIBLIOGRAPHY

Golgi's works, which originally appeared in various journals, were collected in *Opera omnia,* 4 vols. (Milan, 1903–1929). A German trans. of his works is *Untersuchungen ueber den feineren Bau des centralen und peripherischen Nervensystems,* G. Fischer, ed. (Jena, 1894).

Golgi's MSS, partly published drawings (some completed by his students), and scientific and personal effects are in the Museo per la Storia dell'Università di Pavia. Material on Golgi may also be found at the Instituto di Patologia Generale dell' Università di Pavia.

The following works serve as bibliographical sources: Bruno Zanobio, "The Work of Camillo Golgi in Neurology," in *Essays on the History of Italian Neurology. Proceedings of the International Symposium on the History of Neurology. Varenna—30.VIII/1.IX.1961* (Milan, 1963), pp. 179–193; and "L'opera del biologo Camillo Golgi," in *Actes du III Symposium International d'Histoire des Sciences, Turin, 28–30 juillet 1961* (Florence, 1964), pp. 64–84; and Giorgio Pilleri, "Camillo Golgi" in Kurt Kolle, ed., *Grosse Nervenärzte,* 2nd ed., II (Stuttgart, 1970), 3–12.

BRUNO ZANOBIO

GOLITSYN, BORIS BORISOVICH (*b.* St. Petersburg [now Leningrad], Russia, 2 March 1862; *d.* Petrograd [now Leningrad], 16 May 1916), *physics, seismology.*

Golitsyn came from an old family of the nobility. In 1887 he graduated from the hydrographic section of the Maritime Academy; but since he did not wish to serve in the fleet, he went to study abroad, enrolling in the Physics and Mathematics Faculty of the University of Strasbourg. He graduated in 1890 and then returned to Russia. He began to teach at Moscow University in 1891. In 1893 Golitsyn presented to the Faculty of Mathematics and Physics his master's thesis, "Issledovania po matematicheskoy fizike" ("Investigations in Mathematical Physics"). The first part set forth the "general characteristics of dielectrics from the point of view of the mechanical theory of heat" (electrostriction, the dependence of dielectric constants on volume, pressure, and temperature). The second part discussed radiant energy (light pressure, the significance of absolute temperature, and the dependence of radiation on external factors).

What was significantly new in the second part was Golitsyn's departure from the electrodynamics of Michael Faraday and James Clerk Maxwell, by first considering the space occupied by radiation as a kind of medium to which the concept of temperature is applicable. He arrived at the following formulation: "Absolute temperature is conditioned by the sum total of all electrical displacements; and, in particular, the fourth power of the absolute temperature is directly proportional to the sum of the squares of all the electrical displacements which are carried away from the vacuum." In this work Golitsyn presented two adiabatic invariants of thermal radiation: $U\sqrt[3]{v}$ = constant and $T\sqrt[3]{v}$ = constant, where v is a "given volume of ether," U is the quantity of radiant energy in this volume, and T is the absolute temperature of the radiation.

After examining Golitsyn's dissertation, Aleksandr G. Stoletov and Aleksei P. Sokolov, both members of the Faculty of Mathematics and Physics, rendered a sharply negative review. They were not able to see Golitsyn's point of view on temperature radiation in its proper perspective. A heated discussion arose concerning the dissertation. Stoletov solicited opinions on the disputed questions from Hermann Helmholtz, Lord Kelvin, and Ludwig Boltzman—and they agreed generally with Stoletov and Sokolov. Golitsyn was not permitted to defend his dissertation. Court circles found this prohibition insulting to a member of the aristocracy, and consequently Stoletov was passed over as a candidate for membership in the Imperial Academy of Sciences, while Golitsyn was selected to be an adjunct member.

Before 1898 Golitsyn's scientific research was concerned mainly with molecular physics. He examined the problem of critical temperature in great detail. Against the theory of Thomas Andrews he advanced a new notion about conditions of quasi equilibrium based on extremely precise experimental data. Beginning in 1899, Golitsyn started to occupy himself mainly with seismology and seismometry. He laid the foundations of scientific seismometry and developed an improved type of seismograph, one with a galvanometric register. In such a seismograph the pendulum is equipped with coils and oscillates in a field of permanent magnets. Under these conditions an electric current is induced in the coils, the measurement of which permits the precise recording of seismic vibrations.

Through the efforts of Golitsyn, Russian seismometry occupied a leading place in world science at that time; and his seismographs were the prototypes for new apparatus for the study of earthquakes and mechanical vibrations, and for seismic prospecting for useful minerals. In 1908 Golitsyn was elected an academician. International recognition of his great services in seismology was expressed by his election as president of the International Seismic Association at its congress held at Manchester in 1911. In 1916 Golitsyn was made a foreign member of the Royal Society.

BIBLIOGRAPHY

Many of Golitsyn's writings were brought together as *Izbrannye trudy* ("Selected Works"), 2 vols. (Moscow, 1960). His works are listed (under "Galizin") in Poggendorff, IV, 474–475, and V, 408–409.

On Golitsyn's life or work, see G. P. Blok and N. V. Krutikova, "Rukopisi B. B. Golitsyna v arkhive Akademii nauk SSSR" ("Manuscripts of B. B. Golitsyn in the Archive of the Academy of Sciences of the U.S.S.R."), in *Trudy Arkhiva Akademii nauk SSSR,* pt. 10 (1952); A. N. Krylov, "Pamyati B. B. Golitsyna" ("In Memory of B. B. Golitsyn"), in *Priroda,* no. 2 (1918), 171–180; A. S. Predvoditelev, "O fizicheskikh rabotakh B. B. Golitsyna" ("On Golitsyn's Work in Physics"), in Golitsyn's *Izbrannye trudy,* I, 217–240; and A. S. Predvoditelev and N. V. Veshnyakov, "Zhizn i nauchnaya deyatelnost akademika B. B. Golitsyna" ("The Life and Scientific Activity of Academician B. B. Golitsyn"), in Golitsyn's *Izbrannye trudy,* I, 5–12.

See also *Materialy dlya biograficheskogo slovarya deystvitelnykh chlenov imperatorskoy Akademii nauk, 1889–1914* ("Materials for a Biographical Dictionary of Members of the Imperial Academy of Sciences, 1889–1914"), pt. 1 (Petrograd, 1915), 193–218, see entry for Golitsyn; and *Materialy dlya istorii akademicheskikh uchrezhdeny za 1889–1914 gg.* ("Materials for a History of Academic Institutions for the Years 1889–1914"), pt. 1 (Petrograd, 1917), 47–82, on Golitsyn's scientific activity.

J. G. DORFMAN

GOLTZ, FRIEDRICH LEOPOLD (*b.* Posen, Germany [now Poznan, Poland], 14 August 1834; *d.* Strasbourg, France, 4 May 1902), *physiology, encephalology.*

Goltz's father, Heinrich Goltz, a police inspector in Posen and Danzig, died when Friedrich was twelve. His mother, Leopoldine Friederike von Blumenberg, then moved the family to Thorn (now Torun, Poland), where an uncle, Bogumil Goltz, lived. A philosopher, natural scientist, and author, Bogumil Goltz came to have great influence on Friedrich.

Goltz started his medical studies in 1853 at Königsberg. There he attended Hermann Helmholtz' lectures on physiology and general pathology. He was not inclined toward Helmholtz' physical approach but leaned instead toward analysis of the morphological basis of physiological functions and the interpretation of simple observations and animal surgery to arrive at solutions of physiological questions. His doctoral dissertation (20 January 1858), *De spatii sensu cutis,* an investigation of the sense of touch, points in that direction. After two years of surgical training under Ernst Wagner, during which he acquired the techniques for his later brain operations, Goltz was appointed prosector in anatomy at Königsberg, under August Müller. He then became extraordinary professor of anatomy in 1865.

In 1868 Goltz married Agnes Simon, the daughter of Samuel Simon, city councillor in Königsberg. In 1870 he succeeded A. W. Volkmann as professor of physiology in Halle and two years later he was called to the new German university in Strasbourg, the former Faculté de Médecine. He was appointed rector of the university in 1888 and constantly concerned himself with maintaining good relations between the German and French populations of Alsace. He was spirited and witty, a popular teacher, and a great lover of animals. Among his colleagues were such gifted people as J. G. Gaule, Joseph von Mering, Jacques Loeb, Albrecht Bethe, A. Bickel, and J. Richard Ewald. Goltz died of progressive muscle paralysis, asthma, and sclerosis.

The principal subject of Goltz's research was the study of reflex phenomena, particularly in the spinal cord of the frog. Later he was concerned primarily with the analysis of localization phenomena in the brain. He originated a series of tests which for a long time were generally used in university lectures. The Goltz *Kochversuch* ("cooking test," 1860) called for the slow heating of a spinal (decerebrated) frog in a water bath. Because of the gradual increase in stimulation there was no reaction, and Goltz argued that its absence refuted E. F. W. Pflüger's concept of the *Rückenmarksseele* ("spinal cord soul"). His *Klopfversuch* ("tapping test," 1862) also became famous: When the abdominal wall of a frog is tapped, the heart stops momentarily because of the reflex vagus effect. Goltz next investigated the nerve mechanism of frogs during copulation (*Umklammerungsreflex,* or "embracing reflex," 1865). In the same year he demonstrated the famous "croaking reflex" (*Quakreflex*) by stroking the skin on the back of spinal frogs. He reported his findings in *Beiträge zur Lehre von den Funktionen des Nervensystems des Frosches.*

In the following years Goltz analyzed the functions of the labyrinth of the inner ear in frogs and pigeons, thereby succeeding in differentiating the functions of the *nervus octavus* into hearing and equilibrium. He was the first to recognize the importance of the semicircular canals for maintaining equilibrium. In 1874 Goltz proved the existence of reflex centers in dogs for erection, evacuation, and parturition.

Next Goltz concentrated on the study of the functions of the cerebrum (1876). On the basis of tests by Pierre Flourens, Gustav von Fritsch, Julius Hitzig, and Daniel Ferrier, he attempted to obtain, by means of careful surgery, information about the localization or local occurrence of cerebral functions in the center of the brain. At first he partially destroyed portions of the cerebrum, but in later experiments he was able to remove entire lobes, and even a hemisphere. Since he succeeded, with scrupulous care, in keeping the animals alive for several years, he was able to differentiate between the initial irritative symptoms produced by surgery and definite long-term results. He thus arrived at the concept of a reciprocal interchangeability, and even equivalence, of cerebral parts without completely rejecting the localization theory. A dog whose cerebrum had been removed was without intellect, memory, and intelligence.

Regarding animal research as unavoidable, and even essential, Goltz in 1883 protested the antivivisectionist movement. He wrote about his cerebral tests in *Über die Verrichtungen des Grosshirns* (1881) and produced a final report on the dog without a cerebrum in 1892. His research was carried on particularly by C. S. Sherrington and Harvey Cushing.

BIBLIOGRAPHY

I. ORIGINAL WORKS. Goltz's books are *De spatii sensu cutis* (Königsberg, 1858); *Beiträge zur Lehre von den Funktionen des Nervensystems des Frosches* (Berlin, 1869); *Über die Verrichtungen des Grosshirns. Gesammelte Abhandlungen* (Bonn, 1881); and *Wider die Humanaster. Rechtfertigung eines Vivisektors* (Strasbourg, 1883).

His publications in journals include "Beiträge zur Lehre von den Funktionen des Rückenmarks der Frösche," in *Königsberger medizinische Jahrbuch,* **2** (1860), 189–226; "Über Reflexionen vom und zum Herzen," *ibid.,* **3** (1862), 271–274; "Über die physiologische Bedeutung der Bogengänge des Ohrlabyrinths," in *Pflügers Archiv für die gesamte Physiologie des Menschen und der Tiere,* **3** (1870), 172–192; "Über die Funktionen des Lendenmarks des Hundes," *ibid.,* **8** (1874), 460–498; "Über den Einfluss des Nervensystems auf die Vorgänge während der Schwangerschaft und des Gebäraktes," *ibid.,* **9** (1874), 552–565; and "Über die Verrichtungen des Grosshirns I-VII," *ibid.,* **13** (1876), 1–44; **14** (1876), 412–443; **20** (1879), 1–54; **26** (1881), 1–49; **34** (1884), 451–505; **42** (1888), 419–467; **51** (1892), 570–614.

II. SECONDARY LITERATURE. Obituaries are A. Bickel, "Friedrich Goltz †," in *Deutsche medizinische Wochenschrift,* **28** (1902), 403; J. R. Ewald, "Friedrich Goltz," in *Pflüger's Archiv für die gesamte Physiologie des Menschen und die Tiere,* **94** (1903), 1–64, with portrait and complete bibliography; and Heinrich Kraft, "Friedrich Leopold Goltz," in *Münchener medizinische Wochenschrift,* **49** (1902), 965–970.

Shorter biographies are D. Trincker, in *Neue deutsche Biographie,* VI (Berlin, 1964), 636–637, with short bibliography; *Biographische Lexikon der hervorragenden Ärzte aller Zeiten und Völker,* 2nd ed., II (Berlin–Vienna, 1930), 792–793; and K. E. Rothschuh, *Geschichte der Physiologie* (Berlin–Göttingen–Heidelberg, 1953), esp. pp. 186–187, with portrait and list of students.

K. E. ROTHSCHUH

GOMBERG, MOSES (*b.* Elisavetgrad, Russia [now Kirovograd, U.S.S.R.], 8 February 1866; *d.* Ann Arbor, Michigan, 12 February 1947), *organic chemistry.*

Gomberg prepared the first stable free radical, triphenylmethyl, at the University of Michigan in 1900 and pioneered in the development of free-radical chemistry. He was the son of George and Marie Resnikoff Gomberg; his father was the owner of a modest estate in the Ukraine. Young Gomberg entered the Nicolau Gymnasium in Elisavetgrad in 1878. Six years later his father was accused of anticzarist activities. His estate was confiscated and he fled with his family to Chicago, where he and his son, neither of whom had any knowledge of English, worked at menial jobs in the stockyards and elsewhere in the city.

Moses quickly learned English and completed his high school education in Chicago. He then became a student at the University of Michigan, completing his B.S. in 1890. He continued at Michigan as an assistant in chemistry, receiving his M.S. in 1892 and his Ph.D. in 1894. His work was done under Albert B. Prescott, and his dissertation dealt with some reactions of caffeine. Appointed instructor in organic chemistry in 1893, he never severed his connection with the chemistry department at the University of Michigan. Promotion to assistant professor came in 1899, to junior professor in 1902, and to full professor in 1904. From 1927 until his retirement in 1936 he was chairman of the chemistry department.

In order to procure funds for European study, Gomberg carried out analyses of water, minerals, fatty oils, foods, drugs, and patent medicines and served as an expert witness in toxicology cases while he was still a graduate student. Taking a leave of absence in 1896–1897, he spent two terms in Adolf von Baeyer's laboratory in Munich and a term with Victor Meyer in Heidelberg. During this period he turned away from the concentration on analysis which characterized the work of Prescott and his students in order to concentrate on synthetic studies. At Munich he prepared some nitrogen derivatives of isobutyric acid; and at Heidelberg he set out to prepare tetraphenylmethane, a compound which a number of German chemists had unsuccessfully sought to synthesize and which Meyer believed probably could not be synthesized. Meyer suggested that Gomberg undertake a problem more likely to be successful. Gomberg persisted in his objective and, by oxidizing triphenylmethane hydrazobenzene, obtained the corresponding azo compound, which decomposed to tetraphenylmethane on heating at 110–120°C. Although Gomberg was successful in his endeavor, the yield of tetraphenylmethane was poor (2–5 percent).

Upon his return to Michigan, Gomberg sought to prepare hexaphenylethane, the next fully phenylated hydrocarbon of the series. He utilized the classical reaction of a metal on an appropriate halide:

$$2(C_6H_5)_3C\underset{\bullet}{X} + \text{metal} \rightarrow (C_6H_5)_6C_2 + \text{metal halide.}$$

The use of either triphenylmethyl bromide or chloride with sodium failed to yield a product, but substitution of silver for sodium led to a reaction in which a white crystalline product began to separate after heating the reaction mixture for several hours at the boiling point of the benzene solvent. The crystalline product was assumed to be hexaphenylethane, but elementary analysis yielded 87.93 percent carbon and 6.04 percent hydrogen (calculated for hexaphenylethane, $C = 93.83$, $H = 6.17$). Carefully repeated syntheses yielded products giving similar analytical results, and Gomberg was forced to conclude that he was preparing an oxygenated compound (which proved to be the peroxide $[C_6H_5]_6C_2O_2$).

Gomberg repeated the reaction of triphenylmethyl chloride and silver in an atmosphere of carbon dioxide. Now he obtained no solid product at all, but the yellow color of his solution indicated that a reaction had occurred. Removal of the benzene solvent left a colorless solid of unexpectedly high reactivity toward oxygen and halogens. It had been expected that hexaphenylethane would be a colorless solid characterized by chemical inertness. In his first publication on the subject, Gomberg wrote, "The experimental evidence presented above forces me to the conclusion that we have to deal here with a free radical, triphenylmethyl, $(C_6H_5)_3C$. On this assumption alone do the results described above become intelligible and receive an adequate explanation" (*Journal of the American Chemical Society,* **22** [1900], 768).

The announcement of the preparation of a stable free radical was received with skepticism, for most contemporary chemists had become convinced that such chemical species could not exist. Gomberg set out to establish the soundness of his conclusion by carefully studying the properties of his substance and by preparing additional substances showing free-radical properties. He quickly developed an understanding of the experimental conditions necessary for successful synthesis of related compounds. His major research activities during the remainder of his career were aimed toward extending the understanding of free-radical chemistry.

Results of molecular weight determinations by L. H. Cone in Gomberg's laboratory proved to be variable in different solvents and fell closer to the theoretical value for the dimer hexaphenylethane than to that for the monomer triphenylmethyl. This was a matter of grave concern for Gomberg and caused him ultimately to accept the idea that the solution must contain an equilibrium mixture of both substances:

$$(C_6H_5)_3C-C(C_6H_5)_3 \leftrightharpoons 2\ (C_6H_5)_3\ C\cdot$$

Other chemists believed the compound to be merely hexaphenylethane, assuming it to be unstable in the presence of oxygen, halogens, and other highly reactive substances. Gomberg argued that the presence of color supported the free-radical hypothesis. When critics sought to explain the color by use of quinoid structures, Gomberg showed that the addition of oxygen to the solution resulted in loss of color. On standing, the yellow color slowly returned, as if a new equilibrium were being established; but the color could be destroyed again by addition of more oxygen. Change of color with change of temperature also supported the concept of an equilibrium in solution. Jean F. Piccard of Munich showed in 1911 that the colored solution failed to obey Beer's law when diluted; dilution actually brought about intensification of the color, thereby lending support to the equilibrium concept.

Investigators in other laboratories, particularly Wilhelm Schlenk at Jena, brought forth evidence for free radicals in other hexaarylethane systems. By 1911 many organic chemists were willing to concede the existence of stable free radicals in solution, but only when dealing with compounds such as fully substituted ethanes carrying bulky substituents such as phenyl groups, or even better, substituted phenyl groups or naphthyl groups. Free radicals containing nitrogen, sulfur, and oxygen atoms carrying three aryl groups were also prepared in various laboratories, and in 1929 Fritz Paneth bolstered the free-radical concept by establishing evidence for the transient existence of free methyl radicals. Gradually free radicals came to take on great significance in reaction mechanisms.

Gomberg also carried out studies on organometallic compounds, and during World War I he worked on war gases. He was associated with the civilian chemists who originally worked in the Bureau of Mines and were later absorbed by the newly created Chemical Warfare Service. Although the idea of chemical warfare was abhorrent to him, Gomberg accepted the task of developing the commercial synthesis of ethylene chlorohydrin, required as an intermediate for the synthesis of mustard gas. Later, he was commissioned a major in the Ordnance Department and served as an adviser in the production of smokeless powder and high explosives.

During his forty-three years on the Michigan faculty Gomberg was a respected teacher and administrator. As an effective supervisor of graduate students he considered the development of the man as a scientist more important than the production of publications. Two of his students, C. S. Schoepfle and W. E. Bachmann, in their obituary memoir said of him: "Gifted with a remarkable memory, he presented his lectures with the full use of a wealth of historical material and so vividly that they left an indelible imprint on his students. A great teacher and scholar, he inspired his students by his methods and ideals, and his colleagues by the vigor and clarity of his mind. To this greatness, he added an innate kindliness and unassuming modesty that endeared him to all" (*ibid.,* **69** [1947], 2924).

Gomberg was a member of numerous professional societies and was honored by election to the National Academy of Sciences. In 1931 he served as president of the American Chemical Society and at various times was honored by awards administered by it: the Nichols Medal in 1914, the Willard Gibbs Medal in 1925, and the Chandler Medal in 1927.

Although he enjoyed the company of women in a somewhat courtly and reserved manner, Gomberg never married and firmly forbade his graduate students to marry before they finished their degrees. His younger sister Sonja served as his hostess and housekeeper at his cottage in Ann Arbor.

BIBLIOGRAPHY

I. Original Works. There is a bibliography of Gomberg's published papers in C. S. Schoepfle and W. E. Bachmann, "Moses Gomberg, 1866–1947," in *Journal of the American Chemical Society,* **69** (1947), 2924–2925. His original paper on triphenylmethyl appeared in *Berichte der Deutschen chemischen Gesellschaft,* **33** (1900), 3150–3163; and *Journal of the American Chemical Society,* **22** (1900), 757–771. Gomberg published review articles on free-radical chemistry in *Chemical Reviews,* **1** (1924), 91–141, and **2** (1925), 301–314; *Journal of Industrial and Engineering Chemistry,* **20** (1928), 159–164; *Journal of Chemical Educa-

tion, **9** (1932), 439–451; and *Science,* **74** (1931), 553–557.

II. SECONDARY LITERATURE. There is no lengthy biography of Gomberg. The best short sketch is C. S. Schoepfle and W. E. Bachmann, "Moses Gomberg, 1866–1947," in *Journal of the American Chemical Society,* **69** (1947), 2921–2925, repr. in E. Farber, ed., *Great Chemists* (New York, 1961), pp. 1209–1217. There is a short sketch by A. H. White, in *Industrial and Engineering Chemistry,* **23** (1931), 116–117. For an evaluation of Gomberg's role in the history of free-radical chemistry, see A. J. Ihde, in *Pure and Applied Chemistry,* **15** (1967), 1–13, repr. in International Union of Pure and Applied Chemistry, *Free Radicals in Solution* (London, 1967), pp. 1–13. These two publications carry the papers presented at the Centennial Symposium on Free Radicals in Solution, which was held under I.U.P.A.C. sponsorship at the University of Michigan in 1966. These papers reflect the consequences of Gomberg's work.

AARON J. IHDE

GOMPERTZ, BENJAMIN (*b.* London, England, 5 March 1779; *d.* London, 14 July 1865), *mathematics.*

One of three prominent sons of a distinguished mercantile family that emigrated from Holland in the eighteenth century, Gompertz appeared destined for a financial career. Denied matriculation at the universities because he was Jewish, he joined the Society of Mathematicians of Spitalfields in 1797 and educated himself by reading the masters, especially Newton, Colin Maclaurin, and William Emerson. He found in various learned societies the intellectual stimulation that led to many publications and a wide spectrum of accomplishments. Papers to the Royal Astronomical Society on the differential sextant and the aberration of light belie Gompertz's own statement that he was not a practicing astronomer. The Royal Society, of which he was elected a fellow in 1819; the London Mathematical Society, of which he was a charter member; the Society of Actuaries; and the Royal Statistical Society were only a few of the learned and philanthropic organizations to which he gave of his talent and energy.

In 1810 Gompertz married Sir Moses Montefiore's daughter Abigail and joined the stock exchange. In 1820, in a paper to the Royal Society, he applied the method of fluxions to the investigation of various life contingencies. In 1824 he was appointed actuary and head clerk of the newly founded Alliance Assurance Company. A year later he published what is now called Gompertz's law of mortality, which states ". . . the average exhaustion of man's power to avoid death to be such that at the end of equal infinitely small intervals of time he lost equal portions of his remaining power to oppose destruction which he had at the commencement of these intervals." His rigid adherence to Newton's fluxional notation prevented wide recognition of this accomplishment, but he must be rated as a pioneer in actuarial science and one of the great amateur scholars of his day. Augustus De Morgan called Gompertz "the link between the old and new" when he mourned "the passing of the last of the learned Newtonians."

BIBLIOGRAPHY

I. ORIGINAL WORKS. Gompertz's work on life contingencies appeared in the *Philosophical Transactions of the Royal Society:* "A Sketch of the Analysis and Notation Applicable to the Value of Life Contingencies," **110** (1820), 214–294; "On the Nature of the Function Expressive of the Law of Human Mortality, and on a New Mode of Determining the Value of Life Contingencies," **115** (1825), 513–585; and "A Supplement to the Two Papers of 1820 and 1825," **152** (1862), 511–559.

"The Application of a Method of Differences to the Species of Series Whose Sums Are Obtained by Mr. Landen by the Help of Impossible Quantities," *ibid.,* **96** (1806), 174–194, led to *The Principles and Applications of Imaginary Quantities,* 2 vols. (London, 1817–1818). The sequel to these two tracts is *Hints on Porisms . . .* (London, 1850).

A regular contributor to the *Gentleman's Mathematical Companion* from 1796, Gompertz was awarded their annual problem-solution prize every year from 1812 to 1822.

II. SECONDARY LITERATURE. P. F. Hooker, "Benjamin Gompertz," in *Journal of the Institute of Actuaries,* **91,** pt. 2, no. 389 (1965), 203–212, is a competent biography with a complete bibliography of Gompertz's works (twenty-two titles) and works about him (twenty-four titles). Augustus De Morgan, "The Old Mathematical Society," repr. in J. R. Newman, *The World of Mathematics,* IV, 2372–2376, contains a view by a close friend. Also worth reading is De Morgan's obituary in *The Atheneum* (22 July 1865), p. 117. Other informative obituaries are *Monthly Notices of the Royal Astronomical Society,* **26** (1865), 104–109; and M. N. Adler, "Memoirs of the Late Benjamin Gompertz," in *Journal of the Institute of Actuaries,* **13** (Apr. 1866), 1–20.

HENRY S. TROPP

GONSÁLEZ, DOMINGO. See **Gundissalinus, Dominicus.**

GOODRICH, EDWIN STEPHEN (*b.* Weston-super-Mare, England, 21 June 1868; *d.* Oxford, England, 6 January 1946), *comparative anatomy, embryology, paleontology, evolution.*

Goodrich was a son of Rev. Octavius Pitt Goodrich and Frances Lucinda Parker. Among his forebears was Thomas Goodrich, bishop of Ely and lord high chancellor of England, who helped to draw up the

Book of Common Prayer of the Church of England. Goodrich's branch of the family under John Goodrich came to New England in 1630, and settled at Nansewood, Virginia, in 1635. In 1775 the then John Goodrich returned to England, and with Goodrich's death this branch of the family became extinct. When Goodrich was two weeks old his father died, and his mother took him, another son, and a daughter to live with her mother at Pau, France, where he attended the local English school and a French lycée. In 1888 he entered the Slade School at University College, London, as an art student; and while there he became acquainted with E. Ray Lankester, who interested him in zoology. When Lankester became professor of comparative anatomy at Oxford, he made Goodrich his assistant in 1892; this marked the start of the researches which during half a century made Goodrich the greatest comparative anatomist of his day. In 1921 he was appointed Linacre professor of comparative anatomy, a post he held until 1945.

In 1913 Goodrich married Helen L. M. Pixell, a distinguished protozoologist, who helped greatly with his work. His artistic training always stood him in good stead in drawing diagrams of surpassing beauty and clarity while lecturing (students used to insist on photographing the blackboard before it was erased) and in illustrating his books and papers. He also held shows of his watercolor landscapes in London. Goodrich was elected fellow of the Royal Society in 1905 and received its Royal Medal in 1936. He was honorary member of the New York Academy of Science and of many other academies, and honorary doctor of many universities. In 1945 L. S. Berg of Leningrad sent him a message through Julian Huxley: "Please tell him [Goodrich] that though neither I nor my colleagues have ever met him, we all regard ourselves as his pupils." A dapper, tiny, thin man with a dry sense of humor, he always complained when traveling by air that he was not weighed together with his luggage, since his own weight was only half that of an average passenger.

From the start of his researches, most of which were devoted to marine organisms, Goodrich made himself acquainted at first hand with the marine fauna of Plymouth, Roscoff, Banyuls, Naples, Helgoland, Bermuda, Madeira, and the Canary Islands. He also traveled extensively in Europe, the United States, North Africa, India, Ceylon, Malaya, and Java. The most important area of his work involved unraveling the significance of the sets of tubes connecting the centers of the bodies of animals with the outside. There are nephridia, developed from the outer layer inward and serving the function of excretion. Quite different from them are coelomoducts, developed from the middle layer outward, serving to release the germ cells. These two sets of structures may acquire spurious visual similarity when each opens into the body cavity through a funnel surrounded by cilia which create a current of fluid. In some groups the nephridia may disappear (as in vertebrates, where the nephridia may have been converted into the thymus gland), and the coelomoducts then take on the additional function of excretion. This is why man has a genitourinary system. Before Goodrich's analysis, the whole subject was in chaos.

Goodrich established that a motor nerve remains "faithful" to its corresponding segmental muscle, however much it may have become displaced or obscured in development. He showed that organs can be homologous (traceable to a single representative in a common ancestor) without arising from the same segments of the body. Like a tune in music, they can be transposed up or down the scale, for example, the fins and limbs of vertebrates and the position of the occipital arch (the back of the skull), which varies in vertebrates from the fifth to the ninth segment. He distinguished between the different structures of the scales of fishes, living and fossil, by which they are classified and recognized, a fact of fundamental importance when boring into the earth's crust for mineral wealth because the different strata are identified by their fossils. Goodrich's attention was always focused on evolution, to which he made notable contributions, firmly adhering to Darwin's theory of natural selection.

BIBLIOGRAPHY

I. Original Works. A complete bibliography of Goodrich's writings is in the obituary by de Beer (see below). His books include *Cyclostomes and Fishes* (London, 1909); *Living Organisms: An Account of Their Origin and Evolution* (London, 1924); and *Studies on the Structure and Development of Vertebrates* (London, 1930).

II. Secondary Literature. On Goodrich and his work, see Gavin de Beer, "Edwin Stephen Goodrich," in *Obituary Notices of Fellows of the Royal Society of London,* **5** (1947), 477–490; and A. C. Hardy, "Edwin Stephen Goodrich," in *Quarterly Journal of Microscopical Science,* **87** (1947), 317–355.

Gavin de Beer

GOODRICKE, JOHN (*b.* Groningen, Netherlands, 17 September 1764; *d.* York, England, 20 April 1786), *astronomy.*

Goodricke, the British astronomical prodigy of the late eighteenth century whose discoveries laid the foundations of an important branch of stellar astronomy, died at not quite twenty-two years of age. But into this lamentably brief life—and despite the handicap of deafness and dumbness—he managed to compress enough accomplishment to earn a permanent place in the history of science. He was descended from an old family of English country squires, who, raised to baronetcy by the end of the fifteenth century, were occasionally called upon to perform minor diplomatic services. Thus Henry Goodricke, John's father, spent several years in consular service at Groningen, where in 1761 he married Levina Benjamina Sessler.

Scanty records reveal little of Goodricke's early childhood, beyond a suggestion that he became deaf and dumb as a result of a severe illness in early infancy. At the age of eight he was sent from the Netherlands to Edinburgh, to be educated at a school for deaf-mutes which Thomas Braidwood was conducting. Absence of school records conceals the early development of young Goodricke; but his progress must have been satisfactory, for in 1778 he was able to enter Warrington Academy—then a well-known educational institution in the north of England—which made no special provision for handicapped pupils. There, we are told by extant records, ". . . having in part conquered his disadvantage by the assistance of Mr. Braidwood, he attained a surprising proficiency becoming a very tolerable classicist and an excellent mathematician" (Turner, *Historical . . . Academy*). For the latter he had undoubtedly to thank William Enfield, an outstanding teacher and a mathematician of some renown. It was almost certainly he who awakened Goodricke's interest in astronomy and set him on his subsequent career.

Just when Goodricke left Warrington Academy we do not know; but certainly it was not later than 1781, for his *Journal of Astronomical Observations* contains a first entry dated 16 November of that year at York (to which his family had returned from Holland in 1776); it is to this source that we must turn for a description of Goodricke's discoveries.

On 12 November 1782, a few days before the first anniversary of the start of his diary, Goodricke recorded:

> This night I looked at β Persei, and was much amazed to find its brightness altered—it now appears to be of about 4th magnitude. I observed it diligently for about an hour—I hardly believed that it changed its brightness because I never heard of any star varying so quickly in its brightness. I thought it might perhaps be owing to an optical illusion, a defect in my eyes, or bad air; but the sequel will show that its change is true and that I was not mistaken. . . .

Goodricke was not the first to notice the variability of β Persei (or Algol, as it is more commonly known); the Italian astronomer Geminiano Montanari had done so more than a century before (1670) in Bologna. Goodricke was, however, the first to establish that these light changes were periodic. He continued his observations until the end of the season when Algol could be seen above the horizon at York; and it was not until 12 May 1783 that Goodricke communicated (through the good offices of Rev. Anthony Shepherd, then Plumian professor of astronomy at Cambridge) the results of his observations, in the form of a letter read before the Royal Society on 15 May.

This communication, which promptly appeared in print, created considerable interest in astronomical circles, and the Society's council awarded its youthful author one of the two Copley Medals for 1783. Goodricke did indeed deserve it, for not only did he discover the first known short-period variable star but also established a remarkably accurate estimate of its period. (Goodricke's original value for Algol's period was 2 days, 20 hours, 45 minutes—differing from its true period by only 4 minutes. A year later [1784] he revised this period to 2 days, 20 hours, 49 minutes, 9 seconds—a result on which all subsequent observations had little to improve.) At the end of his communication, we find the following sentence, which makes it truly prophetic: "If it were perhaps not too early to hazard even a conjecture on the cause of its variation, I should imagine it could hardly be accounted for otherwise than . . . by the interposition of a large body revolving around Algol . . ." (*Philosophical Transactions of the Royal Society*, **73** [1783], 474).

Nature had denied much to Goodricke but certainly not the gift of a splendid imagination; seldom in the annals of science has the first conjecture of a discoverer been more accurate. Within the remaining short life vouchsafed to him Goodricke discovered, besides that of Algol, the variability of two other naked-eye stars, β Lyrae (1785) and δ Cephei (1786), both of which became prototypes of other classes of variable stars. Unfortunately, Goodricke's bold suggestion that Algol (and β Lyrae) was an eclipsing variable, as they are now called, was made too early to gain speedy acceptance among contemporary astronomers. It was destined to remain a hypothesis until 1889, when the German astronomer Hermann Vogel discovered that Algol is also a spectroscopic binary, whose conjunctions coincide with the minima of light. This established beyond any doubt the binary nature of Algol and similar variables.

In the meantime, Goodricke's short life was fast running out. The last observation recorded in his diary is dated 24 February 1786. In April of that year the Royal Society elected him to fellowship, but he died at York only two weeks later, "in the consequence of a cold from exposure to night air in astronomical observations." The immediate cause of his death is unknown, for he died largely unnoticed. No stone over his tomb at Hunsingore (close to the former family seat of Ribston Hall, Yorkshire) commemorates his final resting place.

BIBLIOGRAPHY

Goodricke's papers published in the *Philosophical Transactions of the Royal Society* are "A Series of Observations On, and A Discovery of, the Period of the Variation of the Light of the Bright Star in the Head of Medusa, Called Algol," **73**, pt. 2 (1783), 474–482; "On the Periods of the Changes of Light in the Star Algol," **74** (1784), 287–292; "Observations of a New Variable Star," **75** (1785), 153–164; and "A Series of Observations on, and a Discovery of, the Period of the Variation of the Light of the Star Marked δ by Bayer, Near the Head of Cepheus," **76** (1786), 48–61.

Biographical information may be found in W. Turner, *Historical Account of Students Educated at the Warrington Academy* (Warrington, 1814).

ZDENĚK KOPAL

GOODSIR, JOHN (*b.* Anstruther, Fife, Scotland, 20 March 1814; *d.* Edinburgh, Scotland, 6 March 1867), *anatomy, marine zoology.*

Goodsir was the eldest of the five sons and one daughter of John Goodsir, a surgeon. Three of his brothers also studied medicine. After attending school in Anstruther until the age of twelve, Goodsir was sent to St. Andrews University, where he studied humanities and natural history, acquiring considerable proficiency in Latin and Greek. As was the custom at that time, he left without taking his degree. His natural predilections were for engineering and chemistry, but his father encouraged his interest in natural history while his mother taught him to draw.

Goodsir matriculated in Edinburgh University in 1830 and studied anatomy, surgery, and natural history under Robert Knox, James Syme, and Robert Jameson. From the beginning his anatomical work was characterized by a high degree of manual dexterity. He surprised his fellow students by making permanent plaster casts of his dissections and was meticulous in articulating skeletons and preserving pathological specimens, believing that "a piece of true dissection ought to turn out an object of wonder and beauty." His father apprenticed him to A. Nasmyth, a dental surgeon, but Goodsir grudged the time the dental work took from his anatomical investigations—which quickly became his absorbing hobby as well as his major study—and Nasmyth agreed to cancel his indentures before the legal term.

In 1835 Goodsir became a licentiate of the Royal College of Surgeons of Edinburgh, joined his father's practice in Anstruther, and began an investigation into the development of teeth. From a microscopic examination of developing jaws at different ages he demonstrated the independent origin of the deciduous and permanent dentitions. This study in the then new field of developmental anatomy was possibly Goodsir's finest piece of work. He communicated his conclusions "On the Origin and Development of the Pulps and Sacs of the Human Teeth" to the British Association in 1838. Although some of these observations on dental embryology had been anticipated by Friedrich Arnold in 1831, Goodsir believed most of his facts were new to science. This work was followed by a study "On the Follicular Stage of Dentition in the Ruminants; With Some Observations on That Process in the Other Orders of Mammals" (1840).

While a student Goodsir formed a close and important friendship with Edward Forbes. He joined local societies and read accounts of various natural history observations, from supposed new fossil fish to the structure of the cuttlefish eye. Goodsir spent a fortnight with Forbes dredging around the Orkney and Shetland Islands in 1839. Their results were jointly presented to the British Association and other joint publications on marine biology soon followed.

In 1840 Goodsir was appointed conservator of human and comparative anatomy in the university museum. He returned to Edinburgh and bought an apartment at 21 Lothian Street which he shared with Forbes. Their home became the headquarters of the Universal Brotherhood of Friends of Truth, a fellowship formed by Forbes some years before and in which Goodsir enjoyed the high rank of Triangle. (The site is now occupied by part of the Royal Scottish Museum.) Goodsir became a member of the Wernerian Society of Edinburgh, the Botanical Society of Edinburgh, the Anatomical and Physiological Society, and the Royal Physical Society, actively participating by communicating papers and holding office.

In 1841 Goodsir succeeded William Macgillivray as conservator of the museum of the Royal College of Surgeons, Edinburgh, and he initiated a series of lectures based on the collection. Some of these lectures were the basis of his *Anatomical and Pathological Observations* (1845) and include fundamental observations on cell structure, a subject for much debate at that time. Goodsir recognized the importance of cell division as the basis of growth and development. He differentiated between the embryonic growth centers of organs and the permanent "centers of nutrition" of the tissues, and established that cells are the active structures involved in glandular secretion.

He thus anticipated by a number of years the work of Rudolf Virchow, who dedicated the first edition of his *Cellularpathologie* (1859) to Goodsir "as one of the earliest and most acute observers of cell-life both physiological and pathological."

In May 1843 Syme offered the curatorship of the university anatomy and pathology museum to Goodsir, who willingly accepted. His brother Harry, a contributor to *Anatomical and Pathological Observations,* assumed his post at the College of Surgeons, but was later lost with John Franklin's polar expedition. Goodsir's fourth brother, Robert, twice voyaged to the Arctic in search of the expedition.

It was Goodsir's ambition to create a teaching museum second to none in Britain. By October 1845 he could report that "an individual studying the collection from the first to the last series may acquire a knowledge of the science from the structures themselves, instead of from books." The collection had been greatly supplemented by zoological specimens collected by Forbes, Harry Goodsir, and himself. Over a thousand carefully dissected and injected specimens were testimony to Goodsir's skill. He became demonstrator of anatomy in May 1844, and in December 1845 was appointed curator of the entire university museum. He communicated a paper "On the Supra-Renal, Thymus and Thyroid Bodies" to the Royal Society, London, in 1846 and was elected a fellow the same year.

With the retirement of Alexander Monro (Tertius) in the spring, a vacancy arose for the chair of anatomy, to which Goodsir had long aspired. Having provided satisfactory evidence of his fitness for anatomical teaching and—even more important in the Edinburgh of 1846—of his religious orthodoxy, Goodsir was elected. From that time he was less active as a scientific author, devoting himself instead to the reorganization of anatomical teaching. He emphasized the tutorial system and his methods came to be regarded as the best in any British university or medical school. He dearly wanted to illustrate his theoretical teaching with practical demonstrations in the surgical wards of a hospital and moved to a larger house in anticipation of becoming a consultant surgeon. When a vacancy did occur at the Edinburgh Royal Infirmary, Goodsir's application was turned down, leaving him a bitterly disappointed man.

In 1850 he started the *Annals of Anatomy and Physiology,* which contained original papers by his pupils and others. After three numbers had been issued the journal was discontinued in 1853, when Goodsir was obliged to withdraw for a year from active work. During the previous summer Goodsir had undertaken the natural history course in addition to his other duties. The extra imposition wore him out and at the end of the course he was "shrunk in features, worn in body, shattered in nerves, and almost a helpless invalid." His health had been deteriorating for a number of years and he now needed a complete rest. He spent a year in Germany and France, being treated for incipient paralysis. During this time he studied German and Italian language and literature. He returned to Germany in 1857 to study ichthyology and subsequently visited the Continent on several occasions to purchase physiological apparatus; he was the first to introduce these costly instruments to Scotland.

Disappointed in his hospital aims, Goodsir moved again, became careless in his domestic habits, and avoided visitors. The paralysis affecting his legs increased until he was able to walk only by concentrating intently on his feet. He keenly felt the loss of his friend Forbes, who had died in 1854. Restlessly he moved twice more before finally settling in the dingy cottage where Forbes had died. There, attended only by his sister, he became more and more of a hermit. But he did not rest from his work.

He began to concern himself with the mathematics of form, trying to perceive an underlying "crystal" arrangement of the fine structure of muscle, bone, and other tissues and organs. This led him to formulate a theory of the triangle as the universal image of nature—the mathematical figure from which both the organic and inorganic worlds are constructed. It is perhaps not without significance that the triangle was one of the outward signs by which Forbes's Universal Brethren were recognized. As his body became increasingly weak Goodsir's speculations became more metaphysical. He drew his strength from the triangle theory of formation which he hoped to complete as the greatest of his works.

Against all advice he commenced his usual course of lectures in November 1866, but before the end of the year he had to give up and confine himself mainly to bed. He died in March 1867, his triangle theory unwritten, and was buried alongside the grave of Forbes.

The significance of Goodsir's contribution to anatomical knowledge should be measured not only by his published writings, but also by his lucid practical demonstrations and inspirational teaching. Many valuable discoveries were incorporated in his lectures but never published. Before him (with the notable exception of John Hunter, whom Goodsir took for a model) anatomy had been regarded as a means to an end—medical practice; Goodsir had the perspective to make it a science in its own right.

BIBLIOGRAPHY

I. Original Works. Goodsir's papers are listed in the Royal Society, *Catalogue of Scientific Papers,* II (1868). Most were republished posthumously in W. Turner, ed., *The Anatomical Memoirs of John Goodsir, F.R.S.,* 2 vols. (Edinburgh, 1868), which contains a number of unpublished lectures, including the ten lectures, "On the Dignity of the Human Body, Considered in a Comparison of Its Structural Relations With Those of the Higher Vertebrata," delivered to the class of anatomy in 1862; two unpublished papers on marine zoology; the full texts of some papers published in abstract only; and an appendix of selected observations from his notebooks on morphology and the action of muscles. The *Anatomical and Pathological Observations* (Edinburgh, 1845), which includes some work by Harry Goodsir, was also republished in the *Anatomical Memoirs.*

Other works for which Goodsir was responsible are *Annals of Anatomy and Physiology,* vol. I, nos. 1–3 (1850–1853); his ed. of Adolph Hannover, *On the Construction and Use of the Microscope* (Edinburgh, 1853); W. Turner, *Atlas of Human Anatomy . . . the Illustrations Selected and Arranged Under the Superintendence of John Goodsir* (Edinburgh, 1857); and his MS on the myology of the horse, which was incorporated in J. Wilson Johnston and T. J. Call, *Descriptive Anatomy of the Horse . . . Compiled from the Manuscripts of Thomas Strangeways . . . and the late Professor Goodsir* (Edinburgh, 1870).

II. Secondary Literature. A comprehensive biographical memoir by H. Lonsdale is prefatory to vol. I of the *Anatomical Memoirs.* This memoir is the source for the quotations in the text and for the entry in *Dictionary of National Biography,* XXII, 137–139. A concise account of Goodsir's work is given by H. W. Y. Taylor in *Report of Proceedings. The Scottish Society of the History of Medicine* (1955–1956), pp. 13–19. Goodsir's reputation among his contemporaries is evidenced by the *Testimonials in Favour of John Goodsir . . . Candidate for the Chair of Anatomy in the University of Edinburgh* (Edinburgh, 1846), which also includes extracts from medical reviews of *Anatomical and Pathological Observations.* Obituaries are in *Edinburgh Medical Journal,* **12** (1867), 959–962; *Transactions and Proceedings of the Botanical Society of Edinburgh,* **9** (1868), 118–127; and *Proceedings of the Royal Society,* **16** (1868), xiv–xvi.

David Heppell

GÖPEL, ADOLPH (*b.* Rostock, Germany, 29 September 1812; *d.* Berlin, Germany, 7 June 1847), *mathematics.*

The son of a music teacher, Göpel was able, thanks to an uncle, the British consul in Corsica, to spend several years of his childhood in Italy, where in 1825–1826 he attended lectures on mathematics and physics in Pisa. His real studies did not begin until 1829, at the University of Berlin. After earning his doctorate there in 1835, he taught at the Werder Gymnasium and at the Royal Realschule before becoming an official at the royal library in Berlin. Since he had little contact with his mathematical colleagues, all we know about him is what C. G. J. Jacobi and A. L. Crelle wrote in the brief accounts they contributed to Crelle's *Journal für die reine und angewandte Mathematik* shortly after his death. Of the two, only Crelle knew him personally, and for but a short time.

In his doctoral dissertation Göpel sought to derive from the periodic continued fractions of the roots of whole numbers the representation of those numbers by certain quadratic forms. Following an eight-year pause after his dissertation, he wrote several works for Grunert's *Archiv der Mathematik und Physik,* for which he was then working. In them he showed thorough familiarity with Jacob Steiner's style of synthetic geometry.

Göpel owes his fame to "Theoriae transcendentium Abelianarum primi ordinis adumbratio levis," published after his death in *Journal für die reine und angewandte Mathematik.* The investigations contained in this paper can be viewed as a continuation of the ideas of C. G. J. Jacobi. The latter had taught that elliptic functions of one variable should be considered as inverse functions of elliptic integrals, but later he also explained them in his lectures as quotients of theta functions of one variable. Moreover, Jacobi had formulated the inverse problem, named for him, for Abelian integrals of arbitrary genus p. From this arose the next task: to solve the problem for $p = 2$. This was done by Göpel and Johann Rosenhain in works published almost simultaneously. In "Theoriae transcendentium . . . ," Göpel started from sixteen theta functions in two variables (analogous to the four Jacobian theta functions in one variable) and showed that their quotients are quadruply periodic. Of the squares of these sixteen functions, four proved to be linearly independent. Göpel linked four more of these quadratics through a homogeneous fourth-degree relation, later named the "Göpel relation," which coincides with the equation of the Kummer surface. Göpel then presented differential equations satisfied by the sixteen theta functions and finally, after ingenious calculations, obtained the result that the quotients of two theta functions are solutions of the Jacobian inverse problem for $p = 2$.

BIBLIOGRAPHY

Göpel's major work is "Theoriae transcendentium Abelianarum primi ordinis adumbratio levis," in *Journal für die reine und angewandte Mathematik,* **35** (1847),

277–312, trans. into German as *Entwurf einer Theorie der Abelschen Transcendenten l. Ordnung,* Ostwalds Klassiker der Exacten Wissenschaften, no. 67 (Leipzig, 1895).

C. G. J. Jacobi and A. Crelle, "Notiz über A. Göpel," in *Journal für die reine und angewandte Mathematik,* **35** (1847), 313–318, was reprinted in the German version of "Theoriae. . . ."

WERNER BURAU

GORDAN, PAUL ALBERT (*b.* Breslau, Germany, 27 April 1837; *d.* Erlangen, Germany, 21 December 1912), *mathematics.*

The son of David Gordan, a merchant, Paul Albert attended Gymnasium and business school, then worked for several years in banks. His early interest in mathematics was encouraged by the private tutoring he received from N. H. Schellbach, a professor at the Friedrich Wilhelm Gymnasium. He attended Ernst Kummer's lectures in number theory at the University of Berlin in 1855, then studied at the universities of Breslau, Königsberg, and Berlin. At Königsberg he came under the influence of Karl Jacobi's school, and at Berlin his interest in algebraic equations was aroused. His dissertation (1862), which concerned geodesics on spheroids, received a prize offered by the philosophy faculty of the University of Breslau. The techniques that Gordan employed in it were those of Lagrange and Jacobi.

Gordan's interest in function theory led him to visit F. B. Riemann in Göttingen in 1862, but Riemann was ailing and their association was brief. The following year, Gordan was invited to Giessen by A. Clebsch, with whom he worked on the theory of Abelian functions. Together they wrote an exposition of the theory. In 1874 Gordan became a professor at Erlangen, where he remained until his retirement in 1910. He married Sophie Deuer, the daughter of a Giessen professor of Roman law, in 1869.

In 1868 Clebsch introduced Gordan to the theory of invariants, which originated in an observation of George Boole's in 1841 and was further developed by Arthur Cayley in 1846. Following the work of these two Englishmen, a German branch of the theory was developed by S. H. Aronhold and Clebsch, the latter elaborating the former's symbolic methods of characterizing algebraic forms and their invariants. Invariant theory was Gordan's main interest for the rest of his mathematical career; he became known as the greatest expert in the field, developing many techniques for representing and generating forms and their invariants. Correcting an error made by Cayley in 1856, Gordan in 1868 proved by constructive methods that the invariants of systems of binary forms possess a finite base. Known as the Gordan finite basis theorem, this instigated a twenty-year search for a proof in case of higher-order systems of forms. Making use of the Aronhold-Clebsch symbolic calculus and other elaborate computational techniques, Gordan spent much of his time seeking a general proof of finiteness. The solution to the problem came in 1888, when David Hilbert proved the existence of finite bases for the invariants of systems of forms of arbitrary order. Hilbert's proof, however, provided no method for actually finding the basis in a given case. Although Gordan was said to have objected to Hilbert's existential procedures, in 1892 he wrote a paper simplifying them. His version of Hilbert's theorem is the one presented in many textbooks.

Apparently unaware of James J. Sylvester's attempts in 1878, Gordan and a student, G. Alexejeff, applied the theory of invariants to the problems of chemical valences in 1900. Alexejeff went so far as to write a textbook on invariant theory that was intended for chemists. After some very hostile criticism from the mathematician Eduard Study and an indifferent reception by chemists, the project of introducing invariants into chemistry was dropped. Gordan made a few more contributions to invariant theory, but in the thirty years following Hilbert's work, interest in the subject declined among mathematicians.

The second major area of Gordan's contributions to mathematics is in solutions of algebraic equations and their associated groups of substitutions. Working jointly with Felix Klein in 1874–1875 on the relationship of icosahedral groups to fifth-degree equations, Gordan went on to consider seventh-degree equations with the group of order 168; and toward the end of his career, equations of the sixth degree with the group of order 360. His work was algebraic and computational, and utilized the techniques of invariant theory. Typical of Gordan's many contributions to these subjects are papers in 1882 and 1885 in which, following Klein's exposition of the general problem, he carries out the explicit reduction of the seventh-degree equation to the setting of the substitution group of order 168.

Gordan made other contributions to algebra and gave simplified proofs of the transcendence of e and π. The overall style of Gordan's mathematical work was algorithmic. He shied away from presenting his ideas in informal literary forms. He derived his results computationally, working directly toward the desired goal without offering explanations of the concepts that motivated his work.

Gordan's only doctoral student, Emmy Noether, was one of the first women to receive a doctorate in

Germany. She carried on his work in invariant theory for a while, but under the stimulus of Hilbert's school at Göttingen her interests shifted and she became one of the primary contributors to modern algebra.

BIBLIOGRAPHY

Further information on Gordan and his work may be found in Charles Fisher, "The Death of a Mathematical Theory," in *Archive for History of Exact Sciences,* **3**, no. 2 (1966), 137–159; and "The Last Invariant Theorists," in *European Journal of Sociology,* **8** (1967), 216–244. See also Felix Klein, *Lectures on the Icosahedron* (London, 1888), and *Lectures on Mathematics* (New York, 1911), lecture 9; Max Noether, "Paul Gordan," in *Mathematische Annalen,* **75** (1914), 1–41, which contains a complete bibliography of Gordan's works; and Hermann Weyl, "Emmy Noether," in *Scripta mathematica,* **3** (1935), 201–220.

C. S. FISHER

GORDON, WALTER (*b.* Apolda, Germany, 3 August 1893; *d.* Stockholm, Sweden, December 1940), *theoretical physics.*

After studying at the University of Berlin, Gordon obtained the Ph.D. there in 1921. He remained until 1929, when he became *Privatdozent*—and later associate professor—at the University of Hamburg. He lost his position there, like other professors of Jewish origin, in the spring of 1933. He became a member of the Institute of Mathematical Physics at the University of Stockholm in the fall of the same year. Through a grant from the Rockefeller Foundation and contributions from organizations for refugee aid and some private sources, he and his wife obtained a meager living. Poor conditions for science at the University of Stockholm, together with a general lack of understanding of existing German political conditions, prevented his obtaining a regular position.

Gordon's thorough mathematical foundation led him to rigorous solutions of important problems of quantum theory. He did not produce many writings, but his publications are of high quality. Some of his results were obtained by others about the same time, because of the intense development of quantum mechanics during the 1920's.

Soon after Erwin Schrödinger's publication of his first papers on wave mechanics in 1926, Gordon made several important contributions to the relativistic generalization of nonrelativistic quantum mechanics: the current-density vector of the scalar wave equation, and the quantitative formula for the Compton effect. That these results were not applicable to the electron—as was generally believed at that time—but to particles obeying Bose statistics, which, however, were discovered later, does not detract from the quality of this work. Soon after the appearance of Dirac's theory of the electron early in 1928, Gordon published two papers containing important contributions to this theory.

In the first paper he gave a rigorous treatment of both states of the Dirac equation in a Coulomb field: the bound states with the characteristic energy values given by the formula, derived earlier by Sommerfeld (before quantum mechanics and spin were known), and the continuous states, his treatment of which was of methodological importance. He returned to the continuous states, but in the nonrelativistic case, in a somewhat later paper containing a thorough study of the continuous wave functions in a Coulomb field, which was important for the problem of particle scattering.

In his next paper Gordon showed that the current-density vector, given by Dirac, can be split into two parts, one being formally equal to the one he himself had derived for the scalar equation—being, so to say, its kinematic part—while the other is connected with the spin of the electron. In his last paper, presented at the Congress of Scandinavian Mathematicians at Stockholm in 1934, he returned to a similar but more general problem, the possible states of a Schrödinger-type wave equation in a multidimensional space, applying it to the probability of a quantity given as a function of the momenta and the coordinates and ending the paper with establishment of the integral equation for the states in a Coulomb field as functions of the momenta.

During almost all of his stay in Sweden, Gordon participated eagerly in the seminars at the Institute of Mathematical Physics, to which his erudition, not merely in physics and mathematics, and his caustic but friendly humor gave a characteristic touch. He also gave lectures, among them a valuable course in group theory.

But Gordon's forced exile, taking him from the congenial and inspiring circle at the Hamburg Institute of Physics, and the uncertainty of his future brought an end to his creative powers. Early in 1937 his health declined, and inoperable stomach cancer was diagnosed. Good medical treatment and the care of his wife enabled him to live a reasonably normal life until the last months of 1940.

BIBLIOGRAPHY

Gordon's writings include "Der Comptoneffekt nach der Schrödingerschen Theorie," in *Zeitschrift für Physik,* **40** (1927), 117–133; "Die Energieniveaus des Wasserstoffatoms nach der Diracschen Quantentheorie des Elektrons," *ibid.,*

48 (1928), 11–14; "Über den Stoss zweier Punktladungen nach der Wellenmechanik," *ibid.,* 180–191; "Der Strom der Diracschen Elektronentheorie," *ibid.,* **50** (1928), 630–632; and "Eine Anwendung der Integralgleichungen in der Wellenmechanik," in *Comptes rendus du huitième Congrès des mathématiciens scandinaves tenu à Stockholm août 1934* (Lund, 1935), pp. 249–255.

On Gordon or his work, see Bertrand Russell, *Introduction to Mathematical Philosophy* (London–New York), trans. into German by E. J. Gumbel and W. Gordon as *Einführung in die mathematische Philosophie* (Munich, 1930), with a foreword by David Hilbert.

OSKAR KLEIN

GORE, GEORGE (*b.* Bristol, England, 22 January 1826; *d.* Birmingham, England, 20 December 1908), *electrochemistry.*

Gore was named for his father, who was a cooper. At the age of twelve he left school and went to work as an errand boy and later as apprentice to a cooper. All his life he was an avid reader and during his early years eagerly pursued an interest in science. In 1851 Gore moved to Birmingham, where he spent the rest of his life. There he was employed as a chemist by a local firm that manufactured phosphorus. Satisfactory phosphorus matches had been introduced into England only recently, and Birmingham had quickly become a center for their manufacture.

At this time Birmingham was also the center of a fast-growing electroplating industry, and Gore's interest in electricity led him to the investigation of plating techniques. From 1854 to 1863 he published many articles on electrodeposition of metals and acquired a reputation as a consultant for local manufacturers. Of particular interest was his study on the properties of electrodeposited antimony. In 1865 he was elected a fellow of the Royal Society for his work in the field of electrochemistry.

Gore published a study of the preparation and properties of anhydrous hydrofluoric acid, which he carried out from 1860 to 1870. In this work he repeated the electrolysis of hydrofluoric acid, using a variety of electrodes, in an attempt to isolate fluorine. In each case a fluoride compound was formed with the material of the anode, but with the use of a special carbon electrode Gore reported that he detected a faint odor resembling that of chlorine. A quantity of fluorine gas sufficient to permit its characterization was not isolated until 1886, by Henri Moissan, who used platinum-iridium electrodes. Gore also conducted an investigation of silver fluoride, which he published in 1870. He found that iodine combined with silver fluoride to produce IF_5.

From 1870 to 1880 Gore was a lecturer in physics and chemistry at King Edward's School in Birmingham. In 1880 he formed the Institute of Scientific Research and served as its director until his death at the age of eighty-two. During these years he was a consultant to industry and continued his research on electrolysis and voltaic cells.

BIBLIOGRAPHY

The 125 scientific papers of George Gore published to 1900 are listed in the Royal Society, *Catalogue of Scientific Papers,* vols. II, VII, X, XV. Among the most important are "On Hydrofluoric Acid," in *Philosophical Transactions of the Royal Society,* **159** (1869), 173–200; and "On Fluoride of Silver," *ibid.,* **160** (1870), 227–246. His books include *The Theory and Practice of Electro-Deposition* (London, 1856); *The Art of Electro-Metallurgy* (London, 1870); *The Scientific Basis of National Progress, Including That of Morality* (London, 1882); *The Art of Electrolytic Separation of Metals* (London, 1890); and *The Scientific Basis of Morality* (London, 1899).

Obituary notices appeared in *Nature,* **79** (1909), 290; *Electrician,* **62** (1909), 467; and *Proceedings of the Royal Society,* **84** (1911), xxi–xxii.

DANIEL P. JONES

GÖRGEY, ARTHUR (*b.* Toporc, Hungary [now Toporec, Czechoslovakia], 30 January 1818; *d.* Visegrád, Hungary, 21 May 1916), *chemistry.*

Görgey came from a very old but impoverished noble family. To please his father he entered the military engineering academy of the imperial army at Tulln, Austria. In 1837 he began active duty as a second lieutenant. Following his father's death in 1845 he left the army, in order to pursue his desire of studying chemistry. He entered the University of Prague, where, after completing his studies, he remained as an assistant to Joseph Redtenbacher. After the Hungarian Revolution of 1848 he returned to Hungary with the hope of obtaining a professorship. In the meantime, though, the Hungarian War of Independence had begun. Görgey immediately joined the newly created Hungarian national army and, as a trained officer, rapidly advanced through the ranks. He so distinguished himself in the battle of Ozora that he was promoted to general and was soon given command of an army. Following several defeats of the Hungarian army, Görgey was named commander-in-chief in 1849. In the so-called Winter Campaign he defeated the Austrian army in several battles and reconquered the capital city of Buda.

Unlike Louis Kossuth, the leader of the Hungarian Revolution, Görgey opposed a complete break with the Habsburg dynasty. When Russia began to give Austria military aid against Hungary and the situation became hopeless, Görgey forced Kossuth, who wanted to continue the fight, to resign. He then took command and surrendered to the Russians on 13 August 1849 near Világos. He was interned by the Austrians at Klagenfurt, where for a time he was a chemist in the gasworks. He returned to his native country following the Austro-Hungarian Agreement of 1867. He received a general's pension and spent the rest of his life justifying his actions.

Görgey remains one of the most disputed personalities in Hungarian history. His military and political activity is the subject of a vast number of books and even of plays; he is sometimes presented as the betrayer of the War of Independence and sometimes as a clever and realistic politician. It is almost completely forgotten in this literature that he is the same Görgey who is cited in organic chemistry textbooks as the discoverer of lauric acid. He made this discovery while carrying out an analysis of coconut oil during his stay in Prague. After saponifying and liberating the fatty acids, he separated them by means of distillation and found in the residue, through fractional crystallization, a component whose analysis indicated an unknown fatty acid consisting of twenty-four (today twelve) carbon atoms.

BIBLIOGRAPHY

Articles by Görgey on lauric acid are "Über die festen, flüchtigen, fetten Säuren des Cocosnussöls," in *Justus Liebigs Annalen der Chemie,* **66** (1848), 290; and *Sitzungsberichte der K. K. Akademie der Wissenschaften zu Wien,* Math.-naturwiss. Klasse (1848), 208. He also wrote an autobiography, *Mein Leben und Wirken in Ungarn,* 2 vols. (Leipzig, 1852).

On Görgey as a chemist, see F. Szabadváry, "Les recherches chimiques du général Görgey," in *Actes du XI Congrès international d'histoire des sciences,* IV (Warsaw, 1965), 78.

FERENC SZABADVÁRY

GOSSELET, JULES-AUGUSTE (*b.* Cambrai, France, 19 April 1832; *d.* Lille, France, 20 March 1916), *geology, paleontology.*

Son of Alexandre Gosselet, a pharmacist in Landrecies, Gosselet lived until the age of eleven in the open countryside, enjoying a freedom interrupted only by the lessons given him by his aunt, who lived in the same house. He then studied at the Institution Courboulis in Landrecies and finally at the *lycée* in Douai, where he received his *bachelier.*

Gosselet enrolled at the École de Pharmacie in Paris and remained in the French capital to take the *cours de candidature;* he then returned to Landrecies for his practical training, which at that time required three years. He occupied himself during this period with the education of his sisters; it proved so much to his taste that he abandoned the career that his father had planned for him in favor of one in education.

He entered the *collège* of Quesnoy, a small town near Landrecies, as assistant teacher of mathematics and remained there while preparing for his *licence,* for which he took the examination in Paris. Although he was unanimously rejected by the jury, his talents were recognized by his examiners; among them was Constant Prévost, who offered him the position of *préparateur* of the geology course at the Sorbonne. He held this post for seven years, identifying, preparing, and cataloging specimens. Of the two teachers who formed his views, Constant Prévost and Edmond Hébert, the former enjoyed trying out theoretical views, while the latter was a strict empiricist. As Charles Barrois aptly observed, Prévost taught his students to soar before they could walk, and Hébert taught them to walk but to remain earthbound.

While in Paris, Gosselet visited the nearby quarries and construction sites, thereby acquiring his views on the parallelism of marine and lacustrine facies.

In 1857 Gosselet presented a detailed section of the quarries at Etroeungt, situated near Landrecies and the Belgian frontier. Here he observed strata forming the transition from the Devonian to the Carboniferous. They were characterized by a mixture of fossils, a finding that opposed accepted ideas of clearly demarcated boundaries between the stages. This study was a prelude to his important researches on primary formations, which he submitted for the doctorate in natural sciences. In 1860 Gosselet became a teacher of physics and chemistry at the *lycée* in Bordeaux. He left secondary teaching in 1864 to become assistant professor of natural history in the Faculty of Science at Poitiers and several months later became professor of geology at Lille. He also assisted the Service de la Carte Géologique de France, for which he made some surveys, and worked for the Service de la Carte Géologique de Belgique.

Gosselet profited from his stay at Bordeaux by studying the shell marls of Saucats and Léognan, as well as the freshwater limestones of northeast Aquitaine and the limestone of Blaye; but it was his appointment to Lille which allowed him to devote himself to the study of the region bounded on the east by the Rhine, on the west by the English Channel, on the north by the Yser, and on the south by Paris. He began with the ancient massifs of the Ardennes.

With the presentation of "L'Ardenne" to the Société Géologique du Nord, Gosselet outlined the principles upon which his deductions were based: the intervention of the paleontological evidence; the notion of the stratigraphic basin, that is, of a depression similar to that of our present seas and surrounded by continents; the important role of faults; and the synchronism of facies. The application of these rules led him to several famous discoveries. He established that two basins had existed since the Devonian: the basin of Dinant and the basin of Namur, separated by an ancient shore, a narrow strip of Silurian. These two basins were gradually filled in, independently and under different bathymetric conditions. Gosselet did not propose an absolute synchronism of the same fauna. His principle is based on the variations of the sediments and the faunal succession under the geographic condition of the area. For Gosselet the paleogeographic reconstruction of a region furnished the essential data for the solution of local stratigraphic problems. He changed considerably the legends of the geological maps of Belgium in particular.

The study of numerous deep boreholes led Gosselet to recognize the continuity of the folding in the two distinct geographic massifs of the Boulonnais and the Ardennes. The paleontological horizons of the Boulonnais were repeated in the same order at the northern flank of the Namur basin. Thus, the coalfields of the Boulonnais were located in the Westphalian, not, as had been thought, in the Lower Carboniferous.

Gosselet determined that the Ardennes was the result of a fold. Since his work, inclined and even horizontal faults have been considered, as well as the vertical ones. He saw that the basin of Dinant—the entire Ardennes—was mobilized by tangential forces and its northern side overthrust the north of Belgium. These studies guided the German Geological Service in the interpretation of the Eifel plateau.

Gosselet was still interested in the cenozoic and mesozoic eras in the geology of the north of France. He mentioned successive seas which have invaded the region from the Triassic to the present. He showed that there was little uniformity in the accumulation conditions of the chalk deposits and no relationship to white marine chalk deposits. Moreover, he confirmed the existence of stepped faults of the Cretaceous (or epi-Cretaceous) strata that must be surmounted in approaching the Paris basin. The relief of the topographic surfaces of the north of France owes its fundamental features to a system of post-Cretaceous fractures. In Flanders these post-Cretaceous faults had, moreover, been preceded by post-Jurassic faults in Artois and post-Carboniferous ones in the north. "Gosselet thus revealed the evolution of a great tectonic line along which the earth's crust had contracted in a persistent and periodic manner since the beginning of time" (C. Barrois, p. 31).

Field studies and materials in historical archives led Gosselet to conclude that from the Tertiary to the present time, Flanders has been sinking at the foot of Artois in an uninterrupted but irregular movement. Gosselet was above all a field man whose observations gave rise to inspired hypotheses.

BIBLIOGRAPHY

I. Original Works. Gosselet's most important writings include *Esquisse géologique du département du Nord et des contrées voisines,* 2 pts. (Lille, 1871–1876); *Esquisse géologique du Nord de la France et des contrées voisines,* 4 pts. (Lille, 1880–1903); *L'Ardenne* (Paris, 1888); and "L'Ardenne," in *Annales de la Société géologique du Nord,* **16** (1889), 64–104.

II. Secondary Literature. On Gosselet or his work, see "Cinquantenaire scientifique de M. Jules Gosselet, 30 novembre 1902," in *Annales de la Société géologique du Nord,* **31** (1902), 157–296; Charles Barrois, "Jules Gosselet 1832–1916," *ibid.,* **44** (1919), 10–47, with portrait; and F. Stockmans, "Gosselet, Jules-Auguste, Alexandre," in *Biographie nationale publiée par l'Académie royale . . . de Belgique,* XXXIV (Brussels, 1967), cols. 425–429.

François Stockmans

GOSSETT, WILLIAM SEALY (also **"Student"**) (*b.* Canterbury, England, 13 June 1876; *d.* Beaconsfield, England, 16 October 1937), *statistical theory.*

The eldest son of Col. Frederic Gossett and Agnes Sealy, Gossett studied at Winchester College and New College, Oxford. He read mathematics and chemistry and took a first-class degree in natural sciences in 1899. In that year he joined Arthur Guinness and Sons, the brewers, in Dublin. Perceiving the need for more accurate statistical analysis of a variety of processes, from barley production to yeast fermentation, he urged the firm to seek mathematical advice. In 1906 he was therefore sent to work under Karl Pearson at University College, London. In the next few years Gossett made his most notable contributions to statistical theory, publishing under the pseudonym "Student." He remained with Guinness throughout his life, working mostly in Dublin, although he moved to London to take charge of a new brewery in 1935. He married Marjory Surtees in 1906; they had two children.

All of Gossett's theoretical work was prompted by practical problems arising at the brewery. The most famous example is his 1908 paper, "The Probable

Error of a Mean." He had to estimate the mean value of some characteristic in a population on the basis of very small samples. The theory for large samples had been worked out from the time of Gauss a century earlier, but when in practice large samples could not be obtained economically, there was no accurate theory of estimation. If an *n*fold sample gives values $x_1, x_2, \cdots x_n$, the sample mean

$$m = \frac{1}{n} \sum x_i$$

is used to estimate the true mean. How reliable is the estimate? Let it be supposed that the characteristic of interest is normally distributed with unknown mean μ and variance σ^2. The sample variance is

$$s^2 = \frac{1}{n} \sum (x_i - m)^2.$$

It was usual to take s as an estimate of σ; if it is assumed that $\sigma = s$, then for any error e, the probability that $|m - \mu| \leqslant e$ can be computed; and thus the reliability of the estimate of the mean can be assessed. But if n is small, s is an erratic estimator of σ; and hence the customary measure of accuracy is invalid for small samples.

Gossett analyzed the distribution of the statistic $z = (m - \mu)/s$. This is asymptotically normal as n increases but differs substantially from the normal for small samples. Experimental results m and s map possible values of z onto possible values of μ. Through this mapping a probability that $|x - \mu| \leqslant e$ is obtained. In particular, for any large probability, say 95 percent, Gossett could compute an error e such that it is 95 percent probable that $|x - \mu| \leqslant e$.

R. A. Fisher observed that the derived statistic $t = (n - 1)^{1/2}z$ can be computed for all n more readily than z can be. What came to be called Student's t-test of statistical hypotheses consists in rejecting a hypothesis if and only if the probability, derived from t, of erroneous rejection is small. In the theory of testing later advanced by Jerzy Neyman and Egon S. Pearson, Student's t-test is shown to be optimum. In the competing theory of fiducial probability advanced by R. A. Fisher, t is equally central.

Gossett was perhaps lucky that he hit on the statistic which has proved basic for the statistical analysis of the normal distribution. His real insight lies in his observation that the sampling distribution of such statistics is fundamental for inference. In particular, it paved the way for the analysis of variance, which was to occupy such an important place in the next generation of statistical workers.

BIBLIOGRAPHY

Gossetts' *"Student's" Collected Papers* were edited by E. S. Pearson and John Wishart (Cambridge–London, 1942; 2nd ed., 1947).

For further biography, consult E. S. Pearson, "Student as Statistician," in *Biometrika,* **30** (1938), 210–250; and "Studies in the History of Probability and Statistics, XVII," *ibid.,* **54** (1967), 350–353; and ". . . XX," *ibid.,* **55** (1968), 445–457.

IAN HACKING

GOULD, AUGUSTUS ADDISON (*b.* New Ipswich, New Hampshire, 23 April 1805; *d.* Boston, Massachusetts, 15 September 1866), *conchology, medicine.*

Gould was born into an old Yankee family. He was the son of Nathaniel Duren Gould and Sally Andrews Prichard. At fifteen he took complete charge of the work on his father's farm while at the same time continuing his studies at the New Ipswich Appleton Academy. In 1821, when he was seventeen, he entered Harvard College where he worked diligently to support himself, and it was during these undergraduate years that his interest in natural history began to develop. Noted among his classmates for his industry and determination, he graduated with respectable grades.

After graduating with a B.A. from Harvard in 1825, he was employed as a private tutor by the McBlair family of Baltimore County, Maryland. Simultaneously, he began the study of medicine and from 1828 to 1829 he studied with James Jackson and Walter Channing at the Massachusetts General Hospital. He received the M.D. in 1830 from Harvard Medical School.

A quiet contemplative man, Gould married Harriet Cushing Sheafe on 25 November 1833. He was a religious man, and for more than thirty years was an active member of the Baptist Church.

Gould's interest in natural history remained keen throughout his life and led him to his first publication. "Lamarck's Genera of Shells." Following the publication of *Cicindelidae of Massachusetts* (Boston, 1833), Gould began his lifelong devotion to the study of mollusks. Six years later, in 1840, he described thirteen new species of shells from Massachusetts, the first of such descriptions that would number 1,100 at the time of his death. Also in 1840, Gould demonstrated his artistic skill by illustrating an article on pupa with thirty drawings of small land snails.

In 1837 the General Court of Massachusetts authorized a geological survey of the state which was to include reports on botany and zoology. Gould was assigned the Invertebrata, exclusive of insects. His preliminary findings were published in a paper entitled, "Results of an Examination of the Species of Shells of Massachusetts and Their Geographical Distribution" (*Boston Journal of Natural History,* **3** [1840], 483–494). This was an epoch-making work since the problem of geographical distribution had received very little attention in other countries and none in the United States. He noted that Cape Cod formed a barrier to some species; of 203 species, eighty were not found south of the Cape and thirty were not found north. Certain species, he noticed, appeared and disappeared suddenly in an area, and he stated that it is necessary to collect data over a period of years to be certain of the distribution.

His *Report on the Invertebrata of Massachusetts* (1841), an octavo volume of almost 400 pages, was the first monograph published in the United States that attempted to describe the entire molluskan fauna of a geographical region. The book was illustrated with more than 200 figures drawn by Gould himself, who said,

> Every species described, indeed almost every species mentioned, has passed under my own eye. The descriptions of species previously known, have been written anew; partly, that they may be more minute in particulars, and partly, with the hope of using language somewhat less technical than is ordinarily employed by scientific men.

The volume gave him an international reputation, and it remains the definitive text on New England mollusks.

In 1846 Gould began his major descriptive work on shells that had been collected by conchologist Joseph Pitty Couthouy during the United States Exploring Expedition, 1838–1842. This work, which forms volume XII of the *United States Exploring Expedition . . .* (1852) was also published under the title "Mollusca and Shells . . ." in *Proceedings of the Boston Society of Natural History* (1846–1850).

When Louis Agassiz came to the United States in 1846, he immediately became a close friend of Gould, with whom he had previously corresponded. Agassiz and Gould collaborated on *Principles of Zoology* (1848), which was published in Boston at the firm of Gould's brother. This work was revised in 1852 and had three additional printings: 1860, 1861, and 1872. A German edition came out in 1851 and a British edition, enlarged by Thomas Wright, was published in 1867.

One of the founders of the Boston Society of Natural History, Amos Binney, died in 1847, leaving an unfinished work, *The Terrestrial Air Breathing Mollusks of the United States,* and instructions in his will that someone be appointed to finish the work. Since Binney had been a man of wealth, no expense was spared. Gould completed the work while Joseph Leidy of Philadelphia did the anatomical drawings. The plates were engraved by Alexander Lawson and the result (published between 1851 and 1857) was one of the most artistic monographs on American Mollusca ever printed in the United States.

During the war with Mexico several collections of shells were made along the western coast of the United States and Mexico by army officers and Gould was selected to identify their collections and to describe new species. Gould was also selected to do the report on mollusks collected by the naturalist William Stimpson for the North Pacific Exploring Expedition of 1853–1855. This work appeared serially from 1859 to 1861 in the *Proceedings of the Boston Society of Natural History.*

The description of the mollusks of the North Pacific Exploring Expedition was Gould's last important work on new material. At the time of his death, he was working on a revision of the *Report on the Invertebrata of Massachusetts,* which was completed by Amos Binney's son, William. According to William H. Dall, Gould's 1841 publication of this report initiated a period in the study of natural history that "was characterized by the broader scope of investigation, the interest in geographical distribution, the anatomy of the soft parts, and the more precise definition and exact discrimination of specific forms" ("Some American Conchologists," p. 97). Fully convinced of Gould's influence, Dall termed this second epoch of American conchology, the "Gouldian Period."

Yet despite the fact that Gould's work in conchology was his greatest contribution to science, his profession always remained that of medicine. According to his daughter, Gould encouraged and advised W. T. G. Morton, the reputed discoverer of ether; helped arrange the first ether demonstration; suggested the use of a valve for the first ether apparatus; gave medical care to some of Morton's first patients; suggested "letheon" as a name for ether; and acted as a mediator between Charles T. Jackson (who claimed original discovery of ether) and Morton.

As if to demonstrate both aspects of his scientific endeavors, Gould was active in both the Boston Society of Natural History and the Massachusetts Medical Society. In the former he served as curator (1831–1838), corresponding secretary (1834–1850), and second vice-president (1860–1866); in the latter he served as president (1865).

BIBLIOGRAPHY

I. ORIGINAL WORKS. An exhaustive bibliography of Gould's publications is in Jeffries Wyman, "Biographical

Memoir of Augustus Addison Gould," in *Biographical Memoirs. National Academy of Sciences,* **5** (1905), 91–113, with adds. by W. H. Dall. The Boston Museum of Science, which holds the material of the old Boston Society of Natural History, has 195 letters relating to Gould; his own annotated copy of *Otia Conchologica,* with notes and sketches laid in; his notebooks and drawings; the MSS for his natural history lectures at Harvard (1834–1836); and sixteen of his letters. Houghton Library at Harvard, the Rare Book Room at the Boston Public Library, the Academy of Natural Sciences of Philadelphia, and the Countway Library of Medicine all contain letters relating to Gould as well.

II. SECONDARY LITERATURE. On Gould or his work, see Harley H. Bartlett, "The Reports of the Wilkes Expedition; and the Work of the Specialists in Science: Gould's 'Mollusca and Shells,' Vol. 12," in *Proceedings of the American Philosophical Society,* **82** (1940), 650–655; Thomas T. Bouve, *Historical Sketch of the Boston Society of Natural History,* Anniversary Memoirs. Boston Society of Natural History (1880), with the life of Gould based on Jeffries Wyman's account (see below), pp. 112–116, with portrait; William H. Dall, "Some American Conchologists," in *Proceedings of the Biological Society of Washington.* **4** (1888), 120–122; and Daniel C. Haskell, *The United States Exploring Expedition, 1838–1842, and Its Publications, 1844–1874* (New York, 1942).

See also Jeffries Wyman, "An Account of the Life and Scientific Career of the Late Dr. A. A. Gould" in *Proceedings of the Boston Society of Natural History,* **11** (1867), 188–205; Richard I. Johnson, *The Recent Mollusca of Augustus Addison Gould,* Bulletin 239. United States National Museum (Washington, D.C., 1964); George E. Gifford, Jr., "The Forgotten Man in the Ether Controversy," in *Harvard Medical Alumni Bulletin,* **40,** no. 2 (1965), 14–19; *Dictionary of American Biography,* VII (New York, 1931), 446–447; and *Dictionary of American Medical Biography* (New York, 1928), pp. 483–484. For a list of societies and institutions of which Gould was a member see the "Biographical Memoir" cited above.

GEORGE E. GIFFORD, JR.

GOULD, BENJAMIN APTHORP (*b.* Boston, Massachusetts, 27 September 1824; *d.* Cambridge, Massachusetts, 26 November 1896), *astronomy.*

The eldest of the four children born to Benjamin Apthorp Gould and Lucretia Dana Goddard, Gould was educated at Boston Latin School (of which his father had been the principal) and Harvard College. Originally intending to take up classical languages, he came under the influence of Benjamin Peirce and his interests shifted to physics and mathematics. After graduation (1844) he taught for a while at Boston Latin School and then sailed to Europe for further study in astronomy; this included a year at Berlin and then work under Gauss at Göttingen, where he received his doctorate (1848).

On returning home, Gould was very depressed by the primitive level of scientific research in his country; but rather than accept a professorship at Göttingen, he vowed to dedicate his efforts to raising the reputation of American astronomy. He did much toward this by founding the *Astronomical Journal* in 1849; although at times forced to operate under extreme difficulties, financial and otherwise, Gould edited the *Journal* for a dozen years, until publication was suspended because of the Civil War.

From 1852 to 1867 Gould was head of the longitude department of the U.S. Coast Survey. He quickly appreciated the utility of the telegraph in determining longitudes and measured the longitude difference between Greenwich and Washington over the first transatlantic cable.

In 1852 Gould was approached concerning the directorship of the Dudley Observatory, recently established by the citizens of Albany, New York. Declining the directorship, he agreed in 1855 to serve, without compensation, as executive officer of the observatory's scientific council, the other members of which were Peirce, Joseph Henry, and A. D. Bache. These scientists, members of the Lazzaroni, were all aware of the poor state of American science and had long been trying to found national institutions for scientific research. Bache, as superintendent of the U.S. Coast Survey, provided the Dudley Observatory with instruments and observers; Gould in particular devoted much effort to converting the observatory into a worthy scientific institution and traveled to Europe to order equipment. The trustees of the observatory agreed to bear financial responsibility for the publication of the *Astronomical Journal,* and in 1857 the *Journal*'s headquarters were transferred there. Gould eventually accepted the directorship and moved to Albany early in 1858. The trustees felt that the observatory should serve the public and had all along been annoyed by delays and unforeseen expenses. Matters came to a head in a vicious newspaper campaign, in which Gould was charged with being incompetent, disloyal, and arrogant. The trustees resolved to remove him from the directorship and to dissolve the scientific council. But the director and the council had much invested in the observatory and refused to abandon it. Finally, on 3 January 1859, Gould was forcibly driven from his home by a band of toughs hired by the trustees, several of his papers being destroyed in the process. He then returned to Cambridge.

During Gould's early associations with the Dudley Observatory he attempted to determine the solar parallax from the Chilean observations of Mars and Venus made by James M. Gilliss, although this material was not entirely adequate for the purpose. After leaving Albany he prepared his "Standard Mean

Right Ascensions of Circumpolar and Time Stars" (1862), the first attempt to combine into one catalog stellar positions determined at a number of observatories. In 1861 he undertook the discussion of the observations made at the U.S. Naval Observatory during the preceding decade, and he subsequently reduced an important series of observations made by Joseph Dagelet at Paris between 1783 and 1785.

Meanwhile, from 1859 to 1864, Gould was greatly involved with his late father's mercantile business. He also became an actuary for the U.S. Sanitary Commission, in which capacity he accumulated extensive data on the vital statistics of military and naval personnel.

In 1861 Gould married Mary Apthorp Quincy, and his subsequent astronomical career owed much to her aid. She helped provide an observatory near Cambridge, and between 1864 and 1867 Gould made meridian observations of faint stars near the north celestial pole. In collaboration with Lewis Rutherfurd he investigated the application of photography to astrometry (1866), specifically to the stars in the Pleiades and Praesepe clusters.

About 1865 Gould resolved to travel to the southern hemisphere for the purpose of charting the southern stars with the detail achieved for the northern stars. With the cooperation of President Domingo Sarmiento he arrived in Córdoba, Argentina, in 1870 to found the Argentine National Observatory. Both the instruments and the accessory supplies had to be obtained from North America or Europe, and there was considerable delay before these materials reached Córdoba. Meanwhile, Gould and his four assistants were not idle; with nothing more than binoculars they determined the magnitudes and positions of all the naked-eye stars in the southern heavens. This was no easy task, and the results were published (1879) in the first volume of the *Resultados del Observatorio nacional argentino en Córdoba,* under the title "Uranometria argentina." This work clearly established "Gould's belt" of bright stars, spread in a broad band inclined at some 20 degrees to the galactic equator.

The observatory slowly took shape, and late in 1872 the first zone observations of the southern stars were made. Most of these observations were completed by 1877, but the onerous task of reduction took several years more; and the "Catálogo de las zonas estelares," comprising positions of 73,160 stars between 23 and 80 degrees south declination, was published as volumes 7 and 8 of the *Resultados* (1884). Parallel with this immense project the "Catálogo General" was prepared, giving more accurate positions, determined as the result of repeated measurements, of 32,448 stars (*Resultados,* **14** [1886]).

Gould returned to Massachusetts in 1885 with some 1,400 photographs of southern star clusters, which he spent much of his remaining years measuring and reducing. After a lapse of a quarter of a century he was also able to resume publication of the *Astronomical Journal,* which he continued to edit until his death.

BIBLIOGRAPHY

There is a complete bibliography of Gould's works following Comstock's memoir (see below), pp. 171–180.

On Gould or his work, see G. C. Comstock, "Biographical Memoir. Benjamin Apthorp Gould," in *Biographical Memoirs. National Academy of Sciences,* **17** (1924), 153–170; A. Hall, "Benjamin Apthorp Gould," in *Popular Astronomy,* **4** (1897), 337–340; and S. C. Chandler, "The Life and Work of Dr. Gould," *ibid.,* 341–347.

BRIAN G. MARSDEN

GOULD, JOHN (*b.* Lyme Regis, England, 14 September 1804; *d.* London, England, 3 February 1881), *ornithology.*

Gould was the son of a gardener and worked at first with his father at Windsor Castle; later he was a gardener in Yorkshire and had the opportunity to observe birds and teach himself taxidermy. The Zoological Society of London was formed in 1826, and after a competition Gould was appointed taxidermist under Nicholas Vigors. He remained with the society until his death. Elizabeth Coxen, whom he married in 1829, was skilled at drawing and took up lithography to help in her husband's publications. She also accompanied him on his travels. They had six children.

In 1830 Gould received a collection of bird skins from the Himalayas, and from them he produced a volume of colored illustrations with text by Vigors. The eighty plates, issued in twenty monthly groups, achieved a high level of accuracy in spite of the absence of living material. No publisher was willing to risk the volume, so Gould published it himself and continued as his own publisher with considerable financial success; his editions were limited to about 250 and were sold mainly on subscription. In all, he issued forty-one volumes in elephant folio containing some 3,000 plates, mostly of birds from all over the world. He also published numerous scientific papers, mainly on new species, which showed his ability in dealing with taxonomic details. The plates, all lithographed and hand-painted, are among the finest bird pictures ever produced: Gould experimented with new techniques and achieved an extraordinary effect conveying the sheen on feathers. The pictures show animals in their natural habitat, and some include fine illustrations of flowers as well; they are on the whole accurate, but Gould has sometimes been criticized for sacrificing correct detail to effect.

Gould's most significant work was *The Birds of Australia.* He issued two volumes of plates and then decided that he must visit Australia before continuing; he and his wife spent 1838–1840 there with an assistant, John Gilbert. They explored Australasia extensively and recorded their findings in notes, drawings, and letters. Issued between 1840 and 1869, the new series of plates, each with a page of description of the species, included notes on distribution and adaptation to the environment, an index of species, and a systematic table. Later he issued a series on Australian mammals, noting the parallels in form and function between marsupial and placental mammals. Gould is probably better remembered in Australia than in his home country; the Gould League of Bird Lovers was founded in Victoria in 1909.

He worked on birds collected by expeditions of the *Beagle* and the *Sulphur* and made plates for their reports. He also issued works on the birds of Europe, Asia, Britain, and New Guinea, and on special groups. In 1843 Gould was elected a fellow of the Royal Society; and during the exhibition of 1851 he displayed his collection of hummingbirds in the gardens of the Zoological Society. He later published a monograph on them. Volumes incomplete at the time of his death in 1881 were finished by R. Bowdler Sharpe, then at the British Museum (Natural History).

Gould, who was almost entirely self-taught, had a rare combination of qualities as naturalist, artist, and businessman which enabled him to leave an extremely valuable record of bird life.

BIBLIOGRAPHY

I. Original Works. His first publication was *A Century of Birds From the Himalaya Mountains* (London, 1831–1832), written with N. A. Vigors; the next was *The Birds of Europe,* 5 vols. (London, 1832–1837). The first attempt at a synopsis of the 4-part *The Birds of Australia and the Adjacent Islands,* 2 vols. (London, 1837–1838), is now very rare and was superseded by *The Birds of Australia,* 7 vols. (London, 1840–1848) and *Supplement* (London, 1851–1869). Of his works on special groups the most important is *A Monograph of the Trochilidae or Humming-Birds,* 5 vols. (London, 1849–1861), and a 5-part *Supplement* (London, 1880–1887). Modern reproductions of some of the plates were issued in a smaller format as *Plates of Birds of Europe, Reproduced,* 2 vols. (London, 1966), with text by A. Rutgers.

II. Secondary Literature. The most useful biography and bibliography of Gould are in R. Bowdler Sharpe, *An Analytical Index to the Works of the Late John Gould, F. R. S., With a Biographical Memoir and Portrait* (London, 1893); both are based on the obituary by Tommaso Salvadori in *Atti della R. Accademia delle scienze* (Turin), **16** (1881), 789–810. Two other good short accounts are G. T. Bettany, in *Dictionary of National Biography,* XXII (London, 1890), 287–288, which includes the bibliography of his separately published works and references to other useful obituaries; and A. H. Chisholm, in *Australian Dictionary of Biography,* I (Melbourne, 1966), 465–467. A popular account is C. L. Barrett, *The Bird Man: A Sketch of the Life of John Gould* (Melbourne–Sydney, 1938). The centenary of Gould's arrival in Australia was celebrated by a commemorative issue of *Emu,* **88,** pt. 2 (Oct. 1938), 89–244, which includes evaluations and information about the location of MSS by Gould, most of which went to Australian libraries.

Assessment of the artistic value of Gould's work can be found in the substantial review in *The Times,* no. 20,897 (3 Sept. 1851), 7; and in S. Sitwell *et al., Fine Bird Books* (London, 1953), pp. 25–40. The plates were dated by F. H. Waterhouse in *Dates of Publication of Some of the Zoological Works of the Late John Gould* (London, 1885); this includes a short biographical sketch but does not cover *The Birds of Europe,* for which Waterhouse did a MS volume of dates (1904), still in the library of the Zoological Society of London.

There is a portrait of Gould at the Linnean Society, of which he was a fellow. His collection of birds from Australia was sold to a collector in Philadephia, but his collection of hummingbirds was bought after his death by the British Museum (Natural History), which published a catalog by A. Günther, *A Guide to the Gould Collection of Humming Birds* (London, 1881; 2nd ed., 1883; 3rd ed., 1884).

Diana M. Simpkins

GOURSAT, ÉDOUARD JEAN-BAPTISTE (*b.* Lanzac, Lot, France, 21 May 1858; *d.* Paris, France, 25 November 1936), *mathematics.*

Goursat completed his elementary and secondary studies at the *collège* of Brive-la-Gaillarde and after only one preparatory year at the Lycée Henri IV in Paris was admitted in 1876 to the École Normale Supérieure. There he began a lifelong association with Émile Picard, whom he credited with being instrumental in his choice of a career. Claude Bouquet, Charles Briot, Jean Darboux, and Charles Hermite were among the faculty who provided inspiration and style to Goursat, who received his D.Sc. in 1881. "Hermite," Goursat said in 1935, "is the first who revealed to me the artistic side of mathematics."

Goursat was devoted throughout his academic career to research, teaching, and the training of future mathematics teachers. In 1879 he was appointed lecturer at the University of Paris, a post he held until 1881, when he was appointed to the Faculty of Sciences of Toulouse. He returned to the École Normale Supérieure in 1885 and remained there until 1897, when he was appointed professor of analysis at the University of Paris. He held this post until he reached the age of mandatory retirement, at which time he became an honorary professor. Simultaneously he was tutor in analysis at the École Polytechnique (1896–1930) and at the École Normale Supérieure, St.-Cloud (1900–1929).

Goursat received numerous honors, including the Grand Prix des Sciences Mathématiques (1886) for "Études des surfaces qui admettent tous les plans de symétrie d'un polyèdre régulier." He was awarded the Prix Poncelet in 1889 and the Prix Petit d'Ormoy in 1891. In 1919 he was elected to the Academy of Sciences. Goursat was also a chevalier of the Legion of Honor and president of the Mathematical Society of France. In 1936 an issue of the *Journal de mathématiques pures et appliquées* was dedicated to him on the occasion of the fiftieth anniversary of his becoming a teacher.

Goursat was a leading analyst of his day. At the University of Paris the "Goursat course" and "Goursat certificate" became synonyms for his course in analysis and its successful completion. One of his earliest works removed the redundant requirement of the continuity of the derivative in Augustin Cauchy's integral theorem. The theorem, now known as the Cauchy-Goursat theorem, states that if a function $f(z)$ is analytic inside and on a simple closed contour C, then

$$\int_C f(z)dz = 0.$$

Goursat's papers on the theory of linear differential equations and their rational transformations, as well as his studies on hypergeometric series, Kummer's equation, and the reduction of Abelian integrals, form, in the words of Picard, "a remarkable ensemble of works evolving naturally one from the other." Goursat introduced the notion of orthogonal kernels and semiorthogonals in connection with Erik Fredholm's work on integral equations. He made original contributions to almost every important area of analysis of his time. His *Cours d'analyse mathématique,* long a classic text in France, contained much material that was original at the time of publication.

Goursat brought warmth to his teaching and the same dedication that he applied to his research. He more than fulfilled the prediction of Darboux, who wrote in 1879: "Student [Goursat] whose development was extremely rapid, excellent mathematician, sure to become as superior a teacher as Appell and Picard." Former students and colleagues alike praised his clarity, precision, orderly teaching, and devotion to his students. His personal warmth and effectiveness are perhaps best summed up in the encomium of a former student and later collaborator, Gaston Julia: ". . . in the name of all those who received . . . not only the treasures of your science, but also the treasures of your heart, let me express . . . our faithful gratitude, . . . having received from you the nourishment of the soul, the bread of science and the example of virtue."

BIBLIOGRAPHY

I. Original Works. Goursat's doctoral thesis was "Sur l'équation différentielle linéaire qui admet pour intégrale la série hypergéometrique," in *Annales scientifiques de l'École normale superieure,* **10,** supp. (1881), 3–142. The Cauchy-Goursat theorem first appeared under the title "Démonstration du théorème de Cauchy," in *Acta mathematica,* **4** (1884), 197–200. This article is reproduced under the same title in *Bihang till K. Svenska vetenskapsakademiens handlingar,* **9,** no. 5 (1884), and essentially the same material appeared under the title "Sur la définition générale des fonctions analytiques, d'après Cauchy," in *Transactions of the American Mathematical Society,* **1** (1900), 14–16. "Études des surfaces qui admettent tous les plans de symétrie d'un polyèdre régulier" was published in *Annales scientifiques de l'École normale supérieure,* **4** (1887), 161–200, 241–312, 317–340.

Goursat's best-known work is *Cours d'analyse mathématique,* 2 vols. (Paris, 1902–1905; 2nd ed., 3 vols., 1910–1913); Earle Raymond Hedrick provided the English trans. of vol. I: *A Course in Mathematical Analysis* (Boston, 1904) and, with Otto Dunkel, of vol. II (Boston, 1917).

Other major works include *Leçons sur l'intégration des équations aux dérivées partielles du premier ordre,* Carlo Bourlet, ed. (Paris, 1891), trans. into German with a preface by Sophus Lie (1893), and a 2nd ed., rev. and enl. by J. Hermann (Paris, 1921); *Le problème de Backlund* (Paris, 1925); and *Leçons sur les séries hypergéométriques et sur quelques fonctions qui s'y rattachent* (Paris, 1936).

Notice sur les travaux scientifiques de M. Édouard Goursat (Paris, 1900), the best single source on Goursat's work up to that year, contains discussions by Goursat of his work in various branches of analysis, listed by topic. The bibliography (104 titles) is listed by journal of publication. The variety of topics and the level of their discussion clearly demonstrate Goursat's breadth and depth of accomplishments.

II. Secondary Literature. The notice on Goursat, in *Larousse mensuel,* no. 151 (Sept. 1919), p. 894, in honor of his election to the Academy of Sciences, is a good survey of Goursat's research contributions to that year.

Jubilé scientifique de M. Édouard Goursat (Paris, 1936) is a collection of speeches delivered to Goursat on 20 Nov. 1935 by former students, colleagues, and associates on the occasion of his fiftieth teaching anniversary. His responses to each address are included. This small vol. consists of encomiums relating to his mathematical and teaching accomplishments. The address of Gaston Julia, with its allusions to Kipling's *Jungle Book,* is particularly delightful. All of the quotations used in the body of this notice were translated from this source.

HENRY S. TROPP

GOUY, LOUIS-GEORGES (*b.* Vals-les-Bains, Ardèche, France, 19 February 1854; *d.* Vals-les-Bains, 27 January 1926), *general physics, optics.*

Almost nothing is known of Gouy's upbringing and education. He spent most of his productive life as a professor at the Faculty of Sciences at the University of Lyons. He was elected correspondent for the Section of General Physics of the Academy of Sciences on 25 November 1901. On 28 April 1913 he was made a nonresident member of the Academy.

Gouy was a prolific researcher, publishing dozens of articles in the major French scientific journals of his day. Most of his significant work was devoted to some of the more obscure problems of optics. By the 1870's, when Gouy began his researches, optical theory had been subjected to a highly developed and fairly rigorous mathematical analysis, and it was felt that most of the major optical problems had been solved. By applying his talents to some of the less obvious areas of optical theory, Gouy was able to make contributions of considerable significance and originality.

Gouy's first major optical paper, published in 1880, dealt with the velocity of light. He showed that in dispersive media it was necessary to distinguish between what is called the group velocity of light (the velocity of a series of light waves subject to direct measurement by J. B. Foucault's method) and the somewhat higher and less easily measured velocity of the individual waves. Lord Rayleigh (John William Strutt) in a later, independent demonstration of Gouy's theory labeled these two velocities the "group-speed" and the "wave-speed," respectively. Both Gouy and Rayleigh derived their results from mathematical theory. A. A. Michelson later confirmed them empirically, using carbon disulfide as a dispersive medium.

In another important paper concerning the propagation of light waves, Gouy demonstrated that spherical waves of weak emission advance more rapidly than plane waves emitted at the same time, by a value that rapidly approaches one-quarter of a wavelength. An analogous consideration led him in 1890 to show that when spherical light waves are sent through the focus of a concave mirror, they "advance" by one-half a wavelength (in other words, the sign of their amplitude is reversed). This he demonstrated from a simple calculation derived from Christian Huygen's analysis of point sources and also proved it experimentally. When two rays of white light are made to interfere with one another after being reflected from plane mirrors, the central fringe is always white. Gouy then showed that when one of these rays is reflected against a concave mirror, the central fringe is black because of the interference resulting from the reversal of the amplitude of the ray that passes through the focus of the concave mirror.

Another area in which Gouy carried on extensive and original experimentation concerned the diffraction produced by the passage of light across the edge of an opaque screen. By concentrating his light on the border of the screen by means of a convergent lens and by using very thin screens with sharply defined edges, he was able to observe deviations of light rays at very large angles. His experimental results showed—contrary to what had been the accepted theory—that the nature of the screen played a large role in determining the degree of diffraction and the manner in which the light waves were polarized. The thickness of the screen and the material of which it was composed were especially important considerations in all experiments of this nature.

Although Gouy's major achievements were in the realm of optics, he also devoted considerable attention to other areas of experimental and mathematical physics. He made important studies on the inductive powers of dielectrics, on electrocapillarity, and on the effects of a magnetic field on electrical discharge in rarefied gases. He was interested in spectroscopy. He investigated the emissive and absorptive powers of colored flames, and he invented a device to feed a constant supply of a salt to a flame in order to allow time to measure its spectroscopic emissions. The device made the air or gas take up the salt in the form of a fine spray before it reached the burner.

Gouy was also interested in phenomena produced by randomness of motion in nature. He was the first, perhaps, to point out that the nature of white light may best be understood as a complex disturbance resulting from a series of highly irregular impulses emanating from the source of light. The prism analyzes the irregular disturbance into constituents of definite wavelength, in the same way that a complex periodic function is analyzed mathematically into its simple harmonic components in a Fourier series. Gouy also made a detailed study of the randomness of Brownian movement in which he demonstrated that despite the irregularity of the movement, there is nevertheless a certain consistency independent of all adventitious circumstances.

Because of the number and variety of his researches, it is difficult to make a general evaluation of Gouy's career. His name is associated with no physical law or theory. He made no important breakthroughs; he opened no new areas of research. Great scientists work at the frontiers of knowledge; Gouy labored in the rear areas where most of the important work had already been accomplished. The significance of his researches was, in a sense, in tidying up the field of physical knowledge by extending already discovered theory into the obscurer areas that had been passed over in the first waves of discovery. His function was to integrate new phenomena into old theory, to extend and complete understanding rather than initiate it. If his work was not as significant as that of the great names in physics, it was nevertheless a vital and necessary part of the development of the science of his era.

BIBLIOGRAPHY

Gouy wrote no major works. A list of his many articles can be found in Poggendorff, IV, 520–521; V, 441–442; and VI, 933.

See the *éloge* of Gouy by Émile Picard in *Comptes rendus hebdomadaires des séances de l'Académie des Sciences,* **182** (1926), 293–295. Another notice by Picard was read to the Academy on 20 December 1937.

J. B. GOUGH

GRAAF, REGNIER DE (*b.* Schoonhoven, Netherlands, 30 July 1641; *d.* Delft, Netherlands, 21 August 1673), *medicine, anatomy, physiology.*

De Graaf began his medical studies in 1660 at Utrecht and continued them at Leiden, where he was a student of Franciscus Sylvius and Johannes van Horne. One of his fellow students was Jan Swammerdam; their friendship was later transformed into violent hostility as a result of priority disputes. As early as 1664 de Graaf published a work on the pancreatic juice; it was immediately translated into French and reprinted many times. After a period in France he received an M.D. degree at Angers in 1665. He established himself as a well-known practicing physician in Delft and privately did scientific research. In spite of his international reputation de Graaf held no university posts, presumably as a result of his being a Roman Catholic. According to a tradition reported by Antoine Portal, he was proposed as successor to Sylvius, but he refused the offer. During this period the Netherlands was involved in successive wars with England and France, a circumstance which did not prevent a remarkable artistic, philosophic, and scientific flowering. Living in Delft at the same time were Anton van Leeuwenhoek and the painter Vermeer. De Graaf was friendly with Leeuwenhoek, whom he introduced to the Royal Society of London in 1673 by a letter which is still preserved.

De Graaf is rightly considered one of the creators of experimental physiology. His reputation was great in his own lifetime, as is evident from the many editions and translations of his works which followed each other in rapid succession. In the eighteenth century Hermann Boerhaave praised him, and Portal devoted twenty pages to him in his *Histoire de l'anatomie et de la chirurgie.* In the nineteenth century Claude Bernard held him in very high esteem and dedicated his meditations on the role of the experimental physiologist to him.

De Graaf published works on very diverse subjects; he also devised the method of the pancreatic fistula. He is known, though, through the term "Graafian follicle," which commemorates his crucial role in the accurate and concrete description of the anatomy and physiology of the female mammalian reproductive organs. The problem of reproduction was vigorously debated around 1665. Many famous writers of the period devoted their works and their speculations to the problems of generation and claimed priority in bitter disputes. Only the name of de Graaf remains. In 1668 he had published a treatise on the male reproductive organs which was immediately reprinted several times; but its contents, showing little originality, are all but forgotten. On the other hand, his treatise on the female reproductive organs constitutes an important step in the history of biology.

For the female mammalian gonad de Graaf adopted the name "ovary," a term proposed at the time by such authors as van Horne and Swammerdam. During this period there appeared the completely new technique of injecting vessels with colored substances, an invention claimed by many, particularly by Swammerdam, who reproached de Graaf with having stolen it from him. The quarrel, often conducted with great bitterness, was sent in letters to the Royal Society for arbitration. According to a story spread by Leeuwenhoek twenty years later, de Graaf died from the exhaustion brought on by the polemic; but it is much more likely that he died of an epidemic illness.

It is easier to grasp the originality of de Graaf's discoveries from his illustrations than from his text. He examined and dissected the ovaries of numerous mammals, including the human, and he succeeded in isolating the ovarian vesicles with their envelopes. In the cow he described the ovary before and after mating and ascertained that its structure changed. He was thus the first to discover the morphological changes of the female gonad which accompany its physiological functions. De Graaf established that the vesicles disappeared to make room for a "glandulous substance projecting from the female testicle." Hence he was the first to recognize the glandular nature of the corpus luteum, a fundamental discovery that was not definitely established until around 1900 and that played an essential role in the development of modern sexual endocrinology. It is beyond doubt that de Graaf correctly depicted the stigma of the corpus luteum, which indicates rupture of the ovarian follicles. His only error was not recognizing the rupture of the follicle. Instead, he supposed that the follicle in its entirety constituted the egg expelled into the Fallopian tube.

The mammalian egg was not discovered until 1827, by Karl Ernst von Baer. The phenomenon of ovulation or follicular rupture was clarified in the course of extended research and debate throughout the nineteenth century but was not definitively established until the first years of the twentieth century. It is remarkable that de Graaf followed the progress of pregnancy in the rabbit from mating until birth. He left several plates illustrating it and was fully aware that the egg traveling in the tube was smaller than the ovarian follicle, but he was unable to explain this, not having observed the follicular rupture. It is very instructive to compare de Graaf's book on the female reproductive organs with the writings of his contemporaries and competitors. One can then see the fundamental differences between the precise details given by de Graaf and those of his colleagues, which are frequently inexact and allow free rein to an often unbridled imagination.

De Graaf's iconography deserves special mention. His likeness was engraved in 1666 by Gérard Edelinck, one of the most celebrated portraitists of the age, and is the frontispiece in a number of editions. A portrait of 1672 has likewise become well known. There is also a drawing of great artistic merit, attributed to Verkolje, which probably represents de Graaf in his laboratory, in the act of dissecting a cadaver. As a second frontispiece to his books there are some symbolic engravings of great iconographic interest. The one in the work on the pancreatic juice (1671) long held the attention of Claude Bernard, who considered it a symbol of experimental physiology in the service of medicine. The plates representing ovaries and internal reproductive organs have been reproduced, particularly in W. M. Bayliss' treatise, which, around 1920, constituted a veritable *summa* of general physiology. In 1943 the famous American endocrinologist and historian of medicine G. W. Corner published a translation of the most important chapters concerning the ovary along with the relevant plates. The present author has published a detailed commentary on these figures and believes that even today the physiology of the ovary can be illustrated by utilizing de Graaf's plates without modification.

BIBLIOGRAPHY

I. Original Works. Complete bibliographies of de Graaf's writings are in the articles by Barge and Daniels. Collections of his works include *Opera omnia* (Lyons, 1678; Amsterdam, 1705, with a short biography). Individual writings mentioned in the text are *De succi pancreatici natura et usu exercitatio anatomico medica* (Leiden, 1664); *De virorum organis generationi inservientibus, de clysteris et de usu siphonis in anatomia* (Leiden-Rotterdam, 1668); *Tractatus anatomico-medicus de succi pancreatici natura et usu* (Leiden, 1671); and *De mulierum organis generationi inservientibus tractatus novus . . .* (Leiden, 1672).

II. Secondary Literature. On de Graaf or his work, see J. A. J. Barge, "Reinier de Graaf, 1641–1941," in *Mededeelingen der Nederlandsche Akademie van Wetenschappen,* Afdeeling Letterkunde **5,** no. 5 (1942), 257–281; W. M. Bayliss, *Principles of General Physiology* (London, 1924), p. 882, cf. p. 253; A. M. Cetto, "Un portrait inconnu de Régnier de Graaf," in *Ciba-Symposium,* **5** (1958), 208–211; G. W. Corner, "On the Female Testes or Ovaries," in *Essays in Biology in Honor of H. M. Evans* (Los Angeles, 1943), p. 686, cf. pp. 121–137; and *The Hormones in Human Reproduction* rev. ed. (Princeton, 1947), p. 281; C. E. Daniels, "De Graaf," in *Biographisches Lexikon der hervorragenden Aerzte aller Zeiten und Völker,* II (Leipzig, 1885), 616; P. Delaunay, *La vie médicale aux XVIe, XVIIe, XVIIIe siècles* (Paris, 1935), p. 556; C. Dobell, *Antony van Leeuwenhoek and His Little Animals* (Amsterdam, 1932), p. 435; E. Gasking, *Investigations Into Generation* (Baltimore, 1967), p. 192; M. Klein, "Histoire et actualité de l'iconographie de l'ouvrage: *De mulierum organis generationi inservientibus* (1672) de R. de Graaf," in *Comptes rendus du 16e Congrès international d'histoire de la médecine, Montpellier, 1958,* I (Brussels, 1959), 316–320, also in *Yperman* (Brussels), **8,** fasc. 9 (1961), 3–7; and "Claude Bernard face au milieu scientifique de son époque," in *Philosophie et méthodologie scientifiques de Claude Bernard* (Paris, 1967), p. 170, cf. pp. 97, 98; J. Lévy-Valensi, *Les médecins et la médecine française au XVIIe siècle* (Paris, 1933), p. 668; J. Needham, *A History of Embryology,* 2nd ed., rev. (Cambridge, 1959), p. 304; E. Nordenskjöld, *Die Geschichte der Biologie* (Jena, 1926), p. 648; A. Portal, *Histoire de l'anatomie et de la chirurgie,* III (Paris, 1770), 214–235; R. C. Punnett, "Ovists and Animalculists," in *American Naturalist,* **62** (1928), 481–507; A. Rey, *De Sylvius à Régnier de Graaf* (Bordeaux, 1930), p. 86, an M.D. diss.; J. Roger, *Les sciences de la vie dans la pensée française du 18e siècle* (Paris, 1963), p. 842; and A. Schierbeek, *Jan Swammerdam 1637–1680, His Life and Works* (Amsterdam, 1967), p. 202.

Marc Klein

GRABAU, AMADEUS WILLIAM (*b.* Cedarburg, Wisconsin, 9 January 1870; *d.* Peking, China, 20 March 1946), *geology, paleontology.*

Grabau was a versatile scientist, a substantial contributor to systematic paleontology, an imaginative pioneer in stratigraphic geology, and a highly respected teacher and prolific writer. After spending the first half of his professional life in the United States, he went to China for the last twenty-five years. Grabau was the son of William Henry Grabau, a Lutheran pastor, and Maria von Rohr Grabau, who died when he was a small boy; he was the third of ten children. He was educated in parochial and public schools, becoming interested in natural history, first in botany and subsequently in paleontology and mineralogy. Correspondence with William O. Crosby at Massachusetts Institute of Technology led to his attending that institution; he received the B.S. in 1896. After a year as instructor he proceeded to graduate study at Harvard, gaining the M.S. and D.Sc. in 1898 and 1900.

Grabau soon became professor of paleontology at Columbia University after a short stay (1899–1901) at Rensselaer Polytechnic Institute in Troy, New York. In the succeeding twenty years he became a leading scientist in paleontology, stratigraphy, and sedimentary petrology, as well as a highly respected teacher. During the hysteria of World War I, Grabau's tenure at Columbia was embittered by accusations of pro-German sympathies and hints and rumors originating at the highest levels. Moving to China in 1920, he became professor of paleontology at the National University and chief paleontologist of the Geological Survey of China.

Grabau married Mary Antin, a Polish immigrant and a distinguished author and sociologist, in 1901. Her health was poor when he left for China, and she remained with a daughter in the United States. Grabau, rather a stocky man, suffered a deterioration of circulation that limited his capacity to work in the field during his later years in the United States; he became an invalid, requiring a wheelchair or requiring crutches after moving to China. Students, associates, and books increasingly became his sources of information.

The principal distinction of Grabau's work is his anticipation of several principles of stratigraphy and paleontology that were to become more generally recognized by later geologists. Of North American stratigraphers of the early years of the century, he seems to have been the best informed on the relationships in foreign lands. Yet he traveled to Europe only once, when he was over forty, and to Asia at the age of fifty. He was imaginative and philosophical. A pioneer in sedimentary petrology, he proposed a genetic classification of sedimentary rocks that strongly influenced advances in the field. Grabau early emphasized the importance of the environment of deposition in determining rock characters and organic assemblages: the field of paleoecology. He produced such theories as the polar control theory of climatic control through the movement of the crust over the interior of the earth, and the pulsation theory, which endeavored to attribute the changing distribution of lands and seas to fluctuations in sea level. Moreover, he made substantial contributions in paleontology, both in the systematic study of fossils of several classes and in the interpretation of their phylogeny and classification.

The relationship of marine bionomy to stratigraphy was the subject of a fifty-page paper published in 1899, a pioneering analysis of knowledge of the living conditions of modern organisms applied to the environment of ancient sedimentary rocks. The article is a masterly outline of the principles of what is now the science of paleoecology. Grabau early emphasized the impact of environment on the fauna and its relationship to the facies of the rocks, that the lateral changes in time-equivalent rocks might be analogous to their succession. In this respect he was a great admirer of Johannes Walther, who held similar views. Grabau was an antagonist of Edward Oscar Ulrich, the popular authority of the early twentieth century who held that faunas relate to marine invasions from several independent oceanic realms; and in general he concurred with Charles Schuchert in his emphasis on environment and lateral facies.

In paleontology Grabau was influenced in his interest in phylogeny and ontogeny by his association at Cambridge with the great paleobiologists Alpheus Hyatt and Robert T. Jackson. His own early studies were directed toward these ends, particularly his work on gastropods. Subsequently he prepared several monographs on such diverse subjects as Chinese Paleozoic corals, Devonian brachiopods, and Permian faunas; these were excellent systematic paleontologic treatises in the manner of the nineteenth-century classic monographs in North America, with attention to anatomic details that might relate to genetic relationships. He had the good fortune to be in Peking when the Peking man was discovered, and he advised on its study.

Grabau's "Classification of Sedimentary Rocks" (*American Geologist,* **33** [1904]) was a portent of the emphasis on the interpretation of origin, as well as texture and composition, in the classification of the deposited rocks. The original terminology was cumbersome in its having Latin-based names formed from

GRABAU

terms for origin, texture, and composition; thus hydrosilicarenyte referred to a marine-laid quartz rock with the texture of sand. The use of a genetic term introduced a subjective element that deterred the direct application of the classification to the rock specimens. Adopted only reluctantly in the beginning, the textural-composition elements became widely used in the middle years of the century, only to be succeeded by other, more sophisticated classifications that further emphasize the aspects he recognized as most pertinent. Thus, Grabau had a great influence in directing the critical study of sedimentary petrology.

Early excursions in the Buffalo, New York, region brought Grabau into contact with the deposits of the continental glaciers. In the 1930's he developed the polar control theory of the distribution of climatic zones through the geologic record. He thought that the poles remained stable with respect to the earth's interior, retaining latitudinal climatic zones, but that the outer crust wandered from these poles. Thus the changing relations of continents to poles caused climatic changes, such as led to glaciation. In his day only a heretic could question the relative permanence of present relationships; half a century later, such a hypothesis came to be appreciably reasonable.

Grabau further believed that the continents once formed a single continental mass, Pangaea, that had been disrupted through relative movements among its dismembered parts. Thus, he was an early protagonist of a theory of continental drift, but one different from those devised by Frank B. Taylor and Alfred Wegener. He thought mountains were rising at the fore of the shifting continental plates and volcanism was at their rear. These theories were ingenious and nearly plausible, for few stratigraphic geologists had Grabau's broad grasp of world geology or his interest in its collation. With the great advances in geophysical science in the latter half of the twentieth century, many such conjectures became subject to more rigorous analysis. Although Grabau could not have anticipated some of this present knowledge, his concepts of the nature of continental movements and climatic zonations have much to commend them.

The pulsation theory attributed the distribution of the principal stratigraphic units to great rhythmic advances and regressions of the seas, which were in turn dependent on restriction and expansion of capacities of ocean basins: eustatic control. He gave distinctive names to his pulsation systems, such as Taconian, Cambrian, Cambrovician, Skiddavian, Ordovician, Silurian, and Siluronian. Fourteen of these cycles were placed in the Paleozoic era, five in the Mesozoic, and two in the Cenozoic, partially to replace the conventional systems. He thought each pulsation had had a duration of about 30 million years, the contraction of seas at the close of each period leading to marked changes in organisms.

Perhaps Grabau thought his pulsation theory was his greatest contribution, for he wrote many volumes endeavoring to relate the distribution of lands and seas to pulsing transgressions and retrogressions and saying that it was further controlled by provincial warping movements accentuating or reversing the effects of the eustatic movements. As has been the case with other endeavors to alter the general geologic classification, based appreciably on historical accidents rather than on clearly natural principles, authorities have never agreed on more ubiquitous natural spans and thus continue to use the established systems.

The greatest effect of Grabau's scientific work probably has been in his contributions to the principles of paleoecology and to the genetic aspects of sedimentary petrology. His stratigraphic work was influential in bringing about a three-dimensional attitude toward sedimentary rock distribution, rather than merely emphasizing the faunal correlation of exposed rock sections. His stratigraphy was dynamic, the source of understanding earth movements. He anticipated the attitudes that became prevalent when the petroleum industry added knowledge of subsurface sections to that of the surface outcrops. The concepts involved in his polar control theory, pulsation theory, and the separation of Pangaea encouraged imaginative syntheses of geologic evidence. This heritage, brought to his students and associates, has contributed far beyond the words and thoughts that he recorded.

The esteem in which Grabau was held was reflected in the honors and prizes that he received but was shown more fittingly in the commemorative volumes that were published by Chinese geologists on his sixtieth birthday and in his burial within the gates of the National University. Among his greatest contributions were the stimulus that he gave to scientific life in China and the instruction and enthusiasm that was productive in his many students. For example, in the first ten years of his residence in China, nineteen of the twenty-five monographs of Palaeontologia sinica were prepared by his students.

Grabau was a fellow of the Geological Society of America, the New York Academy of Science (vice-president, 1906–1907), and the Geological Society of China (vice-president, 1925); corresponding member of the Philadelphia Academy of Sciences and the Deutsche Akademie der Naturforscher; and an honorary member of the Peking Society of Natural History, the China Institute of Mining and Metallurgy, the Academia Sinica, and the Academia Peipinensis.

BIBLIOGRAPHY

I. ORIGINAL WORKS. Grabau was the author of some 300 publications, of which more than a score were substantial monographs and other books. The full bibliography is listed in the publications in the secondary literature. The principal volumes are listed in three categories: paleontological studies, stratigraphic studies, and textbooks and collative works.

The paleontological treatises contain substantial systematic descriptions of fossil organisms. Because his associates were exploring in regions that had not been known, the greatest contributions are to faunas from China: *Phylogeny of Fusus and Its Allies* (Washington, D.C., 1904); *Ordovician Fossils From North China* (Peking, 1922); *Silurian Faunas of Eastern Yunnan* (Peking, 1926); *Paleozoic Corals of China* (Peking, 1928); *Devonian Brachiopods of China* (Peking, 1931); and *Early Permian Fossils of China,* 2 vols. (Peking, 1934–1936). *The Relations of Marine Bionomy to Stratigraphy* (Buffalo, 1899) is a substantial introduction to the field of paleoecology.

In stratigraphic geology, Grabau's first publications were descriptions of stratigraphic sequences in various localities: *Geology and Paleontology of Eighteen Mile Creek and the Lakeshore Sections of Erie County, New York* (Buffalo, 1898); *Guide to the Geology and Paleontology of Niagara Falls and Vicinity* (Albany, 1901); "Classification of Sedimentary Rocks," in *American Geologist,* **33** (1904), 228–247; and *Guide to the Geology and Paleontology of the Schoharie Valley in Eastern New York* (Albany, 1906). *The Monroe Formation of Southern Michigan and Adjacent Regions* (Lansing, Mich., 1910) was prepared with W. H. Sherzer. *The Permian of Mongolia* (New York, 1931) included description of faunas collected on the central Asia expeditions of the American Museum of Natural History. *The Stratigraphy of China* was essentially a summary of knowledge. Probably his best-known work is *The Principles of Stratigraphy* (New York, 1913), repr. with preface by Marshall Kay (New York, 1960), one of the most influential texts of the early twentieth century.

Grabau published *Textbook of Geology,* 2 vols. (New York, 1920–1921), which did not receive wide usage. His five-volume *Paleozoic Formations in the Light of the Pulsation Theory* (Peking, 1936–1938), intended to be the first encyclopedic summary of world stratigraphy, was developed to support his pulsation theory. *Rhythm of the Ages* (Peking, 1940) and the posthumously published, twenty-year-old MS of *The World We Live In* (Taipei, 1961), were popular summaries of his philosophy. *North American Index Fossils* (New York, 1909–1910), written with W. H. Shimer, with illustrations of more than 2,000 distinctive invertebrate fossils, was the standard reference work for more than thirty years. He also published *Principles of Salt Deposition* (New York, 1920).

II. SECONDARY LITERATURE. The full bibliography of Grabau is contained in three biographic papers, H. W. Shimer, in *Proceedings of the Geological Society of America* for 1946 (1947), 161–166; V. K. Ting in *Grabau Anniversary,* the commemorative vol. presented to Grabau on his fiftieth birthday, *Bulletin of the Geological Society of China,* **10** (1931), ix–xviii; and the intro. to *The World We Live In* (Taipei, 1961), xii–xxv.

MARSHALL KAY

GRAEBE, KARL JAMES PETER (*b.* Frankfurt am Main, Germany, 24 February 1841; *d.* Frankfurt, 19 January 1927), *chemistry.*

Graebe's father, for whom he was named, was a soldier and a merchant; his mother, Emmeline Boeddinghaus, was a writer. He entered the Technische Hochschule at Karlsruhe in 1858 but, wishing to become a chemist, he studied with Robert Bunsen at Heidelberg from 1860 to 1862. He then studied at Marburg with Adolph Kolbe, learning a structural approach. After a semester he returned to Heidelberg as Bunsen's assistant.

In 1864 Graebe and his friend C. Diehl joined the firm of Farbwerk Meister, Lucius and Co., in Höchst. Here Graebe worked on the development of iodine dyes but soon developed vision problems and left the company for rest and travel. He then continued his studies with Emil Erlenmeyer at Heidelberg and worked with aromatic oxygen acids. From 1865 to 1869 he was Adolf von Baeyer's assistant at Berlin. Then, after spending a brief time at the Badische Anilin- und Sodafabrik in Mannheim, he went to Leipzig as a *Privatdozent.* In 1870 Graebe became professor at Königsberg, where he encountered difficulty because laboratory facilities were poor and both faculty and students showed little interest in chemistry. He suffered a breakdown and resigned. After his recovery he went to Zurich as a visiting professor. In 1878 he moved to Geneva and taught there until his retirement in 1906. He was a member of the Deutsche Chemische Gesellschaft and served as its president in 1907. He married Albertine Bergdorfer in 1896; they had no children.

Graebe took the work of F. A. Kekulé, published about the time he went to Berlin, as his starting point and studied compounds related to benzene, particularly the quinones. He collaborated with Carl Liebermann, who was then a student, on alizarin. Using Baeyer's zinc-dust reduction method, they showed that alizarin was reduced to anthraquinone, that is, was a derivative of anthracene, not of naphthalene. Within a short time they were also able to synthesize alizarin from anthraquinone and to give the formula for anthracene. The discovery of alizarin eliminated the use of natural madder and spurred the development of the synthetic dye industry. It also pointed out the lack of an adequate patent law.

Graebe continued to work on other organic dyes and quinone derivatives. He and Heinrich von Brunck worked on alizarin blue, found the correct formula, and recognized it as a quinone derivative. With Heinrich Caro, Graebe obtained acridine from anthracene. With Karl Glaser he discovered carbazole, and from this work he was able to analyze pyrene and chrysene. He showed martius yellow to be a derivative of naphthoquinone. Independently of Zdenko Skraup, he synthesized quinoline. He also worked with other organic dyestuffs, such as rosolic acid, euxanthon, and galloflavin.

Since his Berlin days, Graebe had been theoretically interested in the linkage of the oxygens in quinones. He introduced the terms "ortho," "meta," and "para" for disubstituted benzene compounds. He first thought that hydroquinone, which of the three dihydroxybenzenes forms quinone on oxidation, was an ortho compound. But he later decided that it was a para compound. Graebe was also interested in the relationship between color and constitution and proposed that colored compounds contain unsaturated valences or atoms more closely connected than is necessary.

To aid his teaching of chemistry, Graebe became interested in the history of his subject. He wrote articles on leading chemists and completed a history of organic chemistry, only the first volume of which was published.

BIBLIOGRAPHY

I. ORIGINAL WORKS. Graebe's writings include "Ueber Methoxysalysäure," in *Annalen der Chemie und Pharmacie,* **136** (1865), 124–125; "Ueber eine neue Bildungsweise der Methylsalicylsäure," *ibid.,* **142** (1867), 327–330; "Ueber das Verhalten der aromatischen Säuren beim Durchgang durch den thierischen Organismus," *ibid.,* 345–350, written with O. Schultzen; "Untersuchungen ueber die Chinogruppe," *ibid.,* **146** (1868), 1–65; "Ueber Naphthalin," in *Berichte der Deutschen chemischen Gesellschaft,* **1** (1868), 36–38; "Ueber Alizarin und Anthracene," *ibid.,* 49–51, written with C. Liebermann; "Ueber den Zusammenhang zwischen Molecularconstitution und Farbe bei organischen Verbindungen," *ibid.* 106–108, written with C. Liebermann; "Ueber Synthese der Phenanthrens aus Toluol," *ibid.,* **7** (1874), 48–49, written with H. Caro; "Ueber Alizarinblau," in *Annalen der Chemie und Pharmacie,* **201** (1880), 333–354; "Ueber Acridin," in *Berichte der Deutschen chemischen Gesellschaft,* **16** (1883), 2828–2832; and *Geschichte der organischen Chemie* (Berlin, 1920).

Graebe's letters and notes can be found in the Deutsches Museum in Munich, in the Badische Anilin- und Sodafabrik archives at Ludwigshafen, and in the archives of the University of Geneva.

II. SECONDARY LITERATURE. On Graebe or his work, see *Documents pour servir à l'histoire de l'Université de Genève,* III (Geneva, 1883), 36–38; IV (Geneva, 1896), 113–117; V (Geneva, 1909), 31–34; P. Duden and H. Decker, "Nachruf auf Carl Graebe," in *Berichte der Deutschen chemischen Gesellschaft,* **61A** (1928), 9–46; Frankfurt am Main Verein Deutscher Chemiker, "Carl Graebe," in *Zeitschrift für angewandte Chemie,* **40** (1927), 217–218; *Graebe-Feier, Cassel 20.9.1903* (Geneva, 1903); and W. Schlenk, "Carl Graebe," in *Berichte der Deutschen chemischen Gesellschaft,* **60A** (1927), 53.

RUTH GIENAPP RINARD

GRAFF, KASIMIR ROMUALD (*b.* Prochnowo, Germany [now Próchnowo, Poland], 7 February 1878; *d.* Breitenfurt, near Vienna, Austria, 15 February 1950), *astronomy.*

After graduation from the secondary school in Poznan, Graff began his studies of astronomy and physics in 1897 at the University of Berlin, from which he obtained the Ph.D. degree in 1901. From 1898 he was employed at the Urania Observatory in Berlin. In 1902 Graff became assistant astronomer at the Hamburg observatory, and in 1909 when the latter was transferred to Bergedorf, he was appointed associate astronomer. In this position he was obliged to lecture on spherical astronomy. During World War I Graff served as an expert on geodetic surveys. In 1917 he received the honorary title of professor, and at the end of the war he continued photometric observations with instruments of his own design at Bergedorf.

In 1928 he was appointed full professor of practical astronomy at the University of Vienna. There he did his best to modernize the great university observatory. In order to avoid the difficulties in stellar photometry caused by the increasing electric illumination in Vienna, he spent several months every year on the islands of Mallorca and Šolta (Yugoslavia) equipped with instruments of moderate size. Forced to resign from the observatory after the German occupation of Austria in 1938, Graff reassumed the directorship in 1945 but retired three years later. He was a member of the Austrian Academy of Sciences and of the Academia Pontificia Vaticana.

Graff was one of the last of those pioneers in astrophysics who by visual observations promoted photometry and colorimetry, as well as planetary and lunar research. In his stellar photometers he used, instead of "nichols," wedges of gray glass (1914), even copying them photographically in circular form ("Kreiskeilphotometer" [1926]). A combination of assorted wedges of blue and yellow glass for the gradual adjustment of color of an artificial star to that of a natural star was the main part of his colorimeter (1928). Most of his papers contain long lists of stars classified by magnitude and color-type. He made many drawings of the surface features of Mars during its oppositions in 1898, 1901, 1909, and 1924. He occasionally made other observations which cannot be described here in detail. He published valuable textbooks on geographical position-finding and on astrophysics and, in collaboration with M. Beyer, a star atlas.

BIBLIOGRAPHY

I. Original Works. Graff's writings include *Grundriss der geographischen Ortsbestimmung* (Berlin-Leipzig, 1914; 2nd ed., Berlin, 1941; 3rd ed., 1944); *Sternatlas,* 2 pts. (Hamburg, 1925-1927), in collaboration with M. Beyer; *Grundriss der Astrophysik* (Leipzig-Berlin, 1928); and "Physische Beschaffenheit des Planetensystems," in *Handbuch der Astrophysik,* IV (1929), 358-425, and VII (1934), 410-421.

Among his many papers are "Formeln und Hülfstafeln zur Reduktion von Mondphotographien und Mondbeobachtungen," in *Publikationen des Astronomischen Recheninstituts Berlin* (1901); and "Ortsverzeichnis von 580 veränderlichen Sternen," in *Astronomische Abhandlungen der Hamburger Sternwarte in Bergedorf,* **1** (1909), pt. 3. He published at least 170 other papers, the great majority of which are concerned with stellar photometry and colorimetry; the remainder deal with observations of the moon, planets, comets, and eclipses. Most of these papers appeared in the *Astronomische Abhandlungen der Hamburger Sternwarte in Bergedorf* and *Mitteilungen der Hamburger Sternwarte in Bergedorf* (1909-1926); and *Mitteilungen der Universitäts-Sternwarte, Wien,* **1** (1931-1938) and **4** (1947-1950).

II. Secondary Literature. On Graff and his work, see Paul Ahnert, "Kasimir Graff," in *Sterne,* **26** (1950), 186-187, with portrait; Wilhelm Becker, "Kasimir Graff †," in *Astronomische Nachrichten,* **279** (1950), 141-142; and Victor Oberguggenberger, "Kasimir Romuald Graff," in *Almanach. Österreichische Akademie der Wissenschaften,* **100** (1950), 352-358, with portrait.

Konradin Ferrari D'Occhieppo

GRÄFFE, KARL HEINRICH (*b.* Brunswick, Germany, 7 November 1799; *d.* Zurich, Switzerland, 2 December 1873), *mathematics.*

Gräffe was the son of Dietrich Heinrich Gräffe, a jeweler, and Johanna Frederike Gräffe-Moritz. Born in simple circumstances, he studied from 1813 until 1816 with a jeweler in Hannover. Then, almost ready to begin a career as a goldsmith, through unflagging industry he made up his educational deficiencies and in 1821 was accepted as a scholarship student at the Carolineum in Brunswick. In 1824 he entered the University of Göttingen, attended the classes of Bernhard Thibaut and C. F. Gauss, and concluded his studies with the prize-winning dissertation "Die Geschichte der Variationsrechnung vom Ursprung der Differential- und Integralrechnung bis auf die heutige Zeit" (1825).

In 1828 Gräffe became a teacher at the Technische Institut in Zurich, and in 1833 a professor at the Oberen Industrieschule there, working also as a *Privatdozent.* He was appointed extraordinary professor of mathematics at the University of Zurich in 1860. His name remains attached to a method for the numerical solution of algebraic equations, which he invented in response to a prize question posed by the Berlin Academy of Sciences. Let (1) $f(x) = x^n + ax^{n-1} + \cdots a_n = 0$, and let it then be supposed that all roots $\alpha_1, \cdots, \alpha_n$ are real and different from each other: (2) $|\alpha_1| > |\alpha_2| > \cdots > |\alpha_m|$. Let it further be possible to find an equation (3) $F(x) = x^n + A_1x^{n-1} + \cdots A_n = 0$, whose roots are the mth powers $\alpha_1^m, \cdots \alpha_n^m$ of (1). It follows from (2) that (4) $|\alpha_1^m| > \cdots > |\alpha_n^m|$. Since $\alpha_1^m + \cdots + \alpha_n^m = -A_1$, it follows from (4) that $|\alpha_1^m|$, for large m, is approximately equal to A_1, $|\alpha_1^m| \sim A_1$. Correspondingly, $|\alpha_2^m| \sim \left(\frac{A_2}{A_1}\right)$, and so on. One can find an equation (3) with $m = 2$ by constructing $g(x) = (-1)^n f(-x) f(x)$; proceeding in this manner one obtains, with $m = 2^k$, the equation $F(x) = 0$.

The method may be extended to equations with equal roots and to equations with complex roots. The method has found application in modern numerical mathematics.

BIBLIOGRAPHY

A bibliography of Gräffe's works may be found in *Historisch biographische Lexikon der Schweiz,* III (Neuenburg, 1926), 621 ff. His most important work is *Die Auflösung der höheren numerischen Gleichungen* (Zurich, 1837; with additions, 1839).

A biography is Rudolph Wolf, "Carl Heinrich Gräffe; Ein Lebensbild," in *Neue Zürcherzeitung,* nos. 30 and 31 (1874), also pub. separately (Zurich, 1874).

J. J. Burckhardt

GRAHAM, GEORGE (*b.* near Rigg, Cumberland, England, *ca.* 1674; *d.* London, England, 16 November 1751), *scientific instrumentation.*

Graham's father, also called George, died soon after Graham's birth; he was raised by a brother,

William, at nearby Sykeside. In 1688 he apprenticed himself to Henry Aske, a clockmaker in London. His apprenticeship lasted seven years and on 30 September 1695 he gained freedom of the Clockmaker's Company. He was soon employed by Thomas Tompion, the leading clock, watch, and instrument maker. He married Tompion's niece, Elizabeth Tompion, in 1704 and later became Tompion's partner, succeeding to the business in 1713 on Tompion's death. With Tompion, Graham made the original machine (later named an orrery) to demonstrate the motions of heavenly bodies by means of geared models.

In 1715 Graham began experiments to overcome the effects of temperature changes on pendulum length and rate of timekeeping. By 1722 he had devised his mercury-compensated pendulum, which he adjusted and tested carefully before making it public in a paper presented to the Royal Society in 1726. During this period he also invented the deadbeat escapement that certainly contributed to the overall success of his experiments. The combination of escapement and stable pendulum remained in precision clocks until the late nineteenth century. About 1725 Graham invented the cylinder escapement for watches, apparently an improvement inspired by the escapement (somewhat like a duplex in action) patented in 1695 by Tompion, Edward Booth (inventor of repeating clocks and watches), and William Houghton. Graham's design was also deadbeat and had the excellent quality of not being affected by changes in driving power. But his design never enjoyed the popularity in England that it eventually did in France and Switzerland, where it remained in production until the early part of the twentieth century.

In addition to clocks and watches, Graham also made scientific instruments, including barometers, and planetary models like the orrery described above. His precision instrument work began in 1725 with the construction of an eight-foot quadrant for Edmond Halley who had succeeded John Flamsteed as astronomer royal in 1720. This quadrant was used in Halley's work on the right ascension of the moon and adjacent stars. Both coordinates could be read from Graham's single instrument, and it afforded more accuracy and convenience than the separate instruments used by Flamsteed. In this quadrant Graham substituted the vernier for the diagonal scales previously used. The graduations, by his own hand, introduced a new level of accuracy. Besides the usual angular divisions, there was another division into ninety-six parts, produced by bisecting, and used for checking the angular scale. Curiously, although Graham was certainly aware of the different rates of expansion of iron and brass from his pendulum experiments, the graduations were on a brass scale attached to an iron frame. In 1750, to avoid distortions, this quadrant was replaced by one of the same design, but all brass, made by John Bird.

Graham's next important instrument, a twenty-four-and-one-quarter-foot zenith sector, was made for Samuel Molyneux's private observatory at Kew in 1727. With this instrument Graham introduced the great improvement of a micrometer screw to subdivide the vernier divisions. James Bradley used the sector for studies leading to the discovery of the aberration of light from fixed stars (1729). But most of Bradley's work was done with a twelve-and-a-half-foot zenith sector built by Graham particularly for this research. With provision to extend nearly six and one-half degrees on either side of the zenith, Graham's sector permitted observation of about 200 cataloged stars.

It was Graham to whom John Harrison was sent when he came to London to promote his concept of a precision marine clock for finding longitude at sea. Graham spent ten hours going over Harrison's work with him and advised him to build and test his timekeeper before submitting it to the Board of Longitude. Confirming his faith in Harrison's concepts, Graham generously encouraged him with an unsecured, interest-free loan.

Graham's work, particularly his astronomical instruments, gained international fame. His quadrant at Greenwich was copied by other instrument makers for French, Spanish, Italian, and West Indian astronomers. One of his precision clocks was used at Black River, Jamaica, and another at Uppsala, Sweden. When, in 1736, Louis XV sent Pierre Louis Moreau de Maupertius to Tornio, at the head of the Gulf of Bothnia, he took instruments by Graham, including an "instrument des passages," or transit, to help determine if the earth were flattened at the poles in accordance with the theories of Newton and Christian Huygens.

Collaboration between the Royal Society and the French Academy made it desirable, about 1741, that they be able to express weights and measures in mutually intelligible terms. Toward this end Graham employed Jonathan Sisson to prepare two substantial brass rods graduated in conformity with the English standard yard kept in the Tower of London. These were sent to Paris, where one was kept while the other was returned to England inscribed with a graduated half-toise (three Paris feet). Graham had Sisson subdivide both the yard and the half-toise into thirds or feet. Graham himself later devised a beam caliper with a micrometer screw of forty threads per inch and a graduated circular scale divided into twenty parts, read directly by an index pointer to 1/800 inch. He considered the accuracy of this instrument to be equal to half a graduation. This caliper was then used to compare the several standard yards in London at the Court of the Exchequer, Guildhall, Founders' Hall, and the Tower. The greatest variation found was about .040 inch.

Graham's most important contributions were kinematic designs, among them more accurate graduations and micrometer screws for precise subdivisions, including a micrometer eyepiece. His practical experience with scientific observations undoubtedly contributed to his designing and building skills. He trained such followers as Sisson and Bird. The esteem of his contemporaries is revealed both by his election to the council of the Royal Society (1722) and his burial in Westminster Abbey.

BIBLIOGRAPHY

I. Original Works. Graham's works consist of papers presented to the Royal Society of London which appeared in the abridged *Philosophical Transactions of the Royal Society.* The most notable of these is "A Contrivance to Avoid the Irregularities in a Clock's Motion Occasion'd by the Action of Heat and Cold Upon the Rod of the Pendulum," in **34** (1726), no. 392, 40–44.

II. Secondary Literature. For information on Graham, see James Bradley, "An Account of Some Observations Made in London, by Mr. George Graham; and at Black River in Jamaica, by Mr. Colin Campbell, Concerning the Going of a Clock; in Order to Determine the Difference Between the Lengths of Isochronal Pendulums in Those Places," in *Philosophical Transactions of the Royal Society,* **38** (1734), no. 432, 302–314; [Committee of the Royal Society] "An Account of a Comparison Lately Made by Some Gentlemen of the Royal Society, of the Standard of a Yard, and the Several Weights Lately made for Their Use . . .," *ibid.,* **42** (1742/1743), no. 470, 541–556; and "On the Proportions of the English and French Measures From the Standards of the Same Kept at the Royal Society," *ibid.,* pp. 604–606; Nicholas Goodison, *English Barometers, 1680–1860* (New York, 1968), 141–145; and C. Doris Hellman, "George Graham, Maker of Horological and Astronomical Instruments," in *Vassar Journal of Undergraduate Studies,* **5** (May 1931), 221–251.

Also see H. Alan Lloyd, "George Graham, Horologist and Astronomer," in *Horological Journal,* **93,** no. 1118 (Nov. 1951), 708–717; *Some Outstanding Clocks Over 700 Years* (London, 1958); Thomas Reid, *A Treatise on Clock and Watchmaking* (Edinburgh, 1826); and *Dictionary of National Biography* (London, 1891).

Edwin A. Battison

GRAHAM, THOMAS (*b.* Glasgow, Scotland, 21 December 1805; *d.* London, England, 16 September 1869), *chemistry, physics.*

The son of a prosperous manufacturer, Graham entered the University of Glasgow in 1819, at the age of fourteen, and was convinced by the lectures of Thomas Thomson that his calling lay in the field of chemistry. His father, who wanted him to become a minister of the Church of Scotland, was opposed to this choice of vocation, but Graham received encouragement and help from his mother and sister. After receiving the M.A. at Glasgow in 1826, he worked for nearly two years in the laboratory of Thomas Charles Hope at the University of Edinburgh. He then returned to Glasgow, where he taught mathematics and chemistry in a private laboratory. In 1829 he became assistant at the Mechanics' Institution, and in 1830 he succeeded Alexander Ure as professor of chemistry at Anderson's College (later the Royal College of Science and Technology), where he produced his classic work on the phosphates and arsenates (1833).

In 1834 Graham became a fellow of the Royal Society. Three years later he succeeded Edward Turner as professor of chemistry at the University College, London (later the University of London). His time was then fully occupied in teaching, writing, advising on chemical manufactures, and investigating fiscal and other questions for the government. In 1841 he participated in the founding of the Chemical Society and became its first president. With the death of John Dalton in 1844, Graham was left as the acknowledged dean of English chemists, the successor of Joseph Black, Joseph Priestley, Henry Cavendish, William Wollaston, Humphry Davy, and John Dalton. He resigned his professorship in 1854 to succeed Sir John Herschel as master of the mint, a post which ceased to exist upon Graham's death. He died in 1869, an indefatigable but physically broken man.

As a lecturer Graham was well liked by his students, but he was somewhat nervous and hesitant. He was much in demand as a consultant. Most of his work lay in the field of inorganic and physical chemistry, and he is recognized as the real founder of colloid chemistry. His work, usually quantitatively accurate, was original in conception, simple in execution, and brilliant in the results to which it led. Much of his earlier experimental work, some of it not very accurate, is said to have been performed by students and assistants. He received the Royal Medal of the Royal Society twice (1837 and 1863), the Copley Medal of the Royal Society (1862), and the Prix Jecker of the Paris Academy of Sciences (1862). His original and admirable textbook *Elements of Chemis-*

try was widely used, not only in England but also on the Continent, in its much enlarged multivolume translation by Friedrich Julius Otto.

Graham's first original paper, which appeared during his twenty-first year, dealt with spontaneous gas movement, a subject that occupied him throughout his career. In fact, almost all his research is but a development, in different directions, of his early works on gaseous diffusion and water of hydration, as when he showed that Henry's law is not valid for very soluble gases. In another work he found that, like potash, ammonia forms a normal oxalate, binoxalate, and quadroxalate, but that soda forms only a normal oxalate and binoxalate. He also made interesting observations on the glow of phosphorus and the spontaneous flammability of phosphine.

In 1829 Graham published the first of his papers relating specifically to the subject of gaseous diffusion. Although this publication contains the essentials of Graham's law, known to every student of general chemistry, it was in a subsequent paper, for which he was awarded the Keith Prize of the Royal Society of Edinburgh, that he definitely established the principle:

> The diffusion or spontaneous intermixture of two gases in contact is effected by an interchange in position of indefinitely minute volumes of the gases, which volumes are not necessarily of equal magnitude, being, in the case of each gas, inversely proportional to the square root of the density of that gas . . . diffusion takes place between the ultimate particles of gases, and not between sensible masses ["On the Law of the Diffusion of Gases," in *Philosophical Magazine,* **2** (1833)].

Graham maintained that by means of this law the specific gravity of gases could be determined, through experiments on the principle of diffusion, with greater accuracy than by ordinary means. He also pointed out that mixtures of gases could be separated by diffusion, a process employed during World War II at Oak Ridge, Tennessee, to separate the fissionable isotope uranium 235 from the nonfissionable isotope uranium 238.

Graham also measured the effusion of gases through a small hole in a metal plate and found the velocities of flow to be inversely proportional to the square roots of the densities. Yet in his study of the rates of transpiration of gases through capillary tubes, he found that the rates became constant with a certain length of tube and were not simply related to the densities. Later in his career, in "On the Absorption and Dialytic Separation of Gases by Colloidal Septa," Graham began his studies of the penetration of hydrogen through heated metals, a phenomenon which he called "occlusion" and which he explained first by liquefaction of hydrogen and its dissolution in the metal. He later supposed hydrogen to be the vapor of a very volatile metal, hydrogenium, which forms an alloy with the metal. In 1863 he even suggested that the various chemical elements might "possess one and the same ultimate or atomic molecule existing in different conditions of movement."

Graham's major contribution to inorganic chemistry is his paper "Researches on the Arseniates, Phosphates, and Modifications of Phosphoric Acid," in which he elucidated the differences between the three phosphoric acids. This research and the style of the paper are reminiscent of Joseph Black's work on magnesia and the alkalies carried out in Glasgow eighty years earlier. Graham's discovery of the polybasicity of these acids provided Justus Liebig with the clue to the modern concept of polybasic acids. Of this classic work the eminent German chemist and historian of chemistry Albert Ladenburg has said, "so much has seldom been accomplished by a single investigation." Nevertheless, J. J. Berzelius insisted that the three phosphoric acids were isomers of P_2O_5, and as late as 1843 he wrote that Graham's "point of view lacks justification in several respects."

Before Graham's work the relationship between the various phosphates and phosphoric acids was a subject of the greatest confusion. Compounds of one and the same anhydrous acid with one and the same anhydrous base, in different proportions, had long been known, but Graham was the first to establish the concept of polybasic compounds, that is, a class of hydrated acids with more than one proportion of water replaceable by a basic metallic oxide so that several series of salts could be formed. Graham concluded that the individual properties of the phosphoric acids could not be expressed if they were regarded as anhydrides; they must contain chemically combined water essential to their composition. He therefore designated the three modifications of phosphoric acid as phosphoric acid, $\dot{H}^3\overset{\therefore\because}{P}$, that is, $3HO \cdot PO_5$ (modern, $3H_2O \cdot P_2O_5$ or H_3PO_4); pyrophosphoric acid, $\dot{H}^2\overset{\therefore\because}{P}$, i.e., $2HO \cdot PO_5$ (modern, $2H_2O \cdot P_2O_5$ or $H_4P_2O_7$); and metaphosphoric acid, $\dot{H}\overset{\therefore\because}{P}$, i.e., $HO \cdot PO_5$ (modern, $H_2O \cdot P_2O_5$ or HPO_3). In other words, he regarded them respectively as a triphosphate, a biphosphate, and a phosphate of water.

> When one of these compounds is treated with a strong base, the whole or a part of the water is supplanted, but the amount of base in combination with the acid

remains unaltered. There are thus three sets of phosphates, in which the oxygen in the acid being five, the oxygen in the base is three, two, and one ["Researches on the Arseniates . . .," in *Philosophical Transactions of the Royal Society,* **123** (1833)].

Graham summarized the compositions of the three acids of phosphorus and of their sodium salts as shown below. Just as in his demonstration of the relationships to one another of phosphoric acid and the three sodium phosphates, Graham originated the concept of polybasic compounds; so, in his demonstration that the pyrophosphates and metaphosphates are compounds differing from the phosphates by loss of water or metallic base, he originated the concept of anhydro compounds.

Although some isolated investigations on colloids had been carried out before Graham, his publications in this field laid the foundations of colloid chemistry. In "On the Diffusion of Liquids," Graham applied to liquids the exact method of inquiry he had applied to gases twenty years before, and he succeeded in placing the subject of liquid diffusion on about the same footing as that to which he had raised the subject of gaseous diffusion prior to the discovery of his numerical law. He showed that the rate of diffusion was approximately proportional to the concentration of the original solution, increased with rise in temperature, and was almost constant for groups of chemically similar salts at equal absolute (not molecular) concentrations and different with different groups. He believed that liquid diffusion was similar to gaseous diffusion and vaporization with dilute solutions, but with concentrated solutions he noted a departure from the ideal relationship, similar to that in gases approaching liquefaction under pressure. Based on his work on osmosis, Graham developed what he called a "dialyzer," which he used to separate colloids, which dialyzed slowly, from crystalloids, which dialyzed rapidly. He prepared colloids of silicic acid, alumina, ferric oxide, and other hydrous metal oxides, and he distinguished between sols and gels.

Much of the terminology and fundamental concepts of this field are due to Graham:

> As gelatine appears to be its type, it is proposed to designate substances of the class as *colloids* [κόλλα, glue], and to speak of their particular form of aggregation as the *colloidal condition of matter.* Opposed to the colloidal is the crystalline condition. Substances affecting the latter form will be classed as *crystalloids.* . . . Fluid colloids appear to have always a pectous [πηκτός, curdled] modification; and they often pass under the slightest influences from the first into the second condition. . . . The colloidal is, in fact, a dynamical state of matter; the crystalloid being the statical condition.

Graham stated that crystals and crystalloids "appear like different worlds of matter," but he recognized that the essential difference is in the state and that the same substance can exist in the crystalloid or colloid state. He concluded that "in nature there are no abrupt transitions, and the distinctions of class are never absolute."

BIBLIOGRAPHY

I. Original Works. Graham's writings include "On the Absorption of Gases by Liquids," in *Annals of Philosophy,* **12** (1826), 69; "A Short Account of Experimental Researches on the Diffusion of Gases Through Each Other, and Their Separation by Mechanical Means," in *Quarterly Journal of Science and the Arts* (Royal Institution), **27** (1829), 74; "On the Law of the Diffusion of Gases," in *Philosophical Magazine,* **2** (1833), 175, 269, 351; "Researches on the Arseniates, Phosphates, and Modifications of Phosphoric Acid," in *Philosophical Transactions of the Royal Society,* **123** (1833), 253, repr. as Alembic Club Reprint no. 10 (Edinburgh, 1961); *Elements of Chemistry, Including the Application of the Science in the Arts* (London,

TABLE 1

		Oxygen in Soda	Oxygen in Water	Oxygen in Acid	Modern Formulation
First Class	Phosphoric acid	0	3	5	H_3PO_4
	Biphosphate of soda	1	2	5	NaH_2PO_4
	Phosphate of soda	2	1	5	Na_2HPO_4
	Subphosphate of soda	3	0	5	Na_3PO_4
Second Class	Pyrophosphoric acid	0	2	5	$H_4P_2O_7$
	Bipyrophosphate of soda	1	1	5	$Na_2H_2P_2O_7$
	Pyrophosphate of soda	2	0	5	$Na_4P_2O_7$
Third Class	Metaphosphoric acid	0	1	5	HPO_3
	Metaphosphate of soda	1	0	5	$NaPO_3$

1842), trans. into German and enlarged by F. J. Otto as *Ausführliches Lehrbuch der Chemie, physikalische, anorganische, organische* (Brunswick, 1854–1893); "On the Motion of Gases," in *Philosophical Transactions of the Royal Society,* **136** (1846), 573, and **139** (1849), 349; "On the Diffusion of Liquids," *ibid.,* **140** (1850), 1–46; "On Osmotic Force," *ibid.,* **144** (1854), 177–228; "Liquid Diffusion Applied to Analysis," *ibid.,* **151** (1861), 183–224; "Speculative Ideas Respecting the Constitution of Matter," in *Proceedings of the Royal Society,* **12** (1863), 620–623; "On the Absorption and Dialytic Separation of Gases by Colloidal Septa," in *Philosophical Transactions of the Royal Society,* **156** (1866), 399–439; and "On the Occlusion of Hydrogen Gas by Metals," in *Proceedings of the Royal Society,* **16** (1868), 422.

II. SECONDARY LITERATURE. Discussions of Graham's life and work are W. Odling, in *Report of the Board of Regents of the Smithsonian Institution* (1871), pp. 171–216, repr. in E. Farber, ed., *Great Chemists* (New York, 1961), pp. 553–571; J. R. Partington, *A History of Chemistry,* IV (New York, 1964), 265–270, 272–275, 729–732; and M. Speter, "Graham," in G. Bugge, ed., *Das Buch der grossen Chemiker,* II (Weinheim, 1965), 69–77. Discussions of Graham's law are E. A. Mason and R. B. Evans, "Graham's Law: Simple Demonstrations of Gases in Motion. Part I, Theory. Part II, Experiments," in *Journal of Chemical Education,* **46** (1969), 359–364, 423–427; E. A. Mason and B. Kronstadt, "Graham's Law of Diffusion and Effusion," *ibid.,* **44** (1967), 740–744; and A. Ruckstuhl, "Thomas Graham's Study of the Diffusion of Gases," *ibid.,* **28** (1951), 594–596.

GEORGE B. KAUFFMAN

GRAM, HANS CHRISTIAN JOACHIM (*b.* Copenhagen, Denmark, 13 September 1853; *d.* Copenhagen, 14 November 1938), *biology, medicine.*

Gram was the son of Frederik Terkel Julius Gram, a professor of jurisprudence, and Louise Christiane Roulund. He early took up studies in the natural sciences. After receiving a B.A. from the Copenhagen Metropolitan School (1871), he became an assistant in botany (1873–1874) to the zoologist Japetus Steenstrup. But he soon developed an interest in medicine, and in 1878 he obtained the M.D. from the University of Copenhagen. In the following years he was an assistant in various Copenhagen hospitals and in 1882 received the gold medal for a university essay concerning the number and size of human erythrocytes in chlorotics. The following year he defended at Copenhagen his doctoral thesis on the size of the human erythrocytes.

From 1883 to 1885 Gram traveled in Europe, studying pharmacology and bacteriology; in 1884, while working with Friedländer in Berlin, he published his famous microbiological staining method. Gram experimented with staining pneumococci bacteria by modifying Ehrlich's alkaline aniline solutions. Gram stained his preparations with aniline gentian violet, adding Lugol's solution for from one to three minutes. When he then removed the nonspecific attributed stain with absolute alcohol, certain bacteria (pneumococci, for example) retained the color (gram-positive), while other species bleached (gram-negative). Gram himself never used counterstaining for gram-negative microbes, as was later done by Weigert.

Gram spent the next few years as a hospital assistant. In 1891 he was appointed professor of pharmacology at the University of Copenhagen, a position he maintained with inspiring diligence until 1900, although he had also become chief physician in internal medicine at the Royal Frederiks Hospital in 1892. Gram took great interest in the clinical education of young students; he was appointed ordinary professor (1900) and from 1902 to 1909 he published his four-volume *Klinisk-therapeutiske Forelaesninger,* which shows his interest in rational pharmacotherapy in clinical science.

In addition to his university post, Gram had a large private practice in internal medicine; and as chairman of the Pharmacopoeia Commission (1901–1921) he cleared the field of many obsolete therapeutics. After his retirement in 1923 he resumed his former interest in the history of medicine.

Gram was made honorary member of Svenska Läkaresällskapet (1905), Verein für Innere Medizin (1907), and Dansk Selskab for Intern Medicin (1932). Kristiana University (now University of Oslo) awarded him the M.D. *honoris causa* in 1912; and the king awarded him the Dannebrog Commander's Cross, first-class (1912) and the Golden Medal of Merit (1924).

Gram married Louise I. C. Lohse in 1889; she died eleven years later.

BIBLIOGRAPHY

I. ORIGINAL WORKS. A full catalog of Gram's published writings is in O. Preisler, *Bibliotheca medica danica,* VII (Lyngby, 1919), 41; *Index medicus danicus 1913–1927,* II (Copenhagen, 1928), 370–371; and *ibid., . . . 1928–1947* (printed index cards). His more important works include *Blodet hos Klorotiske med Hensyn til Blodlegemernes Tal og Størrelse hos Mennesket* (Copenhagen, 1882); *Undersøgelser over de røde Blodlegemers Størrelse hos Mennesket* (Copenhagen, 1883); "Über die isolierte Färbung der Schizomyceten in Schnitt- und Trockenpräparaten," in *Fortschritte der Medizin,* **2** (1884), 185; *Laegemidlernes Egenskaber og Doser i Tabelform* (Copenhagen, 1897); and *Klinisk-therapeutiske Forelaesninger for de Studerende,* 4 vols. (Copenhagen, 1902–1909).

II. Secondary Literature. See P. Engelstoft, *Dansk biografisk Leksikon,* VIII (1936), 251–252; S. A. Gammeltoft, *Den farmakologiske Undervisnings Historie ved Københavns Universitet* (Copenhagen, 1952), pp. 80–94; H. Okkels, *Farvningstekniken i den mikroskopiske Anatomi* (Copenhagen, 1947), pp. 48–49; C. Sonne, "Nekrolog," in *Acta medica scandinavica,* **98** (1939), 441–443; and H. R. Zeuthen, *Danske Farmakopeer indtil 1925* (Copenhagen, 1927), pp. 258–262.

E. Snorrason

GRAMME, ZÉNOBE-THÉOPHILE (*b.* Jehay-Bodegnée, Belgium, 4 April 1826; *d.* Bois-Colombes, near Paris, France, 20 January 1901), *technology.*

Gramme was born into an educated family of modest means; his father was a clerk in the tax department. Gramme showed no ability as a student but did not lack ingenuity and manual dexterity. He left school at an early age and became a joiner, practicing this trade in the small town of Hannut until he was twenty-two years old. He then moved with his family to Liège, where he remained until 1855. After visiting Brussels, Paris, Lyons, and Marseilles, he settled in Paris as a banister maker. He married Hortense Nysten, a dressmaker from Liège; they lived in Neuilly-sur-Seine, a suburb.

Shortly after he came to Paris, Gramme began to work as a model maker in a firm that specialized in the manufacture of electrical apparatus. This served as his apprenticeship in technology; by 1867 he had become interested in building an improved apparatus for producing alternating current. His success might be said to derive from his characteristic fastidiousness about his person, however. He was appalled by the dirt surrounding the batteries used to produce direct current, and by 1869 he had built a successful—and clean—direct-current dynamo, drawing on the work of Pacinotti (a version of whose machine he had improved) and other earlier physicists who had theorized autoexcitation in revolving machines. Gramme's dynamo, used in metallurgy as well as in the production of electric light, depended upon a ring winding to hold the conductors in place on the surface of the revolving armature. Gramme was the first to give final form to the collector that derives direct current from the revolving armature, and he rapidly saw the possibility of inverting the function of the dynamo to use it as an electrical engine.

Gramme's invention was presented to the Académie des Sciences by the physicist Jules Jamin at the meeting of 17 July 1871. It soon aroused the interest of scientific and industrial circles; and with the help of Marcel Deprez and Arsène d'Arsonval, Gramme was able to accomplish the long-distance transmission of direct-current electricity. Their results were announced to the Academy on 2 December 1872, 25 November 1874, and 11 June 1877. These four notes constitute the whole of Gramme's work published during his lifetime.

Gramme became associated with Hippolyte Fontaine in the further development of his machines; in 1871 they opened a factory—the Société des Machines Magnéto-Électriques Gramme—which manufactured the Gramme ring, Gramme armature, and Gramme dynamo, among other things. The factory grew to great size and the owners prospered. Gramme had a house in Bois-Colombes, complete with gardens and conservatories, built according to his specifications.

Gramme's wife died in 1890, and in 1891 he married Antonie Schentur, who was thirty-six years his junior. In 1901, following Gramme's death, she published a manuscript that he had written in the last two years of his life, containing a number of hypotheses about electricity and magnetism—hypotheses that, unfortunately, most eloquently illustrate Gramme's ignorance of contemporary science as well as his vivid imagination. Indeed, Gramme died semiliterate, without having advanced his mathematical training much beyond the four basic operations of elementary arithmetic.

Gramme was awarded the Volta Prize by Louis Napoleon in 1852. In 1898 he was made Commander of the Order of Leopold I of Belgium. His discoveries of the principles of the dynamo and the electrical engine were of the utmost importance to modern technology.

BIBLIOGRAPHY

I. Original Works. Gramme's writing are "Sur une machine magnéto-électrique produisant des courants continus," in *Comptes rendus hebdomadaires des séances de l'Académie des sciences,* **73** (1871), 175–178; "Sur les machines magnéto-électriques Gramme, appliquées à la galvanoplastie et à la production de lumière," *ibid.,* **75** (1872), 1497–1500; "Sur les nouveaux perfectionnements apportés aux machines magnéto-électriques," *ibid.,* **79** (1874), 1178–1182; "Recherches sur l'emploi des machines magnéto-électriques à courants continus," *ibid.,* **84** (1877), 1386–1389; and *Les hypothèses scientifiques émises par Zénobe Gramme en 1900* (Paris, 1902).

II. Secondary Literature. Biographies are the following (listed chronologically): O. Colson, *Zénobe Gramme, sa vie et ses oeuvres, d'après des documents inédits* (Liège, 1903; 5th ed., 1913); J. Pelseneer, *Zénobe Gramme* (Brussels, 1941); and L. Chauvois, *Histoire merveilleuse de Zénobe Gramme* (Paris, 1963).

Marcel Florkin

GRAMONT, ANTOINE ALFRED ARNAUD XAVIER LOUIS DE (*b.* Paris, France, 21 April 1861; *d.* Savennières, Maine-et-Loire, France, 31 October 1923), *physics, mineralogy.*

Gramont belonged to an aristocratic family and was able to devote himself to scientific research without regard for financial concerns. His first studies, in organic synthesis, were followed by the artificial production of several minerals, including boracite and datholite. He also investigated, in collaboration with Georges Friedel, the pyroelectricity of scolecite.

Beginning in 1894 Gramont specialized in spectroscopy, a field to which he soon contributed new methods. He found that the electric spark of a condenser that is constantly recharged by means of an induction coil (condensed spark) is brighter, shorter, and wider than the spark from a simple coil. In producing the spark on the surface of a compound, Gramont observed a complex spectrum in which each constituent element of the compound, upon being discharged, yielded its own spectrum independently. He termed this spectrum, resulting from the simple superposition of the line spectra of elements composing a body, the "dissociation spectrum."

By suppressing the condenser, Gramont eliminated the spectra of the metalloids and was left with the lines of the metals. At first he confined his studies to the visible portion of the spectrum, but it was obvious that such a technique could constitute a general method of investigation. Through the use of photography it could be extended to the portion of the ultraviolet that passes through the air.

For some twenty years Gramont perfected his method and broadened its field of application. About 1902, with Watteville and Hemsalech, he examined the effect of placing a self-induction coil in the discharge circuit; the result was a weakening of the high-temperature lines and a strengthening of the low-temperature lines. Enlarging the self-induction coil eliminated the lines of the air and then of the metalloids. In order to study the spark spectrum of liquids without interference from lines produced by the electrodes, Gramont generated the spark between the drops forming at the extremities of two capillary tubes (1907). He observed nonconducting substances in the form of solutions in fused salts. At about this same time he discovered the ultimate lines. If a substance is examined in increasingly smaller amounts, the lines likewise become steadily weaker, but their decrease is very irregular: the last visible lines are not the most intense ones of the ordinary spectrum. This discovery facilitated research on traces in general and also, to a degree, opened up the possibilities of quantitative analysis with the spectroscope. Gramont himself obtained some interesting results in this manner.

Gramont died very suddenly, shortly after he had finished correcting the proofs of a major work on spectroscopy written in collaboration with P. E. L. de Boisbaudran, whose career was somewhat similar to his own.

BIBLIOGRAPHY

I. ORIGINAL WORKS. From 1890 to 1921 Gramont published more than 100 communications to the Académie des Sciences in *Comptes rendus hebdomadaires des séances de l'Académie des sciences,* **110–173.** His last work was *Analyse spectrale appliquée à l'analyse chimique* (Paris, 1923), written with P. E. L. de Boisbaudran; Gramont was responsible for pt. 2. See also his *Notice sommaire sur les travaux scientifiques de M. A. de Gramont* (Paris, 1910).

II. SECONDARY LITERATURE. See Edouard Branly, *Rapport sur les travaux de M. A. de Gramont* (Paris, 1913); Charles Fabry, "Arnaud de Gramont (1861–1923)," in *Revue d'optique théorique et instrumentale,* **3** (1924), 153–156; and Albin Haller, "Notice biographique sur Arnaud de Gramont," in *Comptes rendus hebdomadaires des séances de l'Académie des sciences,* **180** (1925), 106–107.

J. PAYEN

GRAND'EURY, CYRILLE (*b.* Houdreville, Meurthe-et-Moselle, France, 9 March 1839; *d.* Malzéville, near Nancy, France, 22 July 1917), *paleobotany.*

Grand'Eury studied first at the École Loritz in Nancy, which later became the École Professionnelle de l'Est. He then attended the École des Mines at St.-Étienne, from which he graduated first in his class in 1859. Grand'Eury worked for several years as an engineer at the Roche-la-Molière mines, but being unable, for reasons of health, to spend prolonged periods in the mines, he then accepted a post as *répétiteur* at the École des Mines at St.-Étienne, where he later became professor of trigonometry. These were his only official positions (1863–1899). In 1885 the Institute named him a corresponding member.

Grand'Eury's first work, on the carboniferous flora of the department of the Loire (1877), touched upon all the topics with which he was to be especially concerned—paleobotanical stratigraphy, the reconstruction of Paleozoic plants, their ecology, and the conditions of formation of coal seams. It also contained a map of the subterranean topography of the basin of the upper Loire and listed new genera and species of plants.

La formation des couches de houille du terrain houiller (géogénie), published in 1887, was the result not only of Grand'Eury's researches in the Loire basin but also of his observations made during ten years of travel in northern Europe, Upper Silesia, and the Urals, and of his studies of the Gard basin. In this work Grand'Eury considered the coal strata, the coal's relationship to the encasing rocks, and the deposition and formation of the coal beds. In 1910 he published a new basic work, *La géologie et la paléontologie du bassin houiller du Gard,* which contained many geological cross sections and columns, together with illustrations of fossil plants and underclays.

Two sections of a planned larger work, *Recherches géobotaniques sur les forêts et sols fossiles et sur la végétation de la flore houillère,* were published before World War I. During the war Grand'Eury's only son and collaborator, Maurice, was killed in action, and the books were never completed.

The study of plant impressions led Grand'Eury to establish for the Massif Central a series of stages that he named for the most abundant representative plants: the cordaitean (lower portion of the St.-Étienne layer), the filicite (middle portion of the same layer), and the *Calamodendron.* He also used names of localities to designate other stages familiar to regional geologists.

His knowledge of the floral succession, applied to mine development, led Grand'Eury to advise the continuation of borings that had been stopped and, thus, to the discovery of new coal deposits. He also drew many scientific hypotheses from this work, notably some concerning the mutation of species.

The study of so many seeds excited Grand'Eury, and as early as 1875 he suspected that a great many of them that he found separately had come from Filicineen-type fronds. He did not describe *Pecopteris pluckeneti,* to which hundreds of tiny seeds are attached, until 1905—after the publications of Robert Kidston (1903) and Oliver and Dukinfield Scott (1904), which were also devoted to seeds in connection with fronds. He concluded that the vegetative organs were comparatively less variable than the reproductive organs, in other words, that a particular foliage will remain constant in the course of evolution but will have different seeds attributed to it.

Grand'Eury was convinced of the necessity of using special generic names for the various organs of a plant. He originated the terms *Cordaianthus* for the inflorescence of the Cordaites, *Cordaicladus* for the axis, *Cordaifloyos* for the bark, and *Cordaixylon* for certain woods. His reconstructions of *Lepidodendra,* of Cordaites, and of other plants from isolated remains of leaves, trunks, and seeds were scientific masterpieces that are still discussed in works on paleobotany.

The observation of mixtures of plant remains—particularly of various fossil rhizomes and roots *in situ*—and detailed surveys of the sections he investigated enabled Grand'Eury to reconstruct the vegetation, to identify both plants living in almost unmixed populations and social plants, and to establish certain conditions of growth.

Grand'Eury was active in the discussion of the deposition of coal. After having been convinced of allochthony, that is, origin by transport, he accepted the concept of deposition at the bottom of large marshy lakes. He stated that one always returned to the idea of a swamp, even if there is only a faint resemblance between coal and peat, in terms of the manner of accumulation of plant debris. The formation took place not on the spot but a short distance away. He also accepted, for certain basins, the existence of a cover of deep water surrounded by large, wooded marshes but held that a uniform conclusion for all basins was not possible. Grand'Eury clearly spoke of a subsidence of the ground necessary for the formation of a coal bed. In the marshy basins such as those he studied, he paid special attention to the schistification of coal, which is due to a water current's carrying sediments that mix with carbonaceous material.

BIBLIOGRAPHY

I. ORIGINAL WORKS. Grand'Eury's writings include "Mémoire sur la flore carbonifère du département de la Loire et du centre de la France étudiée aux trois points de vue botanique, stratigraphique et géognostique," in *Mémoires de l'Académie des sciences de l'Institut de France,* **24,** no. 1 (1877), 1–624; "La formation des couches de houille du terrain houiller (géogénie)," in *Mémoires de la Société géologique de France,* 3rd ser., **4** (1887), 109–196; *La géologie et la paléontologie du bassin houiller du Gard* (St.-Étienne, 1890); and *Recherches géobotaniques sur les forêts et sols fossiles et sur la végétation de la flore houillère,* 3 vols. (Paris–Liège, 1912–1914).

II. SECONDARY LITERATURE. See Paul Bertrand, "C. Grand'Eury. Notice nécrologique," in *Bulletin de la Société géologique de France,* 4th ser., **19** (1920), 148–162; H. Guyot, "Notes sur le paléobotaniste lorrain Cyrille Grand'Eury," in *Bulletin de la Société d'histoire naturelle de Metz,* 3rd ser., **10** (1935), 317–324; and Paul Vuillemin, "L'oeuvre de Cyrille Grand'Eury," in *Revue générale des sciences pures et appliquées,* **28** (1917), 601–604.

F. STOCKMANS

GRANDI, GUIDO (*b.* Cremona, Italy, 1 October 1671; *d.* Pisa, Italy, 4 July 1742), *mathematics.*

At the age of sixteen, Grandi entered the religious order of the Camaldolese and changed his baptismal name of Francesco Lodovico to Guido. His appointment in 1694 as teacher of mathematics in his order's monastery in Florence led him to study Newton's *Principia.* In order to understand it, he was obliged to increase his knowledge of geometry, and made such rapid progress that he was soon able to discover new properties of the cissoid and the conchoid and to determine the points of inflection of the latter curve. When in 1700 Grandi was called to Rome, Cosimo de' Medici encouraged him to stay in Tuscany, by making him professor of philosophy at Pisa. In 1707 he received the honorary post of mathematician to the grand duke, in 1709 he was made a member of the Royal Society of London, and in 1714 he became professor of mathematics at Pisa. Grandi's voluminous scientific correspondence preserved in the library of the University of Pisa testifies to the esteem he enjoyed among the mathematicians of his time.

Grandi also did successful work in theoretical and practical mechanics; his studies in hydraulics evoked considerable interest from the governments of central Italy (for example, the drainage of the Chiana Valley and the Pontine Marshes).

As a collaborator in the publication of the first Florentine edition of the works of Galileo, Grandi contributed to it a "Note on the Treatise of Galileo Concerning Natural Motion," in which he gave the first definition of a curve he called the *versiera* (from the Latin *sinus versus*): Given a circle with diameter *AC,* let *BDM* be a moving straight line perpendicular

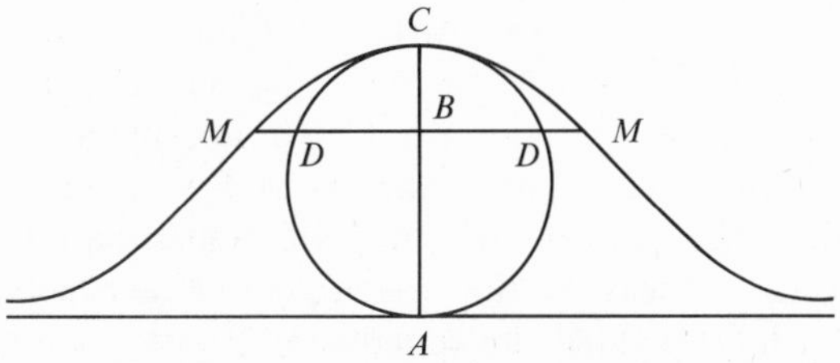

FIGURE 1

to *AC* at *B*, and intersecting the circumference of the circle at *D*. Let point *M* be determined by length *BM* satisfying the proportion $AB:BD = AC:BM$. The locus of all such points *M* is the *versiera*;[1] for a circle of diameter a, tangent to the x-axis at the origin, its Cartesian equation is $x^2y = a^2(a - y)$. The curve is more commonly known as the "witch of Agnesi" as the result of a mistranslation and a false attribution to Maria Gaetana Agnesi, who referred to it in her treatise *Istituzioni analitiche ad uso della gioventù italiana* (1748). Although Fermat had already investigated this particular equation,[2] Grandi's study extended to the more general family of curves of the form

$$y = \frac{a^{(m/n)+1}}{(a^2 + x^2)^{m/2n}},$$

where m and n are positive integers (1710). In an unpublished treatise Grandi also studied a curve known as the strophoid.

Grandi's reputation rests especially on the curves that he named "rodonea" and "clelia," after the Greek word for "rose" and the Countess Clelia Borromeo, respectively. He arrived at these curves in attempting to define geometrically the curves that have the shape of flowers, in particular the multileaved roses. They are represented in polar coordinates by equations of the form

$$\rho = R \sin a\vartheta,$$

in which R is a given line segment and a a positive integer. Grandi communicated the most significant properties of these curves to Leibniz in two letters dated December 1713 but did not make them generally known until ten years later in a memoir presented to the Royal Society of London. He later explained his complete theory in a special pamphlet (1728). Whereas analytic geometry now teaches the study of curves with given equations, Grandi here solved the inverse problem of determining the equations of curves having a preestablished form. The clelias are curves inscribed in a spherical zone, and their projection on a base plane of the zone yields the rodonea.

The *Acta eruditorum* of 4 April 1692 contained, under a pseudonym, the problem of constructing in a hemispheric cupola four equal-sized windows such that the remaining area of the cupola is quadrable. This is known as Viviani's problem, after Vincenzo Viviani who suggested it. It is an indeterminate problem and was solved shortly afterward by Leibniz and by Viviani himself;[3] Grandi also devoted a memoir to it (1699).

The curve

$$y = b \ln(x/a)$$

or

$$x = ae^{y/b},$$

called the logarithmic or logistic curve, was studied by Evangelista Torricelli as early as 1647; Huygens revealed its most important properties in a communication read before the Paris Academy in 1669. In 1701 Grandi demonstrated the theorems enunciated by Huygens.

On a more general level, Grandi's treatise on quadrature of 1703, in which he abandoned the Galilean methods of Cavalieri and Viviani in favor of those of Leibniz, marks the introduction of the

Leibnizian calculus into Italy. Grandi was also the author of several noteworthy and popular textbooks.

NOTES

1. Cf. also Grandi's *Quadratura circuli et hyperbolae.*
2. Cf. *Oeuvres de Fermat,* Charles Henry and Paul Tannery, eds. (Paris, 1891–1922), I, 279–280.
3. Vincenzo Viviani, *Formatione e misura di tutti i cieli* (Florence, 1692).

BIBLIOGRAPHY

I. Original Works. Grandi's writings include *Geometrica divinatio Vivianeorum problematum* (Florence, 1699); *Geometrica demonstratio theorematum Hugenianorum circa logisticam seu logarithmicam* (Florence, 1701); *Quadratura circuli et hyperbolae* (Pisa, 1703, 1710); *De infinitis infinitorum et infinite parvorum* . . . (Pisa, 1710); "Florum geometricarum manipulus," in *Philosophical Transactions of the Royal Society* (1723); *Flores geometrici ex rhodonearum et cloeliarum curvarum descriptione resultantes* . . . (Florence, 1728); *Elementi geometrici piani e solidi di Euclide, posti brevemente in volgare* (Florence, 1731); *Istituzioni di aritmetica pratica* (Florence, 1740); and *Istituzioni geometriche* (Florence, 1741).

II. Secondary Literature. Grandi's letters to Leibniz are in *Leibnizens mathematische Schriften, herausgegeben von C. J. Gerhardt,* 7 vols. and supp. (Berlin and Halle, 1848–1863), IV, 221, 224. There are three works of value by Gino Loria: *Curve sghembe speciali algebriche e trascendenti,* 2 vols. (Bologna, 1925), esp. II, 57; *Curve piane speciali algebriche e trascendenti,* 2 vols. (Milan, 1930), I, 94, 419 ff.; and *Storia delle matematiche,* 2nd ed. (Milan, 1950).

A. Natucci

GRANGER, WALTER WILLIS (*b.* Middletown Springs, Vermont, 7 November 1872; *d.* Lusk, Wyoming, 6 September 1941), *paleontology.*

The son of Charles H. Granger and Ada Byron Haynes, Granger acquired his keen interest in nature as a boy in rural Vermont and began his lifelong career at the American Museum of Natural History in 1890, after only two years of high school. He married Anna Dean of Brooklyn, New York, on 7 April 1904; they had no children. In 1932 he was awarded an honorary D.Sc. by Middlebury College, Vermont. Besides being a member of several scientific societies, he was particularly active in the Explorers Club, of which he was president in 1935–1937 and later an honorary member.

Granger's first years at the American Museum were divided between taxidermy and maintenance work. In 1894 he collected mammal and bird skins in the Rocky Mountains; his interest in fieldwork led to his transfer in 1896 to the department of vertebrate paleontology. In 1909 he was advanced to assistant curator, in 1911 to associate curator, and in 1927 to curator of fossil mammals.

Granger possessed the keen eye, steady hand, and infinite patience essential for finding and collecting delicate fossils. Between 1896 and 1918 he spent nineteen field seasons in the western United States; in 1907 he accompanied Henry F. Osborn to the Fayum in Egypt. From 1897 to 1901 he took part in the excavations for dinosaurs at Bone Cabin, Wyoming, and his first paleontological publication was on some of this material. His major efforts, however, were devoted to the early Tertiary of the Rocky Mountains. His extensive collections of well-preserved fossil mammals formed the basis for numerous systematic revisions and stratigraphic studies.

In 1921 Granger went to China as paleontologist and second in command of the American Museum's Central Asiatic Expeditions, led by Roy Chapman Andrews. During five summers in the Gobi Desert of Mongolia he found and collected a series of faunas ranging in age from Jurassic to Pleistocene. The excitement brought to the expedition members and to the scientific world by the discoveries of the small horned dinosaur *Protoceratops* and accompanying nests of eggs, of tiny Cretaceous mammal skulls, and of the giant *Baluchitherium,* largest of all land mammals, are well told in Andrews' report of the expedition.

Soon after Granger's arrival in China in 1923 he accompanied Dr. Andersson, the leader of the Swedish scientific mission to China, and members of the Chinese Geological Survey to Choukoutien, a locality near Peking where fossil bones had been collected. It was on this visit that the cave deposit which later yielded the remains of Peking man was first brought to the attention of these scientists. Granger was favorably impressed by the richness of the deposit and encouraged the Swedish and Chinese scientists to investigate it fully and advised them on suitable techniques for doing so.

During three winters between the Mongolian trips Granger visited a remote region of Szechwan and obtained an important series of Pleistocene mammals from Chinese collectors who dug out fossil bones and teeth for the Chinese drug markets.

After 1930 Granger's efforts were devoted largely to the necessary curatorial work on the Mongolian collections, to departmental administration, and to editing reports of the Asiatic expeditions. Each summer he found time to spend a few weeks in the field with his skilled preparator and long-time friend

Albert Thomson, and his life ended quietly in the middle of such a congenial excursion.

BIBLIOGRAPHY

I. ORIGINAL WORKS. The most extensive list of Granger's publications is included in the memorial by Simpson (1942). His technical papers are cited in the bibliographies of vertebrate paleontology by O. P. Hay, Carnegie Institution of Washington Publication 390, I (Washington, D.C., 1929), 198; and by C. L. Camp *et al.*, Geological Society of America Special Papers 27 (1940), p. 22; 42 (1942), p. 157; memoir 37 (1949), p. 80.

Granger published an important systematic study of primitive fossil horses in "A Revision of the American Eocene Horses," in *Bulletin of the American Museum of Natural History,* **24** (1908), 221–264; and of primitive ungulates known as condylarths in "A Revision of the Lower Eocene Wasatch and Wind River Faunas," *ibid.,* **34** (1915), 329–361; and, in the same bulletin, several papers on Tertiary geology of the Rocky Mountains. He more characteristically communicated his extensive knowledge of mammalian morphology and relationships orally to his co-workers. In this way he collaborated with William D. Matthew, William K. Gregory, George G. Simpson, *et al.* in twenty papers on the systematics of Eocene mammals; he also contributed importantly to Matthew's major monographs "The Carnivora and Insectivora of the Bridger Basin," in *Memoirs from the American Museum of Natural History,* **9**, pt. 6 (1909), 289–567; and "Paleocene Faunas of the San Juan Basin, New Mexico," in *Transactions of the American Philosophical Society,* n.s. **30** (1937). He was coauthor of 35 reports on vertebrate fossils from Mongolia and China.

Two chapters, "Paleontological Exploration in Eastern Szechuan . . ." and "A Reconnaissance in Yunnan, 1926–1927," were contributed by Granger to R. C. Andrews, *The New Conquest of Asia* (pp. 501–528 and 529–540). He also wrote popular accounts of the Gobi exploration and gracious memorials to W. D. Matthew, in *Journal of Mammalogy,* **12** (1931), 189–194; and to F. B. Loomis, in *Proceedings. Geological Society of America* for 1936 (1937), 173–178.

II. SECONDARY LITERATURE. On Granger or his work, see R. C. Andrews, *The New Conquest of Asia: Natural History of Central Asia,* Reports of Central Asiatic Expedition of the American Museum of Natural History, New York, I, pt. 1 (New York, 1932), 1–453; Donald R. Barton, "The Way of a Fossil Hunter," in *Natural History,* **47** (1941), 172–176; and G. G. Simpson, "Memorial to Walter Granger," in *Proceedings. Geological Society of America* for 1941 (1942), 159–172, with portrait and bibliography of 106 titles.

Brief obituary notices are C. F. Cooper, in *Nature,* **148** (1941), 654–655; J. J. Hickey and J. T. Nichols, in *Abstracts of Proceedings of the Linnaean Society of New York,* **52–53** (1941), 151–152; T. S. Palmer, in *Auk,* **59** (1942), 140; G. G. Simpson, in *Science,* **94** (1941), 338–339; and *News Bulletin. Society of Vertebrate Paleontology,* **4** (1941), 1–2.

JOSEPH T. GREGORY

GRASHOF, FRANZ (*b.* Düsseldorf, Germany, 11 July 1826; *d.* Karlsruhe, Germany, 26 October 1893), *applied mechanics, thermodynamics, machine design.*

Son of a teacher of the humanities, Grashof had a strong practical bent, interrupting his early schooling to work for a locksmith. He went to Berlin in 1844 and spent the following three years at the Gewerbe-Institut, studying mathematics, physics, and machine design as preparation for a career in metallurgy.

After a year as an army volunteer, a career as naval officer seemed attractive; Grashof shipped out as apprentice seaman on a sailing vessel, returning in 1851. Having found himself during this voyage, Grashof realized that he was not suited to a life of physical activity (in part because of myopia) and that his real inclination was to teach engineering sciences.

In 1852 Grashof resumed his studies at Berlin, where he was entrusted with lectures on applied mathematics. Elevated in 1854 to staff membership of the Gewerbe-Institut as teacher of mathematics and mechanics, he was also director of the Office of Weights and Measures.

On 12 May 1856, Grashof was among the twenty-three founders of the Verein Deutscher Ingenieure (VDI). Although no unified Germany then existed, this society was to include the engineers of the twenty-five German states and Grashof was to implement its organization; because of his scientific reputation he was made director of the society and editor of its *Zeitschrift.* The University of Rostock conferred an honorary doctorate in 1860.

Following Ferdinand Redtenbacher's death in 1863, Grashof was named his successor as professor of applied mechanics and the theory of machines at the Polytechnikum in Karlsruhe. He lectured on strength of materials, hydraulics, thermodynamics, and machine design with clarity and precision. He remained in Karlsruhe, rejecting an offer from Aachen and two from Munich.

Although he resigned the editorship of the *Zeitschrift,* Grashof remained director of the VDI and turned much of his attention to technical writing. He was the first to present the fundamental equations of the theory of elasticity, in a text on strength of materials in which he treated flexure, torsion, buckling, plates, and shells. His three-volume *Theoretische Maschinenlehre* (1871–1886) was characterized by sharp insight and critical observation with respect to the limits of accuracy and the admissibility of assumptions; no contemporary English or French work was its equal.

During his lifetime Grashof was recognized as an authority on mechanical engineering in its broadest sense. As teacher and engineer, and as founding member, editor, and long-time director of the VDI, he influenced a generation of engineers by bringing mathematical and scientific considerations to the burgeoning problems of the steam-engine age. Grashof used analysis, supporting and exploiting it with all available experimental work; he shunned the graphical approach of his contemporary Karl Culmann, who founded graphic statics.

Grashof's name is perpetuated in several ways. There is the dimensionless Grashof number of heat transfer in free-convection flow systems (a criterion similar to Reynolds' number of forced convection) for the transition from laminar to turbulent flow. Another Grashof criterion is used in kinematics for establishing whether one link of a four-bar chain can rotate completely. The VDI honored his memory by erecting the Grashof Monument in Karlsruhe and by establishing the annually awarded Grashof Medal, its highest honor for achievements in technology.

Grashof suffered a stroke in 1883 that restricted his activity. In that year he became a member of the Standards Commission; in 1887, he was named a trustee of the Bureau of Standards and received honorary membership in the VDI. A second stroke in 1891 disabled him, and he died two years later, survived by his wife and two children.

BIBLIOGRAPHY

I. Original Works. Grashof published forty-two articles in *Zeitschrift des Vereins deutscher Ingenieure* (1857–1885). His books include *Angewandte Mechanik,* vol. V of Gustave Karsten's *Allgemeine Encyklopädie der Physik* (Leipzig, 1856–1862); *Festigkeitslehre mit Rücksicht auf den Maschinenbau* (Berlin, 1866), 2nd ed., under the title *Theorie der Elastizität und Festigkeit* (Berlin, 1878); *Resultate der mechanischen Wärmetheorie* (Heidelberg, 1870); and *Theoretische Maschinenlehre,* 3 vols. (Leipzig, 1871–1886). Other works are listed in Poggendorff, III, 543.

II. Secondary Literature. On Grashof or his work, see H. Lorenz, "Die wissenschaftlichen Leistungen F. Grashofs," in *Beiträge zur Geschichte der Industrie und Technik,* **16** (1926), 1–12; C. Matschoss, *Männer der Technik* (Düsseldorf, 1925), p. 94; K. Nesselmann, in *Neue deutsche Biographie,* VI (Berlin, 1964), 746; R. Plank, "Franz Grashof als Lehrer und Forscher," in *Zeitschrift des Vereins deutscher Ingenieure,* **70** (1926), 28; and S. Timoshenko, *History of the Strength of Materials* (New York, 1953), p. 133.

Obituaries are in *Zeitschrift des Vereins deutscher Ingenieure,* **37** (1893), 48; and *Transactions of the American Society of Mechanical Engineers,* **15** (1894).

R. S. Hartenberg

GRASSI, GIOVANNI BATTISTA (*b.* Rovellasca, Italy, 27 March 1854; *d.* Rome, Italy, 4 May 1925), *entomology, parasitology.*

The son of Luigi Grassi, a municipal official, and of Costanza Mazzuchelli, a peasant of unusual intelligence, Grassi was educated at Saronno. From 1872 he studied medicine at Pavia, graduating in 1878. He then went to Germany, where he worked at Heidelberg with the zoologist Otto Bütschli and the anatomist Carl Gegenbaur. There Grassi met his future wife, Maria Koenen. In 1883 he was appointed professor of zoology and comparative anatomy at Catania. In 1895 he became professor of comparative anatomy at Rome University, where he remained for the rest of his life. In 1908 he was appointed a senator of the kingdom.

As an anatomist Grassi studied the development of the vertebral column in bony fishes (1883), and as a physician he studied endemic goiter (1903–1917). Some of his more elegant studies were in pure entomology: on bees (1877–1884); on myriapods (1886–1889); and his monumental work on termites (1885–1893). For the latter work he was awarded a Darwin Gold Medal. He also studied the Chetognates (1881, 1883) and the reproduction of eels (1910–1919), and in 1885 he described a new species of spider (*Koenenia mirabilis*), naming it for his wife. Nevertheless, he is remembered today essentially for his studies in parasitology and in practical and applied entomology.

In 1876 in his native Rovellasca Grassi investigated the high mortality of cats and discovered in their bowels large numbers of *Dochmius balsami,* strongly hematophagous little worms very like *Anchylostoma.* In 1878, while still a student at the medical clinic of the University of Pavia and working under Francesco Orsi, he discovered anchylostomiasis in Italy. He made the diagnosis as a result of finding *Anchylostoma* eggs in feces.

Grassi developed a wide knowledge of helminthology, writing first on *Anguillula intestinalis* (or *Rhabdonema strongyloides*) in patients with marshy cachexia (1878–1887). He also studied *Filaria* (1887–1901), *Trichocephalus dispar* (1887), and *Bilharzia* (1888); but he was concerned particularly with the tapeworm. Grassi was the first to demonstrate that *Taenia nana* is able to go through its entire life cycle in one animal, without the need of an intermediate host, a fact that had long been denied. He was also the first to show that the flea *Pulex serraticeps* is the intermediate host of larvae of *Taenia cucumerina* or *elliptica.* Thus he wrote that the swallowing of infected fleas (for example, with milk) might be the reason for *Taenia* in children.

Grassi also made important studies on the parasitic and pathogenic protozoa (1879–1888). Of great practical importance were his studies on the fly (1879–1884): it could swallow, and expel still alive, the spores of *Botrytis* and *Oidium,* the eggs of *Taenia* or *Trichocephalus,* and even bacteria, particularly the cholera bacillus. Grassi then began a campaign to eradicate flies. Grassi made his first observations on malaria in 1890, when in collaboration with Raimondo Feletti he discovered *Plasmodium vivax.* (In 1889 Ettore Marchiafava and Angelo Celli had discovered *Plasmodium falciparum,* the deadliest form of the malarial parasite.) This confirmed the validity of Camillo Golgi's assertions (1885–1889) that the differences in the period (three or four days) and the severity of various malarial fevers arise because of different species of the malarial parasite. Also in collaboration with Feletti, Grassi worked on malaria in 1891 and 1892 and discovered the malaria parasite of birds (*Proteosoma praecox,* very like *Plasmodium vivax*). In 1891 he performed the first inoculation of malaria parasites from one bird into another. But all of Grassi's decisive investigations on the transmission of malaria in man were made between 15 July and 30 November 1898 and reported to the Accademia dei Lincei (see *Rendiconti,* meeting of 22 December 1898).

In 1894 Amico Bignami, in collaboration with Giuseppe Bastianelli, produced a typical malarial fever paroxysm in a healthy man by intradermically injecting a minute drop of blood from a malaria patient. But in 1896 all his attempts to produce malaria in man by the bite of mosquitoes failed. Nevertheless, human malaria from inoculation by mosquito bite—affirmed in 1896 by Bignami and by the English pathologist Patrick Manson in his lectures to the Royal College of Physicians of London—was accepted as most probable. Grassi was struck by the fact that there are always mosquitoes wherever malaria is found, which had already been observed in 1716 by the Italian physician Giovanni Maria Lancisi. Grassi, however, also noted that where mosquitoes abound, malaria is not necessarily present. After deducing that only a particular species of mosquito could transmit malaria to man, it became a question of identifying the species. In August 1898 Grassi discovered that the agent transmitting malaria to man is the female *Anopheles* mosquito, most frequently of the species *A. claviger.*

In November 1898, with the help of Bignami and Bastianelli, Grassi produced experimentally in a healthy man a typical malarial paroxysm of malignant tertian fever, resulting from bites of *Anopheles* mosquitoes. He then demonstrated that all anophelines are capable of becoming the hosts of human malaria parasites during sporogony. In consequence of these demonstrations, Grassi launched a great antimalaria campaign, emphasizing human protection through window screens, prophylaxis with quinine, and the destruction of *Anopheles* with *Gambusia,* which devours its larvae. Above all, Grassi recommended extensive distribution of quinine to all persons in malarial districts, because quinine kills the parasites of malaria and thereby prevents the infection of new anophelines. In 1899 he demonstrated that *Anopheles* is born uninfected and becomes able to transmit malaria only after biting an infected human. Grassi understood the importance of continuous suppressive treatment of malaria with quinine, so as to prevent the occurrence of the asexual blood stages in both uninfected and chronically infected persons.

That Grassi discovered the pathogenic activity of anophelines and, in consequence, is responsible for the victory over human malaria, is undeniable. But the English surgeon Ronald Ross claimed priority and the 1902 Nobel Prize for physiology or medicine was awarded to him; even today this decision is widely accepted. Indeed it was Grassi who first demonstrated the sporogonic cycle of the human malaria parasite (its schizogonic cycle had already been described in 1889 by Golgi). Although unappreciated at the time, Grassi also identified the true agent transmitting malaria in man. Today it is well accepted, in a zoological sense, that while man is the intermediate, the *Anopheles* mosquito is the definitive host of malaria parasites.

Ross made some very important observations on malaria in birds, working from 1896 to 1898 under Manson. In the summer of 1898 he achieved the transmission of experimental malaria in birds by the bite of mosquitoes. He also demonstrated the entire life cycle of *Proteosoma,* the malaria parasite of birds, which concludes as a sporogonic cycle, resulting in the formation of sporozoites that accumulate in the salivary glands of a mosquito. Thus, when the mosquito bites, it inoculates a bird with malaria parasites. Ross also stated that malaria is transmitted in man by the bite of mosquitoes but did not demonstrate this. In addition, in 1898 he did not know of the genus *Anopheles,* nor was he convinced of the mosquito's exclusive importance in transmitting malaria. In 1903 Grassi published his precisely documented vindication, but Ross never acknowledged priority.

Grassi turned to a new field of research—the study of the phylloxera of grapes—which he pursued for several years. On the strength of his first notes, *La questione fillosserica in Italia* (1904), the Italian Ministry of Agriculture requested him to do an exhaustive study of this subject. In 1912 he collected his own observations and those of his collaborators in a precise and monumental analysis of the morphology and biology of the Italian and other European genera of phylloxera. Thus it was possible to begin the fight against this agricultural pest.

Grassi was an extremely private person, and an affectionate husband and father. His forty-two years of teaching and research testify to his deep devotion to science. But his greatest source of pride was that he opened the way to the eradication of malaria. Thus he chose to be buried in the cemetery of Fiumicino, an area that his personal and persevering initiative had rid of the disease.

BIBLIOGRAPHY

Grassi's scientific production was enormous. Alone he wrote more than 250 papers, collaborating on another 100 with his students. For a full listing of his works, see A. Pazzini, "Giovanni Battista Grassi," in *Rivista di biologia,* **19** (1935), 1–46.

For information on Grassi or his work, see A. Corradetti, "L'opera protozoologica di Battista Grassi alla luce degli odierni sviluppi della scienza," in *Rivista di parassitologia,* **15** (1954), 190–199; A. Corti, "Battista Grassi e la trasmissione della malaria," in *Studia ghisleriana,* **1** (1961); C. Golgi, "Sul ciclo evolutivo dei parassiti malarici nella febbre terzana," in *Archivio per le scienze mediche,* **13** (1889), 173–196; and C. Jucci, *Nel centenario della nascita di Battista Grassi* (Milan, 1954).

See also S. Piccini, "Nel centenario della nascita di Battista Grassi," in *Atti del XIV congresso internazionale di Storia della medicina* (Rome–Salerno, Sept. 1954); F. Silvestri, "Commemorazione del Socio Nazionale Giovanni Battista Grassi," in *Atti dell'Accademia nazionale dei Lincei, memorie* (1926); and C. Tumiati, "Giovanni Battista Grassi," in *Vite singolari di grandi medici dell'800* (Florence, 1952), see esp. pp. 125–135 for the clearest assessment of Grassi's priority over Ross.

PIETRO FRANCESCHINI

GRASSMANN, HERMAN GÜNTHER (*b.* Stettin, Germany [now Szczecin, Poland], 15 April 1809; *d.* Stettin, 26 September 1877), *mathematics.*

For a detailed study of his life and work, see Supplement.

GRATIOLET, LOUIS PIERRE (*b.* Ste. Foy-la-Grande, Gironde, France, 6 July 1815; *d.* Paris, France, 16 February 1865), *anatomy, anthropology.*

Gratiolet was the son of a rural physician; his mother was of noble lineage. The father's royalist allegiance disturbed his practice and led to removal to Bordeaux. Here Gratiolet began his studies. Soon turning to Paris, he completed his secondary course at the Collège Stanislas and began, probably in 1834, formal preparation in medicine. While he quickly exhibited uncommon skill and interest in anatomy, he was also successful in the various academic competitions which spurred on the aspiring practical physician (he held internships at the Pitié and Salpetrière hospitals).

Adjacent to the Salpetrière was the Muséum d'Histoire Naturelle, an active center for anatomical studies. Gratiolet frequented the dissection halls of the museum and soon (1839) became a participant in Henri de Blainville's researches. By 1842, having been made Blainville's laboratory assistant, he had renounced practical medicine for a career in science. He nonetheless completed all requirements for a medical degree (1845).

Such auspicious beginnings merely introduced twenty years of acute professional frustration. Gratiolet lectured on anatomy at the museum as Blainville's deputy from 1844 until the latter's death in 1850. Gratiolet's candidacy for his teacher's chair was rejected. He did continue as laboratory assistant and in 1853 was placed in charge of anatomical studies at the museum. He lacked, however, the professorial chair which his scientific achievement and demonstrated instructional capacity deserved. Finally, in 1862, he was named deputy to the professor of zoology in the Faculty of Science, Paris, and received full rights to that chair at the close of 1863. Within sixteen months Gratiolet was dead of apoplexy. He had, reported Paul Broca, "lived only for science."

Gratiolet was an indefatigable investigator and adroit interpreter of animal structure and function. In the former capacity he excelled as a descriptive anatomist, dealing with some of the most difficult material which the organism can present: the vascular and nervous systems, with emphasis on the brain and cranium. Like Blainville, he studied mollusks and concentrated above all on man and the primates. He offered detailed descriptions of the vascular system of such disparate creatures as the hippopotamus and the physician's leech, molluscan organs of generation and generative products, and the osteology of mammals. Gratiolet was a descriptive and comparative

GRATIOLET

anatomist and neither employed vivisection nor attended to pathological lesions and their putative functional correlates. So restricted an approach evoked criticism and should have imposed limits on the scope of the physiological inferences which he evidently conceived to be the primary impulse of his many inquiries. He was a pioneer in the use of embryological material for establishing general zoological affinities (and dissimilarities) and the assessment of the active roles of various structures.

Gratiolet's interpretation of life and particularly of the nature of man began with principles enunciated by Blainville. The organism was an integral whole ceaselessly coping with ever-shifting stimuli from the environment and with the physiological (and, in the case of man, the mental) needs of its own being. Organs of peculiar structure and functional capacity obviously were essential to these tasks. All parts of the body acted cooperatively to share in a given vital act. Body and mind were physiologically conjoined, their activity being most evident in movement guided by instinct or intelligence. Gratiolet was less concerned with animal taxonomy than Blainville had been and accorded slight attention to conspicuous, external parts suitable for classificatory purposes. He struck for the heart of the matter: the form and behavior of those neural and muscular mechanisms without which the higher forms of life are inconceivable.

Thus was produced Gratiolet's first major work: *Mémoire sur les plis cérébraux* (1854). Descriptions of the cerebral folds, or convolutions, of the human brain had long been available; Gratiolet added the careful comparative investigation of the brain form of a wide range of monkeys. On the basis of the distribution and degree of cerebral convolution he emphasized the distinctness of the primates as a group. Gratiolet's anatomical research culminated in the *Anatomie comparée du système nerveux* (1857), a major contribution to mammalian descriptive anatomy. But this comparative anatomy offered far more than description; it presented (part II) Gratiolet's statement on the nature and meaning of intelligence, the opposed roles of "sensation" (a consequence of external stimulus) and "sentiment" (evoked independently within the organism), and man's uniqueness founded on his capacity to reason. These themes were clarified, further developed, and augmented by reflections on the diversity of human races in a notable series of anthropological essays and discussions offered between 1860 and 1865.

Man alone, Gratiolet argued, is to be established as a rational being; only he can speak. Spoken language remained, as it had over the generations since Descartes, the most direct expression of intelligence and the essential criterion of humanity. "This innate and . . . ineffaceable potentiality [for speech] is certainly the most striking, the most noble character of man. . . . Only man can have an idea of an idea, and so on almost to infinity." Implicit in these conclusions was Gratiolet's conviction, and one which comparative anatomy seemed only to confirm and expand, that human intelligence was in some way a function of the cerebral convolutions. One must, he urged, focus on gross structure until the fortunate day arrived that "one might study directly the brain itself."

During the 1860's the question of a localization within the brain (cerebrum) of mental functions was much in dispute. Gratiolet adopted a conservative position: "Generally speaking, I agree with [M. J. P.] Flourens that intelligence is unitary, that the brain is one and that it acts above all as an integral organ [*organ d'ensemble*]." He took this position less on grounds of negative evidence than on the absence of indisputable data confirming any particular case of localization.

Gratiolet, laying groundwork for his anthropological views, accorded complex instinct and simple judgment to both man and animals. But complex judgments required intelligence and hence were, like imagination, man's alone. All men possessed intelligence but their shares, apparently, varied. Gratiolet introduced into the prospering multiple-origins conception of the human races (polygenic theory) the embryological criterion. Claiming that the frontal sutures of the developing cranium in whites closed later than those of other races, he found a splendid opportunity for curious "reflection." "Might not," he mused, "the long persistence of sutures in the white race have some relation to the almost indefinite perfectibility of intelligence among men of this race? . . . might not the brain, among these perfectible men, [thus] remain capable of a slow but continuous growth?" Regrettably, among "idiots and lower [*abruties*] races the cranium is closed upon the brain like a prison." Not only were the races of man different; it was part of their very nature to be so. Lower races were no degraded Caucasians. They were perfect beings but were placed lower on the scale of creation, a scale which, since Gratiolet dismissed transmutationist hypotheses, must be considered as temporally fixed.

Not wholly consistent with this viewpoint was Gratiolet's expression of another, and probably more cherished, notion of why some men are elevated and others depressed: The Caucasian manifests an "instinct for civilization." All whites, from fool to hero, recognized the horrors of that individualism which promotes egoism and scorn for other men and leads to a neglect of social obligation (*devoir*). All whites, Gratiolet's strange apology continued, understood the "usefulness of law [and] the necessity to submit to it." Each must and would sacrifice part of his liberty for the good of the social whole. This remarkable excursus by a cabinet anatomist was not original. It shared fully Blainville's emphasis on physiology as a model for society and thus that special interest, broadcast by Blainville's auditor, Auguste Comte, in the inviolable solidarity of the healthful social organism. It is conservative social doctrine entertained by an anatomist of royalist sentiment and tempered with the epoch's exaggerated interest in racial matters.

Gratiolet displayed patience and industry in the face of constant academic rebuffs. He was exceptionally well-read, particularly in the classics and the literature of philosophy. He commanded deepest friendship, evidencing firm loyalty to his doctrinal allies and candor to all. He was an able and frequent combatant in discussions at the Société d'Anthropologie of Paris, of which he was a founding member. Gratiolet apparently received few or none of the honors due a French scientist of his stature and was overlooked by the Academy of Sciences. Political considerations may have been operative here. Born just after Waterloo and raised in the royalist persuasion, he cast his intellectual foundations in the mold of an outspoken Christian royalist apologist, Blainville. He ably led troops of the National Guard against the republican insurgents of 1848 (but refused decoration for participation in what he called a "civil war") and was obviously neglected by the Bonapartist ministries of the 1850's. In good faith he argued a scientific brief for the autonomy of man, the primacy of the Caucasian race, and the necessary and desirable supremacy of traditional European social forms; and in support of his faith he brought great learning as a naturalist and equal facility as an anatomist.

BIBLIOGRAPHY

I. Original Works. Gratiolet published little before 1850. His principal early contribution was a dissertation for the degree *docteur en médecine* at the Paris Faculty of Medicine: *Recherches sur l'organe de Jacobson* (Paris, 1845). His major anatomical works are two: *Mémoires sur les plis cérébraux de l'homme et des primates,* 1 vol. plus plates (Paris, 1854); *Anatomie comparée du système nerveux considerée dans ses rapports avec l'intelligence,* 2 vols. plus plates (Paris, 1839–1857)—this work was planned and begun by François Leuret but the research, organization, and interpretations of vol. II (1857) are due to Gratiolet.

Gratiolet published over fifty scientific papers, some with collaborators. They are listed in Royal Society, *Catalogue of Scientific Papers 1800–1863* (London, 1868), II, 989–991; and VII [*1864–1873*] (1877), 818. Among the more interesting of these papers are the following: "Mémoire sur les plis cérébraux de l'homme et des primates," in *Comptes rendus hebdomadaires des séances de l'Académie des sciences,* **31** (1850), 366–369, a valuable précis of the 1854 vol.; "Mémoire sur le développement de la forme du crâne de l'homme, et sur quelques variations qu'on observe dans la marche de l'ossification de ses sutures," *ibid.,* **43** (1856), 428–431; "Mémoire sur la microcéphalie considérée dans ses rapports avec la question des caractères du genre humain," in *Mémoires de la Société d'anthropologie de Paris,* **1** (1860), 61–67; "Sur la forme et la cavité cranienne d'un Totonaque, avec réflexions sur la signification du volume de l'encéphale," in *Bulletin de la Société d'anthropologie de Paris,* **2** (1861), 66–81; and "Recherches sur l'anatomie du *Troglydytes aubryi,* chimpanzé d'une nouvelle espèce," in *Nouvelles archives du Muséum d'histoire naturelle* (Paris), **2** (1866), 1–264, written with P. H. E. Alix.

On the evening of 20 January 1865 Gratiolet delivered a lecture on physiognomy at the Sorbonne. This remarkable lecture was soon published—"Considérations sur la physionomie en général et en particulier sur la théorie des mouvements d'expression," in *Annales des sciences naturelles.* Zoologie et paléontologie, 5th ser., **3** (1865), 143–179—as was a posthumous vol. on the subject: *De la physionomie et des mouvements d'expression, suivi d'une notice sur sa vie et ses travaux et de la nomenclature de ses ouvrages, par Louis Grandeau* (Paris, 1865; 4th ed., 1882). In the lecture and book Gratiolet explored the notion that, while spoken language was peculiar to man, animals shared with man another language: facial and bodily movement or "expression."

II. Secondary Literature. Grandeau's essay on Gratiolet (cited above; also published separately [Paris, 1865]) is the most extensive account of the anatomist. Other notices, all quite personal, include Paul Bert, "Éloge de Pierre Gratiolet," in *Bulletin de la Société médicale de l'Yonne* (Auxerre) (1868), 17–37; Paul Broca, "Éloge funèbre de Pierre Gratiolet," in *Mémoires de la Société d'anthropologie de Paris,* **2** (1865), cxii–cxviii; and Edmond Alix, "Notice sur les travaux anthropologiques de Gratiolet," *ibid.,* **3** (1865), lxxi–ciii.

William Coleman

GRAUNT, JOHN (*b.* London, England, 24 April 1620; *d.* London, 18 April 1674), *statistics, demography.*

Graunt, apparently the eldest of seven or eight children born to Henry and Mary Graunt, received some formal "English learning" and, after he was sixteen, was apprenticed in his father's profession of draper. He held various offices in the Freedom of the Drapers' Company and in the city government, and he prospered in his business. In February 1641 he married Mary Scott, who evidently bore him one son and three daughters. Graunt came to know prominent people in London, and before 1650 he had become a friend of William Petty.

After the publication of his only book in January 1662, Graunt was elected, at the request of Charles II, to membership in the Royal Society. He suffered serious losses from the great fire of 1666, and this crisis was worsened by legal harassments occurring after his conversion around that time to Catholicism (earlier he had converted from Puritanism to anti-Trinitarianism). In spite of assistance from Petty, Graunt remained in straitened circumstances until his death.

Graunt's *Natural and Political Observations . . . Upon the Bills of Mortality* was the foundation of both statistics and demography. He had never formally studied mathematics, and the computations in his book were not more complex than what a successful businessman of that time could be expected to know. There has been much speculation over how much assistance Graunt received from Petty in writing the book. Undoubtedly Petty encouraged the undertaking and most likely made some contributions to it, but Graunt seems to deserve the lion's share of credit. He got the idea for his investigation from "having (I know not by what accident) engaged my thoughts upon the *Bills of Mortality,*" which had been published for London since the end of the sixteenth century. These statistics were the primary basis for his study, although he supplemented them with parish christening records and data from a rural area, Romsey in Hampshire (Petty's birthplace).

Since Graunt's treatise was the starting point for two sciences, both his discoveries and the form of his presentation were important. He began by listing the kinds of knowledge that could be gained from analyzing vital statistics. Next, he discussed with impressive sophistication the various kinds of defects in his data—geographical inconsistencies, irregular intervals between recordings, lack of thoroughness, inaccurate age approximations, an ambiguous disease nomenclature, and a bias against honest reporting of certain causes of death, such as syphilis. He published tables of some of the data and some important statistical regularities which he discovered were evident from inspecting the data: a few more boys were born than girls; women tended to live longer than men; the sex ratio was about equal and was stable; the numbers of people dying from most causes except epidemic diseases were about the same from year to year; the mortality rate was high among infants; the frequency of death was higher in urban than in rural areas.

Graunt carried his analysis further by deducing various characteristics of populations from his data. These ingenious attempts indicate a good understanding of the kinds of questions that are significant for demography. Usually he explained his steps in solving problems, but he seldom included the actual calculations; and sometimes he omitted important information. Furthermore, his indirect approach sometimes went beyond the reliable use of his data, and the accuracy of some of his answers was difficult to evaluate. His calculations of the populations of England and Wales and of London are two examples.

Since he did realize the shortcomings of his data, on several occasions Graunt set an excellent example by seeking verification of his estimates by different indirect methods. He introduced the use of statistical samples but did not pursue this subject far enough to determine the sizes of samples or means of selection needed for insuring accuracy. He gave information on infant and old-age mortality which modern demographers have shown contained an implicit life table, but Graunt's method of computing it remains uncertain. He also realized that demographic procedures could be used to make projections concerning both past and future populations. In 1663 he furnished the Royal Society with a brief note on the rate of growth of salmon and the rate of increase of carp in a pond, which indicates that he also saw the value of studying animal populations.

BIBLIOGRAPHY

I. Original Works. Graunt's only book is *Natural and Political Observations Mentioned in a Following Index, and Made Upon the Bills of Mortality* (London, 1662; 2nd ed., 1662; 3rd ed., 1665; 4th ed., Oxford, 1665; 5th ed., London, 1676). The 5th ed. was reprinted in *A Collection of the Yearly Bills of Mortality, From 1657 to 1758 Inclusive. Together With Several Other Bills of an Earlier Date . . .*, presumably edited by Thomas Birch (London, 1759). There is a German trans. by Gottfried Schultz (Leipzig, 1702). There is also a reprint of the 5th ed. in *The Economic Writings of Sir William Petty, Together With the Observations Upon the Bills of Mortality More Probably by Captain John Graunt,* Charles Henry Hull, ed., 2 vols. (Cambridge, 1899; repr. New York, 1963), II, 319–431. Hull also gives a full bibliography of earlier eds. in II, 658–660, 641. There are two reprs. of the 1st ed.: Walter F. Willcox, ed.

(Baltimore, 1939), and B. Benjamin, ed., in *Journal of the Institute of Actuaries,* **90** (1964), 1–61.

Graunt's notes on fish were first published by Thomas Birch in *The History of the Royal Society of London for Improving of Natural Knowledge, From Its First Rise,* 4 vols. (London, 1756–1757), I, 267, 294. Hull quoted the notes from p. 294 following his repr. of Graunt's book, II, 432.

II. SECONDARY LITERATURE. The most important contemporary accounts of Graunt are by John Aubrey and Anthony à Wood: *Aubrey's Brief Lives,* Oliver Lawson Dick, ed. (Ann Arbor, Mich., 1957), pp. 114–115; and Anthony à Wood, *Athenae Oxonienses,* 2nd ed., 2 vols. (London, 1721), I, col. 311. Wood's account has been quoted in full in James Bonar, *Theories of Population From Raleigh to Arthur Young* (London, 1931; facs. repr., 1966), pp. 69–71. There are two modern investigations of his life: C. H. Hull, in *Economic Writings of . . . Petty,* I, xxxiv–xxxviii; and D. V. Glass, "John Graunt and His *Natural and Political Observations,*" in *Notes and Records. Royal Society of London,* **19** (1964), 63–100, see 63–68, notes on 89–94.

The question of Petty's contribution to Graunt's book has been discussed in Glass, *op.cit.,* pp. 78–89, notes on pp. 97–100; Hull, *op. cit.,* I, xxxix–liv; Major Greenwood, *Medical Statistics From Graunt to Farr* (Cambridge, 1948), pp. 36–39; Walter F. Willcox, introduction to Graunt's *Natural and Political Observations* (Baltimore, 1939), pp. iii–xiii; and P. D. Groenewegen, "Authorship of the *Natural and Political Observations Upon the Bills of Mortality,*" in *Journal of the History of Ideas,* **28** (1967), 601–602.

Graunt's contributions to statistics and demography are surveyed and evaluated in B. Benjamin, "John Graunt," in *International Encyclopedia of the Social Sciences,* VI (1968), 253–255; Glass, *op. cit.,* pp. 69–78, notes on pp. 95–97; Hull, *op. cit.,* I, lxxv–lxxix; Greenwood, *op. cit.,* pp. 30–35; Harald Westergaard, *Contributions to the History of Statistics* (London, 1932), pp. 16–23; Ian Sutherland, "John Graunt: a Tercentenary Tribute," in *Journal of the Royal Statistical Society,* **126A** (1963), 537–556; and A. Wolf, F. Dannemann, A. Armitage, and Douglas McKie, *A History of Science, Technology and Philosophy in the 16th & 17th Centuries,* 2nd ed. (New York, 1950), pp. 588–598.

On the background situation for much of the bills of mortality used by Graunt, see Charles F. Mullett, *The Bubonic Plague and England. An Essay in the History of Preventive Medicine* (Lexington, Ky., 1956). Also relevant, and still useful, is the discussion by William Ogle, "An Inquiry Into the Trustworthiness of the Old Bills of Mortality," in *Journal of the Royal Statistical Society,* **55** (1892), 437–460. Norman G. Brett-James has written a very useful paper on the collection of the London data: "The London Bills of Mortality in the 17th Century," in *Transactions of the London & Middlesex Archaeological Society,* **6** (1933), 284–309.

The early reception of Graunt's book is discussed in Robert Kargon, "John Graunt, Francis Bacon, and the Royal Society: the Reception of Statistics," in *Journal of the History of Medicine and Allied Sciences,* **18** (1963), 337–348.

FRANK N. EGERTON, III

GRAVE, DMITRY ALEKSANDROVICH (*b.* Kirillov, Novgorod province, Russia, 6 September 1863; *d.* Kiev, U.S.S.R., 19 December 1939), *mathematics.*

In 1871, after the death of Grave's father, a petty official, the family moved to St. Petersburg. Grave entered the mathematics department of the Physics and Mathematics Faculty of St. Petersburg University in 1881 and studied under P. L. Chebyshev and his pupils A. N. Korkin, I. I. Zolotarev, and A. A. Markov. He began his research while still a student.

After graduating in 1885, Grave continued at St. Petersburg as a postgraduate, and in 1889 he defended his master's thesis. In the same year he started his teaching career at the university as a *Privatdozent.* In 1896 he defended his doctoral dissertation, and in 1899 he became a professor at the University of Kharkov. In 1902 Grave moved to the University of Kiev, where the rest of his work was done.

Grave's mathematical researches were originally connected with Chebyshev's school and were especially influenced by Korkin. In his master's thesis he developed methods originated by C. G. J. Jacobi and Korkin and, taking up a subject proposed by Korkin, contributed to the three-body problem. His doctoral dissertation, the subject of which also was proposed by Korkin, touched upon map projection researches by Euler, Lagrange, and Chebyshev. In it Grave presented a comprehensive study of equal-area plane projections of a sphere, with meridians and parallels being represented on the plane by straight lines and circumferences respectively.

At the beginning of his Kiev period Grave took up algebra and number theory. A brilliant speaker and organizer, he created a school which later became prominent. Among his pupils were Otto J. Schmidt, N. G. Chebotaryov, B. N. Delone, and A. M. Ostrovsky. In 1908–1914 Grave published several original and comprehensive works in algebra and number theory.

He continued his research and teaching activities well after the October Revolution, being elected to the Ukrainian Academy of Sciences (1920) and the Soviet Academy of Sciences (corresponding member from 1924, honorary member from 1929). In this period Grave's interest shifted to mechanics and applied mathematics, then returned to algebra in his last years. His last work on algebraic calculus was conceived as a comprehensive study, of which he was able to publish only two volumes.

BIBLIOGRAPHY

I. ORIGINAL WORKS. Grave published a total of about 180 works; a comprehensive bibliography is in Dobrovolsky (see below). His main works are *Ob integrirovanii chastnykh differentsialnykh uravneny pervogo poryadka* ("On the Integration of Partial Differential Equations of the First Order"; St. Petersburg, 1889), his master's thesis; *Ob osnovnykh zadachakh matematicheskoy teorii postroenia geograficheskikh kart* ("On the Main Problems of the Mathematical Theory of Construction of Geographical Maps"; St. Petersburg, 1896), his doctoral dissertation; *Teoria konechnykh grupp* ("The Theory of Finite Groups"; Kiev, 1908); *Elementarny kurs teorii chisel* ("A Primer in Number Theory"; Kiev, 1909–1910; 2nd ed. 1913); *Arifmeticheskaya teoria algebraicheskikh velichin* ("Arithmetical Theory of Algebraic Quantities"), 2 vols. (Kiev, 1910–1912); *Entsiklopedia matematiki. Ocherk eyo sovremennogo polozhenia* ("Encyclopedia of Mathematics. An Essay on Its Current State"; Kiev, 1912); *Elementy vysshey algebry* ("Elements of Higher Algebra"; Kiev, 1914); and *Traktat po algebraicheskomu analizu* ("Treatise on Algebraic Calculus"), 2 vols. (Kiev, 1938–1939).

II. SECONDARY LITERATURE. Biographies are N. G. Chebotaryov, "Akademik Dmitry Aleksandrovich Grave," in *Sbornik posvyashchenny pamyati akademika D. A. Grave* ("Collected Articles in Memory of Academician D. A. Grave"; Moscow–Leningrad, 1940), pp. 3–14; and V. A. Dobrovolsky, *Dmitry Aleksandrovich Grave* (Moscow, 1968).

The works of Grave are described in a number of general sources on the history of mathematics, such as *Istoria otechestvennoy matematiki* ("History of National Mathematics"), II (Kiev, 1967), 481–486; and A. P. Youschkevitch, *Istoria matematiki v Rossii do 1917 goda* ("History of Mathematics in Russia Until 1917"; Moscow, 1968), pp. 547–554.

A. I. VOLODARSKY

'sGRAVESANDE, WILLEM JACOB (*b.* 'sHertogenbosch, Netherlands, 26 September 1688; *d.* Leiden, Netherlands, 28 February 1742), *physics, mathematics, philosophy.*

'sGravesande was the earliest influential exponent of the Newtonian philosophy in continental Europe, his major work being widely read not only there but also in Britain. His family (originally known as Storm van 'sGravesande) was once important in Delft; like his brothers, he was educated at home by a tutor named Tourton, who was able to encourage his natural mathematical gifts. At Leiden University (1704–1707) he studied law, presenting a doctoral dissertation on the crime of suicide. Again like his brothers, 'sGravesande practiced law at The Hague, where he collaborated with Prosper Marchand and others in founding the *Journal littéraire de la Haye* (1713), a periodical of significance for twenty years in the history of science. He contributed several book reviews and some essays that were reprinted by J. N. S. Allamand in his *Oeuvres philosophiques et mathématiques de Mr. G. J. 'sGravesande* (Amsterdam, 1774). The most celebrated of these (in vol. **12** of the *Journal; Oeuvres,* I, 217–252) was his "Essai d'une nouvelle théorie du choc des corps fondée sur l'expérience" (1722), in which, departing from his customary attachment to the English school, 'sGravesande adopted the Huygens-Leibniz concept of *vis viva,* affirming (prop. X) that "La force d'un corps est proportionelle à sa masse multipliée par le quarré de sa vitesse." For this he was attacked by Samuel Clarke (1728), against whom he defended himself ably.

His association with the English Newtonian philosophers sprang from his appointment as secretary to the Dutch embassy (Wassenaer van Duyvenvoorde and Borsele van den Hooge) sent early in 1715 to congratulate George I on his accession to the English throne. This duty kept 'sGravesande in England for a year. His introduction to English learned society was facilitated by his acquaintance with the three sons of Gilbert Burnet, one of whom, William, proposed 'sGravesande as a fellow of the Royal Society in February 1715; he was elected on 9 June. On 24 March 1715 he was present (with other foreigners) at a demonstration of experiments by J. T. Desaguliers. There is no other mention of his name in the *Journal Book* until, on the brink of returning to The Hague in February 1716, 'sGravesande made a particular offer of his services to the Royal Society. Nevertheless, it is certain that he became acquainted with Newton and other fellows of the society, especially Desaguliers and John Keill, with whom he afterwards corresponded occasionally.

In June 1717, on the recommendation of Wassenaer van Duyvenvoorde, 'sGravesande was called to Leiden as professor of mathematics and astronomy. His inaugural lecture was on the usefulness of mathematics to all the sciences, physics above all (*Oeuvres,* II, 311–328). In 1734 he was additionally named professor of philosophy. By this time Hermann Boerhaave and 'sGravesande were established as the twin luminaries of Leiden, attracting hundreds of foreign students each year. From the outset of his teaching in both physics and astronomy 'sGravesande modeled his lectures on the example of Newton in the *Principia* and *Opticks,* although in later years they incorporated other influences, especially that of Boerhaave. Moreover, he adopted from Keill and Desaguliers the notion of demonstrating to his classes the experimental proof of scientific principles, accumulating an ever larger collection of apparatus, as may be seen from successive editions of his *Physices elementa mathematica, experimentis confirmata. Sive, introductio ad philosophiam Newtonianam* (Leiden, 1720, 1721). The scientific reputation of 'sGravesande is enshrined in this book, which he constantly corrected and amplified in later editions. An "official" English translation prepared by Desaguliers (to whom copies of the Latin original were sent in haste) was also issued in 1720 and 1721, and it passed through six editions. (The booksellers Mears and Woodward printed a rival version under the name of John Keill.) French translations appeared only in 1746 and 1747, but a critical review by L. B. Castel was published in the *Mémoires de Trévoux* in May and October 1721. The book was at once welcomed by British and a number of German scholars. 'sGravesande also published an abbreviated account for student use, *Philosophiae Newtonianae institutiones* (Leiden, 1723, 1728; and ed. Allamand 1744).

In 1721 and again in 1722 'sGravesande visited Kassel at the request of the landgrave to examine the secret perpetual-motion machine constructed by Orffyreus; he was unable to detect a fraud or (apparently) to convince himself that such a device is impossible.

In 1727 he published at Leiden, as a text for his mathematical teaching, *Matheseos universalis elementa. Quibus accedunt, specimen commentarii in Arithmeticam universalem Newtonii: ut et de determinanda forma seriei infinitae adsumtae regula nova* (*Oeuvres,* I, 89–214). This work, translated into Dutch (1728) and English (1752), is of didactic rather than original merit, but it was significant for its invitation to mathematicians to elucidate systematically Newton's *Universal Arithmetick,* which 'sGravesande exemplified by his own explanation of two passages from Newton's book. 'sGravesande found the lighthearted treatment of infinitesimals and the infinite in Bernard de Fontenelle's *Élémens de la géométrie de l'infini* (Paris, 1727) unacceptable, and he maintained his objections in the *Journal littéraire* against Fontenelle's rejoinder (1730).

After commencing the teaching of philosophy, 'sGravesande again published a textbook, *Introductio ad philosophiam, metaphysicam et logicam continens* (Leiden, 1736; repr. 1737, 1756, 1765; Venice, 1737, 1748; French ed., Leiden, 1748)—a work creating some odium for its author by its treatment of the question of necessity and free will. It was republished in *Oeuvres,* II, 1–215, together with some previously unprinted essays on metaphysics discovered by Allamand.

Apart from his own writings, 'sGravesande was active in promoting the publication at Leiden of the works of his greater countryman Christian Huygens, in *Opera varia* (1724) and *Opera reliqua* (1728), both of which he edited; in republishing the writings of his friend John Keill in 1725, as well as in editing Newton's *Arithmetica universalis* (1732); and in compiling the Dutch publication of the *Mémoires de l'Académie royale des sciences contenant les ouvrages adoptés . . .* (The Hague, 1731). Voltaire made a special journey to Leiden in 1736 to secure 'sGravesande's appraisal of his *Élémens de la philosophie de Newton* (London, 1738), writing afterward a warm appreciation of 'sGravesande's kindness and learning.

Although 'sGravesande was by no means the first semipopular exponent of Newtonian science and the experimental method (having been preceded in England by David Gregory, William Whiston, John Keill, and Desaguliers, among others), his *Mathematical Elements of Physics* was easily the most influential book of its kind, at least before 1750. It was a larger, better-argued, and more philosophical work than most of its predecessors; moreover, it leaned heavily on *Opticks* (including the queries) as well as on the *Principia.* One should therefore distinguish between 'sGravesande's roles as an exponent of Newtonian concepts (the rules of reasoning, the theory of gravitational attraction and its applications in celestial mechanics, theory of matter, theory of light, and so forth) and as an exponent of an empiricist methodology disdaining postulated hypotheses. Indeed, 'sGravesande contributed nothing to the progress of mathematical physics, for which one must look to the work of other contemporaries such as the Bernoullis, Pierre Varignon, and Alexis Clairaut. The strength of his exposition was in his perfection of the method of justifying scientific truths either by self-evidence or by appeal to experimental verification in the manner already begun by Keill and Desaguliers, perfected by him through the design of many new instruments constructed by the instrument maker Jan van Musschenbroek, brother of Pieter. (The extant instruments are preserved in the Rijksmuseum voor de Geschiedenis der Natuurwetenschappen at Leiden.) Yet, 'sGravesande's teaching and his *Elements* were by no means the sole vehicle for the introduction of British empiricism to the Continent, although probably they were the most important. He had been anticipated by Boerhaave (although Boerhaave did not employ didactic experiments) and was paralleled by Pieter van Musschenbroek at Utrecht (from 1730; he joined 'sGravesande at Leiden in 1739).

Unlike Newton, 'sGravesande commences his *Elements* with a prefatory discussion of metaphysics and epistemology directed against the Cartesians. The task of physics, he writes, is to determine the laws of nature laid down by the Creator and to unfold their regular operation throughout the universe. In thus examining the true works of God, fictitious hypotheses are to be set aside; but philosophers have differed in their methods of determining the laws of nature and the properties of bodies. "I have therefore thought fit," he continues, "to make good the Newtonian Method, which I have followed in this Work." Since the properties of bodies are not to be learned a priori, who can deny that there are in matter properties not known to us nor essential to matter, which flow from "the free Power of God"? How are the laws of nature to be sought and the three Newtonian laws of motion justified? 'sGravesande replies to these questions in a curious argument. First he asserts Newton's first rule of reasoning (Ockham's Razor). Next, distinguishing the truths of pure mathematics, which are verified by internal consistency, from those of physics ("mixed mathematics"), which depend on the senses, he argues that the latter are justified by analogy: "We must look up as true, whatever being denied would destroy civil Society, and deprive us of the means of living." This seemingly means that the consequences of induction must be true, for 'sGravesande goes on specifically to declare: "In Physics we are to discover the Laws of Nature by the Phenomena, then by induction prove them to be general Laws; all the rest is to be handled mathematically." The definitions of the scope of natural philosophy and of a law of nature (". . . the Rule and Law, according to which God resolved that certain Motions should always, that is, in all Cases, be performed") follow in chapter 1, which is concluded without further discussion by a statement of Newton's three rules of reasoning.

In volume I, 'sGravesande traverses the theory of matter (influences of the queries in *Opticks* are apparent but not marked), elementary mechanics, the five simple machines, Newton's laws of motion, gravity, central forces, hydrostatics and hydraulics, and pneumatics (including a treatment of sound and wave motion). His second volume opens with three chapters on fire, modeled on Boerhaave's ideas rather than Newton's, in whose manifestations he includes electrical phenomena. There follow two books on optics, one on the system of the world, and a final book entitled "The Physical Causes of the Celestial Motions," in which 'sGravesande can explain only that the cause of these motions is the operation of universal gravitation, whose cause is hidden "and cannot be deduced from Laws that are known." All this is treated with the aid of only trivial mathematics but is enriched with extremely numerous experimental illustrations and examples. Newton's ether does not appear, nor his "fits" of easy transmission and reflection, nor the extremely subtle physical speculation of the queries. No doubt the *Elements* owed almost as much of its success to its omissions and simplicity as to its clear and positive treatment of what it did contain. It was, obviously, very different from such later expositions as those of Henry Pemberton and Colin Maclaurin, and in many respects both more stimulating and more original.

BIBLIOGRAPHY

I. Original Works. Besides works mentioned in text, Allamand's *Oeuvres* (vol. I) include 'sGravesande's youthful *Essai de perspective* (Leiden, 1711; English trans., London, 1724) and other minor writings: *Usage de la chambre obscure; Remarques sur la construction des machines pneumatiques; Lettre à Mr. Newton sur une machine inventée par Orffyreus; Remarques touchant le mouvement perpétuel;* and *Lettres sur l'utilité des mathematiques.* The philosophical writings are in vol. II.

II. Secondary Literature. All biographies of 'sGravesande are based on the life by his friend Allamand, prefaced to the *Oeuvres.* See also Pierre Brunet, *Les physiciens hollandais et la méthode expérimentale en France au XVIIIe siècle* (Paris, 1926), *passim;* and *L'introduction des théories de Newton en France au XVIIIe siècle: avant 1738* (Paris, 1931), esp. pp. 97–107; I. Bernard Cohen, *Franklin and Newton* (Philadelphia, 1956), esp. pp. 234–243; C. A. Crommelin, *Descriptive Catalogue of the Physical Instruments of the 18th Century, Including the Collection 'sGravesande-Musschenbroek* (Leiden, 1951); P. C. Molhuysen, P. J. Blok, and K. H. Kossman, *Nieuw Nederlandsch biografisch woordenboek,* VI (Leiden, 1924), cols. 623–627; and A. Thackray, *Atoms and Powers* (Cambridge, Mass., 1970), pp. 101–104.

A. Rupert Hall

GRAY, ASA (*b.* Sauquoit, New York, 18 November 1810; *d.* Cambridge, Massachusetts, 30 January 1888), *botany.*

Gray was the son of Moses Gray and Roxana Howard Gray, who had migrated from New England to upstate New York after the American Revolution. He began his education in local schools at Sauquoit and for a time attended an academy at nearby Clinton, New York. In 1825 he entered Fairfield Academy and after a year began attending medical lectures at Fairfield's College of Physicians and Surgeons of the Western District of the State of New York. Here he came under the influence of a remarkable group of peripatetic medical teachers, including James Hadley, who introduced Gray to chemistry, mineralogy, and especially botany. He began to collect plants during his apprenticeship in Bridgewater, New York, where for a brief time after receiving his M.D. degree in 1831 he practiced medicine.

Already in touch with the leading botanist in the United States, John Torrey of New York, Gray abandoned the practice of medicine in 1832 and spent the next five years in a series of part-time teaching and library positions while increasingly concentrating on botany and making himself so useful to Torrey that he became a full collaborator on the *Flora of North America.* In 1836 he became a member of the scientific corps of the U.S. Exploring Expedition but, tired by the delays in its sailing, he resigned in 1838 to take a professorship at the newly organized University of Michigan. That position entailed Gray's spending a year in Europe, ostensibly to buy a general collection of books for the library but also to make the acquaintance of botanists and to study specimens of American plants in English and Continental herbaria. After his return in 1839, he worked on the *Flora of North America* while waiting in vain for a call from the nearly bankrupt state of Michigan. In 1842 Gray accepted the Fisher professorship of natural history at Harvard University, with the understanding that he could confine his activities to botany and the botanic garden. This milestone in the specialization of natural history made him the only adequately supported professional botanist in the United States and provided the home setting, both physically and institutionally, for the rest of his life.

Gray taught an elementary course in botany and offered a slight amount of advanced work to students of Harvard College, and later the Lawrence Scientific School, for thirty years. In 1848 he married Jane Lathrop Loring, daughter of a Boston lawyer and member of the Harvard Corporation. After 1873 he retired from teaching but continued to live in the house in the botanic garden and to develop the herbarium which ultimately became the property of Harvard. The only real breaks in the routine of his life after 1848 were a series of journeys—to Europe in 1850–1851, 1855, 1868–1869, 1880–1881, and 1887. He collected in the southern Appalachians as a young man and after the completion of the transcontinental railroad was fond of excursions to California, the trans-Mississippi West, and Mexico. Within this framework he lived an active and disciplined life until his last illness, which began in November 1887.

Gray became the leading botanical taxonomist in America in the nineteenth century, not because he was uninterested in physiology or unaware of the major advances made possible by the development of the achromatic microscope, but, rather, because the American setting demanded priority for a program of classification on a continental scale to match the programs of European nations in all parts of the globe not served by local collectors. Torrey and Gray's *Flora of North America* not only accomplished the shift from the Linnaean classification, still prevalent in America in the 1830's, to a natural system modeled on that of A. L. de Jussieu and A. P. de Candolle but also established the practice of thoroughly basing the taxonomy of American plants on the type specimens, until that time largely in the hands of European herbaria. By 1843 the *Flora* had proceeded in the Candollean system, beginning with the Ranunculaceae, through the Compositae, some seventy-six orders. At that point duties at Harvard and the flood of botanical returns from American expansion both westward and overseas in the era of Manifest Destiny made further progress by Torrey and Gray impossible.

Their response to the embarrassment of riches was twofold. Both Gray and Torrey devoted much of their time for the next thirty years to elaborating in reports the plants of collections sent in from the explorations. Some of these publications were in government documents, e.g., the *Reports* of Pacific Railroad Surveys (1855–1857) and the "everlasting" volumes of the botany of the U.S. Exploring Expedition, which were still incomplete at the time of Torrey's death in 1873. Other reports reflected Gray's sponsorship of individual collectors, who accompanied boundary surveys in the West and military expeditions, e.g., *Plantae Fendlerianae Novi-Mexicanae* (1849), *Plantae Wrightianae Texano-Neo-Mexicanae* (1852, 1853), and "Diagnostic Characters of New Species of Phaenogamous Plants, Collected in Japan by Charles Wright, Botanist of the U.S. North Pacific Exploring Expedition" (*Memoirs of the American Academy of Arts and Sciences,* **6** [1859], 377–452). In most cases Gray personally elaborated the orders through Compositae and called on others for other groups. Among the most regular and able collaborators besides Torrey were George Engelmann (especially Coniferae and Cactaceae), William Starling Sullivant (mosses), and Moses Ashley Curtis (fungi).

Gray's other strategy, forced on him by the incompleteness of the *Flora* and the competition of the textbook writer Alphonso Wood, was to modify his scholarly standards and to limit his range to the northeastern United States, thus producing for general use a manual which covered in one volume all the flowering plants and some of the lower plants as well. The *Manual of the Botany of the Northern United States* filled a need that the slower-moving *Flora* could not meet. It went through five editions in Gray's lifetime and has continued to be used in successive editions to the present time. After 1873 Gray minimized his writing of reports in order to return to the *Synoptical Flora of North America.* Much of the progress he made on it in his later years involved reworking in the light of accumulated scholarship the families treated in Torrey and Gray, so that it remained incomplete at his death. In matters of nomenclature and taxonomy Gray dominated American botany as no one before or after him; and if in the 1880's a younger generation was beginning to chafe at his authority his work still made an impressive contribution to the stream of science.

In 1851 Gray had lunch with Charles Darwin at Kew. By 1855 Gray's correspondence with Joseph Dalton Hooker on the geographical distribution of plants so impressed Darwin that he initiated an exchange of letters directly with Gray. Questions from Darwin led Gray to analyze the American flora on the basis of his *Manual* in an important paper, "Statistics of the Flora of the Northern United States" (*American Journal of Science,* **22** [1856], 204–232; **23** [1857], 62–84, 369–403). In 1857 Darwin let Gray in on the secret of the trend of his theory in a letter that became one of the bases of Darwin's priority for the idea of the origin of species by natural selection over Alfred Russel Wallace in the joint publication by Darwin and Wallace in the *Journal of the Linnean Society* in 1858.

Using Darwin's ideas and the collections of plants then coming to him from American expeditions to Japan, Gray explained species and genera of plants which appeared in eastern Asia and eastern North America not as separate creations but as descendants of a Tertiary circum-Boreal flora which had been pushed southward by the Pleistocene glaciation. This exercise in statistics led Gray to "admit that what are termed closely related species may in many cases be lineal descendants from a pristine stock, just as domestic races are." Thus he reached agreement with Darwin's main contention early in 1859, months before the publication of *Origin of Species.* Gray's announcement was the occasion for a full-dress debate with Louis Agassiz, his Harvard colleague who had imported an idealistic philosophy of natural history into the United States and gained an immense popular following.

After the publication of *Origin of Species* Gray was one of the leading reviewers on either side of the Atlantic, insisting on a fair hearing for Darwin in America and serving as agent to secure royalties on the American edition for the author. Until the Civil War distracted Gray's attention, he was through his letters a leading voice in the Darwin circle, urging with Charles Lyell an accommodating strategy in meeting religious objections. Darwin published Gray's commentary from the *Atlantic Monthly* at his own expense as a separate pamphlet under the motto "Natural Selection Not Inconsistent With Natural Theology." Eventually Darwin rejected the strategy suggested by Gray concerning theology and the assertion that natural selection had not damaged the argument from design. Yet Darwin's later years were largely spent on research that involved plants, and Gray figured prominently in his work on the coiling of tendrils and insectivorous plants. Darwin's *The Different Forms of Flowers on Plants of the Same Species* (1877) was dedicated to Gray "as a small tribute of respect and affection."

After the Civil War, Gray occasionally wrote anonymous articles attacking the religious opponents of Darwin, on the one hand, and those who followed T. H. Huxley into agnosticism, on the other. A clergyman, George Frederick Wright, eventually saw that these occasional pieces had a single author who was putting forward a consistent reconciliation of Darwinism and theism. Therefore he assisted Gray in collecting his occasional essays into a book, *Darwiniana* (1876), which firmly coupled Gray's name with the defense of Darwinism, Protestant Christianity, and the argument from design in nature. In 1881 Gray delivered a series of lectures at Yale Divinity School which were published as *Natural Science and Religion.* Their failure to cause a stir is a measure of the accommodation reached by that time between Darwinism and American Protestantism.

Without being a forceful lecturer or teacher, Gray nevertheless was a major force in scientific education in his day. His full line of textbooks shaped botanical education in the United States from the 1840's into the twentieth century. If few of his Harvard undergraduate students became professional botanists, he trained informally and assisted a whole generation of frontier collectors and part-time specialists who formed the rank and file of the botanical profession until German-trained Ph.D.'s began to appear in considerable numbers in the 1870's.

Gray was a more modest institution builder than his colleague Louis Agassiz, but in 1842 he had found Boston and Cambridge with few resources, and he left them a permanent center of botanical study in the Harvard Botanic Garden and the Gray Herbarium. In addition, when he retired from active teaching in 1873, Harvard engaged four men in his place, some of them—e.g., Charles Sprague Sargent—major institution builders themselves. While his relationship with Darwin marks the peak of Gray's career, his imprint on the pursuit of botany in the United States is also pervasive and enduring.

BIBLIOGRAPHY

I. Original Works. Gray's published writings, some 780 titles, are listed in [Sereno Watson and G. L. Goodale], "List of the Writings of Dr. Asa Gray, Chronologically Arranged, With an Index," in *American Journal of Science,* **36** (1888), app., 3–67. The major published collections of his works are *Scientific Papers of Asa Gray,* Charles S. Sargent, ed., 2 vols. (Boston, 1889); *The Letters of Asa Gray,* Jane Loring Gray, ed., 2 vols. (Boston, 1893); and *Darwiniana* (New York, 1876), A. Hunter Dupree, ed. (Cambridge, Mass., 1963).

The major MS collection is preserved in the Harvard University Herbarium, the library of which contains Gray's books, many of them annotated.

II. Secondary Literature. The recent full-scale biography is A. Hunter Dupree, *Asa Gray 1810–1888* (Cambridge, Mass., 1959), which includes notes and bibliography. Also relevant is A. D. Rodgers III, *American Botany, 1873–1892: Decades of Transition* (Princeton, 1944).

A. Hunter Dupree

GRAY, HENRY (*b.* London[?], England, 1825/1827; *d.* London, 8/13 June 1861), *anatomy, physiology.*

For a name as well-known as Gray's, extremely little is known about the man. He was one of four children of a private messenger to George IV and William IV; the family apparently had no financial problems. Essentially nothing is recorded of his preparatory education. On 6 May 1845 Gray entered St. George's Hospital as a perpetual student. He seems very early to have paid considerable attention to anatomical studies, and while still a medical student he won the Royal College of Surgeons' Triennial Prize for an essay entitled "The Origin, Connexion, and Distribution of the Nerves of the Human Eye and Its Appendages, Illustrated by Comparative Dissections of the Eye in the Other Vertebrate Animals." Part of this essay was incorporated into his later paper on the development of the retina.

Gray finished his medical studies and qualified as a member of the Royal College of Surgeons in 1849, and in June of the following year he was appointed house surgeon at St. George's Hospital for the customary twelve months.

Most of Gray's professional career was oriented around St. George's; in 1852 he was demonstrator of anatomy, and after 1853 he was lecturer in anatomy. He was also curator of the St. George's Hospital Museum. In 1852, after publication of his two major papers in the *Philosophical Transactions,* Gray was elected fellow of the Royal Society. In addition he became a fellow of the Royal College of Surgeons and was surgeon to St. James' Infirmary.

Besides his *Anatomy* Gray published several writings, the earliest of which was "On the Development of the Retina and Optic Nerve, and of the Membranous Labyrinth and Auditory Nerve," which incorporated some of the material in his prize essay. His observations were almost exclusively on the chick embryo. He clearly demonstrated that the retina develops from a protrusion of the brain, a point then still being debated. Gray also presented one of the earliest major accounts of the development of the layers of the retina. The labyrinth, he believed, develops in a mode analogous to that of the retina.

Gray's other anatomical paper was "On the Development of the Ductless Glands in the Chick," in which he dealt with the suprarenals, thyroids, and the spleen. On the basis of his observations Gray rejected much of the earlier writings on the embryological origin of each of these glands. From his work he considered it to be proved that these, with the thymus, should be classified in one group, the ductless glands—a classification by no means in general acceptance at that time, which has since developed into what are now known as the endocrine glands. He grouped these three glands on the basis of the similarity of their mode of origin, their structure in the first stages of development, and the manner in which their tissues develop throughout the fetal period. In both of these papers Gray showed a thorough familiarity with the pertinent literature and a high degree of competence in his microscopic observations.

With the support of a grant from the Royal Society, Gray continued his researches on the spleen. These studies culminated in a major treatise, *The Structure and Use of the Spleen,* which was awarded the Astley Cooper Prize in 1853 and was published in 1854. In a historical introduction Gray reviewed most of the previous writings on the spleen. His own observations included the origin of the spleen from the dorsal mesogastrium (often attributed to Johannes Müller) and early, if not initial, descriptions of the closed and open circulations, the lymphatics, and the nerves in the spleen. He also performed ligaturing and chemical experiments on the blood of the spleen.

The work for which Gray is justly most famous and which has become an institution in its own right is his *Anatomy, Descriptive and Surgical* (1858). The great success experienced by Gray's *Anatomy* was not due to lack of competition; there were successful works by Jones Quain, W. J. E. Wilson, Xavier Bichat, J. G. Cloquet, and others in use and readily available in England. Gray was described by a contemporary as a "lucid teacher of anatomy," a lucidity which carried over into his *Anatomy* not only in the logical arrangement of the material but also in the 363 new illustrations. The latter were done from drawings by Henry Vandyke Carter, who executed his drawings from fresh dissections that Gray and he performed. The arrangement of the material and the close relation between the text and the illustrations were Gray's work and show his clear understanding of the fundamentals of his subject. The literary style apparently was greatly polished by the assistance of Timothy Holmes, who also was editor of the third (1863) through ninth (1880) editions of the *Anatomy.* A major innovation, which greatly aided the success of the book was the introduction of remarks on surgical anatomy into an English textbook of anatomy. The reviews of the *Anatomy* often commented on Gray's ability to present, to students and practitioners alike, the practical information which they needed in an accessible form. This accessibility has been one of the great factors in the *Anatomy*'s success and has influenced other writers of anatomy textbooks.

Gray also wrote papers in pathology and is reputed to have made good progress on a major treatise on tumors at the time of his death. He died in June 1861 from smallpox contracted while tending a nephew.

BIBLIOGRAPHY

I. Original Works. Gray's two embryological papers are "On the Development of the Retina and Optic Nerve, and of the Membranous Labyrinth and Auditory Nerve," in *Philosophical Transactions of the Royal Society,* **140** (1850), 189–200; and "On the Development of the Ductless Glands in the Chick," *ibid.,* **142** (1852), 295–309. His books are *The Structure and Use of the Spleen* (London, 1854) and *Anatomy, Descriptive and Surgical* (London, 1858; Philadelphia, 1859). All the American eds. were closely based upon, but were not reprints of, the English eds. Goss (see below) lists both the English and the American series of eds., with their respective editors, through 1959.

II. Secondary Literature. There is a brief obituary in *Proceedings of the Royal Society,* **12** (1862–1863), xi. Two closely related articles which are the basis of much that has been written since are "Henry Gray," in *St George's Hospital Gazette,* **16** (1908), 49–54; and F. K. Boland, "Henry Gray, Anatomist: An Appreciation" in *American Journal of the Medical Sciences,* **136** (1908), 429–435. See also F. N. L. Poynter, "Gray's Anatomy, the First Hundred Years," in *British Medical Journal* (1958), **2,** 610–611; and Charles Mayo Goss, *A Brief Account of Henry Gray F. R. S. and His Anatomy, Descriptive and Surgical During a Century of Its Publication in America* (Philadelphia, 1959).

Wesley C. Williams

GRAY, STEPHEN (*b.* Canterbury, England, 1666; *d.* London, England, 15 February 1736), *electricity.*

The exact date of Gray's birth is uncertain, but records indicate that he was baptized on 26 December 1666. He came from a family of rapidly rising artisans; his grandfather was a carpenter, his father a dyer, his brothers a dyer, a carpenter, and a grocer, and his nephew a gentleman, a Cambridge graduate, and a doctor of medicine. The family understood the value of education. Although Gray followed his father's trade, he learned enough Latin to puzzle out Christoph Scheiner's interminable *Rosa ursina* (1630) when his omnivorous interests led him to sunspots. In science he was perhaps an autodidact, but his letters hint at a period of study in London or perhaps in Greenwich, under his "honoured Friend," the astronomer royal John Flamsteed. A stay in the metropolis would explain much: Gray's command of optics and astronomy; his loyalty to the much older Flamsteed, like himself the son of a tradesman; and his acquaintance with Henry Hunt of Gresham College, a minor functionary of the Royal Society of London. Hunt proved a valuable connection, supplying Gray with the *Philosophical Transactions* and transmitting to their editor the communications they called forth from Canterbury.

Gray's first published paper (1696) describes a microscope made of a water droplet inserted in a tiny hole in a brass plate. The globule "prodigiously magnified" animalcules swimming in it, a property both gratifying and perplexing, since, as Gray noticed, the standard optical theory required rays from bugs so positioned to diverge after refraction. His solution: the rays, if first reflected internally from the back wall of the globule, can be bent by its front surface into a parallel bundle. Although of little consequence itself, this first effort displays the characteristics which would bring Gray, when past sixty, to his capital discoveries in electricity; experiments "for the most part Naturall, being ushered in with very little assistance of Art"; alertness to effects unanticipated by theory; and cautious explanations of anomalies. Encouraged by the Royal Society's reception of his microscope, Gray communicated other ideas for instruments and reports of rarities like mock suns, magnetic sands, and the remains of antediluvian creatures (1699–1701). Then, from 1703 to about 1716, he devoted his scientific energies ("the far Greatest Part of my time that the avocations for a Subsistence would Permitt me") to accurate, quantitative observations of eclipses, sunspots, and (in the hope of improving navigation) the revolutions of Jupiter's satellites.

By his fortieth year Gray was widely known as a

careful and responsible observer. The scrupulous Flamsteed incorporated his results; William Derham solicited his help in experiments on the speed of sound: and the new Plumian professor of natural philosophy, Newton's protégé Roger Cotes, invited him to Cambridge to assist in establishing a new observatory. Against Flamsteed's advice Gray accepted and spent some months in 1707 and 1708 in Cambridge; but the observatory did not materialize, and Gray, who found his employers unexpectedly "mercenary" and their plan to redo Flamsteed's determinations of stellar positions both ignorant and insulting, returned to Canterbury. A bad back had made his trade too strenuous, however, and in 1711 he appealed to Hans Sloane, the secretary of the Royal Society, to intercede for him with the governors of Sutton's Hospital (the London Charterhouse). In June 1719, on the nomination of the prince of Wales, Gray became one of the Charterhouse's eighty "gentleman pensioners," having meanwhile, it is said, assisted in the public lectures of J. T. Desaguliers. The recent conjecture that Newton somehow delayed Gray's entry into the Charterhouse out of hatred for Flamsteed (and hence for his disciple) is baseless; the Newtonians tried to help, and even offered Hunt's old position to Gray, but "the poor man is so very bashful [wrote Sloane's successor, Brook Taylor, in 1713] that I can by no means prevail upon him to think of the business."

On 13 November 1706, Francis Hauksbee (the elder), demonstrator to the Royal Society, appeared before his "Philosophical Masters" armed with a tube of flint glass, with which to try the force of electricity. The tube appreciably outdid the customary generator, amber, and brought Hauksbee close to identifying the cause of electricity with that of the glow producible by chafing glass vessels. The "Strongness of the phenomena together with the facility of operation" of the portentous tube intrigued Gray, and during his stay in Cambridge he amused his nephew and others with experiments designed to map the course of the "Luminous and Electric Effluvium." He rediscovered Otto von Guericke's now famous demonstration that a feather, once drawn to the tube, might be made to hover above it; he found that light was "inherent in the Effluvia" of other electrics; and he conjectured that electrical motions and glows arose from a double stream of fine particles, one shot from the electric and the other an answer from the environment. This scheme, which effluvializes the incoming air current of Niccolo Cabeo's theory and anticipates the afflux of Nollet's system, was to guide Gray to the discovery of conduction.

Sloane did not print Gray's report of the Cantabrigian experiments, chiefly because Hauksbee, to whom it was referred, appropriated its novelties: the hovering feather, the luminous effluvia of wax and sulfur, and, in the form of a revived Cabean theory, the dual currents. Gray did not again bother the Royal Society with electricity until 1720, when he announced the discovery of a new class of nonrigid electrics, including hair, silk, feathers, and—if you please—gilded ox guts. Thereafter again silence, until February 1729, when, having conceded defeat in an attempt to electrify metals by friction, Gray thought to awaken their virtue by exposing them to effluvia from the tube: guided by his earlier theory, he imagined that just as the tube "communicated a Light to [bodies]," it might "at the same Time communicate an Electricity." He took a tube corked at both ends to keep out the dust, a precaution suggested by some old experiments of Hauksbee's. Thinking the corks might alter the tube's power, Gray brought a feather up to its far end, and in great amazement saw the fickle plume go to the cork, not the glass. "I then held the Feather over against the flat End of the Cork, which attracted and repelled many Times together; at which I was much surprized, and concluded that there was certainly an attractive Vertue communicated to the Cork by the excited Tube." It is a classic example of chance favoring the prepared mind.

Gray exploited his discovery by running sticks or threads from the cork to a "receiving Body," a teakettle, for example, or an ivory ball, which he supposed to emit its own effluvia, stimulated by those of the glass passed down the transmitting line. He extended the line to fifty-two feet, the greatest free drop available to him; he had also tried horizontal transmission, through thick threads hung up by pieces of the same material, but without the least success. At this point he visited his young friend Granville Wheler, F. R. S., a wealthy, able scientific amateur with a large country house admirably suited to the new experiments. Wheler suggested that they might send electricity down horizontal lines hung from silk threads narrow enough to prevent the loss of the "Vertue." They managed to transmit for some hundreds of feet before the silk parted under the strain. Quite naturally they replaced it with brass wire of similar bore, which most unexpectedly declined to behave like silk. And so, by attempting to increase the mere quantity of the effect, that is, the distance of transmission, they stumbled upon the fundamental qualitative distinction between insulators and conductors.

For thirty months Gray, Wheler, and another friend, a cousin of Flamsteed's named John Godfrey, enjoyed a monopoly in the study of communicated electricity. They followed two lines of inquiry: (1) the identification of substances which might serve as supporters (insulators) or as receivers and (2) the mapping of the course of transmitted electricity. These results, which conflated induction, conduction, and the mechanism of attraction and repulsion, required too much of the effluvia; serious contradictions, which Gray's group did not recognize, gradually came to light and, by adding their weight to the perplexities raised by the Leyden jar, assisted in forcing the rejection of the effluvial picture.

The publication of the results of Gray's group in 1732 awakened the interest of C. F. Dufay, whose extension and regularization of the phenomena attracted the attention of the learned to the study of electricity. Gray contributed a few further observations, particularly on the appearance of sparks drawn from bodies of different shapes and on the longevity of the electrification of objects encased in tight, dry boxes. These characteristic investigations gave way, in his last days, to a grand cosmic speculation based upon the discovery that a freely suspended conical pendulum would revolve about an electrified body precisely as the planets circle the sun. Cromwell Mortimer, secretary of the Royal Society (which had belatedly admitted Gray in 1732), got wind of the matter and hurried off to the Charterhouse. He found Gray dying. "He hoped [Mortimer reported], if God would spare his Life but a little longer, . . . to be able to astonish the World with a new Sort of *Planetarium* . . . [and] a certain Theory for accounting for the Motions of the Grand *Planetarium* of the Universe." Alas, the pendulum aped the planets only when supported from the hand, driven (as Dufay and Wheler showed) by motions largely involuntary. The Royal Society did Gray no favor by publishing, as his last paper, conjectures so out of keeping with his wonted care and sobriety.

BIBLIOGRAPHY

I. ORIGINAL WORKS. Gray's most important paper is "A Letter . . . Containing Several Experiments Concerning Electricity," in *Philosophical Transactions of the Royal Society,* **37** (1731–1732), 18–44. A bibliography of his published work, drawn up by R. A. Chipman, appears as an appendix to I. B. Cohen, "Neglected Sources for the Life of Stephen Gray," in *Isis,* **45** (1954), 41–50; to it should be added Gray's observations of the solar eclipse of 13 Sept. 1699, published by William Derham in *Philosophical Experiments and Observations of the Late Eminent Dr Robert Hooke . . . and Other Eminent Virtuosos* (London, 1726), p. 343.

A number of Gray's unpublished letters are preserved at the Royal Society of London, the British Museum, and the Royal Observatory (Herstmonceux). R. A. Chipman, "The Manuscript Letters of Stephen Gray," in *Isis,* **49** (1958), 414–433, provides a list which omits letters of 3 Feb. 1696 and 22 May 1696 to Henry Hunt (Royal Society, Guard Book G. 1, fols. 49–50) and an undated note on sunspots (British Museum, Sloane 4039, fol. 332). Chipman, "An Unpublished Letter of Stephen Gray on Electrical Experiments," in *Isis,* **45** (1954), 33–40, prints the letter appropriated by Hauksbee.

II. SECONDARY LITERATURE. Data concerning Gray's family and date of baptism were supplied by the Archivist, Canterbury Cathedral. For published biographical information see J. M. Cowper, *The Roll of the Freemen of the City of Canterbury* (Canterbury, 1903), p. 39; W. P. Courtney, "Stephen Gray, F. R. S.," in *Notes and Queries,* **6** (1906), 161–163, 354; F. Higenbottam, "The Apparition of Mrs. Veal to Mrs. Bargrave at Canterbury, 8th Sept., 1705," in *Archaeologia cantiana,* **78** (1959), 154–166; and the papers of Chipman and Cohen cited above. Estimates of Gray's work will be found in Chipman's papers; J. Priestley, *The History and Present State of Electricity,* 3rd ed. (London, 1775), I, 32–53; E. Hoppe, *Geschichte der Elektrizität* (Leipzig, 1884), pp. 8–11; I. B. Cohen, *Franklin and Newton* (Philadelphia, 1956), pp. 368–371; and, by indirection, in F. Baily, *An Account of the Revd John Flamsteed* (London, 1835), pp. 47, 310.

The important piece of Taylor's regarding Gray's succession to Hunt is in Royal Society Correspondence 82, fol. 5; Hauksbee's role in suppressing Gray's first paper on electricity appears from the Royal Society's *Journal Book,* X, fols. 175, 189–190, 192, and from his published work, for which see R. Home, "Francis Hauksbee's Theory of Electricity," in *Archives for History of Exact Science,* **4** (1967), 203–217.

JOHN L. HEILBRON

GREEN, GEORGE (*b.* Nottingham, England, 1793; *d.* Sneinton, Nottingham, 31 May 1841), *mathematics, natural philosophy.*

For a detailed study of his life and work, see Supplement.

GREEN, JACOB (*b.* Philadelphia, Pennsylvania, 26 July 1790; *d.* Philadelphia, 1 February 1841), *chemistry, biology, botany, dissemination of knowledge.*

Jacob Green was the son of Ashbel Green, prominent Presbyterian clergyman and eighth president of Princeton University. He attended the University of Pennsylvania (B.A., 1807), studied medicine briefly, sold books in Albany, New York, for a few years, took up law, and was admitted to the New York bar.

In 1816 Green moved to Princeton, New Jersey, to live with his father and study theology. He was sidetracked to science when the professor of natural philosophy, Henry Vethake, hired him as an assistant. In 1818 he was elected to a newly created professorship of chemistry, experimental philosophy, and natural history, and held this professorship until it was abolished in 1822.

Green then moved to Philadelphia, delivered a course of public lectures on chemistry, and joined several physicians in founding Jefferson Medical College. He was professor of chemistry at the medical school from 1825 until 1841. During several summers he traveled to Jefferson College (now Washington and Jefferson College) and to Lafayette College, Easton, Pennsylvania, to teach chemistry.

In 1828 Green visited Europe and later published his impressions in *Notes of a Traveller.* He met Michael Faraday, John Dalton, and other scientists but, to his disappointment, not Humphry Davy, who was abroad. In 1830 he published an edition of Davy's *Consolations in Travel.*

Green moved from one science to another, depending upon the circumstances of his life. At the age of nineteen he and his friend Erskine Hazard published *An Epitome of Electricity & Galvanism.* Learning botany largely by independent study, he wrote about plants of New York. Inspired by the skies during evening strolls, he wrote a popular book, *Astronomical Recreations.* As a teacher of chemistry he published three texts. In these activities Green was chiefly a disseminator of science. He advanced science through studies on shells, salamanders, and trilobites, contributing in a small way to the early knowledge of natural history of the United States.

Late in his life Green married and was the father of two children.

BIBLIOGRAPHY

I. ORIGINAL WORKS. Green's works are *An Epitome of Electricity & Galvanism. By Two Gentlemen of Philadelphia* (Philadelphia, 1809), written with Erskine Hazard; *A Catalogue of the Plants Indigenous to the State of New York* (Albany, 1814); *Astronomical Recreations* (Philadelphia, 1824); *Electro-Magnetism* (Philadelphia, 1827); *Text-Book of Chemical Philosophy* (Philadelphia, 1829); *Notes of a Traveller, During a Tour Through England, France, and Switzerland, in 1828,* 3 vols. (New York, 1830); *Consolations in Travel, or the Last Days of a Philosopher. By Sir Humphry Davy . . . With a Sketch of the Author's Life, and Notes, by Jacob Green* (Philadelphia, 1830); *A Monograph on the Trilobites of North America* (Philadelphia, 1832; supp., Philadelphia, 1835); *Syllabus of a Course in Chemistry* (Philadelphia, 1835); and *Chemical Diagrams* (Philadelphia, 1837).

II. SECONDARY LITERATURE. The primary biography is by his father, Ashbel Green; it may be found in James F. Gayley, ed., *History of the Jefferson Medical College of Philadelphia* (Philadelphia, 1858), pp. 31–34, with portrait. More recent accounts are Edgar F. Smith, *Jacob Green, 1790–1841, Chemist* (Philadelphia, 1923), with portrait, abridged in *Journal of Chemical Education,* **20** (1943), 418–427; and George W. Bennett, "Old Jakey Green at Canonsburg," in *Proceedings of the Pennsylvania Academy of Science,* **23** (1949), 218–221.

WYNDHAM DAVIES MILES

GREENOUGH, GEORGE BELLAS (*b.* London, England, 1778; *d.* Naples, Italy, 2 April 1855), *geology.*

Greenough's father, George Bellas, a lawyer, married Sarah, daughter of Thomas Greenough, a surgeon, in 1776. Both parents died when he was a child, and George was brought up by his maternal grandfather, whose surname he assumed in 1795. He entered Eton College in 1789 and Pembroke College, Cambridge, in 1794. He spent three years at Cambridge but did not graduate. Later he went to Göttingen University to study law, and to improve his German he attended the natural history lectures of J. F. Blumenbach. As a result he developed an enthusiasm for science, particularly geology, which lasted all his life. Considerable inherited wealth freed him from the necessity of following a profession.

After returning to England, the controversy between the Huttonians and the Wernerians aroused Greenough's interest. In 1805 he made a two-month tour of Scotland, closely examining the field evidence afforded by basalts and granites. Published extracts from his journal show that he did not fully accept the views of either neptunists or plutonists. A published statement that Greenough had studied under Werner at Freiberg is incorrect, but it is known that on some occasion he met Werner and recorded (in manuscript) an unfavorable impression of him.

In 1807 Greenough was elected both fellow of the Royal Society and a member of Parliament. Soon after, he joined with a dozen other enthusiasts in founding the Geological Society of London. As their first president he upheld the independence of the group and resisted the attempts of Sir Joseph Banks to bring it under the control of the Royal Society. He remained president until 1813 and was elected to further terms in 1818 and 1833. His presidential addresses for 1833 and 1834 were mainly summaries of recent advances in geological science.

Greenough was actively interested in the construction of geological maps, and in 1812 he presented to the Geological Society "nine maps of England with the principal strata sketched in." Its council then requested him to prepare a geological map of England and Wales on a larger scale, which task he undertook with the assistance of other members, although aware that William Smith was already preparing such a map for publication. The completed map was published on 1 May 1820 (see bibliography), five years after Smith's map. Greenough's map was on a slightly smaller scale than Smith's and had much more topographic detail, with hachuring to indicate valleys and escarpments. There was also more geological detail, and the Cretaceous and Upper Jurassic rocks in particular were more accurately delineated. More outcrops of granite and trap were shown, and an interesting feature was the attempt to show the distribution of diluvium, or drift. In the memoir that accompanied the map Greenough claimed that he had not seen Smith's map until it was published and had made very limited use of it. Nonetheless, it seems certain that Greenough did see and use manuscript maps based on Smith's work that were lent to him by John Farey. A revised edition of the map was issued by the Geological Society in 1840 and a third edition in 1865, ten years after Greenough's death. Only in the latter was belated acknowledgment made to William Smith.

In the memoir accompanying the maps, there is very little geology, but Greenough gave many of his notes to W. D. Conybeare and William Phillips, who made frequent use of them in their *Outlines of the Geology of England and Wales* (London, 1822), identifying them as "G. Notes" or simply "G." Greenough also spent many years compiling a geological map of India, which was published in 1854.

In 1819 he published *A Critical Examination of the First Principles of Geology; in a Series of Essays.* These essays were a challenge to those who saw uniformity and regularity in the strata, the skeptical Greenough quoting exceptions for every such assumption. "Before we yield or refuse assent to any proposition," he wrote, "we must sum up probabilities and improbabilities on both sides and strike a balance." But his balance was struck in such a manner that his own views or conclusions were seldom stated, except for his firm belief in the Deluge as the prime cause of valley excavation and a general agreement with the catastrophic theories of Cuvier. This publication, although not well received at the time, was based on wide reading and observation and can be used today as a source book.

When the Royal Geographical Society was founded in 1830, Greenough was elected to its council, and he served as president from 1839 to 1841. His continued interest in geology and geography led him to set off for the East at the age of seventy-six, but he was taken ill and died en route at Naples. In his will he left his extensive library to be divided between the Geological Society of London and the Royal Geographical Society. His collection of rocks and fossils went to University College, London, whose library also possesses a large collection of his manuscripts, including letters, journals, and memoranda.

BIBLIOGRAPHY

I. Original Works. Greenough's published works include *A Critical Examination of the First Principles of Geology; in a Series of Essays* (London, 1819); *Memoir of a Geological Map of England* (London, 1820), accompanying *A Geological Map of England & Wales* (London, 1819)—the map, although dated 1819, was not published until 1820; presidential addresses in *Proceedings of the Geological Society of London,* **2** (1838), 42–70, 145–175; and *General Sketch of the Physical and Geological Features of British India* (London, 1854), a map.

II. Secondary Literature. Obituary notices are in *Quarterly Journal of the Geological Society of London,* **12** (1856), xxvi–xxxiv; and *Journal of the Royal Geographical Society,* **25** (1855), lxxxviii-xc. Passing references are in H. B. Woodward, *The History of the Geological Society of London* (London, 1907); and H. R. Mill, *The Record of the Royal Geographical Society* (London, 1930). Two informative articles by M. J. S. Rudwick, based on Greenough's MSS, are "Hutton and Werner Compared: George Greenough's Geological Tour of Scotland in 1805," in *British Journal for the History of Science,* **1** (1963), 117–135; and "The Foundation of the Geological Society of London: Its Scheme for Co-operative Research and Its Struggle for Independence," *ibid.,* 325–355.

V. A. Eyles

GREENWOOD, ISAAC (*b.* Boston, Massachusetts, 11 May 1702; *d.* South Carolina, 12 October 1745), *natural philosophy, education.*

After graduating from Harvard College, studying science and perhaps medicine in England, and serving on occasional pulpits, Greenwood was installed at Harvard in 1727 as the first Hollis professor of mathematics and natural and experimental philosophy. His contribution to science in America lay in strengthening and modernizing the science program at Harvard College. He had, in 1726, offered the public an experimental course in mechanical philosophy, for which he published a prospectus. To his new professorship he brought this experience, the gift for teaching, a good knowledge of science, keen powers of observation, and an excellent collection of apparatus contributed by Thomas Hollis.

Greenwood's course made use of experiment and demonstration and probably rested heavily upon Newton's work, as did his public lectures. He took an important step to improve the level of Harvard preparation in mathematics in 1729, when he published *Arithmetick, Vulgar and Decimal,* a good textbook. He produced a manuscript text on algebra and seems to have taught Newtonian fluxions. His success was substantial but, after several attempts to reform him, the Harvard Corporation dismissed him in 1738 for excessive drinking. Thereafter, Greenwood sought to set up a private school of experimental philosophy in Boston, delivered lectures in Philadelphia, and went to sea as a tutor. At his death his career was in ruins, but his service to science was best measured by the tradition he developed at Harvard and by the students he inspired, including Professor John Winthrop.

During his professorship Greenwood published three papers in the *Philosophical Transactions of the Royal Society:* one urging the charting of winds, another a study of the effects of damps in wells, and the third a description of an aurora borealis. In response to an English request he made very careful drawings of the inscriptions on Dighton Rock, now understood to have been of Indian origin. Precision and care marked all of this work, but it was less significant than his teaching.

BIBLIOGRAPHY

I. Original Works. Greenwood published a number of items related to his teaching: *An Experimental Course of Mechanical Philosophy* (Boston, 1726); *Course of Philosophical Lectures* (n.d.); *Arithmetick, Vulgar and Decimal: With the Application Thereof to a Variety of Cases in Trade and Commerce* (Boston, [1729]); and *Prospectus of Explanatory Lectures on the Orrery* (Boston, 1734). He also wrote *A Philosophical Discourse Concerning the Mutability and Changes of the Material World* (Boston, 1731) and three papers which appeared in the *Philosophical Transactions of the Royal Society:* "A New Method for Composing a Natural History of Meteors," **35** (1730–1731), 390–402; "A Brief Account of Some of the Effects and Properties of Damps," **36** (1731–1732), 184–191; and "Of an Aurora Borealis Seen in New-England, Oct. 22, 1730," **37** (1732–1733), 55–69. There are Greenwood MSS in the Harvard University archives and in the Massachusetts Historical Society.

II. Secondary Literature. The only good account of Greenwood is Clifford K. Shipton, *Biographical Sketches of Those Who Attended Harvard College; Sibley's Harvard Graduates,* VI (Boston, 1942), 471–482, which includes Frederick G. Kilgour, "Isaac Greenwood and American Science," and the best bibliography.

Brooke Hindle

GREGORY, DAVID (*b.* Aberdeen, Scotland, 3 June 1659; *d.* Maidenhead, Berkshire, England, 10 October 1708), *mathematics, astronomy, optics.*

The eldest surviving son of the laird (also called David) of Kinnairdie in Banffshire, and nephew of James Gregory, David graduated from Marischal College, Aberdeen, and went on to Edinburgh University, where in October 1683—a month before taking his M.A.—he was elected to the chair of mathematics, vacant since his uncle's death in 1675, delivering an inaugural lecture "De analyseos geometricae progressu et incrementis." Staunchly supported by Archibald Pitcairne, an old friend from undergraduate days, he sought conscientiously in his professorial lectures (on elementary optics, astronomy, and mechanics) to impart to his students basic insights into the "new" science of Descartes, John Wallis and, after 1687 (if we are to believe William Whiston) Isaac Newton. Attempts by Gregory in 1684 and 1687 to start a correspondence with Newton failed, but an indirect link with Cambridge was formed in 1685 after a visit to Newton by a mutual acquaintance, John Craig(e).

Increasingly under attack by his fellow professors at Edinburgh for his radical views, Gregory jeopardized his position in 1690 by refusing to swear the required oath of loyalty to the English throne before a visiting parliamentary commission. The retirement of Edward Bernard from the Savilian professorship of astronomy at Oxford in 1691 offered an outlet. Backed by Newton's recommendation of him as "very well skilled in Analysis & Geometry both new & old. . . . understands Astronomy very well . . . & is respected the greatest Mathematician in Scotland," and with Flamsteed's support, Gregory was elected to the chair in face of strong opposition from Edmond Halley (later, after Wallis' death in 1703, to become his companion professor of geometry). In November 1692 he was elected fellow of the Royal Society, but he never took an active part in its affairs except for submitting several papers to its *Transactions.*

During his early years at Oxford, Gregory traveled widely to keep abreast of current developments in science, visiting Johann Hudde and Christian Huygens in Holland in May–June 1693 and Newton at Cambridge in May 1694 and on numerous later occasions in London. His extant Savilian lectures (from 1692) are for the most part a rehash of his Edinburgh *lectiones,* suitably updated; as he told Samuel Pepys, he was concerned to see that his students "should study some Euclid, trigonometry, mechanics, catoptrics and dioptrics, . . . the theory of planets and navigation." His appointment in 1699 as mathematical tutor to the young duke of Gloucester was thwarted by the latter's sudden death; his relations with Flamsteed, a competitor for the post, thereafter rapidly deteriorated, particularly after he joined Newton's committee set up to publish Flamsteed's *Historia coelestis.* Gregory's election in 1705 to the Royal College of Physicians at Edinburgh was purely honorary, but he took a more active role in the Act of Union between England and Scotland in 1707. He married in 1695 and was en route to London to visit his children, sick with smallpox, when he died.

No definitive assessment of Gregory's scientific achievement is possible until a detailed examination of his extant memoranda is made. Doubtless this will reinforce the impression gained from his printed work that a modicum of talent, effectively lacking originality, was stretched a long way. His earliest publication, *Exercitatio geometrica de dimensione figurarum* (1684), was a presentation of a number of manuscript *adversaria* bequeathed to him by his uncle James, interlarded with worked examples from René-François de Sluse's *Miscellanea,* Nicolaus Mercator's *Logarithmotechnia,* and James Gregory's *Geometriae pars universalis* and *Exercitationes* (all 1668) and a citation of Newton's series for the general circle zone communicated to John Collins in 1670 and passed forthwith to Scotland. Ignorant of the general binomial theorem which had been found independently by Newton and his uncle James, Gregory resorted to a brute-force development of the series expansion of the binomial square root by which he accomplished the "dimension" (quadrature and rectification) of various conics, conchoids, the cissoid, the Slusian pearl, and other algebraic curves, while the subtleties of his uncle's use of a Taylor expansion to invert Kepler's equation as an infinite series (first published here, but without any proof) clearly passed him by.

Gregory's *Treatise of Practical Geometry* and *Catoptricae et dioptricae sphaericae elementa* (1695) are printed versions of elementary lectures given at Edinburgh in the 1680's; the latter is often singled out for its appended remark (p. 98) suggesting, on the analogy of the crystalline and vitreous humours "in the Fabrick of the Eye," that an achromatic compound lens might be formed by combining simple lenses of different media, but this insight he might well have had from Newton. His thick folio text on foundations of astronomy, *Astronomiae . . . elementa* (1702), is a well-documented but unimaginative attempt to graft the gravitational synthesis propounded in the first book and especially the third book of Newton's *Principia* onto the findings of traditional astronomy. While respected as a source book it is now chiefly remembered for the remarks by Newton on the *prisca sapientia* of the ancients and their "knowledge" of the inverse-square law of universal gravitation and for the Latin version of Newton's short paper on lunar theory which it reproduces.

Gregory's first collected edition, following Bernard's wish, of *Euclidis quae supersunt omnia* (1703) is a competent gathering of the mathematical and physical writings attributed to Euclid of Alexandria (*Elements, Data, Introductio harmonica, Sectio canonis, Phaenomena, Optica, Catoptrica, Dioptrica, Divisions of figures, De levi et ponderoso*), but the one exciting passage in the preface (on the *Data,* especially 86) again stems from Newton. Of Gregory's articles in the *Philosophical Transactions of the Royal Society* that (1693) on Vincenzo Viviani's "testudo veliformis quadrabilis" is an elegant solution of a tricky but essentially elementary problem; that on the catenary (1697) erroneously derives the correct differential equation of the freely hanging uniform chain (he failed to see the necessity of compounding the tensions at both ends of the curve) and therefrom draws its logarithmic construction and main properties; that (1704) on the Cassini oval or cassinoid briefly sketches its main forms, determining, since it is not convex when its eccentricity is greater than $1/\sqrt{3}$, its inacceptability as a planetary orbit. The poverty of Gregory's astronomical observations merits Flamsteed's jibe of "closet astronomer."

In retrospect, Gregory's true role in the development of seventeenth-century science is not that of original innovator but that of custodian of certain precious papers and verbal communications passed to him by his uncle James and, as privileged information, by Newton.

BIBLIOGRAPHY

I. Original Works. The brief "Index Chartarum," now in Edinburgh University Library, made by Gregory's son David after his father's death, outlines the content of some 400 MSS and memoranda on mathematical, physical, and astronomical topics gathered in four "M.S." (A–D), of which D is "plerumque Jacobi Gregorii." Those (the greater part) still extant are now scattered in the libraries of Edinburgh and St. Andrews universities and the Royal Society, London. Further memoranda are interleaved in "M.S." E (now Christ Church, Oxford, MS 346), essentially a journal of Gregory's scientific activities at Oxford between March 1696 and September 1708. No concordance to these papers is published, but I have in my possession a rough list of the location of the mathematical items made *ca.* 1950 by H. W. Turnbull. Selected extracts, only a small fraction of the total, are reproduced in W. G. Hiscock, *David Gregory, Isaac Newton and Their Circle* (Oxford, 1937) and in Turnbull's ed. of *The Correspondence of Isaac Newton,* III–IV (Cambridge, 1961–1967).

The MS (A57, Edinburgh) of Gregory's first published work, *Exercitatio geometrica de dimensione figurarum sive specimen methodi generalis dimetiendi quasvis figuras* (Edinburgh, 1684)—reviewed by Wallis in *Philosophical Transactions of the Royal Society,* **14,** no. 163 (20 Sept. 1684), 730–732—contains few variants. His "Lectiones opticae ad Acad. Edinburg. 1683" (B11, Edinburgh DC.1.75) remain unprinted, as does his "Geometria de motu: par[te]s [1-5] lect. ad Acad. Edinburg. [1684-1687]" (B12, B15, B16, Edinburgh DC.1.75: incomplete autographs are in the Royal Society and Christ Church; a complete contemporary copy is in Aberdeen University [MS 2171]) except for an Englished fragment "never printed till now" inserted by John Eames and John Martyn in their *Philosophical Transactions Abridged,* VI (London, 1734), 275-276.

Gregory's "Institutionum astronomicarum libri 1 et 2 in usum Academicorum Edinburgensium scripti 1685" (B7, Edinburgh) was later absorbed into his *Astronomia;* the parallel "Geometria practica . . . conscripta 1685" (B6, Edinburgh DC.1.75/DC.5.57; contemporary copy in Aberdeen MS 2171) was subsequently rendered into English (Aberdeen MS 672) by an unknown student and later published by Colin Maclaurin as *A Treatise of Practical Geometry . . . Translated from the Latin With Additions* (Edinburgh, 1745; 9th ed. 1780). His astronomical and medical lectures at Oxford during 1692 to 1697 are preserved in Aberdeen (MS 2206/8). His *Catoptricae et dioptricae sphaericae elementa* (B18) was published by him at Oxford in 1695 (2nd ed., Edinburgh, 1713); with addenda by William Brown it appeared in English as *Dr. Gregory's Elements of Catoptrics and Dioptrics* (London, 1715; enl. ed. by J. T. Desaguliers, London, 1735). The 1694 calculus compendium "Isaaci Newtoni methodus fluxionum ubi calculus differentialis Leibnitij et methodus tangentium Barrovij explicantur et exemplis plurimis omnis generis illustrantur"—variant autographs in St. Andrews (QA33G8D12) and Christ Church; contemporary copies by John Keill in the University Library, Cambridge, Lucasian Papers, and by William Jones, Shirburn 180.H.33—is unprinted.

Gregory's "Notae in Isaaci Newtoni *Principia philosophiae* . . . in anno 1693 conscripta"—original in the Royal Society, amanuensis copy in Christ Church; contemporary transcripts in Edinburgh and Aberdeen (MS GY)—was proposed for publication at Cambridge in 1714, but Nicholas Saunderson could find "nobody that can give me any account of it" (to Jones, February 1714); see S. P. Rigaud, *Correspondence of Scientific Men of the Seventeenth Century,* I (Oxford, 1841),* 264. His weighty *Astronomiae physicae & geometricae elementa* (Oxford, 1702; 2nd ed., Geneva, 1726) was "done into English" as *The Elements of Physical and Geometrical Astronomy* (London, 1715; 2nd ed., 1726); influential reviews appeared in *Philosophical Transactions of the Royal Society,* **23,** no. 283 (Jan.-Feb. 1703), 1312-1320; and *Acta eruditorum* (Oct. 1703), 452-462. Gregory's Latin (pp. 332-336) of Newton's "Theory of the Moon" (Cambridge, Add. 3966.10,82r-83v, published in *Correspondence,* IV [1967], 327-329; Gregory's copy [$C121_2$] is now in the Royal Society) appeared soon after in English as *A New and Most Accurate Theory of the Moon's Motion; Whereby All Her Irregularities May Be Solved* . . . (London, 1702). His supervised edition of ΕΥΚΛΕΙΔΟΥ ΤΑ ΣΩΖΟΜΕΝΑ. *Euclidis quae supersunt omnia. Ex recensione Davidis Gregorii* was published at Oxford in 1703. Gregory's abridgment of Newton's 1671 tract, his "Tractatus de seriebus infinitis et convergentibus" (A56, Edinburgh), is printed in *The Mathematical Papers of Isaac Newton,* III (Cambridge, 1969), 354-372.

In the *Philosophical Transactions of the Royal Society* Gregory published a solution of Viviani's Florentine problem (**18,** no. 207 [Jan. 1694], 25-29); two defenses of his uncle James against Jean Gallois's charges of plagiarism from Roberval (**18,** no. 214 [Nov.-Dec. 1694], 233-236; and **25,** no. 308 [autumn 1706], 2336-2341); a study of the "Catenaria" and a reply to Leibniz's "animadversion" (*Acta eruditorum* [Feb. 1699], 87-91) upon it (**19,** no. 231 [Aug. 1697], 637-652; and **21,** no. 259 [Dec. 1699], 419-426); his observations of the solar eclipse of 13 Sept. 1698 (**21,** no. 256 [Sept. 1699], 320-321); a remark on John Perk's quadrature of a circle lunule (**21,** no. 259 [Dec. 1699], 414-417); and a discourse "De orbita Cassiniana," refuting its claim to be a realistic planetary path (**24,** no. 293 [Sept. 1704], 1704-1706).

II. Secondary Literature. The documented assessment in *Biographia Britannica,* IV (London, 1757), 2365-2372, is still unreplaced. Some biographical complements are given in Agnes M. Stewart, *The Academic Gregories* (Edinburgh, 1901), 52-76. Gregory's Savilian "Oratio inauguralis" on 21 April 1692 is printed, with commentary, by P. D. Lawrence and A. G. Mollond in *Notes and Records. Royal Society of London,* **25** (1970), 143-178; see esp. 159-165; the only modern study in depth of any aspect of Gregory's mathematical and scientific output is C. Truesdell's examination of Gregory's spurious derivation of the catenary's differential equation: "The Rational Mechanics of Flexible or Elastic Bodies, 1638-1788," vol. II of *Euleri opera omnia,* 2nd ser. (Zurich, 1960), pt. 2; see esp. 85-86.

D. T. Whiteside

GREGORY, DUNCAN FARQUHARSON (*b.* Edinburgh, Scotland, 13 April 1813; *d.* Edinburgh, 23 February 1844), *mathematics.*

Duncan Gregory came from a family with a long tradition of interest in science. His great-grandfather, his grandfather, and his father, James, were each professor of medicine at the University of Edinburgh. His great-great-grandfather was the mathematician James Gregory. Gregory attended the Edinburgh Academy, studied for a year in Geneva, and attended the University of Edinburgh. He matriculated at Trinity College, Cambridge, in 1833 and ranked as fifth wrangler in 1837. He remained at Cambridge as lecturer and tutor, and in 1840 he became a fellow of Trinity. Gregory received his M.A. in 1841. At that time he was offered a position at the University of Toronto, but as he was in poor health, he declined it. In 1838 Gregory, together with Robert Ellis, founded the *Cambridge Mathematical Journal.* Gregory was the first editor, and in this role considerably aided George Boole, who submitted his earliest papers to that journal.

Gregory published two books, both designed for use at Cambridge: one on the calculus (1841) and one on applications of analysis to geometry (published posthumously in 1845). His major contribution to mathematics, however, was his theory of algebra. His earliest papers were on differential and difference equations, in which he used a method that came to be known as the calculus of operations. This method involved treating the symbols of operation

$$\frac{d}{dx} \quad \text{or} \quad \Delta$$

as if they were symbols of quantity. In his attempt to justify the validity of this method, Gregory examined the laws governing the combination of these symbols with constants and by iteration. As a result of these studies he came to a definition of algebra as the study of the combination of operations defined not by their specific nature but rather by the laws of combination to which they were subject. This is wholly modern in tone, and that Gregory's work is not more widely known is probably due to the fact that he did not live to create a large-scale abstract algebra to illustrate his view.

BIBLIOGRAPHY

I. Original Works. Gregory's books are *Examples of the Processes of the Differential and Integral Calculus* (Cambridge, 1841) and *A Treatise on the Application of Analysis to Solid Geometry,* William Walton, ed. (Cambridge, 1845). See also *The Mathematical Writings by Duncan Farquharson Gregory,* William Walton, ed. (Cambridge, 1865), which contains almost all of Gregory's published papers. *The Royal Society Catalogue* lists Gregory's works but contains several errors, which are corrected in Clock's thesis (see below).

II. Secondary Literature. Biographical material on Gregory includes a memoir by Robert Ellis, found in the *Mathematical Writings,* pp. xi–xxiv, and the article by H. R. Luard, "D. F. Gregory," in *Dictionary of National Biography.* The significance of his work is discussed in Daniel Arwin Clock, "A New British Concept of Algebra: 1825–1850," Ph.D. diss. (Univ. of Wis., 1964); Elaine Koppelman, "Calculus of Operations: French Influence on British Mathematics in the First Half of the Nineteenth Century," Ph.D. diss. (Johns Hopkins Univ., 1969); and Ernest Nagel, "'Impossible Numbers': A Chapter in the History of Logic," in Studies in the History of Ideas, III (New York, 1935), 429–475.

Elaine Koppelman

GREGORY, FREDERICK GUGENHEIM (*b.* London, England, 22 December 1893; *d.* London, 27 November 1961), *plant physiology.*

Gregory's unusual abilities in mathematics, physics, and chemistry enabled him to foresee the major role that biochemistry and physics would play in physiology and development. This ability, along with his voracious scientific curiosity, extended his work over an enormous range of topics; and it is difficult to select his chief contributions to botanical science. His development of new methods of growth analysis and introduction of the term "net assimilation rate" to denote average photosynthetic efficiency of leaves (i.e., the dry weight of the plant divided by the average area of leaf surface and number of hours of light) were the basis of his early reputation.

With O. N. Purvis he proved that the effect of controlled low (1°C.) temperatures which will convert a "winter" rye to a "spring" rye—the effect known as vernalization—is exerted upon the embryo itself. They showed that excised embryos can be vernalized in the presence of sugar and a minimal oxygen concentration and that the effect is specifically due to temperature. This work and other work with F. J. Richards on mineral nutrition, aimed at determining the physiological causes underlying crop growth, also attracted much attention because of their value to agriculture.

The outcome of Gregory's 1928 visit to the Gazira Research Station in the Anglo-Egyptian Sudan was an increased knowledge of the factors affecting cotton production and provided the basis for strengthening the economy of the Sudan. Although he never returned to Gazira, he advised from London and served on both the Scientific Advisory Committee of the Empire Cotton Growing Corporation and the London Advisory Committee in Agricultural Work in the Sudan. His invention of the resistance porometer and the diffusion porometer enabled sophisticated study of stomatal physiology and the factors controlling transpiration.

All of Gregory's scientific career was spent in association with the Imperial College of Science and Technology, a constituent college of the University of London. The vast number of students and visitors who were influenced by their contact with him represents one of his lasting achievements.

In 1915 Gregory graduated from the Royal College of Science with first-class honors in botany. Having been rejected by the army on physical grounds, he joined the recently founded Research Institute of Plant Physiology at Imperial College under Vernon Blackman. Gregory began his work at Cheshunt Experimental Station, moved to Rothamsted, and finally returned to Imperial College. In 1932 he was appointed assistant director of the Research Institute of Plant Physiology and later succeeded Blackman as professor of plant physiology and director. Elected a member of the Royal Society in 1940, he was awarded its coveted Royal Medal in 1957. In 1956 he was elected a foreign associate of the National Academy of Sciences of the United States.

BIBLIOGRAPHY

I. Original Works. Gregory's works include "Physiological Conditions in Cucumber Houses," in *Report. Experimental and Research Station, Nursery and Market Garden Industries Development Society,* **3** (1917), 19–28; "Studies in the Energy Relation of Plants. I. The Increase in Area of Leaves and Leaf Surface of *Cucumis sativum,*" in *Annals of Botany,* **35** (1921), 93–123; "The Effect of Climatic Conditions on the Growth of Barley," *ibid.,* **40** (1926), 1–26; "Studies in Energy Relations of Plants. II. The Effect of Temperature on Increase in Area of Leaf Surface and in Dry Weight of *Cucumis sativum.* Part I. The Effect of Temperature on the Increase in Area of Leaf Surface," *ibid.,* **42** (1928), 469–507; and "Mineral Nutrition of Plants," in *Annual Review of Biochemistry,* **6** (1937), 557–578.

See also "Physiological Studies in Plant Nutrition. VI. The Relation of Respiration Rate to the Carbohydrate and Nitrogen Metabolism of the Barley Leaf as Determined by Nitrogen and Potassium Deficiency," in *Annals of Botany,* n.s. **1** (1937), 521–561, written with P. K. Sen; "Studies in Vernalization of Cereals. II. The Vernalization of Excised Mature Embryos and of Developing Ears," *ibid.,* n.s. **2** (1938), 237–251, written with O. N. Purvis; and "The Interrelation Between CO_2 Metabolism and Photoperiodism in *Kalanchoë,*" in *Plant Physiology,* **29** (1954), 220–229.

II. Secondary Literature. On Gregory or his work see Helen K. Porter, "Prof. F. G. Gregory, F.R.S.," in *Nature,* **193** (1962), 118; Helen K. Porter and F. J. Richards, "Frederick Gugenheim Gregory 1893–1961," in *Biographical Memoirs of Fellows of the Royal Society,* **9** (1963), 131–153, with complete bibliography; F. C. Steward, "F. G. Gregory 1893–1961," in *Plant Physiology,* **37** (1962), 450; and *The Times* (London), an obituary (30 Nov. 1961), 15a; and a funeral notice (4 Dec. 1961), 12c.

A. D. Krikorian

GREGORY (more correctly **GREGORIE**), **JAMES** (*b.* Drumoak, near Aberdeen, Scotland, November 1638; *d.* Edinburgh, Scotland, late October 1675), *mathematics, optics, astronomy.*

The youngest son of John Gregory, minister of the manse of Drumoak, James Gregory was descended through his father from the fiery Clan Macgregor and through his mother, Janet, from the more scholarly Anderson family, one of whom, Alexander, had been secretary to Viète. Somewhat sickly as a child, he received his early education (including an introduction to geometry) from his mother, but after his father's death in 1651 his elder brother David sent him to Aberdeen, first to grammar school and later to Marischal College. After graduating there and further encouraged by his brother, himself an enthusiastic amateur mathematician, James devoted himself to studies in mathematical optics and astronomy.

In 1662, aware of the lack of scientific opportunities in Scotland, he traveled to London, there publishing *Optica promota* (1663), in which he gathered his earliest researches, and making several influential friends, notably Robert Moray, interim president of the Royal Society in 1660. In April 1663 Moray sought to arrange Gregory's introduction to Christian Huygens in Paris, but this was thwarted by Huygens' absence. Subsequently, to improve his scientific knowledge Gregory went to Italy, studying geometry, mechanics, and astronomy under Evangelista Torricelli's pupil Stefano degli Angeli at Padua (1664–1667) and publishing *Vera circuli et hyperbolæ quadratura* (1667) and *Geometriæ pars universalis* (1668). About Easter 1668 he returned to London; there, backed by John Collins' glowing reviews of his two Italian treatises and much in demand for his fresh contact with recent developments in Italian science, he was elected to the Royal Society on 11 June. Soon after, he made Huygens' attack upon the originality and validity of his *Vera quadratura* and also the publication of Nicolaus Mercator's *Logarithmotechnia* an opportunity for publishing in riposte certain newly composed *Exercitationes geometricæ* of his own.

In late 1668, probably through Moray's intercession, he was nominated to the new chair of mathematics at St. Andrews in Scotland. In 1669, shortly after taking up the post, he married a young widow, Mary Burnet, who bore him two daughters and a son. Much of his time during the next five years was passed in teaching elementary mathematics and the principles of science to his students: "I am now much taken up," he wrote in May 1671, "& hath been so al this winter bypast, both with my publick lectures, which I have twice a week, & resolving doubts which som gentlemen & scholars proposeth to me, . . . al persons here being ignorant of these things to admiration." His London correspondent Collins, a good listener if incapable of appreciating Gregory's deeper insights, was his sole contact with mathematical and scientific developments in the outside world; through him he received extended transcripts of letters written by Isaac Barrow, René-François de Sluse, Huygens, and Newton on a variety of topics, and in return he made Collins privy to many of his researches into equations, infinite series, and number theory.

Early in 1671, when the Académie des Sciences made tentative plans to invite two "Englishmen" (one of them Mercator) to Paris as *pensionnaires,* Moray campaigned actively on Gregory's behalf, but the proposal was not implemented. In 1672 Gregory joined the St. Andrews University "clerk" William Sanders in drafting a scornful reply to a recently published book on hydrostatics by the Glasgow professor George Sinclair: to Sanders' *Great and New Art of Weighing Vanity,* whose title page named as its author "Patrick Mathers, Arch-Bedal to the University of St. Andrews," Gregory contributed a minute dynamical essay, "Tentamina quædam de motu penduli et projectorum." Backed in turn by Sanders, the next year he implemented a long-cherished desire in the face of considerable resistance from his fellow professors, founding at St. Andrews the first public observatory in Britain. Charged with the university's commission, he traveled to London in June 1673 to purchase telescopes and other instruments and to seek John Flamsteed's advice regarding its equipment. Whether or not he did, as he intended, break his return journey at Cambridge to see Newton is not known. His hopes for the new observatory were soon quashed. During his absence the students at St. Andrews had rebelled against their antiquated curriculum, publicly ridiculing the regents; and Gregory, with his radical ideas on introducing the "new" science, was made the scapegoat: "After this the servants of the Colleges got orders not to wait on me at my observations; my salary was also kept back from me; and scholars of most eminent rank were violently kept from me, . . . the masters persuading them that their brains were not able to endure [mathematics]." In 1674 Gregory was glad to accept the newly endowed professorship of mathematics at Edinburgh, "where my salary is double, and my encouragements much greater"; but within a year of his appointment a paralyzing stroke blinded him one evening as he showed Jupiter's satellites through a telescope to his students. A few days later he was dead.

Written in his twenty-fourth year, Gregory's *Optica promota* is—with the notable exception of its "Epilogus"—interesting more for its revelations of the inadequacies of his early scientific training than for its technical novelties. Deprived in Aberdeen of a comprehensive library and contact with any practicing scientist, Gregory nevertheless made good use of available books on optics (Friedrich Risner's 1572 edition of Ibn al-Haytham [Alhazen] and Witelo ["authores perobscuri et prolixi"], Kepler's *Paralipomena,* Kircher's *Ars magna lucis*) and astronomy (Galileo's *Nuncius sidereus,* Kepler's *Astronomia,* Seth Ward's *Astronomia geometrica*). Ignorant of Descartes's *Dioptrique* (1637) and of the sine law of refraction there first publicly announced, in his opening pages Gregory presents an analogical "proof" that all rays incident on a central conic parallel to its main axis are refracted to its further focus for a suitable value of its eccentricity (in fact, as Descartes had shown, when it is the inverse refractive ratio). Departing from the particular cases of infinite and zero refraction when the conic is a circle and a straight line respectively and the parabolic case of reflection (unit negative refraction) and relying on his intuition that the interface is a conic, he "interpolates" the general *mensura refractionis* and then gives his model—equivalent to the sine law he nowhere cites—an experimental basis by displaying its agreement with the refraction tables of Witelo and Kircher.

The following optical propositions (2–59) extend Gregory's Cartesian theorem to systems of conical lenses and also develop the allied properties of reflection in conical mirrors: a neusis construction of the generalized Ibn al-Haytham problem of finding the point(s) of reflection in a general surface (prop. 34) is attained by roughly determining the tangent members of the family of spheroids whose common foci are the object and image points. In his historically significant epilogue Gregory explains how the deficiencies of the conventional pure reflectors and refractors encouraged him to design a compound "catadioptrical" telescope in which their defects were minimized. As an example he sketches "unum hujus perfectissimi generis telescopium" in which a parabolic mirror reflects parallel incident rays to a primary focus, on whose further side they are reflected back through a hole in the center of the first mirror by a small concave elliptical one to a secondary focus and thence through a plano-convex lens to the eye.

In 1663 the London optician Richard Reive was commissioned by Gregory to construct a six-foot "tube" to this design but failed, according to Newton in 1672, to polish its conical mirrors correctly. Newton's own improved design (1668[?]) used a plane mirror to reflect the rays from a spherical main reflector to the side of the telescope tube, and in 1672 through Collins he and Gregory exchanged letters arguing the relative merits of the two mountings. (The 1672 Cassegrain design, in which rays converging on the primary focus are reflected to the secondary focus before they reach it, was dismissed by Gregory as "no great alteration.") The astronomical appendix to the *Optica* (props. 60–90) is of no importance, but it serves to reveal once again Gregory's limited awareness of current scientific research. Much influenced by Seth Ward's *Astronomia* (1656), he here describes at some length geometrical methods for computing solar, lunar, and (hopefully) stellar parallax. A remark (prop. 87, scholium) that the conjunctions of the sun and Earth with Venus or Mercury would have a "pulcherrimum usum" for this purpose ignores the practical difficulties earlier encountered by Jeremiah Horrocks in his observations of the Venus transit in 1639 (first published in 1672). His schemes of planetary computation embody either the Keplerian "hypothesis Ptolemaica" of motion in an excentric circle with equant at the bissextile point or the slightly better Boulliau-Ward hypothesis of elliptical motion round the sun at a focus with mean motion round the second focus.

A still unpublished addendum to the *Optica* (David Gregory, B29, Edinburgh), composed some time after Gregory's arrival in London in 1663, contains a revised discussion of reflections in mirrors and refractions in thin lenses according to the newly encountered sine law of refraction. One theorem, a "notion" of a "burning-glass" (concave leaded spherical glass mirror) was communicated without proof to Collins in March 1673 and published by William Brown in 1715.

By late 1667 a sheen of confidence gleams through Gregory's work. Having absorbed at Padua all that some of the finest intellects in Italian science (Angeli, Gabriele Manfredi, and others) could teach him, he at length emerges fully aware of his hitherto latent mathematical powers. Of the two treatises stemming from his Italian sojourn, the *Vera circuli et hyperbolae quadratura* is the more original. Generalizing a procedure used by Archimedes in his *Measurement of a Circle,* in the case of a general central conic Gregory recursively defines an unbounded double sequence i_n,I_n of inscribed/circumscribed *mixtilinea.* Given a conic arc bounded by its chord and the intersecting tangents at its end points, i_0,I_0 are the inscribed triangle and circumscribed quadrilateral bounding the central sector cut off by the arc and the lines joining its end points to the conic's center. By dividing the arc at the point where it is parallel to its chord, two half-arcs are formed, yielding i_1,I_1 as the total of the two triangles/quadrilaterals inscribed/circumscribed to the two component conic sectors; a similar bisection of the two half-arcs produces corresponding bounding *mixtilinea* i_2,I_2, and so on. Gregory proves (props. 1–5) that i_{n+1}, I_{n+1} are, respectively, the geometric mean of i_n, I_n and the harmonic mean of i_{n+1}, I_n; that is,

$$i_{n+1} = \sqrt{i_n \cdot I_n} \quad \text{and} \quad I_{n+1} = \frac{2i_{n+1} \cdot I_n}{i_{n+1} + I_n}.$$

In the terms of Gregory's "definitiones" 1–10 the general pair i_{n+1}, I_{n+1} forms a "series convergens" (monotonically increasing/decreasing double sequence) of terms "analyticè compositi" (recursively defined by addition, subtraction, multiplication, division, and root extraction) out of the preceding "termini" i_n, I_n; he also proves that as n increases indefinitely, the difference between i_n and I_n becomes arbitrarily small—whence (p. 19) the "ultimi termini convergentes" can be "imagined" to be equal and their common value ($I = \lim_{n\to\infty} i_n = \lim_{n\to\infty} I_n$) is defined to be the "terminatio" (limit) of the "series." As an example of the power of this new terminology and analytical structure he derives purely algebraically the generalized Snell–Huygens inequalities for the central conic: $\frac{1}{3}(i_0 = 2I_0) > I > \frac{1}{3}(4i_1 - i_0)$.

Most tellingly, Gregory reasons that if a "quantitas" (function) can be "compounded" in the "same way" from i_{n+1}, I_{n+1} as from i_n, I_n—say by $\phi(i_n,I_n) = \phi(i_{n+1},I_{n+1})$—then the "terminatio" I is defined by $\phi(i_0,I_0) = \phi(I,I)$. The function $\phi(i_n,I_n)$, i.e.,

$$I_n\sqrt{\frac{i_n}{I_n - i_n}} \cdot \cos^{-1}\sqrt{\frac{i_n}{I_n}};\ \phi(I,I) = I,$$

appropriate to his particular double sequence he was unable to determine, but by considering the "imbalance" of the parametrization $i_n = a^2(a + b)$, $I_n = b^2(a + b)$, and so $i_{n+1} = ab(a + b)$, $I_{n+1} = 2ab^2$, he sought to "prove" not only that ϕ cannot be a rational function, which this makes plausible, but also that it cannot be algebraic, which does not follow at all; in that case I would not be analytically compounded from i_0, I_0 and hence the "true" (algebraic) quadrature of the general conic sector—and of the whole circle in particular—would be impossible. Gregory's ingenious if ultimately ineffective argument was somewhat impercipiently attacked by Huygens when he received a presentation copy of the *Quadratura*: his rebuff, still commonly allowed, that the limit sector I could conceivably be determined in a different, algebraic way from the initial *mixtilinea* i_0, I_0 is in fact invalid since Gregory's argument concerns the structure of the function ϕ, not the passage of i_n,I_n to the limit I (disposed of in the equality $\phi(I,I) = I$). The latter half of the *Quadratura* is of some computational interest: on setting $i_0 = 2$, $I_0 = 4$, then $I = \pi$; while if $i_0 = 99/20$, $I_0 = 18/11$, then $I = \log \text{nat } 10$. These and other circle/hyperbola areas are accurately calculated to fifteen places.

Gregory's second Italian treatise is more eclectic in spirit, being designedly a tool kit of contemporary geometrical analysis of tangent, quadrature, cubature, and rectification problems. In the preface to his *Geometriae pars universalis* he expresses his hope that by "transmuting" the essential defining property of a given curve, it may be changed into one of an already known kind; the "universal part of geometry" presaged in his title is that which comprehends such general methods of geometrical transformation. Under that manifesto Gregory produces a systematic exposition of elementary calculus techniques which he freely admits are largely reworkings and generalizations of approaches pioneered by others. Pierre de Fermat's assignment of linear bounds to a convex arc, itself an improvement of Christopher Wren's 1658 discussion of the cycloid, is developed into a general scheme, demonstrated by an extended Archimedean exhaustion proof, for rectifying an arbitrary "curva simplex et non sinuosa"; Grégoire de St. Vincent's use of a "ductus plani in planum" (the geometrical equivalent of a change of variables under a double integral) is applied to reduce the quadrature of a given plane curve to the "planification" of a "hoof" section of a cylindrical surface and thence to the quadrature of a second curve. Another method of quadrature, that by transform to the subtangential curve, stems from Roberval. A geometrical tangent method is borrowed, again by way of Fermat, from Wren's tract on the cycloid, while an analytical one making use of Jacques de Beaugrand's notation for the vanishing increment "nihil seu serum *o*" of the base variable is a revision of that expounded by Descartes in his 1638 *querelle* with Fermat and published by Claude Clerselier in 1667, illustrated by an example (a Slusian cubic) deriving from Michelangelo Ricci.

Above all, Wren's concept, earlier broached by Roberval and Torricelli in the instance of the Archimedean spiral and Apollonian parabola, of the arc length-preserving "convolution" of a spiral into an equivalent Cartesian curve reappears, much extended and given rigorous exhaustion proof, in Gregory's favorite transform of an "involute" into an "evolute," while vigorous use is made of the Pappus-Guldin theorems relating the quadrature and cubature of solids and surfaces of revolution to their cross-section and its center of gravity. On this basis Gregory was enabled to furnish simple proofs of results in the theory of higher curves and the "infinite" spirals beloved of his tutor Angeli, replacing their previous crude, disparate forms by a logically immaculate, standardized demonstration. But too modern an interpretation of Gregory's book should be avoided: what to us (in prop. 6) may seem a proof of the fundamental theorem of the calculus was for him merely a generalization of William Neil's method for rectifying the semicubical parabola, and its wider significance is not mentioned.

The *Geometria* also affords a glimpse of Gregory's scientific interests at the close of his Italian stay. A proposition on the Fermatian spiral allows him to discourse on its origin (in 1636) as a modified Galilean path of free fall to the earth's center and to comment on the current controversy between Angeli and Giovanni Riccioli on the motion of the earth (one which he reviewed for the Royal Society in June 1668, on his return to London). Again, certain appended nonmathematical passages deal briefly with the optical effect of the apparent twinkling of the stars and with the conjectured composition of cometary tails conceived of as a steamy "exhalation" lit up by the sun and, most important for future physical astronomy, offer the suggestion that the apparent brightnesses of stars of the same magnitude are inversely proportional to the squares of their distances with the corollary that Sirius—taken to be of the same magnitude and brightness as the sun—is 83,190 times its distance.

Mathematics retained its central place in Gregory's affection until his death. Back in London he published a compendium, *Exercitationes geometricæ* , containing primarily an "Appendicula" to his *Vera quadratura* which refuted Huygens' objections to its argument but also appending a number of miscellaneous theorems in geometrical calculus. The "Appendicula" itself is noteworthy for its concluding "theorema" (that if a_n, A_n; b_n, B_n are two convergent Gregorian sequences with respective terminations A, B and if for all r $\phi(a_n, A_n) > \phi(b_n, B_n)$, then $A > B$) and for its twenty-seven narrow upper and lower bounds to the sector of a central conic. Since an "approximatio" to the sector I is said to k-plicate the "true notes" of the *mixtilinea*

$$i_n = 2^{n-1} \sin (I/2^{n-1}), I_n = 2^n \tan (I/2^n)$$

when it compounds i_j, I_j, $j = 0, 1, 2, \ldots, n$ so as to equal $I + O(I^{2k+1})$, Gregory's method clearly made use of the series expansion of one or other of the elementary circle functions. To illustrate the power of the techniques elaborated in his *Geometria,* Gregory also, in ignorance of Harriot's prior resolution, reduced the theory of the plane chart (Mercator map) to "adding secants" (integrating sec x over a given interval, $0 \leq x \leq a$), effecting this elegantly if long-windedly by an involved appeal to a "ductus plani in planum." In addition, he gave analogous quadratures of the tangent, conchoid, and cissoid curves; and, further to expedite the "additio secantium naturalium" near the origin, he elaborated simple rules for integrating $y \approx ax^2 + bx$ and $y \approx ax^3 +$

bx^2, x small. The former of these is the first published instance of "Simpson's" rule. His rigorous geometrical deduction of the Mercator series for $\pm \log (1 \pm x)$ is of minor importance.

After his return to Scotland, Gregory made no further published contribution to pure mathematics, but his private papers reveal that the last half dozen years of his life were ones of intensive research. His executor William Sanders tells us, "His Elements of plain Geometry, with some few propositions of the solids; his Practicall Arithmetick, and Practicall Geometry taught at St. Andrews . . . are but of small moment, being contrived only for the use of such scholars as cannot be at pains to study the Elements." The lost *Tractatus trigonometricus,* in which he reduced "All Trigonometry rectilineal and spherical . . . unto five short canons," on the lines of Seth Ward's *Idea* (1654), was no doubt also intended for professorial lectures. But his real energy was reserved for deeper matters. At Collins' instigation Gregory spent much time on the theory of equations and the location of their roots: achieving success in the case of the reduced cubic and quartic by introducing an appropriate multiplying factor and equating all terms in the resolvent except those involving cube/fourth powers of the unknown to zero, he sought to solve the general quintic in a similar way by adjoining a factor of the fifteenth degree but failed to notice that the resulting equations to zero implied—ineluctably—a sextic eliminant. His papers on Fermatian equations, rational Heronian triangles, and other topics in Diophantine analysis are (much like Newton's contemporary studies, likewise inspired by the appearance of the Samuel Fermat-Jacques de Billy *Diophantus* in 1670) more workmanlike than profound: the "skailzy brods" (writing slates) found on his desk after his death contained his abortive calculations for Jacques Ozanam's unsolvable problem of cubes.

Gregory's letters to Collins are filled with a miscellany of calculus problems, among them his quadrature and rectification of the logarithmic spiral and "evolute" logarithmic curve, which had briefly made its introductory bow in the preface to his *Geometria,* and his construction of the tangent to the "spiralis arcuum rectificatrix" introduced by Collins for use in the "Mariners Plain Chart." His grasp of the subtleties of infinite series in particular quickly matured. His independent discovery of the general binomial expansion in November 1670—in disguised form as that of antilog $((a/c)(\log(b + d) - \log b))$—was matched a month later by his use of a "Newton-Gauss" interpolation formula to insert general means in a given sequence of sines. As a climax, in February 1671 Gregory communicated without proof a number of trigonometrical series, notably those for the natural and logarithmic tangent and secant, and in April 1672 a series solution of Kepler's problem (intended for publication in Collins' edition of Horrocks's *Opera posthuma,* but the bookseller took fright) regarding which he observed that "these infinite serieses have the same success in the roots of equations." Two examples—the series extraction of the root e of the conchoid's defining equation

$$L^2e^2 = (L + a)^2(L^2 - a^2)$$

and the inversion of the Kepler equation

$$a = \sqrt{2re - e^2} + (b - r) \sin^{-1} (\sqrt{2re - e^2}/r)$$

were later published by David Gregory, without direct acknowledgment, in his *Exercitatio geometrica* (1684). Until the printing in 1939 of Gregory's notes, jotted down on the back of a letter from the Edinburgh bookseller Gideon Shaw in January 1671, it seemed likely that these expansions were obtained by straightforward elementary methods, but we now know that he employed, twenty years before even Newton came upon the approach, a Taylor development of a function in terms of its nth-order derivatives.

Of Gregory's scientific pursuits during this last period of his life too little is known. His "Theory of the whole Hydrostaticks comprehended in a few definitions and five or sixe Theorems" (David Gregory, D18) is seemingly lost, although a short 1672 paper in which he proved Huygens' theorem relating atmospheric height logarithmically to barometric pressure still exists in several versions. In our present state of knowledge it seems impossible to determine how far William Sanders drew upon Gregory's hydrostatical ideas in his largely scurrilous *Great and New Art of Weighing Vanity,* but extant preliminary computations in Gregory's hand confirm contemporary report that the appended "Tentamina quædam de motu penduli et projectorum" is uniquely his. Of considerable historical importance as a bridging text between Galileo's *Discorsi* and Newton's *Principia,* these nine small duodecimo pages are a highly original contribution to dynamics. Independently deriving Huygens' Galilean generalization that the square of the instantaneous speed of a body falling freely under simple gravity in a smooth curve is proportional to the vertical distance fallen (and indeed anticipating an objection to Huygens' definition of the fall curve as the limit of a chain of line segments, which Newton put to Huygens in 1673), Gregory deduced the elliptical integral expressing the time of vibration in a circular pendulum and gave its infinite-series expansion for a small arc of swing. Subsequently, framing the supposition that the resistance is constant in magnitude and direction (opposite to that of initial motion), he determined that the resisted path of a projectile under simple gravity is a tilted parabola with main axis parallel to the resultant instantaneous force—a theorem, we now know, which had been found seventy years before by Harriot.

The "Fourty or thereabout of excellent Astronomical propositions invented . . . for the compleeting that art" found after his death doubtless originated in his correspondence with Colin Campbell during 1673–1674 on theoretical astronomy, during the course of which he solved—yet again in ignorance of a prior solution by Harriot—the Keplerian problem of constructing a planetary ellipse, given three focal radii in magnitude and position. Apart from his keen discussion with Newton in 1672 on the respective merits of their "catadioptrical" reflecting telescopes, little evidence has survived of Gregory's continuing interest in optics.

For all his talent and promise of future achievement, Gregory did not live long enough to make the major discovery which would have gained him popular fame. For his reluctance to publish his "several universal methods in Geometrie and analyticks" when he heard through Collins of Newton's own advances in calculus and infinite series, he posthumously paid a heavy price: the "Extracts from Mr Gregories Letters" drawn up by Collins in 1676 for Leibniz' enlightenment were used by Newton in 1712 solely to further his claim to calculus priority and were thereafter forgotten. Gregory's published works had little contemporary impact; his *Vera quadratura* was successfully sabotaged by Huygens, his *Geometria* quickly overshadowed by Barrow's *Lectiones geometricæ.* We are only now beginning to realize the extent and depth of his influence, mathematically and scientifically, on Newton. A comprehensive edition of his work is sorely needed.

BIBLIOGRAPHY

I. ORIGINAL WORKS. Gregory's first published work, *Optica promota, seu abdita radiorum reflexorum & refractorum mysteria, geometricè enucleata; cui subnectitur appendix, subtilissimorum astronomicæ problematôn resolutionem exhibens* (London, 1663), is reprinted in C. Babbage and F. Maseres, *Scriptores optici* (London, 1823), 1–104. His *Vera circuli et hyperbolæ quadratura, in propria sua proportionis specie, inventa & demonstrata* (Padua, 1667; reviewed by John Collins in *Philosophical Transactions of the Royal Society,* **3,** no. 33 [16 Mar. 1668], 640–644) was reprinted by W. J. 'sGravesande in his ed. of *Christiani Hugenii opera varia,* I (Leiden, 1724), 405–482; it was reissued at Padua in 1668 together with Gregory's *Geometriæ pars universalis, inserviens quantitatum curvarum transmutationi & mensuræ* (reviewed by Collins in *Philosophical Transactions of the Royal Society,* **3,** no. 35 [18 May 1668], 685–688), which also contains (pp. 132–151) his discussion of "difficultates quædam physicomathematicæ ex principiis opticis geometricè enodatæ." The same year he published his *Exercitationes geometricæ* (London, 1668), comprising "Appendicula ad veram circuli & hyperbolæ quadraturam" (repr. in *Oeuvres complètes de Christiaan Huygens,* VI [The Hague, 1895], 313–321), sig. A2r–A4r/pp. 1–8; "N. Mercatoris quadratura hyperbolæ geometricè demonstrata/Analogia inter lineam meridianam planispherii nautici & tangentes artificiales geometricè demonstrata; seu, quod secantium naturalium additio efficiat tangentes artificiales. . . ." (repr. in F. Maseres, *Scriptores logarithmici,* II (London, 1791), 2–15), pp. 9–24; and "Methodus facilis & accurata componendi secantes & tangentes artificiales," pp. 25–27.

Gregory's "Tentamina quædam geometrica de motu penduli et projectorum" (repr. in Babbage and Maseres, *Scriptores optici,* pp. 372–376) first appeared as an anonymous appendix (pp. $_2$1–9) to "Patrick Mathers" [William Sanders], *The Great and New Art of Weighing Vanity* (Glasgow, 1672). His report on the moving earth dispute in Italy was published by Henry Oldenburg as "An Account of a Controversy betwixt Stephano de Angelis and John Baptista Riccioli," in *Philosophical Transactions of the Royal Society,* **3,** no. 36 (15 June 1668), 693–698 (repr. with commentary by A. Koyré in "A Documentary History of the Problem of Fall from Kepler to Newton," in *Transactions of the American Philosophical Society,* **45,** [1955], 329–395, esp. 354–358). His two "Answers" to the "Animadversions" of Huygens upon his *Quadratura* (*Journal des sçavans* [2 July and 12 Nov. 1668], repr. in Huygens' *Oeuvres,* VI, 228–230 and 272–276, and in Latin in *Opera varia,* I, 463–466 and 472–476) appeared in *Philosophical Transactions of the Royal Society,* **3,** no. 37 (13 July 1668), 732–735 and no. 44 (15 Feb. 1669), 882–886 (repr. in *Opera varia,* I, 466–471 and 476–481; also Huygens' *Oeuvres,* VI, 240–244 and 306–311).

A number of Gregory's minor mathematical and scientific papers are extant in the Royal Society, London, the University Library, Edinburgh, and also in private possession: these derive from John Collins and Gregory's nephew, David. An incomplete listing of those accessible to the public is given by H. W. Turnbull in *James Gregory Tercentenary Memorial Volume* (London, 1939), pp. 36–43. Extracts from Gregory's correspondence with Collins were published by Newton in *Commercium epistolicum D. Johannis Collins* (London, 1712), pp. 22–26, and by Jean Desaguliers in an appendix to *Dr.* [David] *Gregory's Elements of Catoptrics and Dioptrics,* 2nd ed. (London, 1735). His letters to Robert Bruce were printed by Leslie in *Scots Magazine,* **72** (Aug. 1810), 584–586; those to Colin Campbell by John Gregorson and Wallace in *Archaeologia Scotica,* **3,** Artic. 25 (Jan. 1831), 275–284; those to Collins (with Collins' draft replies) by S. P. Rigaud in his *Corre-*

spondence of Scientific Men of the Seventeenth Century, II (Oxford, 1841), 174–281; the originals of Collins' replies, invaluable for Gregory's mathematical notes upon them, were published by H. W. Turnbull in the *Gregory Volume,* pp. 45–343 (the notes themselves, with lavish commentary, follow on pp. 347–447). Gregory's earliest known letter (to Huygens, in Oct. 1667, accompanying a presentation copy of his *Vera quadratura*) is given in Huygens' *Oeuvres,* VI, 154.

II. SECONDARY LITERATURE. Thomas Birch's article on Gregory in the *Biographia Britannica,* IV (London, 1757), 2355–2365 remains unsuperseded, although it is now partially obsolete. For complements see Agnes M. Stewart, *The Academic Gregories* (Edinburgh, 1901), pp. 27–51; and *University of St Andrews James Gregory Tercentenary: Record of the Celebrations Held . . . July Fifth MCMXXXVIII* (St. Andrews, 1939), pp. 5–11 (H. W. Turnbull's commemoration address, repeated in expanded form in the *Gregory Volume,* pp. 1–15) and pp. 12–16 (G. H. Bushnell's notes on the St. Andrews' observatory). Section VII of the *Gregory Volume* contains summaries of Gregory's *Optica promota* and *Exercitationes* (by H. W. Turnbull, pp. 454–459 and 459–465), his *Quadratura* (by M. Dehn and E. Hellinger, pp. 468–478) and *Geometria* (by A. Prag, pp. 487–509), together with an account by E. J. Dijksterhuis of the Gregory–Huygens squabble (pp. 478–486). A short general survey of Gregory's researches in calculus is given by C. J. Scriba in *James Gregorys frühe Schriften zur Infinitesimalrechnung, Mitteilungen aus dem Mathem. Seminar Giessen,* no. 55 (Giessen, 1957). More specialist mathematical topics are explored by H. W. Turnbull in "James Gregory: A Study in the Early History of Interpolation," in *Proceedings of the Edinburgh Mathematical Society,* 2nd ser., **3** (1933), 151–172; and by J. E. Hofmann, in "Über Gregorys systematische Näherungen für den Sektor eines Mittelpunktkegelschnittes," in *Centaurus,* **1** (1950), 24–37. No study of any aspect of Gregory's scientific achievement exists.

D. T. WHITESIDE

GREGORY, OLINTHUS GILBERT (*b.* Yaxley, England, 29 January 1774; *d.* Woolwich, England, 2 February 1841), *applied mathematics, science education.*

Gregory was one of the band of self-taught or privately tutored mathematicians who swelled the ranks of British mathematics during the eighteenth and early nineteenth centuries. Despite his limited schooling he established a reputation as a writer on scientific subjects, and in 1803, through the patronage of Charles Hutton, he was appointed instructor of mathematics at the Royal Military Academy at Woolwich. In 1821 he succeeded to the professorship and held the post until his retirement in 1838.

Gregory's most important scientific publication, *A Treatise of Mechanics,* appeared in 1806 and went through at least four editions. Although it was a didactic compilation rather than a publication of original research, it was one of the most complete works on pure and applied mechanics that had appeared in English. In purpose and presentation it was an early example of what would now be described as "engineering mechanics." Its theoretical sections covered such topics as the analysis of the flexed beam and the theory of the loaded arch, while its descriptive sections dealt extensively with machine design. The book constituted a contribution to the tradition of applied mathematics and applied mechanics which was then being fostered by the Woolwich mathematicians.

In 1825 Gregory produced another book, *Mathematics for Practical Men,* devoted to "the principles and applications of the mechanical sciences for the use of the younger members of the Institution of Civil Engineers" (which had been founded in 1818 and of which Gregory later became an honorary member). Around this time he also did experimental research on the velocity of sound. From 1802 to 1819 he edited the *Gentleman's Diary* and from 1819 to 1840 the *Ladies' Diary.* On the strength of both his reputation in science and his status as a prominent Dissenter in religion he was included among the group that founded London University, the first nonsectarian university in England.

BIBLIOGRAPHY

Gregory's scientific publications include *A Treatise of Mechanics,* 3 vols. (London, 1806); the first volume of the *Treatise* was translated into German as *Darstellung der mechanischen Wissenschaften,* J. F. W. Dietlein, trans. (Halle, 1824); *Mathematics for Practical Men* (London, 1825); "An Account of Some Experiments Made in Order to Determine the Velocity With Which Sound Is Transmitted in the Atmosphere," in *Philosophical Magazine,* **63** (1824), 401–15.

Gregory also translated one of René Just Haüy's works, *An Elementary Treatise on Natural Philosophy,* 2 vols. (London, 1807).

For additional bibliography see *Dictionary of National Biography* and *British Museum Catalogue of Printed Books.*

HAROLD DORN

GREGORY, WILLIAM (*b.* Edinburgh, Scotland, 25 December 1803; *d.* Edinburgh, 24 April 1858), *chemistry, biology.*

William Gregory was the fourth son of James Gregory, professor of medicine at the University of Edinburgh. William was educated for the medical profession and graduated in 1828 from the University of Edinburgh. After graduation he chose to pursue his interest in chemistry rather than practice medicine. During the next few years he made extended visits to the Continent and worked as assistant to several chemists, most notably Justus Liebig at his Giessen laboratory in 1835. There he developed a primary interest in organic chemistry. Following his work with Liebig, Gregory returned to Edinburgh where he gave public lectures in chemistry.

In 1837 Gregory accepted a lectureship at Anderson College in Glasgow and the next year at a Dublin medical school. Gregory was appointed professor of chemistry at King's College, Aberdeen, in 1839 and remained there, except for an additional year of study with Liebig in 1841, until 1844. Gregory suffered from poor health most of his life and continued to make trips to the Continent to restore his strength. He returned to the University of Edinburgh in 1844 and held the chair of chemistry until his death.

William Gregory is important to the development of chemistry primarily because of his translations into English of the many works of Liebig on organic, agricultural, and physiological chemistry. His own research was devoted chiefly to organic chemistry, especially the separation and analysis of natural products. Gregory investigated the preparation of morphine and codeine from opium and was the first to describe the preparation of isoprene from crude rubber. He also wrote several successful chemical textbooks.

In 1846 Gregory abstracted for a British journal the studies which Karl von Reichenbach had performed in 1845 on animal magnetism. Gregory later translated and published, with a twenty-seven-page preface of his own, Reichenbach's *Researches on Magnetism, Electricity, Heat, Light, Crystallization, and Chemical Attraction, in Their Relations to the Vital Force* (1850). Criticized for both the abstract and the translation of Reichenbach's work, Gregory further incurred the disapproval of his colleagues at the University of Edinburgh with his publication of *Letters to a Candid Inquirer on Animal Magnetism* (1851). In this work he attempted to establish a scientific basis for phenomena such as clairvoyance, thought transference, and unusual sensitivity of subjects who were under the influence of hypnotism. Following Reichenbach, he attributed most of these cases to emanations of a physical fluid, called odyl. His work on animal magnetism went through four editions during the nineteenth century. In addition, he published many pamphlets and papers on this subject. During the last ten years of his life, Gregory also became interested in the study of diatoms, on which he wrote twelve papers.

BIBLIOGRAPHY

I. Original Works. A list of Gregory's published papers, including those on diatoms, can be found in the Royal Society's *Catalogue of Scientific Papers (1800–1863)*, **3** (1869), 8–10. This list does not include Gregory's papers on animal magnetism, many of which were published in *Zoist, A Journal of Cerebral Physiology and Mesmerism, and Their Applications to Human Welfare,* and the *Phrenological Journal* (Edinburgh). These articles include "On the True Scientific Spirit in Which the Claims of Phrenology and Mesmerism Ought to be Examined," in *Phrenological Journal* (1847), pp. 1–28; "On Animal Magnetism," in *Zoist,* **9** (1851), 423–424; and "On the Theory of Imagination as the Cause of Mesmeric Phenomena, and On Money Challenges in Mesmerism," *ibid.,* **10** (1852), 1–37.

Gregory's important books include *Outlines of Chemistry, for the Use of Students* (London, 1845); *Letters to a Candid Inquirer on Animal Magnetism* (Edinburgh, 1851); *Handbook of Organic Chemistry* (London, 1852); and *Elementary Treatise on Chemistry* (Edinburgh, 1855). He also edited, with Justus Liebig, the 1842 and 1847 rev. eds. of Edward Turner, *Elements of Chemistry.*

Gregory's translations of Liebig's works include *Instructions for Chemical Analysis of Organic Bodies* (Glasgow, 1839); *Animal Chemistry* (Cambridge, 1842); *Chemistry in its Applications to Agriculture and Physiology* (London, 1847); *Researches on the Chemistry of Food* (London, 1847); *Researches on the Motion of the Juices in the Animal Body* (London, 1848); *Familiar Letters on Chemistry* (London, 1851); and *Principles of Agricultural Chemistry* (London, 1855). See also his trans. of Karl von Reichenbach, *Researches on Magnetism, Electricity, Heat, Light, Crystallization, and Chemical Attraction, in Their Relations to the Vital Force* (London, 1850).

II. Secondary Literature. A brief sketch of Gregory's life may be found in the *Dictionary of National Biography,* VIII, 548. The following are obituaries: *Edinburgh New Philosophical Journal,* **8** (1858), 171–175; *Proceedings of the Royal Society of Edinburgh,* **4** (1857–1862), 121–122; *Transactions of the Botanical Society of Edinburgh,* **6** (1857–1860), 75–79; and *Journal of the Chemical Society,* **12** (1860), 172–175. An extensive review of Gregory's work on animal magnetism appeared in the *British and Foreign Medico-Chirurgical Review,* **8** (1851), 378–431.

Daniel P. Jones

GREN, FRIEDRICH ALBRECHT CARL (*b.* Bernburg, Germany, 1 May 1760; *d.* Halle, Germany, 26 November 1798), *chemistry, physics.*

The eldest son of a Swedish immigrant hatter, Gren was destined for the clergy. But the death of his father forced him to abandon his formal education and prepare for a pharmaceutical career. After an apprenticeship characterized by oppressive servitude and his own private study of botany and chemistry, Gren went to Offenbach am Main as a journeyman pharmacist in 1779. For health reasons, he proceeded to Erfurt the following year. There he administered the apothecary shop owned by Wilhelm B. Trommsdorff, professor of chemistry, botany, and materia medica, and father of the chemist Johann B. Trommsdorff.

Instructed and encouraged by his employer, Gren prepared a manuscript for a chemistry text and entered into correspondence with Lorenz von Crell, editor of Germany's leading chemical journal. Upon the elder Trommsdorff's death in 1782, Gren first attempted to establish a chemical factory in Bernburg, then entered Helmstedt University, in the duchy of Brunswick. There he assisted Crell (who had arranged a scholarship for him), studied medicine and science, and lectured on chemistry.

In 1783 Gren went on to Halle University, where he continued his studies, gave chemistry lectures, and served as research assistant to Wenceslaus Karsten, professor of mathematics and physics. He took an M.D. in 1786 and a Ph.D. in 1787 and then quickly rose to professor of physics and chemistry in Halle's medical faculty in 1788. He remained in this post until his death ten years later.

Gren made his mark on German scientific life as an author of texts, a journal editor, and a theorist in chemistry and physics. Both his sense of the inadequacy of existing works and his need for additional income led him to devote much time to writing textbooks. The books were well received, some continuing to appear long after his death. Chemistry was the subject of his first text, the *Systematisches Handbuch der gesammten Chemie* (1787–1790; 3rd ed., 1806). He subsequently published *Grundriss der Naturlehre* (1788; 6th ed., 1820), *Grundriss der Pharmakologie* (1790), *Handbuch der Pharmakologie* (1791–1792; 3rd ed., 1814–1815) and *Grundriss der Chemie* (1796; 4th ed., 1818; English translation, 1800).

Inspired by the example of his former teacher and patron Crell, Gren founded a periodical for the "mathematical and chemical branches of natural science." Under his editorship, the *Journal der Physik* (1790–1794), which was succeeded by the *Neues Journal der Physik* (1795–1797), soon became Germany's most exciting scientific journal. After Gren's death, it was continued by his colleague Ludwig Wilhelm Gilbert, and subsequent editors, as the *Annalen der Physik* (1799–present).

Gren first attracted attention as a theorist by proposing that phlogiston has negative weight in his *Dissertatio inauguralis physico-medica sistens observationes et experimenta circa genesin aëris fixi et phlogisticati* (1786). His pride in the phlogiston theory's German origins apparently led him to try to rescue it from the difficulties created by the new discoveries with gases. Although equally nationalistic, most German chemists rejected Gren's proposal as absurd, embracing instead Richard Kirwan's system, which identified hydrogen as phlogiston. Undaunted, Gren continued to campaign for the negative weight of phlogiston until 1790, when the physicist Johann Tobias Mayer persuaded him to abandon the view with arguments based on the motion of pendulums.

That same year Gren announced that the empirical cornerstone of Lavoisier's antiphlogistic theory lacked grounding—pure red calx of mercury (mercuric oxide) did not yield any gas when it was reduced. Two years later his claim was supported by Johann Friedrich Westrumb, a widely respected experimentalist. A bitter debate ensued between Lavoisier's German proponents (notably Sigismund Friedrich Hermbstädt and Martin Heinrich Klaproth in Berlin) and the German phlogistonists (notably Gren, Westrumb, and J. B. Trommsdorff). The turning point in the antiphlogistic revolution in Germany came by mid-1793, when Gren and his allies were discredited.

As a consequence of this defeat, Gren soon adopted the compromise phlogiston theory of Johann Gottfried Leonhardi and Jeremias Benjamin Richter. This theory differed but slightly from Lavoisier's, treating phlogiston (the basis of light) as a component of all substances which could be oxidized. Gren's support of this theory helped prepare the way for the ultimate acceptance of Lavoisier's theory. In the mid-1790's, Gren also helped prepare the way for the penetration of Kant's "dynamic system" into German chemistry and physics by giving it very favorable, if brief, attention in his publications.

BIBLIOGRAPHY

I. Original Works. A complete list of Gren's publications through 1795 appears in his autobiography in Johann Kaspar Philipp Elwert, *Nachrichten von dem Leben und den Schriften jeztlebender teutscher Aerzte, Wündärzte, Thierärzte, Apotheker und Naturforscher* (Hildesheim, 1799), pp. 171–185.

II. Secondary Literature. For information on Gren see Wolfram Kaiser and Karl-Heinz Krosch, "Zur Geschichte der Medizinischen Fakultät der Universität Halle," in *Wissenschaftliche Zeitschrift: Mathematisch-naturwissenschaftliche Reihe,* **13** (1964), 160–176; Dietrich Ludwig Gustav Karsten, "Kurze Nachrichten von dem Leben des Professors Gren zu Halle," in *Neue Schriften,* **2** (1799), 404–413; an article by Hans Schimank in *Neue deutsche Biographie,* VII (Berlin, 1966), 45–46 (Gren was a Lutheran, not a Calvinist as Schimank maintains); J. R. Partington, *A History of Chemistry,* III (London, 1962), 575–577, 620–625, 632–636; Alexander Nicolaus Scherer,

"Friedrich Albrecht Carl Gren," in *Allgemeines Journal der Chemie,* **2** (1799), 357–416, 615–618; and Johann Bartholomai Trommsdorff, "Kurze Biographie des verewigten Friedrich Albrecht Carl Gren," in *Journal der Pharmacie,* **6** (1799), 367–375.

For further information on Gren's role in the antiphlogistic revolution, see Karl Hufbauer, "The Formation of the German Chemical Community, 1700–1795," diss. (Univ. of Cal., Berkeley, 1970), chs. 6 and 7.

KARL HUFBAUER

GRESSLY, AMANZ (*b.* Bärschwyl, Switzerland, 17 July 1814; *d.* Bern, Switzerland, 13 April 1865), *geology, stratigraphy, paleontology.*

Born at La Verrerie, a glassworks of Bärschwyl established by his grandfather, Gressly was first educated at home, then at Laufon, Solothurn, Lucerne, and Fribourg. As a medical student at Strasbourg, he came under the influence of Phillipe Louis Voltz and Jules Thurmann of Porrentruy in the Swiss Jura. Their interest inspired him to become a geologist. This was during the period of subdivision of major units of the geological column. Some of the geological column (A. G. Werner's Secondary and Tertiary) had been subdivided earlier in relatively undisturbed sedimentary sequences, such as those of southern England (William Smith, Robert Bakewell) and the Paris basin (Georges Cuvier, Alexandre Brongniart).

To reach this stage of geological chronology, simple petrography and the principle of faunal succession had been sufficient. The extensions of the subdivisions to the disturbed sequences of mountainous regions required a new geometric perspective which the engineer Voltz could well appreciate and which in the hands of his protégé Thurmann (1832) were to begin the science of tectonics. But beyond the application of new mechanical and architectural considerations, the theoretical framework of geology required the abandonment of simplistic Wernerian doctrines of simultaneous worldwide depositions of lithologically similar formations—the "onionskin" view of stratigraphy. Gressly made a major contribution to this development, by his identification and definition of the concept of facies or "aspects de terrain," an accomplishment of his first significant work, "Observations géologiques sur le Jura Soleurois" (1838), written at the age of twenty-two. This work and his extensive collections of fossils (Rollier mentions 25,000 specimens [1911]) brought him to the attention of Louis Agassiz, who engaged him as assistant at Neuchâtel. Agassiz made free use of Gressly's abilities and fossils for his own monographs. When Agassiz departed for America in 1846, he carried with him a substantial part of Gressly's fossil collections. This departure aggravated Gressly's state of melancholia; already by 1845, he had spent time in a sanitarium. Nevertheless, Agassiz was always profuse in his published acknowledgments of Gressly's high abilities.

Gressly's close associations with Agassiz's other abandoned assistants, Eduard Desor and Carl Vogt, continued, although his employment after the departure of Agassiz was in what would now be described as engineering geology for the construction of the alpine railroads. In this capacity he described the geologically rewarding tunnels of Hauenstein, des Loges, and Mont-Sagne. In 1859 he experienced what Wegmann described as immense pleasure in finding, on the modern coast of Sète on the French Riviera, the ecological zones he had deduced from his studies of the Jura while a student. In 1861 Gressly accompanied Vogt on a six-month voyage to the high latitudes. An indefatigable field geologist and collector in his native Jura, Gressly was described perhaps romantically as something of a folk figure. The painter Auguste Bachelin was one of his few close friends and sketched him often at Combe-Varin, which he made headquarters with Desor. A rapid mental decline began in 1864, and he died within a year.

The chronostratigraphic rock unit of Thurmann's researches in the Bernese Jura had been the terrain, a term roughly equivalent to formation, which Gressly used (as one example) for the Portlandian series of the Upper Jurassic group of strata. Recognizing the striking variations within the horizontal extensions of the terrains of the Solothurn Jura, he characterized the facies as a distinguishable petrographic aspect always accompanied by the same faunal assemblage and rigorously excluding some of the genera and species common to other facies. Twenty-three years before he ever saw the sea, he described this law of dissociation as reflecting conditions at the time of sedimentation, with modern processes as a guide to the ancient environment. He proposed as a general law that every facies of a terrain presents quite distinct petrographic and geognostic or paleontologic characteristics in marked contrast with those of other facies, either on the same stratigraphic level or generally characteristic of the terrain. Further, petrographically and geognostically similar facies of distinct terrains are characterized by analogous faunal assemblages, even succeeding each other vertically through a series of superposed terrains.

Gressly derived a series of paleoecological rules from his observations, noting, for example, that the diversity of facies increases vertically with a rising series and decreases with a sinking series (corresponding to conditions of receding and advancing seas, respectively). This work of 1838 alone establishes Gressly as a pioneer in, if not the founder of paleogeography. Wegmann wrote of him, "In creating this vision of superposed paleogeographies, he added a fourth dimension to his perspective."

BIBLIOGRAPHY

I. ORIGINAL WORKS. Gressly's own publications were very few. Among them are "Geognostische Bemerkungen über den Jura der nordwestlichen Schweiz, besonders des Kantons Solothurn und der Grenz-Partien der Kantone Bern, Aargau und Basel," in *Neues Jahrbuch für Mineralogie, Geognosie, und Petrefactenkunde* (1836), pp. 659–675, short version in *Bibliothèque universelle* (1837), pp. 194–197; "Résumé d'observations géologiques sur les modifications du Jura des cantons de Soleure et d'Argovie," in *L'Institut,* **4** (1836), 92–93; "Description géologique des montagnes du Jura Soleurois et Argovien," *ibid.,* 126–128: "Note sur les restes de mammiteres trouvés dans le portlandien de Soleure," *ibid.,* 165–166.

Also see "Observations géologiques sur les terrains des chaînes Jurassiques du canton de Soleure et des contrées limitrophes," in *Verhandlungen der Schweizerischen naturforschenden Gesellschaft* (1837), pp. 126–132; "Observations géologiques sur le Jura Soleurois," in *Neue Denkschriften der Schweizerischen naturforschenden Gesellschaft,* **2** (1838), 1–112; **4** (1840), 113–241; **5** (1841), 235–349; "Uebersicht der Geologie des nordwestlichen Aargau's," in *Neues Jahrbuch fur Mineralogie Geognosie, und Petrefactenkunde* (1844), pp. 153–163, short version in *Bulletin de la Société neuchâteloise des sciences naturelles,* **1** (1844–1846), 166–168; "Nouvelles données sur les faunes tertiaires d'Aljoi," in *Actes de la Société helvétique des sciences naturelles* (1853), pp. 251–261; "Ossements fossiles d'un saurien gigantesque de la famille des Dinosauriens," in *Bulletin de la Société neuchâteloise des sciences naturelles,* **4** (1856–1857), 13–16; "Études géologiques sur le Jura Neuchâtelois," in *Mémoires de la Société neuchâteloise des sciences naturelles,* **4** (1859), 1–159, written with E. Desor; *Briefe aus dem Norden. Der Bund* (Bern, 1861). pp. 246–251, 281–284; "Erinnerungen eines Naturforschers aus Südfrankreich," in *Album von Combe-Varin* (Zurich, 1861), pp. 201–296; "Differenzialheber (Wasserstandsmesser)," in *Mitteilungen der Naturforschenden Gesellschaft in Bern* (1866), 228–233; and "Uebersicht der geologischen Verhaltnisse der Umgebungen Oltens in Bezug auf den Hauenstein Tunnel (1853)," in *Mitteilungen der Naturforschenden Gesellschaft in Solothurn,* **8** (1928), 1–40.

II. SECONDARY LITERATURE. For works on Gressly, see Kurt Meyer, "Amanz Gressly, ein Solothurner Geologe (1814–1865)," in *Mitteilungen der Naturforschenden Gesellschaft in Solothurn,* no. 22 (1966), 1–79; L. Rollier, "Lettres d'Amand Gressly, le géologue jurassien (1814–1865)," in appendices, *Actes de la Société Jurassienne d'émulation,* **16** (1911), **17** (1912), **18** (1913); and *Imprimerie du petit Jurassien* (Moutier, 1911), with biographical and bibliographical sketch and portrait.

Also see Emil Kuhn-Schnyder, in *Neue deutsche Biographie;* J. Thurmann. "Essai sur les soulèvements jurassiques du Porrentruy," 2 vols., I (Porrentruy, 1832), 1–84; II (Strasbourg, 1836), 1–51; and Eugene Wegmann, "L'exposé original de la notion de faciès par A. Gressly (1814–1865)," in *Sciences de la terre,* **9,** no. 1 (1962–1963), 83–119, with facsimile reproductions of critical parts of Gressly's 1838 definition of facies.

CECIL J. SCHNEER

GREW, NEHEMIAH (*b.* Mancetter, Warwickshire, England, 1641; *d.* London [?], England, 25 March 1712), *plant morphology, plant anatomy.*

Grew was the son of Obadiah Grew, a clergyman and schoolmaster, and Ellen Vicars. After early education at Coventry, he took his B.A. in 1661 at Cambridge, where he was a member of Pembroke Hall. Further study at Cambridge being impossible owing to his religious nonconformity, he qualified for the M.D. at the University of Leiden. Returning to England, Grew practiced first at Coventry and later in London. He relied almost entirely on medicine as a means of livelihood for the rest of his life. He first married Mary Huetson, who died in 1685, then Elizabeth Dodson, by whom he had at least one son and two daughters.

The Royal Society became the focal center of Grew's activities, for in 1672 he was persuaded by some of the fellows, notably John Wilkins, the bishop of Chester, to move from Coventry to London to take up more seriously the study of plant anatomy, in which he had become interested. Fifty pounds were raised by subscription among the fellows to induce him to make this change. Through the Royal Society, Grew also came into contact with Robert Hooke, whose diverse activities included pioneering studies in the field of microscopy. The compound microscope was just coming into use. Hooke was instructed to make the Society's microscope available to Grew. By 1677 both Hooke and Grew were secretaries of the Royal Society.

As a medical man Grew had been interested in the structure of animals before turning to plants. His philosophy and religious beliefs made him regard both plants and animals as "contrivances of the same Wisdom" and he therefore concluded that it would be just as rewarding to study the structure of plants as that of animals. Similar views had already been expressed by Francis Glisson, one of the founders of the Royal Society, in a published passage which Grew subsequently quoted in the preface to his first important book, *The Anatomy of Vegetables Begun.*

Grew was no narrow-minded specialist: besides plant anatomy he was interested in the occurrence of crystalline materials in plant tissues. He also described and illustrated the intestines and related organs of many different kinds of animals. In 1672 he discussed the nature of snow and noticed that it is composed of "icicles" of determined form. By 1675 he was interested in the taste of plants and attempted to classify them accordingly. In 1681 Grew's *Musaeum Regalis Societatis* appeared, a thick volume which not only listed but described in detail, sometimes with illustrations, the objects in the Society's museum at Gresham College. In 1701 Grew published his last great work, *Cosmologia sacra.* This religious and philosophical treatise reflects the beliefs in which he was brought up and which served as a background to his scientific work.

Grew's chief claim to scientific distinction rests on his outstanding contribution to plant anatomy. The suggestion made by some botanists that Grew merely copied Marcello Malpighi's results by referring to the manuscript of his *Anatome plantarum* between the time of its submission to the Royal Society for publication and its ultimate appearance cannot be taken seriously. A careful perusal of Thomas Birch's *History of the Royal Society,* as well as the writings of Agnes Arber and W. Carruthers, shows that there are no grounds for the view that his results were secondhand. Indeed, Grew went to some trouble to demonstrate to fellows of the Royal Society instances in which Malpighi was in advance of him. For example, Malpighi was the first to demonstrate spiral thickenings in vessels. Malpighi and Grew appear, in fact, to have held each other in high scientific regard. Yet communication must have been impeded, for Malpighi could not read English and was less able than Grew to express himself correctly in Latin.

Grew communicated his ideas on plant anatomy to the Royal Society in a series of "discourses" which were so well received that he was asked to publish them in book form. Grew's first three scientific books are much shorter than the fourth, which repeats and elaborates the contents of the first three. The publication of *The Anatomy of Plants* (1682) was therefore the highlight of Grew's career as a plant anatomist. An examination of the text and the profuse illustrations in this great work reveals the tremendous advance in knowledge which it represents. Grew was so successful partly because he started with naked-eye observations and then passed on to higher magnifications. He next elucidated the structures of stems and roots by the combined use of transverse, radial, and tangential longitudinal sections—still the practice today—and also studied obliquely cut surfaces.

Grew's primary aim was to discover the physiological functions of the various tissues. In this he was only partially successful, not surprisingly, for such mechanisms as the ascent of sap and the translocation of foodstuffs are still only partly understood. In Grew's time much energy was dissipated in trying to establish physiological similarities between plants and animals. For example, attempts were made to discover a circulatory system in plants comparable with that in animals. On 23 June 1672 Grew was "desired" by the Royal Society "to discover, whether, whilst plants are growing, there be a peristaltic motion in them." On 7 May 1673 he pointed out to the Society that roots have the power to overcome the resistance of the soil as they grow downward as well as to absorb nourishment. This suggested to some of those present that the downward movement of the roots was sustained by muscular action. In such circumstances it is not surprising that Grew became involved in a controversy with Martin Lister which was mainly an argument about the flow of fluids in the plant body. Grew was more successful in recognizing structural differences in plants with different taxonomic affinities, and in so doing he foreshadowed the modern study of systematic anatomy.

Grew confirmed the existence of cells, already seen by Robert Hooke, but he had no idea that they contain the living substance, protoplasm. But Grew went further than Hooke, for he noted the vessels in wood, the fibers in bark, and the parenchyma of the pith and cortex. Indeed, he was responsible for introducing the term "parenchyma." Grew found that the root consists of a skin, a "cortical body" commonly called the "barque," and a "ligneous body" or vascular core. He found that the cortical body pierces the ligneous body by "inserted pieces," which are evidently the structures now called medullary rays. In the ligneous body he described annual rings. He likened the vessels and fibers, together with the inserted pieces, to the warp and woof of a piece of cloth. He searched in vain to find valves in the vessels. The ascent of sap in the vessels was accounted for by capillarity, and he thought that the vessels were kept supplied with sap from neighboring parenchyma cells which served as cisterns. Grew believed that the sap rises through the wood only during the spring and that it moves through the bark at other times of the year. His concept of vessels was that their structure resembled a ribbon twisted spirally around an imaginary cylindrical object. He and many anatomists who followed him believed that the wood is in some way derived from the bark. Grew recognized the stomata as orifices or "passports" in the skin of leaves, but Malpighi seems to have understood their structure more completely.

Grew made important contributions to plant morphology as well as to anatomy. For example he studied flowers, fruits, and seeds, along with the vegetative organs. In the flower he termed the calyx the "emplacement," the corolla the "foliature," and the stamens and styles the "attire." On pollination he observed that the pollen "falls down upon the seed case or womb and touches it with a prolific virtue or subtle and vivific effluvia."

Unfortunately, Grew worked in circumstances that afforded no opportunity to teach students, and consequently, except for what he published, his knowledge died with him. Grew and Malpighi were more accurately informed about plant structure than their immediate successors, and it was not until the time of the German plant anatomist, Hugo von Mohl (1805–1872), that any really fundamental advances in the subject were made.

BIBLIOGRAPHY

I. ORIGINAL WORKS. Grew's scientific writings are *The Anatomy of Vegetables Begun. With a General Account of Vegetation Founded Thereon* (London, 1672); *An Idea of a Phytological History Propounded. Together With a Continuation of the Anatomy of Vegetables, Particularly Prosecuted Upon Roots, and an Account of the Vegetation of Roots, Grounded Chiefly Thereupon* (London, 1673); *The Comparative Anatomy of Trunks, Together With an Account of Their Vegetation Grounded Thereupon* (London, 1675); and *The Anatomy of Plants With an Idea of a Philosophical History of Plants and Several Other Lectures Read Before the Royal Society* (London, 1682). He also wrote *Musaeum Regalis Societatis or a Catalogue and Description of the Natural and Artificial Rarities Belonging to the Royal Society and Preserved at Gresham College. Whereunto is Subjoyned the Comparative Anatomy of Stomachs and Guts* (London, 1681); and *Cosmologia sacra or a Discourse of the Universe as It Is the Creature and Kingdom of God. . . .* (London, 1701).

The following are among the MSS concerning Grew's activities to be found in the library of the Royal Society: "Letter Book," V (1672), 443–446, and VI (1673), 321, dealing with the controversy with Martin Lister; and "Register Book," III (4 Apr. 1672), dealing with the structure of snow; IV (25 Mar. 1675), the description and classification of tastes of plants; V (8 Feb. 1676), on animal anatomy, and (8 Mar.), on salts in plant tissues. There are others in both the *Letter Book* and the *Register Book,* but it is impossible to cite all of them here.

II. SECONDARY LITERATURE. See Agnes Arber, "Tercentenary of Nehemiah Grew (1641–1712)," in *Nature,* **147** (1941), 630–632; "The Relation of Nehemiah Grew and Marcello Malpighi," in *Chronica botanica,* **6** (1941), 391–392; and "Nehemiah Grew and Marcello Malpighi," in *Proceedings of the Linnean Society of London* (1941), 218–238; Thomas Birch, *History of the Royal Society of London,* 4 vols. (London, 1660–1687); W. Carruthers, "On the Life and Work of Nehemiah Grew," in *Journal of the Royal Microscopical Society,* **129** (1902), 129–141; Robert Hooke, *Micrographia or Some Physiological Descriptions of Minute Bodies Made by Magnifying Glasses With Observations and Inquiries Thereupon* (London, 1665; facs. ed., New York, 1961); M. Malpighi, *Anatome plantarum* (London, 1675; 1679); C. R. Metcalfe, "A Vista in Plant Anatomy," in W. B. Turrill, ed., *Vistas in Botany* (London, 1959), pp. 76–98; and Julius von Sachs, *History of Botany (1530–1860)*, trans. by Henry E. F. Garnsey, rev. by Isaac Bayley Balfour (Oxford, 1906), p. 229–241.

CHARLES R. METCALFE

GRIESS, JOHANN PETER (*b.* Kirchhosbach, Germany, 6 September 1829; *d.* Bournemouth, England, 30 August 1888), *chemistry.*

The son of a blacksmith, Griess began his advanced studies in Kassel at the Polytechnic, aimed at an agricultural career, then went on to Jena and Marburg. He was a rebellious and idle student, always in trouble with the authorities, but after a short period at the well-known tar distillery at Offenbach he became more subdued and returned to Marburg to work under A. W. H. Kolbe. His career was launched in 1858, when A. W. von Hofmann, who had been impressed by an early paper, invited him to London.

Griess struck everyone both by the eccentricity of his dress and by the excellence of his work. After three years a well-executed investigation for Allsopp and Sons, the brewers, brought him an appointment as chemist in their brewery at Burton-on-Trent, which he held until his death. Griess married Louisa Anna Mason in 1869; they had two sons and two daughters. He became a fellow of the Royal Society and was one of the founders of the Institute of Chemistry.

Griess's main contribution to chemistry had nothing to do with brewing but stemmed from the early discovery which Hofmann had noted, the formation of a new type of organic nitrogen compound by the action of nitrous acid on certain amines. Between 1860 and 1866 Griess developed the chemistry of this diazo reaction, which was mainly of theoretical interest at first, extending the work of Rafaelle Piria and Ernst Gerland, who had noted the action of nitrous fumes on anthranilic acid, yielding salicylic acid and nitrogen. Griess found that the reaction with picramic acid in alcohol yielded a new type of nitrogen compound for which he devised the name diazodinitrophenol, the first use of the term "diazo." Studies on aniline produced explosive compounds too unstable to have any application. Further studies with other reactions showed that the diazo reaction was a versatile route to new compounds, but it was not until 1864 that, by coupling diazotized aniline with naphthylamine, Griess opened up the general way to a new class of coloring substances. The azo dyes came under intense investigation and thousands were patented.

In 1884 Griess, simultaneously with Böttiger, discovered dyes capable of coloring cotton without a mordant. None of Griess's patents proved lucrative, although others made fortunes. He died content with his position as a practicing brewery chemist pursuing organic research as a hobby.

BIBLIOGRAPHY

A list of Griess's writings may be found in Poggendorff, III, 548-549; and IV, 533.

Several sketches of Griess's life derive from E. Fischer, in *Berichte der Deutschen Chemischen Gesellschaft,* **24** (1891), 1007-1078, with portrait. An appreciation of his chemical work in relation to the structure of dyes is in F. A. Mason, in *Journal of the Society of Dyers and Colourists,* **46** (Feb. 1930), 33-39. See also H. Grossmann, in G. Bugge, ed., *Das Buch der grossen Chemiker,* II (Berlin, 1930), 217-228.

FRANK GREENAWAY

GRIFFITH, RICHARD JOHN (*b.* Dublin, Ireland, 20 September 1784; *d.* Dublin, 22 September 1878), *geology.*

Griffith was the son of Richard Griffith, a wealthy merchant and a member of parliament. His father decided he should follow a career in engineering and mining, and in 1800 sent him to London to study chemistry and mineralogy under William Nicholson, chemist and editor of the *Journal of Natural Philosophy.* This was followed by visits to mining areas, first in England and Wales, and then in Scotland. In Edinburgh, Griffith attended the classes of Thomas Hope, professor of chemistry, and Robert Jameson, professor of natural history; in 1807 he was elected a fellow of the Royal Society of Edinburgh. In 1808 he was nominated as an honorary member of the recently formed Geological Society of London, a clear indication that he had already attracted some esteem.

Griffith returned to Ireland and in 1809 was appointed engineer to a commission inquiring into the nature and extent of the Irish bogs. His reports, published in 1810-1812, contained some geological details. When Richard Kirwan died in 1812, Griffith succeeded him as inspector general of the royal mines in Ireland; in the same year he was appointed mining engineer to the Royal Dublin Society. His duties for the Society were to investigate and report on the coalfields and mining areas, and he was also required to give public lectures on the geology of Ireland.

Griffith's friend G. B. Greenough, president of the Geological Society of London, suggested that he prepare a geological map of Ireland. This was the beginning of an undertaking that eventually resulted in the publication of the first geological map of Ireland. When Griffith was lecturing on geology in 1815, he exhibited a map he had prepared; but there is no record of its contents, and it was not published. Twenty years passed before the question of publication really arose.

The results of Griffith's first coalfield investigation, made for the Royal Dublin Society, were published in 1814 as *Geological and Mining Report on the Leinster Coal District.* This was accompanied by a colored geological map on a scale of .75 inch to the mile and several geological sections. A second report, on the Connaught coal district, also with geological map and sections, was published in 1818. In these reports Griffith stated that although he used Wernerian terms, he expressly dissociated himself from any theoretical implications. A third report, on the coal districts of the Ulster counties of Tyrone and Antrim, although prepared in 1818, did not appear in print until 1829. This was accompanied by sections but not a map.

There was still no suitable topographical map of Ireland to serve as a basis for a large-scale geological map, but in 1825 a trigonometrical survey under the Board of Ordnance was begun, principally to provide a basis for the equitable adjustment of local taxation. On Griffith's recommendation, the survey was to be executed on a scale of six inches to the mile (in England it was on a scale of two inches to the mile). The actual boundaries of the civil units had first to be determined; and since this was not the work of military surveyors, a special Boundary Department was set up with Griffith as director. This work was carried out in advance of the Ordnance Survey and was completed in 1844.

In 1829 Griffith was appointed commissioner for the general valuation of lands, an office which he held until 1868. Shortly afterward he resigned his post with the Royal Dublin Society but declared his intention of continuing his researches toward the completion of a geological map of all Ireland. With over 100 officials working under him, and traveling throughout the country, Griffith was well placed to obtain the information he required. The Board of Ordnance surveyors were also collecting geological information; but since they were following a plan that began in the north of Ireland, their notes were mostly confined to that area.

In 1835 the British Association for the Advancement of Science met in Dublin, and at the meeting Griffith exhibited a manuscript geological map of Ireland which he had prepared from his notes. Although this map does not seem to have been preserved, its main features were copied by John Phillips and shown in his *Index Geological Map of the British Isles,* issued in 1838, on a scale of about twenty-eight miles to the inch. Phillips acknowledged the use of Griffith's "valuable and yet unpublished map." On this map the southwest of Ireland is colored almost entirely as "clay slate and grauwacke slate," or "primary" rocks.

Soon after Phillips' map appeared, a colored geological map of Ireland by Griffith, on a scale of ten miles to the inch, was published in an atlas of maps accompanying the second report of the Irish Railway Commission, dated 13 July 1838. The report included a twenty-five-page "Outline of the Geology of Ireland," and this and the map were also issued separately. This map showed some major advances in Griffith's geological knowledge, such as the substitution of large areas of "old conglomerate" and "Old Red Sandstone" where Phillips' map had shown "clay slate."

The publication of a large-scale (four miles to the inch) map had been delayed by the fact that the topographical map was not yet complete, but in 1838 Griffith colored geologically an unfinished proof impression and exhibited it in August at the British Association meeting at Newcastle-on-Tyne. The engraved map, uncolored, was published in March 1839. Colored copies were supplied to order. It was remarkably detailed, with tablets for twenty-six different colors to indicate the various stratigraphic horizons, as well as different igneous and metamorphic rocks. A noteworthy feature was Griffith's division of the Carboniferous Limestone into five different groups. The main divisions of the strata were retained in later editions of the map, although the number of subdivisions was greatly increased. A reduction of the map (on a scale of about sixteen miles to the inch), dated 1853, had thirty-seven colored tablets; and the final revised edition of the large-scale map, issued in 1855, had over forty. The subdivisions were lithological and did not imply any relative age.

Griffith's particular interest in the Carboniferous Limestone rocks led him to amass a large collection of fossils from the formation; and he employed Frederick McCoy, a young paleontologist, to describe them in a well-illustrated and valuable publication, *A Synopsis of the Characters of the Carboniferous Limestone Fossils of Ireland,* published in 1844 at Griffith's own expense. This was followed by a similar work on the Silurian fossils of Ireland, collected by Griffith and described by McCoy.

In 1854 Griffith was awarded the Wollaston Medal of the Geological Society of London for his services to geological science and particularly for his geological map of Ireland. On the final revised edition, dated 1855, Griffith stated that he had taken some boundaries in the southeast from those on the recently published maps of the Irish Geological Survey. The official survey had begun in 1845, but publication had been delayed until 1855, when the one-inch topographical maps were ready. As the maps of the Survey and the accompanying memoirs were published, Griffith's map gradually became out-of-date.

Griffith was created a baronet in 1858. He continued to hold some public offices and was widely consulted. In 1869, when he was eighty-five, he testified before a select committee of inquiry into valuation; this evidence contains much of interest concerning Griffith's work.

BIBLIOGRAPHY

I. Original Works. A long, but not complete, list of Griffith's papers is in the unsigned obituary in *Geological Magazine* (see below). There is also a list in Royal Society, *Catalogue of Scientific Papers,* III (1866), 17–18.

Works by Griffith published separately are *First Report to the Commissioners on the Bogs of Ireland,* Parliamentary Report (1810) and subsequent reports (1811–1812); *Geological and Mining Report on the Leinster Coal District* (Dublin, 1814); *Geological and Mining Survey of the Connaught Coal District* (Dublin, 1818); *Geological and Mining Surveys of the Coal Districts of the Counties of Tyrone and Antrim* (Dublin, 1829); *Outline of the Geology of Ireland and Geological Map of Ireland,* accompanying *Second Report of the Railway Commissioners* (Dublin, 1838); *A General Map of Ireland to Accompany the Report of the Railway Commissioners Shewing the Principal Physical Features and Geological Structure of the Country* (Dublin, 1839, 1846, 1855); and *Geological Map of Ireland to Accompany the Instructions to Valuators* (Dublin, 1853). Griffith also wrote *Notice Respecting the Fossils of the Mountain Limestone of Ireland as Compared with Those of Great Britain, and Also With the Devonian System* (Dublin, 1842); and, jointly with F. McCoy, *A Synopsis of the Characters of the Carboniferous Limestone Fossils of Ireland* (Dublin, 1844) and *A Synopsis of the Silurian Fossils of Ireland* (Dublin, 1846).

II. Secondary Literature. A lengthy, unsigned obituary notice in *Geological Magazine,* **5** (11 Dec. 1878), 524–528, is the source of several other notices. Some additional biographical details are in H. F. Berry, *History of the Royal Dublin Society* (London, 1915), pp. 162 ff. A very detailed account of the progress of Griffith's map and its geological changes is given by Maxwell Close, "Anniversary Address to the Royal Geological Society of Ireland," in *Journal of the Royal Geological Society of Ireland,* n.s. **5** (1880), 132–148. Some further information is given in A. G. Davis, in "Notes on Griffith's Geological Maps of Ireland," in *Journal of the Society for the Bibliography of Natural History,* **2** (1950), 209–211. A valuable commentary is R. C. Simington and A. Farrington, "A Forgotten Pioneer, Patrick Ganly, Geologist, Surveyor, and Civil Engineer," in *Journal of the Department of Agriculture, Republic of Ireland,* **46** (1949), 2–16; in this paper the geological work of one of Griffith's assistants is described, with much background information.

JOAN M. EYLES

GRIFFITH, WILLIAM (*b.* Ham Common, Surrey, England, 4 March 1810; *d.* Malacca, India, 9 February 1845), *botany.*

Griffith, youngest son of Thomas Griffith, a London merchant, was the great-grandson of Jeremiah Meyer, historical painter to George II and a founder of the Royal Academy. He was educated for the medical profession and was apprenticed to a surgeon in the West End of London. In 1829 he began attending classes at the University of London, as one of John Lindley's students. Here Griffith became acquainted with Nathaniel Wallich, who had collected plants extensively in the Himalayas and Burma. Griffith studied in Paris under the anatomist Charles Mirbel, to whose famed dissertation on *Marchantia polymorpha* was appended Griffith's note on *Targionia hypophylla.* He also studied medical botany with William Anderson at Sir Hans Sloane's garden in Chelsea, where he became acquainted with Franz Bauer, the botanical artist at Kew Gardens, whom he admired for his accurate observations.

Griffith went to India in 1832 as an assistant-surgeon in the service of the East India Company and remained there until his death. In 1835, with Wallich and John MacClelland, a soil expert, he went to Assam as part of the delegation seeking to establish tea production in India. Afterward, Griffith traveled in India and neighboring countries, collecting plants; he was the first European to enter many of these areas. Griffith's goal was to write a flora of India. It was not to be an ordinary flora, since he planned to include information on the ecology, physiology, morphology, and anatomy of the native plants as well as a list of them. A fellow of the Linnean Society, Griffith regularly corresponded with J. D. Hooker, George Bentham, and Robert Wight. In 1842, at Hooker's recommendation, he became director of the Calcutta Botanical Gardens during Wallich's absence and served as professor of botany at Calcutta Medical College. In 1844, anticipating leave to England, Griffith married Miss Henderson, the sister of his brother's wife; but in January 1845 he contracted hepatitis (most likely a complication from repeated malaria attacks) and died the following month. His personal papers were willed to the East India Company, and a rough edition compiled by Griffith's nonbotanical friend MacClelland was published at Calcutta. The papers and a herbarium (estimated at 12,000 species) were shipped to England, where they are in the library of the herbarium at Kew Gardens.

Griffith observed the cryptogams as no earlier worker had, correctly describing the four-tiered antheridia of *Anthoceros* and the minute perispore elaters of *Equisetum.* He believed that all land plants reproduced by a sexual system similar to that of the angiosperms, involving pistils, anthers, and seeds. In attempting to make cryptogams and phanerogams conform, he divided the lower land plants into three classes: the "cryptogamic" plants, including ferns, anthocerotes, lycopods, and horsetails, believed to have no obvious sex organs; the "gymnospermous" plants, *Azolla, Salvinia,* and *Chara,* bearing naked "ovules" analogous to conifers; and the "pistilligerous" plants, the mosses and liverworts, fully equal to angiosperms because they possessed both pistils (archegonia) and anthers (antheridia).

His theories about seed plants were more accurate; Griffith was the first to observe pollen grains in the pollen chamber of a *Cycas* ovule. He attempted to explain the angiospermous ovule and established that the embryo sac exists prior to pollination. He also recognized the necessity of pollen-tube penetration into the nucellus for fertilization. His descriptions of ovules in the Loranthaceae and Santalaceae are noteworthy. Unfortunately, Griffith was unable to ascertain the ultimate fate of the pollen tube; he confused the suspensor of the embryo with the tip of the pollen tube, thus giving tentative approval to Matthias Schleiden's erroneous concept that the embryo comes from the tip of the pollen tube. Griffith's misunderstanding of fertilization in angiosperms undoubtedly contributed to his confusion about sexuality in cryptogams.

By 1850 Wilhelm Hofmeister had confirmed many of Griffith's observations, although his conclusions differed. Hofmeister discovered the function of the pollen tube in embryogeny, thus comprehending the true point of fertilization. He was able to extrapolate this knowledge to the cryptogams and thereby discovered alternation of generations in land plants. Griffith was an astute observer who possessed virtually all the data that Hofmeister later used. It is fair to suppose that had Griffith lived, he might have preceded Hofmeister in recognizing alternation of generations. Certainly he would have become a noted botanist of the nineteenth century.

BIBLIOGRAPHY

I. ORIGINAL WORKS. Griffith's shorter writings are listed in Royal Society, *Catalogue of Scientific Papers,* X, 18–19.

The following longer works were arranged by J. MacClelland and published as *Posthumous Papers: Journals of Travels in Assam, Burma, Bootan, and the Neighboring Countries* (Calcutta, 1847); *Icones plantarum asiaticarum,* 4 vols. (Calcutta, 1847–1854); *Notulae ad plantas asiaticas,* 4 vols. (Calcutta, 1847–1854); *Itinerary Notes of Plants Collected in the Khasyah and Bootan Mountains 1837–1838, in Afghanistan and Neighboring Countries 1839–1841* (Calcutta, 1848); and *Palms of British East India* (Calcutta, 1850).

II. SECONDARY LITERATURE. See the unsigned "Obituary of W. Griffith," in *Proceedings of the Linnean Society of London,* **1** (1838–1848), 239–244; "Obituary of W. Griffith," in *London Journal of Botany,* **4** (1845), 371–375; I. H. Burkill, *Chapters on the History of Botany in India* (Nasik, 1965), pp. 37–74; W. Hofmeister, "La formation de l'embryon des phanérogames," in *Annales des sciences naturelles,* 4th ser., **12** (1859), 1–71; W. J. Hooker, ed., "Works of the Late William Griffith, Esq., F. L. S.," in *London Journal of Botany,* **7** (1848), 446–449; J. M. Lamond, "The Afghanistan Collection of William Griffith," in *Notes from the Royal Botanic Garden, Edinburgh,* **30** (1970), 159–175; and W. H. Lang, "William Griffith, 1810–1845," in F. S. Oliver, ed., *Makers of British Botany* (Cambridge, 1913), 177–191.

ANN M. HIRSCH-KIRCHANSKI
STEFAN J. KIRCHANSKI

GRIGNARD, FRANÇOIS AUGUSTE VICTOR (*b.* Cherbourg, France, 6 May 1871; *d.* Lyons, France, 13 December 1935), *chemistry.*

Grignard developed the reaction that became one of the most fruitful methods of synthesis in organic chemistry. The son of Marie Hébert and Théophile Henri Grignard, foreman and sailmaker at the marine arsenal, Grignard attended the lycée at Cherbourg, the École Normale Spéciale at Cluny, and the University of Lyons. After fulfilling his military service from 1892 to 1893, he completed his studies in mathematics at Lyons and, influenced by a classmate from Cluny, overcame his dislike of chemistry and became an assistant in the chemistry department. He soon began a long association with Philippe Antoine Barbier, the head of the department, who in 1898 investigated the conversion of an unsaturated ketone into the corresponding tertiary alcohol by using methyl iodide and magnesium instead of zinc as called for by the Saytzeff method. When Grignard was looking for a doctoral thesis topic, Barbier recommended that he take up the study of this variation on the Saytzeff reaction.

A survey of the literature on organomagnesium compounds convinced Grignard that such an intermediate compound was formed in Barbier's reaction. He also learned of the difficulties other workers had experienced with organomagnesium compounds which ignite spontaneously in air or in carbon dioxide. He found, however, that E. Frankland in 1859 and J. Wanklyn in 1861 had solved a similar problem with zinc alkyls by keeping them in anhydrous ether. Adapting their method, Grignard treated magnesium turnings in anhydrous ether with methyl iodide at room temperature, preparing what came to be known as the Grignard reagent, which could be used for reaction with a ketone or an aldehyde without first being isolated. On hydrolyzing with dilute acid, the corresponding tertiary or secondary alcohol was produced in much better yield than Barbier had been able to obtain.

Grignard's discovery was reported in a short paper at a meeting of the Académie des Sciences in May 1900. Although he was frequently opposed, Grignard held to the view throughout his life that the organomagnesium compounds he prepared had the formula RMgX and that in anhydrous ether they existed as the etherate which most likely had the formula $(C_2H_5)_2O(R)MgX$.

Grignard submitted his thesis on organomagnesium compounds and their applications in synthesis and received the doctor of physical sciences degree at Lyons on 18 July 1901. The complete thesis was published by the university, and within the year a full abstract appeared in *Chemisches Zentralblatt.* Grignard's method of synthesis thus became widely known and firmly established. By 1908 more than 500 papers dealing with the Grignard reaction had been published. In his thesis Grignard described the preparation of carboxylic acids by the action of carbon dioxide on his reagent; secondary alcohols from aldehydes or formic esters; tertiary alcohols from ketones, esters, acid halides, or anhydrides; and unsaturated hydrocarbons in place of tertiary alcohols. He reported that alcohols react with organomagnesium compounds, as does water, to produce hydrocarbons and that aromatic bromides lead to products analogous to the aliphatic compounds.

Grignard was awarded the Cahours Prize of the Institut de France in 1901 and the Berthelot Medal in 1902. He became lecturer in chemistry at Besançon in 1905, returned to Lyons in 1906 and moved to Nancy in 1909 where he became professor of organic chemistry in 1910. That year he married Augustine Marie Boulant, and Roger, the first of two children, was born in 1911.

In November 1912 the Nobel Prize for chemistry was awarded jointly to Grignard, for his 1900 discovery of the role of organomagnesium compounds in synthesis, and Paul Sabatier, for his discoveries in catalytic hydrogenation made fifteen years earlier. Continuing his research on organomagnesium compounds, Grignard investigated their reactions with epoxides, glycols, and with cyanogen to produce nitriles. In army service from 1914 to 1919 he worked primarily on toluene production and war gases. He succeeded Barbier at Lyons in the fall of 1919, remaining there the rest of his life.

In addition to his organometallic researches, Grignard investigated terpenes; structure determination by ozonization; the condensation of carbonyls; and the cracking, hydrogenation, and dehydrogenation of hydrocarbons.

In recognition of his monumental contributions to chemistry, Grignard was a member or honorary member in the world's major chemical and scientific societies. Honorary doctorates were conferred on him by Louvain in 1927, Brussels in 1930, and an honorary professorship by Nancy in 1931.

BIBLIOGRAPHY

I. ORIGINAL WORKS. Grignard announced the discovery of his method of synthesis in "Sur quelques nouvelles combinaisons organométalliques du magnésium et leur application à des synthèses d'alcools et d'hydrocarbures," in *Comptes rendus de l'Académie des sciences,* **126** (1898), 1322. His doctoral thesis, "Sur les combinaisons organomagnésiennes mixtes et leur application à des synthèses d'acides, d'alcools et d'hydrocarbures," in *Annales de l'Université de Lyon,* **6** (1901), 1-116, was also published in Paris later in 1901. Toward the end of his life Grignard began editing a handbook, *Traité de chimie organique,* 23 vols. (Paris, 1935-1954), and his son, Roger, in collaboration with Jean Cologne published his lectures as *Précis de chimie organique* (Paris, 1937).

Lists of Grignard's publications, positions, and honors appear in Charles Courtot, "Notice sur la vie et les travaux de Victor Grignard (1871-1935)," in *Bulletin. Société chimique de France,* **5**, no. 3 (1936), 1433-1472. A collection of addresses by and about Grignard was published by A. Rey, *Victor Grignard (In Memoriam)* (Lyons, 1936).

II. SECONDARY LITERATURE. Biographical details and evaluations of Grignard's work are given by Charles Courtot in his paper listed above; Henry Gilman, "Victor Grignard," in *Journal of the American Chemical Society,* **59** (1937), 17-19; and Heinrich Rheinboldt, "Fifty Years of the Grignard Reaction," in *Journal of Chemical Education,* **27** (1950), 476-488. For a more recent treatment of the Grignard reaction see Rudolph M. Salinger, "The Structure of the Grignard Reagent and the Mechanism of Its Reactions," in Arthur F. Scott, ed., *Survey of Progress in Chemistry* (New York, 1963), pp. 301-324.

A. ALBERT BAKER, JR.

GRIJNS, GERRIT (*b.* Leerdam, Netherlands, 28 May 1865; *d.* Utrecht, Netherlands, 11 November 1944), *physiology.*

Grijns was the son of Cornelis Dirk Grijns, a merchant, and Janetta Christina Seret. He attended the Gymnasium at Delft and started his medical studies at the University of Utrecht in 1885. In 1901 he took his M.D. degree, offering a thesis entitled "Bijdrage tot de physiologie van den Nervus opticus." For this investigation he had to work at night, since the very sensitive galvanometer he used was disturbed by traffic during the day. In March 1893 Grijns passed the final examination that gave him the right to practice. A scholarship enabled him to study physiology for six months at Leipzig, under Carl Ludwig. After marrying Johanna Gesina de Wilde on 15 September 1893, Grijns left for the Netherlands East Indies as a medical officer. In his first years in the Far East he treated many patients suffering from beriberi, a disease then very common and of unknown origin.

The Dutch government had, in 1886, sent out the Pekelharing-Winkler commission with instructions to investigate the cause of beriberi. They concluded that most probably an infectious agent, a coccus, was the causative agent. Christiaan Eijkman, later winner of the Nobel Prize in physiology or medicine, was charged with the continuation of their studies. At Batavia, Java, he had a small laboratory for pathological anatomy and bacteriology at his disposal. Grijns became his co-worker but had to join the Atjeh expedition in Sumatra in 1895-1896. Here he observed patients with beriberi but had no time for thorough investigations.

On Eijkman's return to the Netherlands in 1896, Grijns was appointed to continue his investigations. The former had pointed to the close resemblance of human beriberi to polyneuritis gallinarum and had established that feeding only completely polished (overmilled) rice caused polyneuritis in fowls, but that incompletely polished (or husked by hand) rice prevented or even cured the disease. Eijkman firmly believed a bacterium or a poison to be the cause even several years after Grijns, in 1901, had advanced the idea that a deficiency of "protective substances" was the causative factor and that the absence in food of not only proteins, carbohydrates, fats, and minerals, but also of other (still unknown) substances, could result in disease. This idea of "partial hunger" became the starting point and the basis of the modern theory of vitamins. At the same time Grijns gave lessons in anatomy at the School for Native Doctors (S.T.O.V.I.A.) and later taught physiology and ophthalmology, on which he wrote a simple textbook. Except for an interruption during 1902-1904, when he was on leave in Europe because of ill health, he pursued his research until 1912, when he became director of the laboratory.

In 1917 Grijns returned to the Netherlands, and in 1921 he was appointed professor of animal physiology at the State Agricultural University, Wageningen. In the academic year 1929–1930 he served as vice-chancellor. In the year of his retirement (1935), on his seventieth birthday, a committee of honor presented him an English translation of his publications on nutrition (1900–1911) and of his thesis. Because of his brilliant and immensely fruitful idea on nutritional deficiency, he was awarded in 1940 the Swammerdam Medal, inscribed "Hodiernae Nutrimentorum Doctrinae Conditor atque Pater" ("Founder and Father of the Modern Doctrine of Nutrition").

BIBLIOGRAPHY

I. Original Works. Grijns's classic publications appeared in *Geneeskundig tijdschrift voor Nederlandsch-Indië* (1901–1910). They appeared in English in his *Research on Vitamins 1900–1911* and *Physiology of the Nervus opticus,* his thesis, both translated and republished on the occasion of his seventieth birthday (Gorinchem, 1935). His inaugural address was *Nieuwere gezichtspunten in de voedingsleer* (Gorinchem, 1921).

II. Secondary Literature. No full biography of Grijns is available. The best, although short, is inserted in *Research on Vitamins* (see above). Some short notes, all in Dutch, are the following (listed chronologically): E. Brouwer, "Prof. Dr. G. Grijns," in *Landbouwkundig tijdschrift,* **44,** no. 531 (Mar. 1932); N. H. Swellengrebel, "Toespraak tot Prof. Grijns," in *Nederlands tijdschrift voor geneeskunde,* **85** (1941), 120–123, with Grijns's answer; B. C. P. Jansen, "In Memoriam Prof. Dr. G. Grijns," *ibid.,* **90** (1946), 240–241, with portrait; S. Postmus, "Gerrit Grijns 1865–1944," in *Voeding,* **16** (1955), 3–4; and J. F. Reith, "Christiaan Eijkman en Gerrit Grijns," *ibid.,* **32** (1971), 180–195.

Gerrit A. Lindeboom

GRIMALDI, FRANCESCO MARIA (*b.* Bologna, Italy, 2 April 1618; *d.* Bologna, 28 December 1663), *astronomy, optics.*

His father, Paride Grimaldi, a silk merchant and member of a wealthy family of noble blood, settled in Bologna in 1589. Paride's first wife died childless, and, about 1614, he married Anna Cattani (or Cattanei). Of her six sons five survived; Francesco Maria was the fourth born, the third surviving. With his father deceased and his mother in possession of her grandfather's chemist's shop, Francesco Maria and his brother Vincenzo Maria, one year older, entered the Society of Jesus on 18 March 1632. Of Francesco's first three years in the novitiate, it is known that the third was spent at Novellara. Following this he went to Parma in 1635 to begin studying philosophy. Within a year that house was closed, and he was transferred to Bologna.

In 1636 he went to Ferrara for the second year of his three-year course in philosophy, while the third year, 1637–1638, was spent in Bologna again. From 1638 to 1642 Grimaldi taught rhetoric and humanities in the College of Santa Lucia at Bologna. From 1642 to 1645 he studied theology. Further study in philosophy brought him a doctorate in 1647, and he was then appointed to teach philosophy. Within a year, however, consumption undermined his health, making it necessary for him to transfer to a less time-consuming task, the teaching of mathematics. According to Riccioli, Grimaldi was well prepared to teach all branches of mathematics—geometry, optics, gnomonics, statics, geography, astronomy, and celestial mechanics. By 1651 he had determined to take the full vows for priesthood and did so on 1 May.

During the 1640's and especially in the 1650's Grimaldi was very active in astronomical and related studies. From 1655 to the end of his life his scientific efforts were devoted essentially to the preparation of *De lumine.* His death came shortly after finishing this work, at the end of an eight-day illness characterized by high fever and headaches.

The astronomical work of Grimaldi was closely tied to the career and interests of Giovanni Battista Riccioli (1592–1671), a Jesuit since 1614, who taught theology for a long time before gaining permission to pursue his love of astronomy. Riccioli was prefect of studies at Bologna and had been dispensed from all teaching in order to prepare his *Almagestum novum* when Grimaldi came under his influence. In 1640 Grimaldi conducted experiments on free fall for Riccioli, dropping weights from the Asinelli tower and using a pendulum as timer. He found that the square of the time is proportional to the distance of free fall from rest. Riccioli credited him as being absolutely essential to the completion, in 1651, of *Almagestum novum,* remarking especially on Grimaldi's ability to devise, build, and operate new observational instruments. Grimaldi's contributions included such measurements as the heights of lunar mountains and the height of clouds. He is responsible for the practice of naming lunar regions after astronomers and physicists.

An especially noteworthy contribution was his selenograph of the moon, a composite from telescopic observations of many phases, accurate and correct enough so that he must have used crossed hairs and a micrometer with his eyepiece. The use of a micrometer eyepiece seems also to have been made in the triangulation and leveling procedures carried out to establish the meridian line for Bologna. In this project, completed by 1655, Riccioli and Grimaldi collaborated with Montalbini and G. D. Cassini. The results were reported in Riccioli's *Geographiae et Hydrographiae Reformatae* (1661). Grimaldi appears to have been responsible for much of the tabular material in the second volume of Riccioli's *Astronomia Reformata* (1665), especially on the fixed stars.

Grimaldi's primary contribution to positive science was the discovery of optical diffraction. A comprehensive treatise on light, the complete descriptive title is *A physicomathematical thesis on light, colors, the rainbow and other related topics in two books, the first of which adduces new experiments and reasons deduced from them in favor of the substantiality of light. In the second, however, the arguments adduced in the first book are refuted and the Peripatetic teaching of the accidentality of light is upheld as probable.* The title page also states that he deals with "the previously unknown diffusion of light; the manner and causes of reflection, refraction, and diffraction; vision and the intentional species of visibles and audibles; the substantial effluvium of the magnet, which pervades all bodies; and in a special argument the atomists are attacked." A final descriptive element appears on the subtitle page preceding book II, where he notes that, in any case, "permanent colors are nothing other than light." If we take Grimaldi at his word, he is presenting two possible basic theses about the nature of light. It may be substance, or it may be accident, i.e., a quality of some other substance. His personal choice appears in his preface to the work, where he says he would be delighted by a student who would be persuaded that the experiments supporting the substantiality of light have no force and who could confirm better than he "the doctrine which we personally embrace and finally sustain in the present opuscule." At various places in book I he prescinds from a substantial theory of light in arguing a proposition, e.g., prop. 10, which deals with the nature of the propagation of light. His position in book I is thus not always in support of the substantial theory of light. As a philosopher he stands against the certainty of either hypothesis, each called an "opinion," on the nature of light. He says ultimately that the many experiments of book I, albeit persuasive, "do not in any way lead to the substantiality of light" (II, 2).

Grimaldi's position on the substance-accident question is better understood by a look at the whole book and what it deals with. Book I (sixty propositions, 472 pages) devotes the first twenty-seven propositions (229 pages) essentially to the four modes of light, the porous nature of bodies, and the propagation of light. Thereafter book I deals with colors and the rainbow (props. 28–60, 244 pages). The substance-accident question is not much debated after prop. 27, nor is it made a necessary basis for the treatment of colors and the rainbow. While books I and II present opposing views on the substantial nature of light, they agree on other major points. In both books Grimaldi opposes any corpuscular theory of light. In both books he is concerned to show color to be nothing more than a modification of light. Color is not the addition of something else to light. Both books agree on the fluid nature of light phenomena. Light may be a fluid substance or the accidents of some other fluid substance(s). Grimaldi expressly chooses the latter version of a fluid theory.

The discussion of diffraction (book I, prop. 1, pp. 1–11) is the basis for introducing a fluid, but not necessarily substantial, view of light. The experiments on diffraction are clear and well described by Grimaldi. He used bright sunlight introduced into a completely darkened room via a hole about 1/60 inch across. The cone of light thus produced was projected to a white screen at an angle so as to form an elliptical image of the sun on the screen. At a distance of ten to twenty feet from the slit he inserted a narrow opaque rod into the cone of light to cast a shadow on the screen. The border of this shadow, he noted, is not clear, and the size of the shadow is far beyond what rectilinear projection would predict. Having demonstrated this, he proceeded to his description of external diffraction bands. These bands are never more than three, and they increase in intensity and in width nearer to the shadow. The series of bands nearest the shadow has a wide central band of white with a narrow violet band nearer the shadow and a narrow red band away from the shadow. Grimaldi warned that the red and violet bands must be observed closely to avoid mistaking the series for alternating bands of light and dark. After describing these parallel bands, he turned to examine the effect of varying the shape of the opaque object. In place of the rod he used a step-shaped object to cast a shadow with two rectangular corners. Still describing external bands, he carefully described the curvature of the bands around the outer corner and continuing to follow the shadow border. When the series approaches the inner corner of the step-shaped shadow, it intersects perpendicularly another series approaching parallel to the other side of this corner. He noted that as they cross each other the colors "are either augmented intensively or are mixed." Nothing more about the appearance of these intersecting bands is found in the description.

In the diffraction experiments he now turned to a description of internal fringes. Here he omitted naming the colors or their order. His diagram shows two pairs of twin contiguous tracks following the border of an L-shaped shadow. These bands are said to appear only in pairs, while the number increases with the width of the obstacle and its distance from the screen. The bands bend around in a semicircle at the end of the L, remaining continuous. At the corner of the L he made a further observation. Here not only do the bands curve around to follow the shadow outline, but a shorter and brighter series of colors appears. He showed these as five feather-shaped fringes radiating from the inside corner of the L and perpendicularly crossing the previously described internal paired tracks of light. The nature of this phenomenon seems to have impressed him as being like the wash of a moving ship.

The final diffraction experiment allowed a cone of light to pass first through two parallel orifices, the first being 1/60 inch and the second being 1/10 inch in diameter. The distances between the holes and between the screen and second hole are equal, at least twelve feet each. The screen is parallel to the orifices. The screen holds a circle of direct illumination just over 1/5 inch across. The circle is significantly wider than rectilinear propagation allows and the border is colored red in part, blue in part. Neither the width nor order of these colors is given.

These diffraction experiments showed Grimaldi that a new mode of transmission of light had been discovered and that this mode contradicts the notion of an exclusively rectilinear passage of light. Diffraction thus gave prima facie evidence for a fluid nature of light. The name "diffraction" comes from the loss of uniformity observed in the flow of a stream of water as it "splits apart" around a slender obstacle placed in its path. He discussed other fluid phenomena analogously with light. To explain color and the varieties of color he decided that a "change in agitation" of the luminous flow is responsible. A light ray is conceived like a column of fluid in vibration, but not regular vibration. Lighter colors are said to result from a greater density of rays and darker colors from a lower density.

In performing his diffraction experiments, Grimaldi gives measurements only where they will show the nonrectilinear propagation of light. No quantities are given for the sizes or distances of the colored fringes in any of his experiments. No notion of periodicity occurred to him.

Knowledge of his work appears in the work of both Hooke and Newton. Hooke performed his first series of diffraction experiments later in 1672, after the notice of Grimaldi's book in the *Philosophical Transactions.* Hooke referred to it, however, as inflexion and may have encountered diffraction phenomena independently. Newton was aware of Grimaldi's work, but only at secondhand, crediting Honoré Fabri as the source of his knowledge on diffraction. At first (1675) Newton described and attempted to account for only the internal fringes. His description shows that he could not have performed the experiment. By 1686 he came to deny the existence of internal fringes on the basis of experiments. In the *Opticks* he described and tried to explain only the external fringes, which he never ceased to regard as a sort of refraction. The essence of Newton's contribution to the knowledge of diffraction is his set of careful measurements, which made clear the periodic nature of the phenomenon.

BIBLIOGRAPHY

I. ORIGINAL WORKS. The sole work published under Grimaldi's name or written by him is the posthumous *Physico-mathesis de lumine, coloribus, et iride, aliisque adnexis libri duo, in quorum primo asseruntur nova experimenta, & rationes ab iis deductae pro substantialitate luminis. In secundo autem dissolvuntur argumenta in primo adducta, et probabiliter sustineri posse docetur sententia peripatetica de accidentalitate luminis. Qua occasione de hactenus incognita luminis diffusione, de reflexionis, refractionis, ac diffractionis modo et causis, de visione, deque speciebus intentionalibus visibilium et audibilium, ac de substantiali magnetis efluvio omnia corpora pervadente, non pauca scitu digna proferuntur, et speciale etiam argumento impugnantur atomistae* (Bologna, 1665).

II. SECONDARY LITERATURE. The sources for Grimaldi's life and personality are minimal. A brief elogium by Giovanni Battista Riccioli is appended to the printed text of Grimaldi's book. Riccioli is also responsible for detailed information on Grimaldi's family in an "Epitome genealogiae Grimaldae gentis," in *Almagestum novum, astronomiani veterum novumque,* I, pt. 2 (Bologna, 1651). A useful biography appears in Angelo Fabrioni, *Vitae Italorum,* III (Pisa, 1779), 373–381.

Other sources with significant amounts of information are the brief (none as long as thirty pages) publications of Roberto Savelli, *Grimaldi e la rifrazione* (Bologna, 1951) and *Nel terzo centenario del "De lumine" di F. M. Grimaldi* (Ferrara, 1966); and esp. of Giorgio Tabarroni, *P. F. M. Grimaldi, bolognese iniziatore della ottica-fisica* (Bologna, 1964) and *Nel terzo centenario della morte de F. M. Grimaldi* (Bologna, 1964).

The best account of his astronomical work is the *Almagestum novum,* which indicates some forty items of which Grimaldi was the source. Jiří Marek, "Les notions de la théorie ondulatoire de la lumière chez Grimaldi et Huyghens," in *Acta historiae rerum naturalium necnon technicarum,* **1** (1965), 131–147, is too eager to attribute ideas to Grimaldi that are not his. The review of *De lumine* cited in the text is *Philosophical Transactions of the Royal Society of London,* **6,** no. 79 (22 Jan. 1672), 3068–3070.

By far the most useful discussion to date of Grimaldi

and his work is Francis A. McGrath, "Grimaldi's Fluid Theory of Light," M.Sc. diss. (University College, London, 1969).

For the importance of Grimaldi's work to Newton, see Roger H. Stuewer, "A Critical Analysis of Newton's Work on Diffraction," in *Isis,* **61** (1970), 188–205.

BRUCE S. EASTWOOD

GRINNELL, JOSEPH (*b.* Indian agency forty miles from Fort Sill [now Oklahoma], 27 February 1877; *d.* Berkeley, California, 29 May 1939), *zoology.*

Grinnell's Quaker father, Fordyce Grinnell, was a physician in the Indian service. He tried private practice in Tennessee but returned to the service in 1880 and went to Dakota Territory, where Joseph found welcome friends among the Indian children. Joseph's mother, Sarah Pratt Grinnell, also a Quaker, was, like her husband, descended from early New England stock. The family moved to Pasadena, California, in 1885, to Pennsylvania in 1888, and returned to Pasadena in 1891. Joseph attended Pasadena High School and earned his B.A. in 1897 at Throop Polytechnic Institute (now California Institute of Technology), spending all his free time making a collection of local birds.

In 1896 he seized an opportunity to spend the summer in Alaska, where he collected birds avidly, and he returned there in 1898 with a group of goldseekers for eighteen months, during which time his success with birds was much greater than was the group's with gold. Grinnell began graduate work at Stanford University, but his studies were interrupted by typhoid fever. After his recovery (M.A., 1901) he taught at Throop Polytechnic from 1903 to 1908, first as instructor and then as professor.

A chance acquaintance with Annie M. Alexander, a generous benefactress of the new Museum of Vertebrate Zoology at the University of California, led the way for Grinnell to become director of the museum in 1908, a position he held until his death. Under his direction, the museum expanded from its original small building to become a large wing of the zoology building at Berkeley. After receiving his Ph.D. (Stanford, 1913), Grinnell also served at Berkeley, advancing from assistant to full professor of zoology.

Grinnell entered zoology at an exciting time, along with an enthusiastic circle at Stanford and vicinity which included, among others, Walter K. Fisher; Edmund Heller; Robert Evans Snodgrass; Grinnell's professor, Charles H. Gilbert; and the university's president, David Starr Jordan. The initial phase of exploration and classification in zoology had largely been completed and the role of the environment was coming under intense study.

Having informally agreed not to enter Stanford's preempted field of fishes, the Museum of Vertebrate Zoology elected to collect the terrestrial vertebrates of California and adjacent regions. Grinnell worked almost entirely within that ecologically diverse state, comparing animal species that were separated by natural barriers or that varied because of diversity of altitude or climate. He led a seven-year survey of the fauna of a cross section of the Sierra Nevada and another of the Mount Lassen area. He recognized from field studies that no two species can occupy the same ecologic niche and remain separate species, a concept usually attributed to G. F. Gause from later experimental studies.

A painstaking observer, a voluminous notetaker, and a precise writer, Grinnell contributed extensively to the knowledge of distribution and ecology of Californian vertebrates. With dismay he observed the deleterious effects of the state's growing population on the natural environment and became an active conservationist. A tree-surrounded meadow in the Northern California Coast Range Reserve, where he and his wife often camped, is dedicated to their memory.

BIBLIOGRAPHY

I. ORIGINAL WORKS. Grinnell's bibliography, listed in the memorial by his wife cited below, contains more than 550 titles. Among his most significant regional studies are "An Account of the Mammals and Birds of the Lower Colorado Valley With Especial Reference to the Distributional Problems Presented," in *University of California Publications in Zoology,* **12** (1914), 51–294; the valuable *Animal Life in the Yosemite: An Account of the Mammals, Birds, Reptiles, and Amphibians in a Cross Section of the Sierra Nevada* (Berkeley, 1924), written with Tracy I. Storer; and *Vertebrate Animals of Point Lobos Reserve, 1934–35,* Carnegie Institution Publication no. 481 (Washington, D. C., 1936).

Two definitive lists of special value are *Fur-Bearing Mammals of California: Their Natural History, Systematic Status, and Relations to Man,* 2 vols. (Berkeley, 1937), written with J. S. Dixon and J. M. Linsdale; and *Game Birds of California* (Berkeley, 1918), written with H. C. Bryant and T. I. Storer. Grinnell devoted his Sundays to compiling a bibliography on California birds, "Bibliography of California Ornithology," in 3 pts. in *Pacific Coast Avifauna,* no. 5 (15 May 1909); no. 16 (15 Sept. 1924); no. 26 (8 Dec. 1939).

II. SECONDARY LITERATURE. The memorial by his wife, Hilda Wood Grinnell, "Joseph Grinnell: 1877–1939," in *Condor,* **42,** no. 1 (1940), 3–34, is a remarkably straightforward detailed account of Grinnell's life. His Stanford days were touched on in Walter K. Fisher, "When

Joseph Grinnell and I Were Young," *ibid.,* pp. 35-38. His characteristics and impact on students were presented in Alden H. Miller, "Joseph Grinnell," in *Systematic Zoology,* **13,** no. 4 (1964), 235-242.

ELIZABETH NOBLE SHOR

GRISEBACH, AUGUST HEINRICH RUDOLF (*b.* Hannover, Germany, 17 April 1814; *d.* Göttingen, Germany, 9 May 1879), *botany, taxonomy.*

Grisebach was the son of the auditor general Rudolph Grisebach and Louise Meyer, his second wife. His uncle Georg Friedrich Wilhelm Meyer was a well-known botanist and the first to instruct the young Grisebach in botany. As a boy Grisebach began to collect plants and acquired a good knowledge of the native flora. He studied medicine and natural history at Göttingen (1832-1834) and at Berlin (1834-1836) and was *Privatdozent* at Berlin and, from 1837, at Göttingen. In 1839-1840 he traveled through the Balkan peninsula and northwestern Asia Minor. This most important journey of his life led him through regions that were for the greater part botanically unexplored. The two books he published about this journey established his reputation as a botanical taxonomist and phytogeographer. While a student he had explored the western Alps (1833), and later he traveled to Norway (1842), southern France and the Pyrenees (1850), and the Carpathian Mountains (1852). In 1841 he became associate professor, and in 1847 full professor, at the University of Göttingen. He declined various offers of professorships elsewhere.

His scientific career is marked by the close connection of traditional taxonomic investigations and phytogeographic studies. In taxonomy and floristic botany he began his work with a monograph on the genus *Gentiana.* He specialized in Malpighiaceae, Gramineae, and the genus *Hieracium,* and studied the flora of southeastern Europe, Central America and Argentina. His works on the flora of these regions are still well known and used, although of course outdated in detail. *Flora of the British West Indian Islands* has recently been reprinted, and there is a detailed commentary by Stearn.

Grisebach was far ahead of his time in proposing a work, "Flora Europaea," of which only a fragment appeared after his death. Grisebach was not one of the great taxonomists of the time. He was perhaps not primarily interested in the problems of systematics but rather in floristic botany as one of the cornerstones of the great structure of synthetic phytogeography that he envisioned.

In phytogeography, for which he coined the modern term "geobotany" (*Geobotanik*) in 1866, Grisebach was especially influenced by the ideas of Alexander von Humboldt about the effect of climate on the composition of flora, particularly on the so-called physiognomic plant types. Grisebach's main work, *Die Vegetation der Erde nach ihrer klimatischen Anordnung* (1872), drew on his floristic studies, various travels in Europe, his great herbarium, and an intensive study of the contemporary literature. The extent of his reading is apparent in his *Berichte über die Leistungen in der Pflanzengeographie* (1841-1853 and 1868-1876) forerunners of modern "progress reports." His herbarium was of use in such tasks as the calculation of the numbers of endemic species in different parts of the Mediterranean. In the *Vegetation der Erde* Grisebach gave a lively picture of the earth's plants emphasizing the effect of climate on the composition and distribution of the flora. It has been noted that he had an amazing ability to describe the vegetation of countries that he himself had never seen. Grisebach extended the system of physiognomic plant types (*Vegetationsformen*) founded by Humboldt to comprise fifty-four forms, an idea revived and refined in recent times. The limitations of his work are to be found in his relative disregard of historical factors and the imperfect knowledge of the physiological foundations of ecology of his time. Nevertheless, this book has been of great importance as one of the first comprehensive reviews of knowledge of the earth's vegetation.

BIBLIOGRAPHY

I. ORIGINAL WORKS. A complete bibliography of Grisebach's writings compiled by his son Eduard appeared in Grisebach's posthumous *Gesammelte Abhandlungen und kleinere Schriften zur Pflanzengeographie* (Leipzig, 1880) and was reprinted by Stearn, in *Journal of the Arnold Arboretum, Harvard University,* **46** (1965), 250. A short bibliography can be found in the necrology by Reinke (see below).

His most important works are *Genera et species Gentianearum* (Stuttgart-Tübingen, 1838); *Reise durch Rumelien und nach Brussa im Jahre 1839,* 2 vols. (Göttingen, 1841); *Spicilegium florae Rumelicae et Bithynicae,* 2 vols. (Brunswick, 1843-1844); *Flora of the British West Indian Islands* (London, 1859-1864; repr. 1963); *Catalogus plantarum Cubensium* (Leipzig, 1866); *Die Vegetation der Erde nach ihrer klimatischen Anordnung,* 2 vols. (Leipzig, 1872; 2nd ed., 1884-1885); *Plantae Lorentzianae* (Göttingen, 1874); and *Symbolae ad Floram argentinam* (Göttingen, 1879).

II. SECONDARY LITERATURE. The most detailed biographical notes have been published by J. Reinke in *Botanische Zeitung,* **37** (1879), 521-534. This is supplemented (especially as concerns his family) by E. Grisebach,

Geschichte der Familie Grisebach (Hamburg, 1936). The article by O. Drude, in *A. Petermanns Mitteilungen aus J. Perthes Geographischer Anstalt,* **25** (1879), 269–271, emphasizes the importance of his works for phytogeography. There are short biographies by E. Wunschmann, in *Allgemeine deutsche Biographie,* XLIX (Leipzig, 1904), and by H. Dolezal, in *Neue deutsche Biographie,* VII (Berlin, 1966), with an extensive bibliography of secondary literature.

GERHARD WAGENITZ

GRISOGONO, FEDERICO, also known as **Federicus De Chrysogonis** (*b.* Zadar, Dalmatia, Yugoslavia, 1472; *d.* Zadar, 2 January 1538), *cosmography, astrology.*

Grisogono, the son of Antonio de Grisogono and Catarina Giorgi, belonged to one of the most illustrious families of the town of Zadar (Zara). After military adventures in Italy and in France, he studied philosophy and medicine at Padua. He received a doctorate from the University of Padua (1506 or 1507) and then taught astrology and mathematics there. But the career of professor was hardly suitable for this rich aristocrat, and in 1508 he returned to Zadar. He spent the remainder of his life in his native city, administering his property, holding municipal offices, practicing medicine, and making astronomical observations. In 1512 he visited Venice and was prosecuted for his politico-astrological predictions.

In his medical publications Grisogono appears as an aggressive advocate of astrology. His chief contribution to science concerns the theory of the tides. He supposed that the tides result from the combined action of the sun and the moon and that each of these celestial bodies exerts an attraction on the waters lying not only below its zenith position but also, at the same time and with the same intensity, below its nadir. This hypothesis allowed Grisogono to construct a mathematical model which predicted high tide quite accurately, particularly its second appearance during the day.

BIBLIOGRAPHY

I. ORIGINAL WORKS. Only two books by Grisogono are known: *Speculum astronomicum terminans intellectum humanum in omni scientia* (Venice, 1507); and *De modo collegiandi, pronosticandi et curandi febres, nec non de humana felicitate ac denique de fluxu et refluxu maris* (Venice, 1528). The chapter on the tides from the latter was republished in J. P. Galluci, *Theatrum mundi et temporis* (Venice, 1588).

II. SECONDARY LITERATURE. Grisogono's life and medical work are described in M. D. Grmek, "Prinosi za poznavanje života i rada F. Grisogona," in *Radovi instituta Jugoslavenske akademije u Zadru,* **15** (1968), 61–91. An analysis of his hypothesis on the tides is given in Ž. Dadić, "Tumačenja pojave plime i oseke mora u djelima autora s područja Hrvatske," in *Rasprave i gradja za povijest nauka,* **2** (1966), 87–143. Remarks on Grisogono's astrological work can be found in L. Thorndike, *History of Magic and Experimental Science,* V (New York, 1941), 314; and in K. Sudhoff, *Iatromathematiker* (Breslau, 1902), pp. 47–48.

M. D. GRMEK

GRODDECK, ALBRECHT VON (*b.* Danzig, Germany [now Gdansk, Poland], 25 August 1837; *d.* Clausthal, Germany, 18 July 1887), *geology, mineralogy.*

An uncle was a well-known Prussian mine superintendent and through him Albrecht must have come in contact with the mining and metallurgical industry. Groddeck attended the Gymnasium in Danzig until 1856. In 1857 he decided to study metallurgy; but he first worked in the mining industry until 1860. Then he went to the universities of Berlin and Breslau for theoretical training. During vacations he visited the mines of Silesia, and subsequently also those of Mansfeld and the Oberharz, most of which are stratabound deposits. This fact may have left a lasting influence on his patterns of thought in ore genesis. Subsequently he spent two semesters at the mining school at Clausthal. Among his professors, F. D. A. Roemer had the strongest influence on him.

Groddeck worked for a short time as a chemist for mining companies, and in 1864 he was employed as an instructor in mining and ore dressing at Clausthal. In 1867 Roemer retired and Groddeck added mineralogy, geognosy, and paleontology to his teaching schedule and simultaneously became acting director of the school.

During the same year he had presented a doctoral thesis to the philosophy faculty of the University of Göttingen, published the year before under the title "Ueber die Erzgänge des nordwestlichen Oberharzes" (*Zeitschrift der Deutschen geologischen Gesellschaft,* **18** [1866], 693–776). On 1 January 1871 he moved up to the post of director of the School of Mines and on 16 June 1872 he obtained the title *königlicher Bergrath.* In 1880 he passed the technical subjects on to a younger professor, but he soon took over a course in ore geology, a subject he had introduced into the curriculum.

It is obvious that Groddeck's teaching and administrative responsibilities were extremely heavy. This may explain why he was not a prolific writer. Nevertheless, he cooperated in the detailed mapping of the Harz Mountains. He mainly concentrated on two research topics: Roemer had contributed to the paleontological knowledge of the Harz region and other areas; Groddeck continued this work by investigating the lithologic sequences, primarily in the Harz Mountains, as reflected in his booklet *Abriss der Geognosie des Harzes* (1871–1883). His second topic, which historically is probably much more significant and original, was the link between lithology and ore geology. Here he made a major step in a direction that was almost entirely lost for 80 years and which has been rediscovered only recently. It was an observational classification of ore deposits, taking into account the facts of congruence between the host rock and the deposits. In his textbook on economic ore deposits, he came very close to stating that conformable or congruent deposits were contemporaneous, and noncongruent deposits epigenetic. This idea is reflected in his book in the following classification of mineral deposits (p. 84):

I. Bedrock deposits (formed in situ)

Formed with country rock:

- A. Layered deposits
  - 1. massive ore strata
  - 2. coprecipitation ore strata (of disseminated ore matter)
  - 3. lenticular ore layers (or strings)
- B. Massive (nonlayered) deposits

Formed later than enclosing rock:

- C. Cavity fillings
  - 1. fissure fillings or dikes
    - a. dikes in massive rocks
    - b. dikes in layered rocks
  - 2. fillings of caves
- D. Metamorphic mineral deposits

II. Weathering deposits (detrital deposits)

Groddeck's fifty-seven types of ore deposits were classified first according to geometric criteria (layered, vein type, and so on) and second according to composition. In this morphologic trend he was closest of all his contemporaries to the general trend of objectivation, that is, of an introduction of observational as against interpretative criteria in scientific classifications. In botany, zoology, and crystallography, this observational pattern had been followed since the first half of the eighteenth century, whereas in geology, especially in ore geology, old mythologic theories of magic ore sources were still fashionable, and because of Pošepný, had again become accepted dogma in 1890. Consequently, Groddeck was clearly a forerunner of the modern approach, especially the modern French morphological school of thought.

Because of his teaching and administrative duties, his early death, and probably also his less active links with foreign researchers, Groddeck was not very influential in his field, and apparently not nearly as well known in Anglo-Saxon countries as Pošepný, who traveled in North America and whose book on ore deposits was translated into English as early as 1895. Pošepný, and in part also von Cotta, were strong proponents of an almost pan-epigenetic theory of ore genesis, whereas Groddeck showed an independent new approach, linking observations in the country rock with his genetic interpretations. For this independent observation and interpretation of ore features he was rediscovered after 1958; an English translation of his 1879 book on ore deposits is presently being prepared.

His keen scientific mind also led him to propose other new genetic solutions to old problems, thus far explained by complicated hypotheses based more on ideas (projections of ideas) than on observations. For example, he showed with both observation and a sound logic of relations, that the tectonic structure of the Oberharz diabase consists of a simple, compressed saddle-shaped fold. He also proved that the adinole schist of the Oberharz is a normal bed concordant with the siliceous Culm schist, again demonstrating that he was ahead of his time in regard to genetic understanding. He also pioneered observations and interpretations of wall rock alterations. Groddeck's work therefore deserves a more important place in the history of geology than it has up to now been accorded.

BIBLIOGRAPHY

I. Original Works. A bibliography of Groddeck's works is in Poggendorff, III, 551–552; IV, 537. His major publications are *Abriss der Geognosie des Harzes,* 2 vols. (1871–1883); and his textbook, *Die Lehre von den Lagerstätten der Erze* (Leipzig, 1879).

II. Secondary Literature. See A. K. Lossen, "Albrecht von Groddeck," in *Jahrbuch der Preussischen geologischen Landesanstalt u. Bergakademie zu Berlin, 1887* (1888), 109–132; and "Albrecht von Groddeck," in *Neues Jahrbuch für Mineralogie, Geologie und Paläontologie,* **1** (1888), 24.

W. Fischer, *Gesteins- und Lagerstättenbildung im Wandel der wissenschaftlichen Anschauung* (Stuttgart, 1961), refers often to Groddeck's work, but does not fully appreciate the role of his work as compared to that of Cotta and Pošepny.

G. C. Amstutz

GROSSETESTE, ROBERT (*b.* Suffolk, England, *ca.* 1168; *d.* Buckden, Buckinghamshire, England, 9 October 1253), *natural philosophy, optics, calendar reform.*

Grosseteste was the central figure in England in the intellectual movement of the first half of the thirteenth century, yet the only evidence for his life before he became bishop of Lincoln in 1235 is to be found in fragmentary references by Matthew of Paris and other chroniclers, by Roger Bacon, and occasionally in charters, deeds and other records.[1] His birth has been variously dated between 1168 and 1175, but since he is described as "Magister Robertus Grosteste" (the first appearance of his name) in a charter of Hugh, bishop of Lincoln, of probably 1186–1190, the earlier date is the more likely. Tradition places his birth in Suffolk, of humble parentage. He may have been educated first at Lincoln, then at Oxford, and was in the household of William de Vere, bishop of Hereford, by 1198, when a reference by Gerald of Wales suggests that he may have had some knowledge of both law and medicine. After that it seems likely that he taught at Oxford in the arts school until the dispersion of masters and scholars during 1209–1214. He must have taken his mastership in theology, probably at Paris, during this period, some time before his appointment as chancellor of the University of Oxford, although with the title *magister scholarum,* probably about 1214–1221, when he must have lectured on theology.

Grosseteste was given a number of ecclesiastical preferments and sinecures, including the archdeaconry of Leicester in 1229; but in 1232 he resigned them all except for a prebend at Lincoln, writing to his sister, a nun: "If I am poorer by my own choice, I am made richer in virtues."[2] From 1229 or 1230 until 1235 he was first lecturer in theology to the Franciscans, who had come to Oxford in 1224. His influence there was profound and continued after he left Oxford in 1235 for the see of Lincoln, within the jurisdiction of which Oxford and its schools came. He contributed largely to directing the interests of the English Franciscans toward the study of the Bible, languages, and mathematics and natural science. Indispensable sources for this later period of his life are his own letters and those of his Franciscan friend Adam Marsh.

Grosseteste's career thus falls into two main parts, the first that of a university scholar and teacher and the second that of a bishop and ecclesiastical statesman. His writings fall roughly into the same periods: to the former belong his commentaries on Aristotle and on the Bible and the bulk of a number of independent treatises, and to the latter his translations from the Greek. Living at a time when the intellectual horizons of Latin Christendom were being greatly extended by the translations into that language of Greek and Arabic philosophical and scientific writings, he took a leading part in introducing this new learning into university teaching. His commentary on Aristotle's *Posterior Analytics* was one of the first and most influential of the medieval commentaries on this fundamental work. Other important writings belonging to the first period are his commentary on Aristotle's *Physics,* likewise one of the first; independent treatises on astronomy and cosmology, the calendar (with intelligent proposals for the reform of the inaccurate calendar then in use), sound, comets, heat, optics (including lenses and the rainbow), and other scientific subjects; and his scriptural commentaries, especially the *Moralitates in evangelica, De cessatione legalium, Hexaëmeron* and commentaries on the Pauline Epistles and the Psalms. Having begun to study Greek in 1230–1231, he used his learning fruitfully during the period of his episcopate by making Latin translations of Aristotle's *Nicomachean Ethics* and *De caelo* (with Simplicius' commentary), of the *De fide orthodoxe* of John of Damascus, of Pseudo-Dionysius and of other theological writings. For this work he brought to Lincoln assistants who knew Greek; he also arranged for a translation of the Psalms to be made from the Hebrew and seems to have learned something of this language.

Although in content a somewhat eclectic blend of Aristotelian and Neoplatonic ideas, Grosseteste's philosophical thinking shows a strong intellect curious about natural things and searching for a consistently rational scheme of things both natural and divine. His search for rational explanations was conducted within the framework of the Aristotelian distinction between "the fact" (*quia*) and "the reason for the fact" (*propter quid*). Essential for the latter in natural philosophy was mathematics, to which Grosseteste gave a role based specifically on his theory, expounded in *De luce seu de inchoatione formarum* and *De motu corporali et luce,* that the fundamental corporeal substance was light (*lux*). He held that light was the first form to be created in prime matter, propagating itself from an original point into a sphere and thus giving rise to spatial dimensions and all else according to immanent laws. Hence his conception of optics as the basis of natural science. *Lux* was the instrument by which God produced the macrocosm of the universe and also the instrument mediating the interaction between soul and body and the bodily senses in the microcosm of man.[3] Grosseteste's rational scheme included revelation as well as reason, and he was one of the first medieval thinkers to attempt to deal with the conflict between the Scriptures and the new Aristotle. Especially interesting are his discussions of the problems of the eternity or creation of the world, of the relation of will to intellect, of angelology, of divine knowledge of particulars, and of the use of allegorical interpretations of Scripture.

Grosseteste's public life as bishop of Lincoln was informed by both his outlook on the universe as a scholar and his conception of his duties as a prelate dedicated to the salvation of souls. Analogous to corporeal illumination was the divine illumination of the soul with truth. He extended the luminous analogy to illustrate the relationship between the persons of the Trinity, the operation of divine grace through free will like light shining through a colored glass,[4] and the relation of pope to prelates and of bishops to clergy: as a mirror reflects light into dark places, he said in asserting his episcopal rights against the cathedral chapter of Lincoln, so a bishop reflects power to the clergy.[5]

In practice Grosseteste was governed by three principles: a belief in the supreme importance of the cure of souls; a highly centralized and hierarchical conception of the church, in which the papacy, under God, was the center and source of spiritual life and energy; and a belief in the superiority of the church over the state because its function, the salvation of souls, was more vital. Such views were widely accepted, but Grosseteste was unique in the ruthlessness and thoroughness with which he applied them, for example, in opposing the widespread use of ecclesiastical benefices to endow officials in the service of the crown or the papacy. As a bishop he had attended the First Council of Lyons in 1245, and in a memorandum presented to the pope there in 1250 he expounded his views on the unsuitability of such appointments while accepting the papal right to dispose of all benefices. Likewise, his opposition to the obstruction of the disciplinary work of the church by any ecclesiastical corporation or secular authority brought him into conflict both with his own Lincoln chapter and with the crown over royal writs of prohibition when secular law clashed with church law and when churchmen were employed as judges or in other secular offices. Grosseteste was a close friend of Simon de Montfort and took charge of the education of his sons, but the degree to which he shared in or influenced Montfort's political ideals has probably been exaggerated. Above all he was a bishop with an ideal, an outstanding example of the new type of ecclesiastic trained in the universities.

Scientific Thought. Some of Grosseteste's scientific writings can be dated with reasonable certainty, and most of the others can be related to these in an order based on internal references and on the assumption that the more elaborated version of a common topic is the later.[6] From the evidence for his method of making notes on his reading and thoughts to be worked up into finished essays and commentaries,[7] and from these writings themselves, it may be assumed that many of them arose out of his teaching in the schools. Gerald of Wales's description of Grosseteste at Hereford as a young clerk with a manifold learning "built upon the sure foundation of the liberal arts and an abundant knowledge of literature"[8] is borne out by what is probably his earliest work, *De artibus liberalibus.* In this attractive introduction he described how the seven liberal arts at once acted as a *purgatio erroris* and gave direction to the gaze and inclination of the mind (*mentis aspectus et affectus*). Of particular interest is his treatment of music, of which his love became proverbial, and of astronomy. As for Boethius, music for him comprised the proportion and harmony not only of sounds produced by the human voice and by instruments but also of the movements and times of the celestial bodies and of the composition of bodies made of the four terrestrial elements—hence the power of music to mold human conduct and restore health by restoring the harmony between soul and body and between the bodily elements, and the related power of astronomy through its indication of the appropriate times for such operations and for the transmutation of metals. Related to this essay was his phonetical treatise *De generatione sonorum,* which he introduced with an account of sound as a vibratory motion propagated from the sounding body through the air to the ear, from the motion of which arose a sensation in the soul.

Grosseteste developed his mature natural philosophy through a logic of science based on Aristotle and through his fundamental theory of light. In their present form most of the works concerned were almost certainly written between about 1220 and 1235. *De luce* and *De motu corporali et luce,* with his cosmogony and cosmology of light, seem to date from early in this period. The structure of the universe generated by the original point of *lux* was determined, first, by the supposition that there was a constant proportion between the diffusion or "multiplication" of *lux,* corresponding to the infinite series of natural numbers, and the quantity of matter given cubic dimensions, corresponding to some finite part of that series. Second, the intensity of this activity of *lux* varied directly with distance from the primordial source. The result was a sphere denser and more opaque toward the center. Then from the outermost boundary of the sphere *lumen* emanated inward to produce another sphere inside it, then another, and so on, until all the celestial and elementary spheres of Aristotelian cosmology were complete. Another seemingly early work in this series, *De generatione stellarum,* shows Grosseteste dependent on Aristotle in many things but not in all, for he argued that the stars were composed of the four terrestrial elements. Later, in his commentary on the *Physics,* he contrasted the imprecise and arbitrary way man must measure spaces and times with God's absolute measures through aggregates of infinites.

In all these writings Grosseteste made it clear that by *lux* and *lumen* he meant not simply the visible light which was one of its manifestations, but a fundamental power (*virtus, species*) varying in its manifestation according to the source from which it was propagated or multiplied and in its effect according to its recipient. Thus he showed in *De impressionibus elementorum* how solar radiation effected the transformation of one of the four terrestrial elements into another and later, in *De natura locorum,* how it caused differences in climate. An explanation of the tides begun in *De accessione et recessione maris* or *De fluxu et refluxu maris* (if this work is by him)[9] was completed in *De natura locorum,* in which he argued that the rays of the rising moon released vapors from the depth of the sea which pushed up the tide until the moon's strength increased so much that it drew the vapors through the water, at which time the tide fell again. The second, smaller monthly tide was caused by the weaker lunar rays reflected back to the opposite side of the earth from the stellar sphere.

In *De cometis et causis ipsarum* Grosseteste gave a good example of his method of falsification in arguing that comets were "sublimated fire" separated from their terrestrial nature by celestial power descending from the stars or planets and drawing up the "fire" as a magnet drew iron. Later, in *De calore solis* (*ca.* 1230–1235), he produced perhaps his most elegant exercise in analysis by reduction to conclusions falsified either by observation or by disagreement with accepted theory, finally leaving a verified explanation. He concluded that all hot bodies generated heat by the scattering of their matter and that the sun generated heat on the earth in direct proportion to the amount of matter incorporated from the transparent medium (air) into its rays.

Grosseteste set out and exemplified the formal structure of his mature scientific method in his *Commentaria in libros posteriorum Aristotelis,* his *Commentarius in viii libros physicorum Aristotelis,*[10] and four related essays giving a geometrical analysis of the natural propagation of power and light. It seems likely that he began the commentary on the *Posterior Analytics* when he was still a master of arts, that is, before 1209, and completed it over a long period, finishing after 1220 and probably nearer the end of the decade. The commentary on the *Physics* was written later, likewise certainly over a period of years, probably around 1230. It has striking parallels with some of the scientific topics of the *Hexaëmeron* but shows less than even the limited knowledge of Greek found in this work, suggesting that it just precedes it.

For Grosseteste, as for Aristotle, a scientific inquiry began with an experienced fact (*quia*), usually a composite phenomenon. The aim of the inquiry was to discover the reason for the fact (*propter quid*), the proximate cause or natural agent from which the phenomenon could be demonstrated:

> Every thing that is to be produced is already described and formed in some way in the agent, whence nature as an agent has the natural things that are to be produced in some way described and formed within itself, so that this description and form itself, in the very nature of things to be produced before they are produced, is called knowledge of nature.[11]

His method of discovering the causal agent was to make first a *resolutio,* or analysis of the complex phenomenon into its principles, and then a *compositio,* or reconstruction and deduction of the phenomenon from hypotheses derived from the discovered principles. He verified or falsified these hypotheses by observation or by theory already verified by observation.

Besides this double method, Grosseteste used in the analysis of the causal agent as the starting-point of demonstration another Aristotelian procedure, that of the subordination of some sciences to others, for example, of astronomy and optics to geometry and of music to arithmetic, in the sense that "the superior science provides the *propter quid* for that thing of which the inferior science provides the *quia.*"[12] But mathematics provided only the formal cause; the material and efficient causes were provided by the physical sciences. Thus "the cause of the equality of the two angles made on a mirror by the incident ray and the reflected ray is not a middle term taken from geometry, but is the nature of the radiation generating itself in a straight path . . . ."[13] The echo belonged formally to the same genus as the reflection of light, but the material and efficient causes of the propagation of sound had to be sought in its fundamental substance: "the substance of sound is *lux* incorporated in the most subtle air . . . ."[14] This introduced a fundamental addition to the very similar discussion of the propagation of sound in *De artibus liberalibus* and *De generatione sonorum.*

Grosseteste developed his geometrical analysis of the powers propagated from natural agents in the four related essays written most probably in the period 1231–1235. He said in the first, *De lineis, angulis et figuris seu de fractionibus et reflexionibus radiorum:* "All causes of natural effects have to be expressed by means of lines, angles and figures, for otherwise it would be impossible to have knowledge *propter quid* concerning them."[15] The same power produced a physical effect in an inanimate body and a sensation in an animate one. He established rules for the operation of powers: for example, the power was greater the shorter and straighter the line, the smaller the incident angle, the shorter the three-dimensional pyramid or cone; every agent multiplied its power spherically. Grosseteste discussed the laws of reflection and refraction (evidently taken from Ptolemy) and their causes, and went on in *De natura locorum* to use Ptolemy's rules and construction with plane surfaces to explain refraction by a spherical burning glass. "Hence," he resumed, "these rules and principles and fundamentals having been given by the power of geometry, the careful observer of natural things can give the causes of all natural effects by this method." This was clear "first in natural action upon matter and later upon the senses . . . ."[16]

An example of the analysis of a power's producing sensation is provided by Grosseteste's *De colore.* The *resolutio* identified the constituent principles: color was light incorporated by a transparent medium; transparent mediums varied in degree of purity from earthy matter; light varied in brightness and in the multitude of its rays. In the *compositio* he asserted that the sixteen colors ranging from white (bright light, multitudinous rays, in a pure medium) to black were produced by the "intension and remission" of these three variable principles. "That the essence of color and a multitude of the same behaves in the said way," he concluded, "is manifest not only by reason but also by experiment, to those who know the principles of natural science and of optics deeply and inwardly. . . . They can show every kind of color they wish to visibly, by art [*per artificium*]."[17]

The last of these four essays, *De iride seu de iride et speculo,* is the most complete example of Grosseteste's method and his most important contribution to optics. The *resolutio* proceeds through a summary of the principle of subordination and its relation to demonstration *propter quid* into a discussion of the division of optics into the science of direct visual rays, of reflected rays, and of refracted rays, in order to decide to which part the study of the rainbow belonged. It was subordinate to the third part, "untouched and unknown among us until the present time";[18] and it is his treatment of refraction that has the greatest interest.

> This part of optics [*perspectiva*], when well understood, shows us how we may make things a very long distance off appear to be placed very close, and large near things appear very small, and how we may make small things placed at a distance appear as large as we want, so that it is possible for us to read the smallest letters at an incredible distance, or to count sand, or grain, or seeds, or any sort of minute objects.[19]

The reason, as he had learned from Euclid and Ptolemy, was "that the size, position and arrangement according to which a thing is seen depends on the size of the angle through which it is seen and the position and arrangement of the rays, and that a thing is made invisible not by great distance, except by accident, but by the smallness of the angle of vision." Hence "it is perfectly clear from geometrical reasons how, by means of a transparent medium of known size and shape placed at a known distance from the eye, a thing of known distance and known size and position will appear according to place, size and position."[20]

Grosseteste followed this account of magnification and diminution by refracting mediums with an apparently original law of refraction, according to which the refracted ray, on entering a denser medium, bisected the angle between the projection of the incident ray and the perpendicular to the interface. "That the size of the angle in the refraction of a ray may be determined in this way," he concluded, "is shown us by experiments similar to those by which we discovered that the reflection of a ray upon a mirror takes place at an angle equal to the angle of incidence."[21]

It was also evident from the principle that nature always acts in the best and shortest way. Grosseteste went on to use a construction of Ptolemy's to show how to locate the refracted image, claiming again that this "is made clear to us by the same experiment and similar reasonings"[22] as those used in a similar construction for locating the reflected image. The first of these references to experimental verification, since it would have been so inaccurate, may throw doubt on all such references by Grosseteste. As was true for the majority of medieval natural philosophers, most of these references came from books or from everyday experience. Clearly his interest was directed primarily toward theory. Yet he advocated and was guided by the principle of experiment and developed its logic.

Besides these works related to optics, Grosseteste wrote important treatises on astronomical subjects. In *De sphaera,* of uncertain date between perhaps 1215 and 1230, and *De motu supercaelestium,* possibly after 1230, he expounded elements of both Aristotelian and Ptolemaic theoretical astronomy. In a later work, *De impressionibus aëris seu de prognosticatione,* dating apparently from 1249, he discussed astrological influences and, again, his mature explanation of the tides.

More original were Grosseteste's four separate treatises on the calendar: *Canon in kalendarium* and *Compotus;* correcting these, *Compotus correctorius,* probably between 1215 and 1219; and *Compotus minor,* with further corrections, in 1244. He showed that with the system long in use, according to which nineteen solar years were considered equal to 235 lunar months, in every 304 years the moon would be one day, six minutes, and forty seconds older than the calendar indicated. He pointed out in the *Compotus correctorius* (cap. 10) that by his time the moon was never full when the calendar said it should be and that this was especially obvious during an eclipse. The error in the reckoning of Easter came from the inaccuracy both of the year of 365.25 days and of the nineteen-year lunar cycle.

Grosseteste's plan for reforming the calendar was threefold. First, he said that an accurate measure must be made of the length of the solar year. He knew of three estimates of this: that of Hipparchus and Ptolemy, accepted by the Latin computists; that of al-Battānī; and that of Thābit ibn Qurra. He discussed in detail the systems of adjustments that would have to be made in each case to make the solstice and equinox occur in the calendar at the times they were observed. Al-Battānī's estimate, he said in the *Compotus correctorius* (cap. 1), "agrees best with what we find by observation on the advance of the solstice in our time." The next stage of the reform was to calculate the relationship between this and the mean lunar month. For the new-moon tables of the *Kalendarium,* Grosseteste had used a multiple nineteen-year cycle of seventy-six years. In the *Compotus correctorius* he calculated the error this involved and proposed the novel idea of using a much more accurate cycle of thirty Arab lunar years, each of twelve equal months, the whole occupying 10,631 days. This was the shortest time in which the cycle of whole lunations came back to the start. Grosseteste gave a method of combining this Arab cycle with the Christian solar calendar and of calculating true lunations. The third stage of the reform was to use these results for an accurate reckoning of Easter. In the *Compotus correctorius* (cap. 10), he said that even without an accurate measure of the length of the solar year, the spring equinox, on which the date of Easter depended, could be discovered "by observation with instruments or from verified astronomical tables."[23]

As with Grosseteste's optics, it was Roger Bacon who first took up his work on the calendar; and Albertus Magnus first made serious use of his commentary on the *Posterior Analytics,* as did John Duns Scotus of that on the *Physics.* These attentions marked the beginning of a European reputation that continued into the early printing of his writings at Venice, the collecting of his scientific manuscripts by John Dee, and interest in them by Thomas Hobbes.[24]

NOTES

1. See D. A. Callus, ed., *Robert Grosseteste.*
2. *Epistolae,* H. R. Luard, ed., p. 44.
3. E.g., *Hexaëmeron,* British Museum MS Royal 6.E.V (14 cent.), fols. 147v–150v; L. Baur, "Das Licht in der Naturphilosophie des Robert Grosseteste," in *Abhandlungen aus dem Gebiete der Philosophie und ihrer Geschichte. Eine Festgabe zum 70. Geburtstag Georg Freiherrn von Hertling* (Freiburg im Breisgau, 1913), pp. 41–55.
4. *De libero arbitrio,* caps. 8 and 10, in L. Baur, *Die philosophischen Werke des Robert Grosseteste,* pp. 179, 202.
5. *Epistolae,* pp. 360, 364, 389.
6. For the basic work on this question, see Baur, *Die philosophischen Werke;* and S. H. Thomson, *The Writings of Robert Grosseteste*—with the revisions by Callus, "The Oxford Career of Robert Grossetest," *Robert Grosseteste;* A. C. Crombie, *Robert Grosseteste and the Origins of Experimental Science* (1953, 1971); and R. C. Dales, "Robert Grosseteste's Scientific Works," *Commentarius in viii libros.*
7. From William of Alnwick, as first noticed by A. Pelzer. See Callus, "The Oxford Career of Robert Grosseteste," pp. 45–47.
8. Giraldus Cambrensis, *Opera,* J. S. Brewer, ed., I (London, 1861), 249.
9. See R. C. Dales, "The Authorship of the *Questio de fluxu et refluxu maris* Attributed to Robert Grosseteste," in *Speculum,* **37** (1962), 582–588.
10. See the ed. by Dales. Grosseteste wrote probably about 1230 a summary of Aristotle's views in his *Summa super octo libros physicorum Aristotelis.*
11. *Commentarius in viii libros physicorum Aristotelis,* lib. I, Dales, ed., pp. 3–4.
12. *Commentaria in libros posteriorum Aristotelis,* I, 12 (1494), fols. 11r–12r.
13. *Ibid.,* I, 8, fol. 8r.
14. *Ibid.,* II, 4, fol. 29v.
15. *De lineis, angulis et figuris,* in Baur, *Die philosophischen Werke,* pp. 59–60.
16. *De natura locorum, ibid.,* pp. 65–66.
17. *De colore, ibid.,* pp. 78–79.
18. *De iride, ibid.,* p. 73. See L. Baur, *Die Philosophie des Robert Grosseteste,* pp. 117–118; Crombie, *Robert Grosseteste* (1971), pp. 117–124.
19. *De iride,* in Baur, *Die philosophischen Werke,* p. 74.
20. *Ibid.,* p. 75.
21. *Ibid.,* pp. 74–75.
22. *Ibid.,* p. 75.
23. *Compotus,* R. Steele, ed., pp. 215, 259.
24. See Crombie, *Robert Grosseteste* (1971); A. Pacchi, "Ruggero Bacone e Roberto Grossetesta in un inedito hobbesiano del 1634," in *Rivista critica di storia della filosofia,* **20** (1965), 499–502; and *Convenzione e ipotesi nella formazione della filosofia naturale di Thomas Hobbes* (Florence, 1965).

BIBLIOGRAPHY

I. ORIGINAL WORKS. The earliest-dated printed ed. of a work by Grosseteste is *Commentaria in libros posteriorum Aristotelis* (Venice, 1494; 8th ed., 1552). It was followed by his *Summa super octo libros physicorum Aristotelis* (Venice, 1498; 9th ed., 1637); *Libellus de phisicis lineis angulis et figuris per quas omnes actiones naturales com-

plentur (Nuremburg, 1503); *De sphaera,* pub. as *Sphaerae compendium* (Venice, 1508; 5th ed., 1531); and *Compotus correctorius* (Venice, 1518). His *Opuscula* (Venice, 1514; London, 1690) includes *De artibus liberalibus, De generatione sonorum, De calore solis, De generatione stellarum, De colore, De impressionibus elementorum, De motu corporali, De finitate motus et temporis* (appearing first as the concluding section of his commentary on the *Physics*), *De lineis, angulis et figuris, De natura locorum, De luce, De motu supercaelestium,* and *De differentiis localibus.* All these essays, with *De sphaera* and the hitherto unprinted *De cometis, De impressionibus aëris* and *De iride,* were published by L. Baur in *Die philosophischen Werke des Robert Grosseteste* (see below). For further modern texts see *Canon in Kalendarium,* ed. by A. Lindhagen as "Die Neumondtafel des Robertus Lincolniensis," in *Archiv för matematik, astronomi och fysik* (Uppsala), **11,** no. 2 (1916); *Compotus, factus ad correctionem communis kalendarii nostri,* R. Steele, ed., in Roger Bacon, *Opera hactenus inedita,* VI (Oxford, 1926), 212 ff.; S. H. Thomson, "The Text of Grosseteste's *De cometis,*" in *Isis,* **19** (1933), 19–25; and "Grosseteste's *Questio de calore, de cometis* and *De operacionibus solis,*" in *Medievalia et humanistica,* **11** (1957), 34–43; *Commentarius in viii libros physicorum Aristotelis . . .,* R. C. Dales, ed. (Boulder, Colo., 1963); and R. C. Dales, "The Text of Robert Grosseteste's *Questio de fluxu et refluxu maris* with an English Translation," in *Isis,* **57** (1966), 455–474. See also *Roberti Grosseteste episcopi quondam Lincolniensis epistolae,* H. R. Luard, ed. (London, 1861).

II. SECONDARY LITERATURE. For the fundamental work of identifying and listing Grosseteste's writings see L. Baur, *Die philosophischen Werke des Robert Grosseteste, Bishop von Lincoln,* vol. IX of Beiträge zur Geschichte der Philosophie des Mittelalters (Münster, 1912); and S. H. Thomson, *The Writings of Robert Grosseteste Bishop of Lincoln 1235–1253* (Cambridge, 1940). For further discussions of his scientific writings with references to additional items, see D. A. Callus, "The Oxford Career of Robert Grosseteste," in *Oxoniensia,* **10** (1945), 42–72; D. A. Callus, ed., *Robert Grosseteste, Scholar and Bishop* (Oxford, 1955); A. C. Crombie, *Robert Grosseteste and the Origins of Experimental Science, 1100–1700* (Oxford, 1953; 3rd ed., 1971) and the comprehensive bibliography therein; and R. C. Dales, "Robert Grosseteste's Scientific Works," in *Isis,* **52** (1961), 381–402. The basic modern biography is still F. S. Stevenson, *Robert Grosseteste, Bishop of Lincoln* (London, 1899), while Callus, *Robert Grosseteste,* judiciously sums up more recent scholarship. The pioneering account of his scientific thought is L. Baur, *Die Philosophie des Robert Grosseteste, Bischofs von Lincoln,* XVIII, nos. 4–6 of Beiträge zur Geschichte der Philosophie des Mittelalters (Münster, 1917).

A. C. CROMBIE

GROSSMANN, ERNST A. F. W. (*b.* Rothenburg, near Bremen, Germany, 16 February 1863; *d.* Munich, Germany, 17 March 1933), *astronomy.*

Grossmann began to study astronomy in 1884 at Göttingen, where he took his doctorate under A. C. W. Schur and Leopold Ambronn in 1891. He was assistant at the Göttingen observatory from 1891 to 1896, at Moritz Kuffner's observatory in Vienna from 1896 to 1898, at the Leipzig observatory from 1898 to 1902, and at the Kiel observatory from 1902 to 1905. In 1905 he became observer at Munich, where he lived for the rest of his life. He retired in 1928.

Grossmann was an enthusiastic and important worker with meridian instruments. All of his work was devoted to questions concerning fundamental astrometric measurements. After examining systematic errors in measurements of double stars in his dissertation, he made careful observations with the meridian circles of all the observatories where he worked. One main area of his research was the theory of atmospheric refraction; his very important examination of existing observations resulted in a value for the constant of refraction of 60.15″, which is still used.

Grossmann's observations of fundamental right ascensions near the celestial pole indicated clearly that the values adopted at that time were affected by systematic errors. Although his attempts to measure stellar parallaxes by a meridian circle were unsuccessful, they convinced astronomers that the photographic method is better. In 1921 he showed that existing observations of the planet Mercury were not sufficiently accurate to permit determination of a reliable value of the relativistic motion of its perihelion. It was more than twenty years later that a new comprehensive discussion of all observations of Mercury made between 1765 and 1937, which was undertaken by the U.S. Naval Observatory at Washington, showed convincingly that the observed value of the motion of perihelion was in agreement with the theory of relativity.

BIBLIOGRAPHY

Grossmann's major works are "Untersuchungen über die astronomische Refraktion," in *Abhandlungen der K. Bayerischen Akademie der Wissenschaften,* Math.-phys. Kl., **28,** no. 9 (1917), 1–72; "Die Bewegung des Merkurperihels nach den Arbeiten Newcombs," in *Astronomische Nachrichten,* **214** (1921), 41–54; and "Parallaxenbestimmungen am Meridiankreise," in *Neue Annalen der K. Sternwarte in München,* **5,** no. 1 (1926), 1–173.

There is no secondary literature.

F. SCHMEIDLER

GROSSMANN, MARCEL (*b.* Budapest, Hungary, 9 April 1878; *d.* Zurich, Switzerland, 7 September 1936), *mathematics.*

Grossmann was the son of Jules Grossmann, a businessman, and Henriette Lichtenhahn. He took his final secondary school examination in 1896 in Basel, where his family had moved. He then studied mathematics at the Zurich Polytechnikum (later named the Eidgenössische Technische Hochschule) and in 1900 became an assistant to the geometer W. Fiedler. He earned his doctorate from the University of Zurich in 1912 with a work entitled *Über metrische Eigenschaften Kollinearer Gebilde* (Frauenfeld, 1902). He became a teacher at the cantonal school in Frauenfeld in 1901 and at the Oberrealschule in Basel in 1905. He was appointed professor of descriptive geometry at the Eidgenössische Technische Hochschule in 1907. In 1903 he married Anna Keller.

Grossmann was a classmate of Albert Einstein. When Einstein sought to formulate mathematically his ideas on general relativity theory, he turned to Grossmann for assistance. Grossmann discovered that the law of gravitation could be stated in terms of the absolute differential geometry first developed by E. Christoffel (1864), and later by M. M. G. Ricci together with T. Levi-Civita (1901). Grossmann and Einstein set forth their fundamental discoveries in the joint works cited in the bibliography.

Grossmann was a teacher of outstanding ability and he gave many mathematicians and engineers their training in geometry. His lectures were published in textbooks that enjoyed a large success.

BIBLIOGRAPHY

I. Original Works. Grossmann's works include *Der mathematische Unterricht an der Eidgenössischen Technischen Hochschule,* Commission Internationale de l'Enseignement-mathématique, no. 7 (Basel–Geneva, 1911); "Mathematische Begriffsbildungen zur Gravitationstheorie," in *Vierteljahrsschrift der Naturforschenden Gesellschaft in Zurich,* **58** (1913), 291–297; and *Darstellende Geometrie* (Leipzig, 1915), with many other eds.

He collaborated with Einstein on "Entwurf einer verallgemeinerten Relativitätstheorie und einer Theorie der Gravitation," in *Zeitschrift für Mathematik und Physik,* **62** (1913), 1–38; the work is in 2 parts: I, "Physikalischer Teil" (pp. 1–22), is by Einstein, and II, "Mathematischer Teil" (pp. 23–38), is by Grossmann. The other collaboration is "Kovarianzeigenschaften der Feldgleichungen," *ibid.,* **63** (1914), 215–225.

II. Secondary Literature. For information on Grossmann, see F. Bäschlin, "Marcel Grossmann," in *Schweizerische Zeitschrift für Vermessungswesen, Kulturtechnik und Photogrammetrie,* **34** (1936), 243 ff.; L. Kollros, "Prof. Dr. Marcel Grossmann," in *Verhandlungen der Schweizerischen naturforschenden Gesellschaft,* **118** (1937), 325–329, with portrait and bibliography; and W. Saxer, "Marcel Grossmann," in *Vierteljahrsschrift der Naturforschenden Gesellschaft in Zurich,* **81** (1936), 322–326, with bibliography.

Johann Jakob Burckhardt

GROTE, AUGUSTUS RADCLIFFE (*b.* Aigburth, near Liverpool, England, 7 February 1841; *d.* Hildesheim, Germany, 12 September 1903), *entomology.*

Grote was the son of Friedrich Rudolf Grote, a German from Danzig, and Anna Radcliffe, daughter of a Welsh ironmaster. As a youth he immigrated to Staten Island, New York, where his parents had purchased a farm. Grote's formal education was interrupted by the panic of 1857, and although by his own account he continued his studies on the Continent, the only degree he is known to have taken was the honorary M.A. conferred in 1874 by Lafayette College in Pennsylvania.

Grote's first papers on the Lepidoptera were published in 1862, and he rapidly became an authority on the taxonomy of the order, especially that of the noctuid moths. Many of his early studies were written with Coleman T. Robinson. For almost two decades, except for a residence of several years in Demopolis, Alabama, Grote held various positions at the Buffalo (New York) Society of Natural Sciences. After the death of his father in 1880 he left his work at the society and the editorship of the *North American Entomologist* and returned to Staten Island.

Pressed by debts in the following year, Grote sold his valuable collection of Lepidoptera to the British Museum, and permanently left the United States in 1884. He took up residence in Bremen and later in Hildesheim, where he became an honorary curator of the Roemer-Museum. He died of endocarditis. Grote married twice. His first wife, Julia, died after the birth of their second child; his second wife, Gesa Maria, survived him.

One of the leading American entomologists of the nineteenth century, Grote was the first in the United States to study the Noctuidae in real depth, giving attention to the insufficient or confusing species descriptions of some European taxonomists. Although he investigated most areas of lepidopterology, his greatest contribution was the accurate description of a vast number of species. Almost 1,250 of Grote's names are included (many as synonyms) in current checklists, as are over 140 credited to Grote and Robinson.

Grote published over 600 papers in numerous journals. A composer and accomplished organist, he also found time to write poetry and popular articles on science. Although neither a Fiske nor a Huxley, he entered the controversy over science and religion, and several of his books suggested a logical conciliation on the basis of relative value.

BIBLIOGRAPHY

I. ORIGINAL WORKS. Citations for most of Grote's entomological papers and checklists are included in W. Horn and S. Schenkling, *Index Litteraturae Entomologicae . . . bis inklusive 1863,* II (Berlin, 1928), 465; and W. Derksen and U. Scheiding-Göllner, *Index Litteraturae Entomologicae 1864–1900,* II (Berlin, 1965), 212–221.

Among his full-length works are the semipopular *An Illustrated Essay on the Noctuidae of North America* (London, 1882) and the two books on science and religion, *Genesis I–II: An Essay on the Bible Narrative of Creation* (New York, 1880), and *The New Infidelity* (New York, 1881). Grote's poetry was collected as *Rip van Winkle: A Sun Myth and Other Poems* (London, 1882).

II. SECONDARY LITERATURE. The only extensive biographical summary is Ronald S. Wilkinson, intro. to the repr. ed. of Grote's *An Illustrated Essay on the Noctuidae of North America* (Hampton, Middlesex, 1971), in which the earlier lit. is cited. Grote's own autobiographical sketch was used by C. J. S. Bethune in his obituary, "Professor Augustus Radcliffe Grote," in *Report of the Entomological Society of Ontario . . . 1903* (1904), 109–112.

RONALD S. WILKINSON

GROTH, PAUL HEINRICH VON (*b.* Magdeburg, Germany, 23 June 1843; *d.* Munich, Germany, 2 December 1927), *mineralogy, crystallography.*

Following a trip to St. Petersburg in 1840 Groth's father, Philipp Heinrich August Groth, lived in Magdeburg and then, from 1845, worked in Dresden as a portrait painter. His mother, Marie Steffen, was a daughter of a businessman in Frankfurt an der Oder. After attending the Kreuzschule in Dresden from 1855 to 1862, Groth studied at the Freiberg Mining Academy and at the Dresden Polytechnical School. In 1865 he entered the University of Berlin to study physics and mineralogy. He received his doctorate in 1868 and until 1870 was an assistant to the physicist Gustav Magnus. He qualified as a lecturer at the University of Berlin in 1870 and from 1870 to 1872 taught mineralogy and geology at the mining academy in Berlin. In April 1872 he assumed the new professorship of mineralogy at the University of Strasbourg, where he established a mineral collection whose catalog (1878) was considered a model of the type. On 1 September 1883 he succeeded F. von Kobell as professor of mineralogy at the University of Munich and as director of the Bavarian State Collection, which he enlarged primarily in the areas of Alpine minerals and of mineral deposits. He retired on 1 April 1924 and devoted his time to the history of science.

Groth's first mineralogical work (1866) dealt with the titanite he discovered in the Plauenscher Grund, near Dresden, a substance that J. D. Dana named grothite in 1867. (A silicate probably related to harstigite was named grothine by F. Zambonini in 1913.) As a student of F. A. Breithaupt, Groth paid particular attention to paragenesis of minerals. In 1885, in Dauphiny, he accounted for the dependence of axinite-epidote occurrences in amphibole schists and of anatase-turnerite occurrences in gneiss by the leaching of the surrounding rock. His *Topographische Übersicht der Minerallagerstätten* (1917) was one of the best surveys in its time.

Groth's most important contribution to science was his explanation of the connections between chemical composition and crystal structure. Although he did not succeed in determining the optical properties of potassium permanganate through interpolation from isomorphic mixtures with potassium perchlorate, he did recognize the crystallographic peculiarities of mixed crystals. Comparison of the analogies between crystals of the same system with similar interfacial angles led him to a new definition of isomorphism (1874) as requiring the capacity to form homogeneous mixed crystals (isomorphic mixtures) as well as the growth of crystals of each end member in solution with the other.

Systematic measurements of the influences on the crystal form of benzene derivatives with the substitution of hydroxyl, nitro, and ammonia groups, or halides or alkali metals led Groth to call this influence "morphotropy" (1870) and to conceive of, for example, mononitrophenol, dinitrophenol, and trinitrophenol as a morphotropic series. In this regard he also spoke of the morphotropic force of an element or a group of atoms, asserting that the manifestation of such a force depended on the specific morphotropic force of the atom or group of atoms (or both) that is being substituted on (1) the chemical nature of the compound in which the substitution takes place, (2) the crystal system of the compound being altered, and (3) the position of the entering group relative to the other atoms in the molecule. Sometimes the elastic deforming force changes only an axial length, but it may also cause a predictable change in the crystal system. The deforming effect is necessarily greater in regular crystals than in other crystal systems, because in the former a change of angle is not possible without a change in the system.

In 1870 Groth began the lectures that he published in 1876 as the textbook *Physikalische Krystallographie.* With his students he systematically investigated the optical, thermal, elastic, magnetic, and electrical properties of crystals. In 1871 Groth improved the polariscope, the stauroscope, the axial-angle instrument, and the goniometer and combined them into a universal instrument. In 1890 he simplified the reflecting goniometer and modified Koch and Emil Warburg's device for determining the coefficients of elasticity in circular plates. His most important finding came in 1876, when he determined that crystallographically equivalent orientations are also always physically equivalent and hence that every geometric plane of symmetry of a crystal is also a physical plane of symmetry.

In 1895, in the third edition of *Physikalische Krystallographie,* Groth presented for the first time a derivation based on Leonard Sohncke's ideas of the crystal forms from the simplest to the highest symmetry and discussed the theory of the space lattice. In 1904 he provided this definition:

> A crystal consists of regular systems of points, placed within each other, each of which is formed of similar atoms; each of these systems of points belongs to a number of lattices, placed within each other, each of which is formed of similar atoms in parallel position; all the lattices of such a structure are congruent, that is, their elementary parallelepiped is the same [*Zeitschrift für Kristallographie,* **54** (1915), 67].

During the period in which other physicists and mineralogists showed scant interest in the space lattice theory, Groth "maintained, through his teaching in Munich, the Sohnckian tradition" (Max von Laue, *Geschichte der Physik* [1947], p. 119).

In accordance with this definition Groth treated structural change resulting from substitution of another atom or group of atoms (or both) as a homogeneous deformation and expressed the dimensions of the unit cell by the topical parameters ψ, χ, ω, of his co-worker W. Muthmann (1894), in the equations

$$\psi = \sqrt[3]{\frac{V}{ac \sin \beta \sin \gamma \sin A}}; \; \chi = a\psi; \; \omega = c\psi,$$

where in the triclinic case a, b, c are the axial lengths (expressed as a ratio $a:1:c$) and α, β, γ are the angles. V is molecular weight divided by density, or equivalent weight; and A is the angle opposite side α in the spherical triangle with sides α, β, γ (*Einleitung in die chemische Krystallographie,* p. 26).

In his *Chemische Krystallographie* (1906–1919) Groth compiled crystallographic and physical data on more than 7,000 substances, thereby facilitating their positive identification; but his data did not enable him to give a complete explanation of the relationships between chemical composition and crystal form—and above all he could not explain atomic structures. There is a certain element of tragedy in the fact that the first X-ray structural analyses of diamond, sphalerite, rock salt, fluorite, pyrite, and calcite misled Groth (1914) into thinking that molecules could no longer be mentioned in connection with crystals and were confined to gases, liquids, and colloids. In crystallization, molecules necessarily assumed a reciprocal orientation, a parallel or "twin" position.

> In the union of two or more molecules into a single crystal particle there emerge, in the place of the earlier, internal atomic bonds, bonds between the atoms of adjacent molecules. . . . That parts of the molecule's internal bonds enter into the crystal structure is shown by the . . . previously observed relationship between the structure of the chemical molecule and the crystal structure, that is, crystal form [*Berichte der Deutschen chemischen Gesellschaft,* **47** (1914), 2064].

Here Groth was thinking especially of the persistence of organic ring bonds. Earlier he had pointed out the limited tendency to crystallization of very large organic molecules and the preservation of enantiomorphic molecules in the crystal structure, but he was unwilling to accept a molecular lattice.

Groth's importance to modern structural research and to chemistry has been aptly expressed by E. H. Kraus:

> Many of his views on morphotropy and isomorphism, and on chemical crystallography in general have become firmly embodied in chemical literature. Furthermore, the remarkable advances in our knowledge of crystal structure as the result of the development of X-ray analysis, dating from 1912, are in large measure due to Groth's long and enthusiastic advocacy of the point system theory of crystal structure [*American Mineralogist,* **13** (1928), 96].

Groth was a member of the academies of science of Munich, St. Petersburg, and Vienna, of the National Academy of Sciences of the United States, the Accademia dei Lincei of Rome, the Royal Society, and the Geological Society of London, whose Wollaston Medal he received in 1908. He was also an honorary member of the Mineralogical Society of London, the Mineralogical Society of America, the French Society of Mineralogy and Geology, the Chemical Society of London, and the German Chemical Society, and received honorary doctorates from the universities of Cambridge, Geneva, and Prague. Groth founded the *Zeitschrift für Kristallographie und Mineralogie* in 1877 and from that year until 1920 edited its first fifty-five volumes.

BIBLIOGRAPHY

I. ORIGINAL WORKS. Groth's writings include *Tabellarische Übersicht der einfachen Mineralien* (Brunswick, 1874; 2nd ed., 1882; 3rd ed., 1889; 4th ed., 1898); *Physikalische Krystallographie* (Leipzig, 1876; 2nd ed., 1885; 3rd. ed., 1895; 4th ed., 1905); *Die Mineraliensammlung der Kaiser-Wilhelm-Universität Strassburg* (Strasbourg, 1878); *Grundriss der Edelsteinkunde* (Leipzig, 1887); *Führer durch die Mineraliensammlung des bayerischen Staates in München* (Munich, 1891); *Einleitung in die chemische Krystallographie* (Leipzig, 1904); *Chemische Krystallographie,* 5 vols. (Leipzig, 1906–1919), also in photocopy (University Park, Pa., 1959); *Elemente der physikalischen und chemischen Krystallographie* (Munich–Berlin, 1921); *Mineralogische Tabellen* (Munich, 1921), written with K. Mieleitner; *Entwicklungsgeschichte der mineralogischen Wissenschaften* (Berlin, 1926, repr. 1970); and "Vorgeschichte, Gründung und Entwicklung der *Zeitschrift für Kristallographie* in den ersten fünfzig Jahren," in *Zeitschrift für Kristallographie,* **66** (1928), 1–21.

There is a full bibliography by K. Mieleitner, "Verzeichnis der Arbeiten P. H. von Groth's" in *Zeitschrift für Kristallographie,* **58** (1923), 3–6, a special issue commemorating Groth's eightieth birthday; and in Poggendorff.

II. SECONDARY LITERATURE. On Groth or his work, see G. Menzer, in *Neue deutsche Biographie,* VII (1966), 167–168; and C. Schiffner, in *Aus dem Leben alter Freiberger Bergstudenten* (Freiberg, 1935), pp. 339–341. The numerous obituaries are listed by Menzer and Poggendorff.

WALTHER FISCHER

GROTTHUSS, THEODOR (CHRISTIAN JOHANN DIETRICH) VON (*b.* Leipzig, Germany, 20 January 1785; *d.* Geddutz, near Jelgava, Courland, Russia [now Lithuanian S.S.R.], 26 March 1822), *chemistry, physics.*

Grotthuss came from an old and distinguished family of Courland chancellery nobility. He was born while his parents were abroad. His father, an amateur composer and collector of natural science material, died while still young. Grotthuss lived on his mother's estate, Geddutz, and received a good education there. From 1803 to 1808 he completed his education in science in Leipzig, Paris, Naples, and Rome, and was an auditor at the École Polytechnique in Paris, studying with Antoine de Fourcroy, Claude Berthollet, Louis Vauquelin, and Domenico Morrichini, among others. In 1805, while in Italy, he presented an original explanation of the electrolysis of water, which postulated that molecules of water and salt are polarized and, under the influence of the electric poles, form in the solution electromolecular chains whose members at each end are discharged at the opposite poles of the current. The mechanism of electroconductivity according to Grotthuss was generally accepted until the appearance of the electrolytic dissociation theory and is now used to explain the anomalous high electroconductivity of hydrogen and hydroxyl ions.

After his return from France, Grotthuss spent the last part of his life on his mother's estate, not far from Jelgava, the capital of Courland, where in seclusion he conducted scientific experiments and constructed new theories; only in 1812, to save himself from Napoleon's invasion, did he go to St. Petersburg for six months. Grotthuss reported the results of his work to the Courland Society of Literature and Art, of which he was an active member; he had his articles published in the proceedings of this society, as well as in German journals of chemistry and physics (Johann Schweigger's *Journal für Chemie und Physik,* L. W. Gilbert's *Annalen der Physik,* Adolph Gehlen's *Neues allgemeines Journal der Chemie*) and in A. N. von Scherer's *Allgemeine nordische Annalen der Chemie,* published in St. Petersburg from 1819 to 1822. His articles and notes amount to more than seventy.

In the period from 1808 to 1822 Grotthuss discovered experimentally the basic laws of photochemistry (that a chemical reaction can be caused only by the light absorbed by a substance and that the chemical effect of light is proportional to the time of exposure [1818]), produced original theories on the nature of phosphorescence and color (1815), and attempted to develop a unified electromolecular conception of various chemical and physical phenomena (which anticipated certain elements of the modern kinetic-molecular theory). In studying the flames of gas mixtures Grotthuss came to the conclusion that components of the mixtures (i.e., individual gases such as H_2 and O_2) react among themselves only at a certain concentration (pressure), that a gas mixture in a narrow tube will not ignite, and that a spark or an open flame is necessary for an explosion (1811). Humphry Davy used these results in his construction of the miner's safety lamp (1815). In later years Grotthuss and Davy carried on a polemic concerning the explanation for the action of this lamp.

Grotthuss worked out detailed methods for obtaining, and studied the properties of, thiocyanic (sulfocyanic) acid and its salts, and discovered an analytical application of the reaction of trivalent iron and divalent cobalt with thiocyanides (1817–1818). At the same time as J. W. von Goethe, who was investigating sulfur sources at Bad Berka, Grotthuss suggested that sulfur sources in nature were formed as a result of the reduction of gypsum deposits by organic substances (1816). He worked on the analysis of meteorites and proposed original theories of their origins (1819–1821). He first observed the phenomenon of electrostenolysis in passing an electric current through very narrow cracks (1818).

Grotthuss was a very versatile chemist and physicist whose research received well-deserved recognition from his contemporaries, especially in Germany and Russia. He was elected a corresponding member of the Turin and Munich academies of science and an honorary member of the Société Galvanique in Paris. Many of Grotthuss' ideas contributed to the theoretical development of the kinetic theory, the theory of electrolytic dissociation, the electromagnetic theory of light, and contemporary theories of luminescence.

In the last years of his life Grotthuss' hereditary illness grew acute; as a result of his great suffering he committed suicide at the age of thirty-seven. He left his estate, archives, and library to found a chair of physics and chemistry at Jelgava, and in his will he freed his serfs from their taxes and obligations.

Grotthuss' scientific legacy in the field of electrochemistry was "discovered" by Wilhelm Ostwald, who did much to popularize it, at the end of the nineteenth century.

BIBLIOGRAPHY

I. ORIGINAL WORKS. Grotthuss' writings include *Physisch-chemische Forschungen* (Nuremberg, 1820); and *Abhandlungen über Elektrizität und Licht,* R. Luther and A. von Oettingen, eds. (Leipzig, 1906), Ostwald's Klassiker der exacten Wissenschaften, no. 152.

II. SECONDARY LITERATURE. On Grotthuss or his work, see W. Ostwald, *Elektrochemie, ihre Geschichte und Lehre* (Leipzig, 1896), pp. 309–316 and *passim;* J. Stradins, "The Work of Theodore Grotthuss and the Invention of the Davy Safety Lamp," in *Chymia,* **9** (1964), 125–145; and *Theodor Grotthuss, 1785–1822* (Moscow, 1966).

J. P. STRADINS

GROVE, WILLIAM ROBERT (*b.* Swansea, Wales, 11 July 1811; *d.* London, England, 1 August 1896), *electrochemistry, physics.*

Grove was the only son of John Grove, magistrate and deputy lieutenant for Glamorganshire, and his wife, Anne Bevan. He was educated privately and at Brasenose College, Oxford, graduating B.A. in 1832 and M.A. in 1835. He became a barrister, but apparently because of ill health soon turned from law to science, toward which he had always had an inclination. He soon gained a reputation in the comparatively new but rapidly growing science of electrochemistry, particularly with his development of the Grove cell, an improved form of voltaic cell which became very popular. It was used, for example, by Faraday in his lecture demonstrations at the Royal Institution.

Grove was elected a fellow of the Royal Society in 1840 and from 1841 to 1846 was professor of experimental philosophy at the London Institution. In 1837 he had married Emma Maria Powles, who died in 1879; they had two sons and four daughters. In order to meet the financial needs imposed by a growing family, although without entirely abandoning scientific pursuits, Grove returned to the practice of law and became a Queen's Counsel in 1853. In 1856 he defended William Palmer, the "Rugeley poisoner," in a famous murder trial. He became a judge in 1871, and although it was thought that his special knowledge would be particularly valuable in trying cases involving infringement of patents, it was found that he became more interested in the subject of the patent, sometimes suggesting improvements, than in the bare legal aspects of the case.

One of the main defects of early zinc-copper cells was polarization, due to the accumulation of a film of hydrogen bubbles on the surface of the copper plate—this film not only had a high resistance, thus weakening the current, but produced a back emf. Polarization was overcome to some extent as early as 1829 by Antoine-César Becquerel, who used two liquids separated by a porous partition. In the first practical application of the two-liquid principle, devised by J. F. Daniell, the copper sulfate solution in contact with the copper plate was separated from the sulfuric acid containing the zinc plate by unglazed earthenware. This arrangement gave a reasonably constant emf of about 1.1 volts.[1]

After relating a number of experiments[2] using different metals and electrolytes as well as different containers, Grove described what was to become the standard form of his battery, consisting of zinc in dilute sulfuric acid and platinum in concentrated nitric acid (or a mixture of nitric and sulfuric acids), giving an emf of nearly two volts. In 1841 the platinum was replaced by carbon in Bunsen's adaptation of the cell.

It is important that the cell described above should not be confused with what Grove came to call his "gas battery," which was, in fact, the earliest fuel cell; its possibilities have only recently been exploited. In a postscript to the letter describing his first experiments on voltaic cells, Grove described how, when test tubes of hydrogen and oxygen were separately placed over two platinum strips, sealed into and projecting through the bottom of a glass vessel containing dilute sulfuric acid so that half of each strip was in contact with the acid and half exposed to the gas, a current flowed through a wire connecting the projecting ends.[3] In subsequent experiments Grove obtained a powerful current using hydrogen and chlorine, and appreciable currents with other pairs of gases. Grove realized that the electrical energy resulted from the chemical energy liberated when hydrogen and oxygen combined and that this electrical energy could be used to decompose water (he did in fact carry out the electrolysis of water with current from his gas battery). This realization stimulated thoughts which had been engaging him for some time: "This battery establishes that gases in combining and acquiring a liquid form evolve sufficient force to decompose a similar liquid and cause it to acquire a gaseous form. This is to my mind the most interesting effect of the battery; it exhibits such a beautiful instance of the correlation of natural forces."[4]

The concept underlying this observation was first briefly enunciated in a lecture given in January 1842 on the progress of physical science since the opening of the London Institution and was then developed in a series of lectures given during the following year. The substance of these lectures constituted the material for Grove's book, *On the Correlation of Physical Forces,* first published in 1846. New material was added to each of the five subsequent editions. The work was an early statement of the principle of the conservation of energy, one of several at about this time.[5]

Describing, in 1845, some experiments that he had carried out four or five years earlier on the possibility of using arc lighting in mines, Grove claimed that his lack of success led him to the idea of sealing a helix of platinum wire in a glass vessel and igniting it by an electrical current; the resulting device seems to have been the earliest form of the filament lamp.[6]

In 1846 Grove gave the first experimental proof of dissociation. He showed that steam in contact with a strongly heated platinum wire was dissociated into hydrogen and oxygen. He also showed that the reactions

$$CO_2 + H_2 = CO + H_2O$$
$$CO + H_2O = CO_2 + H_2$$

could take place under the same conditions. He expressed the view that the platinum wire merely rendered the chemical equilibrium unstable and that the gases restored themselves to a stable equilibrium according to the circumstances. Among other observations, he first drew attention to the striated appearance of rarefied gases in discharge tubes.

Grove was one of the original members of the Chemical Society, and at the jubilee meeting in 1891 he said, "For my part, I must say that science to me generally ceases to be interesting as it becomes useful." There is therefore perhaps some irony in the fact that so much of his work led to important practical consequences, yet his contribution to the concept of energy conservation (for which, it is plain from the prefaces to the successive editions of his book, he felt he was insufficiently credited) was overshadowed by the work of others. A member of the Council of the Royal Society in 1846 and 1847 and one of its secretaries in the following two years, he played a leading part in the society's reform movement.[7] He was knighted in 1872.

NOTES

1. Grove denied that the ideas which led to the development of his cell owed anything to Daniell, a denial which led to a sharp exchange of letters between the two men; see *Philosophical Magazine,* **20** (1842), 294–304; **21** (1842), 333–335, 421–422; **22** (1843), 32–35.
2. The evolution of the cell is described in the papers listed in the bibliography. The fullest account of its refinements and mode of action is in *Philosophical Magazine,* **15** (1839), 287–293.
3. For an explanation in modern terms and the contemporary significance of this experiment, see K. R. Webb, "Sir William Robert Grove (1811–1896) and the Origins of the Fuel Cell," in *Journal of the Royal Institute of Chemistry,* **85** (1961), 291–293; and J. W. Gardner, *Electricity Without Dynamos* (Harmondsworth, 1963), pp. 42 and 49 ff.
4. *Philosophical Magazine,* **21** (1842), 420.
5. See T. S. Kuhn, "Energy Conservation as an Example of Simultaneous Discovery," in M. Clagett, ed., *Critical Problems in the History of Science* (Madison, Wis., 1959), pp. 321–356.
6. *Philosophical Magazine,* **27** (1845), 442–446.
7. See H. Lyons, *The Royal Society 1660–1940* (Cambridge, 1944), pp. 259 ff.

BIBLIOGRAPHY

I. Original Works. Grove's only book is *On the Correlation of Physical Forces* (London, 1846; 6th ed., with reprints of many of Grove's papers, 1874). His papers are listed in the Royal Society *Catalogue of Scientific Papers,* III (London, 1869), 31–33. The main papers on the Grove cell are "On Voltaic Series and the Combination of Gases by Platinum," in *Philosophical Magazine,* **14** (1839), 127–130 (see 129–130 for the postscript describing the first experiments on the "gas battery"); "On a New Voltaic Combination," *ibid.,* 388–390; and "On a Small Voltaic Battery of Great Energy; Some Observations on Voltaic Combinations and Forms of Arrangement; and on the Inactivity of a Copper Positive Electrode in Nitro-Sulphuric Acid," *ibid.,* **15** (1839), 287–293. See also *Report of the Ninth Meeting of the British Association for the Advancement of Science Held at Birmingham in August 1839* (London, 1840), pp. 36–38. Papers on the gas battery are "On a Gaseous Voltaic Battery," in *Philosophical Magazine,* **21** (1842), 417–420; and "On the Gas Voltaic Battery," in *Philosophical Transactions of the Royal Society,* **133** (1843), 91–112; **135,** (1845), 351–361.

Other papers referred to in the text are "On the Application of Voltaic Ignition to Lighting Mines," in *Philosophical Magazine,* **27** (1845), 442–446; "On Certain Phenomena of Voltaic Ignition, and the Decomposition of Water Into its Constituent Gases by Heat," in *Philosophical Transactions of the Royal Society,* **137** (1847), 1–21; and "On the Electro-Chemical Polarity of Gases," *ibid.,* **142** (1852), 87–101 (the first mention of his observation of "striae" appears at the end of this paper). See also "On the Striae Seen in the Electrical Discharge *in vacuo,*" in *Philosophical Magazine,* **16** (1858), 18–22; and "On the Electrical Discharge and Its Stratified Appearance in Rarefied Media," in *Proceedings of the Royal Institution of Great Britain,* **3** (1858–1862), 5–10.

II. SECONDARY LITERATURE. On Grove and his work, see the short obituary notice by A. Gray in *Nature,* **54** (1896), 393–394; K. R. Webb, "Sir William Robert Grove (1811–1896) and the Origins of the Fuel Cell," in *Journal of the Royal Institute of Chemistry,* **85** (1961), 291–293; and J. G. Crowther, "William Robert Grove," in *Statesmen of Science* (London, 1965), pp. 77–101, which is concerned mainly with Grove's contributions toward the reforms in the Royal Society.

E. L. SCOTT

GRUBB, HOWARD (*b.* Dublin, Ireland, February 1844; *d.* Monkstown, Ireland, 17 September 1931), *optical engineering.*

Grubb's father, Thomas, engineer to the Bank of Ireland, established a factory for the manufacture of machine tools and telescopes. Grubb studied civil engineering at Trinity College, Dublin, but in 1865 left his studies to assist his father in the construction of a Cassegrain reflecting telescope of forty-eight inches aperture for Melbourne, Australia. He took control of the factory in 1868 and moved into larger premises in Rathmines, Dublin. In 1871 he married Mary Hester Walker, the daughter of a physician from Louisiana.

At Rathmines, between 1890 and 1914, Grubb made upwards of ninety first-class telescope objectives from five inches to twenty-eight inches in diameter and most of the necessary tubes and mountings. The completion, in 1887, of a twenty-seven-inch equatorial refractor, together with a forty-five-foot dome and three smaller domes for the Royal Observatory, Vienna, established his reputation as a maker of large telescopes of improved design. One of his most important undertakings was the construction in the 1890's of seven identical photographic telescopes, each with a thirteen-inch objective and ten-inch guider. All seven were used in the *Carte du Ciel,* an international photographic survey of the entire heavens. He also worked on four larger photographic refractors from twenty-four inches to twenty-six and a half inches in aperture, and on several reflecting telescopes, among them a forty-inch for the Simeiz Observatory, Crimea.

Grubb patented (1900) a novel form of optical gunsight and perfected the submarine periscope, two instruments which he made in quantity during World War I. In 1914 the business was moved to St. Albans, England, and continued there until 1925, when a new company under the name of Sir Howard Grubb, Parsons and Company was formed, with headquarters at Newcastle-upon-Tyne. Grubb, then 81 years of age, returned to Dublin.

Grubb was elected a fellow of the Royal Society of London in 1883 and knighted in 1887. He received the Cunningham Gold Medal of the Royal Irish Academy in 1881 and the Boyle Medal of the Royal Dublin Society in 1912. He was appointed scientific advisor to the Commissioners of Irish Lights in 1913 in succession to Sir Robert Ball. He was an honorary member of the Royal Institute of Engineers of Ireland and held the honorary degree of master of engineering from the University of Dublin.

BIBLIOGRAPHY

I. ORIGINAL WORKS. Grubb's publications include "Telescopic Objectives and Mirrors: Their Preparation and Testing," in *Nature,* **34,** 85; "Polar Telescopes," in *Transactions of the Royal Dublin Society,* 2nd and 3rd series; "Automatic Spectroscope for Dr. Huggins' Sun Observations," in *Monthly Notices of the Royal Astronomical Society,* **31,** 36; "On the Choice of Instruments for Stellar Photography," *ibid.,* **47,** 309; "New Arrangement of Electric Control for the Driving Clock of Equatorials," *ibid.,* **48,** 352; "On a New Form of Ghost Micrometer," *ibid.,* **41,** 59, written with E. C. Burton; and "Telescopes of the Future," in *Observatory,* **1** (1877), 55.

II. SECONDARY LITERATURE. The main sketches of Grubb's life and work are obituary notices in *Proceedings of the Royal Society,* **135A** (1932), iv–ix; and *Monthly Notices of the Royal Astronomical Society,* **92,** no. 4 (1932), 253–255. Grubb's activities in telescope making are discussed in H. C. King, *The History of the Telescope* (London, 1955).

H. C. KING

GRUBB, THOMAS (*b.* 1800; *d.* Dublin, Ireland, 19 September 1878), *optical engineer.*

Grubb was a self-taught Irish mechanic, engaged by the Bank of Ireland to construct and develop machines for printing bank notes. He established a small private observatory near Charlemont Bridge, Dublin, and about 1830, on an adjoining site, he opened a factory for the manufacture of machine tools and reflecting telescopes.

In 1835 Grubb constructed a fifteen-inch equatorial newtonian-cassegrainian reflector for Armagh Observatory, in which, for the first time, a triangular system of balanced levers shared the weight of the primary speculum. He used a similar system in a twenty-inch reflector made for Glasgow Observatory, and with such success that it was adopted, with modifications, by William Parsons, earl of Rosse, for his thirty-six-inch and seventy-two-inch reflectors at Parsonstown.

Grubb's greatest achievement was his construction, at Charlemont Bridge Works, of a forty-eight-inch equatorial cassegrainian reflector for Melbourne, Australia. This telescope, completed in 1867, was hailed as a triumph of engineering and optical skill. Intended for photography, it had several novel features, among them counterpoises to reduce the pressure of the polar axis on the bearings. But once on site, the instrument required almost constant adjustment and the mirrors of speculum metal (through no fault of Grubb's) soon became tarnished. These defects and others temporarily destroyed confidence in this type of telescope and unfortunately delayed its development for some thirty years.

After 1865 Grubb was assisted by his son, Howard, who in 1868 took control of the factory and moved into larger premises in Rathmines, Dublin. A member of the Royal Irish Academy, Grubb became a fellow of the Royal Society in 1864 and a fellow of the Royal Astronomical Society in 1870.

BIBLIOGRAPHY

I. Original Works. A work by Grubb is "On Illuminating the Wires of Telescopes," in *Monthly Notices of the Royal Astronomical Society,* **3** (1836), 177–179.

II. Secondary Literature. Short biographies are given in *Dictionary of National Biography* and *Observatory,* **2** (1878), 203. Further references appear in "Obituary Notice of Sir Howard Grubb," in *Proceedings of the Royal Society,* **135A** (1932), iv–ix. Grubb's activities in telescope making are discussed in H. C. King, *The History of the Telescope* (London, 1955).

H. C. King

GRUBENMANN, JOHANN ULRICH (*b.* Trogen, Appenzell, Switzerland, 15 April 1850; *d.* Zurich, Switzerland, 16 March 1924), *mineralogy, petrography.*

Grubenmann was the only surviving child of Johann Kaspar Grubenmann and Katharina Eugster. Among Grubenmann's ancestors was the distinguished Johann Ulrich Grubenmann, who in 1775 erected the wooden bridge across the Rhine at Schaffhausen, a milestone in the history of wide-spanned wooden bridges. At the time of Grubenmann's birth the family was living in extremely reduced circumstances and the boy had to contribute to its means by hard work during his school years. Through scholarships and the help of friends he was able to complete his education and in 1874 he obtained the diploma of certified teacher in natural sciences from the Swiss Federal Institute of Technology. That year he was elected professor of chemistry, mineralogy, and geology at the cantonal school of Frauenfeld, which he also served as rector from 1880 to 1888.

In 1876 Grubenmann married Ida Caroline Baumer; she died in 1880, a month after the birth of their son Max Alfred. He married a second time in 1881 and, by his wife Lisette Augusta, had a son, Max Carl, and a daughter, Ida Clara.

In addition to his teaching responsibilities, Grubenmann carried out petrographic fieldwork in the volcanic area of Hegau, Germany, and in the Alps. He also visited the volcanic districts of Italy and spent some time studying in Munich (1875–1876) and Heidelberg (1886). He received the Ph.D. from the University of Zurich in 1886 with a thesis on the "basalts" (now called olivine melilithites) of Hegau. Two years later he qualified as *Privatdozent* at Zurich and on the death of G. A. Kenngott became professor of mineralogy and petrography and director of the Mineralogical and Petrographical Institute of the Institute of Technology and the University of Zurich. He also was dean of the Faculty of Philosophy (1896–1898) at Zurich and chairman of the division for natural sciences (1907–1909) and rector (1909–1911) at the Institute of Technology. He retired in 1920 but remained scientifically active. In 1921 Grubenmann founded *Schweizerische mineralogische und petrographische Mitteilungen,* which he edited until his death.

Grubenmann devoted himself to the study of metamorphic rocks at a time when petrographic research was mostly occupied with the seemingly genetically simpler rocks of magmatic origin. From the outset he recognized the importance of a physicochemical approach to his studies. In recognition of his achievements and those of his Viennese friends and colleagues F. Becke and F. Berwert, the Viennese Academy of Science entrusted the three scientists with the task of studying the crystalline schists of the eastern Alps. Their researches culminated in the publication of the classic treatise "Ueber Mineralbestand und Struktur der kristallinen Schiefer" (1903). A further result of these studies was Grubenmann's publication of *Die kristallinen Schiefer* (1904–1907), which went through two editions. Part 1 of the third edition, entitled *Die Gesteinsmetamorphose,* was published separately in 1924 in collaboration with Grubenmann's pupil and successor Paul Niggli.

Grubenmann's work was based entirely on observations in nature. He proceeded from the recognition that the mineral composition of metamorphic rocks of a given chemical composition must depend upon the conditions of pressure and temperature (P-T conditions) prevailing at the time of their formation. Accordingly, he created a rock classification in which for each of twelve chemically defined groups or orders the mineral compositions for varying P-T conditions were systematically studied.

The American scientist C. R. Van Hise had already distinguished between two main zones of rock formation within the earth's crust. One zone was characterized by the relatively low values of pressure and temperature normally found in the upper regions of the earth's crust. The second zone was dominated by relatively high values of pressure and temperature such as normally belong to the deeper regions. These two genetic zones were known as the epizone and katazone respectively. Studies carried out by Grubenmann on the rocks of the southern flank of the Gotthard massif indicated the necessity of recognizing a third, so-called mesozone, lying between the two other zones and having intermediate P-T conditions. This extension of the zonal principle proved most useful in later studies. For each of the twelve previously mentioned orders Grubenmann examined and defined the typomorphic mineral composition prevailing in each of the three zones. He proposed a nomenclature based on these relationships and his terminology is widely accepted.

Although rocks were Grubenmann's chief preoccupation, he was also interested in mineralogy. An important publication in this field was his monograph (1899) on the magnificent rutilated quartzes from Piz Aul, Graubünden, which he acquired for the Zurich collection. Grubenmann was also a successful organizer. He expanded the Minerological and Petrographical Institute by adding a chemical laboratory that produced numerous chemical analyses, mostly of metamorphic rocks, and where, perhaps for the first time in Europe, students were given the opportunity for systematic training in rock analyses. Grubenmann founded and for twenty-five years presided over the Swiss Geotechnical Commission whose task it was to locate natural raw materials in Switzerland. On his initiative a series of monographs dealing with building stones, roofing slates, clay deposits, and coal and peat occurrences were published.

BIBLIOGRAPHY

I. Original Works. Grubenmann's works include "Die Basalte des Hegaus, eine petrographische Studie," inaug. diss. (Univ. of Zurich, 1886); "Prinzipien und Vorschläge zu einer Klassifikation der kristallinen Schiefer," in *Collected Works of the Tenth International Geological Congress, Mexico* (1896); "Ueber die Rutilnadeln einschliessenden Bergkristalle vom Piz Aul im Bündneroberland," in *Neujahrsblatt der Naturforschenden Gesellschaft in Zurich,* **101** (1899); *Die kristallinen Schiefer,* 2 vols. (Berlin, 1904–1907; 2nd ed. 1910); *Ueber einige schweizerische Glaukophangesteine* (Stuttgart, 1906); "Struktur und Textur der metamorphen Gesteine," in *Fortschritte der Mineralogie, Kristallographie und Petrographie,* **2** (1912); and *Die Gesteinsmetamorphose* (Berlin, 1923), written with P. Niggli.

The treatise "Ueber Mineralbestand und Struktur der kristallinen Schiefer" was published under Friedrich Becke's name in *Denkscriften der Akademie der Wissenschaften,* **75** (1903).

II. Secondary Literature. For information on Grubenmann, see J. Jakob and A. H. Schinz, "Verzeichnis der Publikationen von Prof. Dr. U. Grubenmann, herausgegeben auf seinen 70. Geburtstag, den 15. April 1920," in *Vierteljahrsschrift der Naturforschenden Gesellschaft in Zurich,* **65** (1920), with complete bibliography; P. Niggli, "Prof. Dr. U. Grubenmann," in *Verhandlungen der Schweizerischen naturforschenden Gesellschaft* (Lucerne, 1924); and R. L. Parker, "Prof. Dr. U. Grubenmann," in *Zentralblatt für Mineralogie, Geologie, und Paläontologie* (1924).

The Swiss author Arnold Kübler (once a pupil of Grubenmann) gives an extremely lively portrait of the university professor in his novel *Oeppi der Student* (Zurich, 1947), in which Grubenmann appears under the pseudonym "Zwiesand."

Conrad Burri

GRUBER, MAX VON (*b.* Vienna, Austria, 6 July 1853; *d.* Berchtesgaden, Germany, 16 September 1927), *hygiene.*

Gruber, the youngest of five children, grew up in the center of the old section of Vienna. His father, Ignaz, a general practitioner and otologist who had published a two-volume textbook on chemistry, awakened Max's interest in that field; and from his mother, Gabriele Edle von Menninger, he inherited his love for nature. After graduating from the Schottengymnasium he entered the First Chemical Institute of the University of Vienna as demonstrator (5 April 1876) even before completing his medical studies and went on to become an assistant. From 1879 to 1883 Gruber improved his knowledge of chemistry and physiology under Max von Pettenkofer and Karl von Voit in Munich and Karl Ludwig in Leipzig.

Hans Buchner, who worked with Gruber under Pettenkofer, encouraged him to concentrate on bacteriology. He called Gruber's attention to the work of Carl Wilhelm von Naegeli, who concerned himself with bacteriology from the botanist's point of view. Whereas Naegeli and Theodor Billroth believed in the unlimited variability of bacteria and Ferdinand Cohn, followed by Robert Koch, supported a rigid constancy of bacterial characteristics, Gruber recognized that bacteria possess a variability within limits partially determined by the culture medium. The establishment of this theory was important for the differentiation of the categories of bacteria and gained significance for Gruber in his examinations of cholera vibrios, enabling him to distinguish them from other vibrios.

Gruber was made lecturer in Vienna at the age of twenty-nine; less than two years later he became associate professor and head of the newly established Institute for Hygiene at the University of Graz, Austria. He was particularly concerned with public health, and during this period he successfully combated the cholera epidemic which had broken out in southern Austria in 1885–1886.

After the death of Josef Nowak, Gruber became associate professor at Vienna on 23 March 1887; and on 10 December 1891 he was named full professor, the second to occupy the chair of hygiene established in 1875 at the University of Vienna. He was handicapped in his new post by the limited space in the makeshift quarters of the Institute for Hygiene and by the troublesome administrative duties and difficulties with the authorities. These obstacles weighed so heavily on Gruber that after the death of his first wife in 1888, and despite being a member of the Vienna Academy of Sciences, he attempted to resign his chair and find employment as head of a laboratory in Munich or at the Jenner Institute in London, under Joseph Lister.

In October 1902 Gruber succeeded Hans Buchner as director of the Institute for Hygiene in Munich. He held the post until his voluntary retirement in 1923, on the occasion of his seventieth birthday. From then until his death, he concentrated completely on his duties as president of the Bavarian Academy of Sciences.

While in Vienna, Gruber discovered the agglutination which gained him international fame. He and his English student Herbert Edward Durham found that the blood serum of animals inoculated with typhoid or cholera bacteria some time before agglutinated these bacteria. The significance of this phenomenon in nature is that even though the bacteria are not killed by the specific agglutinins, they become more susceptible to the attack of the unspecific alexins of the body. These results were announced by Durham on 3 January 1896, in *Proceedings of the Royal Society,* and by Gruber himself on 28 February 1896, to the Society of Physicians in Vienna. Shortly afterward these findings were published in *Münchener medizinische Wochenschrift* (3 March 1896), *Semaine médicale* (4 March 1896), and *Wiener klinische Wochenschrift* (12 March 1896). The priority of Gruber's discovery, contested at the time by Richard Pfeiffer, has long since been fully recognized.

The practical application of the agglutination reaction in the determination of unknown bacteria by means of artificially produced agglutinating animal sera was proved by Gruber in joint research with Albert Sidney Grünbaum, his other English student. The reverse problem of diagnosing typhoid fever by showing evidence of specific agglutinins in the serum of patients was correctly recognized and presented by Grünbaum on 9 April 1896 to the Fourteenth Congress of Internal Medicine in Wiesbaden. Gruber and Grünbaum could furnish proof of this with only two patients, however, because the occurrence of typhoid fever had greatly diminished since the introduction to Vienna of a central water supply from mountain springs in 1873. On 26 June 1896 Ferdinand Widal lectured at the Société Médicale des Hôpitaux de Paris on the serological diagnosis of typhoid fever, based on patients from Paris. This diagnostic method today is called the Gruber-Widal reaction.

The side-chain theory of antibodies, established by Paul Ehrlich and generally recognized around the turn of the century but nevertheless primarily hypothetical, was attacked by Gruber in 1901 in a paper published jointly with Clemens von Pirquet. Following a reply by Ehrlich, Gruber and Pirquet, whose views had been confirmed experimentally, voiced their opinion once more in 1903. They received recognition and support not only from the medical school in Vienna but also from far beyond the boundaries of their country.

BIBLIOGRAPHY

I. Original Works. Gruber's writings include "Über die als 'Kommabacillen' bezeichneten Vibrionen von Koch und Finkler-Prior," in *Wiener medizinische Wochenschrift,* **35,** nos. 9–10 (1885), 261–264, 297–301; "Über active und passive Immunität gegen Cholera und Typhus, sowie über die bacteriologische Diagnose der Cholera und des Typhus," in *Wiener klinische Wochenschrift,* **9,** nos. 11–12 (1896), 183–186, 204–209; "Theorie der activen und passiven Immunität gegen Cholera, Typhus und verwandte Krankheitsprozesse," in *Münchener medizinische Wochen-*

schrift, **44,** no. 9 (1896), 206–207, written with H. Durham; "14. Congress für Innere Medizin, Wiesbaden 1896," in *Verhandlungen des Kongress für innere Medizin* (1896), pp. 207–227; "Neue Früchte der Ehrlich'schen Toxinlehre," in *Wiener klinische Wochenschrift,* **16** (1903), 791–793; "Wirkungsweise und Ursprung der aktiven Stoffe in den präventiven und antitoxischen Seris," *ibid.,* 1097–1105; "Geschichte der Entdeckung der spezifischen Agglutination," in R. Kraus and C. Levaditi, eds., *Handbuch der Immunitätsforschung und experimentellen Therapie,* I (Jena, 1914), 150–154; and "Dankrede anlässlich der Feier seines 70. Geburtstages," in *Münchener medizinische Wochenschrift,* **70** (1923), 1038–1039.

II. SECONDARY LITERATURE. On Gruber or his work, see N. W. Forst, "Max von Gruber," in *Geist und Gestalt,* II (Munich, 1959), 242–247; E. Glaser, "Max Gruber," in *Wiener medizinische Wochenschrift,* **74** (1927), 1330; R. Grassberger, "Max v. Gruber," in *Wiener klinische Wochenschrift,* **40** (1927), 1304–1306; K. B. Lehmann, "Max v. Gruber (6 Juli 1923)," in *Münchener medizinische Wochenschrift,* **70** (1923), 879–881; and "Zum Gedächtnis Max v. Gruber. 6 Juli 1853 bis 16 September 1927," *ibid.,* **74** (1927), 1838–1839; E. Lesky, *Die Wiener medizinische Schule im 19. Jahrhundert* (Graz-Cologne, 1965), 595–602 and *passim;* G. Rath, "Max(imilian) Franz Maria Ritter v. Gruber," in *Neue deutsche Biographie,* VII (Berlin, 1966), 177–178; and K. Süpfle, "Max v. Gruber zum Gedächtnis," in *Deutsche medizinische Wochenschrift,* **53** (1927), 1869–1870.

H. FLAMM

GRUBY, DAVID (*b.* Kis-Kér, Hungary [now Bačko Dobro Polje, Yugoslavia], 20 August 1810; *d.* Paris, France, 14 November 1898), *microbiology, medical mycology, parasitology.*

At the time of his death Gruby was known mainly as an eccentric physician famous for the extravagant cures prescribed for his distinguished patients, who had included Frédéric Chopin, Alexandre Dumas *père,* Heinrich Heine, Alphonse Lamartine, Alphonse Daudet, George Sand, Ambroise Thomas, and Franz Liszt. These prescriptions were actually clever applications of psychosomatic medicine. It was only slowly realized that in the short period of his scientific activity Gruby had made very original and important contributions to science—indeed, he founded an important branch of modern medicine, discovering the dermatomycoses, a group of skin diseases caused by parasitic lower plants.

Gruby was one of seven or eight children of a poor Jewish peasant in a village of Baczka, a fertile district of southern Hungary. Although in his birthplace he could have received only an elementary education, he very early showed great interest in reading and studying. He received his first instruction in secular knowledge from a medical student who worked as a substitute teacher in Kis-Kér and lodged in Gruby's father's home. Gruby left Kis-Kér about 1824 or 1825 to seek further education in Pest. His early years had been marked by great poverty, hardship, and prejudice, although some of the reported stories may be more fiction than truth. His great talent and determined pursuit of his aim enabled him to succeed, against all the odds, in completing his secondary studies at the Piarist Gymnasium in Pest. In 1828 Gruby went to Vienna to study medicine. According to the list of medical students of 1836 he was then in the fifth year of his studies. He passed the first examination on 13 February 1838, the second on 18 March 1839, and graduated on 5 August 1839.

The time he took for his studies seems unusually long for a gifted student, but in order to earn a living Gruby seems to have acquired some special technical knowledge: he is reported to have built himself an accurate clock and a microscope which was, for the time, an excellent instrument. In his microscopic studies Gruby was encouraged and guided by two young teachers who were beginning their distinguished careers at the Vienna medical school: Joseph Berres, from 1831 professor of anatomy, and Karl Rokitansky, from 1833 prosector and a year later associate professor of pathological anatomy. Some of Gruby's early microscopic observations on pathological morphology were included in his dissertation, which contains microscopic observations (with 103 illustrations) on the pathology of body fluids—mucus, sputum, pus, pseudomembranes, coagula, and saliva—and compares pathological with normal findings. His attempt at microscopic differentiation of pus from other pathological substances was a careful, original investigation in a new field of medicine. Gruby demonstrated, among other things, that every one of the studied body fluids contained living elements (leukocytes). He republished his dissertation as the first part of a larger treatise on microscopic pathology, but the other planned parts never appeared.

Gruby also made preparations to be sold to various institutions and gave courses in microscopy, which enabled him to meet many visiting foreign physicians, such as William Bowman and P. J. Roux. It was Roux who suggested to Gruby—who could not find a suitable position because he refused to give up his religion—that he move to Paris, the great center of medical learning. Microscopy was little practiced there, and thus Paris offered a promising field for an experienced young man.

Gruby settled in Paris in 1840. Assisted by friends, he worked in the Foundling Hospital under the distinguished pediatrician Jacques François Baron and, urged by some foreign students, he began to give courses in microscopic anatomy and pathology which were attended by Claude Bernard, François Magendie, Henri Milne-Edwards, Pierre Flourens, and many foreign scientists.

At this time Gruby began to announce his discoveries of various microscopic fungi that produce skin diseases. In 1841 he found a fungus in favus, a contagious skin disease marked by round yellow crusts resembling honeycomb, usually situated over hair follicles and accompanied by intense itching. The following year he described *Trichophyton ectothrix,* a microscopic cryptogam, found at the roots of a man's beard, which caused the disease *Sycosis barbae.* Shortly afterward he discovered *Oidium albicans* (*Monilia albicans*), the cause of thrush in infants. In 1843 Gruby described another fungus, which he called *Microsporum audouini,* in honor of Jean Victor Audouin. In man *Microsporum* causes a form of tinea (ringworm) that is also called microsporia or Gruby's disease. Another form of ringworm, caused by *Trichophyton tonsurans,* was discovered and described by Gruby in 1844. The cause of favus, *Achorion schoenleini,* was first described by J. L. Schönlein, who was not certain whether it was the cause or a manifestation of the disease. Gruby showed that the disease could be produced experimentally in man or animals by inoculating the specific mold. His clinical descriptions were generally inadequate, but his descriptions of the microscopic features were so excellent that when his findings were later rediscovered and confirmed, not much could be added to his original reports. The idea of a plant parasite as a cause of disease in man was something quite new in the era before Pasteur; and Gruby was responsible for the firm establishment of this conception by his findings and experiments, against the doubts, opposition, and ridicule of many contemporary physicians.

In 1843 Gruby discovered an animal parasite in the blood of the frog that he called, because of its corkscrew shape, *Trypanosoma;* the name has been used for this important genus ever since. In the same year he described, in association with his friend Onésime Delafond, professor at the veterinary school at Alfort, another parasitic hematozoon in the dog microfilaria. They also showed (1852) that the disease could be induced in a healthy dog by intravenous transfusion of defibrinated blood from an infected animal. In 1859 Gruby described and depicted a parasitic mite (*Acarus*) producing skin disease called *Erythema autumnale.*

In 1847–1848, in the early period of general anesthesia administered by inhalation, Gruby made experiments on animals with ether and chloroform, which contributed to the knowledge of their effects on several bodily functions. He also emphasized the higher toxicity and quicker action of chloroform as compared with ether.

After 1845 Gruby published only a few papers, eventually spending all his time and energy on his medical practice. The cause of his loss of interest in scientific endeavor remains unknown.

BIBLIOGRAPHY

I. Original Works. Gruby's inaugural diss., *Observationes microscopicae ad morphologiam pathologicam* (Vienna, 1839), repub. in 1840 with the subtitle *Morphologia fluidorum pathologicorum, tomi primi, pars prima,* seems to be his only book on science. He published over 30 short papers, 21 of them in *Comptes rendus hebdomadaires des séances de l'Académie des sciences,* **13-34** (1841–1852). Six of them were written in collaboration with O. Delafond, and about 20 date from 1841–1845. Some of Gruby's papers were soon translated into German or English. Six of them, representing the foundation of medical mycology, were published "as a monument *aere perennius* of Gruby's scientific achievement" in an English trans. by S. J. Zakon and T. Benedek: "David Gruby and the Centenary of Medical Mycology 1841–1941," in *Bulletin of the History of Medicine,* **16** (1944), 155–168. A bibliography of Gruby's works was collected by R. Blanchard (1899) and is included (with some additions) in the biographies by L. Le Leu (1908), A. P. M. Salaun (1935), and B. Kisch (1954).

II. Secondary Literature. A full biography is B. Kisch, "David Gruby (1810–1898)," pt. 2 of "Forgotten Leaders in Modern Medicine," in *Transactions of the American Philosophical Society,* n.s. **44** (1954), 193–226. Of the older appreciations the most important are R. Blanchard, "David Gruby (1810–1898)," in *Archives de parasitologie,* **2** (1899), 43–74; L. Le Leu, *Le Dr. Gruby. Notes et souvenirs* (Paris, 1908), a volume of notes and recollections by Gruby's last (from 1888) private secretary; and A. P. M. Salaun, *La vie et l'oeuvre de David Gruby* (Bordeaux, 1935). There are several short biographies, such as T. Rosenthal, "David Gruby (1810–1898)," in *Annals of Medical History,* n.s. **4** (1932), 339–346; and several appreciations of his discoveries in the field of dermatomycoses: E. Podolsky, "David Gruby (1810–1898) and the Fungus Growth," in *Medical Annals of the District of Columbia,* **26** (1957), 24–26, 60; J. H. Rille, "David Gruby," in *Dermatologische Wochenschrift,* **83** (1926), 512–526; and J. Théodoridès, "L'oeuvre scientifique du Docteur Gruby," in *Revue d'histoire de médecine hébraïque,* **27** (1954), 27–38, 138–143.

V. Kruta

GUA DE MALVES, JEAN PAUL DE (*b.* near Carcassonne, France, *ca.* 1712; *d.* Paris, France, 2 June 1786), *mathematics, mineralogy, economics.*

Very little is known of de Gua's life, and even the

precise date and place of his birth are not established. According to Condorcet, he was struck by the contrast between the opulence of his first years and the privation that followed the ruin of his parents, Jean de Gua, baron of Malves, and Jeanne de Harrugue, in the wake of the bankruptcy of John Law in 1720. He planned an ecclesiastical career; while it seems that he never became a priest, this training nevertheless permitted him to obtain several benefices and pensions. After a stay in Italy he appears to have participated for a few years in the activities of the short-lived Société des Arts, a sort of scientific and technical academy founded in 1729 by Louis de Bourbon-Condé, prince of Clermont. In any case, he gradually acquired a thorough grounding in science.

De Gua's first publication (1740) was a work on analytic geometry inspired by both Descartes's *Géométrie* (1637) and Newton's *Enumeratio linearum tertii ordinis* (1704). Its principal aim was to develop a theory of algebraic plane curves of any degree (Descartes's "lignes géométriques") based essentially on algebra. Nevertheless, he drew on infinitesimal methods in order to simplify various calculations and recognized that their use is indispensable, particularly for everything involving the transcendental curves ("mécaniques"). De Gua was especially interested in tangents, asymptotes, and singularities: multiples, points, cusps, and points of inflection. In this area he skillfully used coordinate transformations and systematically made use of an "algebraic" or "analytic" triangle, obtained by a 45° rotation of Newton's parallelogram. The use of the latter had been popularized by the *Enumeratio* and by the commentaries of several of Newton's disciples, among them Brook Taylor, James Stirling, and s'Gravesande. The use of perspective allowed de Gua to associate the different types of points at a finite distance with various infinite branches of curves. Among his other contributions, he explicitly asserted that if a cubic admits three points of inflection, the latter are aligned. He also introduced two new types of cubics into the enumeration undertaken by Newton and Stirling, among others.

De Gua's treatise contributed to the rise of the theory of curves in the eighteenth century and partially inspired the subsequent works of Euler (1748), Gabriel Cramer (1750), A. P. Dionis du Séjour, and M. B. Goudin (1756). The fame of this work led to de Gua's election to the Royal Academy of Sciences as adjoint geometer on 18 March 1741, replacing P. C. Le Monnier. He presented several mathematical memoirs, two of which, published at the time, deal with the number of roots of an algebraic equation according to their nature and sign and with the famous rule of Descartes. However, on 3 June 1745, following a dispute de Gua renounced the pursuit of a normal academic career and requested that his modest position of associate be made honorary. Although he continued his scientific research, he seems to have moved away from the study of mathematics during this period. Not until the time of the reorganization of 23 April 1785 did he resume his place at the Academy, this time as a pensioner in the new class of natural history and mineralogy, which was closer to his new interests. Moreover, it seems that the contents of the several mathematical memoirs on spherical trigonometry and the geometry of polyhedra that he subsequently published in the *Histoire* of the Academy for 1783 date for the most part from the 1740's.

The career of de Gua was marked by several incidents which certainly resulted, at least in part, from difficulties inherent in his personality. His stay at the Collège Royal (Collège de France) was abnormally brief. Appointed on 30 June 1742 to the chair of Greek and Latin philosophy, which was vacant following the death of Joseph Privat de Molières, de Gua actually filled this post until 26 July 1748, when he resigned; he was replaced by P. C. Le Monnier. Like his predecessors and his successor, de Gua gave to his instruction an orientation having no connection with the official title of the chair; he dealt successively with Newtonian epistemology, differential and integral calculus, the principles of mathematics, arithmetic, and the philosophy of Locke—without, however, publishing anything based on his teaching.

Another incident took place during the same period. In 1745 the publisher A. F. Le Breton had joined with the Paris booksellers A. C. Briasson, M. A. David, and L. Durand for the purpose of publishing a much enlarged French version of the famous *Cyclopaedia* of Ephraim Chambers. Apparently appreciating de Gua's wide-ranging abilities, they made him responsible for the scientific material in the edition in a contract signed on 27 June 1746 in the presence of Diderot and d'Alembert, who acted both as witnesses and as consultants. The agreement was annulled on 3 August 1747. On 16 October 1747 de Gua, who had meanwhile mortgaged his other income to repay a portion of the advances he had received from the booksellers, was replaced by d'Alembert and Diderot as director of this project, which was to become the celebrated *Encyclopédie.*

De Gua next turned his attention to philosophy and political economy, translating works by George Berkeley and Matthew Decker, as well as a debate in the House of Commons that he introduced with a long "Avant-propos" on the problem of the interest rate on loans. At the same time he was actively interested in prospecting for gold in Languedoc and addressed several memoirs on this subject to the government. Having obtained, in 1764, an exploitation permit valid for twenty years, he undertook an unsuccessful venture that partially ruined him. In 1764 he published a work on mineral prospecting and composed the first six volumes of a series of *mémoires périodiques* on subjects in philosophy, science, economics, and so on; the series was never published—for lack, it seems, of official authorization. De Gua also was interested in lotteries, but beginning in the 1760's he specialized in mineralogy and conchology, which explains his change of sections at the Academy in 1785.

This disordered scientific activity and a taste for the unusual give to de Gua's work a special character. The interest of his first mathematical writings evokes regrets that he did not persevere in this direction.

BIBLIOGRAPHY

I. Original Works. Among de Gua's writings are *Usages de l'analyse de Descartes pour découvrir, sans le secours du calcul différentiel, les propriétés, ou affections principales des lignes géométriques de tous les ordres* (Paris, 1740); five mathematical memoirs in *Histoire de l'Académie royale des sciences:* "Démonstration de la règle de Descartes . . .," 72–96, and "Recherches des nombres des racines réelles ou imaginaires . . .," 435–494, in the volume for 1741 (Paris, 1744) and "Trigonométrique sphérique, déduite très brièvement . . .," 291–343, "Diverses mesures, en partie neuves, des aires sphériques et des angles solides . . .," 344–362, and "Propositions neuves . . . sur le tétraèdre . . .," 363–402, in the volume for 1783 (Paris, 1786); and *Projet d'ouverture et d'exploitation de minières et mines d'or et d'autres métaux aux environs du Cézé, du Gardon, de l'Eraut* [*sic*] *et d'autres rivières du Languedoc, du Comté de Foix, du Rouergue etc.* (Paris, 1764). He translated several works from English into French: George Berkeley, *Dialogues entre Hylas et Philonaüs contre les sceptiques et les athées* (Amsterdam, 1750); Matthew Decker, *Essai sur les causes du déclin du commerce étranger de la Grande Bretagne,* 2 vols. (n.p., 1757); and *Discours pour et contre la réduction de l'intérest naturel de l'argent, qui ayant été prononcés en 1737, dans la Chambre des communes du parlement de la Grande Bretagne, occasionnèrent en ce pays la réduction de 4 à 3%* . . . (Wesel–Paris, 1757)—"Avant-propos du traducteur," pp. i–clxviii, is by de Gua. With J. B. Romé de l'Isle he edited *Catalogue systématique et raisonné des curiosités de la nature et de l'art, qui composent le cabinet de M. Davila* . . . (Paris, 1767), for which he wrote I, pt. 2, 71–126: "Coquilles marines."

II. Secondary Literature. On de Gua or his work, see the following (listed chronologically): the *éloge* of M. J. A. N. Condorcet, read 15 Nov. 1786, in *Histoire de l'Académie royale des sciences pour l'année 1786* (Paris, 1788), pt. 1, 63–76; X. de Feller, ed., *Dictionnaire historique,* IV (Paris, 1808), 238; J. J. Weiss, in Michaud, ed., *Biographie universelle,* XVIII (Paris, 1817), 575–576, also in new ed., XVIII (Paris, 1857), 1–2; J. M. Quérard, *La France littéraire,* III (Paris, 1829), 494–495; Guyot de Fère, in F. Hoefer, ed., *Nouvelle biographie générale,* XXII (Paris, 1859), col. 278; Poggendorff, I, 967–968; *Intermédiare des mathématiciens,* VIII (1901), 158, and XI (1904), 148–149; P. Sauerbeck, "Einleitung in die analytische Geometrie der höheren algebraïschen Kurven nach der Methoden von Jean-Paul de Gua de Malves. Ein Beitrag zur Kurvendiskussion," in *Abhandlungen zur Geschichte der mathematischen Wissenschaften,* **15** (1902), 1–166; G. Loria, "Da Descartes e Fermat a Monge e Lagrange. Contributo alla storia della geometria analitica," in *Atti dell'Accademia nazionale dei Lincei. Memorie,* classe di scienze fisiche, matematiche e naturale, 5th ser., **14** (1923), 777–845; N. Nielsen, *Géomètres français du XVIIIe siècle* (Copenhagen–Paris, 1935), pp. 195–200; L. P. May, "Documents nouveaux sur l'*Encyclopédie,*" in *Revue de synthèse,* **15** (1938), 5–30; G. Loria, *Storia delle matematiche* (Milan, 1950), pp. 668–689, 739–740, 758, 851; and C. B. Boyer, *History of Analytic Geometry* (New York, 1956), pp. 174–175, 184, 194.

René Taton

GUCCIA, GIOVANNI BATTISTA (*b.* Palermo, Italy, 21 October 1855; *d.* Palermo, 29 October 1914), *mathematics.*

The son of Giuseppe Maria Guccia and Chiara Guccia-Cipponeri, Guccia belonged, through his father, to the noble Sicilian family of the marquis of Ganzaria. As a young man he was an ardent sportsman and was particularly interested in horsemanship. He studied first at Palermo, then at the University of Rome, where he was one of Luigi Cremona's best students. In 1880 he defended a thesis dealing with a class of surfaces representable, point by point, on a plane. Shortly before, he had presented a communication on certain rational surfaces dealt with in this work to the congress of the French Association for the Advancement of Science at Rheims and had been publicly congratulated by J. J. Sylvester. After returning to Palermo, Guccia pondered some grand schemes of theoretical research. In 1889 he was appointed to the newly created chair of higher geometry at the University of Palermo, a post he held for the rest of his life.

The path that Guccia followed throughout his career was that of the great Italian geometers of the nineteenth century. For them the synthetic method, aided by intuition, was the ideal instrument of discovery, more efficacious than the calculus, of which the artifices often conceal the logical structures and the relationships among the elements of a figure. To be sure, the role of algebra is not negligible, but it should be limited to what is linear, for the establishment of certain principles, and then give way to the intuitive method. Guccia's works concern primarily Cremona's plane transformations, the classification of linear systems of plane curves, the singularities of curves and of algebraic surfaces, and certain geometric loci which permit the projective properties of curves and surfaces to be deduced.

In studying the classification of linear systems of types 0 and 1, Guccia was inspired by the method used by Max Nöther to demonstrate that every Cremona transformation is the product of a finite number of quadratic transformations. Guccia's results were completed in 1888 by Corrado Segre, and the question was taken up in 1897 by Guido Castelnuovo in his memoir on linear systems of curves traced on an algebraic surface. In studying the singular points and singular curves of a surface, Guccia discovered theorems analogous to those for linear systems of curves. Although the majority of Guccia's publications are very short, they all contain original ideas and new relations profitably used by other geometers. This is particularly true of his researches on projective involutions, which laid the foundation for the generalizations of Federico Enriques and Francesco Severi. Occasionally, Guccia himself generalized from partial results, as in the case of the projective characteristics of plane algebraic curves and of their linear systems (where he introduced a projective definition of polars), which he extended to surfaces and to gauche curves.

In a period when knowledge of the geometry of algebraic surfaces was extremely limited, Guccia made a useful contribution. It was immediately exploited and absorbed by other mathematicians who, more attracted than he by analytical procedures, achieved greater fame. Compared with the work of his teacher Cremona, Guccia's is on a lower plane, if not in subtlety at least in extent and significance. Yet Guccia's chief merit lies elsewhere: his name remains associated with the foundation of the Circolo Matematico di Palermo.

In 1884, five years before his appointment to the university, Guccia had the idea of establishing a mathematical society in Palermo, for which he would furnish the meeting place, a library, and all necessary funds. His generous offer was favorably received, and on 2 March 1884 the society's provisional statutes were signed by twenty-seven members. The goal was to stimulate the study of higher mathematics by means of original communications presented by the members of the society on the different branches of analysis and geometry, as well as on rational mechanics, mathematical physics, geodesy, and astronomy. The group's activity was soon known abroad through the *Rendiconti del Circolo matematico di Palermo,* the first volume of which consisted of four sections appearing in July 1885, September 1886, December 1886, and September 1887. On 7 November 1887 Joseph Bertrand presented this volume to the Académie des Sciences of Paris, emphasizing its high scientific standard. On 26 February 1888 new statutes for the society authorized the election of foreign corresponding members, and the *Rendiconti* thereby became an international review. Guccia, who had placed his personal fortune at the disposal of the Circolo, established a mathematical publishing house in Palermo in 1893. To the *Rendiconti* he added *Supplemento ai Rendiconti del Circolo matematico di Palermo, Indici delle pubblicazioni del Circolo matematico di Palermo,* and *Annuario biografico del Circolo matematico di Palermo.* He also took personal charge of the editing of all these publications.

BIBLIOGRAPHY

I. Original Works. The list of mathematical works drawn up by de Franchis (see below) contains forty-four titles. Lectures given at the University of Palermo in 1889–1890 appeared as *Teoria generale delle curve e delle superficie algebriche* (Palermo, 1890). His longer arts. include "Teoremi sulle trasformazioni Cremoniane nel piano. Estensione di alcuni teoremi di Hirst sulle trasformazioni quadratiche," in *Rendiconti del Circolo matematico di Palermo,* **1** (1884–1887), 27, 56–57, 66, 119–132; "Generalizzazione di un teorema di Noether," *ibid.,* 139–156; "Sulla riduzione dei sistemi lineari di curve ellittiche e sopra un teorema generale delle curve algebriche di genere *p,*" *ibid.,* 169–189; "Sui sistemi lineari di superficie algebriche dotati di singolarità base qualunque," *ibid.,* 338–349; "Sulle singolarità composte delle curve algebriche piane," *ibid.,* **3** (1889), 241–259; "Ricerche sui sistemi lineari di curve algebriche piane, dotati di singolarità ordinarie," *ibid.,* **7** (1893), 193–255, and **9** (1895), 1–64; and "Un théorème sur les courbes algébriques planes d'ordre *n,*" in *Comptes rendus hebdomadaires des séances de l'Académie des sciences,* **142** (1906), 1256–1259.

II. Secondary Literature. See Michele de Franchis, "XXX anniversario della fondazione del Circolo matematico di Palermo . . .," in *Supplemento ai Rendiconti del Circolo matematico di Palermo,* **9** (1914), 1–68; and "G. B. Guccia, cenni biografici . . .," in *Rendiconti del Circolo matematico di Palermo,* **39** (1915), 1–14.

Pierre Speziali

GUDDEN, JOHANN BERNHARD ALOYS VON (*b.* Cleves, Germany, 7 June 1824; *d.* Lake Starnberg, near Schloss Berg, Germany, 13 June 1886), *psychiatry, neuroanatomy.*

Gudden was the third of seven sons of Johannes

Gudden, a landed proprietor in Lower Rhineland, and Bernhardine Fritzen. His feeling for exact observation and his aptitude for study became evident at an early age. After passing the final secondary school examination in the fall of 1843, he studied medicine in Bonn, Halle, and Berlin, where he passed the state medical examination with distinction in 1848. His dissertation, *Quaestiones de motu oculi humani* (1848), dealing with one of his fields of later research, revealed the originality of his investigations. It is possible that during his student years he was already in contact with the heads of psychiatric institutions, such as Maximilian Jacobi at Siegburg, near Bonn; August Damerow at Nietleben, near Halle; and Karl Wilhelm Ideler at the Charité in Berlin. Entry into the field of psychiatry was possible only through these institutions; the subject was rarely treated separately in the universities.

In 1849 Gudden obtained a position at the Siegburg asylum as an intern under Maximilian Jacobi, one of the leading German somatic psychiatrists. He married the latter's granddaughter Clarissa Voigt in 1855; they had nine children. From 1851 to 1855 Gudden worked with Wilhelm Roller at Illenau, a hospital known even outside Germany for its outstanding organization.

In 1855 Gudden was appointed director of the newly founded Werneck asylum near Würzburg. He supervised the transformation of the baroque palace, built by Balthasar Neumann, into Germany's most modern asylum; this achievement earned him a reputation as an excellent organizer. In the treatment of the mentally disturbed he rejected the methods of the older psychiatric schools at Siegburg and Illenau. Despite their humane conceptions these schools had continued the use of physical force and believed that "moral influence" and "educational" strictness were beneficial. An advocate of the principle of no restraint, Gudden championed, earlier than Wilhelm Griesinger and Ludwig Meyer, a liberal and humane orientation in the treatment of the mentally ill. Going beyond even John Conolly, he granted his patients an unprecedented measure of personal freedom. He insisted that proper treatment required communal social life for the patients, constant contact between physicians and patients, and a well-trained staff with a strong sense of duty.

In his articles "Ueber die Entstehung der Ohrblutgeschwulst" and "Ueber die Rippenbrüche bei Geisteskranken," Gudden demonstrated that reddening of the ears, rib fractures, and bedsores (which he considered an attendant symptom of mental illness, produced by injury to the "trophic nerve") were the consequences of mechanical therapy and insufficient care.

In 1869 Gudden became director of the recently constructed cantonal mental hospital in Burghölzli, near Zurich, and professor of psychiatry at the University of Zurich. Following the death of August Solbrig in 1872 he was named director of the district mental hospital in Munich; his practical talents were decisive in gaining him this appointment. Soon afterward he was also named professor of psychiatry at the University of Munich. The hospital, built by Solbrig in 1859, was enlarged and reorganized under Gudden's supervision, as was a second institution in Gabersee in 1883. Both were distinguished by the rational arrangement and distribution of their facilities. From 1870 Gudden was a coeditor of the *Archiv für Psychiatrie und Nervenkrankheiten.* He was ennobled in 1875.

In 1886, after he and other psychiatrists had examined records pertaining to the case, Gudden gave his opinion on the mental illness of Ludwig II of Bavaria. They diagnosed it as paranoia (what would now be called the paranoid form of schizophrenia). On the basis of this diagnosis, the king was relieved of all official duties. On 12 June 1886 he was taken by Gudden, who treated him with great consideration, to Schloss Berg, on Lake Starnberg, which was to serve as the king's residence. The following morning Gudden took a quiet walk with the king; they were accompanied by several attendants. That evening, at about 6:30, Gudden went for another walk with the king, this time without attendants. A few hours later both were found drowned in the lake, not far from the shore. (The evidence leaves little doubt that during the walk Ludwig suddenly ran into the shallow lake and that Gudden followed in order to restrain him; the powerful forty-year-old king then probably overpowered Gudden and drowned himself.)

In an early work, *Beiträge zur Lehre von den durch Parasiten bedingten Hautkrankheiten* (Stuttgart, 1855), Gudden conclusively verified through skillful clinical observations that scabies is a parasitic disease caused by mites. His major scientific work was, however, in three fields: care of the mentally ill, craniology, and cerebral anatomy. The last two were closely related, both by common experimental procedures and by the results obtained.

Through his practical work as well as through his publications on treatment of the mentally ill, most of which dealt with hospital administration, Gudden contributed significantly to liberating mental patients from treatment by physical force. In therapy his main concerns were that the hospital be rationally organized, that the personnel be properly trained, and that the curable—and even the incurable—patients be able to move about as freely as possible. Gudden's research did not deal with clinical psychopathology, an area which was investigated by his student Emil Kraepelin. Gudden was skeptical of systematic reflections that went beyond the individual case. In nosology he followed Griesinger's classification.

Gudden published his *Experimentaluntersuchungen über das Schädelwachstum* in 1874. In this work he showed that the growth of the cranium is essentially the result of interstitial processes; and he discovered that when sense organs and parts of the brain are extirpated, the cranial bones are also affected.

In cerebral anatomy, too, Gudden used extirpation in his research. Building on the observations of Ludwig Türck and Augustus Waller on secondary degeneration, he developed, through an ingenious combination of anatomical and experimental pathological investigations, the "Gudden method." By systematically destroying, on one side only, parts of the nervous system and of the brain in a newborn animal, he was able to induce atrophy of the conducting paths and centers; this made it possible, by means of a comparative examination of the two sides in the full-grown animal, to determine the functions of nerve fibers and nuclei. This method, which is still in use, allowed him to classify nerves that had previously been considered anatomically and physiologically similar into separate systems according to function and origin. Thus Gudden was the first to set forth many of the neuroanatomical facts generally accepted today concerning the paths, origins, and termini of the nerves, as well as many concerning the nuclei of the cranial nerves (the crossing of the optic nerve, the tractus opticus, the fornix, corpus mamillare, interpeduncular ganglion, and nuclei of the nerves of the eye muscle, among others). During his years in Munich he amassed, with his "Gudden microtome" (later improved by Auguste Forel), one of the world's largest collections of brain-tissue preparations.

Gudden was very cautious in drawing physiological conclusions from his research. He confined himself for the most part to recording morphological data, which he constantly reexamined under altered experimental conditions. His writings are characterized by their conciseness and by a wealth of carefully observed details. It took some time, however, for the scientific reliability of his findings to be recognized. He lacked the kind of intuitive inspiration possessed by, for instance, Theodor Meynert, whose research on cerebral anatomy he approved. Gudden's students Emil Kraepelin, Franz Nissl, Auguste Forel, and Sigbert Ganser all described him as having a commanding and magnetic personality. At the time of his death he was editing the results of his neuroanatomical research, the majority of which were still unpublished.

BIBLIOGRAPHY

I. Original Works. Gudden's writings include *Quaestiones de motu oculi humani* (Halle, 1848), his diss.; "Das Irrenwesen in Holland," in *Allgemeine Zeitschrift für Psychiatrie,* **10** (1853), 458–480; "Zur relativ verbundenen Irrenheil- und Pflegeanstalt," *ibid.,* **16** (1859), 627–632; "Über die Entstehung der Ohrblutgeschwulst," *ibid.,* **17** (1860), 121–138; **19** (1862), 190–220; **20** (1863), 423–430; *Beitrag zur Lehre von der Scabies,* 2nd ed. (Würzburg, 1863); *Der Tagesbericht der Kreisirrenanstalt Werneck* (Würzburg, 1869); "Ueber einen bisher nicht beschriebenen Nervenfaserstrang im Gehirn der Säugethiere und Menschen," in *Archiv für Psychiatrie und Nervenkrankheiten,* **2** (1870), 364–366; "Anomalien des menschlichen Schädels," *ibid.,* 367–373; "Ueber die Rippenbrüche bei Geisteskranken," *ibid.,* 682–692; "Experimentaluntersuchungen über das peripherische und centrale Nervensystem," *ibid.,* 693–723; *Experimentaluntersuchungen über das Schädelwachsthum* (Munich, 1874); "Ueber die Kreuzung der Fasern im Chiasma n. optici," in *Albrecht von Graefes Archiv für Ophthalmologie,* **20,** no. 2 (1874), 249–268; **21,** no. 3 (1875), 201–203; **25,** no. 1 (1879), 1–56; **25,** no. 4 (1879), 237–246; "Ueber ein neues Mikrotom," in *Archiv für Psychiatrie und Nervenkrankheiten,* **5** (1875), 229–244; "Ueber den Tractatus peduncularis transversus," *ibid.,* **11** (1881), 415–423; "Mittheilung über das Ganglion interpedunculare," *ibid.,* 424–427; "Ueber zwei verschiedene Fasersysteme im N. opticus," in *Tageblatt der Eisenacher Naturforscherversammlung* (1882), 307–310; "Ueber das Corpus mamillare und die sogenannten Schenkel des Fornix," in *Allgemeine Zeitschrift für Psychiatrie,* **41** (1884), 697–701; "Ueber die neuroparalytische Entzündung," *ibid.,* 714–715; *Jahresbericht der Kreisirrenanstalt München* (1885); "Ueber die Sehnerven, den Sehtractus, etc.," in *Allgemeine Zeitschrift für Psychiatrie,* **42** (1885), 347–348; "Ueber die Einrichtung von sogenannten Ueberwachungsstationen," *ibid.,* 454–456; and "Ueber die Frage der Lokalisation der Functionen der Grosshirnrinde," *ibid.,* 478–497. Other articles are in *Korrespondenzblatt für schweizer Ärzte* (1871), no. 5; (1872), no. 4; and in *Ärztliche Intelligenzblatt* (1884).

R. Grashey collected and edited Gudden's published and unpublished works on cerebral anatomy in the lavishly illustrated *B. v. Gudden. Gesammelte und hinterlassene Abhandlungen* (Wiesbaden, 1889).

II. Secondary Literature. On Gudden or his work, see Sigbert Ganser, in Theodor Kirchhoff, ed., *Deutsche Irrenärzte,* II (Berlin, 1924), 47–58; Hubert Grashey, "Nekrolog auf Bernhard von Gudden," in *Archiv für Psy-*

chiatrie und Nervenkrankheiten, **17** (1886), i–xxix; and "Nachtrag zum Nekrolog," *ibid.,* **18** (1887), 898; Ernst Grünthal, in Kurt Kolle, ed., *Grosse Nervenärzte,* I (Stuttgart, 1956), 128–134; Emil Kraepelin, "Bernhard von Gudden, ein Gedenkblatt," in *Münchener medizinische Wochenschrift,* **33** (1886), 577–580, 603–607; H. Laehr, in *Allgemeine Zeitschrift für Psychiatrie,* **43** (1887), 163–168; Theodor Meynert, in *Wiener medizinische Blätter,* **9** (1886), 24; and *Allgemeine Zeitschrift für Psychiatrie,* **43** (1887), 177–186; Franz Nissl, "Bernhard von Guddens hirnanatomische Experimentaluntersuchungen," in *Zeitschrift für Psychiatrie,* **51** (1895), 527; James W. Papez, in Webb Haymaker, ed., *The Founders of Neurology* (Springfield, Ill., 1953), pp. 45–48; E. Rehm, "König Ludwig II. und Professor Gudden," in *Psychologische neurologische Wochenschrift,* **38** (1936), 45; Hugo Spatz, "Bernhard von Gudden," in *Münchener medizinische Wochenschrift,* **103** (1961), 1277–1282; and Wallenberg, in *Archiv für Psychiatrie,* **76** (1925), 21–46.

HANS HENNING SCHROTH

GUDERMANN, CHRISTOPH (*b.* Vienenburg, near Hildesheim, Germany, 25 March 1798; *d.* Münster, Germany, 25 September 1852), *mathematics.*

Gudermann's father was a teacher. After graduating from secondary school Gudermann was to have studied to become a priest, but in Göttingen he studied, among other things, mathematics. From 1823 he was a teacher at the secondary school in Kleve; and from 1832 until his death he taught at the Theological and Philosophical Academy in Münster, first as associate professor, and from 1839 as full professor, of mathematics.

Gudermann's scientific work forms part of German mathematics in the second quarter of the nineteenth century. The characteristic feature of this period is that the ideas of transforming mathematics had been expressed or indicated, but understanding and realizing them in results or comprehensive theories was still beyond the capabilities of the mathematicians; this was achieved only in the second half of the century. Much preparatory work had to be carried out for this transformation. As soon as comprehensive, sufficiently accurate and general theories had been established, the preparatory work was forgotten. This was also the fate of Gudermann's work; he is known as the teacher of Karl Weierstrass rather than as an original thinker.

The depth of Gudermann's understanding of the contemporary trends in mathematics is substantiated by the topic which he discussed in his own work. C. F. Gauss's influence on Gudermann is still unclear, but the topic he chose is close to the intellectual environment of Gauss and his followers. Basically, Gudermann considered only two groups of problems: spherical geometry and the theory of special functions.

His book *Grundriss der analytischen Sphärik* (1830) deals with the former. He considered the study of spherical geometry important for several reasons. In the introduction he pointed out that a plane was a special case of a spherical surface, that is, a sphere with an infinite radius. For this reason and because of its constant curvature there exist many similarities between spherical geometry and plane geometry; yet at the same time Gudermann considered scientifically more interesting the study of cases in which this similarity no longer holds. As part of this program he sought to establish an analytical system for spherical surfaces akin to that formed by the coordinate system in planimetry. But he had to admit the existence of insurmountable difficulties if the required simplicity of the analytical means was to be preserved. At some points in the book Gudermann came close to problems which were important for non-Euclidean geometry but did not stress them, nor did he explicitly mention this aspect.

Gudermann devoted much more attention to the theory of special functions. After the earlier works of Leonhard Euler, John Landen, and A. M. Legendre (Gauss's results were still in manuscript), Niels Abel's studies on elliptical functions, published mostly in A. L. Crelle's *Journal für die reine und angewandte Mathematik,* represented an important divide in treating this area. In 1829 Carl Jacobi's book *Fundamenta nova theoriae functionum ellipticarum* was published. At the time Gudermann was one of the first mathematicians to expand on these results. Beginning with volume **6** (1830) of Crelle's *Journal,* he published a series of papers which he later summarized in two books: *Theorie der Potenzial- oder cyklisch-hyperbolischen Functionen* (1833) and *Theorie der Modular-Functionen und der Modular-Integrale* (1844), which were to have had a sequel which was never written.

In these books Gudermann went back to the origin of the theory of special functions—the problems of integral calculus—and stressed the genetic connection between simply periodic functions and elliptical functions. Since he did not neglect the requirements of integral calculus, he saw the necessity of arranging the theory to allow for numerical calculations. The key appeared to be in the development of the functions into infinite series and infinite products and in the use of suitable transformations. This made it possible to present extensive numerical tables in his first book and to work through to the nucleus of the theory of special functions in his second book, indicating the way which subsequently proved to be exceptionally fruitful. Thus he also came close to Gauss's intentions. Gudermann also introduced a notation for elliptical functions—*sn, cn,* and *dn*—which was adopted. He himself called elliptical functions "Modularfunctionen." It was pointed out later that Gudermann's work had an excess of special cases which in time lost interest.

Gudermann's work drew deserved attention in Germany in the 1830's. Since he was one of the few university professors to treat the problems of elliptical functions systematically, Karl Weierstrass came from the University of Bonn in 1839–1840 to attend Gudermann's lectures and presented "Über die Entwicklung der Modularfunctionen" as a *Habilitationsschrift* in 1841.

Gudermann was one of the first to realize Weierstrass' mathematical talent and scientific ability. Weierstrass, using Gudermann's idea of the development of functions into series and products, formed the principal, mighty, and accurate tool of the theory of functions.

BIBLIOGRAPHY

I. Original Works. Gudermann's books include *Grundriss der analytischen Sphärik* (Cologne, 1830); *Theorie der Potenzial- oder cyklisch-hyperbolischen Functionen* (Berlin, 1833); *Theorie der Modular-Functionen und der Modular-Integrale* (Berlin, 1844); and *Über die wissenschaftliche Anwedung der Belagerungs-Geschütze* (Münster, 1850).

II. Secondary Literature. See *Neue deutsche Biographie,* VII, 252–253; F. Klein, *Vorlesungen über die Entwicklung der Mathematik im 19. Jahrhundert,* I (Berlin, 1926), 278 f.; *Encyklopädie der mathematischen Wissenschaften,* II (Leipzig, 1913); and R. Sturm, "Gudermanns Urteil über die Prüfungsarbiet von Weierstrass (1841)," in *Jahresbericht der Deutschen Mathematiker-Vereinigung,* **19** (1910), 160.

Luboš Nový

GUENTHER, ADAM WILHELM SIEGMUND (*b.* Nuremberg, Germany, 6 February 1848; *d.* Munich, Germany, 3 February 1923), *mathematics, geography, meteorology, history of science.*

Guenther was the son of a Nuremberg businessman, Ludwig Leonhard Guenther, and Johanna Weiser. In 1872 he married Maria Weiser; they had one daughter and three sons, one of whom was the political economist and sociologist Gustav Adolf Guenther.

Guenther studied mathematics and physics from 1865 at Erlangen, Heidelberg, Leipzig, Berlin, and Göttingen. He received his doctorate from Erlangen with *Studien zur theoretischen Photometrie* (1872). He participated in the Franco-Prussian War and then took the teaching examination for mathematics and physics. In 1872 he became a teacher at Weissenburg, Bavaria, and immediately qualified for university lecturing at Erlangen with *Darstellung der Näherungswerte der Kettenbrüche in independenter Form* (Erlangen, 1872–1873). Guenther went to the Munich Polytechnicum as a *Privatdozent* in mathematics in 1874 and to Ansbach in 1876 as professor of mathematics and physics at the Gymnasium. From 1886 to 1920 he was professor of geography at the Munich Technische Hochschule, and from 1911 to 1914 he was rector of this school. A member of the Liberal party, he served in the German Reichstag from 1878 to 1884 and in the Bavarian Landtag from 1884 to 1899 and from 1907 to 1918. During World War I he headed the Bavarian flying weather service, beginning in 1917.

Guenther's numerous books and journal articles encompass both pure mathematics and its history and physics, geophysics, meteorology, geography, and astronomy. The individual works on the history of science, worth reading even today, bear witness to a thorough study of the sources, a remarkable knowledge of the relevant secondary literature, and a superior descriptive ability. Although it is true that his compendia contain a great many names and references, only hint at particulars, and are outdated today, they are nevertheless characteristic of their time.

BIBLIOGRAPHY

I. Original Works. Guenther's principal writings are *Zur reinen Mathematik: Lehrbuch der Determinantentheorie* (Erlangen, 1875; 2nd ed., 1877); *Die Lehre von den gewöhnlichen verallgemeinerten Hyperbelfunktionen* (Halle, 1881); and *Parabolische Logarithmen und parabolische Trigonometrie* (Leipzig, 1882).

On physics, geography, and related fields, see *Einfluss der Himmelskörper auf Witterungsverhältnisse,* 2 vols. (Halle, 1877–1879); *Lehrbuch der Geophysik und physikalischen Geographie,* 2 vols. (Stuttgart, 1884–1885), 2nd ed. entitled *Handbuch der Geophysik* (1897–1899); *Handbuch der mathematischen Geographie* (Stuttgart, 1891); and *Didaktik und Methodik des Geographie-Unterrichtes* (Munich, 1895).

Works on the history of science include *Vermischte Untersuchungen zur Geschichte der mathematischen Wissenschaften* (Leipzig, 1876); *Ziele und Resultäte der neueren mathematisch-historischen Forschung* (Erlangen, 1876); *Antike Näherungsmethoden im Lichte moderner Mathematik* (Prague, 1878); "Geschichte des mathematischen Unterrichtes im deutschen Mittelalter bis zum Jahre 1525," in *Monumenta Germaniae paedagogica,* III (Berlin,

1887); "Abriss der Geschichte der Mathematik und Naturwissenschaften im Altertum," in *Handbuch der klassischen Altertumswissenschaften,* 2nd ed., V. supp. 1 (1894): *Geschichte der anorganischen Naturwissenschaften im 19. Jahrhundert* (Berlin, 1901); *Entdeckungsgeschichte und Fortschritte der Geographie im 19. Jahrhundert* (Berlin, 1902); *Geschichte der Erdkunde* (Vienna, 1904); and *Geschichte der Mathematik,* I, *Von den aeltesten Zeiten bis Cartesius* (Leipzig, 1908; repr., 1927).

Guenther was coeditor of *Zeitschrift für mathematischen und naturwissenschaftlichen Unterricht* (1876–1886); *Zeitschrift für das Ausland* (1892–1893); *Münchener geographische Studien* (from 1896); *Mitteilungen zur Geschichte der Medizin und der Naturwissenschaften* (from 1901); and *Forschungen zur bayerischen Landeskunde* (1920–1921).

II. SECONDARY LITERATURE. Obituaries include E. von Drygalski, in *Jahrbuch der bayerischen Akademie der Wissenschaften* (1920–1923), pp. 79–83; *Geographische Zeitschrift,* **29** (1923), 161–164; L. Günther, in *Lebensläufe aus Franken,* IV (1930), 204–219; W. Schüller, in *Zeitschrift für mathematischen und naturwissenschaftlichen Unterricht,* **56** (1925), 109–113; H. Wieleitner, in *Mitteilungen zur Geschichte der Medizin und der Naturwissenschaften,* **22** (1923), 1–2; and August Wilhelm, in *Neue deutsche Biographie,* VI (1966), 266–267.

J. E. HOFMANN

GUERICKE (GERICKE), OTTO VON (*b.* Magdeburg, Germany, 20 November 1602; *d.* Hamburg, Germany, 11 May 1686), *engineering, physics.*

Guericke was the son of Hans Gericke and Anna von Zweidorff. As the scion of a patrician family long established in Magdeburg he was destined to participate in political life. He was registered in the Faculty of Arts at the University of Leipzig from 1617 to 1620; attended the University of Helmstedt in 1620; and studied law at Jena in 1621 and 1622. Guericke then went to Leiden, where in addition to studying law he also attended lectures on mathematics and engineering, especially fortification.

Upon his return to Germany Guericke was elected an alderman of the city of Magdeburg in 1626; in the same year he married Margarethe Alemann, who died in 1645 (his second wife was Dorothea Lentke, whom he married in 1652). In 1630 he assumed the additional duties of city contractor. After the destruction of the city in 1631, Guericke worked in Brunswick and Erfurt as an engineer for the Swedish government; from 1635 he performed the same duties for the electorate of Saxony. This dual position allowed Guericke to serve Magdeburg throughout the Thirty Years' War, during which time he acted as envoy to the changing occupation powers. He further represented Magdeburg at the subsequent peace conferences and later at the Imperial Diet in Regensburg.

Diplomacy consumed much of Guericke's time from 1642 to 1666. He was also mayor of Magdeburg (1646–1676). He devoted his brief leisure to scientific experimentation, however, and his attendance at international congresses and princely courts allowed him to take part in the exchange of scientific ideas. Guericke presented some of his own experiments on several occasions at Regensburg in 1653–1654 and again in 1663 at the court of the Great Elector in Berlin. He also learned of new scientific developments in such circumstances; at Osnabrück in 1646 he first heard of Descartes's new physics and at Regensburg he was introduced to the experiments of Torricelli, who was working on the problem of the vacuum, as was Guericke himself, but from another point of view.

Indeed, Guericke had been preoccupied ever since his student days at Leiden with the question of the definition of space. A convinced Copernican, he was particularly concerned with three fundamental questions: (1) What is the nature of space? Can empty space exist, or is space always filled and empty space only a *spatium imaginarium,* a logical abstraction? (2) How can individual heavenly bodies affect each other across space, and how are they moved? (3) Is space, and therefore the heavenly bodies enclosed in it, bounded or unbounded?

Descartes's conception of space and matter as equivalent and his denial of a vacuum led Guericke to propose an experiment designed to resolve the old conflict between plenists and vacuists. Guericke posited that if the air were pumped out of a strong container and no other new material allowed to take its place the vessel would implode if Descartes's assertions were true. Soon after he returned from Osnabrück in 1647 Guericke made a suction pump using a cylinder and piston to which he added two flap valves; he then used this apparatus to pump water out of a well-caulked beer cask. Air entered the cask, however, as was evidenced by whistling noises. When Guericke repeated the experiment with the beer cask sealed within a second larger one that he had also filled with water, the water that he pumped out was replaced by water seeping in from the larger vessel.

In an attempt to solve the sealing problem Guericke ordered the construction of a hollow copper sphere with an outlet at the bottom. He pumped the air directly out of this apparatus which thereupon imploded. This result would seem to indicate that Descartes was right; but Guericke still thought otherwise on the basis of his earlier experiments. He had a new apparatus made, and with this his experiment succeeded. Guericke thus invented the air pump, or, rather, discovered the pumping capacity of air. He had thought that the air within the vessel would sink, as had the water in his previous devices, and that it would be evacuated from the bottom; later experiments, however, in which the outlet was placed at arbitrary points on the copper sphere proved that the air left in the container during the process of evacuation was distributed evenly throughout the interior space.

This discovery of the elasticity of the air represents perhaps the most important result of Guericke's experiments. From it he was led to investigate the decrease of the density of the air with height and to theorize concerning empty space beyond the atmosphere of heavenly bodies; to study variations of air pressure corresponding to changes in the weather (taking mean air pressure to correspond to a water column twenty Magdeburg ells high, he succeeded in 1660 in making barometric weather forecasts); to propose systematic weather reporting through a network of observation stations; to come to know the ponderability of air within air; and finally, to draw further conclusions about a variety of phenomena connected with vacuums, most of which he demonstrated experimentally, especially the work capacity of air, by which he refuted the theory of *horror vacui.*

The most famous of Guericke's public experiments is the one of the Magdeburg hemispheres, in which he placed together two copper hemispheres, milled so that the edges fit together snugly. He then evacuated the air from the resulting sphere and showed that a most heavy weight could not pull them apart. Contrary to legend, the demonstration was performed with a team of horses for the first time in Magdeburg in 1657 (not Regensburg in 1654) and repeated at court in Berlin in 1663. Guericke also made other, less dramatic, public demonstrations of the effectiveness of air pressure on several occasions in Regensburg; these Regensburg experiments were reported by Gaspar Schott in *Mechanica hydraulico-pneumatica* (1657) and *Technica curiosa* (1664), and were supplemented with additional information that Guericke communicated by letter.

Schott's books as well as other foreign publications of Guericke's experiments (for example, works of M. Cornaeus and S. Lubieniecky) stimulated Huygens and Boyle, among others, to repeat and extend the experiments and to set to work upon an improved air pump. Guericke himself was occupied with the same project; he improved his pump with hydraulic sealing and devised a stationary installation for it (it occupied two floors of his house). In 1663 Guericke developed a portable pump modeled on one of Boyle's and constructed one especially for his visit to Berlin in that year. (Three examples of this type of pump survive, one each in Munich, Lund, and Brunswick.)

Guericke's experimental work, however, represents only one facet of his attempt to reach a complete physical world view. He drew upon his Copernicanism to construct the foundations for such a system. Guericke's celestial physics were further based upon the notion that the heavenly bodies interacted with each other across empty space through magnetic force; here he turned to the earlier work of Gilbert and Kepler. Their magnetic hypotheses had been refuted by Athanasius Kircher (in *Magnes sive De arte magnetica,* 1641); joining the argument, Guericke sought to modify Gilbert's magnetism experiments by making use of materials mimicking the actual composition of the earth. To this end Guericke cast a sphere composed of a variety of minerals with a large proportion of sulfur—in later experiments he used pure sulfur—and showed that it possessed the *virtutes mundanae,* that is, such powers as attraction and the ability to move other bodies. By rubbing the sphere of sulfur, Guericke had actually produced static electricity; but since he did not recognize these electrical effects as special phenomena, but as demonstrations of the *virtutes* of a celestial body, he cannot properly be credited with the invention of the first electrical machine.

Having dealt with the problems of empty space and the movement of heavenly bodies, Guericke concerned himself further with the question of the boundedness of space and the number of worlds therein. He conceived of fixed stars as suns with planetary systems, each of which exerts a sphere of force (*orbis virtutis, sphaera activitatis*); these systems border on each other and do not interact—each heavenly body rather possesses a specific center of gravity for a specific *virtus conservativa,* which he interpreted as its source of cohesion. Thus, in opposition to Aristotelian cosmography, an immaterial boundary of space becomes inconceivable. Giordano Bruno had already speculated about an infinite universe containing an infinite number of worlds, but his ideas had been unacceptable because only God was considered infinite—all of God's creation must be finite. Guericke overcame this objection by redefining the notion of nothingness. By his reasoning, empty space as a mere receptacle for God's creations is nothingness and is not created. Empty space is therefore independent of God and the created universe—indeed, it precedes the latter. Therefore empty space cannot be bounded. Neither can the number of worlds be bounded, although such a number is not infinite (since there are no infinite numbers). Likewise it is not limited, since there is no greatest number and no end to the series of numbers. Infinite space is thus a conceptual possibility.

Such speculations about the heavenly bodies quite naturally led Guericke to the study of astronomy. He explained planetary orbits as exactly circular and concentric, effected by the rotating *orbis virtutis* of the sun, and interpreted the apparent eccentricities as a result of the different densities of the atmosphere.

In 1666 Guericke was made a noble and his family name became von Guericke. In 1681 he retired from his public offices and went to live in Hamburg with his son, a magistrate of Brandenburg. He spent the rest of his life there.

BIBLIOGRAPHY

I. Original Works. Guericke's most important published work is *Experimenta nova, ut vocantur, de vacuo spatio* . . . (Amsterdam, 1672; repr. Aalen, 1962).

His letters to Schott, Lubieniecky, Leibniz, and others may be found in Hans Schimank, trans. and ed., with the collaboration of Hans Gossen, Gregor Maurach, and Fritz Krafft, *Otto von Guerickes Neue (sogenannte) Magdeburger Versuche über den leeren Raum, nebst Briefen, Urkunden und anderen Zeugnissen seiner Lebens- und Schaffensgeschichte* (Düsseldorf, 1968), which also contains a full bibliography by Krafft current through 1967.

II. Secondary Literature. In addition to Schimank, above, see Alfons Kauffeld, *Otto von Guericke: Philosophisches über den leeren Raum* (Berlin, 1968); Fritz Krafft, "Experimenta nova. Untersuchungen zur Geschichte eines wissenschaftlichen Buches. I," in Eberhard Schmauderer, ed., *Buch und Wissenschaft* . . . (Düsseldorf, 1969), XVII, 103–129, in the series Technikgeschichte in Einzeldarstellungen; and "Sphaera activitatis—orbis virtutis," in *Sudhoffs Archiv: Zeitschrift für Wissenschaftsgeschichte,* **54** (1970), 113–140.

Fritz Krafft

GUERTLER, WILLIAM MINOT (*b.* Hannover, Germany, 10 March 1880; *d.* Hannover, 21 March 1959), *metallography, metallurgy.*

Guertler was the son of Alexander Guertler, a physician. After graduating from the Gymnasium in Hameln in 1899 he studied variously until 1904 at the Technische Hochschule in Hannover, the University of Munich, and the University of Göttingen, from which he earned the doctorate in 1904 under Gustav Tammann. He worked as Tammann's assistant until 1906. From 1906 to 1908 Guertler was an assistant at the Technische Hochschule in Berlin; in 1908 he joined the faculty as a doctor of engineering.

In the academic year 1908–1909 Guertler was a research associate at the Massachusetts Institute of Technology; he worked there again in 1911. From 1909 to 1914 he worked, without pay, with A. Doeltz at the Metallurgical Institute of the Berlin Technische Hochschule. He was head assistant at the Institute in 1917, became professor there in the same year, and eventually served as deputy director (1921–1928) and director (1929). In 1930 he was appointed to teach at the Institute for Applied Metallurgy; he was promoted to professor and director of the institute in 1933. In 1936 he assumed the additional posts of professor and director of the Institute for Metallurgy and the Science of Materials at the Technische Hochschule in Dresden. He reached retirement age in 1945 and from then until 1956 was a guest professor at the Technical University in Istanbul and at M.I.T.

Guertler's lifework concerned pure and applied metallurgy, which he developed into an independent scientific discipline. He did not restrict himself to a purely academic approach to the subject but rather sought to consider all aspects of the study of metals—both theoretically and technologically—and to apply his results in the metal industry. At the beginning of his researches he systematically investigated the constitution of metals; he was especially interested in the conductivity of alloys. He discovered that the value of the conductivity of a compound composed of several metals is always less than the sum of the conductivities of the components. Through his work on nomenclature Guertler established many new metallurgical concepts, including segregation and peritectonics. He also developed new alloys, largely those of nonferrous metals and most notably those of silver and aluminum. In 1926 he was selected to give the Campbell Memorial Lecture; he also made lecture tours in India, Japan, and the United States.

Guertler was, moreover, a pioneer in the scientific organization of his field. Besides writing books—particularly the handbook *Metallographie* (begun in 1912)—he founded such periodicals as the *Internationale Zeitschrift für Metallographie* in 1911 (called *Zeitschrift für Metallkunde* after 1919). Further, he established the German Metallographic Society and the German Society for Technical Röntgenology.

BIBLIOGRAPHY

I. Original Works. Guertler wrote more than 300 scientific papers and books and was awarded some 100 patents for his methods and devices. For bibliography, see Poggendorff, V, 462–463; VI, pt. 2, 973–974; and VIIa, pt. 2, 314–315.

His many papers and monographs include his diss. *Über wasserfreie Borate und über Entglasung* (Leipzig, 1904); "Die elektrische Leitfähigkeit der Legierungen," in *Zeit-*

schrift für anorganische Chemie, **51** (1906), 397–433; **54** (1907), 58–88; see also Guertler's paper on electric conductivity in *Physikalische Zeitschrift,* **9** (1908), 29–36, 404–405; **11** (1910), 476–479; "Stand der Forschung über die elektrische Leitfähigkeit der kristallisierten Metallegierungen," in *Jahrbuch der Radioaktivität und Elektronik,* **5** (1908), 17–81; **6** (1909), 127; "Beiträge zur Kenntnis der Elektrizitätsleitung in Metallen und Legierungen," *ibid.,* **17** (1920), 276–292, 298–299; "Vereinheitlichung der Benennung metallischer Produkte," in *Zeitschrift für Metallkunde,* **11** (1919), 200; *Richtlinien zur Gewinnung eines Überblicks über den Aufbau von Dreistoffsystemen,* no. 1 in the series Forschungsarbeiten zur Metallkunde, of which Guertler was editor (Berlin, 1923); *Sechs Vorlesungen zur Einführung in das Verständnis der modernen Spezialstähle,* Forschungsarbeiten zur Metallkunde, no. 8 (Berlin, 1928); "Colloidal Conditions in Metal Crystals," in J. Alexander, ed., *Colloid Chemistry,* III (New York, 1931), 439–448.

See also, under his editorship, *Metallographie. Ein ausführliches Lehr- und Handbuch der Konstitution und der physikalischen, chemischen und technischen Eigenschaften der Metalle und metallischen Legierungen,* I–III (Berlin, 1912–1935), of which Guertler is also author of numerous parts; *Metalltechnischer Kalender* (Berlin, 1922); *Vom Erz zum metallischen Werkstoff* (Leipzig, 1929), vol. I of *Der metallische Werkstoff,* ed. with W. Leitgebel; *Einführung in die Metallkunde,* 2 vols. (Leipzig, 1943), later published as *Metallkunde,* I (Berlin, 1954) and the new series of *Archiv für Metallkunde.*

II. Secondary Literature. On Guertler and his work, see W. Claus, "William M. Guertler. Zum 60. Geburtstag am 10.3.1940," in *Metall: Wirtschaft, Wissenschaft, Technik,* **19** (1940), 175–176; F. Erdmann-Jesnitzer, "William Guertler †," in *Bergakademie,* **11** (1959), 334; B. Trautmann, "Guertler, William Minot," in *Neue deutsche Biographie,* VII (1966), 287–288; and "William Guertler †," in *Zeitschrift für Metallkunde,* **50** (1959), 239.

Hans-Günther Körber

GUETTARD, JEAN-ÉTIENNE (*b.* Étampes, Seine-et-Oise, France, 22 September 1715; *d.* Paris, France, 6 January 1786), *geology, natural history, botany.*

A versatile scientist trained in medicine and chemistry, Guettard gradually acquired knowledge of the various branches of natural history. Although always concerned to some degree with all these fields, most of his career, especially after about 1746, was devoted to geology, and his reputation now rests upon two achievements: his discovery of the volcanic nature of Auvergne, and his attempt to construct a geological map of France.

Guettard's schooling in Étampes, nearby Montargis, and Paris was less important in shaping his career than was the influence of his maternal grandfather, François Descurain, a physician and apothecary in Étampes, as well as an amateur botanist and friend of Bernard de Jussieu. Guettard's early activities followed the pattern set by Descurain. While studying in Paris, he was introduced, probably by Jussieu, to naturalist-physicist René Antoine Ferchault de Réaumur and by 1741 had become curator of Réaumur's natural history collection. As Réaumur's assistant, he also conducted experiments on the regeneration of marine polyps. In 1742 he was admitted to the Faculté de Médecine de Paris, and on 3 July 1743 was elected to the Académie Royale des Sciences as an *adjoint botaniste.* At the same time he began to take field trips in the Loire Valley and in Normandy and to form his own natural history collection. His first major publication, *Observations sur les plantes* (1747), was a botanical study of the environs of Étampes, based upon a manuscript by his grandfather.

By 1747 Guettard had become *médecin botaniste* to Louis, duc d'Orléans, the two men having in common not only their religious views—both were devout Jansenists—but also their interest in the chemical analysis of minerals and rocks. After the duke's death in 1752, his son, Louis-Philippe, continued to support Guettard and he was given rooms in the Palais-Royal. With a laboratory at his disposal and an assured income, Guettard was free to devote himself entirely to scientific research. The remainder of his career is remarkable for his many long field trips, the development of a large scientific correspondence, and the publication of numerous articles often of the length and character of small monographs.

All of Guettard's scientific work bears the stamp of the Baconian naturalist who consciously avoided the formulation of theories. He attacked the ideas of the natural theologians, the cosmology and geology of Buffon, and the biology of Charles Bonnet, labeling all such systems premature, scientifically unsound, or philosophically dangerous and tending toward materialism. Although his own work is not free of preconceptions, Guettard tried to avoid drawing conclusions from his data. Thus, while his studies of sedimentation and erosion provided the kind of evidence other geologists were using to suggest an extension of the time scale beyond the biblical 6,000 years, Guettard's own writings contain no hint of such ideas. Similarly, his studies of the comparative anatomy of fossil and living forms led him only to deny repeatedly the likelihood that species can become extinct. It was therefore left to his contemporaries and successors to recognize the implications of Guettard's work.

Most of Guettard's field trips within France—he also traveled in the Low Countries, Italy, Switzerland, and Poland—were undertaken to supply data for a national geological survey and are thus of relatively small intrinsic interest apart from the larger project. A notable exception was his voyage to Auvergne in 1751, accompanied by his friend Chrétien-Guillaume de Lamoignon de Malesherbes. During this journey Guettard noticed that volcanic rocks were often used in the construction of local roads and dwellings; he examined the quarries and concluded that the whole region was volcanic. This discovery was announced in his "Mémoire sur quelques montagnes de la France qui ont été des volcans" (*Mémoires de l'Académie royale des sciences pour l'année 1752* [1756], pp. 27–59). He did not pursue the subject further, but this memoir induced several of his contemporaries to study the geological history of Auvergne, and the region very soon became a tourist attraction. Years later the priority of Guettard's discovery was challenged by Barthélemy Faujas de Saint-Fond in his *Recherches sur les volcans éteints du Vivarais et du Velay* (1778). Whether or not anyone had in fact anticipated Guettard, as Faujas claimed, it is certain that Guettard's discovery was made independently and was the first public announcement.

In the well-known controversy over the nature of columnar basalt, Guettard at first supported the view that these formations were not volcanic in origin. However, after visits to Italy in 1771 and 1772 and the vicinity of Montpellier in 1771, he began to have doubts, and these doubts were confirmed when in 1775 he explored the neighborhood of Montélimar in Dauphiné. His change of opinion about the origin of columnar basalt was announced in his *Mémoires sur la minéralogie du Dauphiné* (1779).

Guettard's work as a geological cartographer began before 1746, the year in which he presented what he called a preliminary "mineralogical map" of France to the Académie Royale des Sciences. His travels and reading had called his attention to "a certain regularity" in the distribution of minerals and rocks over the earth's surface, and he decided to plot his data on a map. The result was his "Mémoire et carte minéralogique sur la nature & la situation des terreins qui traversent la France & l'Angleterre" (*Mémoires de l'Académie royale des sciences pour l'année 1746* [1751], pp. 363–392), which was followed in later years by memoirs and maps dealing with the Middle East, part of North America, Poland, and Switzerland, as well as preliminary (unpublished) maps of Italy and Corsica. These maps show, by means of conventional chemical symbols, the location of rock formations and mineral deposits, and they are also marked off in regions labeled *Bandes*. Each *Bande* was characterized by the predominance of certain deposits, so that in France, for example, he could outline three such concentric zones: the Sandy Band (primarily sandstones and limestones) with its center near Paris, the Marly Band, and the Schistose or Metalliferous Band. Although superposition was sometimes noted, the scheme was basically not a stratigraphic one. Guettard hoped eventually to clarify the relationships between the systems of bands outlined for neighboring geographical regions, and he also expected that his maps would enable scientists to find or predict the locations of useful or valuable mineral deposits, building materials, and agricultural and industrial soils. As late as 1784, he was still perfecting his initial mineralogical map of France.

In 1766 Guettard and Lavoisier were commissioned by Henri Bertin, minister and secretary of state in charge of mining, to prepare a geological survey of France. The collaboration of Guettard and Lavoisier had actually begun before that date, and among the several field trips they took together was their famous geological tour of Alsace, Lorraine, and Franche-Comté in 1767. By 1777 they had completed sixteen quadrangles, while bringing an almost equal number to partial completion, out of a projected total of some 200 maps. The survey passed into the hands of Antoine Monnet in 1777, and he published thirty-one quadrangles in the *Atlas et Description minéralogiques de la France* (1780), which he later issued in a second edition containing forty-five quadrangles. The rest of the survey was never executed.

The maps of the *Atlas* feature the chemical symbols used by Guettard, but he intentionally omitted the system of bands so that the survey would not appear to be based on any one geological theory; in addition, Lavoisier used the margin of each quadrangle for a vertical section designed to show the stratigraphic arrangement of the earth's crust. Monnet's maps followed a somewhat similar pattern. Although employing chemical symbols on geological maps was popular for a time, the maps of the *Atlas* had no close imitators; contemporaries and later geologists, with the notable exception of Nicolas Desmarest, found these maps to be models of observational accuracy, but the cartographic techniques of Guettard and Lavoisier were superseded by those developed in subsequent decades by such men as A. G. Werner, William Smith, Georges Cuvier, and Alexandre Brongniart.

Among Guettard's many other achievements were his identification of trilobites in the slates of Anjou and his discovery in France of sources of kaolin and petuntse needed in the manufacture of good porcelain. As a botanist, he remained a defender of the Linnaean system against its many critics. When the Académie Royale des Sciences was reorganized in 1785, he became a pensionnaire in the division of botany and agriculture. Upon his death, his natural history collection and library of more than 3,500 titles were sold and their fate is uncertain. His unpublished papers include memoirs on subjects botanical and geological, the latter including studies of virtually every French province. Toward the end of his life, Guettard searched for funds to support the publication of these papers, but without success. The papers then passed into the hands of Lavoisier, Guettard's scientific executor, whose efforts to have some of them published also failed.

BIBLIOGRAPHY

I. ORIGINAL WORKS. Works by Guettard include *Observations sur les plantes,* 2 vols. (Paris, 1747); *Mémoires sur la minéralogie du Dauphiné,* 2 vols. (Paris, 1779); *Mémoires sur différentes parties de la physique, de l'histoire naturelle; des sciences et des arts, & c.,* 5 vols. in 6 (Paris, 1768–1786). Guettard contributed to *Atlas et Description minéralogiques de la France, Entrepris par ordre du Roi . . . Première Partie* (Paris, 1780), in which the maps are the work of Guettard, Lavoisier, and Monnet, and the text the work of Monnet; for an analysis, see the Lavoisier bibliographies cited below.

Guettard also contributed to J. B. de La Borde, E. Béguillet, *et al., Description générale et particulière de la France . . .,* 4 vols. (Paris, 1781–1784), continued as *Voyage pittoresque de la France,* 8 vols. (Paris, 1784–1800). He translated Pliny the Elder, *Histoire naturelle,* 12 vols. (Paris, 1771–1782), and published more than seventy articles in the *Mémoires de l'Académie royale des sciences,* with a few in *Observations sur la physique, sur l'histoire naturelle et sur les arts* and *Journal oeconomique.*

More than twenty-five cartons and volumes of Guettard's MSS are in the Central Library of the Muséum National d'Histoire Naturelle, Paris. Travel journals and other documents are in the archives of the Académie des Sciences, Paris, and the Olin Library, Cornell University, Ithaca, New York. One journal has been published, with minor modifications, by A. Vernière, "Note sur les environs de Vichy et sur la découverte des volcans éteints de l'Auvergne (d'après un manuscrit autographe de Guettard, 1751)," in *Revue scientifique du Bourbonnais et du centre de la France,* **14** (1901), 5–13. Additional letters are in the Municipal Library of Clermont-Ferrand, Puy-de-Dôme, and can be found among the papers of Pierre-Michel Hennin, Library of the Institut de France, Paris. Single letters of importance are published in Buffon, *Les époques de la nature,* Jacques Roger, ed., *Mémoires du Muséum National d'Histoire Naturelle,* ser. C, **10** (Paris, 1962), cxxxix, n. 7; and René Fric, "Une lettre de Guettard à Monnet au sujet des prismes basaltiques," in *Bulletin historique et scientifique de l'Auvergne,* **78** (1958), 91–96.

II. SECONDARY LITERATURE. For works on Guettard see Aimé de Soland, "Étude sur Guettard," in *Annales de la Société linnéenne de Maine-et-Loire,* **13, 14, 15** (1871–1873), 32–88; Gavin de Beer, "The Volcanoes of Auvergne," in *Annals of Science,* **18** (1962), 49–61; M. J. A. N. C. Condorcet, "Éloge de M. Guettard," in *Histoire de l'Académie royale des sciences pour l'année 1786* (1788), pp. 47–62; Denis I. Duveen and Herbert S. Klickstein, *A Bibliography of the Works of Antoine Laurent Lavoisier 1743–1794* (London, 1954); Denis I. Duveen, *Supplement to a Bibliography of the Works of Antoine Laurent Lavoisier 1743–1794* (London, 1965); Roland Lamontagne, "La participation canadienne à l'oeuvre minéralogique de Guettard," in *Revue d'histoire des sciences et de leur applications,* **18** (1965), 385–388; A.-L. Letacq, "Notice sur les travaux scientifiques de Guettard aux environs d'Alençon & de Laigle (Orne)," in *Bulletin de la Société linnéenne de Normandie,* **5** (1891), 67–85; R. Michel, "À propos de la découverte des Volcans éteints de l'Auvergne et du Vivarais: Notes sur deux géologues du XVIIIe siècle, Guettard (1715–1786) et Faujas de Saint-Fond (1741–1819)," in *Revue des sciences naturelles d'Auvergne,* **11** (1945), 37–53; and R. Rappaport, "The Geological Atlas of Guettard, Lavoisier, and Monnet: Conflicting Views of the Nature of Geology," in Cecil J. Schneer, ed., *Toward a History of Geology* (Cambridge, Mass., 1969).

RHODA RAPPAPORT

GUIBERT, NICOLAS (*b.* St. Nicolas-de-Port, Lorraine, *ca.* 1547; *d.* Vaucouleurs, France, *ca.* 1620), *chemistry.*

Little is known of Guibert's family and early life. A Catholic, he studied medicine at the University of Perugia and, after receiving his degree, traveled in Italy, France, Germany, and Spain. During this period, Guibert became well known as an alchemist, working for several important persons, including Francesco de' Medici, grand duke of Tuscany, and Cardinal Granvelle, viceroy of Naples and a leader of Philip II's Spanish faction at Rome. He also associated for a time with Giambattista della Porta in Naples. Settling in the Italian town of Casteldurante, Guibert established a successful medical practice and in 1578 was appointed chief medical authority of one of the papal states. He held this position until leaving Italy at the end of 1579 to work as alchemist for Otto Truchsess, archbishop of Augsburg, whom he advised to commission a translation of Paracelsus' complete works into Latin.

Guibert's growing frustration with alchemical pursuits, however, accentuated his dissatisfaction with the obscurity and pretensions of much of sixteenth-century alchemy, and he emerged finally as a vehement critic of the profession. His first published attack came in 1603. In *Alchymia ratione et experientia ita demum viriliter impugnata et expugnata,* Guibert attempted to refute the major alchemical literature by demonstrating that alchemy is false and that most important alchemical treatises are of no authority. He branded the *Tabula smaragdina* and other alchemical writings attributed to Ibn-Sīnā, Albertus Magnus, and Thomas Aquinas as spurious. Moreover, the works whose authorship he accepted as genuine, such as the writings of Arnald of Villanova, Roger Bacon, Agrippa, and Paracelsus (the "limb of Satan"), were condemned by him as quackery and heresy. Despite its often exaggerated tone and unsubstantiated claims concerning the literature, Guibert's *Alchymia* did serve to reinforce several significant, albeit not widely held, ideas. Most important was his demonstration that metals are distinct species and not transmutable; he rejected the common argument for the transmutation of metals based on analogy to the organic realm—such as the change from larva to butterfly—and contradicted the influential belief that iron can be changed into copper.

His attack on the fundamental tenets of alchemy elicited a vigorous response from Andreas Libavius, the famous German iatrochemist, whose *Defensio alchymiae transmutatoriae opposita Nicolai Guiberti* (Ursel, 1604) defends the apparent conversion of metals—as in iron-copper replacement reactions—as genuine transmutations. Libavius further asserted that the growth and change of plants and animals afforded a valid analogy for maintaining the reality of chemical transmutations. Guibert, in turn, attacked Libavius' position in detail in his second major work, *De interitu alchymiae* (1614). The controversy concerning alchemy was part of the broader debate, which persisted throughout the sixteenth and seventeenth centuries, on the relations between occult science, natural magic, and emerging modern science. Guibert's rejection of alchemy derived from his revulsion from the activities of those charlatans who styled themselves scientists; from an orthodox Catholic suspicion of heresy in Renaissance Neoplatonism and the Hermetic revival of the sixteenth century; and, finally, from a recognition of certain theoretical and experimental inconsistencies of alchemy.

BIBLIOGRAPHY

I. Original Works. Guibert's scientific works include *Assertio de murrhinis, sive de iis quae murrhino nomine exprimuntur* (Frankfurt, 1597); *Alchymia ratione et experientia ita demum viriliter impugnata et expugnata* (Strasbourg, 1603); and *De interitu alchymiae metallorum transmutatoriae tractatus aliquot. Adiuncta est eiusdem apologia in sophistam Libavium, alchymiae refutatae furentem calumniatorem* (Toul, 1614).

II. Secondary Literature. Information on Guibert's life and work may be found in Dom Calmet, *Contenant la bibliothèque Lorraine,* vol. IV of *Histoire de Lorraine* (Nancy, 1751), 454–455; and F. Hoefer, ed., *Nouvelle biographie générale,* XXII (Paris, 1858), 518. The most reliable assessment of Guibert's scientific work is Lynn Thorndike, *A History of Magic and Experimental Science* (New York, 1941), V, 648, and VI, 244–247, 451–452. See also James R. Partington, *A History of Chemistry* (London, 1961), II, 268.

Martin Fichman

GUIDI, GUIDO, also known as **Vidus Vidius** (*b.* Florence, Italy, 10 February 1508; *d.* Pisa, Italy, 26 May 1569), *anatomy, surgery.*

Guidi belonged through his father, Giuliano di Guido dei Guidi, to a family of physicians, and through his mother, Costanza, he was descended from the famous painter Domenico Ghirlandaio. A part of his success can be explained by his capacity to unite science and art harmoniously. After becoming a doctor of medicine Guidi practiced in Rome and Florence. In 1542 he went to Paris and Fontainebleau, bringing to Francis I two splendidly illustrated manuscripts containing the Greek transcription and Latin translation of several classic treatises on surgery. The illustrations in these manuscripts have long been attributed to Francesco Primaticcio, but they were very probably done by the painter Francesco Salviati and his pupils.

In Paris, Guidi was named royal physician and became the first professor of medicine at the Collège Royal. He lived in the private residence of Benvenuto Cellini, and it was there that he had his *Chirurgia* printed, one of the most beautiful scientific books of the Renaissance. Greatly envied by the Faculty of Medicine, Guidi had to leave Paris after the death of Francis I in 1547. His new patron, Cosimo I de' Medici, named him professor of philosophy and medicine at the University of Pisa in 1548. At Pisa, Guidi carried out important anatomical investigations, recorded in a manuscript (*Anatomia*) composed around 1560, which is preserved in Cosimo I de' Medici's library. Guidi became a priest and was given the high church office of provost of Pescia. He was also the consul of the Academy of Florence.

In his *Chirurgia* of 1544 Guidi presents himself above all as a humanist anxious for the faithful restoration of classical knowledge. On the other hand, the *Anatomia* is the work of a scientist fully conscious of the Vesalian revolution and seeking his inspiration from nature. Unfortunately, this treatise was printed, under the title *De anatome corporis humani,* in a posthumous edition with hideous illustrations and maladroit additions by Guido Guidi, Jr., Guidi's nephew. This explains the negative judgments of several historians of medicine and their claims that Guidi plagiarized Vesalius and Falloppio.

Guidi's true merits can be established only after study of the original version of his anatomical work (MS II, III 32, Biblioteca Nazionale, Florence), a study which has not yet been made. Guidi certainly described the vertebrae, the cartilaginous structures, and the bones of the cranium better than any of his predecessors. His name is still attached to the *canalis vidianus* of the sphenoid bone and to the nerve that traverses this canal. Moreover, he made important and original studies of the mechanism of the articulations in the human body resulting from its vertical position in relation to the mechanism of the quadruped articulations. It is interesting to note that his anatomical work concluded with a group of experiments on living animals (for example, ligature of the blood vessels). The first professor of medicine at the Collège de France thus inaugurated the method of vivisection that was to bring such fame to that chair.

In his writing on practical medicine Guidi remained within classical Galenism. Nevertheless, this conservatism did not prevent him from describing a new childhood disease (chicken pox) or from inventing an original method for tracheotomy.

BIBLIOGRAPHY

I. Original Works. The MSS of Guidi's works are preserved in the Bibliothèque Nationale, Paris (particularly MS. lat. 6866), and in the Biblioteca Nazionale and Biblioteca Riccardiana, Florence. The most important of his works to be printed in his lifetime is *Chirurgia e Graeco in Latinum conversa, Vido Vidio Florentino interprete, cum nonnulis ejusdem Vidij commentarijs* (Paris, 1554). The posthumous writings prepared by Guido Guidi, Jr., are *Universae artis medicinalis pars quae ad curationum morborum spectat* (Frankfurt, 1596); *Ars medicinalis,* 3 vols. (Venice, 1611), which contains the first printed edition of the treatise "De anatome corporis humani"; and *Opera omnia medica chirurgica et anatomica* (Frankfurt, 1668).

II. Secondary Literature. The older biographies are S. Salvini, "Guido Guidi consolo," in *Fasti consolari dell' Accademia Fiorentina* (Florence, 1717), pp. 115–123, and P. B., "Elogio di Monsig. Guidi," in *Elogi degli uomini illustri di Toscana,* III (Lucca, 1772), 250–256. More recent publications are H. Omont, *Collection des chirurgiens grecs avec dessins attribués au Primatice* (Paris, 1908); W. Brockbank, "The Man Who Was Vidius," in *Annals of the Royal College of Surgeons of England,* **19** (1956), 269–295; C. E. Kellett, "The School of Salviati and the Illustrations to the *Chirurgia* of Vidus Vidius," in *Medical History,* **2** (1958), 264–268; and M. D. Grmek, "La période parisienne dans la vie de Guido Guidi anatomiste de Florence et professeur au Collège de France," in *Atti della VI biennale dello Studio Firmano* (Fermo, 1965), pp. 191–200.

M. D. Grmek

GUIGNARD, JEAN-LOUIS-LÉON (*b.* Mont-sous-Vaudrey [Jura], France, 13 April 1852; *d.* Paris, France, 7 March 1928), *botany.*

After completing his preliminary education in Mont-sous-Vaudrey, where his parents earned a livelihood by farming, Guignard went on to receive his secondary school diploma (*baccalauréat ès lettres*) in Besançon. From 1871 to 1874 he worked as an apprentice in several pharmacies in Paris. Then in 1874 he enrolled in the Paris School of Pharmacy and concurrently pursued studies at the Faculty of Sciences. Guignard also competed successfully for an appointment to an internship in pharmacy in the Paris municipal hospitals where he served with distinction from 1876 to 1882.

From this formative period, Guignard emerged in 1882 with an advanced qualification in pharmacy (*diplôme supérieure*) and a doctorate in natural sciences from the Faculty of Sciences. Two outstanding theses crowned his scholastic achievement: a study of the embryo sac in angiosperms for his *diplôme supérieure* in pharmacy and a brilliant investigation of the embryogeny in leguminous plants for his *docteur ès sciences naturelles.* Both works immediately established him as a botanist of considerable ability.

His student years behind him, Guignard worked briefly as an assistant and aide-naturalist at the Museum of Natural History. In 1883 he left for Lyons where he became professor of botany at the Faculty of Sciences and director of the botanical garden of that city. Appointed professor of botany at the Paris School of Pharmacy in 1887, he served in that capacity until 1927 and was also director of the school from 1900 to 1910. Guignard was elected to many learned societies including the Botanical Society of France (president, 1894); the Paris Academy of Medicine; Academy of Sciences (president, 1919); Society of Biology (vice-president, 1894); and the National Society of Agriculture of France.

Guignard's publications dating from 1880 represented more than four decades of botanical investigation. His most important contributions were to embryology, cytology, fertilization, the morphology and development of the seed, and his study of reproductive organs in plants. Of considerable interest too was his research on the sites of specific plant principles, organs of secretion, and his work in bacteriology.

In 1882 Guignard demonstrated that the embryo sac in flowering plants always develops from one of the hypodermal cells of the nucellus and described the general character of the eight-nucleate embryo sac in thirty-six families of monocotyledons and dicotyledons. Shortly after, in 1883, Guignard observed the longitudinal division of chromosomes in karyokinesis, thus confirming W. Fleming's findings. But even more important was his confirmation in 1889 of meiosis in plants, a phenomenon discovered a year earlier by E. Strasburger.

Double fertilization in angiosperms was discovered by Guignard in 1899 independently of S. Nawaschin, who had announced his discovery of the same phenomenon at a scientific meeting in Kiev, Russia, in 1898. In the meantime, Guignard had expanded the scope of his work to include such studies as the morphology of bacteria; pollen formation; the role of the centrosome and related bodies; the development and structure of the male gamete in *Fucus,* liverworts, mosses and ferns; the localization of hydrocyanic acid, glycosides and enzymes in plants; the growth and development of the seed, especially the tegmen, and investigations of organs of secretion in *Laminaria* and *Copaifera.*

From 1900 to 1922, Guignard continued his research on fertilization, embryogeny, and pollen formation, while devoting a major portion of his time to studying the sites of production in plants of sulfurated and cyanogenetic glycosides and their enzymes. His findings, published in 1906, on the poisonous nature of the Java bean (*Phaseolus lunatus* L.) showed that the toxicity was due to its hydrocyanic content and led to a ban on the importation of the bean into France. Guignard also developed a sensitive test for determining hydrocyanic acid in plants by means of sodium picrate paper. Grafting experiments with cyanogenetic plants convinced Guignard that, except when two species of the same genus were grafted, there was no migration of cyanogenetic glycosides between graft and stock; each retained, in this respect, chemical autonomy.

After 1907 there was a marked decline in the number of Guignard's scientific publications. His most significant scientific accomplishments had been made by the turn of the century, and his work on the localization of plant principles had brought him to the threshold of a new field of inquiry, the study of plant biosynthesis.

BIBLIOGRAPHY

I. Original Works. For a comprehensive listing of Guignard's publications, see P. Guérin, "Léon Guignard, 1852–1928," in *Bulletin des sciences pharmacologiques,* **35** (1928), 374–380.

II. Secondary Literature. The fullest account of Guignard's life and work will be found in P. Guérin, cited above, pp. 354–380. See also R. Souèges, "Léon Guignard," in *Figures pharmaceutiques françaises* (Paris, 1953), pp. 203–208. A good discussion of Guignard's contributions to plant embryology is included in R. Souèges, *L'embryologie végétale, résumé historique,* 2 vols., II (Paris, 1934), 19–21 and *passim.*

For Guignard's work in cytology, see Maurice Hocquette, "Morphologie, anatomie, cytologie," in A. Davy de Virville, *et al., Histoire de la Botanique en France* (Paris, 1954), pp. 147–149, 151; and A. Hughes, *A History of Cytology* (London–New York, 1959), pp. 66, 70–72.

Alex Berman

GUILLANDINUS. See **Wieland, Melchior.**

GUILLAUME, CHARLES ÉDOUARD (*b.* Fleurier, Switzerland, 15 February 1861; *d.* Sèvres, France, 13 June 1938), *metallurgy, physics.*

Guillaume's father, Édouard Guillaume, returned to Switzerland, his family's original home, from London, where he had managed a clockmaking firm. His knowledge of science was considerable, and he was his son's first teacher. The latter was admitted at the age of seventeen to the Zurich Polytechnikum, where he studied not only the prescribed scientific subjects but also German and French literature. He used to say that François Arago's *Éloges académiques* had exerted a profound influence on him.

In 1883 Guillaume entered the International Bureau of Weights and Measures at Sèvres, near Paris. He remained there throughout his career and became its director. In 1911 he was elected a corresponding member of the physics section of the Académie des Sciences.

Guillaume's first works were devoted to the mercury thermometer; upon completion of these studies he published a treatise on thermometry which made available to physicists the methods perfected by the International Bureau of Weights and Measures. He next participated in the preparation of the national meters, a fundamental work which marked the origin of modern metrology and permitted the presentation in 1889, at the first Conference on Weights and Measures, of the complete collection of standardized meters destined for the different countries.

Since 1890, Guillaume was led to undertake investigations on metal alloys. Studies had been made at Sèvres on a ferronickel (an alloy of iron with 24 percent nickel and 2 percent chromium) that had just been created at the Imphy Works in Nièvre. This alloy was more expansible than the iron or the nickel composing it. While studying an alloy containing slightly more nickel, Guillaume observed that this small variation in composition resulted in an alloy less expansible than the constituent metals. He undertook a methodical study of ferronickels and showed that with 36 percent nickel, one obtained an alloy, which he called invar, that expanded ten times less than iron and that even possessed a zero coefficient of dilatation after appropriate tempering, drawing, and rolling.

This alloy immediately found numerous applications, particularly in clockmaking. Guillaume also helped to solve another problem—compensation in ordinary watches—through his discovery of elinvar, an alloy whose elasticity does not vary with temperature.

These successes gave Guillaume an important role in the International Physics Congress, held in Paris in 1900, and earned him the 1920 Nobel Prize in physics. Moreover, he had the pleasure of seeing that his work would be brilliantly continued at the International Bureau of Weights and Measures by the physicist Albert Pérard, who succeeded him as director. In addition, Albert Portevin and Pierre Chevenard obtained very satisfactory results in developing his researches on nickel alloys.

BIBLIOGRAPHY

Guillaume's works include "Sur la dilatation des aciers au nickel," in *Comptes rendus hebdomadaires des séances de l'Académie des sciences,* **124** (1897), 176; "Recherches sur les aciers au nickel. Propriétés métrologiques," *ibid.,* 752; "Recherches sur les aciers au nickel. Propriétés magnétiques et déformations permanentes," *ibid.,* 1515; "Recherches sur les aciers au nickel. Dilatations aux températures élevées; résistance électrique," *ibid.,* **125** (1897), 235, errata, p. 342; "Recherches sur les aciers au nickel. Variations de volumes des alliages irréversibles," *ibid.,* **126** (1898), 738; "Nouvelles recherches sur la dilatation des aciers au nickel," *ibid.,* **136** (1903), 303; "Changements passagers et permanents des aciers au nickel," *ibid.,* 357; "Variations du module d'élasticité des aciers au nickel," *ibid.,* 498; "Sur la théorie des aciers au nickel," *ibid.,* 1638; "L'anomalie de dilatation des aciers au nickel," *ibid.,* **152** (1911), 189; "Coefficient du terme quadratique dans la formule de dilatation des aciers au nickel," *ibid.,* 1450; "Modification de la dilatabilité de l'invar par des actions mécaniques ou thermiques," *ibid.,* **163** (1916), 655; "Écrouissage et dilatabilité de l'invar," *ibid.,* 741; "Homogénéité de dilatation de l'invar," *ibid.,* 966; "Recherches métrologiques sur les aciers au nickel," in *Travaux et mémoires du Bureau international des poids et mesures,* **17** (1927); "Les anomalies des aciers au nickel et leurs applications," in *Revue de métallurgie,* **25** (1928), 35.

GEORGES CHAUDRON

GUILLET, LÉON ALEXANDRE (*b.* Saint Nazaire, France, 11 July 1873; *d.* Paris, France, 9 May 1946), *metallurgy.*

Guillet entered the École Centrale des Arts et Manufactures near the top of his class and received his engineering degree in 1897. In 1902 he submitted his thesis for the doctorate in physical sciences to the Faculté des Sciences of Paris; it dealt with the alloys of aluminum. He was named *suppléant* professor of metallurgy at the Conservatoire National des Arts et Métiers in 1906, and in 1908 he became titular holder of that chair. In 1911 he was appointed to the chair of metallurgy at the École Centrale des Arts et Manufactures, and in 1923 he became that school's director. He was elected a member of the Académie des Sciences in 1925, in the division of applications of science to industry.

Throughout his career Guillet never separated science from its applications, for he was convinced that modern industry, and especially metallurgy, must no longer be content with the empiricism that had prevailed for so long in the factories; instead, factories should have research departments. In 1905 Guillet was named director of the laboratory of one of the largest automobile factories of de Dion and Bouton, in Puteaux, near Paris; and he transformed this laboratory into the first department of scientific research to be organized in an industrial plant.

Guillet's scientific work was related almost entirely to the theory of alloys. The research that contributed most to his reputation was that concerning special steels, that is, those made with nickel, manganese, chromium, and tungsten. From special steels he turned to the study of bronzes and brasses. He also made original contributions to experimental measurements, principally in his research on thermal treatments of alloys.

During World War I, Guillet was assigned to the naval yards of Penhoët, where he was concerned in particular with tempering projectiles. His results were used in France and in several allied countries.

Guillet, like Henry Le Chatelier, who was to a certain degree his patron, was a trainer of men. He had around him a group of disciples, some of whom became very well-known engineers and scientists. As director of the École Centrale des Arts et Manufactures, Guillet was responsible for the notable progress of this school. Speaking of his directorship, he declared: "I spent the happiest years of my life there, and that was because those were the years during which I was best able to work for others."

Guillet was an active member of the Académie des Sciences; he had a special gift for clearly mediating scientific discussions.

BIBLIOGRAPHY

Guillet's articles include "Contribution à l'étude des alliages d'aluminium," thesis (Paris, 1902); "Contribution à l'étude des alliages aluminium-fer et aluminium-manganèse," in *Comptes rendus hebdomadaires des séances de l'Académie des sciences,* **134** (1902), 236; "Sur la micrographie des aciers au nickel," *ibid.,* **136** (1903), 227; "Nouvelles recherches sur la cémentation des aciers au carbone et des aciers spéciaux," *ibid.,* **138** (1904), 1600; "Propriétés et constitution des aciers au chrome," *ibid.,* **139** (1904), 426; "Constitution et propriétés des aciers au tungstène," *ibid.,* 519; "Propriétés et constitution des aciers au molybdène," *ibid.,* 540; "Sur la trempe des bronzes," *ibid.,* **140** (1905), 307; "Comparaison des propriétés, essais de classification des aciers ternaires," *ibid.,* **141** (1906), 107; "Constitution des alliages cuivre-aluminium," *ibid.,* 464; "Sur les points de transformation et la structure des aciers nickel-chrome," *ibid.,* **156** (1913), 1774; "Sur les alliages de cuivre, de nickel et d'aluminium," *ibid.,* **158** (1914), 704; "Sur la trempe des laitons à l'étain," *ibid.,* **172** (1921), 1038; and "Influence de l'écrouissage sur la resistivité des métaux et des alliages," *ibid.,* **176** (1923), 1800.

His books include *Notice sur ses travaux scientifiques* (Paris, 1907, 1923); *Traitements thermiques des produits métallurgiques* (Paris, 1909); *L'enseignement technique supérieur à l'après guerre* (Paris, 1918); *Précis de métallographie microscopique et de macrographie* (Paris, 1918), written with A. Portevin; *Additif à la notice sur ses travaux scientifiques* (Paris, 1925); and *Les métaux légers et leurs alliages: Aluminium, magnésium, glucinium, métaux alcalins et alcalino-terreux* (Paris, 1936).

GEORGES CHAUDRON

GUILLIERMOND, MARIE ANTOINE ALEXANDRE (*b.* Lyons, France, 19 August 1876; *d.* Lyons, 1 April 1945), *botany.*

Born into a family of physicians in which science was held in esteem, Guilliermond experienced the premature death of his father and several years later of his mother, who had been remarried to a physician. Sensitive and shy, he wished to teach and conduct research. His teachers were Maurice Caullery, Eugène Bataillon, and, in cryptogamy, Louis Matruchot. His teaching career was brilliant: beginning as a lecturer in agricultural botany at the Faculté des Sciences in Lyons, he went to the University of Paris in 1913 as lecturer in botany at the Faculty of Sciences and in 1935 succeeded Pierre Augustin Dangeard to the chair of botany at the Sorbonne. Much tried by France's military misfortunes, he fell ill and retired in 1942. He died three years later. He had belonged to the Académie des Sciences since 1935.

Guilliermond's brilliant investigations were conducted in two profoundly different areas requiring different mental orientations. His first works dealt with lower organisms: blue-green algae (cyanophyceae), bacteria, and especially yeasts, to which he devoted his doctoral thesis, *Recherches cytologiques sur les levures et quelques moisissures à formes levures* (1902). Were yeasts, as Oscar Brefeld held, more highly evolved forms of fungi? It was believed that they possessed a primitive structure with diffuse chromatin, but Guilliermond's studies, which form the basis of our scientific knowledge of the yeasts, established as well the indisputable presence of a nucleus and its division at the time of budding. At first he thought the nucleus divided by amitosis. Later, progress in technique permitted him and his students to demonstrate that mitosis was in fact taking place. He also recognized the vacuoles and their content, which is precipitable in metachromatic corpuscles.

It was undoubtedly in the field of the sexuality of the yeasts that Guilliermond made the greatest progress: he established the occurrence of isogamous copulation before the formation of the ascus (*Schizosaccharomyces octosporus*) and of heterogamous copulation (*Zygosaccharomyces chevalieri*). He detected the copulation of the ascospores of various *Saccharomyces,* which allowed him to distinguish between haplobiontic and diplobiontic yeasts. Researches on the filamentous Endomycetaceae revealed analogous processes in this family and permitted the formulation of a classically accepted hypothesis regarding the phylogeny of the yeasts.

Guilliermond's studies on the formation of the ascus among the higher Ascomycetes yielded important results. For example, through the tiny Pezizaceae *Humaria rutilans,* which possess the largest chromosomes among the fungi, he was able to demonstrate the characteristics of three successive mitoses of the ascus: heterotypic, homeotypic, and typical. Along the same lines, his research on the cytology of bacteria and especially of the Cyanophyceae contributed to the establishment of the then classically accepted type of these cells. (The electron microscope has since revealed the inaccuracy of this type.)

Because the yeasts provided the greatest continuity to Guilliermond's first group of investigations, as a complete botanist he wished to become acquainted with the greatest number of forms. It was as a systematist that he published *Les levures* (1911) and later drew up the tables of yeasts in the *Tabulae biologicae.*

The second area of Guilliermond's work is completely different. In the period in which physicochemical biology was actively developing, he wished, as a plant cytologist, to establish a close contact with animal cytology. His researches therefore dealt with the morphological constituents of the cytoplasm.

It had been known since 1910 that the chondriosomes, or mitochondria, consisting of a lipoprotein complex much richer in lipids than is cytoplasm, must play an important role in secretory phenomena. Also known was the importance of the vacuole system for cellular physiological phenomena. Through various means, such as plasmolysis, vital stains, mitochondrial techniques, and the ultramicroscope, the attempt could be made to answer a series of questions: Are there organelles other than the vacuoles which can arise *de novo* in the cell? Is it possible for the amidon to be formed not in the plasts but in the cytoplasm and even in the chondriosomes? What is the significance of the Golgi apparatus, revealed by silver stains, which seems to be attached sometimes to the vacuome, sometimes to the chondriome, and sometimes to be an autonomous formation?

Since the electron microscope did not then exist, the ultramicroscope presented the cytoplasm as a homogeneous gel, and these problems were approached *in situ* in the cell (and often in the living state). It is then possible to understand how courageous was Guilliermond's research and how valuable the results obtained—for example, affirmation that only the vacuoles can be formed again. Furthermore, the attraction that this research held for many students provided Guilliermond with an excellent group with which to pursue this work.

BIBLIOGRAPHY

Works by Guilliermond include *Recherches cytologiques sur les levures et quelques moisissures à formes levures* (Lyons, 1902), his doctoral diss.; "Remarques sur la caryocinèse des Ascomycètes," in *Annales mycologici,* **3** (1905), 344; "Recherches cytologiques et taxinomiques sur les Endomycétacées," in *Revue générale de botanique,* **21** (1909), 353; "Nouvelles observations sur la sexualité des levures," in *Archiv für Protistenkunde,* **28** (1912), 52; *Traité de cytologie végétale* (Paris, 1933), written with G. Mangenot and L. Plantefol; *Précis de biologie végétale* (Paris, 1937), written with G. Mangenot; and *Introduction á l'étude de la cytologie,* 3 vols. (Paris, 1938).

LUCIEN PLANTEFOL

GUINTER, JOANNES (*b.* Andernach, Germany, *ca.* 1505; *d.* Strasbourg, France, 4 October 1574), *medicine.*

Nothing is known of Guinter's family, except that it was obscure and impoverished, or of his earliest education. He is said to have left Andernach at the age of twelve in quest of learning, studying successively at Utrecht, Deventer, and Marburg, in which last place he completed his humanistic and philosophical studies. Thereafter for a brief period he taught in a preparatory school at Goslar, Saxony, where he recouped his funds and was able to proceed to Louvain for further study and also some teaching of Greek, and then to Liège. At some undetermined earlier time Guinter seems to have begun the study of medicine at Leipzig, and about 1527 he proceeded from Liège to Paris to continue that study. He received the baccalaureate in medicine on 18 April 1528 after two witnesses had sworn to the fact of his previous studies at Leipzig. On 4 June 1530 he was promoted licentiate and on 29 October 1532 received the M.D. degree. He was accepted as a regent doctor by the Paris Faculty of Medicine on 6 February 1533, and on 7 November 1534 he was named one of the two professors of medicine at a salary of twenty-five livres.

As part of his academic duties Guinter was responsible for the annual winter course in human anatomy, and it was inevitable during the pre-Vesalian period that his approach would be Galenic. The procedure followed was in the medieval pattern, with Guinter lecturing to the class while a barber or surgeon performed the actual dissection in order merely to illustrate and confirm Galen's anatomy. However, Guinter himself appears occasionally to have dissected, although his technique left much to be desired. One of his pupils during the period 1533–1536, the later distinguished anatomist Andreas Vesalius, referred to Guinter's anatomical instruction in strongly condemnatory terms, even declaring: "I do not consider him an anatomist, and I should willingly suffer him to inflict as many cuts upon me as I have seen him attempt on man or any other animal—except at the dinner table." Nevertheless, it is to Guinter's credit that he did attempt to teach his students some comparative anatomy and was willing to allow them to gain some experience by participation in the actual dissection. It was in conjunction with his anatomical course that he published a dissection manual, *Institutiones anatomicae* (Paris, 1536), in four books, dealing first with the more corruptible internal organs and then with those less susceptible to putrefaction. Thus the work followed the form first made popular by Mondino da Luzzi (1316), that is, the medieval method of dissection based upon a limited amount of dissection material. Guinter acknowledged the assistance of his student Vesalius in preparation of the work, probably the dissection and preparation of anatomical specimens. Although Guinter's manual, preceded only by those of Mondino and Berengario da Carpi (1522), contained no genuine anatomical contributions, it did advocate that anatomy, hitherto considered as chiefly fit for study by surgeons, was fundamental to the education of the physician.

Guinter was one of the major Greek scholars of his day, a fact first disclosed by the publication of his *Syntaxis Graeca* (Paris, 1527). In particular he devoted this scholarship to translations of the classical writers on medicine, and in the *Commentaries* of the Faculty of Medicine of Paris he was recognized as having translated the larger part of Galen's writings and all those of Paul of Aegina. The considerable bulk of Guinter's translations is explained by his method, according to which, as he declared, he translated each day as much as his secretary could write out from dictation, after which Guinter edited the version for publication. Despite the speed with which he translated, his versions appear to have held up well before the criticism of later editors. Guinter's most important translations were his version of the first nine books of Galen's anatomical treatise, *De anatomicis administrationibus* (Paris, 1531), and *De Hippocratis et Platonis placitis* (Paris, 1534), the latter considered by Guinter to be his most significant contribution to knowledge of classical Greek medicine. He also translated the writings of Paul of Aegina, *Opus de re medica* (Paris, 1532); Caelius Aurelianus, *Liber celerum vel acutarum passionum* (Paris, 1533); and Oribasius, *Commentaria in aphorismos Hippocratis* (Paris, 1533). Guinter was responsible for the introduction and popularization of a number of Greek anatomical terms, such as dartos, pericranium, urachus, and colon, that were to replace the inexact and confusing medieval anatomical nomenclature and thus lead to greater precision in anatomical description.

Owing to the growing pressure of religious orthodoxy in France, Guinter, a Lutheran, left Paris in 1538 for Metz and after about two years went to Strasbourg, where he was provided with a chair of Greek studies at the Gymnasium. At the same time he developed a medical practice, but criticism of his double occupation compelled him to relinquish his academic position in 1556. Although he continued his studies of the classical Greek physicians, producing a translation of the writings of Alexander of Tralles in 1549 and a revised edition in 1556, most of his later publications reflected his interest as a practicing physician. His book of advice on how to avoid the plague, *De victus et medicinae ratione cum alio tum pestilentiae tempore observanda commentarius* (Strasbourg, 1542), was translated into French by Antoine Pierre in 1544 and by Guinter in 1547 as *Instruction très utile par laquelle un chacun se pourra maintenir en santé, tant au temps de peste, comme autre temps.* Further works on this subject were *Bericht, Regiment und Ordnung wie die Pestilenz und die pestilenzialische Fieber zu erkennen und zu kuriren* (Strasbourg, 1564) and *De pestilentia commentarius in quatuor dialogos distinctus* (Strasbourg, 1565). Guinter also produced *Commentarius de balneis et aquis medicatis* (Strasbourg, 1565); a general study of medicine containing some autobiographical material, *De medicina veteri et nova* (Basel, 1571); and a collection of writings on obstetrics published posthumously by Joannes Georg Schenck a Grafenberg, *Gynaeciorum commentarius, de gravidarum, parturientium, puerperarum et infantium cura* (Strasbourg, 1606). Guinter was entombed in the church of St. Gallus in Strasbourg.

BIBLIOGRAPHY

There are many references to Guinter, most of them unfortunately containing serious errors. In particular his name is usually given erroneously as Günther, Gonthier, Guinther, or even Winter, and an almost unshakable legend places his birth in 1487. These two points are given special attention in Edouard Turner, "Jean Guinter d'Andernach 1505–1574," in *Gazette hebdomadaire de médecine et de chirurgie,* 2nd ser., **18** (1881), 425, 441, 505. Turner's essay includes the best bibliography of Guinter's long list of publications, which is also given *in extenso* in J. J. Höveler, "Ioannes Guinterius Andernacus," in *Jahresbericht über das Progymnasium zu Andernach für das Schuljahr 1898–99* (Andernach, 1899), pp. 3–21. Höveler, however, accepts the legendary date for Guinter's birth. Some further information is to be found in *Commentaires de la Faculté de médecine de l'Université de Paris (1516–1560*), M.-L. Concasty, ed. (Paris, 1964). Guinter as an anatomist is treated in C. D. O'Malley, *Andreas Vesalius of Brussels 1514–1564* (Berkeley–Los Angeles, 1964); and there is a bibliography of eds. of Guinter's *Institutiones anatomicae,* including those revised by Vesalius, in Harvey Cushing, *Bio-bibliography of Andreas Vesalius,* 2nd ed. (Hamden, Conn., 1962). Some autobiographical information is to be found in the prefaces to Guinter's various translations and in his *De medicina veteri et nova* (Basel, 1571).

C. D. O'MALLEY

GULDBERG, CATO MAXIMILIAN (*b.* Christiania [now Oslo], Norway, 11 August 1836; *d.* Christiania, 14 January 1902), *chemistry, physics.*

Guldberg was the eldest of the nine children of Carl August Guldberg, a minister and owner of a bookshop and printing office, and Hanna Sophie Theresia Bull. When Guldberg was eleven years old, his father was appointed minister at Nannestad, about fifty miles north of Christiania. Although the foundation for Guldberg's later delight in outdoor life, hunting, and fishing was laid in his father's remote parish, he could not get a satisfactory education there, and at the age of thirteen he was sent to live with his maternal grandmother at Fredrikstad. There he entered secondary school, where he excelled in mathematics.

Because the school in Fredrikstad could not grant admission certificates for the university, in 1853 Guldberg went to Christiania, where he spent his last school year in a private Latin school; he then matriculated at the University of Christiania in 1854, the same year as his friend Peter Waage. At the university Guldberg majored in mathematics and studied physics and chemistry. While still a student, he worked independently on advanced mathematical problems, and his first published scientific paper, "On the Contact of Circles" (University of Christiania publication [Christiania, 1861]), won the crown prince's gold medal.

In 1859 he graduated in science and obtained a modest position as teacher at Nissen's secondary school in Christiania. In 1860 he was appointed teacher of mathematics at the Royal Military Academy. The next year, by means of a scholarship, he made a one-year study tour of France, Switzerland, and Germany. In 1862 he qualified for a position in applied mechanics at the Royal Military College, and in 1863 he was appointed a teacher of advanced mechanics at the same school. He held these two positions until his death. He was awarded a scholarship in 1867 at the University of Christiania, where he became professor of applied mathematics in 1869.

Guldberg and Waage, whose names are linked for their joint discovery of the law of mass action, were also closely related through marriage. Guldberg married his cousin Bodil Mathea Riddervold, the daughter of cabinet minister Hans Riddervold; the couple had three daughters. Waage married her sister. The collaboration between the two friends and brothers-in-law on the studies of chemical affinity that were to lead to the law of mass action began immediately after Guldberg's return from abroad in 1862. The first report of their results was presented by Waage on 14 March 1864 before the Norwegian Academy of Sciences and published the following year in the Academy's proceedings. But the report remained almost completely unknown to scientists, a fate also suffered by a more detailed description of their theory published in French in 1867. The theory did not become generally known until Wilhelm Ostwald, in a paper published in 1877, adopted the law of mass action and proved its validity by new experiments. Although the law had had several forerunners, the combined efforts of the theorist Guldberg and the empiricist Waage led to the first general mathematical and exact formulation of the role of the amounts of reactants in chemical equilibrium systems. In 1878 Jacobus Henricus van't Hoff, apparently without any knowledge of Guldberg and Waage's work, derived the law from reaction kinetics.

Although the law of mass action is Guldberg's greatest contribution to physical chemistry, it is not his only one. Some of his early work published in Norwegian did not get the publicity it deserved. He devoted much time to a search for a general equation of state for gases, liquids, and solids from a kinetic molecular approach. In 1867, nineteen years before van't Hoff, he introduced the ideal gas equation in the form $pV = 2T$. In 1869 he developed the concept of "corresponding temperatures" and deduced an equation of state valid for all liquids of certain types. In 1890 he formulated the rule that the reduced boiling temperatures of most liquids are close to 2/3, a relationship discovered independently by P. A. Guye. In addition, Guldberg made valuable contributions to the thermodynamics of solution and of dissociation, and he discovered and correctly explained cryohydrates. He wrote many articles on various practical problems and a number of textbooks on mathematics and mechanics. He was editor of the *Polyteknisk tidsskrift,* an active member and officer of scientific societies, and the recipient of many honors.

BIBLIOGRAPHY

I. Original Works. Guldberg and Waage's various papers on the law of mass action have been abridged and translated into German by Richard Abegg as *Untersuchungen über die chemischen Affinitäten,* in Wilhelm Ostwald, Klassiker der exakten Wissenschaften, CIV (Leipzig, 1899). Their first paper, "Studier over Affiniteten," published in Norwegian in *Forhandlinger i Videnskabs-selskabet i Christiania,* (1865), 35–45, appears in facsimile, along with a number of articles on the law, in Haakon Haraldsen, ed., *The Law of Mass Action: A Centenary Volume 1864–1964* (Oslo, 1964).

II. Secondary Literature. A biography of Guldberg and a discussion of his work by Haakon Haraldsen appears on pp. 19–26 and 32–35 of the centenary volume cited above and on pp. 172–174 of Abegg's trans. Also see J. B. Halvorsen, "C. M. Guldberg," in *Norsk Forfatter-Lexikon,* II (Christiania, 1888), 447; Elling Holst, "C. M. Guldberg," in *Nordisk Universitetstidsskrift,* **2** (1902), 321; H. Goldschmidt, "C. M. Guldberg," in *Fordhandlinger Videnskabs-Selskabet Christiania,* no. 1 (1903), 1; Sophus Torup, "C. M. Guldberg," in *Norsk biografisk leksikon,* V (Oslo, 1931), 76; T. Hiortdahl, "Den Fysisk-Kemiske Forening, Tidsskr. Kemi, Farmaci og Terapi," in *Pharmacia,* **14** (1917), 240; Kåre Fasting, "Teknikk og Samfunn," in *Den Polytekniske Forening 1852–1952* (Oslo, 1952); and Gunnar Oxaal, *Teknisk Ukeblad* (1954), pp. 306, 308.

George B. Kauffman

GULDIN, PAUL (*b.* St. Gall, Switzerland, 12 June 1577; *d.* Graz, Austria, 3 November 1643), *mathematics.*

Guldin was of Jewish descent but was brought up as a Protestant. He began work as a goldsmith and as such was employed in several German towns. At the age of twenty he was converted to Catholicism and entered the Jesuit order, changing his first name, Habakkuk, to Paul. In 1609 he was sent to Rome for further education. Guldin taught mathematics at the Jesuit colleges in Rome and Graz. When a severe illness obliged him to suspend his lecturing, he was sent to Vienna, where he became professor of mathematics at the university. In 1637 he returned to Graz, where he died in 1643.

In 1582 the Gregorian calendar was introduced in western Europe, and it met with a great deal of opposition among both scientists and Protestants; one of the opponents was the famous chronologist Sethus Calvisius. To refute him and to defend Pope Gregory XIII and his fellow Jesuit Christoph Clavius, Guldin published his first work, *Refutatio elenchi calendarii Gregoriani a Setho Calvisio conscripti* (Mainz, 1618).

In 1622 Guldin published a physicomathematical dissertation on the motion of the earth caused by alteration of the center of gravity. In it he made the assumption that every unimpeded large body whose center of gravity does not coincide with the center of the universe is moved in such a way that it will coincide with the latter. In the fourteenth century the doctrine of centers of gravity had begun to play a role in the mechanics of large bodies. In his *Quaestiones super libros quattuor de caelo et mundo Aristotelis,* Jean Buridan argued that geological processes are always causing a redistribution of the earth's matter and therefore are continually changing its center of gravity. But the center of gravity always strives to be at the center of the universe, so the earth is constantly shifting about near the latter. Guldin accepted Buridan's hypothesis but was also well-informed about the objection which Nicole Oresme had formulated in his *Le livre du ciel et du monde.*

In 1627 a correspondence on religious subjects developed between Guldin and Johannes Kepler. On the occasion of his journey from Ulm to Prague, which he undertook to solicit funds from Emperor Rudolph II for the publication of the Rudolphine Tables (Ulm, 1627), Kepler wrote on his objections to the Catholic religion to Guldin. In his answer Guldin tried to refute them with theological arguments drawn up for him by a fellow Jesuit. Kepler's reply ended the correspondence.

Guldin's main work was *Centrobaryca seu de centro gravitatis trium specierum quantitatis continuae,* in four volumes (Vienna, 1635–1641). In the first volume Guldin determined the centers of gravity of plane rectilinear and curvilinear figures and of solids in the Archimedean manner. Against Niccolò Cabeo's attacks in *Philosophia magnetica* (1629) directed toward his theory concerning the motion of the earth, Guldin reproduced in volume I his dissertation of 1622 and a note in which he discussed Cabeo's arguments. The appendix to volume I contains tables of quadratic and cubic numbers and an exposition of the use of logarithms referring to Adriaan Vlacq's *Arithmetica logarithmica* (1628).

Volume II contains what is known as Guldin's theorem: "If any plane figure revolve about an external axis in its plane, the volume of the solid so generated is equal to the product of the area of the figure and the distance traveled by the center of gravity of the figure" (ch. 7, prop. 3, p. 147). This theorem has been much discussed in terms of possible plagiarism from the early part of book VII of Pappus' *Collectio* (*ca.* A.D. 300). However, the theorem cannot have been taken from the first published edition of the *Collectio,* the Latin translation of Federico Commandino (Venice, 1588), because that text shows obvious lacunae. Guldin attempted to prove his theorem by metaphysical reasoning, but Bonaventura Cavalieri pointed out the weakness of his demonstration and proved the theorem by the method of indivisibles. Volume II treats the properties of the Archimedean spiral and the conic sections, their lengths and surfaces, the determination of the center of gravity of a sector of a circle and of a segment of a circle and a parabola, the rise of solids of revolution, and the application of the Guldin theorem to them.

In volume III Guldin determined the surface and the volume of a cone, a cylinder, a sphere, and other solids of revolution and their mutual proportions. In his *Stereometria doliorum* (1615) Kepler determined the volumes of certain vessels and the areas of certain surfaces by means of infinitesimals, instead of the long and tedious method of exhaustions. In volume IV Guldin severely attacked Kepler for the lack of rigor in his use of infinitesimals. He also criticized Cavalieri's use of indivisibles in his *Geometria indivisibilibus* (1635), asserting not only that the method had been taken from Kepler but also that since the number of indivisibles was infinite, they could not be compared with one another. Furthermore, he pointed out a number of fallacies to which the method of indivisibles appeared to lead.

In 1647, after the death of Guldin, Cavalieri published *Exercitationes geometricae sex,* in which he defended himself against the first charge by pointing out that his method differed from that of Kepler in that it made use only of indivisibles, and against the second by observing that the two infinities of elements to be compared are of the same kind.

BIBLIOGRAPHY

Guldin's writings are listed in the text. A very good account of his works may be found in C. Sommervogel, *Bibliothèque de la Compagnie de Jésus,* II (Brussels–Paris, 1891), 1946–1947.

On Guldin or his work, see the following (listed chronologically): C. J. Gerhardt, *Geschichte der Mathematik in Deutschland* (Munich, 1877), pp. 129–130; L. Schuster, *Johann Kepler und die grossen kirchlichen Streitfragen seiner Zeit* (Graz, 1888), pp. 217–228, 233–243; M. Cantor, *Vorlesungen über Geschichte der Mathematik,* II (Leipzig, 1900), 840–844; H. G. Zeuthen, *Geschichte der Mathematik im 16. und 17. Jahrhundert* (Leipzig, 1903), pp. 240, 241, 293; G. A. Miller, "Was Paul Guldin a Plagiarist?," in *Science,* **64** (1926), 204–206; P. Ver Eecke, "Le théorème dit de Guldin considéré au point de vue historique," in *Mathésis,* **46** (1932), 395–397; R. C. Archibald, "Notes and Queries," in *Scripta mathematica,* **1** (1932), 267; P. Duhem, *Le système du monde,* IX (Paris, 1958), 318–321; C. B. Boyer, *The History of the Calculus and Its Conceptual Development* (New York, 1959), pp. 121, 122, 138, 139; and J. E. Hofmann, "Ueber die *Exercitatio geometrica* des M. A. Ricci," in *Centaurus,* **9** (1963), 151, 152.

H. L. L. BUSARD

GULLAND, JOHN MASSON (*b.* Edinburgh, Scotland, 14 October 1898; *d.* Goswick, England, 26 October 1947), *organic chemistry, biochemistry.*

Gulland's father was professor of medicine at Edinburgh University; his mother was the daughter of David Masson, professor of English literature at the same university. His own studies in chemistry at that university were interrupted by war service, and he graduated in 1921. At the universities of St. Andrews and Manchester he and Robert Robinson established the structures of an important group of alkaloids including morphine. From 1924 Gulland was at Oxford with W. H. Perkin, Jr., and worked on strychnine and brucine; but the routine of degradation and synthesis began to pall, and his interest turned to biochemical problems of wider significance. He is remembered mainly for his work on the chemistry of nucleic acids, for which he was elected a fellow of the Royal Society in 1945. He carried out this work at the Lister Institute of Preventive Medicine, London (1931–1936), and as professor of chemistry at University College, Nottingham (1936–1947).

Gulland was one of the first to use methods other than those of classical chemistry to study the structure of nucleic acids. In early work he showed spectroscopically that the pentose residue was attached to the 9 position rather than the 7 position in the purine nucleosides. Later, with Elisabeth Jackson (1938), he found that the enzymatic hydrolysis of ribonucleic acid (RNA) gave evidence that the RNA nucleosides, like those of deoxyribonucleic acid (DNA), were linked by phosphate ester groups through the 3′ and 5′ positions. Owing to the difficulty of preparing pure enzymes, such evidence was then regarded with suspicion, and there was subsequently much confusion about the nature of the internucleotide link in RNA. The role of cyclic phosphates in the hydrolysis of RNA was not understood until the 1950's, when Gulland's evidence for the 3′–5′ link in RNA was seen to be valid.

Electrometric titration of DNA, done with D. O. Jordan and H. F. W. Taylor (1947), proved the existence of the hydrogen bonding which was an essential feature of the famous "double helix" of J. D. Watson and Francis Crick (1953). An earlier type of helical structure put forward by Linus Pauling and E. J. Corey had envisaged the phosphate groups as closely packed inside a single helix, the bases projecting radially on the outside. The Watson-Crick structure, on the other hand, required that two helices be linked by hydrogen bonds between the base pairs adenine-thymine and guanine-cytosine.

Gulland and his co-workers found that the primary phosphoric acid groups of DNA were readily titratable and thus, as was later realized, were on the outside of the double helix. With D. O. Jordan and J. M. Creeth, Gulland showed that the amino and amido groups of the bases were titratable only after treatment at extreme acid or alkaline pH, that is, only after there had been a breakdown into smaller molecular units, as confirmed by a decrease in viscosity and disappearance of streaming birefringence (1947). Rosalind Franklin and Raymond Gosling used Gulland's titrations as the main evidence in favor of the double helix, to which they had been led by their own crystallographic studies (1953).

The full solution of most of the problems tackled by Gulland was usually a little beyond the reach of the techniques of the day; he did not think that "easy" research was worth doing. His striking appearance, personal charm, and skill with words made him a memorable teacher. He died in a railway accident and was survived by his wife and two daughters.

BIBLIOGRAPHY

I. ORIGINAL WORKS. There is a not quite complete bibliography of Gulland's works in the obituary notice of the Royal Society, cited below. Among his earliest publications, written with R. Robinson, are "The Morphine Group. Part I. A Discussion of the Constitutional Problem," in *Journal of the Chemical Society,* **123** (1923), 980; and "The Constitution of Codeine and Thebaine," in *Memoirs of the Manchester Literary and Philosophical Society,* **69** (1924–1925). For his work on purine nucleosides see "Spectral Absorption of Methylated Xanthines and Constitution of the Purine Nucleosides," in *Nature,* **132** (1933), 782, written with E. R. Holiday.

His papers on RNA nucleosides, written with Elisabeth M. Jackson, include "Phosphoesterases of Bone and Snake Venoms," in *Biochemical Journal,* **32** (1938), 590–596; "5-Nucleotidase," *ibid.,* 597–601; "The Constitution of Yeast Nucleic Acid," in *Journal of the Chemical Society* (1938), p. 1492; and "The Constitution of Yeast Ribonucleic Acid. Part III. The Nature of the Phosphatase-Resistant Group," *ibid.* (1939), p. 1842.

For works on Gulland's other researches, see "Some Aspects of the Chemistry of Nucleotides," *ibid.* (1944), p. 208; "Deoxypentose Nucleic Acids. Part II. Electrometric Titration of the Acidic and Basic Groups of the Deoxypentose Nucleic Acid of Calf Thymus," *ibid.* (1947), p. 1131, written with D. O. Jordan and H. F. W. Taylor; and "Deoxypentose Nucleic Acids. Part III. Viscosity and Streaming Birefringence of Solutions of the Sodium Salt of the Deoxypentose Nucleic Acid of Calf Thymus," *ibid.,* p. 1141, written with J. M. Creeth and D. O. Jordan.

II. SECONDARY LITERATURE. Obituaries by R. D. Haworth appeared in *Obituary Notices of Fellows of the Royal Society of London,* **6,** no. 17 (1948), 67–82, and in *Journal of the Chemical Society* (1948), pp. 1476–1482; the former has a portrait. See also J. W. Cook, in *Nature,* **160** (1947), 702–703.

For the significance of Gulland's work on nucleic acids, see D. M. Brown and A. R. Todd, "Evidence on the Nature of the Chemical Bonds in Nucleic Acids," in E. Chargaff and J. N. Davidson, eds., *The Nucleic Acids,* I (New York, 1955), 409–445; R. E. Franklin and R. G. Gosling, in *Nature,* **171** (1953), 740–741; D. O. Jordan, *The Chemistry of Nucleic Acids* (London, 1960), pp. 67–68, 140–153, 169–170, and *passim;* and J. D. Watson, *The Double Helix* (London, 1968), p. 183.

KATHLEEN R. FARRAR

GULLSTRAND, ALLVAR (*b.* Landskrona, Sweden, 5 June 1862; *d.* Uppsala, Sweden, 21 July 1930), *ophthalmology, geometrical optics.*

Allvar Gullstrand was the son of a prominent physician who was city physician of Landskrona. Under the influence of his father he began the study of medicine in 1880 and soon specialized in physiological optics. He studied in Uppsala, Vienna, and Stockholm. He finished his medical studies in 1884 and obtained the license to practice medicine in 1888. After receiving his doctorate in 1890, he was appointed in 1892 as lecturer at the Royal Caroline Institute. At the same time he worked as chief physician at an ophthalmological clinic and in 1892 was appointed head of the eye clinic in Stockholm.

In 1894 Gullstrand became professor of ophthalmology at the University of Uppsala, where he received an honorary degree in 1907. Six years later, the university created a special chair for him, without teaching obligations, in physiological and physical optics. Gullstrand also received an honorary degree from the University of Jena, and in 1911 from the University of Dublin. That same year, the Nobel Prize in physiology or medicine was awarded to him for his investigations of the dioptrics of the eye.

Allvar Gullstrand's greatest achievements lie in the field of ophthalmological optics, the study of the human eye as an optical system. This study engendered his interest in geometrical optics. He then drew the attention of the optical designers to several misconceptions and so made important contributions to this field as well.

Gullstrand started his work in ophthalmology with a paper on the astigmatism of the cornea. He became interested in the accommodation mechanism of the human eye and in an exact theory discussed the influence which the layers of the crystalline lens play. This was a difficult mathematical problem which had not been attacked in detail before. It led to the conception of a new and more accurate model of the human eye, a big step beyond Helmholtz. This is described in Gullstrand's masterly commentaries on the occasion of his reediting Helmholtz' *Handbook of Physiological Optics.* These commentaries contain by far the clearest and best description of all of Gullstrand's ideas on geometrical and physiological optics.

Gullstrand invented a slit lamp, which, in combination with a microscope, allowed him to locate exactly a foreign body in the eye with respect to all three dimensions. He designed aspheric lenses for aphakic eyes, that is, eyes from which the lens has been removed as a result of cataracts. He investigated the effect of the rotation of the eye around the fulcrum, and through his friendship with M. von Rohr many of his ideas led to the construction of optical instruments, particularly the great Gullstrand ophthalmoscope, which was manufactured by Zeiss.

In the field of geometrical optics Gullstrand wrote many extensive papers that went beyond the frontiers of optical knowledge for his time. He developed the theory of the fourth-order aberration of a general optical ray, independent of the axis of a rotational symmetry system. Especially, he made contributions to the knowledge of umbilic points, that is, points in which the two principal curvatures are the same. He then investigated how the characteristic quantities of general bundles change with refraction, thus obtaining what he called the system laws of optical systems. But Gullstrand did not restrict himself solely to the consideration of spherical surfaces; one of his longest papers deals with the construction and tracing through of aspheric surfaces.

Unacquainted with the work of H. R. Hamilton, he solved difficult mathematical problems simply by developing the necessary quantities in a series around the coordinates of the principal ray. He considered mathematical methods, such as the calculus of variation and vector methods, to be false ornaments. This prejudice makes his papers long and clumsy, but they contain a number of valuable and little-known results. H. Boegehold, C. W. Oseen, and the writer have endeavored to give simpler derivations of his beautiful results. However, there are limitations to his method. In the case of a branch point, for example, the series development does not work.

Gullstrand was a fighter, discovering several inaccuracies in the normal treatment of optical problems; he spent much of his time studying these inaccuracies, which were mostly a result of approximate pictures being applied to describe finite realities. For instance, the Sturm conoid described an astigmatic bundle as a bundle of rays going through two straight lines perpendicular to each other and to the principal ray. Gullstrand showed that such a manifold bundle of rays is not a normal system, that is, it cannot originate from an object point. Another fallacy was that the collinear image formation, which is the coordination of lines in object and image space such that the rays from any object point unite in a fixed image point, could not have been taken as an approximation to the real image formation, because the former cannot be obtained by optical means (with the trivial exception of the plane mirror). Unfortunately, books are still published disregarding these simple truths.

Gullstrand represents a scientist of very rigorous standards, and as such, he was highly respected by his peers for his intelligence and integrity. His advice was widely sought, even outside his special sphere of interest; among other honors, he was a member and later president of the Nobel Prize committee.

BIBLIOGRAPHY

I. ORIGINAL WORKS. Gullstrand's works include "Objektive Differential-Diagnostik und photographische Abbildung von Augenmuskellahmungen," in *Kungliga Svenska vetenskapsakademiens handlingar,* **18** (1892); "Allgemeine Theorie der monochromatischen Aberrationen und ihre nächsten Ergebnisse für die Ophthalmologie," in *Nova acta Regiae Societatis scientiarum upsaliensis* (1900); "Die Farbe der Macula centralis retinae," in *Archiv für Ophthalmologie,* **62** (1905), 1–72, 378; "Die reelle optische Abbildung," in *Kungliga Svenska vetenskapsakademiens handlingar,* **41** (1906), 1–119; "Tatsachen und Fiktionen in der Lehre von der optischen Abbildung," in *Archiv für Optik* (1907), 1–41, 81–97; and "Die optische Abbildung in heterogenen Medien und die Dioptrik der Kristallinse des Menschen," in *Kungliga Svenska vetenskapsakademiens handlingar,* **43** (1908), 1–58.

See also *Einführung in die Methoden der Dioptrik des Auges des Menschen* (Leipzig, 1911); "Die reflexlose Ophthalmoskopie," in *Archiv für Augenheilkunde,* **68** (1911), 101–144; "Das allgemeine optische Abbildungssystem," in *Kungliga Svenska vetenskapsakademiens handlingar,* **55** (1915), 1–139; "Ueber aspharische Flächen in optischen Instrumenten," *ibid.,* **60** (1919), 1–155; "Optische Systemsgesetze zweiter und dritter Ordnung," *ibid.,* **63** (1924), 1–175; and "Einiges über optische Bilder," in *Naturwissenschaften,* **14** (1926), 653–664.

II. SECONDARY LITERATURE. For information about Gullstrand and his work see H. Boegehold, "Ueber die Entwicklung der Theorie der optischen Instrumente seit Abbe," in *Ergebnisse der exakten Naturwissenschaften,* **8** (1929), 1–146; M. Herzberger, "Allvar Gullstrand," in *Optica acta,* **3** (1960), 237–241; J. W. Nordenson, "Allvar Gullstrand," in *Klinische Monatsblatter für Augenheilkunde,* pp. 560–566; C. W. Oseen, "Allvar Gullstrand," in *Kungliga Svenska vetenskapsakademiens årsbok,* (1937); "Une méthode nouvelle de l'optique géometrique," in *Kungliga Svenska vetenskapsakademiens handlingar,* **3** (1936), 1–41; and M. von Rohr, "Allvar Gullstrand," in *Zeitschrift für ophthalmologische Optik,* **18** (1930), 129–134.

MAXIMILIAN J. HERZBERGER

GUNDISSALINUS, DOMINICUS, also known as **Domingo Gundisalvo** or **Gonsález** (*fl.* Toledo, Spain, second half of the twelfth century), *science translation, philosophy of science.*

Gundissalinus' date of birth is unknown, although conjecture has offered 1110; there is some evidence that he was still alive in 1190. He was archdeacon of Segovia, but his intellectual activity was centered at Toledo, where a flourishing school of translators, under the patronage of such archbishops as Raymond of Toledo, introduced a considerable amount of Arabic and Judaic materials to the Latin West during the twelfth century.

Many of the translations were done with the collaboration of two scholars, one knowledgeable in Arabic, the other in Latin, with a vernacular serving as common ground. The translations attributed to Gundissalinus were probably done in this fashion, although only in the manuscripts of the translation of the *De anima* of Ibn Sīnā (Avicenna) is Gundissalinus' name specifically linked with that of a co-translator, Abraham ibn Daūd (Avendauth). In addition to the *De anima,* Gundissalinus' name has been connected with translations of Ibn Sīnā's *Sufficientia* and *Metaphysics,* as well as a portion of his *Posterior Analytics,* together with the *Logic* and *Metaphysics* of al-Ghazzālī; the *Fons vitae* of Ibn Gabirol; the *De intellectu,* the *Fontes questionum,* the *De scientiis,* the *Liber excitativus ad viam felicitatis,* and the *De ortu scientiarum* of al-Fārābī; the *De intellectu* of al-Kindī; and the *Liber de definitionibus* of Isaac Israeli.

Gundissalinus was the author of five philosophical works which drew heavily on the Arabic-Judaic materials of his translations as well as on Latin sources. He was the first to provide the Latin West with an introduction to Arabic-Judaic Neoplatonism and the first to blend this tradition with the Latin Christian Neoplatonism of Boethius and Augustine. His *De unitate* is such a syncretic work. It is rich in aphorisms which were quoted frequently during the Middle Ages, for example, "Quidquid est ideo est quia unum est." Gundissalinus' *De anima,* likewise a compilation from his translations, is essentially a presentation of Avicennian psychology and ideas from Ibn Gabirol, although it utilizes material from other sources, such as Augustine and the treatise *On the Difference Between Soul and Spirit* of Qusṭā ibn Lūqā.

Gundissalinus' *De processione mundi* is taken from numerous sources: Ibn Sīnā, Ibn Gabirol, al-Ghazzālī, al-Fārābī, Boethius, Porphyry, the *Epistola de anima* of Isaac de Stella, possibly the *De deo Socratis* of Apuleius, and his own *De unitate.* Its editor, Georg Bülow, considers it a late work. The *De processione* was used in the thirteenth century by both William of Auvergne (William of Paris) and Thomas Aquinas. Gundissalinus' *De immortalitate animae,* again dependent on Arabic materials, is a well-written treatise proving the indestructibility of the soul, using arguments based on the soul's own nature which were to become standard in the Middle Ages. The *De immortalitate* was reworked in the thirteenth century by William of Auvergne.

The *De divisione philosophiae* is a classification of the sciences which served as a source for later classification schemes. It incorporates al-Fārābī's work on the classification of the sciences (the *De ortu scientiarum*) and utilizes a wide variety of other sources: classical Latin, Arabic, and Aristotelian. Since it draws on Gerard of Cremona's translation of the Arabic mathematician al-Nayrīzī, the *De divisione* was likely written after 1140, since Gerard's translating activity probably did not begin before that year. The *De divisione* begins with a prologue followed by a section containing six definitions of philosophy taken from various sources.

The sciences are classified into three major groups: propaedeutic sciences, including grammar, poetics, and rhetoric; logic; and philosophical sciences. The latter are further divided into theoretical and practical sciences. The theoretical sciences are subdivided in turn into physics, mathematics, and theology. Physics contains eight subjects, and mathematics has seven. Following this discussion, Gundissalinus inserts a section from Ibn Sīnā's *Posterior Analytics.* Treatment of the practical sciences, which include politics, economics, and ethics, concludes the treatise.

Gundissalinus' classification transcends the conventional subject matter of the *trivium* and the *quadrivium.* He includes a section on medicine as a branch of physics, and the seven subjects subsumed under mathematics include discussions of *scientiae de aspectibus, de ponderibus,* and *de ingeniis,* in addition to the four subjects of the *quadrivium.* The *De divisione* was directly used by Robert Kilwardby in his own treatise on classification, and its influence is further revealed in the works of Michael Scot, Vincent of Beauvais, and Thierry of Chartres.

BIBLIOGRAPHY

I. Original Works. Editions of Gundissalinus' writings include M. Menéndez y Pelayo, *Historia de los heterodoxos españoles,* I (Madrid, 1880), 691–711, text of *De processione mundi;* Paul Correns, "Die dem Boethius fälschlich zugeschrieben Abhandlung des Dominicus Gundisalvi *De unitate,*" in *Beiträge zur Geschichte der Philosophie des Mittelalters,* **1,** no. 1 (1891), 1–11; Georg Bülow, "Des Dominicus Gundissalinus Schrift von der Unsterblichkeit der Seele," *ibid.,* **2,** no. 3 (1897), 1–38; Ludwig Baur, "Dominicus Gundissalinus *De divisione philosophiae,*" *ibid.,* **4,** nos. 2–3 (1903), 1–142; Georg Bülow, "Des Dominicus Gundissalinus Schrift von dem Hervorgange der Welt (*De processione mundi,*" *ibid.,* **24,** no. 3 (1925), 1–54; and J. T. Muckle, "The Treatise *De anima* of Dominicus Gundissalinus," in *Mediaeval Studies,* **2** (1940), 23–103.

II. Secondary Literature. On Gundissalinus or his work, see M. T. D'Alverny, "Avendauth?" in *Homenaje a Millás-Vallicrosa,* I (Barcelona, 1954), 19–43, esp. the arts. by P. Alonso listed in ftn. 14, pp. 24–25, including "Las fuentes literarias de Domingo Gundisalvo," in *Al-Andalus,* **11** (1947), 209–211; C. Bäumker, "Les écrits philosophiques de Dominicus Gundissalinus," in *Revue thomiste,* **5** (1897), 723–745; and "Dominicus Gundissalinus als philosophischer Schriftsteller," in *Beiträge zur Geschichte der Philosophie des Mittelalters,* **25,** nos. 1–2 (1927), 255–275; D. A. Callus, "Gundissalinus' *De anima* and the Problem of Substantial Form," in *New Scholasticism,* **13** (1939), 338–355; A. H. Chroust, "The Definition of Philosophy in the *De divisione philosophiae* of Dominicus Gundissalinus," *ibid.,* **25** (1951), 253–281; P. Duhem, *Le système du monde,* III (Paris, 1958), 177–181; E. Gilson,

History of Christian Philosophy in the Middle Ages (New York, 1955), pp. 235–239, 652–653; Nicholas M. Haring, "Thierry of Chartres and Dominicus Gundissalinus," in *Mediaeval Studies,* **26** (1964), 271–286; R. W. Hunt, "The Introductions to the *Artes* in the Twelfth Century," in *Studia Mediaevalia in Honor of R. J. Martin* (Bruges, 1948), pp. 85–112; L. Löwenthal, *Pseudo-Aristoteles über die Seele. Eine psychologische Schrift des 11. Jahrhunderts und ihre Beziehung zu Salomo ibn Gabirol (Avicebron)* (Berlin, 1891), pp. 77–113; J. Teicher, "Gundissalino e l'Agostonismo avicennizante," in *Rivista di filosofia neoscholastica* (May 1934), pp. 252–258; and L. Thorndike, *A History of Magic and Experimental Science,* II (New York, 1923), 78–82.

More general works are A. Jourdain, *Recherches critiques sur l'âge et l'origine des traductions d'Aristote* (Paris, 1819), pp. 107–119; Artur Schneider, "Die abenländische Spekulation des zwölften Jahrhunderts in ihrem Verhältnis zur aristotelischen und jüdisch-arabischen Philosophie," in *Beiträge zur Geschichte der Philosophie des Mittelalters,* **17**, pt. 4 (1915), 39–72; M. Steinschneider, *Die europäischen Übersetzungen aus dem arabischen bis Mitte des 17. Jahrhunderts* (Graz, 1956), pp. 40–50, 260–261; and R. de Vaux, *Notes et textes sur l'avicennisme latin aux confins des xii*^e^ *et xiii*^e^ *siècles* (Paris, 1934), pp. 141–142.

CLAUDIA KREN

GUNTER, EDMUND (*b.* Hertfordshire, England, 1581; *d.* London, England, 10 December 1626), *navigation, mathematics.*

Little is known of Gunter's origins or the details of his life. Of Welsh descent, he was educated at Westminster School and Christ Church, Oxford, graduating B.A. in 1603 and M.A. in 1605. He subsequently entered holy orders, became rector of St. George's, Southwark, in 1615, and received the B.D. degree later that year. In March 1619 he became professor of astronomy at Gresham College, London, retaining this post and his rectorship until his sudden death at the age of forty-five.

Gunter's contributions to science were essentially of a practical nature. A competent but unoriginal mathematician, he had a gift for devising instruments which simplified calculations in astronomy, navigation, and surveying; and he played an important part in the English tradition—begun in 1561 by Richard Eden's translation of Martín Cortes' *Arte de navegar* and furthered by William Borough, John Dee, Thomas Harriot, Thomas Hood, Robert Hues, Robert Norman, Edward Wright, and others—which put the theory of navigation into a form suitable for easy use at sea. Gunter's works, written in English, reflected the practical nature of his teaching and linked the more scholarly work of his time with everyday needs; the tools he provided were of immense value long afterward.

Gunter's first published mathematical work was the *Canon triangulorum* of 1620, a short table, the first of its kind, of common logarithms of sines and tangents. His account of his sector, in the *De sectore et radio* of 1623, had circulated in manuscript for sixteen years before its publication. The sector, a development from Hood's, included sine, tangent, logarithm, and meridional part scales; its uses included the solution of plane, spherical, and nautical triangles (the last formed from rhumb, meridian, and latitude lines). With improvements, the British navy used it for two centuries, and it was also a precursor of the slide rule. Gunter solved such problems as finding the sun's amplitude from its declination and the latitude of the observer by adding similar scales to the seaman's cross-staff. Comparison of the amplitude with the sun's direction, measured by a magnetic compass, was known to give the compass variation; but although Gunter's own observations in 1622 at Limehouse were about five degrees less than Borough's 1580 results there, a statement of the secular change of variation awaited the further decrease observed by Gunter's Gresham successor, Henry Gellibrand.

Gunter's other inventions may have included the so-called Dutchman's log for measuring a ship's way. Henry Briggs acknowledged his suggested use of arithmetical complements in logarithmic work and the terms cosine, contangent, and such are probably Gunter's own; his use of the decimal point and his decimal notation for degrees are to be noted. Gunter's chain, used in surveying, is sixty-six feet long and divided into 100 equal links, thus allowing decimal measurement of acreage. Largely following Willebrord Snell, Gunter took a degree of the meridian to be 352,000 feet; this decision gave English seamen a much improved result.

BIBLIOGRAPHY

I. ORIGINAL WORKS. Gunter's chief works went through six eds. by 1680 and were successively augmented by their editors. They are *Canon triangulorum, sive tabulae sinuum et tangentium artificialium ad radium 10000.0000. & ad scrupula prima quadrantis* (London, 1620)—the British Museum copy (C.54.e.10) is bound with Henry Briggs's rare *Logarithmorum chilias prima* (London, n.d. [probably 1617]) and contains copious MS additions; *De sectore et radio. The Description and Use of the Sector in Three Bookes. The Description and Use of the Crosse-Staffe in Other Three Bookes. . . .* (London, 1623), a work of great practical importance; and *The Description and Use of His Majesties Dials in White-Hall Garden* (London, 1624)—the British Museum copy (C.60.f.7) gives evidence of Gunter's friendship with Ben Jonson—describes the large complex of dials, which stood until about 1697. A copy of the enl. 2nd ed. of his works, entitled *The Description and Use of the Sector, Crosse-staffe, and Other Instruments: With a Canon of Artificiall Lines and Tangents, to a Radius of 100,000,000 Parts, and the Use Thereof in Astronomie, Navigation, Dialling and Fortification, etc.* . . . (London, 1636), was bought by Newton for five shillings in 1667 and may be seen, much thumbed, in the library of Trinity College, Cambridge (NQ.9.160); it includes the vexed method of "middle latitude," probably first put forth by Ralph Handson in his 1614 version of Bartolomäus Pitiscus' *Trigonometria* but not used by Gunter himself. The 1653 ed. of the works, amended by Samuel Foster and Henry Bond, contains an early printed statement of the logarithmic result for the integral of the secant function or meridional parts—Gunter's meridian scale, like Wright's earlier one, came from the simple addition of secants; and he was doubtless unaware of Harriot's unpublished calculation of them as (in effect) logarithmic tangents, completed in 1614: he was not, anyway, interested in such theoretical niceties.

II. SECONDARY LITERATURE. There is little need to refer to the brief early biographical sketches by John Aubrey, Charles Hutton, and John Ward. Accounts of aspects of Gunter's scientific contributions and their contexts are given in James Henderson, *Bibliotheca tabularum mathematicarum Being a Descriptive Catalogue of Mathematical Tables. Part 1. Logarithmic Tables* (*A. Logarithms of Numbers*) (Cambridge, 1926); and, extensively, in David W. Waters, *The Art of Navigation in England in Elizabethan and Early Stuart Times* (London, 1958), which gives detailed references to the relevant work of his contemporaries, of whom Briggs, Harriot, and Wright are the most important in this context. Christopher Hill, *Intellectual Origins of the English Revolution* (Oxford, 1965), covers the wider background, with much detail on the Gresham College circles. E. G. R. Taylor, *The Mathematical Practitioners of Tudor and Stuart England* (London, 1954), is useful but often infuriating on documentation. A more recent survey of the mathematical and navigational references is in J. V. Pepper, "Harriot's Unpublished Papers," in *History of Science*, **6** (1968), 17–40. The scientific correspondence of the later seventeenth century contains references to Gunter but does not add much of substance.

JON V. PEPPER

GÜNTHER, JOHANN. See **Guinter, Joannes**

GURVICH, ALEKSANDR GAVRILOVICH (*b.* Poltava, Russia, 27 September 1874; *d.* Moscow, U.S.S.R., 27 July 1954), *biology.*

Gurvich was the son of a notary, G. K. Gurvich; his elder brother, L. G. Gurvich, was a prominent specialist in petroleum chemistry. He graduated from the Faculty of Medicine of the University of Munich in 1897 and from 1899 to 1901 was an assistant in the department of anatomy in the University of Strasbourg. From 1901 to 1905 he lived in Bern, where he did his early work on the histophysiology of kidney cells and studied mitoses in amphibian eggs that had been put through a centrifuge. In 1904 he published *Morphologie und Biologie der Zelle.*

From 1907 to 1917 Gurvich was professor of anatomy and histology at the Higher Courses for Women in St. Petersburg. *Atlas und Grundriss der Embryologie* appeared in German, Spanish, and Russian between 1907 and 1909; *Vorlesungen der allgemeinen Histologie* was published in 1913. At the same time, in 1912, he began the investigations into the processes of morphogenesis that were to lead him to the theory of the biological field.

Gurvich served as professor of histology at the University of Simferopol (Crimea) from 1918 to 1924; he held the same position from 1924 to 1929 at the University of Moscow. He was head of the department of experimental biology of the Institute of Experimental Medicine in Leningrad from 1930 to 1942. In 1942 he returned to Moscow to assume the same post at the All-Union Institute of Experimental Medicine, which became the Academy of Medical Sciences in 1944; his own department became the Institute of Experimental Biology, with him as its director.

From 1948 until the end of his life Gurvich continued his experimental work at his home laboratory. He had begun his scientific work in histology, cytology, and embryology, with a later concentration on the problem of mitosis—particularly on the causes of cell division. The latter led him to the discovery of the resolving factor of mitosis—that is, of weak shortwave ultraviolet radiation, which he called mitogenetic rays. His researches in this field paved the way for further developments in molecular biology and resulted in establishment of the chain of processes occurring in cells after mitogenetic irradiation and the applicability of spectral analysis of mitogenetic rays (various fermentative processes with various spectral characteristics being the source of radiation).

Gurvich's early researches on morphogenesis allowed him to establish that the arrangement of morphological structures—the regular movement of cells and change in their form in the process of development—is governed by the character of the vector field. This became known as the theory of the biological field. He published seventeen monographs and more than 120 special works. His ideas were developed in the works of his wife, L. D. Gurvich, his daughter, A. A. Gurvich, S. J. Salkind, G. M. Frank, M. A. Baron, L. J. Blacher, and L. V. Belousov, among others.

BIBLIOGRAPHY

Gurvich's publications include "Über Determination, Normierung und Zufall in der Ontogenese," in *Archiv für Entwicklungsmechanik der Organismen*, **30** (1910), 133–193;

"Über den Begriff des embryonalen Feldes," *ibid.,* **51** (1922), 383–415; "Die Natur des spezifischen Erregers der Zellteilung," in *Archiv für mikroskopische Anatomie und Entwicklungsmechanik,* **100** (1923), 11–40; *Das Problem der Zellteilung physiologisch betrachtet* (Berlin, 1926); "Sur les rayons mitogénétiques et leur identité avec les rayons ultraviolets," in *Comptes rendus hebdomadaires des séances de l'Académie des sciences,* **184** (1927), 903–904, written with G. M. Frank; *Die histologischen Grundlagen der Biologie* (Jena, 1930); *Die mitogenetische Strahlung* (Berlin, 1932; 2nd ed., Jena, 1959), written with L. D. Gurvich; and *Teoria biologicheskogo polya* ("The Theory of the Biological Field"; Moscow, 1944).

On Gurvich's life and work, see L. V. Belousov, A. A. Gurvich, S. J. Salkind, and N. N. Kanneguiser, *Aleksandr Gavrilovich Gurvich (1874–1954)* (Moscow, 1970).

L. J. BLACHER

GUTBIER, FELIX ALEXANDER (*b.* Leipzig, Germany, 21 March 1876; *d.* Jena, Germany, 4 October 1926), *chemistry.*

Gutbier was the son of Carl F. Gutbier, a factory owner, and Fanny Thilo. He studied chemistry at the Technische Hochschule in Dresden under Walter Hempel and Fritz Foerster, then at the University of Erlangen with Otto Fischer, and finally at the University of Zurich under Alfred Werner. He received his doctorate in 1899 under Otto Fischer with the dissertation "Beiträge zur Kenntnis der Rosinduline." After becoming Fischer's assistant, he qualified for university lecturing in 1902 with *Studien über das Tellur* and was appointed *Privatdozent* in chemistry at the University of Erlangen. He refused an offer in 1907 to move to the University of Montevideo, and in the same year he was named extraordinary professor at Erlangen. In 1912 he was called to the Technische Hochschule in Stuttgart as professor of electrochemistry and chemical technology. Later he became professor of inorganic chemistry there and director of the Institute for Inorganic Chemistry and Inorganic Chemical Technology. From 1920 to 1922 he was rector of the Technische Hochschule. He was called to the University of Jena as professor of inorganic chemistry and director of the chemistry laboratory in 1922. In Jena, from 1924 until 1926, he was dean of the Faculty of Mathematics and Natural Sciences, which was founded through his initiative and was independent of the Faculty of Philosophy. From Easter 1926 until his death he was rector of Jena. Gutbier's first wife was Olga Fischer, daughter of Otto Fischer; they had two sons. His second wife was Gertrud Gaugler.

Gutbier's scientific publications treat many branches of inorganic chemistry; only in the beginning of his career was he concerned with problems in organic chemistry with his teacher Otto Fischer. While in Erlangen he became involved in inorganic chemistry. His analytical, inorganic, and atomic weight investigations included a special interest in tellurium. Gutbier turned his attention to the chemistry of coordination complexes and colloid chemistry. Beginning with the colloids of tellurium, he went on to the description of the metallic colloids silver, gold, platinum and the platinum metals, and of other colloidal elements. He also examined protective colloids and their specific effectiveness. In addition, he obtained a wealth of results in the chemistry of coordination complexes. Particularly noteworthy are the findings on hexachloro and hexabromo salts and of many metallic acids.

In all these investigations very different reactions were studied: for example, those of hydrogen sulfide with selenious acid, of oxygen with ruthenium, of hydrogen peroxide with tellurium, the catalytic effect of platinum black on hydrazine, and the receptivity for hydrogen induced by the presence of palladium, platinum, rhodium, and iridium. In addition, Gutbier worked out quantitative determinations and methods of separation for tellurium, palladium, and selenium, and for tungstic acid by means of nitrone; he also formulated separation methods for palladium and tin by means of dimethylglyoxime and electrolysis, respectively.

Because of his ability in analytic chemistry and his work on palladium, tellurium, and bismuth, Gutbier also succeeded in the difficult field of atomic weight determination. His researches in physical chemistry include the electrolysis of bismuth salt solutions and the preparation of selenium colloids through electrolysis and of mercury colloids through sputtering.

Gutbier also had a great interest in the history of chemistry, as shown in his work on Henri Moissan (1908) and in his essay on Goethe, Grand Duke Karl August, and chemistry in Jena (1926).

His activity as a teacher found expression in Gutbier's *Lehrbuch der qualitativen Analyse,* his monograph *Chemiestudium und Chemieunterricht,* and in his collaborative efforts with L. Birckenbach: *Praktische Anleitung zur Massanalyse* and *Praktische Anleitung zur Gewichtsanalyse.* His technical aptitude is evident in his invention of the high-speed dialyzer in the course of his work on colloid chemistry.

Gutbier was above all an experimental chemist who was able to inspire numerous students and co-workers through his organizational skills. He published about 260 papers.

BIBLIOGRAPHY

Gutbier's books include *Zur Erinnerung an Henri Moissan* (Erlangen, 1908); *Praktische Anleitung zur Gewichts-*

analyse, 2nd ed. (Stuttgart, 1919), written with L. Birckenbach; *Lehrbuch der qualitativen Analyse* (Stuttgart, 1920); *Praktische Anleitung zur Mass analyse,* 4th ed. (Stuttgart, 1924), written with L. Birckenbach; and *Goethe, Karl August und die Chemie in Jena* (Jena, 1926).

Part of his doctoral diss. was published in the complete works of Otto Fischer, and part appeared as "Über Thio-N-methyl-Pyridon und -Chinolon," in *Berichte der Deutschen chemischen Gesellschaft,* **33** (1900), 3358–3359.

A systematic bibliography of his journal articles is in Poggendorff, VI, 983–984.

F. HEIN

GUTENBERG, BENO (*b.* Darmstadt, Germany, 4 June 1889; *d.* Pasadena, California, 25 January 1960), *seismology.*

Gutenberg was the son of Hermann Gutenberg, a soap manufacturer, and Pauline Hachenburger Gutenberg. He attended the Realgymnasium and Technische Hochschule in Darmstadt, taking intensive courses in mathematics, physics, and chemistry. He intended to specialize in mathematics and physics at the University of Göttingen, but an interest in weather forecasting and climatology led him to Emil Wiechert's course on instrumental observation of geophysical phenomena at the new geophysical institute there. He took all of Wiechert's courses until he was told that he had learned practically all that was known in seismology. For his Ph.D. (1911) he elected to study microseisms.

From 1911 until 1918 (with an interruption for army service) Gutenberg was assistant at the International Seismological Association in Strasbourg; in 1918 he became *Privatdozent* at the University of Frankfurt-am-Main, where he was appointed professor of geophysics in 1926. His father died that year, and Gutenberg also undertook the management of the family business.

In 1930 Gutenberg accepted a professorship at the California Institute of Technology. This post also provided him with research facilities at the Seismological Laboratory of the Carnegie Institution there, which had an extensive network of seismograph stations, together with good recording instruments; it became part of the California Institute of Technology in 1936 and Gutenberg was its director from 1947 to 1958.

Gutenberg began in seismology with the most complex and frustrating topic in the field: the origin of microseisms. In his thesis and a number of later papers he considered most of the presently known sources for microseismic disturbances. Soon thereafter he produced his most elegant piece of research: following earlier suggestions by Wiechert and by R. D. Oldham, he computed the travel times of waves that would be affected by a low-velocity core of the earth, searched seismograms for them, demonstrated the existence of the core and measured its depth (2,900 kilometers) to an accuracy that still stands.

Gutenberg's early interest in meteorology led him to studies of the structure of the upper atmosphere. Noting the curious ring zones of silence and signal around strong air blasts, he derived the general curves for temperature in the ionosphere.

With Charles F. Richter, he derived improved travel-time curves for earthquakes (and determinations of velocity within the earth) while similar work was being done by Harold Jeffreys and Keith Bullen. The difference in approach is well exemplified by the derivation of these curves. The Jeffreys-Bullen curves were derived by statistical methods from a large volume of data from many sources; those by Gutenberg and Richter were from fewer data, from seismograms individually examined. Gutenberg derived improved methods of epicenter and depth determinations (using advanced instruments developed by Hugo Benioff), extended Richter's magnitude scale to deep-focus shocks, and, with Richter, determined the quantitative relations between magnitude, energy, intensity, and acceleration.

Studies of amplitude variations of compressional waves gave Gutenberg initial evidence that low-velocity layers existed within the earth. Using precise determinations of focal depth, he determined the variation of travel times as a function of source depth and thus the fine-scale variations of velocity in the upper mantle, demonstrating the existence of a low-velocity channel at a depth of between 100 and 200 kilometers. This channel is essential to theories of crustal movements.

One widely quoted hypothesis of Gutenberg's has proved invalid. From studies of surface wave velocities, and of reflection of compressional waves beneath the oceans, he concluded that the Atlantic basin was nearly continental in average structure as contrasted with the "truly oceanic" structure of the Pacific. Later work at sea has shown that the anomaly he found was due primarily to the much larger proportion of the Atlantic occupied by the mid-ocean ridge.

With Richter, Gutenberg redetermined the locations of all major earthquakes, showing both the patterns of seismicity and the geometry of the deep-focus earthquakes. Both seismologists and geologists are indebted to Gutenberg. Among the former he will be remembered best for his studies of the core and for his travel times and thorough studies of the phases of earthquake arrivals in "On Seismic Waves"; the latter use *Internal Constitution of the Earth* (which he edited, and wrote large portions of) and *Seismicity of the Earth* as standard sources.

BIBLIOGRAPHY

I. ORIGINAL WORKS. Among Gutenberg's more outstanding works are "On Seismic Waves," in four pts., in *Beiträge zur Geophysik,* **43** (1934); **45** (1935); **47** (1936); and **54** (1939), written with C. F. Richter, which contains much of his work on earthquake travel times and studies in teleseisms; *Internal Constitution of the Earth* (New York, 1939; 2nd ed., 1951); and *Seismicity of the Earth* (New York, 1941), written with Richter, which gives the worldwide geography of earthquakes in a useful format.

A revision of the travel times is "Epicenter and Origin Time of the Main Shock on July 21 and Travel Time of Major Phases," in G. B. Oakeshott, ed., *Earthquakes in Kern County, California During 1952,* California Division of Mines Bulletin 171 (San Francisco, 1955), pp. 157–163. For Gutenberg's summary of seismologic research at three stages over a span of two decades, see *The Physics of the Earth's Interior,* International Geophysics Series, vol. I (New York, 1959). Richter's memorial, cited below, includes a bibliography.

II. SECONDARY LITERATURE. Gutenberg's life and contributions to seismology are summarized in H. Jeffreys, "Beno Gutenberg," in *Quarterly Journal of the Royal Astronomical Society,* **1** (1960), 239–242; and C. F. Richter, "Memorial to Beno Gutenberg, 1889–1960," in *Proceedings of the Geological Society of America for 1960* (1962), pp. 93–104. Sidelights on Gutenberg's early years appear in "Fifteenth Award of the William Bowie Medal," in *Transactions of the American Geophysical Union,* **34,** no. 3 (1953), 353–355.

GEORGE G. SHOR, JR.
ELIZABETH NOBLE SHOR

GUY DE CHAULIAC. See **Chauliac, Guy de.**

GUYE, CHARLES-EUGÈNE (*b.* St. Christophe, Switzerland, 15 October 1866; *d.* Geneva, Switzerland, 15 July 1942), *physics, electromagnetism, molecular physics.*

Guye was a member of a distinguished Swiss family. With his older brother, Philippe-Auguste (1862–1922), he pioneered in investigating phenomena on the borderline between physics and chemistry. Philippe-Auguste, primarily a chemist, was interested in electrochemical synthesis and is known for his precision studies of atomic weights. He was a founder of the *Journal de chimie physique.* Charles-Eugène became primarily a physicist. Interested in electromagnetism and molecular size determinations, he gained recognition for his precise measurements of variation of the mass of electrons as a function of their velocity, and as director of physical laboratories at the University of Geneva. Together and separately, the two Guyes achieved distinction in their different disciplines by devising experimental means for analyzing interface phenomena in physical chemistry and chemical physics.

Four years after Philippe-Auguste, Charles-Eugène left his native town in the canton of Vaud for Geneva, where he began his scientific career in the 1880's with experimental demonstrations of rotatory polarization in optically active crystals and liquids. Studying with Jacques-Louis Soret and Charles Soret, he obtained his doctorate with a thesis on this subject in 1889 at the University of Geneva. There both Guyes were active most of their lives. Significantly, in 1894 Charles-Eugène was called to a professorship at Zurich's Polytechnique. Remaining there for six years, he achieved intellectual independence and was aroused to new scientific interests through teaching electrical engineering. At Zurich Guye's research was in alternating currents, polyphasic generators, and hysteresis phenomena. Albert Einstein was one of his students.

In 1900 Guye returned to Geneva when offered a permanent professorship in experimental physics. He remained there through his retirement in 1930. Most active in the laboratory during the first two decades of the twentieth century, Guye studied electric arcs, their explosive potentials and spontaneous rotations. Bolometry, induction coefficients, and analysis of electrical measuring instruments were his specialties. By designing highly accurate instruments for such work, Guye found important new applications for his apparatus in determining the diameters of molecules and investigating the interior structures of solid-state materials.

With the advent of H. A. Lorentz' theory of the electron and Max Abraham's rival theory, Guye became interested in using his apparatus to test for evidences of the FitzGerald-Lorentz contraction hypothesis and transformation equations. It seemed to him that a crucial experiment ought to be possible to decide between Lorentz' idea of a deformable electron with a shape dependent on velocity and Abraham's notion of permanently spherical electrons. The opportunity seemed all the more inviting as Einstein's special theory of relativity, which was based upon Lorentz' work, began to stir controversy after 1905, while on the other hand, W. Kauffmann's experiments appeared to support Abraham and contradict the predictions of Lorentz and Einstein.

For fully a decade after 1907 Guye carried through a series of increasingly elaborate experiments with charged particles moving through electromagnetic fields. Collaborating with M. Ratnowsky and Charles Lavanchy, Guye was able to develop very precise techniques for measuring particle deflections within carefully controlled electric and magnetic fields. In 1916 and 1921 Guye published these methods and pronounced results in favor of the Lorentzian formulas and Einsteinian theory. Thereafter his reputation rose as a most able experimenter among the world's physicists, but the greater fame of his brother, whom he outlived by two decades, overshadowed Charles-Eugène.

Of French extraction, culture, and spirit, Guye served his profession and university long and well; first as dean of the Faculty of Sciences (1910–1914); then as consulting editor of *Helvetica physica acta* and editor of *Archives de Genève* (1919–1927). He served the Swiss government as a member of its Commission on Weights and Measures (1915–1931) and served as a member of the Solvay Institute of the University of Brussels (1925–1934). In 1927 he was honored to become a correspondent of the French Académie des Sciences, and many other French honors followed. The several small books that he published in later years on the evolution of statistical thermodynamics and on reductionism in physics and biology show the breadth of his interests and the vitality of his mind.

BIBLIOGRAPHY

I. ORIGINAL WORKS. Guye's works include *L'évolution physicochimique* (Paris, 1922), trans. by J. R. Clarke as *The Evolution of Physical Chemistry* (London, 1925); and *Les limites de la physique et de la biologie* (Geneva, 1936). There is a bio-bibliography in *Documents pour servir à l'histoire de l'Université de Genève,* VI (1938), 69–71; IX (1944), 32 f.

II. SECONDARY LITERATURE. An anonymous work about Guye is "Au Professor C. E. Guye à l'occasion de son soixante-dixième anniversaire," in *Helvetica physica acta,* **9** (1936), 511–514. See also Émile Briner, "Ch.-E. Guye (1866–1942)," in *Journal de chimie physique,* **40** (1943), 1–4; Louis de Broglie, "Notice sur la vie et les travaux de Charles-Eugène Guye," in *Comptes rendus de l'Académie des sciences,* **215** (1942), 209–211; *Historisch-biographisches Lexikon der Schweiz,* IV (Neuenburg, 1927), 25; and Poggendorff, IV, 986 f.; VIIa, 324.

LOYD S. SWENSON, JR.

GUYER, MICHAEL FREDERIC (*b.* Plattsburg, Missouri, 17 November 1874; *d.* New Braunfels, Texas, 1 April 1959), *zoology.*

Guyer was the son of Michael Guyer and Sarah J. Thomas. From 1890 to 1892 he attended the University of Missouri and then spent two years at the University of Chicago, where he received the B.S. degree in 1894. He was a teaching assistant in zoology at the University of Nebraska from 1895 to 1896 under Henry B. Ward. In 1897 he taught high school in Lincoln, Nebraska, and received the M.S. degree the same year. His election to Phi Beta Kappa and Phi Kappa Phi honorary societies attested to his scholastic ability. Guyer returned to the University of Chicago in 1897, holding a three-year fellowship; there he worked out his doctoral dissertation, on pigeon spermatogenesis, under Charles Otis Whitman. In 1899 he married Helen M. Stauffer; a son, Edwin Michael, was born on 25 November 1900, the year in which Guyer received his Ph.D.

Guyer became professor of zoology at the University of Cincinnati, also in 1900, and served as head of the department until 1911. At Cincinnati he continued his research on spermatogenesis of guinea fowl, chickens, and hybrids between them; wrote a text on *Animal Micrology* (1906); and, with W. O. Pauli, published a manual of physiology. He also advised both the Medical School (on premedical education) and the Cincinnati Zoological Garden. From 1908 to 1909 he studied at Paris and the Naples Biological Station.

In 1911 Guyer was brought to the University of Wisconsin by its president, Charles R. Van Hise, to be chairman of the department of zoology, a position he held until his retirement in 1945. At Wisconsin he taught animal biology, heredity and eugenics, and cytology. His book *Being Well Born* (1916) aroused widespread interest in human heredity and pointed out its significance, in certain cases, as a predisposing factor to crime, disease, and mental deficiency, as well as its possible role in the improvement of the human species. His *Animal Biology* (1931) quickly became a leading textbook of introductory zoology, going through four editions.

Guyer's continuing interest in medical education led to his appointment in the early 1920's to the National Commission on Medical Education and shortly thereafter to the Wisconsin Basic Science Board, an examining body for prospective Wisconsin physicians. In both of these bodies he exerted a strong influence, stressing the importance of basic sciences in the premedical and medical curricula.

As a cytologist he was one of the first to determine, with a margin of error of about 2 percent, the chromosome number in human spermatocytes. From 1917 to 1930 his main research effort was directed toward inducing hereditary eye defects by injecting antilens serum into pregnant rabbits as eyes were beginning to form in their unborn fetuses. This research held the intriguing possibility that the units of heredity in the germ cells might be altered by antibody action. His papers on these investigations stimulated research elsewhere, which, although it failed in the end to substantiate his main thesis, led to better knowledge about placental transmission of antibodies and other immunological problems. After 1930 he and his students turned to studies on the growth of cancer cells and their susceptibility to certain chemicals, such as palladium.

In his later years Guyer published biological reflections on his own species in *Speaking of Man* (1942). He retired from teaching in 1945 and subsequently spent much time in Arizona and Texas to conserve his health. During his years of teaching he supervised the doctoral research of over two dozen graduate students.

BIBLIOGRAPHY

Some of Guyer's more significant publications are *Animal Micrology* (Chicago, 1906; 5th ed., 1948); *Being Well Born* (Indianapolis, 1916; 2nd ed., 1927); "Transmission of Induced Eye Defects," in *Journal of Experimental Zoology,* **31** (1920), 171–223; "Soma and Germ," in *American Naturalist,* **59** (1925), 97–114; *Animal Biology* (New York, 1931; 4th ed., 1948); and *Speaking of Man* (New York, 1942).

LOWELL E. NOLAND

GUYONNEAU DE PAMBOUR, F. M. See **Pambour, F. M. Guyonneau de.**

GUYOT, ARNOLD HENRI (*b.* Boudevilliers, Switzerland, 28 September 1807; *d.* Princeton, New Jersey, 8 February 1884), *geography, glacial geology.*

At the University of Neuchâtel, Guyot's studies were classical while his early interest in nature was satisfied by collecting insects and plants. In 1825 he went to Germany to continue his education. He studied first at Karlsruhe, where he lived with the family of Alexander Braun, who was often visited by Louis Agassiz and Karl Schimper during their vacations. He later went to Berlin to prepare for the ministry. Guyot eventually abandoned theology for science, however, and terminated his education in 1835 with a doctoral dissertation on the natural classification of lakes.

Soon after, Guyot left Berlin for Paris, having accepted the responsibility of educating the sons of the Count de Pourtalès-Gorgier. While in this position he traveled extensively in Europe for four years. In the spring of 1838, Agassiz met Guyot in Paris, and finding him unconvinced about his new concept of a glacial age, urged him to visit the Alpine glaciers that summer. Guyot spent six weeks in the Alps making a series of fundamental observations on the moraines, the differential flow of glaciers, and the banded structure of the ice (blue bands). These results, although presented orally at the meeting of the Geological Society of France in Porrentruy, in September 1838, were not published because Agassiz and Guyot had decided to collaborate on a major work in which Agassiz would study the glaciers and Guyot the erratic boulders in the plains of Switzerland.

In the following years, Guyot saw with pleasure—and also with some bitterness—most of his conclusions confirmed by Agassiz, Edward Forbes, and others. But since Guyot's original work had not been published, he did not receive proper credit for these findings. In 1847 Agassiz published only one volume, *Système glaciaire,* of the joint work, which he alone had written. It was not until 1883, after Agassiz's death, that a short summary of Guyot's contributions to the project was published.

Guyot returned to Neuchâtel in 1839, and was appointed professor of history and physical geography at the academy there. His major study of the distribution of erratic boulders in Switzerland was undertaken between 1840 and 1847. By tracing the boulders to their original outcrops along the northern slope of the Alps, he recognized eight erratic basins demonstrating the former existence of gigantic Alpine glaciers, as postulated by Agassiz. But Guyot wrote very little on the subject, having planned to publish a complete account of his investigation in the second volume of Agassiz's work which never appeared.

The revolution of 1848 led to the suppression of the academy in June of that year, and Guyot followed Agassiz to America. At the Lowell Technological Institute in Boston he taught comparative physical geography. His lectures, *Earth and Man,* published in 1849, represent a far-reaching synthesis in which he visualized a divine law of progress common to Genesis, the evolution of the earth, and the history of humanity. In his later years, as shown by his work *Creation* (1884), he partially accepted the doctrine of evolution through natural causes.

In 1854 Guyot was appointed professor of physical geography and geology at Princeton. He spread the new concept of geographic education by means of field studies, and for that purpose prepared, between 1861 and 1875, a series of specially designed textbooks and wall maps which became very popular.

Under the auspices of the Smithsonian Institution, Guyot established the instrumental and geographic requirements for a national system of meteorological stations. In order to find the best location for these

GUYTON DE MORVEAU

stations, he undertook a systematic topographical survey of the entire Appalachians from Vermont to North Carolina, a gigantic task which he completed in 1881 with the survey of the Catskills.

In his honor, the term "guyot" is applied to a seamount, generally deeper than 200 meters, whose top is a relatively smooth platform. Originally proposed by H. H. Hess in 1946 after extensive investigations in the Pacific, this term is now in common use throughout the world.

BIBLIOGRAPHY

I. ORIGINAL WORKS. Guyot's chief work is *Earth and Man, or Lectures on Comparative Physical Geography in Its Relation to the History of Mankind,* translated from the French by C. C. Felton (Boston, 1849). A collection of meteorological and physical tables, with other tables useful in practical meteorology, prepared for and published by the Smithsonian Institution are in Smithsonian Institution Publication no. 538 (Washington, D.C., 1852; other eds., 1859, 1884), p. 747.

Other works by Guyot include "On the Topography of the State of New York," in *American Journal of Science,* 2nd ser., **8** (1852), 272–276; "On the Appalachian Mountain System," *ibid.,* **31** (1861), 157–187; "On the Physical Structure and Hypsometry of the Catskill Mountain Region," *ibid.,* 3rd ser., **19** (1880), 429–451; "Observations sur les glaciers," in *Bulletin de la Société des sciences naturelles de Neuchâtel,* **13** (1883), 156–159, with a letter of introduction, pp. 151–156; and *Creation, or the Biblical Cosmogony in the Light of Modern Science* (New York, 1884).

II. SECONDARY LITERATURE. For works about Guyot, see J. D. Dana, "Memoir of Arnold Guyot (1807–1884)," in *Biographical Memoirs. National Academy of Sciences,* **2** (1886), 309–347, which has a complete list of Guyot's publications; and C. Faure, "Vie et travaux d'Arnold Guyot," in *Globe,* **23** (1884), 3–72.

ALBERT V. CAROZZI

GUYTON DE MORVEAU, LOUIS BERNARD (*b.* Dijon, France, 4 January 1737; *d.* Paris, France, 2 January 1816), *chemistry, aeronautics.*

The son of Antoine Guyton, a lawyer, and Marguerite Desaulle, Guyton was educated in Dijon at the Godran (Jesuit) College and the Faculty of Law, and from 1756 to 1762 he practiced there as an advocate. Dijon was the capital of the French province of Burgundy and the seat of one of the provincial *parlements,* or royal courts of law, which had both political and judicial functions; and in 1762 Guyton entered the *parlement* as *avocat-général du roi,* one of the public prosecutors. He then added "de Morveau" to his name, the designation being that of a family property, and until 1789 he was often called Monsieur de Morveau. During the French Revolution he became Guyton-Morveau, then Guyton, and finally Guyton-Morveau again.

The suppression of the Jesuits in France in 1763 resulted in the closing of many schools run by them. Various plans for educational reform were advanced, including Guyton's *Mémoire sur l'éducation publique* (1764), which contains detailed proposals for a large college in each province. He believed that a wide range of subjects should be taught, with less emphasis on classics than hitherto, and made the interesting suggestion that mathematics, physics, natural history, and chemistry should be included in the final two years. He quoted from many classical and modern authors and had obviously studied his subject with the thoroughness that was to characterize all his future work.

Guyton ably performed his heavy parliamentary duties until he retired in 1782 with a pension and the title of *avocat général honoraire.* Some of his speeches were published in *Discours publics et éloges* (3 vols., 1775–1782), one of the most important being his criticism, in 1767, of the local variations of the law in France—where there were, he said, one people, one legislator, and 285 legal codes. He was praised by Voltaire, and in 1771 he outlined a scheme for a new code applicable to the whole country; but the collapse of the old system, like that of education, was to come only with the Revolution, and its reform with Napoleon.

A long poem satirizing the Jesuits—*Le rat iconoclaste ou le Jésuite croqué*—was published anonymously at Dijon in 1763. It was known to be Guyton's work; and after hearing it read, the Académie des Sciences, Arts et Belles-Lettres of Dijon elected him as an *honoraire* on 20 January 1764. His early contributions to its meetings were literary but he became interested in chemistry, which was often discussed at the Academy, and in 1768 he installed a laboratory in his new house. He was entirely self-taught, studying initially the books of A. Baumé and P. J. Macquer.

Another member of the Dijon Academy, J. P. Chardenon, was engaged in research on combustion and calcination; and after his death in 1769 Guyton continued the work. His results were published in "Dissertation sur le phlogistique," the first essay in a volume entitled *Digressions académiques* (1772). Chardenon had speculated about the reason why metals gain weight on calcination, but Guyton pointed out that no one had, in fact, proved that every metal invariably gains weight. This he now did, in a careful and accurate piece of quantitative work that shows that he had developed into a competent chem-

 GUYTON DE MORVEAU

ist. He also proved that decreases in weight occasionally observed by earlier chemists were due to some effect other than calcination. In order to explain why a metal containing phlogiston weighs less than its calx, he modified Chardenon's theory, believing that phlogiston was specifically lighter than all other substances, however subtle, and therefore appeared to lighten anything containing it weighed in any medium whatsoever. Guyton was as unconvincing as Chardenon, who had considered only weighings in air, and his theory gained no support. The experimental part of Guyton's essay, however, was influential; for his proof of the gain in weight was one of the factors that led Lavoisier to investigate combustion and calcination.

Digressions académiques also contained a discussion of chemical affinity in which Guyton elaborated the theory, earlier suggested by Buffon, that ultimate particles of matter attracted each other by a force obeying Newton's inverse-square law—the relation was complicated in that at short distances their shapes had to be considered, for they could not be regarded as point masses. He hoped that the shapes of these particles might eventually be inferred from a study of crystals, but he gave no specific examples. In 1773 Guyton measured the forces of cohesion between mercury and other metals and thought that these could be related to the affinities supposed to be responsible for the formation of amalgams. He returned several times to this problem of measuring affinities, but with no more success than his contemporaries Richard Kirwan and C. F. Wenzel.

In 1772 Guyton became vice-chancellor of the Dijon Academy and was elected a correspondent of the Paris Académie des Sciences. During a visit to Paris in 1775 he was introduced to pneumatic chemistry by Lavoisier, and he soon became convinced that a portion of the air was absorbed during combustion and calcination, causing the gain in weight. He abandoned his former theory but still believed in phlogiston and thought, like Macquer, that it was released at the same time that air was absorbed.

This theory was taught in the public course of chemistry, published as *Élémens de chymie* (3 vols., 1777–1778), that Guyton gave in the Dijon Academy every year from 1776, assisted by Hugues Maret and J. F. Durande. The arrangement of the lectures and book was determined by Guyton's theory that the mutual attraction between the ultimate particles of different kinds of matter could cause one substance to dissolve in another, and that a chemical change was possible only as a result of such a solution. Every reaction therefore required a solvent, and a chapter was devoted to each of twenty solvents: fire, air, and water; nine acids; three alkalies; four oily substances; and mercury.

In order to keep his course up to date, Guyton read widely in several languages. He also translated a number of books and memoirs, his annotated edition of T. O. Bergman's *Opuscules physiques et chymiques* (2 vols., 1780–1785) being especially important. He also added notes to C. W. Scheele's *Mémoires de chymie* (1785), translated by his close friend Claudine Picardet, the wife of another Dijon academician.

A reformer by nature, Guyton became the leading critic of the current chemical nomenclature, in which the name of a substance was hardly ever related to its constitution but was derived from such unsystematic origins as the name of its discoverer, its place of occurrence, or its appearance. Macquer and Bergman proposed certain reforms; and Guyton had been influenced by both of them when, in 1780, he was commissioned by the publisher Panckoucke to write the chemical volumes of the *Encyclopédie méthodique.* All the articles had been arranged in one alphabetical sequence in the *Encyclopédie* of Diderot and D'Alembert and also in the supplementary volumes (1776–1777) to which Guyton contributed fourteen chemical articles, but in the new work each subject was to be treated in one or more separate volumes.

Guyton was about to write a comprehensive treatise on chemistry, and he now had a chance to reform the nomenclature completely. In 1782 he published his initial proposals. They were concerned mainly with acids, bases, and salts, but the principles he laid down were universally applicable. The most important was that the simplest substances should have the simplest names, and that names of compounds should recall their components. The old, unsystematic names were excluded. Thus, oil of vitriol (named from its oily appearance) and Epsom salt (named from its place of occurrence) became vitriolic acid and vitriol of magnesia, respectively. These reforms were welcomed by Macquer and Bergman and were adopted by chemists in France, England, and other countries.

From the beginning of his scientific career, Guyton was interested in metallurgy and mineralogy. In 1769 he investigated the use of coal instead of charcoal in blast furnaces, and in 1777 he described a special flux of powdered glass, borax, and charcoal for assaying iron ores. There were several different theories of the relation between iron and steel; and research led Guyton to discover in 1786, independently of G. Monge, C. A. Vandermonde, and C. L. Berthollet (*Observations sur la physique,* **29** [1786], 210–221), that cast iron, wrought iron, and steel differed only in carbon content. He was often consulted by directors of mines and foundries in Burgundy, and he devised a portable set of apparatus for analyzing minerals in the field. He wanted to reform the nomenclature of minerals on the same lines as chemical nomenclature, but in this he was less successful.

Guyton always attached importance to the applications of science, and he intended the laboratory of the Dijon Academy to be used for the public benefit. In 1782, for example, he examined several white pigments, hoping to find a substitute for the poisonous white lead. Zinc calx (oxide) proved satisfactory, and it was manufactured and sold at the Academy by the laboratory steward, J. B. Courtois, the father of Bernard Courtois. Several times Guyton was personally involved in industry. From about 1780, with three partners, he manufactured saltpeter at Dijon. The enterprise, which was taken over by the elder Courtois in 1788, led to the development of a new analytical method. Saltpeter (potassium nitrate) was made by mixing decayed animal manure (containing nitrates) with wood ashes (containing potash), leaching with water, and evaporating. If too much potash was added, the saltpeter was contaminated with potassium chloride, so generally some nitrate was wasted in the mother liquor. Guyton determined the amount of chloride in a sample of mother liquor by adding lead nitrate solution of known concentration until all the chloride was precipitated; this enabled him to calculate how much potash was needed to form the maximum quantity of saltpeter free from chloride. This was one of the earliest applications of volumetric analysis.

Soda manufacture was another of Guyton's interests. In 1783 he visited le Croisic, in Britanny, and set up a factory to prepare soda (sodium carbonate) by a method discovered by Scheele: the action of atmospheric carbon dioxide on a paste of slaked lime (calcium hydroxide) and concentrated brine (impure sodium chloride, prepared by solar evaporation of sea water). Some soda was made, but the enterprise lasted only a few years. Guyton's only profitable industrial venture was a glassworks, run in conjunction with a coal mine, which he opened in 1784 at St. Bérain sur Dheune, in Burgundy.

Despite his many activities in chemistry Guyton found time to contribute to a new and exciting application of science. In November and December 1783 the balloon flights of J. F. Pilatre de Rozier and J. A. C. Charles attracted widespread attention, and the Dijon Academy decided to make its own balloon, to be filled with "inflammable gas." Guyton tested various gases. The gas from zinc and sulfuric acid (hydrogen) was the lightest but expensive to prepare, so he rapidly developed a large-scale plant for generating a heavier but cheaper gas by the dry distillation of vegetable matter. The iron retorts leaked, however, and eventually hydrogen was used. Guyton made two flights, with Claude Bertrand, an astronomer, on 25 April 1784, and with C. A. H. Grossart de Virly, lawyer and amateur chemist, on 12 June 1784. During the second flight an attempt was made to steer the balloon with manually operated oars and a rudder, a method that was theoretically sound and seems to have been partly successful but required too much effort for sustained flight.

Full accounts of the preliminary calculations and experiments, as well as descriptions of the construction of the balloon and the large-scale production of gas, were published in *Description de l'aérostate* (1784), an important treatise that added to Guyton's international reputation. In Dijon, however, all was not well. For several years the Academy had been accumulating substantial debts, and some of the literary members believed that the expenses of the laboratory and the chemical course were responsible. A bitter dispute developed in 1786 when Maret, the secretary, died and Guyton accepted the office in addition to that of chancellor, which he had held since 1781. The atmosphere became so unpleasant that for over a year he stayed away from the Academy. When he returned at the end of 1787, he resumed his activities as chancellor, but not secretary, and gave the annual course, which was now an account of antiphlogistic chemistry.

After the publication in 1786 of volume I, part 1, of *Encyclopédie méthodique, chymie,* Guyton began to prepare the article "Air" for part 2. This was to include an account of combustion and descriptions of the gases in the atmosphere, and they would have to be named according to the theory that he accepted. He made a journey to Paris in February 1787 and stayed there for about seven months. Discussions with Lavoisier soon led him to adopt the antiphlogistic theory without reservation; and he collaborated with Lavoisier, Berthollet, and Fourcroy in writing *Méthode de nomenclature chimique* (1787), in which the nomenclature, more extensively revised than in 1782, was designed so that names of substances agreed with their constitutions according to the new theory. Vitriolic acid, for example, now considered to be a compound of sulfur and oxygen, was called sulfuric acid, and was distinguished from sulfurous acid, which contained less oxygen. Guyton also joined Lavoisier and his colleagues on the editorial board of *Annales de chimie,* the journal that was founded in 1789; but his scientific work, including the *Encyclopédie méthodique, chymie,* which he handed over to Fourcroy after the publication of part 2 in 1789, was now interrupted by the French Revolution.

In August 1789 Guyton became president of the Dijon Patriotic Club; and in 1790 he was elected *procureur général syndic* of the Côte d'Or, one of the new "departments" into which Burgundy was divided. He held this important administrative post until elected to the National Assembly in August 1791. This took him to Paris, where he remained for the rest of his life. In 1792 he became a deputy to the National Convention, which declared France a republic, and he was among the majority who voted for the execution of Louis XVI in January 1793. Guyton became secretary of the Committee of General Defense on 3 January 1793, and from 6 April to 11 July he was president of the first Committee of Public Safety, at a time when most of its nine members were men of moderate opinions trying to secure national unity while engaged in a desperate war. But in July the moderates, including Guyton, were removed; and under Robespierre the committee took steps that redeemed the military situation but led to the Terror.

During 1794 Guyton was concerned mainly with the applications of science to the war. He helped J. A. A. Carny to devise simplified methods of making saltpeter and gunpowder, and he was a lecturer at the intensive courses on gunpowder and cannon manufacture that were given at Paris in February and March to men from all parts of France. He was one of the organizers of the first military air force—the *Compagnie d'Aérostiers*—and on 26 June 1794 he witnessed the French victory over the Austrians at Fleurus, Belgium, when observers in a captive balloon threw out messages with reports on the Austrian positions. As political commissioner attached to the army he accompanied it to Brussels and returned to Paris on 31 July, four days after Robespierre's downfall. From 6 October 1794 to 3 February 1795 he again served on the Committee of Public Safety, which now had limited powers. Although elected to the Conseil des Cinq-Cents after the Convention was dissolved in 1795, he joined none of its committees and retired from politics in 1797.

One of the first members of the Institut de France when it was founded in 1795, Guyton was president of the class of mathematical and physical sciences in 1807. He was twice director of the École Polytechnique (1798–1799, 1800–1804), and as a professor from its founding in 1794 until 1811 he taught and did research there. In 1798 he liquefied ammonia by cooling the dry gas to $-44°C.$ with a mixture of ice and calcium chloride. Under his direction C. B. Desormes and N. Clément proved in 1801 (independently of W. Cruickshank) that carbon formed two oxides, the lower one being the "heavy inflammable air" that had puzzled earlier chemists; in 1803 he devised a pyrometer consisting of a platinum rod which, as it expanded, caused a pointer to move over a circular scale. But, as in his Dijon days, Guyton's interests were too wide for him to be able to make great contributions to experimental chemistry. It was as a reformer of nomenclature, a teacher, and a systematizer that he made his name. And he was always concerned with the applications of chemistry.

Guyton did important research on the disinfection of air, a subject that first interested him in 1773, when he was consulted about the problem of putrid emanations from corpses in the crypt of a Dijon church. Believing the disease-carrying particles accompanied the volatile alkali (ammonia) given off by decaying flesh, he filled the church with marine (hydrochloric) acid fumes, which he hoped would precipitate the emanation with the ammonia. The treatment did, in fact, remove the odor, and it was later used successfully in prisons and hospitals. In England, Sir James Carmichael Smyth independently introduced the use of nitric acid fumes, and Guyton subsequently made the investigation described in his *Traité des moyens de désinfecter l'air* (1801). He found that his original theory was incorrect, for ammonia was not always evolved from decaying flesh; and he now thought that the disinfectant action was due to oxygen, which the antiphlogistic chemists assumed to be in all acids. Oxymuriatic acid (chlorine) was believed to contain a high proportion of oxygen, and Guyton found it to be an effective disinfectant—an interesting example of a satisfactory procedure based on a theory that was soon shown to be false. A simple apparatus for producing chlorine from common salt, sulfuric acid, and manganese dioxide was described in his book, which was translated into five languages. For this service to humanity he was admitted to the Legion of Honor in 1805, and in 1811 he became a baron of the empire.

In 1799, Napoleon appointed Guyton administrator of the mints, an important post, for there were nine mints in France and the number later increased. He left office at the Bourbon restoration in 1814 but resumed when Napoleon returned from Elba. He finally retired on 7 July 1815, three weeks after Waterloo.

Some of the men responsible for the execution of Louis XVI were exiled by Louis XVIII, but Guyton was left in peace. He died six months later and was survived by the former Mme. Picardet, whom he had married in 1798, after the death of her first husband. They had no children.

BIBLIOGRAPHY

I. Original Works. Details of the various eds. and trans. of Guyton's books, and references to his most important contributions to periodicals, are given in W. A.

Smeaton, "L. B. Guyton de Morveau: A Bibliographical Study," in *Ambix,* **6** (1957), 18–34.

II. Secondary Literature. Georges Bouchard, *Guyton-Morveau, chimiste et conventionnel* (Paris, 1938) is a reliable biography but includes few details of Guyton's scientific work. Some aspects of this have been discussed in a series of articles by W. A. Smeaton: "The Contributions of P. J. Macquer, T. O. Bergman and L. B. Guyton de Morveau to the Reform of Chemical Nomenclature," in *Annals of Science,* **10** (1954), 87–106; "The Early History of Laboratory Instruction in Chemistry at the École Polytechnique, Paris, and Elsewhere," *ibid.,* 224–233; "Guyton de Morveau's Course of Chemistry in the Dijon Academy," in *Ambix,* **9** (1961), 53–69; "Guyton de Morveau and Chemical Affinity," *ibid.,* **11** (1963), 55–64; "Guyton de Morveau and the Phlogiston Theory," in I. B. Cohen and R. Taton, eds., *Mélanges Alexandre Koyré,* I (Paris, 1964), 522–540; "L. B. Guyton de Morveau: Early Platinum Apparatus," in *Platinum Metals Review,* **10** (1966), 24–28; "The Portable Chemical Laboratories of Guyton de Morveau, Cronstedt and Göttling," in *Ambix,* **13** (1966), 84–91; "Louis Bernard Guyton de Morveau and His Relations With British Scientists," in *Notes and Records. Royal Society of London,* **22** (1967), 113–130; and "Is Water Converted Into Air? Guyton de Morveau Acts as Arbiter Between Priestley and Kirwan," in *Ambix,* **15** (1968), 75–83.

There are numerous references to Guyton in Roger Tisserand, *Au temps de l'Encyclopédie: L'Académie de Dijon de 1740 à 1793* (Paris, 1936), a book based on a study of the archives of the Dijon Academy, which are now in the Archives Départementales de la Côte d'Or, Dijon. Guyton's early theory of calcination is discussed in J. R. Partington and D. McKie, "Historical Studies on the Phlogiston Theory. Part I," in *Annals of Science,* **2** (1937), 361–404; and, with more emphasis on the experimental work, in H. Guerlac, *Lavoisier—The Crucial Year* (Ithaca, N.Y., 1961), pp. 125–145. An account of Guyton's contributions to volumetric analysis is E. Rancke Madsen, *The Development of Titrimetric Analysis Till 1806* (Copenhagen, 1958), pp. 83–101. There is a discussion of his reform of chemical nomenclature in M. P. Crosland, *Historical Studies in the Language of Chemistry* (London, 1962), pp. 153–192. His work on disinfection is described in Lars Oberg, "De mineralsura rökningarna. En episod ur desinfektionsmedlens historia," in *Lychnos* (1965–1966), pp. 159–180, with English summary. There is an evaluation of his research on white pigments in R. D. Harley, *Artists' Pigments c. 1600–1835* (London, 1970), pp. 162–168. An annotated English trans. of his article "On the Nature of Steel and Its Proximate Principles" is in C. S. Smith, ed., *Sources for the History of the Science of Steel 1532–1786* (Cambridge, Mass.-London, 1968), pp. 257–274.

W. A. Smeaton

GWYNNE-VAUGHAN, DAVID THOMAS (*b.* Llandovery, Wales, 12 March 1871; *d.* Reading, England, 4 September 1915), *botany.*

Gwynne-Vaughan was the eldest child of Henry Thomas Gwynne-Vaughan and Elizabeth Thomas. He was educated at Monmouth Grammar School and Christ's College, Cambridge, where he held a scholarship and graduated with a first class in part I of the natural sciences tripos in 1893. He left Cambridge without taking part II and taught science for a year until, in 1894, he was invited to work at the Jodrell Laboratory, Kew, under D. H. Scott. There, using plants cultivated at Kew, he began to specialize in microscopic studies of plant anatomy, particularly the arrangement of vessels in the stem.

At the British Association for the Advancement of Science meeting in 1896 he read a paper on "The Arrangement of the Vascular Bundles in Certain Nymphaeaceae," and on the strength of this, Frederick Bower offered him a post in his laboratory in Glasgow. He held this post from 1897 to 1907, working mainly on the anatomy of Pteridophyta, while also lecturing and writing a book on practical botany with Bower.

Before settling in Glasgow, Gwynne-Vaughan was able to make two expeditions. During 1897 and 1898 he went up the Amazon and Purus rivers to report on rubber production for a commercial syndicate. Although he was fascinated by the wealth of plant life, this trip offered little opportunity for collection. After another short period at Kew he spent most of 1899 in the Malay Peninsula, collecting and observing with W. W. Skeat.

From 1907 to 1909 Gwynne-Vaughan was head of the department of botany at Birkbeck College, London, and then in 1909 moved, as professor of botany, to the Queen's University of Belfast where he stayed until 1914. He then assumed the chair of botany at University College, Reading, a position he held, in spite of illness, until his death in 1915. In 1911 he married Helen C. I. Fraser, a cytologist who had succeeded him at Birkbeck College and who continued to work there.

Gwynne-Vaughan was active in the British Association beginning with the formation of its botanical section in 1895, and was secretary and recorder of the section for some years. He was also a member of the Royal Irish Academy, a fellow of the Linnean Society of London, and a fellow of the Royal Society of Edinburgh.

His first research, published as "On a New Case of Polystely in Dicotyledons" (*Annals of Botany* [1896]), reported a complete series of transitions between polystely and astely within the Nymphaeaceae. This was expanded and illustrated in a paper to the Linnean Society in 1897 which gave details of the morphology of the leaf and showed how the ontogeny of the individual leaf repeats the successive forms of the seedling leaves. His work on polystely in *Primula* (1897) showed that in this genus the gametostelic condition is more primitive than the dialystelic condition, and the apical region is not simplified. These new examples and interpretations extended the basic work that had been done on polystely by P. E. Van Tieghem.

Next Gwynne-Vaughan moved to an extensive work, "Observations on the Anatomy of Solenostelic Ferns" (1901-1903), in which he showed that the apparent segmentation of the stele is late development rather than a primitive feature, and he named broken-up portions of the central stele "meristeles." Development of the dictyostele in both young plants and lateral shoots are illustrated to show that they are similar and that the structure of the dictyostele is due to overlapping leaf gaps.

He also worked briefly on the morphology of *Equisetum*. He studied some of the Marattiales (tree ferns) and Algae and in 1908 he published his view that the xylem vessels of ferns had openings in the vertical walls. But work by F. Halft (1910) and N. Bancroft (1911) did not support this.

Gwynne-Vaughan's interest in the ontogeny of fern vessels was now extended to the study of the phylogeny of the fossil Osmundaceae, undertaken in a fruitful collaboration with the paleontologist Robert Kidston of Stirling. Through their research the structure of specimens from all over the world was traced back to the Permian. The sequence was sufficiently complete to show how anatomic changes correlated with successive geological strata, with progression from the protostele to the solenostele. This work, "On the Fossil Osmundaceae" (1907-1914), was published in a series of five papers by the Royal Society of Edinburgh, which awarded the MacDougall-Brisbane Medal to Gwynne-Vaughan in 1910.

BIBLIOGRAPHY

I. Original Works. Gwynne-Vaughan's first paper, "On a New Case of Polystely in Dicotyledons," is in *Annals of Botany,* **10** (1896), 288-291; the expanded version, "On Some Points in the Morphology and Anatomy of the Nymphaeaceae," is in *Transactions of the Linnean Society of London,* 2nd ser., **5** (1897), 287-229. Other works include "On Polystely in the Genus *Primula,*" in *Annals of Botany,* **11** (1897), 307-325; and "Observations on the Anatomy of Solenostelic Ferns," *ibid.,* **14** (1901), 71-98; **17** (1903), 689-742.

Practical Botany for Beginners (London-New York, 1902), written with F. O. Bower, is Gwynne-Vaughan's only book. The classic series of papers "On the Fossil Osmundaceae," written with R. Kidston, is in *Transactions of the Royal Society of Edinburgh,* **45** (1907), 759-780; **46** (1908), 213-232; **46** (1909), 651-667; **47** (1910), 455-477; **50** (1914), 469-480.

II. Secondary Literature. The most useful obituaries are F. O. Bower in *Proceedings of the Royal Society of Edinburgh,* **36** (1916), 334-339; and D. H. Scott in *Annals of Botany,* **30** (1916), i-xxiv. Gwynne-Vaughan's collection of anatomical slides is held in the botany department of the University of Glasgow, and a typescript catalogue (1920) of the collection is in the library of the British Museum (Natural History).

Diana M. Simpkins

GYLLENHAAL, LEONHARD (*b.* Ribbingsberg, Sweden, 3 December 1752; *d.* Höberg, near Skara, Sweden, 13 May 1840), *entomology.*

Gyllenhaal was a major in the army, a landed proprietor, and an amateur scientist who became one of Sweden's foremost authorities on Coleoptera (a distinction that he shared with another amateur, C. J. Schönherr). His interest in nature was apparent early; as a child he was an avid collector of natural specimens, including plants, insects, and minerals. As he progressively concentrated on Coleoptera, Gyllenhaal had a special building constructed in the gardens of Höberg, his estate in Västergötland, for the housing and study of his collection. He generously shared his specimens with other collectors and institutions.

Gyllenhaal's chief importance rests in one work, *Insecta Suecica descripta* (1808-1827). The title of this four-volume work would indicate that the author had intended a survey of all of Sweden's insects, or at least more of them than the beetles. This wide design was not realized, and the book is concerned entirely with Coleoptera—conceived on the highest level and executed in the most minute detail, it became known and used throughout the world.

Gyllenhaal became a member of the Royal Swedish Academy of Science in 1809 but published only one paper in its *Handlingar.* He was never closely involved with the Academy or its work, in part because of his age (he was fifty-seven at the time of his election) and because he did not like to leave Höberg, preferring to work undisturbed in his research building.

Gyllenhaal's extensive collection of Coleoptera is now in the Zoological Museum of the University of Uppsala. Because of the number of its type specimens it is of great value to researchers even today.

BIBLIOGRAPHY

Gyllenhaal's works are "Instrumenta cibaria insectorum aliquot Sueciae descripta," in *Nova acta Regiae Societatis scientiarum upsaliensis,* **6** (1799), 117-132; *Insecta Suecica*

HAAK

descripta. Classis I. Coleoptera sive Eleutherata, 4 vols.: I-III (Skara, 1808-1813), IV (Leipzig, 1827); and "Ammärkningar rörande ett av Carl de Geer under namn af Attelabus glaber beskrifvet insect," in *Kungliga Svenska vetenskapsakademiens handlingar* (1817), pp. 137-141. In addition, he contributed many articles on beetles to Schönherr's monumental *Synonymia insectorum* (Paris, 1833-1845).

BENGT-OLOF LANDIN

HAAK, THEODORE (*b.* Neuhausen, near Worms, Germany, 25 July 1605; *d.* London, England, May 1690), *learned correspondence, translation.*

Haak's father, Theodor, attended the University of Heidelberg; but little is known about him before he married Maria Tossanus, the daughter of the Reformed theologian Daniel Tossanus (Toussaint), who after escaping the St. Bartholomew's Day massacre in France became court preacher at Heidelberg and later professor of theology and rector of the university. Through the marriages of his mother's sisters, Haak was related to a cousin, the Reformed theologian at Leiden, Friedrich Spanheim (1600–1649), and to J. F. Schloer (an uncle), who was counselor of state to Frederick IV, the elector palatine. A grandson of Schloer's settled in England, where he became a fellow of the Royal Society and of the College of Physicians; it was at his house that Haak died. Thus Haak was closely related to Continental families who were important in the Reformed church, in high state office, and in the learned world at Heidelberg and Leiden. As a conveyor of knowledge and information between England and the Continent, Haak's long and active life shows the importance of these family connections.

During 1625–1626 Haak studied at Oxford and Cambridge, then returned to Germany. In 1628 or 1629 he took up residence at Gloucester Hall (now Worcester College), then one of the Calvinist centers at Oxford, where he studied theology and mathematics. He left at the end of 1631, was ordained deacon in 1632, and settled in London. During the next few years he was active in the Palatine Collections for the benefit of the exiled ministers of the Palatinate, spending part of his time in Heidelberg. Little is known about his life during the late 1630's until he settled permanently in England toward the end of 1638, but by 1635 he was in touch with Samuel Hartlib and his circle, probably through his cousins in the Schloer family. In 1656 Haak married Elizabeth Genne, who died in 1669. He and his family were naturalized British citizens late in 1656.

Given his religious views, Haak naturally sided with Parliament during the 1640's. He undertook a largely unsuccessful diplomatic mission to the Continent and Denmark (1643–1644) but later turned down similar offers, preferring to remain in London, where he performed important work as a translator, for example, to the secretary of state, John Thurloe. His services gained him a pension and financial independence. He declined an offer to become secretary to the elector, Charles Louis, at Heidelberg, accepting instead a position as his unofficial agent in London. At this time John Wilkins was the elector's private chaplain. In 1645 the Westminster Assembly, whose secretary was John Wallis, engaged Haak to make a translation of the *Dutch Bible and Annotations,* a work that had been prepared at the request of the Synod of Dort. This immense task was completed in 1657, after many interruptions.

In 1647 Haak wrote to Marin Mersenne that the proper use and enjoyment of knowledge lie in its free communication, so that it may serve the general good, in accordance with the divine intent. Twenty years later, in a letter that accompanied a copy of Thomas Sprat's *History of the Royal Society,* Haak wrote to Governor John Winthrop of Connecticut about the need for mankind to improve "the treasures God hath communicated to them so abundantly throughout all the world," thus "more and more reconciling the estrangedness of the minds of mankind amongst themselves, that they may be willing to listen to more and more and still better Truths and Union." He hoped that the *History* would not only "revive and quicken" the governor himself to mind his "engagement and interest," but that he in turn would "excite and animate many others also to consort and cooperate for the advancement of so universal a Benefit as the scope of this Society holds forth, and their endeavours promise to all the world." In these words Haak stated the aspirations that were shared by Hartlib's Comenian group and by the members of the early Royal Society, two groups which show considerable overlap. Natural philosophy, i.e., the study of God's manifest revelation in creation, is an ennobling activity; it leads to piety, peace, order, and a sense of community among all mankind. The study of natural philosophy is the crucial prerequisite for the successful achievement of Comenian pansophy.

When Comenius arrived in London in September 1641, he was received by Hartlib, Joachim Hübner, John Pell, John Dury, and Haak. At that time Haak had already served Hartlib and his Comenian scheme. Late in 1639, through his command of French, Haak initiated a correspondence with Mersenne, then widely known as the chief figure in a group that was dedicated to the discussion and exchange of learned and scientific knowledge. The first letter was accompanied by copies of Comenius' *Pansophiae prodromus* (1639) and Pell's *Idea of Mathematics,* and both authors now began to correspond directly with Mersenne. Unfortunately we do not have Haak's letters; but the nineteen letters from Mersenne to Haak, written within little more than a year, show a lively exchange of books and information on the sorts of subjects that interested Hartlib and that later figured both in the early scientific meetings in England before 1660 and in the Royal Society after that date.

There is therefore good reason to accept John Wallis' account, although written many years later, that it was Haak who at London in 1645—"if not sooner"—"gave the first occasion, and first suggested those meetings" which have the best claim to be considered the beginnings of "the Royal Society of London for improving Natural Knowledge." In May 1647 Haak resumed his correspondence with Mersenne, who had been traveling extensively in Italy and France for much of the time between October 1644 and the early part of 1647; four more letters followed until July 1648, although it is not clear whether Mersenne answered. (He was ill much of that time and died on 1 September 1648.) Haak's letters appear unmistakably related to the scientific meetings then being held in London, for he refers to experiments being performed by a group of which he was a member.

During the following years Haak was busy with translation and was in touch with Pell, Hartlib, and Dury, among others. Within a year of the first meeting of the as yet unnamed Royal Society, Haak was proposed for membership by John Wilkins, thus becoming an original member of the Society. Less than a year later, in late August 1662, he received a letter from his old friend, the Leiden philologist J. F. Gronovius, "expressing his high sense of the usefulness of the design of the Society" (Birch, I, 108). It was Gronovius who in 1639 had taken Haak's letter with Pell's and Comenius' books to Mersenne in Paris. Until the end of his life nearly thirty years later, Haak regularly attended the meetings of the Royal Society, from time to time serving on various committees. He made a few communications but was chiefly active in the promotion and maintenance of correspondence with the learned world abroad, especially in Germany. He proposed a considerable number of visiting Germans for membership, he translated letters, and about 1680 he acted as intermediary in the correspondence between Hooke and Leibniz.

During the last two decades of his life, Haak was very close to Hooke; for periods of several years they saw each other at least once a week, sometimes eating or drinking tea together, holding conferences with learned friends, and playing chess. Like Hooke, Haak appears to have taken a special and continuing interest in that old Comenian project, a universal language. Haak and Hooke also talked much about books and book purchases. Haak had known Milton since the late 1640's, when both did translation work for the Council of State. He began but seems never to have finished a translation of *Paradise Lost* into German.

Haak's own letters and writings tell us very little about himself, and our knowledge of his private life is sparse; but all his contemporaries agree that he was an exceptionally kind-hearted and generous man. By virtue of his work, beliefs, and activities, he charted a well-nigh archetypal course during a long life that covered most of the seventeenth century.

BIBLIOGRAPHY

I. ORIGINAL WORKS. Among Haak's translations are German versions of two pieces by the Puritan divine, Daniel Dyke the Elder: *The Mystery of Self-Deceiving* (London, 1615), in German under the title *Nosce teipsum* (Basel, 1638); and a *Treatise of Repentance* (London, 1631), in German as *Nützliche Betrachtung . . . der wahren Busse,* first published with *Nosce teipsum* (Frankfurt, 1643). Both were several times reissued together in German. The important Mersenne correspondence is in Cornelis de Waard *et al.,* eds., *Correspondance de Marin Mersenne* (Paris, 1932–), VIII (1963), IX (1965), X (1967), XI (1970), and in future volumes. Two of the letters from 1647 and 1648 are in Harcourt Brown, *Scientific Organizations in Seventeenth Century France* (Baltimore, 1934), pp. 268–272. The letters to John Winthrop are in "Correspondence of the Founders of the Royal Society With Governor Winthrop of Connecticut," in *Proceedings of the Massachusetts Historical Society 1878,* **16** (1879), 206–251. The Haak-Hooke-Leibniz letters have so far been only partially published: see C. I. Gerhardt, ed., *Die philosophischen Schriften von G. W. Leibniz,* 7 vols. (Berlin, 1875–1890), VII, 16–20. There is also material relevant to this correspondence and to Haak in general in the letters of Johann von Gloxin to Leibniz in Leibniz, *Sämtliche Schriften und Briefe,* 1st ser., *Allgemeiner und historischer Briefwechsel,* III (Leipzig, 1938). Haak's activity in the Royal Society can be traced in Thomas Birch, *The History of the Royal Society,* 4 vols. (London, 1756–1757).

II. SECONDARY LITERATURE. There is an excellent monograph by Pamela R. Barnett, *Theodore Haak, F.R.S. (1605–1690)* (The Hague, 1962). The bibliography gives a full listing of the primary sources, both unprinted and printed, and of the secondary material; this book also presents the first printing of the translation of *Paradise Lost,* which covers bks. I–III and the opening lines of bk. IV. Miss Barnett's solid scholarship and good insight into

HAAR

the period transcend much recent but inferior writing on the events in which Haak was involved. Her "Theodore Haak and the Early Years of the Royal Society," in *Annals of Science,* **13** (Dec. 1957), 205–218, is also commendable.

Useful and suggestive information about the German intellectual milieus with which Haak was in touch will be found in Leopold Magon, "Die drei ersten deutschen Versuche einer Übersetzung von Miltons 'Paradise Lost,'" in Karl Bischoff, ed., *Gedenkschrift für Ferdinand Josef Schneider* (Weimar, 1956), pp. 39–82. Among much inferior writing on the subject, R. H. Syfret, "The Origins of the Royal Society," in *Notes and Records. Royal Society of London,* **5** (Apr. 1948), 75–137, still stands out as basically sound and reliable. Birch's *History* should be supplemented by Henry W. Robinson and Walter Adams, eds., *The Diary of Robert Hooke 1672–1680* (London, 1935); and R. T. Gunther, *Early Science in Oxford. The Life and Work of Robert Hooke,* X (Oxford, 1935), pp. 69–265, the diary from Nov. 1688 to Aug. 1693.

HANS AARSLEFF

HAAR, ALFRÉD (*b.* Budapest, Hungary, 11 October 1885; *d.* Szeged, Hungary, 16 March 1933), *mathematics.*

Alfréd was the son of Ignatz Haar and Emma Fuchs. While a student at the Gymnasium in Budapest, he was a collaborator on a mathematical journal for high schools and in 1903, his last year at the Gymnasium, he won first prize in the Eötvös contest in mathematics. He had started studying chemistry, but his success in the contest induced him to switch to mathematics. From 1904 he studied in Göttingen; in 1909 he took his Ph.D. degree as a student of D. Hilbert and that year became a *Privatdozent* at the University of Göttingen.

In 1912, after a short time at the Technical University of Zurich, he returned to Hungary and succeeded L. Fejér at Klausenburg University, first as extraordinary professor and then, from 1917, as ordinary professor. When Klausenburg became Rumanian he went to Budapest with his colleague F. Riesz. Together they continued their activity at Szeged University, where in 1920 they founded *Acta scientiarum mathematicarum,* a journal of great reputation. In 1931 Haar became a corresponding member of the Hungarian Academy of Sciences.

Haar did work in analysis. Although not formally abstract, it is so close to the abstract method that it still looks modern. His doctoral thesis had dealt with orthogonal systems of functions. Twenty years later he returned to the same subject. Haar first extended what was known on divergence, summation, and oscillation for the Fourier system to other orthogonal systems, in particular to solutions of Sturm-Liouville problems. He discovered a curious orthogonal system according to which every continuous function can be developed into an everywhere converging series; its elements are discontinuous functions admitting, at most, three values. Later he became interested in multiplicative relations of orthogonal systems and characterized their multiplication tables. This research led him to the character theory of commutative groups as a precursor of Pontryagin on duality.

In complex functions Haar did work on splitting lines of singularities and on asymptotics. As one of the first applications of Hilbert's integral methods in equations and of Dirichlet's principle, Haar in 1907 studied the partial differential equation $\triangle\triangle u = 0$; with T. von Kármán he put this method to use in elasticity theory. Haar also wrote a number of papers on Chebyshev approximations and linear inequalities.

Two of Haar's shorter papers (1927–1928) that greatly influenced problems and methods in partial differential equations in the 1930's concern the equation

$$F(x,y,z,p,q) = 0,$$

which is usually dealt with by the method of characteristics. Since this method presupposes the existence of the second instead of the first derivative of the solutions, one may ask whether there exist solutions which escape the methods of characteristics. Under rather broad conditions, Haar answered this question in the negative.

Haar's most important contribution to variational calculus (1917–1919) features an analogous principle, Haar's lemma, an extension of Paul du Bois-Reymond's to double integrals: If

$$\iint_B \left(u\frac{\partial f}{\partial x} + v\frac{\partial f}{\partial y} \right) dxdy = 0$$

for all continuously differentiable f which vanish on the boundary of B, then there is a w such that

$$\frac{\partial w}{\partial x} = -v, \frac{\partial w}{\partial y} = u.$$

Haar's lemma allows one to deal with variational problems like

$$\iint_B f(p,q,x,y,z)\, dxdy = \text{minimum},$$

without supplementary assumptions on the second derivative of the unknown function z. He applied his lemma to variational problems like Plateau's. A multitude of papers by others show the influence this lemma exerted on the whole area of variational calculus.

The notion to which Haar's name is most firmly attached is Haar's measure on groups. In 1932 Haar showed, by a bold direct approach, that every locally compact group possesses an invariant measure which assigns positive numbers to all open sets. An immediate consequence of this theorem was the analytic character of compact groups (J. Von Neumann). It was somewhat later applied to locally compact Abelian groups by Pontryagin. The theorem is now one of the cornerstones of those areas of mathematics where algebra and topology meet.

BIBLIOGRAPHY

See *Alfréd Haar: Gesammelte Arbeiten* (Budapest, 1959), B.S.-Nagy, ed.

H. FREUDENTHAL

HAAS, ARTHUR ERICH (*b.* Brünn, Moravia [now Brno, Czechoslovakia], 30 April 1884; *d.* Chicago, Illinois, 20 February 1941), *physics, history of physics.*

After studying physics at Vienna and Göttingen, Haas received his doctorate at Vienna in 1906 and then turned enthusiastically to the history of physics. In order to qualify as a lecturer he submitted to the Philosophy Faculty of the University of Vienna a dissertation on the history of the energy principle. His paper was the cause of considerable puzzlement to the physicists who were responsible for passing an initial judgment on it, and it was decided that he should prepare an additional work in pure physics.

In fulfilling the faculty's assignment, Haas followed the latest publications in physics and thereby came across the unsolved problem of black-body radiation toward the end of 1909. He studied J. J. Thomson's *Electricity and Matter,* the contents of which are reflections on atomic structure, while reading an essay by Wilhelm Wien in the *Encyclopädie der mathematischen Wissenschaften* in which the suggestion was put forth that the energy element "can be derived from a universal property of the atom." Seizing upon this idea, Haas became the first to apply a quantum formula to the clarification of atomic structure. In the process he substituted real atoms for the more formal than physical Planck oscillators in the radiation cavity.

Haas's quantum rule $E_{pot} = h\nu$ agrees, for the ground state, with the condition later stated by Niels Bohr; and thus Haas obtained the correct "Bohr" radius of the hydrogen atom. But, characteristically, he wrote down only the equation solved for the action quantum, i.e., $h = 2\pi e\sqrt{r \cdot m}$. Therefore, like Wien he considered the dimensions of the atom as fundamental, from which the action quantum can then be derived. Within a numerical factor of eight Haas also correctly derived the Rydberg constant from the action quantum h, the velocity of light c, and the fundamental magnitudes of the electron, e and m. He achieved this relation by a very formal second hypothesis, namely, that the frequency derived from his quantum rule corresponds with the constant of Balmer's equation.

Although Haas's theorem failed to take into account the excited states—and therefore the connection with spectroscopic data—it was nevertheless a remarkable forerunner of Bohr's atomic theory. Yet in February 1910 Haas's ideas were termed a "carnival joke" by Viennese physicists and only slowly found recognition.

In 1913, through the intervention of Karl Sudhoff, Haas became an associate professor of the history of science at the University of Leipzig. Sudhoff, then head of the German historians of science and medicine, had been favorably impressed by Haas's first address at Cologne in 1908 and also managed to get him the editorship of volume V of Poggendorff. At the end of World War I Haas returned to Vienna, where he gradually turned from the history of physics to physics. In 1920 he calculated—independently of F. Wheeler Loomis and Adolf Kratzer—the correct formulas for the isotope effect in rotational spectra. After several offers of guest lectureships he finally immigrated to the United States in 1935. From 1936 until his death he was professor of physics at the University of Notre Dame.

Haas's work in the history of physics was inspired by his interest in older as well as modern theories. (He was influenced by Mach's and Ostwald's interest in the history of science.) Haas possessed the "conviction that no other method is as suited as the historical for facilitating the understanding of physical principles and for clarifying and deepening the knowledge of their significance" (*Die Grundgleichungen der Mechanik . . .*, preface). His numerous books written from this point of view, often based on his lectures and addresses, are masterpieces of clear exposition which were widely disseminated and translated into many languages.

BIBLIOGRAPHY

I. ORIGINAL WORKS. Haas's writings include *Die Entwicklungsgeschichte des Satzes von der Erhaltung der Kraft* (Vienna, 1909), his *Habilitationsschrift; Die Grundgleichungen der Mechanik, dargestellt auf Grund der geschichtlichen Entwicklung* (Leipzig, 1914); *Einführung in die theoretische Physik,* 2 vols. (Leipzig, 1919–1921); and *Der erste Quantenansatz für das Atom* (Stuttgart, 1965), repr. of 1910 papers with extensive biography and bibliography by A. Hermann.

Among Haas's works in the history of physics are *Die Entwicklungsgeschichte des Satzes von der Erhaltung der Kraft* (Vienna, 1909); *Der Geist des Hellenentums in der modernen Physik* (Leipzig, 1914); and "Die ältesten Beobachtungen auf dem Gebiet der Dioptrik," in *Archiv für die Geschichte der Naturwissenschaften und der Technik,* **9** (1920–1922), 108–111.

II. SECONDARY LITERATURE. See A. Hermann, "Arthur Erich Haas und der erste Quantenansatz für das Atom," in *Sudhoffs Archiv für Geschichte der Medizin und der Naturwissenschaften,* **49** (1965), 255–268; and *Genesis of Quantum Theory* (Cambridge, Mass., 1971), ch. 5.

A. HERMANN

HAAS, WANDER JOHANNES DE (*b.* Lisse, Netherlands, 2 March 1878; *d.* Bilthoven, Netherlands, 26 April 1960), *physics.*

De Haas was first educated to be a notary, but then studied physics at Leiden University where he was assistant to H. Kamerlingh Onnes. In 1912 he wrote his doctoral thesis, "On the Compressibility of Hydrogen Gas at Low Temperatures." After working in Berlin and at the Physikalische Reichsanstalt in Potsdam, de Haas was assistant to H. A. Lorentz, his father-in-law and at that time director of the physics division in the Teyler Institute at Haarlem. De Haas first became a professor of physics at the Technische Hogeschool, Delft, in 1917. He left for Groningen University in 1922, and from 1924 to 1948 was professor at Leiden University.

Together with W. H. Keesom, de Haas was director of the Kamerlingh Onnes Laboratory of Experimental Physics, initially one of the few laboratories in the world where low-temperature work was systematically carried out. In 1922 he became a member of the Royal Netherlands Academy of Science and Letters at Amsterdam. His health was never very good, but with the help of his wife (a theoretical physicist) he was able to maintain his international scientific contacts and to execute the duties of his laboratory directorate. Although he specialized in magnetism, de Haas found time to dabble in many different branches of physics.

The general trend of de Haas's work is shown by his early work at Berlin. There, in 1915, he performed an experiment suggested by Einstein, known as the Einstein-de Haas effect: the sudden magnetization of a suspended iron cylinder in a vertical solenoid causes a momentary torque in the cylinder. The theoretical foundation for this effect is that the unidirectional aligning of the spinning electrons in the magnetic field also aligns their mechanical moments, resulting in a torque pulse.

The experimental results of later scientists indicated that the ratio of the magnetic to the mechanical moment differed by a factor of two from the original classic expectation. This is the fundamental "half-integer quantization" for the spinning electron, as compared to the integer quantization for the orbital moment, a difference which runs through the whole development of modern atomic physics.

Pioneering with simple apparatus was de Haas's favorite conception of experimental physics. But he was also aware of the need for organization and routine techniques that had been introduced in the Leiden laboratory by Kamerlingh Onnes. Together with E. C. Wiersma, de Haas was a leader in the production of extremely low temperatures by adiabatic demagnetization of precooled magnetized material. Other lines of research led to the so-called Van Alphen-de Haas effect on the anomalous behavior of the resistance of a metal crystal in a magnetic field, and to magneto-optic researches on crystals, mainly done and published by Jean Becquerel. During World War II de Haas succeeded in preventing a large amount of uranium ore from being taken to Germany. After the war this uranium was useful in starting the Netherlands-Norway joint establishment for nuclear energy at Kjeller (Norway).

BIBLIOGRAPHY

For information on the Einstein-de Haas effect see "Experimenteller Nachweis der Ampèreschen Molekularströme," in *Verhandlungen der Deutschen physikalischen Gessellschaft,* **17** (1915), 152–170, written with Einstein. Also see E. Beck, *Annalen der Physik,* **60** (1919), 109. Other of de Haas's publications are in *Proceedings. K. Nederlandse akademie van wetenschappen* and in *Physica* (The Hague). A biography of de Haas may be found in *Jaarboek van de K. Akademie van wetenschappen gevestigd te Amsterdam* (1959–1960), 300; on the World War II period see also S. A. Goudsmit, *ALSOS* (Schuman, N.Y., 1947), where de Haas is called "Professor X."

J. A. PRINS

HAAST, JOHANN FRANZ JULIUS VON (*b.* Bonn, Germany, 1 May 1822; *d.* Christchurch, New Zealand, 16 August 1887), *geology.*

Haast was the only son of Mathias Haast and Anna Ruth. His father, a merchant, was elected burgomaster at Bonn. Haast studied geology and mineralogy at the University of Bonn, where, tradition says, he rescued the prince consort from drowning in the Rhine. Although he did not graduate, he worked for a time with August Krantz, a mineral dealer—leading a somewhat undistinguished life gripped by wanderlust and rendered more unsettled by the early death of his first wife, Antonia Schmitt.

Haast's opportunity for a more rewarding career came in 1858 with his appointment to advise an English shipping firm on the prospects of encouraging German immigration to New Zealand. Exploration and scientific appraisal of resources was exactly the kind of work for which Haast longed. Immediately after fulfilling his contract to the shipping firm, he joined the explorer Ferdinand von Hochstetter in his explorations of New Zealand (1859), traveling extensively throughout both islands. Among the areas he visited was a volcanic wilderness closely controlled by the Maoris and, because of later outbursts of fighting, not revisited by Europeans for several decades.

Through the fame attendant on his journeys with Hochstetter, Haast was engaged to make a topographic and geologic survey of the west coast of South Island by the Nelson provincial government. He and his team discovered a new coalfield at Westport and reported on other coal and gold resources (1860).

A crisis arose at the South Island port of Lyttelton, situated in the heart of an ancient volcano which the authorities had hoped to pierce by a tunnel to the nearby city of Christchurch. The contractors had struck a hard lava flow and refused to go on. Hurrying to the scene, Haast made a rapid and competent survey of the geology to convince the workers that the amount of hard rock was limited. Work was resumed on the tunnel, which provided a vital link between city and port.

Haast was rewarded with appointment as geologist for Canterbury province (1861). He was naturalized as a British subject in the same year and made Christchurch his home. There he married Mary Dobson, daughter of the provincial engineer Edward Dobson and, like his first wife, musically gifted. Haast contributed enormously to the intellectual and cultural life of Christchurch. He founded the Philosophical Institute of Canterbury in 1862, the Canterbury Museum in 1870, the Canterbury Collegiate Union with Bishop Harper, later to become the University of Canterbury, and the Imperial Institute. When the provincial geological survey was concluded, he became director of the Canterbury Museum and professor of geology at the university. He also served as a member of the senate of the University of New Zealand.

A pioneer scientist in a largely unexplored land, Haast had interests that ranged far and wide. He collected new plants from the Southern Alps; he inquired into problems of early human settlement of New Zealand; and he gained great immediate attention through his discovery of bones of the gigantic moa and a giant extinct eagle which he named *Harpagornis.* Most of his research was devoted to geologic and topographic surveys of Canterbury province and the west coast. These activities were closely related, and he never perpetrated the modern error of divorcing current geological processes from the study of ancient rocks. Haast thus accurately recognized that most of the Canterbury plains were composed of rubble fans, formed as glacial outwash, rather than accepting more fanciful theories, then current, involving torrential deposition as drift.

A forceful, ebullient man who was well aware of having "made himself" and willing, according to C. A. Fleming, to prove and underline the point by festooning himself with honors, Haast naturally made both scientific and personal enemies. He scathingly condemned the brilliant government geologist Alexander McKay for "poaching" his moa bones, and he repeatedly resisted and opposed with his provincial experience geological theories advanced on a national scale by the small but excellent team of geologists in the New Zealand Geological Survey. As a result he found a natural ally in another great geologist, F. W. Hutton, in opposing the towering figure of nineteenth-century science in New Zealand, Sir James Hector. It would be difficult to allow that Haast matched either of these two contemporaries in scientific achievement, and politically and administratively he was much less significant than Hector. His ebullience, a certain lack of originality, and his geographically circumscribed field of work told against him. Yet some of his concepts live on, and to this day there is a recognizable Canterbury outlook on geology established by Haast.

BIBLIOGRAPHY

I. Original Works. Haast's writings include *Report of a Topographical and Geological Examination of the Western Districts of the Nelson Province* (Nelson, N.Z., 1861); "Notes on the Geology of the Province of Canterbury," in *Government Gazette, Province of Canterbury,* **9** (1862); "Report on the Geology of the Malvern Hills, Canterbury," in *Report. Geological Explorations,* **7** (1871–1872), 1–88; and *Geology of the Provinces of Canterbury and Westland, New Zealand* (Christchurch, 1879).

II. Secondary Literature. On Haast or his work, see P. Burton, *The New Zealand Geological Survey 1865–1965,* Information Series, Department of Scientific and Industrial Research no. 52 (1965); C. A. Fleming, "Haast, Sir Julius von, K.C.M.G., F.R.S. (1822–87)," in A. H. McLintock, ed., *An Encylopaedia of New Zealand,* I (Wellington, 1966), 892–893; H. F. von Haast, *The Life and Times of Sir Julius von Haast* (New Plymouth, N.Z., 1948); and J. B. Waterhouse, "A Historical Survey of the pre-Cretaceous Geology of New Zealand," in *New Zealand Journal of Geology and*

ḤABASH AL-ḤĀSIB

Geophysics, **8** (1965), pt. 6, 931–998; **10** (1967), pt. 4, 923–981.

J. B. WATERHOUSE

ḤABASH AL-ḤĀSIB, AḤMAD IBN ʿABDALLĀH AL-MARWAZĪ (*b.* Marw, Turkestan [now Mary, Turkmen S.S.R.]; *d.* 864–874), *trigonometry, astronomy.*

Little is known of Ḥabash's life and family. He worked at Baghdad as astronomer under the ʿAbbāsid caliphs al-Maʾmūn and al-Muʿtaṣim, but he may not have belonged to the small group that collaborated in the Mumtaḥan observations. He made observations from 825 to 835 in Baghdad. Abū Jaʿfar ibn Ḥabash, the son of Ḥabash, was also a distinguished astronomer and an instrument maker.

Works. The biographers Ibn al-Nadīm, Ibn al-Qifṭī, and Ḥājjī Khalīfa ascribe the following works to Ḥabash:

1. A reworking of the *Sindhind.*
2. The *Mumtaḥan Zīj,* the best known of his works, which relies on Ptolemy and is based on his own observations. Ibn Yūnus called it *al-Qānūn* ("The Canon").
3. The *Shāh Zīj,* the shortest of his *ziyajāt.*
4. The *Damascene Zīj.*
5. The *Maʾmūnī Zīj* (or *Arabic Zīj*). This and the *Damascene Zīj* are based on the Hijra calendar rather than on the Yazdigird or Seleucid eras.
6. On the *Rukhāmāt* and Measurements.
7. On the Celestial Spheres.
8. On Astrolabes.
9. On the Oblique and Perpendicular Planes.
10. On the Distances of the Stars.

Since not all of these works are extant, it is almost impossible to determine how many *ziyajāt* Ḥabash wrote and their titles. Two manuscripts on the tables of Ḥabash are preserved, one in Istanbul (Yeni Cami, no. 784) and the other in Berlin (no. 5750). These are not copies of his original works. There has been criticism of the Yeni Cami copy, suggesting that it is a revision of Ḥabash's *zīj* by Kūshyār ibn Labbān. In one way or another the introduction and the passages have come to us in their original forms and can be used, as can the Berlin manuscript, as the sources on Ḥabash.

Trigonometry. Ḥabash's trigonometric contributions are very important.

Sines. In the *Sūrya-Siddhānta* (A.D. 400) a table of half chords is given. A special name for the function which we call the sine is first found in the works of Āryabhaṭa I (A.D. 500). Besides half chord he also uses the term *jya* or *jiva.* In the Islamic world this word was transcribed as *jayb.* Al-Khwārizmī (*ca.* 825) was the first to prepare a table of sines. Ḥabash followed him by constructing such a table for

$$\theta = 0;0^\circ, 0;15^\circ, 0;30^\circ, 0;45^\circ, 1;0^\circ \cdots 90;0^\circ.$$

Versed sine. Among the trigonometric functions the versed sine (versine) also attracted attention. We know that it was mentioned in the *Sūrya-Siddhānta,* and a table for the versed sine is given in Āryabhaṭa. In Islam astronomers used special names to distinguish the versed sine, such as *jayb maʿkūs* (used by Ḥabash), *jayb mankūs* (used by al-Khwārizmī), and *sahm.* Ḥabash may be the first who clearly defined the sine and the versed sine as follows: "A perpendicular from the circumference to the diameter is the sine (*jayb mabsūṭ*) of the arc between the diameter and the perpendicular; the distance between the circumference and the perpendicular upon the diameter is the versed sine (*jayb maʿkūs*) of the abovementioned arc." He showed that if $A < 90^\circ$, the versed sine $= 60^P - \cos A = 1 - \cos A$; and if $A > 90^\circ$, the versed sine$=60^P + \cos A = 1 + \cos A$. Also, if $A < 90^\circ$, the versed sine $<$ sine; if $A > 90^\circ$, the versed sine $>$ sine; and if $A = 90^\circ$, the versed sine $=$ sine.

Tangent. The *Sūrya-Siddhānta* and other Hindu works mention the shadows, particularly in connection with astronomy. Ḥabash seems to have been the first to compile a table of tangents for

$$\theta = 0;0^\circ, 0;30^\circ, 1;0^\circ \cdots 90;0^\circ.$$

The function of *umbra extensa* (the length of shadow) is defined as

$$h = P\frac{\cos h}{\sin h},$$

$P =$ the length of gnomon. For the computation of the *umbra extensa* from the altitude of the sun, he gives the following steps (see Figure 1):

$$\frac{KR}{P} = \frac{RO}{S}$$
$$KR = \sin h$$
$$RO = \cos h$$
$$P = 12$$
$$S = \textit{umbra extensa}$$
$$\frac{\sin h}{12} = \frac{\cos h}{S}$$
$$S = \frac{\cos h}{\sin h}12.$$

In addition to finding the *umbra extensa* from the altitude of the sun, Ḥabash presents the following equations:

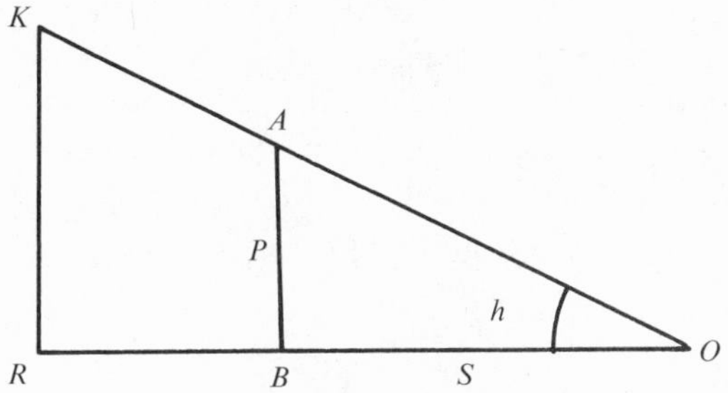

FIGURE 1

$$\text{hypotenuse} = \sqrt{S^2 + P^2}.$$

$$\sin h = \frac{P}{\sqrt{S^2 + P^2}} \cong .$$

Spherical Astronomy. For the solution of problems in spherical astronomy, transformations of coordinates, time measurements, and many other problems, Ḥabash gives astronomical tables of functions which are standard for all *ziyajāt*.

He gives the general rule for calculating the declination of the sun (the first declination, *al-mayl al-awwal*) (see Figure 2):

$$\sin \delta\odot = \sin \varepsilon \cdot \sin \lambda$$

$$\text{obliquity of ecliptic } \varepsilon = 23;\ 35°.$$

The declination depends not only on λ but also on the value of the obliquity of the ecliptic.

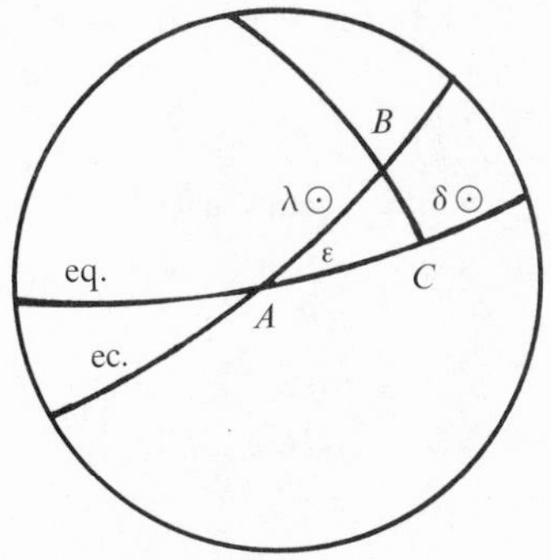

FIGURE 2

The culmination of the sun is defined. (See Figure 3.) If the declination of the sun is northern, $h = (90 - \phi) + \delta\odot$. If the declination of the sun is southern, $h = (90 - \phi) - \delta\odot$.

The time of day, measured from sunrise, is proportional to the altitude of the sun, i.e., the "arc of revolution" (*al-dā'ir min al-falak*). Islamic astronomers gave many trigonometric functions showing the relations between the time and the altitude of the sun. The first exact solution was given by Ḥabash and proved by Abu'l-Wafā' and al-Bīrūnī. This function

ḤABASH AL-ḤĀSIB

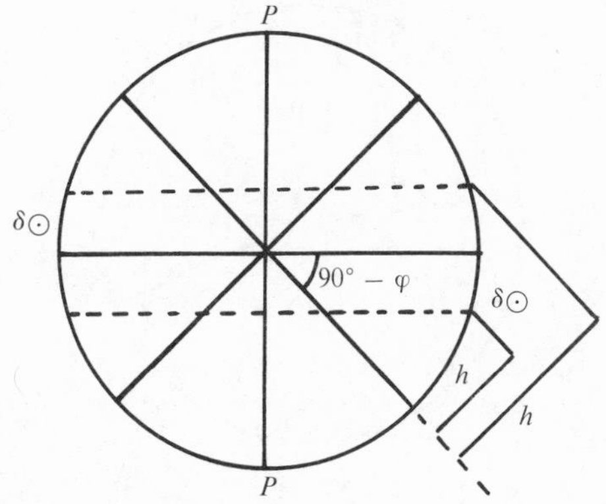

FIGURE 3

is equivalent to the function given by Brahmagupta in his *Khaṇḍakhādyaka:*

$$\text{vers } t = \text{vers } P - \frac{\sin h \cdot \text{vers } P}{\sin \text{alt} \cdot \text{merid}},$$

where P = half of the length of daylight
h = altitude of the sun
t = time
vers P = day sine (*jayb al-nahār;* Sanskrit, *antyā*).

Then he computes the altitude of the sun from the time:

$$\sin h = \frac{(\text{vers } P - \text{vers } t) \sin \text{alt} \cdot \text{merid.}}{\text{vers } P}.$$

Ḥabash calculates the length of daylight, i.e., equation of daylight (*ta'dīl al-nahār*), which al-Khwārizmī calls the ascensional difference. (See Figure 4.)

$$\frac{KD}{DG} = \frac{KL}{LM} \cdot \frac{ME}{EG}$$

$$\frac{\sin \phi}{\cos \phi} = \frac{\cos \delta\odot}{\sin \delta\odot} \cdot \frac{\sin ME}{R}$$

$$\sin ME = R\,\frac{\sin \phi \cdot \sin \delta \odot}{\cos \phi \cdot \cos \delta \odot}$$

$$\sin ME = R\, tg\, \phi \cdot tg\, \delta\odot.$$

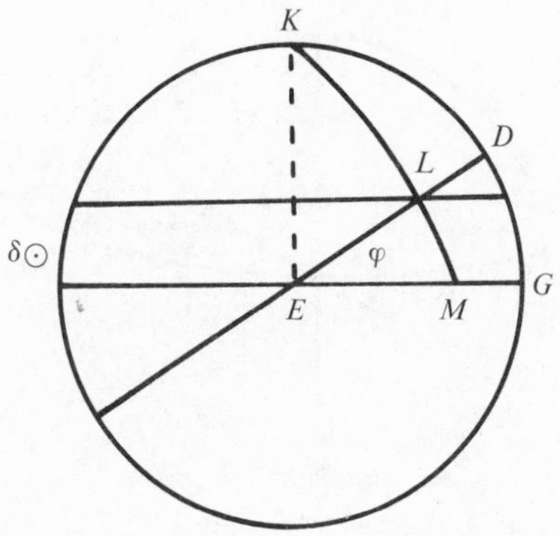

FIGURE 4

ḤABASH AL-ḤĀSIB

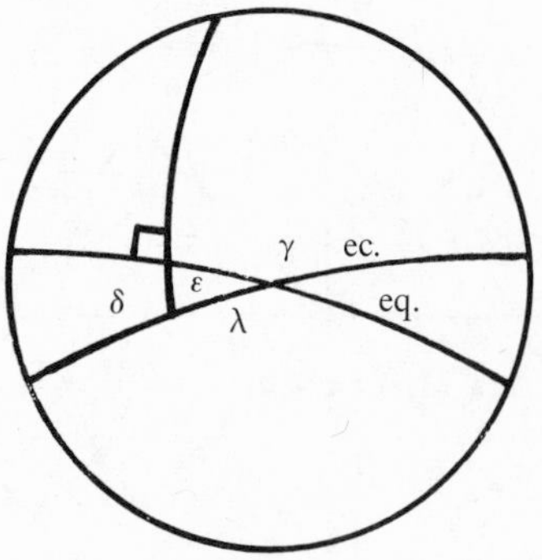

FIGURE 5

He shows that if the declination of the sun is northern, the length of daylight = the equation of daylight + 90°; and if the declination of the sun is southern, the length of daylight = 90° − the equation of daylight. The equation of daylight is tabulated for the planets, the sun, and the moon. With the aid of this table one can easily find the arc of daylight.

The ascensions (*maṭāliʿ al-burūj*) or rising times in the right sphere (*al-falak al-mustaqīm*), i.e., right ascension, is defined (see Figure 5) as

$$\frac{\sin \lambda \cdot \cos \varepsilon}{\cos \delta}.$$

Ḥabash prepared such tables because of the right ascension's astrological importance.

The ascension for a particular latitude is called the oblique ascension. Ḥabash showed that if the arbitrary point P on the ecliptic is between the vernal and autumnal equinoxes, the right ascension − 1/2 equation of daylight = oblique ascension; and if it is between the autumnal and vernal equinoxes, the right ascension + 1/2 equation of daylight = oblique ascension.

Ḥabash prepared tables for the seven climates. According to him the first climate (*iqlīm*) was that portion of the northern hemisphere in which

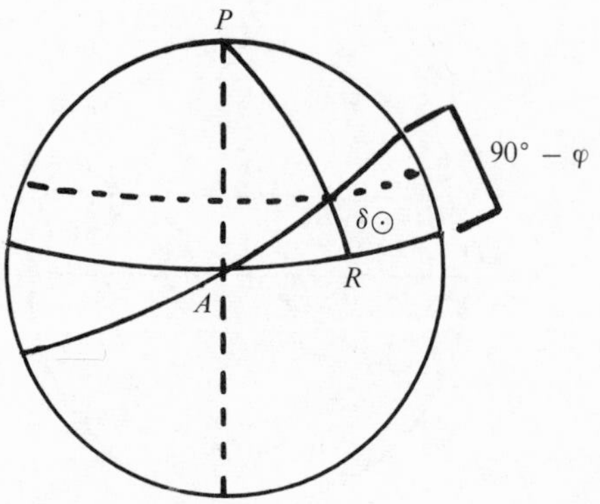

FIGURE 6

$13 \leq$ max. $D \leq 13 - 0.50$, i.e., a band of a half-hour advance in length of daylight.

For finding the ortive amplitude (*jayb al-mashriq*) Ḥabash gives the following function (see Figure 6):

$$\text{Ortive amplitude } AR = \frac{\sin \delta\odot}{\cos \phi}$$

$$\delta\odot = \text{declination of the sun.}$$

Astronomy. Ḥabash generally follows Ptolemy, but some sections of his work are distinctly non-Ptolemaic.

Theory of the Sun. Ḥabash compiled tables of mean motion of the sun for 1, 31, 61, 91, ··· 691 and 1, 2, 3, 4, 5, ··· 30 Hijra years; for 1, 2, 3, 4, ··· 29 days; for 1, 2, 3, 4, ··· 24 hours; and for 10, 20, 30, ··· 60 minutes. The mean motion of the sun is 384;55,14° per Hijra year and 0;59,8° per day (the value given in the *Almagest*). He computed the eccentricity of the sun 2^P5^1 (2; 1°).

Ḥabash divided half of the ecliptic into eighteen parts, each part called *kardaja.* The Arabic-Persian term *kardaja* (pl., *kardajāt*) is usually derived from the Sanskrit *kramajya.* It seems to have stood for a unit length of arc. He also prepared equation tables of the sun (*taʿdīl al-shams*) for each degree of anomaly.

Methods for the calculation of the equation of the sun were given by Ḥabash. This classical procedure was given in the *Almagest* and followed by the Islamic astronomers. If the mean motion $\bar{\lambda}$ or anomaly is given, to find λe, i.e., the true motion of the sun (see Figure 7):

$$\text{If } \bar{\lambda} < 90^\circ$$

$$e = \text{eccentricity}$$

$$\operatorname{tg} \lambda e = \frac{ED}{BD}$$

$$ED = \sin \bar{\lambda} \cdot e$$

$$BD = MD + MB$$

$$MD = \cos \bar{\lambda} \cdot e$$

$$\operatorname{tg} \lambda e = \frac{\sin \bar{\lambda} \cdot e}{\cos \bar{\lambda} \cdot e + 60^P}.$$

The converse of the problem, i.e., given λ, determine $\bar{\lambda}$, is set out. This equation gives the following approximate solution (see Figure 8):

$$\text{If } \lambda < 90^\circ$$

$$\operatorname{tg} \lambda e = \frac{ED}{BD}$$

$$ED = \sin \lambda \cdot e.$$

Since the angle λe is small, Ḥabash supposed $BD = BC$, i.e., 60^P:

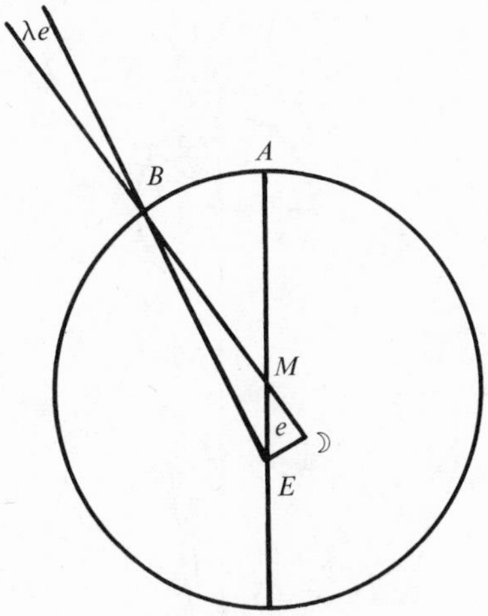

FIGURE 7

$$BE = 60^P - EC$$
$$EC = \cos\lambda \cdot e$$
$$BE = 60^P - \cos\lambda \cdot e$$
$$\operatorname{tg}\lambda e = \frac{e \sin\lambda}{60^P - (e \cdot \cos\lambda)}.$$

Ḥabash gave another rule to solve the above problem:

$$\sin\lambda e = \frac{ED}{60^P}$$
$$ED = \sin\lambda \cdot e$$
$$\sin\lambda e = \frac{\sin\lambda \cdot e}{60^P}.$$

This function is correct, but the independent variable is λ rather than $\bar{\lambda}$. If $\bar{\lambda}$ replaces λ, this will lead to the equation $\lambda = \lambda - e \sin\lambda$, which is known as Kepler's equation. The equivalent of this equation is found in Tamil astronomy in south India.

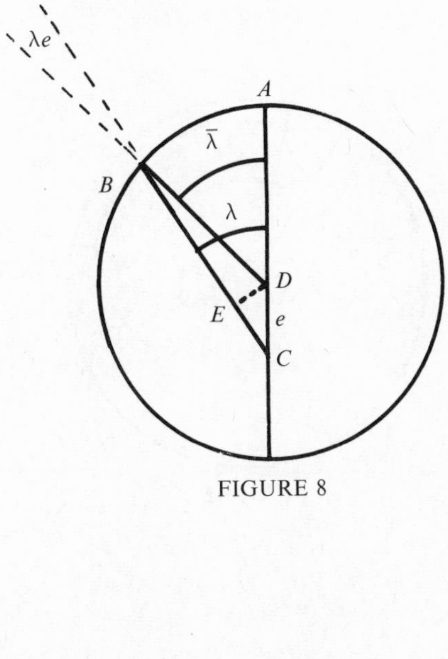

FIGURE 8

ḤABASH AL-ḤĀSIB

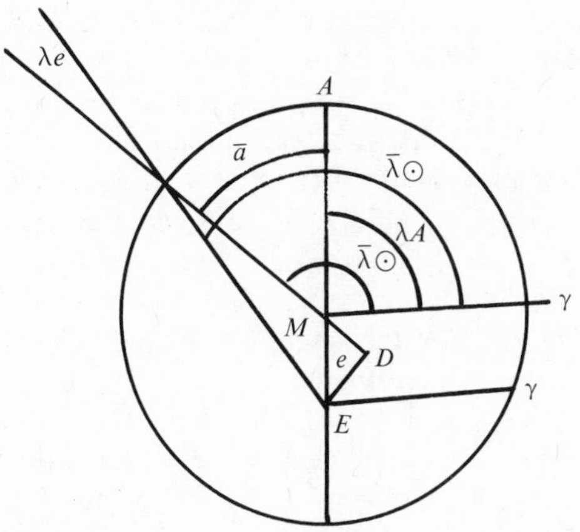

FIGURE 9

From the mean position Ḥabash found the true position of the sun (see Figure 9):

If $\bar{\lambda}\odot > \lambda A$

and $\bar{\lambda}\odot - \lambda A < 90°$,

anomaly $\bar{a} = \bar{\lambda}\odot - \lambda A$,

where $\bar{\lambda}\odot$ = mean longitude of the sun

and λA = longitude of the apogee.

Thus, $$\operatorname{tg}\lambda e = \frac{\sin\bar{a} \cdot e}{\cos\bar{a} \cdot e + 60^P}$$

and $\bar{\lambda}\odot = \lambda e$ = true position of the sun.

He also computed from the true position the mean position of the sun (see Figure 10). The true position B, i.e., λB, is given:

$$\lambda B - \lambda A = \angle AEB = a$$
$$\sin\lambda e = \frac{\sin a \cdot e}{60^P}$$
$$\bar{\lambda}B = \lambda B + \lambda e.$$

By applying these methods Ḥabash calculated the

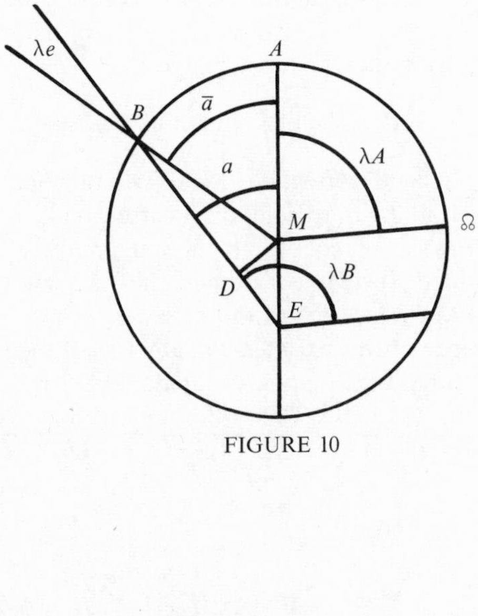

FIGURE 10

ḤABASH AL-ḤĀSIB

entrance of the sun into the zodiacal signs and compiled tables for them.

Lunar Theory. Ḥabash constructed several tables for the longitudinal and latitudinal motions of the moon for periods of thirty lunar years, for years, for months, for days (13;10,35°, the value given in the *Almagest*), for hours (0;32,27°), and for fractions of hours. He also drew up tables for general lunar anomaly and for the equation of the moon (*taʿdīl al-qamar*) in four columns.

Ḥabash's technique for computing the true longitude of the moon was based on the model of the lunar motion given by Ptolemy in book V of the *Almagest*. The most essential deviation from the previous tables consisted in the arrangement of all corrections of the mean positions so that they are never negative. As Neugebauer remarks, this constituted a great practical advantage over the Ptolemaic method. (See Figure 11.)

The true place of the moon is determined as follows:

M = movable center of eccenter
δ_0 = apparent radius of epicyle when in apogee of eccenter
G = "true apogee" of epicycle
F = "mean apogee" of epicycle
W_0 = maximum angular distance possible between F and G
F_0 = point on the epicycle such that $F = W_0$
$\bar{a}$ = "mean anomaly" of moon counted from F_0
W = angular distance between G and F_0
$a = \bar{a} + w_1$, "true anomaly" counted from G
λ = "true longitude" of the moon counted from γ_0.

The "first correction," W_1:

$$\bar{\lambda}\odot - \bar{\lambda}☾ = K$$

The function of K is tabulated in the first column of the table, called "equation of the moon (*taʿdīl al-qamar*)." It gives the distance from G to F_0, the value given in *Almagest* V, except that Ḥabash had added W_0, which makes W nonnegative.

$$\bar{a} + \text{the first equation} = a.$$

The "second correction," W_2, is a function of a, tabulated in the third column. It corresponds in value to *Almagest* V, 8, col. 4, but the maximum equation δ_0 is added to it. It is assumed that the epicycle is located at the apogee of the eccenter. When it is in the perigee of the eccenter, the amount of the excess of the epicyclic equation is tabulated in the fourth column of the table. This is the function of K (corresponding to *Almagest* V, 8, col. 5); the result will be

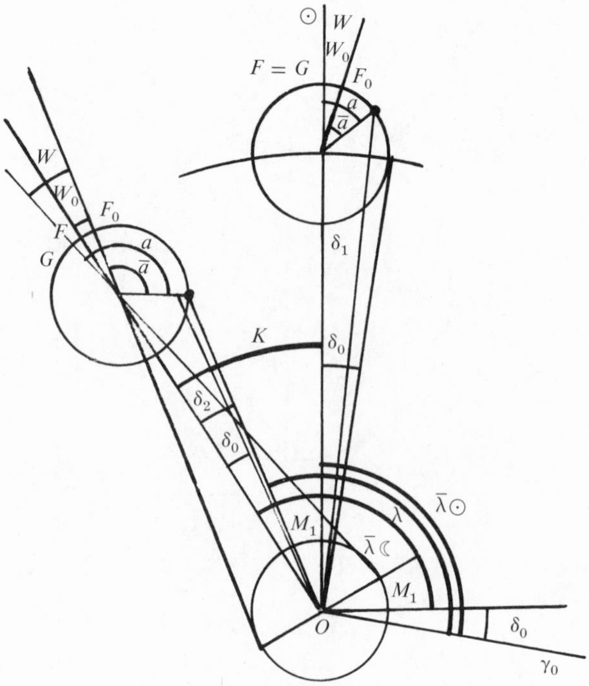

FIGURE 11

obtained by multiplying the value of the fourth column by the second: $\delta = W_2 + \mu\gamma$.

If $a < 180°$, the result will be subtracted from or added to the true center. Finally Ḥabash obtains

$$\lambda = \bar{\lambda} - \delta.$$

Latitude of the Moon. The latitude of the moon for a given moment is determined by means of a table prepared for one degree. The true place of the moon (λ☾) is added to the mean position of the ascending node (−λ☊). Because of the longitude of the ascending node, the distance of the node from γ_0 is counted in a negative direction. This total, *A*, is the argument with which the table of the latitude of the moon is entered.

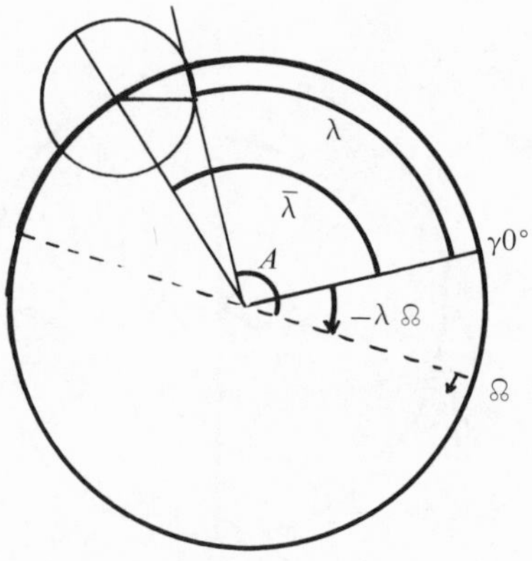

FIGURE 12

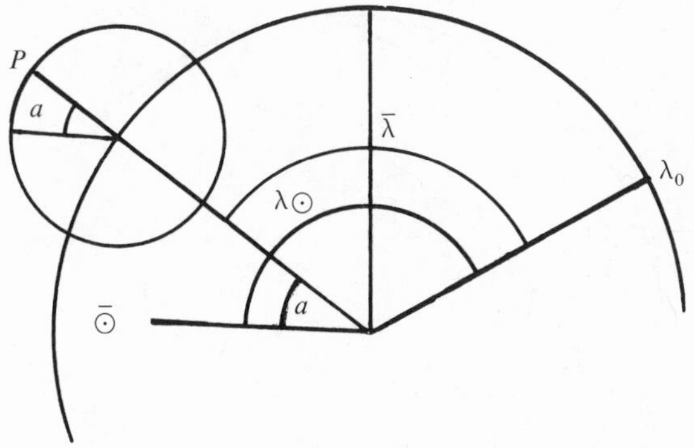

FIGURE 13

Theory of the Planets. For finding the longitudes of the planets Ḥabash prepared several tables for mean motions, in longitude and latitude, and the equations. His procedure for finding the true longitude of a planet for a given moment t is based on the Ptolemaic method (*Almagest* XI).

For outer planets (see Figure 13):

$$\bar{a} = \bar{\lambda}\odot - \bar{\lambda},$$

where $\lambda\odot$ = mean longitude of the sun
λ = mean longitude of the planet
$\bar{a}$ = anomaly or argumentum.

It implies that the radius of the planet on the epicycle is always parallel to the direction from 0 to the mean sun.

Inner Planets. For inner planets $\bar{\lambda} = \bar{\lambda}\odot$, and the anomaly can be found from the tables. (See Figure 14.)

For the outer planets he first found the mean longitude $\bar{\lambda}$, mean anomaly a, and the longitude of the apogee λA of the planet (see Figure 15): $\bar{\lambda} - \lambda A = \bar{K}$.

He found the distance of the center C of the epicycle from the apogee for the given moment. According to the Ptolemaic planetary theory, the planet makes its regular motion not around the point O but around E, i.e., the "equant." The center of the defer-

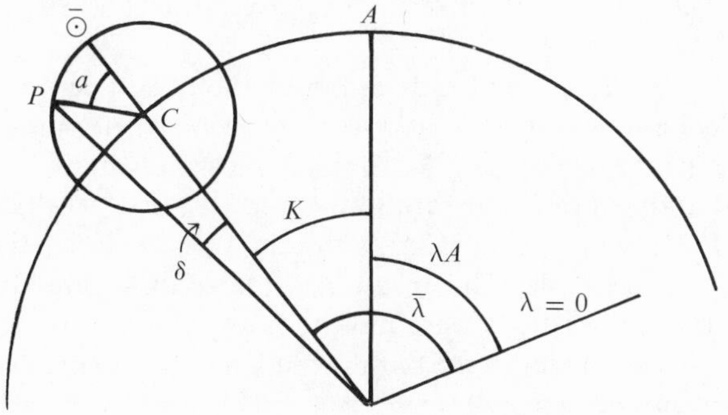

FIGURE 14

ḤABASH AL-ḤĀSIB

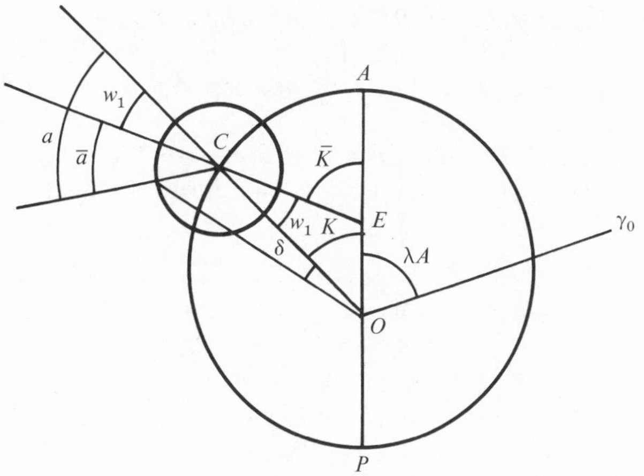

FIGURE 15

ent falls between O and E. Then he found the epicyclic equation as seen from O. Thus the true anomaly, a, counted from true apogee, is found. Ḥabash tabulated this difference, $W_1 = a - \bar{a}$, as function $\bar{K}$, in the first column. This is called the "first correction": $a = W_1 + \bar{a}$.

Then he computed the distance of C from A, i.e., K, as seen from A. This difference is also equal to the angle W_1:

$$K = \bar{K} - W_1.$$

If $$\bar{K} < 180^\circ$$

$$K = \bar{K} - W_1$$
$$a = \bar{a} + W_1.$$

Then comes the "second correction," W_2. This depends not only on the true anomaly a but also on the position of the epicycle. If it is exactly in the apogee, this amount of correction will be less than W_2 by the amount μA tabulated in column 4 as the function a:

$$\delta = W_2 - \mu A \cdot \gamma.$$

γ is found as a function of K in the second column.

All these procedures are correct only if the value found in the second column is negative. If it is positive, the second column is multiplied by the value found in the fifth column, then subtracted from the fourth. The true longitude of the planet is

$$\lambda = \lambda A + K + \delta.$$

Latitude of the Planets. The procedure for calculating the latitude of the superior planets is based on Ptolemaic method (*Almagest* XIII, 6). The table of latitudes was prepared in three columns. Ḥabash used the same numeric values as Ptolemy (*Almagest* XIII, table 5). According to him, the latitudes can be found

ḤABASH AL-ḤĀSIB

by the addition of two components: the inclination of the epicycle about its second diameter (β_1) and the angle at the line of nodes between the deferent and ecliptic planes (β_2).

The first and second columns are functions of anomaly $a{:}b_1(a)$ and $b_2(a)$. The third column is the function θ.

$$\text{Mars} = \theta = \lambda$$
$$\text{Jupiter} = \theta = \lambda - 20°$$
$$\text{Saturn} = \theta = \lambda + 50°$$
$$c(\theta)$$
$$\beta_1 = b_1 \cdot c$$
$$\beta_2 = b_2 \cdot c$$

The latitude of the planet $\beta = \beta_1 + \beta_2$.

For the inferior planets (based on Ptolemaic method, *Almagest* XIII, 6), one enters the latitude table with the truly determined anomaly and records the corresponding numbers in the first and the second columns. These are the functions of a: $b_1(a)$ and $b_2(a)$.

One finds the determined true longitude of the planets. For Venus, $A = \lambda -$ the longitude of apogee. For Mercury, if the determined true anomaly is in the first fifteen rows,

$$A = \lambda - 10°;$$

if it is in those that follow,

$$A = \lambda + 10°.$$

Next,
$$A + 90° = \theta \text{ for Venus}$$
$$A + 270° = \theta \text{ for Mercury.}$$

One enters the table with that value and finds the corresponding number in the third column. This is the function $c(\theta)$.

Then, $b_1 \cdot c =$ the first latitude $= \beta_1$.

If θ is in the first fifteen rows, the planet is northern. If it is in those that follow, it is southern. If θ is after the first fifteen rows at the same time that a is in the first fifteen rows, the planet is northern.

Next, one enters the latitude table with

$$\theta \text{ for Venus}$$
$$\theta + 180° \text{ for Mercury}$$

and finds the corresponding value in the third column. This is the function of θ or $\theta + 180°$: $c(\theta)$ or $c(\theta + 180°)$. Then $b_1c =$ the second latitude $= \beta_2$. If (θ) or $(\theta + 180°)$ is in the first fifteen rows and $a < 180°$, the planet has a northern latitude. If $a > 180°$, it has a southern latitude. If (θ) or $(\theta + 180°)$ is below the first fifteen rows and $a < 180°$, the planet has a southern latitude; and if $a > 180°$, the planet has a northern latitude. Then

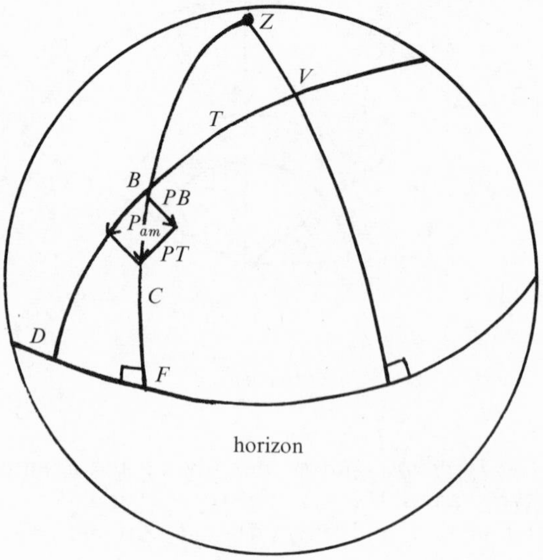

FIGURE 16

$c^2 + C^2/6 = \beta_3$ for Venus. If the planet has northern latitude, $\beta = \beta_2 + \beta_3$ and $C^2 = 3C^2/4 = \beta_3$ for Mercury. If the planet has southern latitude, $\beta = \beta_2 + \beta_3$.

Parallax (Ikhtilāf al-Manẓar) Theory. Ḥabash had two entirely different methods for determining the parallax, i.e., parallax in longitude P_λ and parallax in latitude P_β. One of them may seem a transition between that of Ptolemy and the later Islamic astronomers. This solution depends on the first sine (*al-jayb al-awwal*) that can be formulated (see Figure 16):

$$\frac{\sin BV}{\sin FB} \quad \frac{\sin DB}{\cos DB}$$

equal cos B and the second sine, which is equal to sin B. Without proof he states that

$$\sin P_\lambda = (\text{first sine})\,(\sin P_{am}).$$

P_{am} is measured according to Ptolemy (see Figure 17):

$$\sin P_\beta = \frac{(\sin P_{am})\,(\text{first sine})}{\cos P_\beta}.$$

The other method seems to derive from the *Sūrya-Siddhanta*.

The technique for determining the longitude component is of great interest. Ḥabash first determined t (see Figure 18), then used it as argument in the parallax table. The result was called the first parallax. He added this to t and with that value entered the parallax table. The result was the second parallax. These operations were repeated until the fifth parallax—a quarter of the parallax in longitude, expressed in hours.

For finding the lunar parallax in latitude Ḥabash

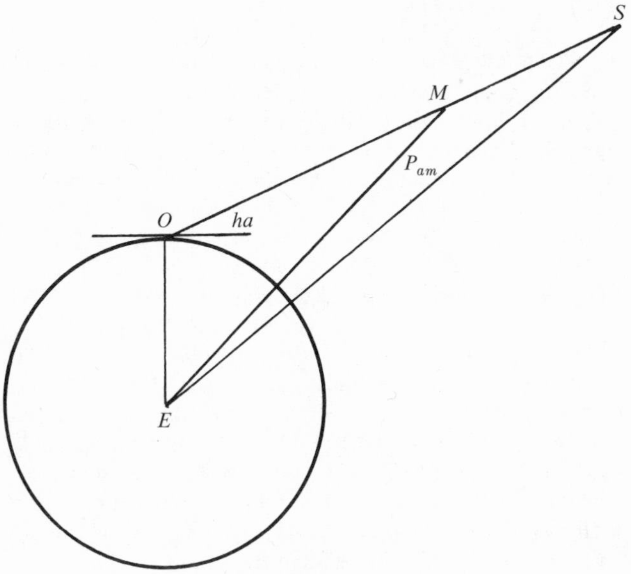

FIGURE 17

used A as an argument, and the corresponding value of the function was to be doubled (see Figure 18). This would be the lunar parallax in latitude.

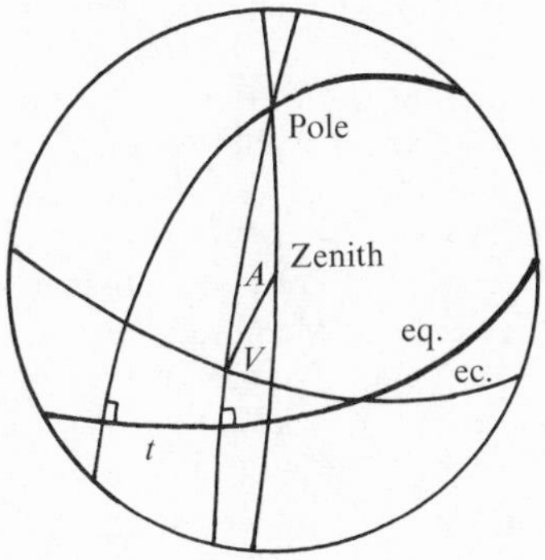

FIGURE 18

Visibility Theory (*Ru'yat al-Hilāl*). Habash may have been the first astronomer to engage in the computation of the new crescent. Like the ancient Babylonians and the Jews, the Muslims depended on visual observation of the new crescent for their religious and secular calendars. This led the Muslim astronomers to realize that the knowledge of the visibility of the new crescent is an essential task of astronomy. Ḥabash used the following method for the determination of the visibility of the new crescent. He added twenty or thirty minutes to the time of sunset, thus obtaining the mean position of the moon at the time when the new crescent becomes visible. Then the true position of the sun, the moon, and the head were needed for the above-mentioned time (see Figure 19). Thus, $\lambda - \lambda\odot = \lambda_1$, which Maimonides called the first elongation.

ḤABASH AL-ḤĀSIB

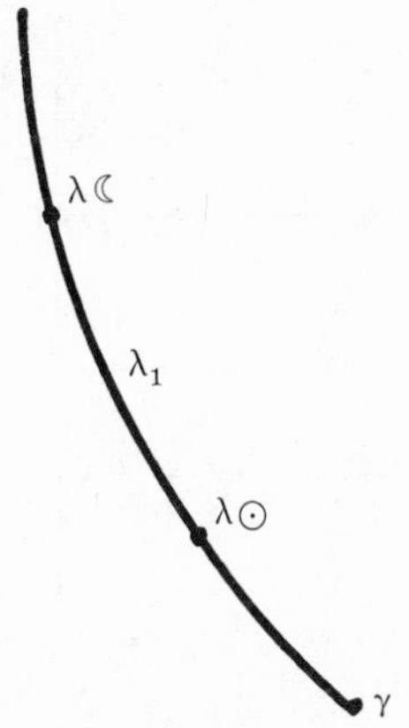

FIGURE 19

For an observer on the surface of the earth, the moon M would appear in a lower position M_1 because of the parallax.

$$\frac{\text{Diameter of the earth}}{\text{The distance of the moon to the center of the earth}} = \text{parallax of the moon } P_{am}.$$

Then the parallax in latitude P_β and longitude P_λ can be obtained (see Figure 20). Thus, $\lambda_1 - P\lambda = \lambda_2$, which Maimonides called the second elongation. The

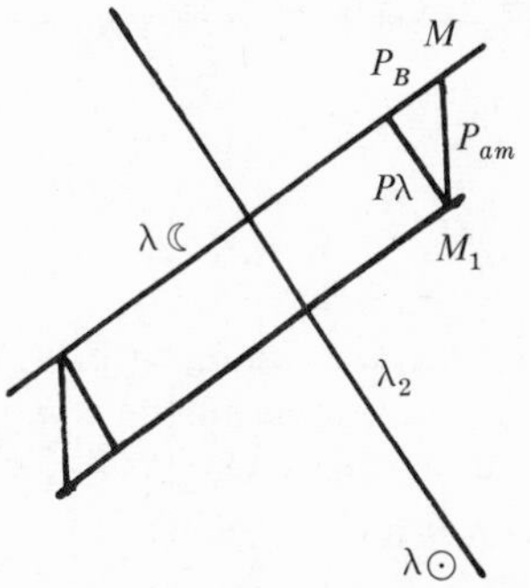

FIGURE 20

true latitude of the moon (Maimonides called it the first latitude) was subtracted from or added to the parallax in latitude, depending on the variable position of the moon:

$$M_\beta - P_\beta = M_{1\beta} \text{ (second latitude).}$$

From this second latitude one can derive half of the day arc of the moon, and from that the equation of the day of the moon is obtained. This equation of the moon is added to or subtracted from the longitude of the moon. Thus the point of the ecliptic O (see Figure 21), which sets simultaneously with the moon, is obtained: $\lambda_2 - C = \lambda_3 O$.

Then the arc of the equator QA, which sets simultaneously with the arc of the ecliptic, λ_3, is calculated

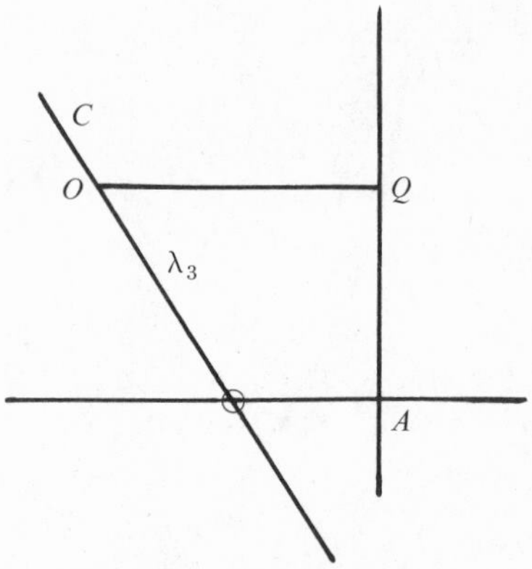

FIGURE 21

(see Figure 22). This is the difference between the rising times of the moon and the sun. This time difference is multiplied by the surplus of the moon in one hour and divided by fifteen. The result K is

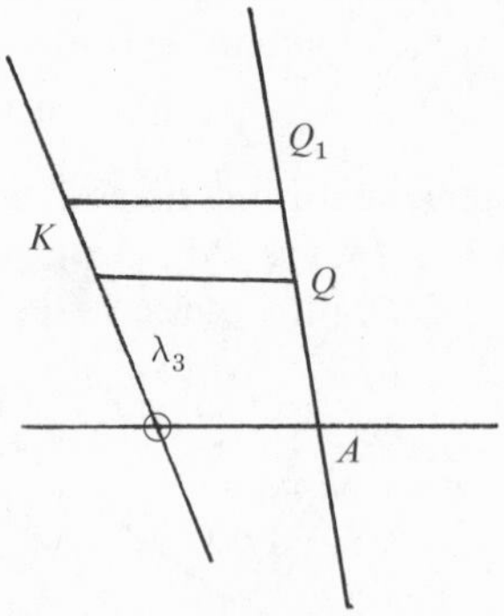

FIGURE 22

added to the true longitude of the moon, i.e., the distance cut by the moon during that time is added to get the distance between the moon and the sun at sunset. Then (see Figure 23)

$$\angle Q_1AR = 90^\circ - \Phi$$
$$\sin Q_1R = \cos \Phi \cdot \sin QA.$$

If $QR > 10^\circ$, the moon will be visible on that day. If $QR < 10^\circ$, the moon will not be visible.

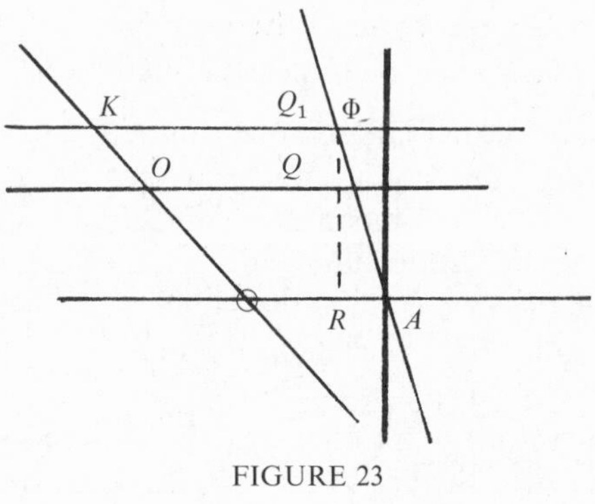

FIGURE 23

BIBLIOGRAPHY

The following works may be consulted for further information: A. Braunmühl, *Vorlesungen über Geschichte der Trigonometrie* (Leipzig, 1900); G. Caussin, *Le livre de la grande Hakémite,* vol. VII of Notices et Extraits des MSS (Paris, 1804); S. Gandz, J. Obemann, and O. Neugebauer, *The Code of Maimonides. Book Three. Treatise Eight; Sanctification of the New Moon* (New Haven, 1956); J. Hamadanizadeh, "A Medieval Interpolation Scheme for Oblique Ascensions," in *Centaurus,* **9** (1963), 257–265; E. S. Kennedy, "An Islamic Computer for Planetary Latitudes," in *Journal of the American Oriental Society,* **71** (1951), 12–21; and "Parallax Theory in Islamic Astronomy," in *Isis,* **47** (1956), 33–53; E. S. Kennedy and M. Agna, "Planetary Visibility Tables in Islamic Astronomy," in *Centaurus,* **7** (1960), 134–140; E. S. Kennedy and Janjanian, "The Crescent Visibility Table in Al-Khwārizmī's Zij," *ibid.,* **11** (1965), 73–78; E. S. Kennedy and Ahmad Muruwwa, "Bīrūnī on the Solar Equation," in *Journal of Near Eastern Studies,* **17** (1958), 112–121; E. S. Kennedy and Sharkas, "Two Medieval Methods for Determining the Obliquity of the Ecliptic," in *Mathematics Teacher,* **55** (1962), 286–290; E. S. Kennedy and W. R. Transue, "A Medieval Iterative Algorism," in *American Mathematical Monthly,* **63,** no. 2 (1956), 80–83; Ḥājjī Khalīfa, *Kashf al-Ẓunūn,* S. Yaltkaya, ed., 2 vols. (Istanbul, 1941–1943); E. Kramer, *The Main Stream of Mathematics* (New York, 1951); Ibn al-Nadīm, *Fihrist,* Flügel, ed., I (1871); N. Nadir, "Abūl-Wāfā' on the Solar Altitude," in *Mathematics Teacher,* **53** (1960), 460–463; C. A. Nallino, *Al-Battānī Opus astronomicum,* 3 vols. (Brera, 1899–1907), see vols. I and III; O. Neugebauer, "The Transmission of Planetary Theories in Ancient and Medieval Astronomy," in *Scripta mathematica,* **22** (1956); "Studies in Byzantine Astronomical Terminology," in *Transactions of the American Philosophical Society,* **50** (1960); "The Astronomical Tables of Al-Khwārizmī," in *Hist. Filos. Skrifter. Danske Videnskabernes Selskab,* **4,** no. 2 (1962); and "Thâbit ben Qurra 'On the Solar Year' and 'On the Motion of the Eighth Sphere,'" in *Transactions of the American Philosophical Society,* **106** (1962), 264–299; Ibn al-Qifṭī, *Ta'rīkh al ḥukamā',* Lippert, ed. (Berlin, 1903); G. Sarton, *Introduction to the History of Science,* I (Baltimore, 1927), 545, 550, 565, 667; A. Sayili, "Habeş el Hasib'in 'El Dimişki' adiyla Maruf Zîci'nin Mukaddemesi," in *Ankara üniversitesi dil ve tarih-coğrafya fakültesi dergisi,* **13** (1955), 133–151; C. Schoy, "Beiträge zur arabischen Trigonometrie," in *Isis,* **5** (1923), 364–399; D. E. Smith, *History of Mathematics,* II (London, 1925); and H. Suter, *Die Mathematiker und Astronomen der Araber und ihre Werke* (Leipzig, 1900).

S. TEKELI

HABER, FRITZ (*b.* Breslau, Germany [now Wrocław, Poland], 9 December 1868; *d.* Basel, Switzerland, 29 January 1934), *chemistry.*

Haber's mother died when he was born. His father, who sold pigments and dyestuffs, was one of

Germany's largest importers of natural indigo. Haber's early schooling was at the *Volksschule* and the St. Elisabeth Gymnasium. He attended the universities of Berlin and Heidelberg and the Charlottenburg Technische Hochschule; the latter school awarded him the Ph.D. in 1891. After little more than a year of employment at three different factories, Haber entered the Eidgenössische Technische Hochschule at Zurich, Switzerland, as a postdoctoral student in chemical technology and studied principally with Georg Lunge. Six months spent in his father's business proved to be unsatisfactory, and he became an assistant to Ludwig Knorr at the University of Jena and then to Hans Bunte at the Karlsruhe Technische Hochschule. He received *Privatdozent* status at the Baden school following publication of his first book, *Experimentelle Untersuchungen über Zertsetzgung und Verbrennung von Kohlenwasserstoffen* ("Experimental Studies on the Decomposition and Combustion of Hydrocarbons" [Munich, 1896]).

This record of his research exemplifies the work for which Haber became famous: theoretical studies, done with insight and thoroughness, in areas of growing practical importance. The thermal decomposition of hydrocarbons had been investigated extensively by Marcelin Berthelot twenty-five years earlier; Haber criticized Berthelot's conclusions as arbitrary. He found the carbon-to-carbon linkage in hydrocarbons to have a greater thermal stability than the carbon-to-hydrogen linkage in aromatic compounds; the reverse was true for aliphatic compounds. This rule has been shown to be subject to exceptions.

In 1901 Haber married Dr. Clara Immerwahr, also a chemist. A son, Hermann, was born in June 1902. During the autumn of 1917, two and one-half years after the death of his first wife, he married Charlotta Nathan. Two children, Eva and Ludwig, were born; the marriage ended in divorce in 1927.

After being named *Privatdozent,* Haber turned to problems of physical chemistry, although he had no formal education in this area. He had the help of his colleague Hans Luggin, a pupil of Svante Arrhenius, but Haber considered himself self-taught in the field. He first investigated the electrochemical reduction of nitrobenzene and showed the importance of electrode potential. He studied the nature and rate of the electrode process for the quinine-quinol system and, interested in the nature and rate of the electrode process, did not emphasize the application to the measurement of hydrogen ion concentration. Later he devised a glass electrode to measure hydrogen ion concentration through the electric potential across a piece of thin glass. Other electrochemical subjects investigated by Haber include fuel cells; measurement of the free energy of oxidation of hydrogen, carbon monoxide, and carbon; and the electrolysis of crystalline salts. At the end of his career he had an active interest in electrochemistry, studying autoxidation; application of Planck's quantum theory to chemistry was the basis of most of his later work. In 1898 he published his *Grundriss der technischen Elektrochemie auf theoretischer Grundlage* at Munich and was promoted to associate professor. As an indication of his growing reputation, in 1902 the Deutsche Bunsen-Gesellschaft sent him on a sixteen-week study tour of the United States. His report on chemical education and electrochemical industry in the country was acclaimed in Europe and America.

In 1905 Haber's *Thermodynamik technischer Gasreaktionen Vorlesungen* was published at Munich, and in 1906 he was given a full professorship. Gilbert Lewis and M. Randall's classic text, *Thermodynamics and the Free Energy of Chemical Substances*, published in 1923, described Haber's book as "a model of accuracy and critical insight."

Haber's outstanding accomplishment in chemistry, during the first decade of the twentieth century, involved a gas reaction. He was one of many scientists interested in nitrogen fixation. As in virtually all his work, the problem had both theoretical and practical significance, and he looked into several possible solutions. Walther Nernst, a leader in physical chemistry, obtained data at variance with Haber's for the combination of nitrogen and hydrogen to form ammonia. Nernst presented measurements from experiments done at high pressure and can be considered the first to accomplish the synthesis under these conditions. (Henry Le Chatelier had been the first to try the high-pressure synthesis, but an explosion induced him to forsake the venture.) Haber considered the difference in values a personal challenge. Working with Robert Le Rossignol, a student from the Isle of Jersey, and assisted by the mechanic Kirchenbauer, he performed high-pressure experiments and confirmed his earlier results, done at atmospheric pressure, which Nernst had questioned. A constant used by Nernst in his calculations—not his heat theorem—was later shown to be the cause of the erroneous values.

Haber went on to commercial exploitation of the synthesis of ammonia. His calculations showed that about 8 percent ammonia was available at pressures of 200 atmospheres and temperatures of 600°C. However, it was through the work of others that the process came to be the first successful high-pressure industrial chemical reaction. Such practical problems as a satisfactory, long-lasting container for the operation were solved under the direction of Carl Bosch and his associates at the Badische Anilin- und

Sodafabrik. Nonetheless, users and students of high-pressure techniques came to Haber's laboratory for instruction.

In 1912 Haber became director of the Kaiser Wilhelm Institute for Physical Chemistry and Electrochemistry at Dahlem, on the outskirts of Berlin. His friend Richard Willstätter was codirector, with Ernst Beckmann, of the first of these Kaiser Wilhelm research institutes, for chemistry.

At the start of World War I, Haber placed himself and his laboratory at the service of his country. Assigned problems involving the supply of war materials, he showed xylene and solvent naphtha to be good substitutes for toluene as an antifreeze in benzene motor fuel. The War Ministry consulted Walther Nernst about using irritants to drive the Allies out of their trenches so that open warfare might be resumed; Haber was given a share in solving this problem. Dianisidine chlorosulfonate, an irritant powder suggested by Nernst, and the lacrimator xylyl bromide proved to be ineffective. Haber's laboratory studied other irritants and the investigation came to a close in December 1914 with an explosion when a few drops of dichloromethylamine were added to a few cubic centimeters of impure cacodyl chloride. Otto Sackur, an outstanding physical chemist, was killed.

Haber developed the use of chlorine gas as a war weapon; by the end of January 1915 the preliminary laboratory research was completed. On 11 April 1915 about 5,000 cylinders of the gas were distributed, and the chemical was released over a 3.5-mile front near Ypres, Belgium. German military leaders later admitted that had massive attacks rather than the small test been done, German victory would have been assured. Instead, the Allies soon developed gases and the weapon on both sides was no longer intended to move men but to kill them.

In 1916 Haber became chief of the Chemical Warfare Service; and although he was only a captain, every detail of chemical offense, defense, supply, and research came under his supervision. By that time his process of nitrogen fixation was used in supplying Germany with nitrogen compounds, needed for fertilizers and for the explosives that provided staying power after the United States's entry into the war.

In November 1919 Haber was awarded the Nobel Prize in chemistry. The honor was denounced by some French, British, and American scientists, which dealt another blow to his spiritual and physical condition. Having put all his energies into the war, he was obliged to share personally in Germany's defeat. To be condemned as inhuman by fellow scientists also involved in war work deeply troubled him.

During the early postwar years Haber continued his patriotic efforts. He was the leading figure in appeals for the Notgemeinschaft, the Emergency Society for German Science. His most noteworthy contribution, although a failure, was to search the oceans for gold, in the hope of extracting enough to pay the war reparations demanded by the Allies. Nineteenth-century analyses had shown that some samples of seawater contained nearly twice as much as the lowest-grade land deposit that was profitable to operate. Unfortunately, Haber did not verify the published results, later established as much too high, and an extraction scheme was devised without ascertaining the exact amount of gold and its form in seawater. Several ocean trips were undertaken in vain, but a very accurate method for gold analysis was found.

Haber's other activities during the postwar years proved more fruitful. His institute became one of the great scientific research centers in the world. During his tenure as director the Kaiser Wilhelm Institute for Physical Chemistry and Electrochemistry was credited with more than 700 publications in scientific journals. As at Karlsruhe and as head of chemical warfare, Haber showed himself to be a talented leader. He displayed versatility in handling a variety of subject matters in both academic and military situations. He was able to conform to a military environment and provide at other times a liberal and independent atmosphere to his associates. Beginning as an organic chemist, he contributed to every branch of physical chemistry as well as to peripheral sciences. He was a pure and applied scientist able to bridge the gap between the purist and the engineer. Men rather than accomplishments were the products of his direction; many outstanding physical chemists of the first half of the twentieth century started their careers with him.

The Haber Colloquium, a research seminar at his institute, began in October 1919 and soon attracted scientists from all parts of Europe. Haber's contribution was clarity and the ability to abstract, spiced with satire and wit. His ability to think about and discuss material from the hydrogen atom to the flea, presented by expert lecturers, was greatly admired. As other commitments took him away from the meetings, they lost their verve and attendance dropped.

He was always engrossed in research projects and activities, and he had an extraordinary ability to concentrate, staying with problems both scientific and nonscientific. His speaking, reading, and writing habits were in this same mold. His best appreciated speeches were given at a commemoration for Justus Liebig, with whom he has been compared, and on